Prepare for Class "Read the Book"

Feature	Description	Benefit	Page
	Every chapter begins with....		
Chapter Opening Article & Project	Each chapter begins with a current article and ends with a related project.	The Article describes a real situation. The Project lets you apply what you learned to solve a related problem.	247, 349
	Every section begins with....		
Learning Objectives 1	Each section begins with a list of objectives. Objectives also appear in the text where the objective is covered.	These focus your studying by emphasizing what's most important and where to find it.	269
	Most sections contain...		
PREPARING FOR THIS SECTION	Most sections begin with a list of key concepts to review, with page numbers.	Ever forget what you've learned? This feature highlights previously learned material to be used in this section. Review it, and you'll always be prepared to move forward.	269
Now Work the 'Are You Prepared?' Problems	Special problems that support the Preparing for This Section feature.	Not sure you need the Preparing for This Section review? Work the 'Are You Prepared?' problems. If you get one wrong, you'll know exactly what you need to review and where to review it!	269, 279
"Now Work" PROBLEMS	These follow most examples, and direct you to a related exercise.	We learn best by doing. You'll solidify your understanding of examples if you try a similar problem right away, to be sure you understand what you've just read.	278
WARNING	Warnings are provided in the text.	These point out common mistakes and help you to avoid them.	301
Explorations and **Seeing the Concept**	These represent graphing utility activities to foreshadow a concept or solidify a concept just presented.	You will obtain a deeper and more intuitive understanding of theorems and definitions.	100, 275
In Words	These provide alternative descriptions of select definitions and theorems.	Does math ever look foreign to you? This feature translates math into plain English.	271
Calculus Icon	These appear next to information essential for the study of calculus.	Pay attention–if you spend extra time now, you'll do better later!	276
Showcase *New!* **EXAMPLES**	These examples provide "how-to" instruction by offering a guided, step-by-step approach to solving a problem.	With each step presented on the left and the mathematics displayed on the right, students can im... see how each of th...	183–184
Model It! Examples and Problems	Marked with ●. These are examples and problems that require you to build a mathematical model from either a verbal description or data.	...he form, ...her, the ...on an ...m. These problems ...develop models that will allow ...u to describe the problem mathematically and suggest a solution to the problem.	323, 332

Practice "Work the Problems"

Feature	Description	Benefit	Page
"Assess Your Understanding" contains a variety of problems at the end of each section.			
'Are You Prepared?' Problems	These assess your retention of the prerequisite material you'll need. Answers are given at the end of the section exercises. This feature is related to the Preparing for This Section feature.	Do you always remember what you've learned? Working these problems is the best way to find out. If you get one wrong, you'll know exactly what you need to review and where to review it!	269, 279
Concepts and Vocabulary	These short-answer questions, mainly Fill-in-the-Blank and True/False items, assess your understanding of key definitions and concepts in the current section.	Learning math is more than memorization – it's about discovering connections. These problems help you understand the 'big ideas' before diving into skill building.	280
Skill Building	Correlated to section examples, these problems provide straightforward practice.	It's important to dig in and develop your skills. These problems provide you with ample practice to do so.	280–281
Mixed Practice	These problems offer comprehensive assessment of the skills learned in the section by asking problems that relate to more than one concept or objective. These problems may also require you to utilize skills learned in previous sections.	Learning mathematics is a building process. Many concepts are interrelated. These problems help you see how mathematics builds on itself and also see how the concepts tie together.	281
Applications and Extensions	These problems allow you to apply your skills to real-world problems. These problems also allow you to extend concepts leamed in the section.	You will see that the material learned within the section has many uses in everyday life.	281–284
Discussion and Writing	"Discussion and Writing" problems are colored red. These support class discussion, verbalization of mathematical ideas, and writing and research projects.	To verbalize an idea, or to describe it clearly in writing, shows real understanding. These problems nurture that understanding. Many are challenging but you'll get out what you put in.	284
"Now Work" Problems	Many examples refer you to a related homework problem. These related problems are marked by a pencil and yellow numbers.	If you get stuck while working problems, look for the closest Now Work problem and refer back to the related example to see if it helps.	276

Review "Study for Quizzes and Tests"

Feature	Description	Benefit	Page
Chapter Reviews at the end of each chapter contain...			
"Things to Know"	A detailed list of important theorems, formulas, and definitions from the chapter.	Review these and you'll know the most important material in the chapter!	342–343
"You Should Be Able To..."	Contains a complete list of objectives by section, examples that illustrate the objective, and practice exercises that test your understanding of the objective.	Do the recommended exercises and you'll have mastery over the key material. If you get something wrong, review the suggested page numbers and try again.	343–344
Review Exercises	These provide comprehensive review and practice of key skills, matched to the Learning Objectives for each section.	Practice makes perfect. These problems combine exercises from all sections, giving you a comprehensive review in one place.	344–347
CHAPTER TEST	About 15–20 problems that can be taken as a Chapter Test. Be sure to take the Chapter Test under test conditions—no notes!	Be prepared. Take the sample practice test. This will get you ready for your instructor's test. If you get a problem wrong, watch the Chapter Test Prep video.	348
CUMULATIVE REVIEW	These problem sets appear at the end of each chapter, beginning with Chapter 2. They combine problems from previous chapters, providing an ongoing cumulative review.	These are really important. They will ensure that you are not forgetting anything as you go. These will go a long way toward keeping you constantly primed for quizzes and tests.	348–349
CHAPTER PROJECTS	The Chapter Project applies what you've learned in the chapter. Additional projects are available on the Instructor's Resource Center (IRC).	The Project gives you an opportunity to apply what you've learned in the chapter to solve a problem related to the opening article. If your instructor allows, these make excellent opportunities to work in a group, which is often the best way of learning math.	349

Precalculus: Enhanced with Graphing Utilities

Volume 2

Michael Sullivan

Michael Sullivan, III

Custom Edition for Montgomery College

Taken from:

Precalculus: Enhanced with Graphing Utilities, Fifth Edition
Michael Sullivan and Michael Sullivan, III

Custom Publishing

New York Boston San Francisco
London Toronto Sydney Tokyo Singapore Madrid
Mexico City Munich Paris Cape Town Hong Kong Montreal

Cover Art: Courtesy of PhotoDisc/Getty Images.

Excerpts taken from:
Precalculus: Enhanced with Graphing Utilities, Fifth Edition
by Michael Sullivan, Michael Sullivan, III

Published by Prentice Hall
Upper Saddle River, New Jersey 07458

Printed in the United States of America

10 9 8 7 6 5 4 3 2 1

2008360979

AY

Pearson Custom Publishing
is a division of

PEARSON

www.pearsonhighered.com

ISBN 10: 0-555-05053-X
ISBN 13: 978-0-555-05053-8

BRIEF CONTENTS

For the Next Generation

Shannon, Patrick, and Ryan (Murphy)
Maeve and Sean (Sullivan)

Michael S., Kevin, and Marissa (Sullivan)
Kaleigh, Billy, and Timmy (O'Hara)

Contents

List of Applications

Calculus

Carpentry. *See also* **Construction**

Chemistry

Combinatorics

Communications

Computers and computing

Construction

Photo Credits

Chapter 1 Pages 1 and 54, Alamy Images; Page 19, Peter Arnold, Inc.; Page 25, Kendra Luck, CORBIS-NY; Page 32, Kathy McLaughlin/The Image Works; Page 50, AP Wide World Photos.

Chapter 2 Pages 55 and 124, ROB & SAS, CORBIS-NY; Page 69, NASA/Jet Propulsion Laboratory; Page 111, Tony Freeman/PhotoEdit, Inc.

Chapter 3 Pages 125 and 172, MonicaGraff/The Image Works; Page 161, Erin Garvey/Photolibrary.com.

Chapter 4 Pages 173 and 244, Dr. Jeremy Burgess/Photo Researchers, Inc.; Page 212, Corbis Digital Stock.

Chapter 5 Pages 247 and 349, Alamy Images; Page 304, The Granger Collection; Page 312, NASA/GESC/Tom Stack & Associates, Inc.; Page 313, Tony Freeman/PhotoEdit, Inc.; Page 318, Jim Pickerell/The Image Works; Page 333, ©Theo Allofs/Corbis/Bettmann.

Chapter 6 Pages 351 and 437, Professor Vijay Panchang, Ph.D, P.E., Texas A&M University, Galveston; Page 363, Doug Pensinger/Getty Images; Page 410, P. Berndt/Custom Medical Stock Photo, Inc.

Chapter 7 Pages 439 and 507, Reuters Limited.

Chapter 8 Pages 509 and 560, Getty Images/PhotoDisc; Page 521, eStock Photography; Page 544, Nelson Hancock/Rough Guides Dorling Kindersley; Page 546, Richard Megna/Fundamental Photographs, NYC.

Chapter 9 Pages 561 and 636, Joseph Drivas/Getty Images; Page 586, Engraving By P. Dupin/Corbis/Bettmann; Page 595, Corbis/Bettmann; Page 605, Library of Congress.

Chapter 10 Pages 637 and 704, Lynette Cook/Photo Researchers, Inc.; Page 656, Scott McDonald/Hedrich Blessing.

Chapter 11 Pages 705 and 801, Steven Rubin/The Image Works; Page 759, Corbis/Bettmann.

Chapter 12 Pages 803 and 847, NASA/GFSC/Tom Stack & Associates, Inc.; Page 829, The Granger Collection; Page 842, Corbis/Bettmann.

Chapter 13 Pages 849 and 877, Photofest; Page 870, The Granger Collection.

Chapter 14 Pages 879 and 918, NASA/GFSC/Tom Stack & Associates.

Appendix A Page A15, AP Wide World Photos, Page A22, #51, Whole Spirit Press; #52, Red River Press, Inc.; Page A76, Alamy Images.

Trigonometric Functions

6

Surf's Up: Using Models To Predict Huge Waves

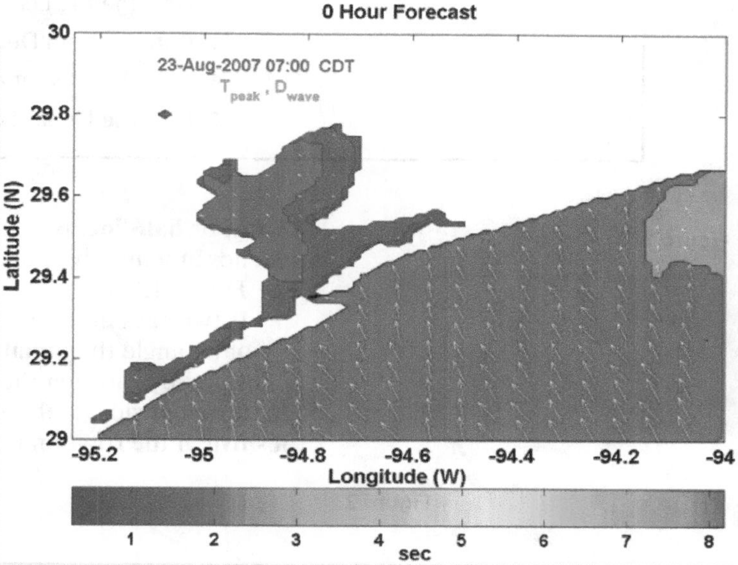

GALVESTON, Feb. 15, 2005—If you are a ship captain and there might be 50-foot waves headed your way, you would appreciate some information about them, right?

That's the idea behind a wave model system a Texas A&M University at Galveston professor has developed. His detailed wave prediction system is currently in use in the Gulf of Mexico and the Gulf of Maine.

Vijay Panchang, head of the Department of Maritime Systems Engineering, doesn't make waves; he predicts what they will do, when they will do it, and how high they will get.

Using data provided daily from NOAA [National Oceanic and Atmospheric Administration] and his own complex mathematical models, Panchang and research engineer Doncheng Li provide daily wave model predictions for much of the Texas coast, the Gulf of Mexico, and the Gulf of Maine. Their simulations, updated every 12 hours, provide a forecast for two days ahead.

Because the models use wind data, tsunamis that are created by undersea earthquakes cannot be predicted. But that is not to say his modeling system does not come up with some big waves.

His wave model predicted big waves in November 2003 in the Gulf of Maine, and it was accurate; waves as high as 30 feet were recorded during one storm even in coastal regions.

Last summer during Hurricane Ivan, a buoy located 60 miles south of the Alabama coast recorded a whopping 60-foot wave. "There may have been higher waves because right after recording the 60-foot wave, the buoy snapped and stopped functioning," he says.

Source: Science Daily www.sciencedaily.com/releases/2005/02/050222193810.htm. Posted February 23, 2005.

—See Chapter Project I—

A Look Back

In Chapter 2, we began our discussion of functions. We defined domain and range and independent and dependent variables; we found the value of a function and graphed functions. We continued our study of functions by listing properties that a function might have, like being even or odd, and we created a library of functions, naming key functions and listing their properties, including the graph.

A Look Ahead

In this chapter we define the trigonometric functions, six functions that have wide application. We shall talk about their domain and range, see how to find values, graph them, and develop a list of their properties.

There are two widely accepted approaches to the development of the trigonometric functions: one uses right triangles; the other uses circles, especially the unit circle. In this book, we develop the trigonometric functions using the unit circle. In Section 8.1, we introduce trigonometric functions using right triangles.

Outline

6.1 Angles and Their Measure

PREPARING FOR THIS SECTION *Before getting started, review the following:*

- Circumference and Area of a Circle (Appendix A, Section A.2, p. A16)
- Uniform Motion (Appendix A, Section A.8, p. A72)

Now Work the 'Are You Prepared?' problems on page 361.

OBJECTIVES
1. Convert between Decimals and Degrees, Minutes, Seconds Forms for Angles (p. 354)
2. Find the Arc Length of a Circle (p. 356)
3. Convert from Degrees to Radians and from Radians to Degrees (p. 356)
4. Find the Area of a Sector of a Circle (p. 359)
5. Find the Linear Speed of an Object Traveling in Circular Motion (p. 360)

Figure 1

A **ray,** or **half-line,** is that portion of a line that starts at a point V on the line and extends indefinitely in one direction. The starting point V of a ray is called its **vertex.** See Figure 1.

If two rays are drawn with a common vertex, they form an **angle.** We call one ray of an angle the **initial side** and the other the **terminal side.** The angle formed is identified by showing the direction and amount of rotation from the initial side to the terminal side. If the rotation is in the counterclockwise direction, the angle is **positive;** if the rotation is clockwise, the angle is **negative.** See Figure 2.

Figure 2

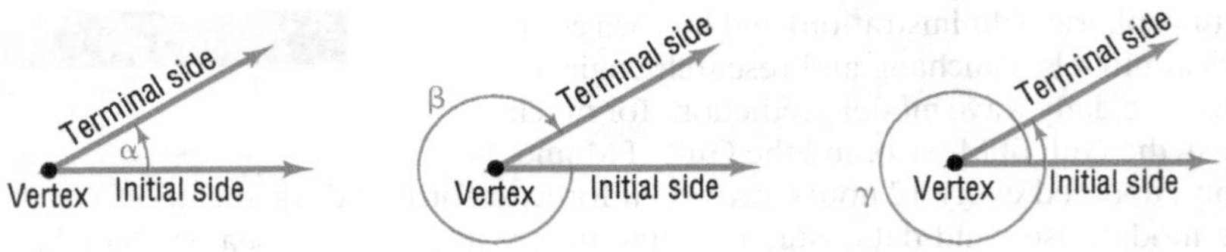

Lowercase Greek letters, such as α (alpha), β (beta), γ (gamma), and θ (theta), will often be used to denote angles. Notice in Figure 2(a) that the angle α is positive because the direction of the rotation from the initial side to the terminal side is counterclockwise. The angle β in Figure 2(b) is negative because the rotation is clockwise. The angle γ in Figure 2(c) is positive. Notice that the angle α in Figure 2(a) and the angle γ in Figure 2(c) have the same initial side and the same terminal side. However, α and γ are unequal, because the amount of rotation required to go from the initial side to the terminal side is greater for angle γ than for angle α.

An angle θ is said to be in **standard position** if its vertex is at the origin of a rectangular coordinate system and its initial side coincides with the positive x-axis. See Figure 3.

Figure 3

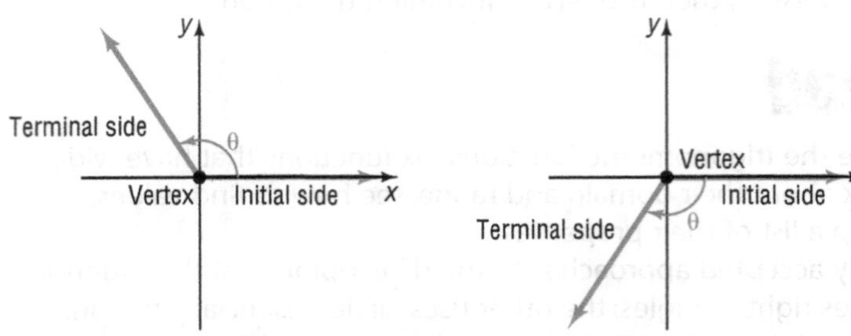

(a) θ is in standard position; θ is positive
(b) θ is in standard position; θ is negative

When an angle θ is in standard position, the terminal side will lie either in a quadrant, in which case we say that θ **lies in that quadrant,** or the terminal side will lie on the x-axis or the y-axis, in which case we say that θ is a **quadrantal angle.** For example, the angle θ in Figure 4(a) lies in quadrant II, the angle θ in Figure 4(b) lies in quadrant IV, and the angle θ in Figure 4(c) is a quadrantal angle.

Figure 4

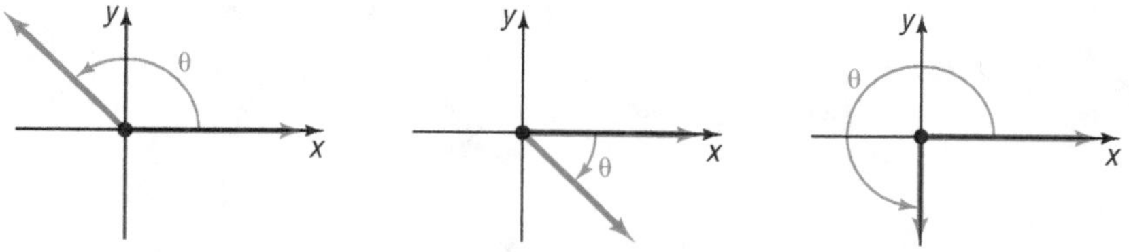

(a) θ lies in quadrant II **(b)** θ lies in quadrant IV **(c)** θ is a quadrantal angle

We measure angles by determining the amount of rotation needed for the initial side to become coincident with the terminal side. The two commonly used measures for angles are *degrees* and *radians*.

Degrees

HISTORICAL NOTE *One counterclockwise rotation is 360° due to the Babylonian year, which had 360 days in it.* ■

The angle formed by rotating the initial side exactly once in the counterclockwise direction until it coincides with itself (1 revolution) is said to measure 360 degrees, abbreviated 360°. **One degree, 1°**, is $\frac{1}{360}$ revolution. A **right angle** is an angle that measures 90°, or $\frac{1}{4}$ revolution; a **straight angle** is an angle that measures 180°, or $\frac{1}{2}$ revolution. See Figure 5. As Figure 5(b) shows, it is customary to indicate a right angle by using the symbol ⊾.

Figure 5

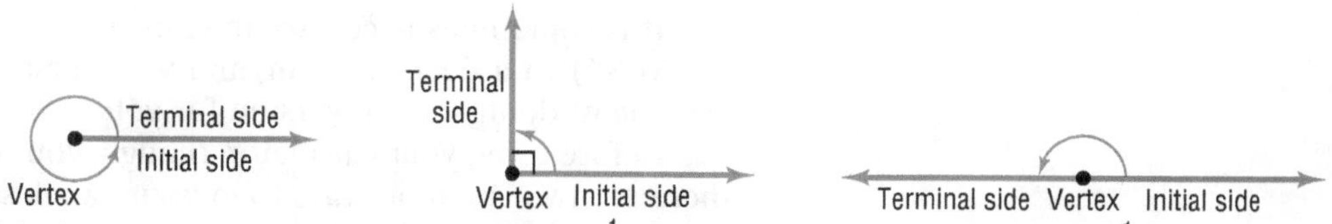

(a) 1 revolution counterclockwise, 360° **(b)** right angle, $\frac{1}{4}$ revolution counterclockwise, 90° **(c)** straight angle, $\frac{1}{2}$ revolution counterclockwise, 180°

It is also customary to refer to an angle that measures θ degrees as an angle *of* θ degrees.

EXAMPLE 1 **Drawing an Angle**

Draw each angle.

(a) 45° (b) −90° (c) 225° (d) 405°

Solution (a) An angle of 45° is $\frac{1}{2}$ of a right angle. See Figure 6.

(b) An angle of −90° is $\frac{1}{4}$ revolution in the clockwise direction. See Figure 7.

Figure 6

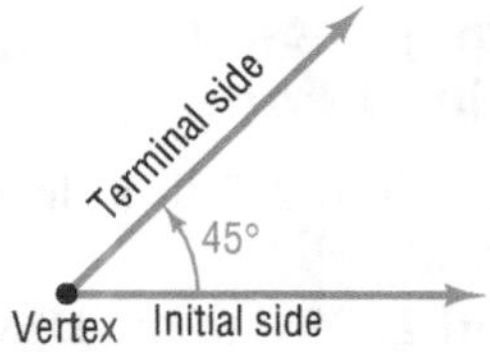

Figure 7

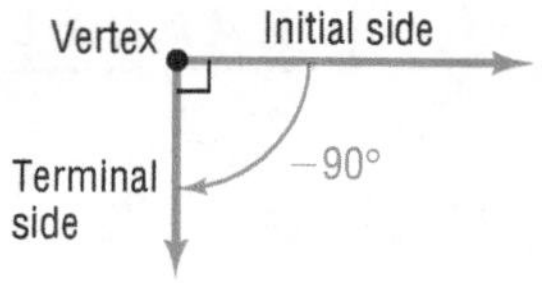

(c) An angle of 225° consists of a rotation through 180° followed by a rotation through 45°. See Figure 8.

Figure 8

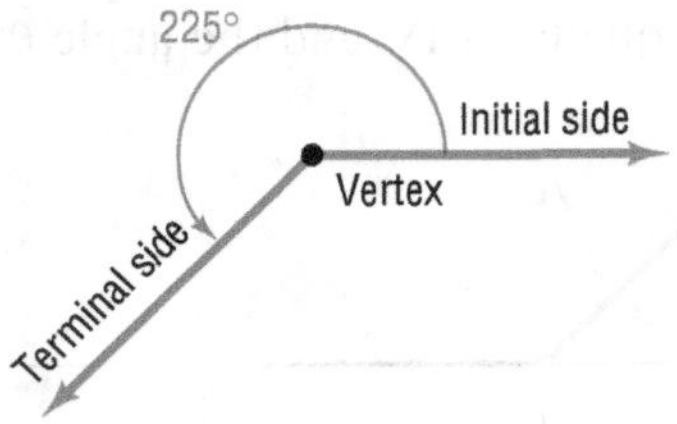

(d) An angle of 405° consists of 1 revolution (360°) followed by a rotation through 45°. See Figure 9.

Figure 9

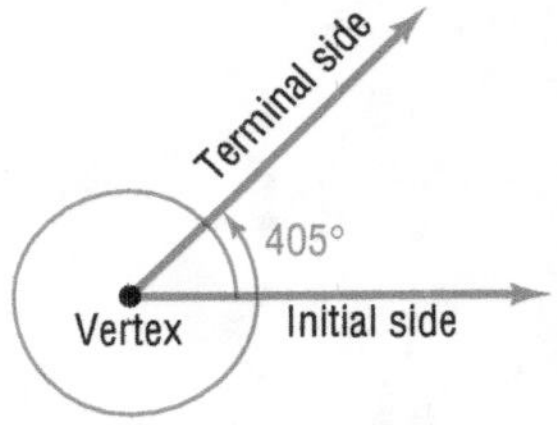

Now Work PROBLEM 11

1 Convert between Decimals and Degrees, Minutes, Seconds Forms for Angles

Although subdivisions of a degree may be obtained by using decimals, we also may use the notion of *minutes* and *seconds*. **One minute,** denoted by **1′**, is defined as $\frac{1}{60}$ degree. **One second,** denoted by **1″**, is defined as $\frac{1}{60}$ minute, or equivalently, $\frac{1}{3600}$ degree. An angle of, say, 30 degrees, 40 minutes, 10 seconds is written compactly as 30°40′10″. To summarize:

$$1 \text{ counterclockwise revolution} = 360^\circ \qquad \textbf{(1)}$$
$$1^\circ = 60' \qquad 1' = 60''$$

It is sometimes necessary to convert from the degree, minute, second notation (D°M′S″) to a decimal form, and vice versa. Check your calculator; it should be capable of doing the conversion for you.

Before using your calculator, though, you must set the mode to degrees because there are two common ways to measure angles: degree mode and radian mode. (We will define radians shortly.) Usually, a menu is used to change from one mode to another. Check your owner's manual to find out how your particular calculator works.

Now let's see how to convert from the degree, minute, second notation (D°M′S″) to a decimal form, and vice versa, by looking at some examples:

$$15^\circ 30' = 15.5^\circ \quad \text{because} \quad 30' = 30 \cdot 1' = 30 \cdot \left(\frac{1}{60}\right)^\circ = 0.5^\circ$$

$1' = \left(\frac{1}{60}\right)^\circ$

$$32.25^\circ = 32^\circ 15' \quad \text{because} \quad 0.25^\circ = \left(\frac{1}{4}\right)^\circ = \frac{1}{4} \cdot 1^\circ = \frac{1}{4}(60') = 15'$$

$1^\circ = 60'$

EXAMPLE 2

Converting between Degrees, Minutes, Seconds, and Decimal Forms

(a) Convert 50°6′21″ to a decimal in degrees. Round the answer to four decimal places.

(b) Convert 21.256° to the D°M′S″ form. Round the answer to the nearest second.

Algebraic Solution

(a) Because $1' = \left(\frac{1}{60}\right)^\circ$ and $1'' = \left(\frac{1}{60}\right)' = \left(\frac{1}{60}\cdot\frac{1}{60}\right)^\circ$, we convert as follows:

$$\begin{aligned} 50°6'21'' &= 50° + 6' + 21'' \\ &= 50° + 6\cdot\left(\frac{1}{60}\right)^\circ + 21\cdot\left(\frac{1}{60}\cdot\frac{1}{60}\right)^\circ \\ &\approx 50° + 0.1° + 0.0058° \\ &= 50.1058° \end{aligned}$$

(b) We proceed as follows:

$$\begin{aligned} 21.256° &= 21° + 0.256° \\ &= 21° + (0.256)(60') && \text{Convert fraction of degree to minutes; } 1° = 60'. \\ &= 21° + 15.36' \\ &= 21° + 15' + 0.36' \\ &= 21° + 15' + (0.36)(60'') && \text{Convert fraction of minute to seconds; } 1' = 60''. \\ &= 21° + 15' + 21.6'' \\ &\approx 21°15'22'' && \text{Round to the nearest second.} \end{aligned}$$

Graphing Solution

(a) Figure 10 shows the solution using a TI-84 Plus graphing calculator.

Figure 10

So $50°6'21'' = 51.1058°$ rounded to four decimal places.

(b) Figure 11 shows the solution using a T1-84 Plus graphing calculator.

Figure 11

So $21.256° = 21°15'22''$ rounded to the nearest second.

Now Work PROBLEMS 23 AND 29

In many applications, such as describing the exact location of a star or the precise position of a ship at sea, angles measured in degrees, minutes, and even seconds are used. For calculation purposes, these are transformed to decimal form. In other applications, especially those in calculus, angles are measured using *radians*.

Radians

A **central angle** is a positive angle whose vertex is at the center of a circle. The rays of a central angle subtend (intersect) an arc on the circle. If the radius of the circle is r and the length of the arc subtended by the central angle is also r, then the measure of the angle is **1 radian.** See Figure 12(a).

For a circle of radius 1, the rays of a central angle with measure 1 radian subtend an arc of length 1. For a circle of radius 3, the rays of a central angle with measure 1 radian subtend an arc of length 3. See Figure 12(b).

Figure 12

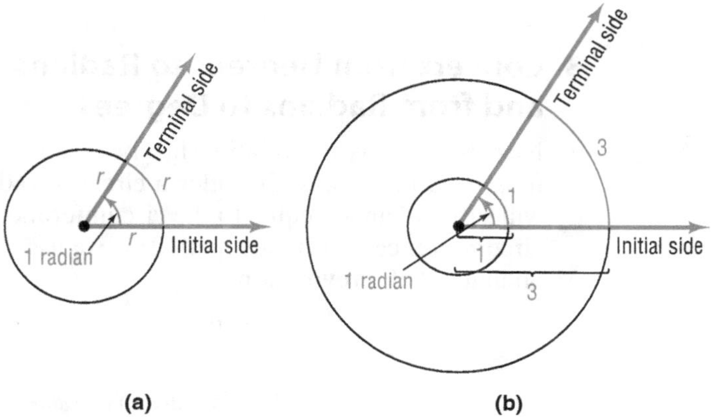

2 Find the Arc Length of a Circle

Figure 13

$\dfrac{\theta}{\theta_1} = \dfrac{s}{s_1}$

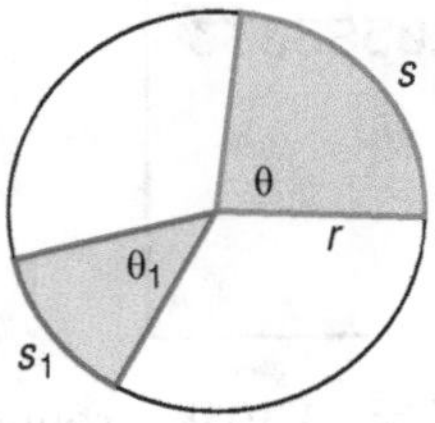

Now consider a circle of radius r and two central angles, θ and θ_1, measured in radians. Suppose that these central angles subtend arcs of lengths s and s_1, respectively, as shown in Figure 13. From geometry, we know that the ratio of the measures of the angles equals the ratio of the corresponding lengths of the arcs subtended by these angles; that is,

$$\frac{\theta}{\theta_1} = \frac{s}{s_1} \qquad (2)$$

Suppose that $\theta_1 = 1$ radian. Refer again to Figure 12(a). The length s_1 of the arc subtended by the central angle $\theta_1 = 1$ radian equals the radius r of the circle. Then $s_1 = r$, so equation (2) reduces to

$$\frac{\theta}{1} = \frac{s}{r} \quad \text{or} \quad s = r\theta \qquad (3)$$

THEOREM

Arc Length

For a circle of radius r, a central angle of θ radians subtends an arc whose length s is

$$s = r\theta \qquad (4)$$

NOTE Formulas must be consistent with regard to the units used. In equation (4), we write

$$s = r\theta$$

To see the units, however, we must go back to equation (3) and write

$$\frac{\theta \text{ radians}}{1 \text{ radian}} = \frac{s \text{ length units}}{r \text{ length units}}$$

$$s \text{ length units} = r \text{ length units} \frac{\theta \text{ radians}}{1 \text{ radian}}$$

Since the radians cancel, we are left with

$$s \text{ length units} = (r \text{ length units})\theta \qquad s = r\theta$$

where θ appears to be "dimensionless" but, in fact, is measured in radians. So, in using the formula $s = r\theta$, the dimension for θ is radians, and any convenient unit of length (such as inches or meters) may be used for s and r. ■

EXAMPLE 3 **Finding the Length of an Arc of a Circle**

Find the length of the arc of a circle of radius 2 meters subtended by a central angle of 0.25 radian.

Solution We use equation (4) with $r = 2$ meters and $\theta = 0.25$. The length s of the arc is

$$s = r\theta = 2(0.25) = 0.5 \text{ meter}$$

Now Work PROBLEM 71

3 Convert from Degrees to Radians and from Radians to Degrees

Figure 14

1 revolution = 2π radians

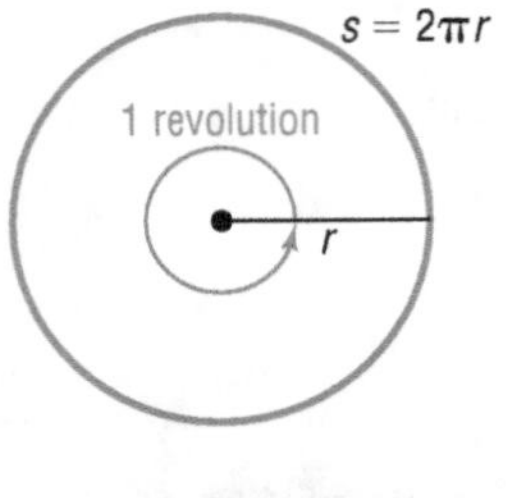

Next we discuss the relationship between angles measured in degrees and angles measured in radians. Consider a circle of radius r. A central angle of 1 revolution will subtend an arc equal to the circumference of the circle (Figure 14). Because the circumference of a circle equals $2\pi r$, we use $s = 2\pi r$ in equation (4) to find that, for an angle θ of 1 revolution,

$$s = r\theta$$

$$2\pi r = r\theta \qquad \theta = 1 \text{ revolution; } s = 2\pi r$$

$$\theta = 2\pi \text{ radians} \qquad \text{Solve for } \theta.$$

From this we have,

$$1 \text{ revolution} = 2\pi \text{ radians} \tag{5}$$

Since 1 revolution $= 360°$, we have

$$360° = 2\pi \text{ radians}$$

Dividing both sides by 2 yields

$$180° = \pi \text{ radians} \tag{6}$$

Divide both sides of equation (6) by 180. Then

$$1 \text{ degree} = \frac{\pi}{180} \text{ radian}$$

Divide both sides of (6) by π. Then

$$\frac{180}{\pi} \text{ degrees} = 1 \text{ radian}$$

We have the following two conversion formulas:

$$1 \text{ degree} = \frac{\pi}{180} \text{ radian} \qquad 1 \text{ radian} = \frac{180}{\pi} \text{ degrees} \tag{7}$$

EXAMPLE 4 Converting from Degrees to Radians

Convert each angle in degrees to radians.

(a) 60° (b) 150° (c) −45° (d) 90° (e) 107°

Solution

(a) $60° = 60 \cdot 1 \text{ degree} = 60 \cdot \frac{\pi}{180} \text{ radian} = \frac{\pi}{3} \text{ radians}$

(b) $150° = 150 \cdot 1° = 150 \cdot \frac{\pi}{180} \text{ radian} = \frac{5\pi}{6} \text{ radians}$

(c) $-45° = -45 \cdot \frac{\pi}{180} \text{ radian} = -\frac{\pi}{4} \text{ radian}$

(d) $90° = 90 \cdot \frac{\pi}{180} \text{ radian} = \frac{\pi}{2} \text{ radians}$

(e) $107° = 107 \cdot \frac{\pi}{180} \text{ radian} \approx 1.868 \text{ radians}$

Example 4, parts (a)–(d), illustrates that angles that are "nice" fractions of a revolution are expressed in radian measure as fractional multiples of π, rather than as decimals. For example, a right angle, as in Example 4(d), is left in the form $\frac{\pi}{2}$ radians, which is exact, rather than using the approximation $\frac{\pi}{2} \approx \frac{3.1416}{2} = 1.5708$ radians. When the fractions are not "nice," we use the decimal approximation of the angle, as in Example 4(e).

Now Work PROBLEMS 35 AND 61

EXAMPLE 5 Converting Radians to Degrees

Convert each angle in radians to degrees.

(a) $\frac{\pi}{6}$ radian (b) $\frac{3\pi}{2}$ radians (c) $-\frac{3\pi}{4}$ radians

(d) $\frac{7\pi}{3}$ radians (e) 3 radians

Solution

(a) $\frac{\pi}{6}\text{ radian} = \frac{\pi}{6}\cdot 1\text{ radian} = \frac{\pi}{6}\cdot\frac{180}{\pi}\text{ degrees} = 30°$

(b) $\frac{3\pi}{2}\text{ radians} = \frac{3\pi}{2}\cdot\frac{180}{\pi}\text{ degrees} = 270°$

(c) $-\frac{3\pi}{4}\text{ radians} = -\frac{3\pi}{4}\cdot\frac{180}{\pi}\text{ degrees} = -135°$

(d) $\frac{7\pi}{3}\text{ radians} = \frac{7\pi}{3}\cdot\frac{180}{\pi}\text{ degrees} = 420°$

(e) $3\text{ radians} = 3\cdot\frac{180}{\pi}\text{ degrees} \approx 171.89°$

Now Work PROBLEM 47

Table 1 lists the degree and radian measures of some commonly encountered angles. You should learn to feel equally comfortable using degree or radian measure for these angles.

Table 1

Degrees	0°	30°	45°	60°	90°	120°	135°	150°	180°
Radians	0	$\frac{\pi}{6}$	$\frac{\pi}{4}$	$\frac{\pi}{3}$	$\frac{\pi}{2}$	$\frac{2\pi}{3}$	$\frac{3\pi}{4}$	$\frac{5\pi}{6}$	π
Degrees		210°	225°	240°	270°	300°	315°	330°	360°
Radians		$\frac{7\pi}{6}$	$\frac{5\pi}{4}$	$\frac{4\pi}{3}$	$\frac{3\pi}{2}$	$\frac{5\pi}{3}$	$\frac{7\pi}{4}$	$\frac{11\pi}{6}$	2π

EXAMPLE 6 Finding the Distance between Two Cities

See Figure 15(a). The latitude of a location L is the angle formed by a ray drawn from the center of Earth to the Equator and a ray drawn from the center of Earth to L. See Figure 15(b). Glasgow, Montana, is due north of Albuquerque, New Mexico. Find the distance between Glasgow (48°9′ north latitude) and Albuquerque (35°5′ north latitude). Assume that the radius of Earth is 3960 miles.

Figure 15

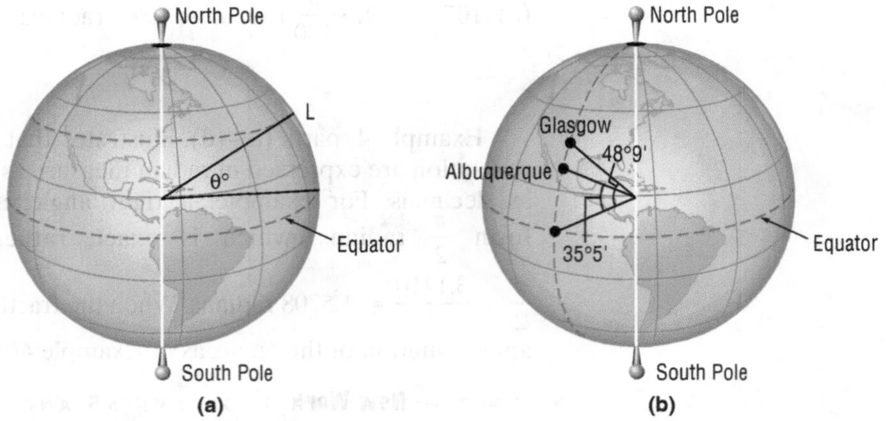

Solution The measure of the central angle between the two cities is $48°9' - 35°5' = 13°4'$. We use equation (4), $s = r\theta$, but first we must convert the angle of $13°4'$ to radians.

$$\theta = 13°4' \underset{4' = \left(\frac{4}{60}\right)^\circ}{\approx} 13.0667° = 13.0667 \cdot \frac{\pi}{180} \text{ radian} \approx 0.228 \text{ radian}$$

We use $\theta = 0.228$ radian and $r = 3960$ miles in equation (4). The distance between the two cities is

$$s = r\theta = 3960 \cdot 0.228 \approx 903 \text{ miles}$$

NOTE If the measure of an angle is given as 5, it is understood to mean 5 radians; if the measure of an angle is given as 5°, it means 5 degrees. ■

When an angle is measured in degrees, the degree symbol will always be shown. However, when an angle is measured in radians, we will follow the usual practice and omit the word *radians*. So, if the measure of an angle is given as $\frac{\pi}{6}$, it is understood to mean $\frac{\pi}{6}$ radian.

Now Work PROBLEM 101

4 Find the Area of a Sector of a Circle

Figure 16

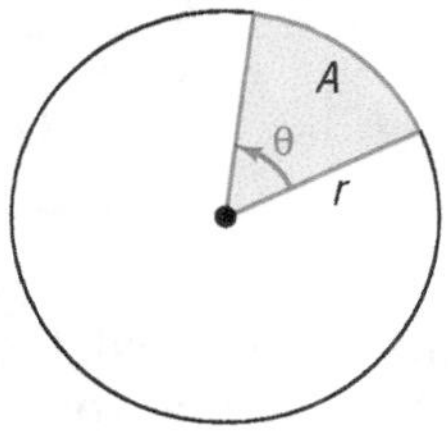

Consider a circle of radius r. Suppose that θ, measured in radians, is a central angle of this circle. See Figure 16. We seek a formula for the area A of the sector (shown in blue) formed by the angle θ.

Now consider a circle of radius r and two central angles θ and θ_1, both measured in radians. See Figure 17. From geometry, we know the ratio of the measures of the angles equals the ratio of the corresponding areas of the sectors formed by these angles. That is,

Figure 17 $\frac{\theta}{\theta_1} = \frac{A}{A_1}$

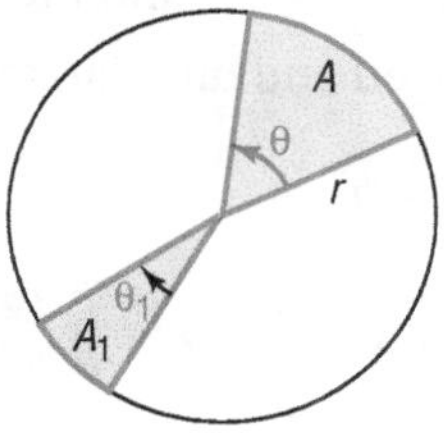

$$\frac{\theta}{\theta_1} = \frac{A}{A_1}$$

Suppose that $\theta_1 = 2\pi$ radians. Then A_1 = area of the circle $= \pi r^2$. Solving for A, we find

$$A = A_1\frac{\theta}{\theta_1} \underset{\substack{A_1 = \pi r^2 \\ \theta_1 = 2\pi}}{=} \pi r^2 \frac{\theta}{2\pi} = \frac{1}{2}r^2\theta$$

THEOREM

Area of a Sector

The area A of the sector of a circle of radius r formed by a central angle of θ radians is

$$A = \frac{1}{2}r^2\theta \tag{8}$$

EXAMPLE 7 **Finding the Area of a Sector of a Circle**

Find the area of the sector of a circle of radius 2 feet formed by an angle of 30°. Round the answer to two decimal places.

Solution We use equation (8) with $r = 2$ feet and $\theta = 30° = \frac{\pi}{6}$ radian. [Remember, in equation (8), θ must be in radians.]

$$A = \frac{1}{2}r^2\theta = \frac{1}{2}(2)^2\frac{\pi}{6} = \frac{\pi}{3}$$

The area A of the sector is 1.05 square feet, rounded to two decimal places.

Now Work PROBLEM 79

5 Find the Linear Speed of an Object Traveling in Circular Motion

We have already defined the average speed of an object as the distance traveled divided by the elapsed time in Appendix A, Section A.8.

Figure 18 $v = \frac{s}{t}$

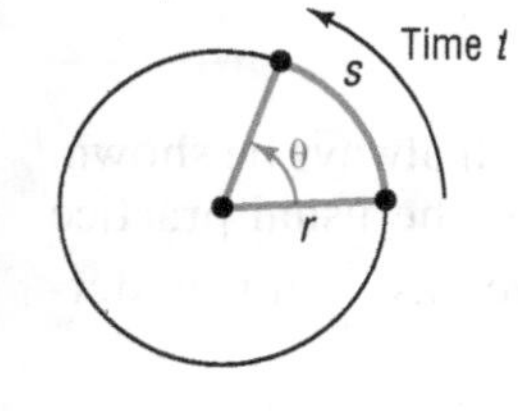

DEFINITION

Suppose that an object moves around a circle of radius r at a constant speed. If s is the distance traveled in time t around this circle, then the **linear speed** v of the object is defined as

$$v = \frac{s}{t} \tag{9}$$

As this object travels around the circle, suppose that θ (measured in radians) is the central angle swept out in time t. See Figure 18.

DEFINITION

The **angular speed** ω (the Greek letter omega) of this object is the angle θ (measured in radians) swept out, divided by the elapsed time t; that is,

$$\omega = \frac{\theta}{t} \tag{10}$$

Angular speed is the way the turning rate of an engine is described. For example, an engine idling at 900 rpm (revolutions per minute) is one that rotates at an angular speed of

$$900\frac{\text{revolutions}}{\text{minute}} = 900\frac{\cancel{\text{revolutions}}}{\text{minute}} \cdot 2\pi\frac{\text{radians}}{\cancel{\text{revolution}}} = 1800\pi\frac{\text{radians}}{\text{minute}}$$

There is an important relationship between linear speed and angular speed:

$$\text{linear speed} = v = \underset{\substack{\uparrow \\ (9)}}{\frac{s}{t}} \underset{\substack{\uparrow \\ s = r\theta}}{=} \frac{r\theta}{t} = r\left(\frac{\theta}{t}\right) \underset{\substack{\uparrow \\ (10)}}{=} r \cdot \omega$$

So

$$v = r\omega \tag{11}$$

where ω is measured in radians per unit time.

When using equation (11), remember that $v = \frac{s}{t}$ (the linear speed) has the dimensions of length per unit of time (such as feet per second or miles per hour), r (the radius of the circular motion) has the same length dimension as s, and ω (the angular speed) has the dimensions of radians per unit of time. If the angular speed is given in terms of *revolutions* per unit of time (as is often the case), be sure to convert it to *radians* per unit of time using the fact that 1 revolution $= 2\pi$ radians before attempting to use equation (11).

EXAMPLE 8 **Finding Linear Speed**

A child is spinning a rock at the end of a 2-foot rope at the rate of 180 revolutions per minute (rpm). Find the linear speed of the rock when it is released.

Solution Look at Figure 19. The rock is moving around a circle of radius $r = 2$ feet. The angular speed ω of the rock is

$$\omega = 180\frac{\text{revolutions}}{\text{minute}} = 180\frac{\cancel{\text{revolutions}}}{\text{minute}} \cdot 2\pi\frac{\text{radians}}{\cancel{\text{revolution}}} = 360\pi\frac{\text{radians}}{\text{minute}}$$

Figure 19

From equation (11), the linear speed v of the rock is

$$v = r\omega = 2 \text{ feet} \cdot 360\pi \frac{\text{radians}}{\text{minute}} = 720\pi \frac{\text{feet}}{\text{minute}} \approx 2262 \frac{\text{feet}}{\text{minute}}$$

The linear speed of the rock when it is released is 2262 ft/min ≈ 25.7 mi/hr.

Now Work PROBLEM 97

Historical Feature

Trigonometry was developed by Greek astronomers, who regarded the sky as the inside of a sphere, so it was natural that triangles on a sphere were investigated early (by Menelaus of Alexandria about AD 100) and that triangles in the plane were studied much later. The first book containing a systematic treatment of plane and spherical trigonometry was written by the Persian astronomer Nasir Eddin (about AD 1250).

Regiomontanus (1436–1476) is the person most responsible for moving trigonometry from astronomy into mathematics. His work was improved by Copernicus (1473–1543) and Copernicus's student Rhaeticus (1514–1576). Rhaeticus's book was the first to define the six trigonometric functions as ratios of sides of triangles, although he did not give the functions their present names. Credit for this is due to Thomas Finck (1583), but Finck's notation was by no means universally accepted at the time. The notation was finally stabilized by the textbooks of Leonhard Euler (1707–1783).

Trigonometry has since evolved from its use by surveyors, navigators, and engineers to present applications involving ocean tides, the rise and fall of food supplies in certain ecologies, brain wave patterns, and many other phenomena.

6.1 Assess Your Understanding

'Are You Prepared?' *Answers are given at the end of these exercises. If you get a wrong answer, read the pages listed in red.*

1. What is the formula for the circumference C of a circle of radius r? What is the formula for the area A of a circle of radius r? (p. A16)

2. What is the formula for uniform motion? (p. A72)

Concepts and Vocabulary

3. An angle θ is in _____ _____ if its vertex is at the origin of a rectangular coordinate system and its initial side coincides with the positive x-axis.

4. On a circle of radius r, a central angle of θ radians subtends an arc of length $s =$ _____; the area of the sector formed by this angle θ is $A =$ _____.

5. An object travels around a circle of radius r with constant speed. If s is the distance traveled in time t around the circle and θ is the central angle (in radians) swept out in time t, then the linear speed of the object is $v =$ _____ and the angular speed of the object is $\omega =$ _____.

6. ***True or False*** $\pi = 180$.

7. ***True or False*** $180° = \pi$ radians.

8. ***True or False*** On the unit circle, if s is the length of the arc subtended by a central angle θ, measured in radians, then $s = \theta$.

9. ***True or False*** The area A of the sector of a circle of radius r formed by a central angle of θ degrees is $A = \frac{1}{2}r^2\theta$.

10. ***True or False*** For circular motion on a circle of radius r, linear speed equals angular speed divided by r.

Skill Building

In Problems 11–22, draw each angle.

11. $30°$ **12.** $60°$ **13.** $135°$ **14.** $-120°$ **15.** $450°$ **16.** $540°$

17. $\frac{3\pi}{4}$ **18.** $\frac{4\pi}{3}$ **19.** $-\frac{\pi}{6}$ **20.** $-\frac{2\pi}{3}$ **21.** $\frac{16\pi}{3}$ **22.** $\frac{21\pi}{4}$

In Problems 23–28, convert each angle to a decimal in degrees. Round your answer to two decimal places.

23. $40°10'25''$ **24.** $61°42'21''$ **25.** $1°2'3''$ **26.** $73°40'40''$ **27.** $9°9'9''$ **28.** $98°22'45''$

In Problems 29–34, convert each angle to $D°M'S''$ form. Round your answer to the nearest second.

29. $40.32°$ **30.** $61.24°$ **31.** $18.255°$ **32.** $29.411°$ **33.** $19.99°$ **34.** $44.01°$

In Problems 35–46, convert each angle in degrees to radians. Express your answer as a multiple of π.

35. $30°$ **36.** $120°$ **37.** $240°$ **38.** $330°$ **39.** $-60°$ **40.** $-30°$

41. $180°$ **42.** $270°$ **43.** $-135°$ **44.** $-225°$ **45.** $-90°$ **46.** $-180°$

In Problems 47–58, convert each angle in radians to degrees.

47. $\frac{\pi}{3}$ **48.** $\frac{5\pi}{6}$ **49.** $-\frac{5\pi}{4}$ **50.** $-\frac{2\pi}{3}$ **51.** $\frac{\pi}{2}$ **52.** 4π

53. $\frac{\pi}{12}$ **54.** $\frac{5\pi}{12}$ **55.** $-\frac{\pi}{2}$ **56.** $-\pi$ **57.** $-\frac{\pi}{6}$ **58.** $-\frac{3\pi}{4}$

In Problems 59–64, convert each angle in degrees to radians. Express your answer in decimal form, rounded to two decimal places.

59. $17°$ **60.** $73°$ **61.** $-40°$ **62.** $-51°$ **63.** $125°$ **64.** $350°$

In Problems 65–70, convert each angle in radians to degrees. Express your answer in decimal form, rounded to two decimal places.

65. 3.14 **66.** 0.75 **67.** 2 **68.** 3 **69.** 6.32 **70.** $\sqrt{2}$

In Problems 71–78, s denotes the length of the arc of a circle of radius r subtended by the central angle θ. Find the missing quantity. Round answers to three decimal places.

71. $r = 10$ meters, $\theta = \frac{1}{2}$ radian, $s = ?$

72. $r = 6$ feet, $\theta = 2$ radians, $s = ?$

73. $\theta = \frac{1}{3}$ radian, $s = 2$ feet, $r = ?$

74. $\theta = \frac{1}{4}$ radian, $s = 6$ centimeters, $r = ?$

75. $r = 5$ miles, $s = 3$ miles, $\theta = ?$

76. $r = 6$ meters, $s = 8$ meters, $\theta = ?$

77. $r = 2$ inches, $\theta = 30°$, $s = ?$

78. $r = 3$ meters, $\theta = 120°$, $s = ?$

In Problems 79–86, A denotes the area of the sector of a circle of radius r formed by the central angle θ. Find the missing quantity. Round answers to three decimal places.

79. $r = 10$ meters, $\theta = \frac{1}{2}$ radian, $A = ?$

80. $r = 6$ feet, $\theta = 2$ radians, $A = ?$

81. $\theta = \frac{1}{3}$ radian, $A = 2$ square feet, $r = ?$

82. $\theta = \frac{1}{4}$ radian, $A = 6$ square centimeters, $r = ?$

83. $r = 5$ miles, $A = 3$ square miles, $\theta = ?$

84. $r = 6$ meters, $A = 8$ square meters, $\theta = ?$

85. $r = 2$ inches, $\theta = 30°$, $A = ?$

86. $r = 3$ meters, $\theta = 120°$, $A = ?$

In Problems 87–90, find the length s and area A. Round answers to three decimal places.

87.
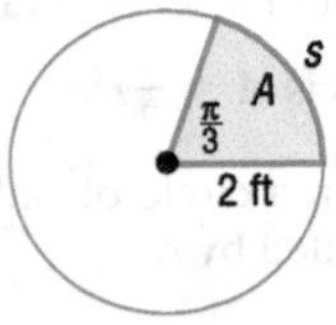

88.
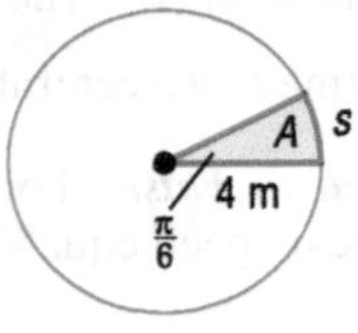

89.
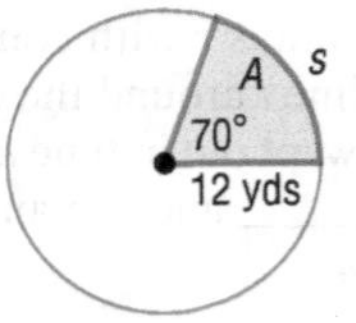

90.
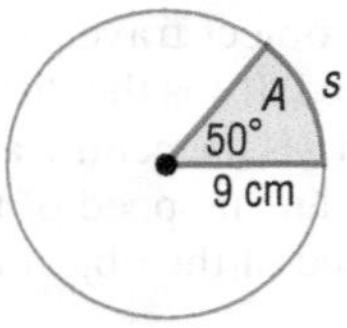

Applications and Extensions

91. Movement of a Minute Hand The minute hand of a clock is 6 inches long. How far does the tip of the minute hand move in 15 minutes? How far does it move in 25 minutes? Round answers to two decimal places.

92. Movement of a Pendulum A pendulum swings through an angle of 20° each second. If the pendulum is 40 inches long, how far does its tip move each second? Round answers to two decimal places.

93. Area of a Sector Find the area of the sector of a circle of radius 4 meters formed by an angle of 45°. Round the answer to two decimal places.

94. Area of a Sector Find the area of the sector of a circle of radius 3 centimeters formed by an angle of 60°. Round the answer to two decimal places.

95. Watering a Lawn A water sprinkler sprays water over a distance of 30 feet while rotating through an angle of 135°. What area of lawn receives water?

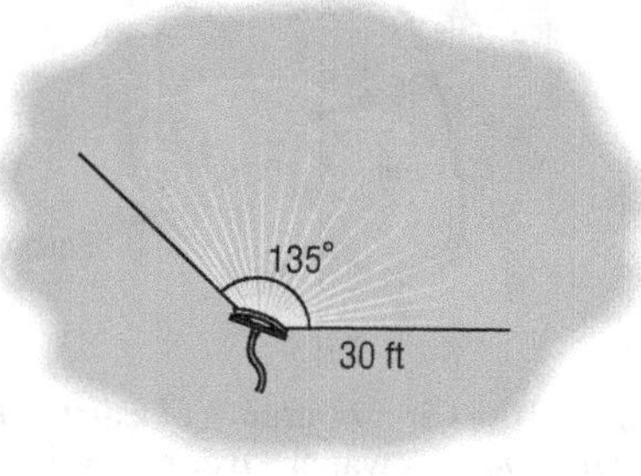

96. Designing a Water Sprinkler An engineer is asked to design a water sprinkler that will cover a field of 100 square yards that is in the shape of a sector of a circle of radius 15 yards. Through what angle should the sprinkler rotate?

97. Motion on a Circle An object is traveling around a circle with a radius of 5 centimeters. If in 20 seconds a central angle of $\frac{1}{3}$ radian is swept out, what is the angular speed of the object? What is its linear speed?

98. Motion on a Circle An object is traveling around a circle with a radius of 2 meters. If in 20 seconds the object travels 5 meters, what is its angular speed? What is its linear speed?

99. Bicycle Wheels The diameter of each wheel of a bicycle is 26 inches. If you are traveling at a speed of 35 miles per hour on this bicycle, through how many revolutions per minute are the wheels turning?

100. Car Wheels The radius of each wheel of a car is 15 inches. If the wheels are turning at the rate of 3 revolutions per second, how fast is the car moving? Express your answer in inches per second and in miles per hour.

In Problems 101–104, the latitude of a location L is the angle formed by a ray drawn from the center of Earth to the Equator and a ray drawn from the center of Earth to L. See the figure.

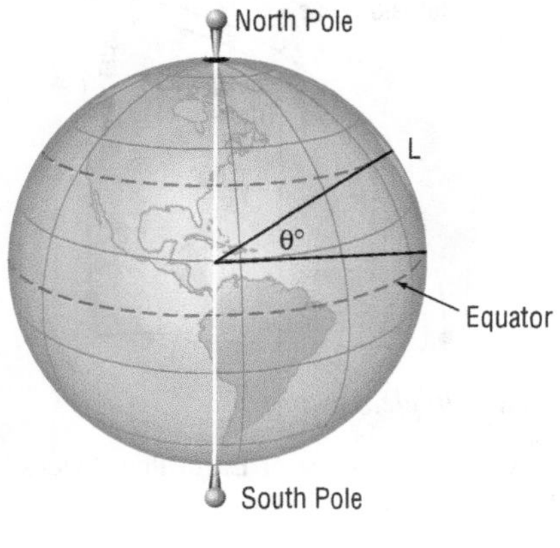

101. Distance between Cities Memphis, Tennessee, is due north of New Orleans, Louisiana. Find the distance between Memphis (35°9′ north latitude) and New Orleans (29°57′ north latitude). Assume that the radius of Earth is 3960 miles.

102. Distance between Cities Charleston, West Virginia, is due north of Jacksonville, Florida. Find the distance between Charleston (38°21′ north latitude) and Jacksonville (30°20′ north latitude). Assume that the radius of Earth is 3960 miles.

103. Linear Speed on Earth Earth rotates on an axis through its poles. The distance from the axis to a location on Earth 30° north latitude is about 3429.5 miles. Therefore, a location on Earth at 30° north latitude is spinning on a circle of radius 3429.5 miles. Compute the linear speed on the surface of Earth at 30° north latitude.

104. Linear Speed on Earth Earth rotates on an axis through its poles. The distance from the axis to a location on Earth 40° north latitude is about 3033.5 miles. Therefore, a location on Earth at 40° north latitude is spinning on a circle of radius 3033.5 miles. Compute the linear speed on the surface of Earth at 40° north latitude.

105. Speed of the Moon The mean distance of the moon from Earth is 2.39×10^5 miles. Assuming that the orbit of the moon around Earth is circular and that 1 revolution takes 27.3 days, find the linear speed of the moon. Express your answer in miles per hour.

106. Speed of Earth The mean distance of Earth from the Sun is 9.29×10^7 miles. Assuming that the orbit of Earth around the Sun is circular and that 1 revolution takes 365 days, find the linear speed of Earth. Express your answer in miles per hour.

107. Pulleys Two pulleys, one with radius 2 inches and the other with radius 8 inches, are connected by a belt. (See the figure.) If the 2-inch pulley is caused to rotate at 3 revolutions per minute, determine the revolutions per minute of the 8-inch pulley.

[**Hint:** The linear speeds of the pulleys are the same; both equal the speed of the belt.]

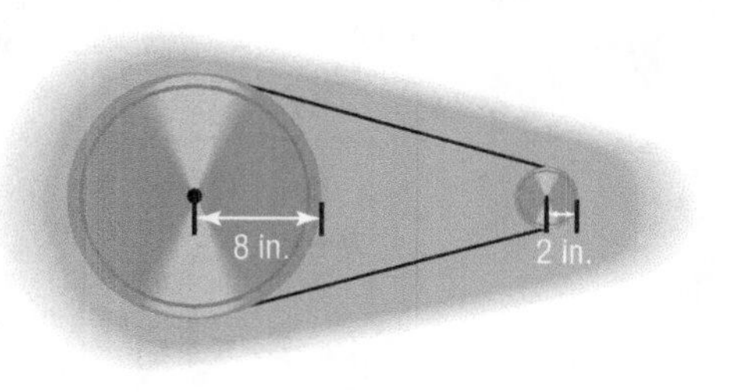

108. Ferris Wheels A neighborhood carnival has a Ferris wheel whose radius is 30 feet. You measure the time it takes for one revolution to be 70 seconds. What is the linear speed (in feet per second) of this Ferris wheel? What is the angular speed in radians per second?

109. Computing the Speed of a River Current To approximate the speed of the current of a river, a circular paddle wheel with radius 4 feet is lowered into the water. If the current causes the wheel to rotate at a speed of 10 revolutions per minute, what is the speed of the current? Express your answer in miles per hour.

110. Spin Balancing Tires A spin balancer rotates the wheel of a car at 480 revolutions per minute. If the diameter of the wheel is 26 inches, what road speed is being tested? Express your answer in miles per hour. At how many revolutions per minute should the balancer be set to test a road speed of 80 miles per hour?

111. The Cable Cars of San Francisco At the Cable Car Museum you can see the four cable lines that are used to pull cable cars up and down the hills of San Francisco. Each cable travels at a speed of 9.55 miles per hour, caused by a rotating wheel whose diameter is 8.5 feet. How fast is the wheel rotating? Express your answer in revolutions per minute.

112. Difference in Time of Sunrise Naples, Florida, is approximately 90 miles due west of Ft. Lauderdale. How much sooner would a person in Ft. Lauderdale first see the rising Sun than a person in Naples? See the hint.

[**Hint:** Consult the figure. When a person at Q sees the first rays of the Sun, a person at P is still in the dark. The person at P sees the first rays after Earth has rotated so that P is at the location Q. Now use the fact that at the latitude of Ft. Lauderdale in 24 hours an arc of length $2\pi(3559)$ miles is subtended.]

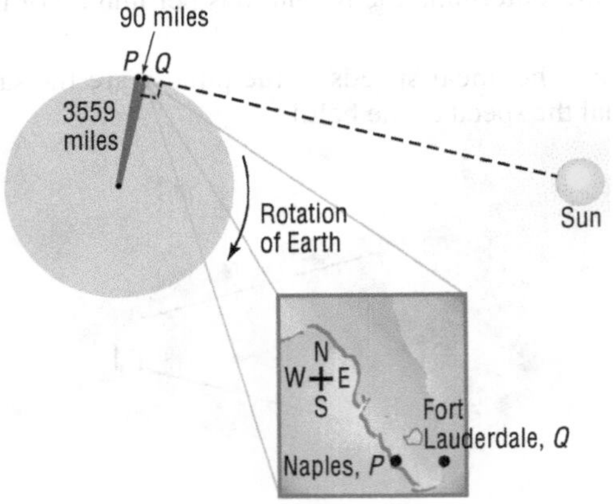

113. Keeping Up with the Sun How fast would you have to travel on the surface of Earth at the equator to keep up with the Sun (that is, so that the Sun would appear to remain in the same position in the sky)?

114. Nautical Miles A **nautical mile** equals the length of arc subtended by a central angle of 1 minute on a great circle* on the surface of Earth. (See the figure on the top, right of the page.) If the radius of Earth is taken as 3960 miles, express 1 nautical mile in terms of ordinary, or **statute,** miles.

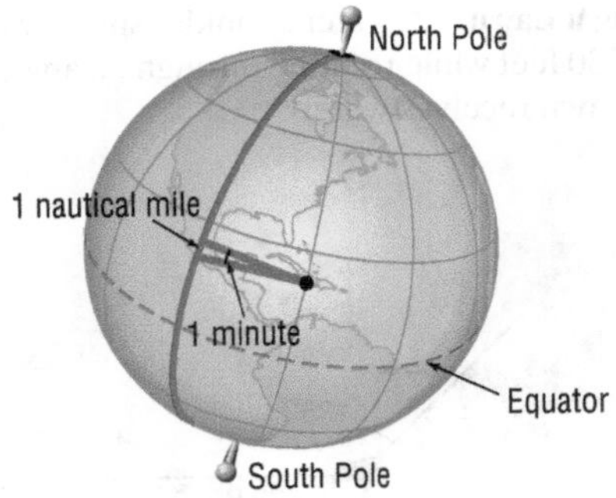

115. Approximating the Circumference of Earth Eratosthenes of Cyrene (276–194 BC) was a Greek scholar who lived and worked in Cyrene and Alexandria. One day while visiting in Syene he noticed that the Sun's rays shone directly down a well. On this date 1 year later, in Alexandria, which is 500 miles due north of Syene he measured the angle of the Sun to be about 7.2 degrees. See the figure. Use this information to approximate the radius and circumference of Earth.

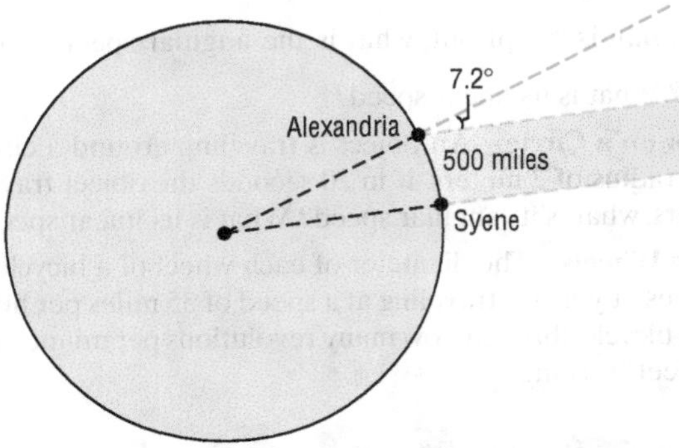

116. Designing a Little League Field For a 60-foot Little League Baseball field, the distance from home base to the nearest fence (or other obstruction) on fair territory should be a minimum of 200 feet. The commissioner of parks and recreation is making plans for a new 60-foot field. Because of limited ground availability, he will use the minimum required distance to the outfield fence. To increase safety, however, he plans to include a 10-foot wide warning track on the inside of the fence. To further increase safety, the fence and warning track will extend both directions into foul territory. In total the arc formed by the outfield fence (including the extensions into the foul territories) will be subtended by a central angle at home plate measuring 96°, as illustrated.

(a) Determine the length of the outfield fence.

(b) Determine the area of the warning track.

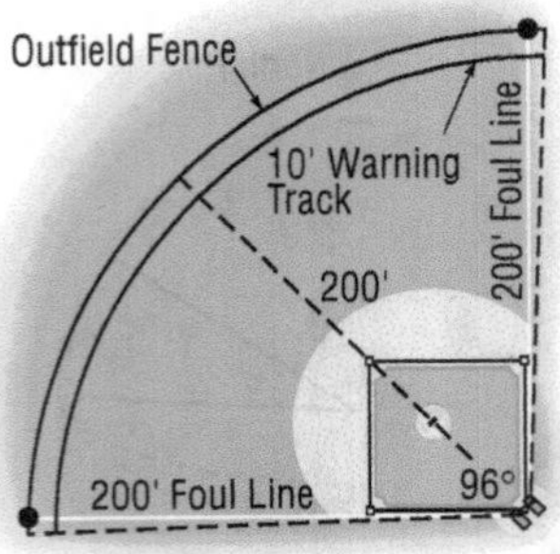

Source: www.littleleague.org

*Any circle drawn on the surface of Earth that divides Earth into two equal hemispheres.

[**Note:** There is a 90° angle between the two foul lines. Then there are two 3° angles between the foul lines and the dotted lines shown. The angle between the two dotted lines outside the 200-foot foul lines is 96°.]

117. Pulleys Two pulleys, one with radius r_1 and the other with radius r_2, are connected by a belt. The pulley with radius r_1 rotates at ω_1 revolutions per minute, whereas the pulley with radius r_2 rotates at ω_2 revolutions per minute. Show that $\frac{r_1}{r_2} = \frac{\omega_2}{\omega_1}$.

Discussion and Writing

118. Do you prefer to measure angles using degrees or radians? Provide justification and a rationale for your choice.
119. What is 1 radian? What is 1°?
120. Which angle has the larger measure: 1 degree or 1 radian? Or are they equal?
121. Explain the difference between linear speed and angular speed.
122. For a circle of radius r, a central angle of θ degrees subtends an arc whose length s is $s = \frac{\pi}{180} r\theta$. Discuss whether this is a true or false statement. Give reasons to defend your position.
123. Discuss why ships and airplanes use nautical miles to measure distance. Explain the difference between a nautical mile and a statute mile.
124. Investigate the way that speed bicycles work. In particular, explain the differences and similarities between 5-speed and 9-speed derailleurs. Be sure to include a discussion of linear speed and angular speed.
125. In Example 6, we found that the distance between Albuquerque, New Mexico, and Glasgow, Montana, is approximately 903 miles. According to *mapquest.com,* the distance is approximately 1300 miles. What might account for the difference?

'Are You Prepared?' Answers

1. $C = 2\pi r$; $A = \pi r^2$ **2.** $d = r \cdot t$

6.2 Trigonometric Functions: Unit Circle Approach

PREPARING FOR THIS SECTION *Before getting started, review the following:*

- Geometry Essentials (Appendix A, Section A.2, pp. A14–A19)
- Unit Circle (Section 1.5, p. 45)
- Symmetry (Section 1.2, pp. 19–21)
- Functions (Section 2.1, pp. 56–64)

Now Work the 'Are You Prepared?' problems on page 378.

OBJECTIVES
1. Find the Exact Values of the Trigonometric Functions Using a Point on the Unit Circle (p. 367)
2. Find the Exact Values of the Trigonometric Functions of Quadrantal Angles (p. 368)
3. Find the Exact Values of the Trigonometric Functions of $\frac{\pi}{4} = 45°$ (p. 370)
4. Find the Exact Values of the Trigonometric Functions of $\frac{\pi}{6} = 30°$ and $\frac{\pi}{3} = 60°$ (p. 371)
5. Find the Exact Values of the Trigonometric Functions for Integer Multiples of $\frac{\pi}{6} = 30°$, $\frac{\pi}{4} = 45°$, and $\frac{\pi}{3} = 60°$ (p. 374)
6. Use a Calculator to Approximate the Value of a Trigonometric Function (p. 375)
7. Use a Circle of Radius r to Evaluate the Trigonometric Functions (p. 376)

We are now ready to introduce trigonometric functions. The approach that we take uses the unit circle.

The Unit Circle

Recall that the unit circle is a circle whose radius is 1 and whose center is at the origin of a rectangular coordinate system. Also recall that any circle of radius r has circumference of length $2\pi r$. Therefore, the unit circle (radius $= 1$) has a circumference of length 2π. In other words, for 1 revolution around the unit circle the length of the arc is 2π units.

The following discussion sets the stage for defining the trigonometric functions using the unit circle.

Let t be any real number. We position the t-axis so that it is vertical with the positive direction up. We place this t-axis in the xy-plane so that $t = 0$ is located at the point $(1, 0)$ in the xy-plane.

If $t \geq 0$, let s be the distance from the origin to t on the t-axis. See the red portion of Figure 20(a).

Now look at the unit circle in Figure 20(a). Beginning at the point $(1, 0)$ on the unit circle, travel $s = t$ units in the counterclockwise direction along the circle, to arrive at the point $P = (x, y)$. In this sense, the length $s = t$ units is being **wrapped** around the unit circle.

If $t < 0$, we begin at the point $(1, 0)$ on the unit circle and travel $s = |t|$ units in the clockwise direction to arrive at the point $P = (x, y)$. See Figure 20(b).

Figure 20

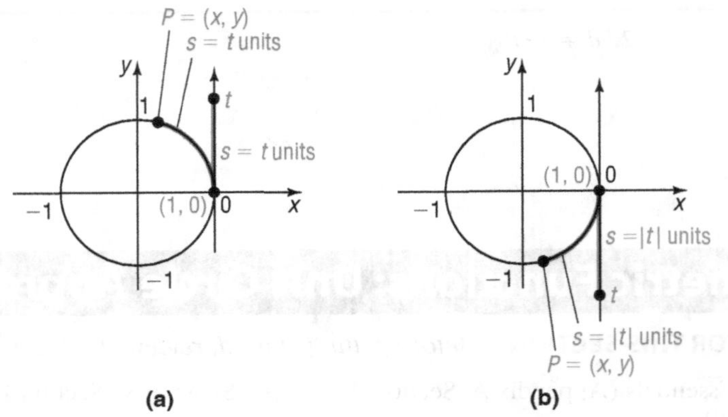

If $t > 2\pi$ or if $t < -2\pi$, it will be necessary to travel around the unit circle more than once before arriving at the point P. Do you see why?

Let's describe this process another way. Picture a string of length $s = |t|$ units being wrapped around a circle of radius 1 unit. We start wrapping the string around the circle at the point $(1, 0)$. If $t \geq 0$, we wrap the string in the counterclockwise direction; if $t < 0$, we wrap the string in the clockwise direction. The point $P = (x, y)$ is the point where the string ends.

This discussion tells us that, for any real number t, we can locate a unique point $P = (x, y)$ on the unit circle. We call **P the point on the unit circle that corresponds to t.** This is the important idea here. No matter what real number t is chosen, there is a unique point P on the unit circle corresponding to it. We use the coordinates of the point $P = (x, y)$ on the unit circle corresponding to the real number t to define the **six trigonometric functions of t.**

DEFINITION Let t be a real number and let $P = (x, y)$ be the point on the unit circle that corresponds to t.

The **sine function** associates with t the y-coordinate of P and is denoted by

$$\sin t = y$$

In Words

The sine function takes as input a real number t that corresponds to a point $P = (x, y)$ on the unit circle and outputs the y-coordinate. The cosine function takes as input a real number t that corresponds to a point $P = (x, y)$ on the unit circle and outputs the x-coordinate.

The **cosine function** associates with t the x-coordinate of P and is denoted by

$$\cos t = x$$

If $x \neq 0$, the **tangent function** associates with t the ratio of the y-coordinate to the x-coordinate of P and is denoted by

$$\tan t = \frac{y}{x}$$

If $y \neq 0$, the **cosecant function** is defined as

$$\csc t = \frac{1}{y}$$

If $x \neq 0$, the **secant function** is defined as

$$\sec t = \frac{1}{x}$$

If $y \neq 0$, the **cotangent function** is defined as

$$\cot t = \frac{x}{y}$$

Notice in these definitions that if $x = 0$, that is, if the point P is on the y-axis, then the tangent function and the secant function are undefined. Also, if $y = 0$, that is, if the point P is on the x-axis, then the cosecant function and the cotangent function are undefined.

Because we use the unit circle in these definitions of the trigonometric functions, they are sometimes referred to as **circular functions.**

1 Find the Exact Values of the Trigonometric Functions Using a Point on the Unit Circle

EXAMPLE 1 **Finding the Values of the Six Trigonometric Functions Using a Point on the Unit Circle**

Let t be a real number and let $P = \left(-\frac{1}{2}, \frac{\sqrt{3}}{2}\right)$ be the point on the unit circle that corresponds to t. Find the values of $\sin t$, $\cos t$, $\tan t$, $\csc t$, $\sec t$, and $\cot t$.

Figure 21

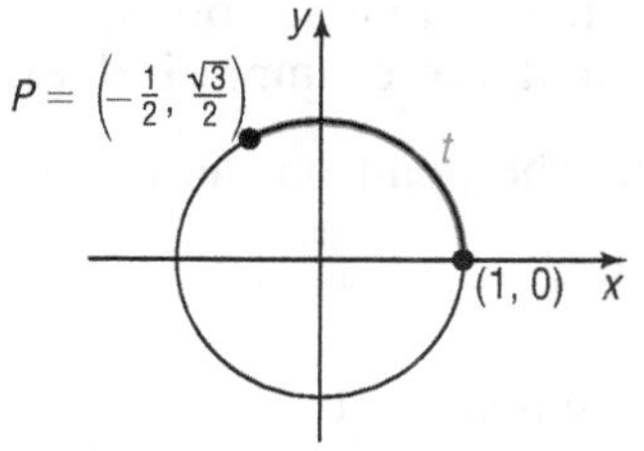

Solution See Figure 21. We follow the definition of the six trigonometric functions, using $P = \left(-\frac{1}{2}, \frac{\sqrt{3}}{2}\right) = (x, y)$. Then, with $x = -\frac{1}{2}$ and $y = \frac{\sqrt{3}}{2}$, we have

$$\sin t = y = \frac{\sqrt{3}}{2} \qquad \cos t = x = -\frac{1}{2} \qquad \tan t = \frac{y}{x} = \frac{\frac{\sqrt{3}}{2}}{-\frac{1}{2}} = -\sqrt{3}$$

$$\csc t = \frac{1}{y} = \frac{1}{\frac{\sqrt{3}}{2}} = \frac{2\sqrt{3}}{3} \qquad \sec t = \frac{1}{x} = \frac{1}{-\frac{1}{2}} = -2 \qquad \cot t = \frac{x}{y} = \frac{-\frac{1}{2}}{\frac{\sqrt{3}}{2}} = -\frac{\sqrt{3}}{3}$$

WARNING When writing the values of the trigonometric functions, do not forget the argument of the function.

$\sin t = \frac{\sqrt{3}}{2}$ correct

$\sin = \frac{\sqrt{3}}{2}$ incorrect

Now Work PROBLEM 11

Trigonometric Functions of Angles

Let $P = (x, y)$ be the point on the unit circle corresponding to the real number t. See Figure 22(a). Let θ be the angle in standard position, measured in radians, whose terminal side is the ray from the origin through P. See Figure 22(b). Since the unit circle has radius 1 unit, if $s = |t|$ units, then from the arc length formula $s = r\theta$, we have $\theta = t$ radians. See Figures 22(c) and (d).

Figure 22

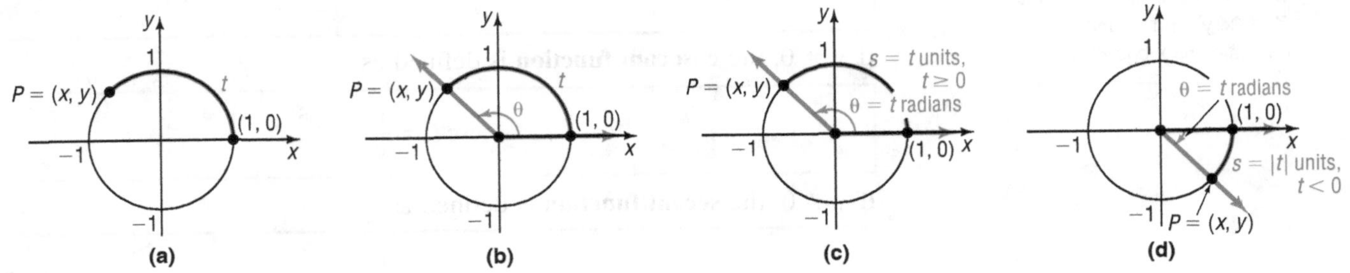

The point $P = (x, y)$ on the unit circle that corresponds to the real number t is the point P on the terminal side of the angle $\theta = t$ radians. As a result, we can say that

$$\underset{\text{Real number}}{\sin t} = \underset{\theta = t \text{ radians}}{\sin \theta}$$

and so on. We can now define the trigonometric functions of the angle θ.

DEFINITION If $\theta = t$ radians, the **six trigonometric functions of the angle θ** are defined as

$\sin\theta = \sin t$	$\cos\theta = \cos t$	$\tan\theta = \tan t$
$\csc\theta = \csc t$	$\sec\theta = \sec t$	$\cot\theta = \cot t$

Even though the trigonometric functions can be viewed both as functions of real numbers and as functions of angles, it is customary to refer to trigonometric functions of real numbers and trigonometric functions of angles collectively as the *trigonometric functions*. We shall follow this practice from now on.

If an angle θ is measured in degrees, we shall use the degree symbol when writing a trigonometric function of θ, as, for example, in $\sin 30°$ and $\tan 45°$. If an angle θ is measured in radians, then no symbol is used when writing a trigonometric function of θ, as, for example, in $\cos\pi$ and $\sec\frac{\pi}{3}$.

Finally, since the values of the trigonometric functions of an angle θ are determined by the coordinates of the point $P = (x, y)$ on the unit circle corresponding to θ, the units used to measure the angle θ are irrelevant. For example, it does not matter whether we write $\theta = \frac{\pi}{2}$ radians or $\theta = 90°$. The point on the unit circle corresponding to this angle is $P = (0, 1)$. As a result,

$$\sin\frac{\pi}{2} = \sin 90° = 1 \quad \text{and} \quad \cos\frac{\pi}{2} = \cos 90° = 0$$

2 Find the Exact Values of the Trigonometric Functions of Quadrantal Angles

To find the exact value of a trigonometric function of an angle θ or a real number t requires that we locate the point $P = (x, y)$ on the unit circle that corresponds to t. This is not always easy to do. In the examples that follow, we will evaluate the trigonometric functions of certain angles or real numbers for which this process is relatively easy. A calculator will be used to evaluate the trigonometric functions of most other angles.

EXAMPLE 2 Finding the Exact Values of the Six Trigonometric Functions of Quadrantal Angles

Find the exact values of the six trigonometric functions of:

(a) $\theta = 0 = 0°$ (b) $\theta = \frac{\pi}{2} = 90°$

(c) $\theta = \pi = 180°$ (d) $\theta = \frac{3\pi}{2} = 270°$

Solution (a) The point on the unit circle that corresponds to $\theta = 0 = 0°$ is $P = (1, 0)$. See Figure 23(a). Then

Figure 23

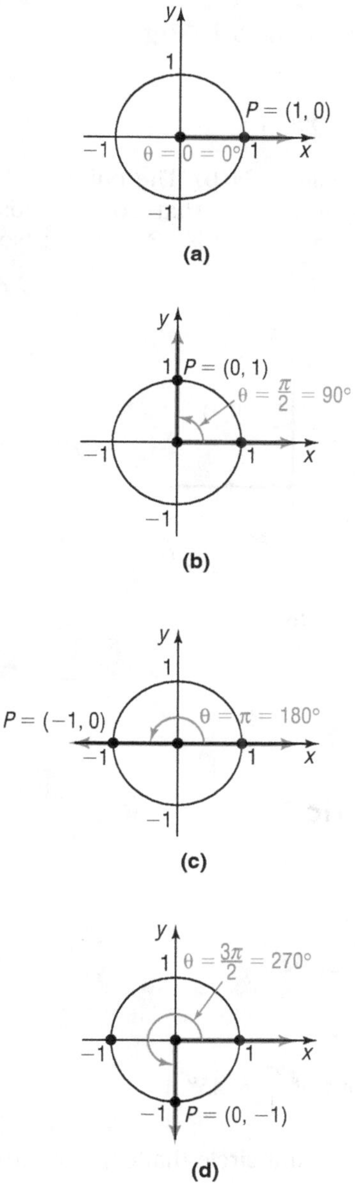

$$\sin 0 = \sin 0° = y = 0 \qquad \cos 0 = \cos 0° = x = 1$$

$$\tan 0 = \tan 0° = \frac{y}{x} = 0 \qquad \sec 0 = \sec 0° = \frac{1}{x} = 1$$

Since the y-coordinate of P is 0, $\csc 0$ and $\cot 0$ are not defined.

(b) The point on the unit circle that corresponds to $\theta = \frac{\pi}{2} = 90°$ is $P = (0, 1)$. See Figure 23(b). Then

$$\sin\frac{\pi}{2} = \sin 90° = y = 1 \qquad \cos\frac{\pi}{2} = \cos 90° = x = 0$$

$$\csc\frac{\pi}{2} = \csc 90° = \frac{1}{y} = 1 \qquad \cot\frac{\pi}{2} = \cot 90° = \frac{x}{y} = 0$$

Since the x-coordinate of P is 0, $\tan\frac{\pi}{2}$ and $\sec\frac{\pi}{2}$ are not defined.

(c) The point on the unit circle that corresponds to $\theta = \pi = 180°$ is $P = (-1, 0)$. See Figure 23(c). Then

$$\sin \pi = \sin 180° = y = 0 \qquad \cos \pi = \cos 180° = x = -1$$

$$\tan \pi = \tan 180° = \frac{y}{x} = 0 \qquad \sec \pi = \sec 180° = \frac{1}{x} = -1$$

Since the y-coordinate of P is 0, $\csc \pi$ and $\cot \pi$ are not defined.

(d) The point on the unit circle that corresponds to $\theta = \frac{3\pi}{2} = 270°$ is $P = (0, -1)$. See Figure 23(d). Then

$$\sin\frac{3\pi}{2} = \sin 270° = y = -1 \qquad \cos\frac{3\pi}{2} = \cos 270° = x = 0$$

$$\csc\frac{3\pi}{2} = \csc 270° = \frac{1}{y} = -1 \qquad \cot\frac{3\pi}{2} = \cot 270° = \frac{x}{y} = 0$$

Since the x-coordinate of P is 0, $\tan\frac{3\pi}{2}$ and $\sec\frac{3\pi}{2}$ are not defined.

Table 2 on the next page summarizes the values of the trigonometric functions found in Example 2.

Table 2

Quadrantal Angles							
θ (Radians)	θ (Degrees)	$\sin\theta$	$\cos\theta$	$\tan\theta$	$\csc\theta$	$\sec\theta$	$\cot\theta$
0	0°	0	1	0	Not defined	1	Not defined
$\frac{\pi}{2}$	90°	1	0	Not defined	1	Not defined	0
π	180°	0	−1	0	Not defined	−1	Not defined
$\frac{3\pi}{2}$	270°	−1	0	Not defined	−1	Not defined	0

There is no need to memorize Table 2. To find the value of a trigonometric function of a quadrantal angle, draw the angle and apply the definition, as we did in Example 2.

EXAMPLE 3 **Finding Exact Values of the Trigonometric Functions of Angles That Are Integer Multiples of Quadrantal Angles**

Find the exact value of:

(a) $\sin(3\pi)$ (b) $\cos(-270°)$

Solution (a) See Figure 24(a). The point P on the unit circle that corresponds to $\theta = 3\pi$ is $P = (-1, 0)$, so $\sin(3\pi) = y = 0$.

(b) See Figure 24(b). The point P on the unit circle that corresponds to $\theta = -270°$ is $P = (0, 1)$, so $\cos(-270°) = x = 0$.

Figure 24

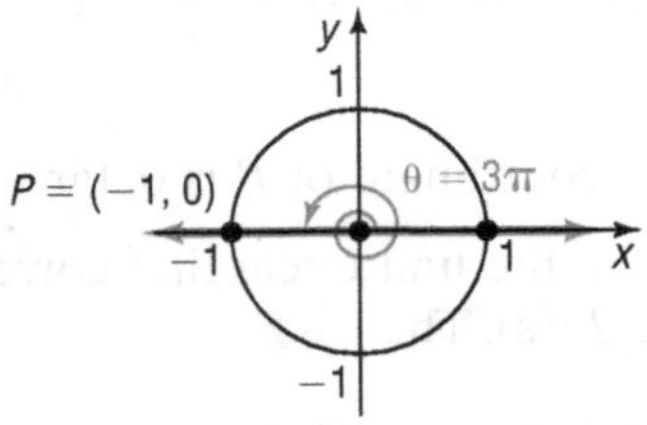

(a)

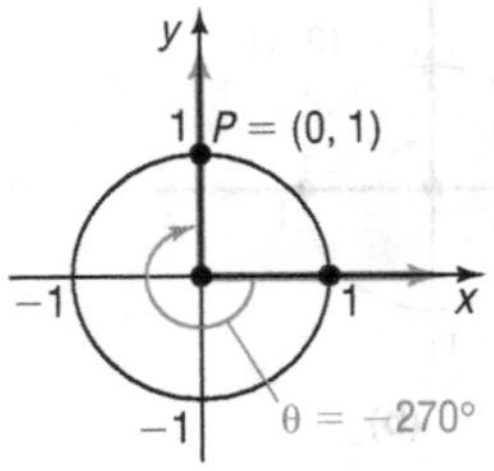

(b)

Now Work PROBLEMS 19 AND 59

3 Find the Exact Values of the Trigonometric Functions of $\frac{\pi}{4} = 45°$

EXAMPLE 4 **Finding the Exact Values of the Trigonometric Functions of $\frac{\pi}{4} = 45°$**

Find the exact values of the six trigonometric functions of $\frac{\pi}{4} = 45°$.

Solution We seek the coordinates of the point $P = (x, y)$ on the unit circle that corresponds to $\theta = \frac{\pi}{4} = 45°$. See Figure 25. First, we observe that P lies on the line $y = x$. (Do

Figure 25

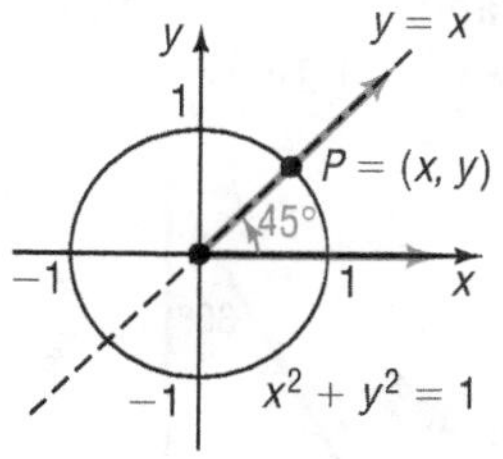

you see why? Since $\theta = 45° = \frac{1}{2} \cdot 90°$, P must lie on the line that bisects quadrant I.) Since $P = (x, y)$ also lies on the unit circle, $x^2 + y^2 = 1$, it follows that

$$x^2 + y^2 = 1$$
$$x^2 + x^2 = 1 \quad y = x, x > 0, y > 0$$
$$2x^2 = 1$$
$$x = \frac{1}{\sqrt{2}} = \frac{\sqrt{2}}{2} \qquad y = \frac{\sqrt{2}}{2}$$

Then

$$\sin\frac{\pi}{4} = \sin 45° = \frac{\sqrt{2}}{2} \qquad \cos\frac{\pi}{4} = \cos 45° = \frac{\sqrt{2}}{2} \qquad \tan\frac{\pi}{4} = \tan 45° = \frac{\frac{\sqrt{2}}{2}}{\frac{\sqrt{2}}{2}} = 1$$

$$\csc\frac{\pi}{4} = \csc 45° = \frac{1}{\frac{\sqrt{2}}{2}} = \sqrt{2} \qquad \sec\frac{\pi}{4} = \sec 45° = \frac{1}{\frac{\sqrt{2}}{2}} = \sqrt{2} \qquad \cot\frac{\pi}{4} = \cot 45° = \frac{\frac{\sqrt{2}}{2}}{\frac{\sqrt{2}}{2}} = 1$$

EXAMPLE 5 **Finding the Exact Value of a Trigonometric Expression**

Find the exact value of each expression.

(a) $\sin 45° \cos 180°$

(b) $\tan\frac{\pi}{4} - \sin\frac{3\pi}{2}$

(c) $\left(\sec\frac{\pi}{4}\right)^2 + \csc\frac{\pi}{2}$

Solution

(a) $\sin 45° \cos 180° = \underset{\text{From Example 4}}{\frac{\sqrt{2}}{2}} \cdot \underset{\text{From Table 2}}{(-1)} = -\frac{\sqrt{2}}{2}$

(b) $\tan\frac{\pi}{4} - \sin\frac{3\pi}{2} = \underset{\text{From Example 4}}{1} - \underset{\text{From Table 2}}{(-1)} = 2$

(c) $\left(\sec\frac{\pi}{4}\right)^2 + \csc\frac{\pi}{2} = \left(\sqrt{2}\right)^2 + 1 = 2 + 1 = 3$

Now Work PROBLEM 33

4 Find the Exact Values of the Trigonometric Functions of $\frac{\pi}{6} = 30°$ and $\frac{\pi}{3} = 60°$

Consider a right triangle in which one of the angles is $\frac{\pi}{6} = 30°$. It then follows that the third angle is $\frac{\pi}{3} = 60°$. Figure 26(a) illustrates such a triangle with hypotenuse of length 1. Our problem is to determine a and b.

We begin by placing next to this triangle another triangle congruent to the first, as shown in Figure 26(b). Notice that we now have a triangle whose angles are each 60°. This triangle is therefore equilateral, so each side is of length 1.

Figure 26

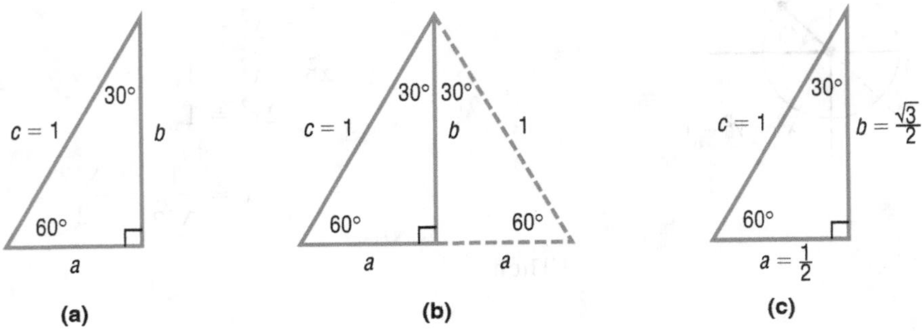

This means the base is $2a = 1$, and so $a = \frac{1}{2}$. By the Pythagorean Theorem, b satisfies the equation $a^2 + b^2 = c^2$, so we have

$$a^2 + b^2 = c^2$$

$$\frac{1}{4} + b^2 = 1 \qquad a = \frac{1}{2},\ c = 1$$

$$b^2 = 1 - \frac{1}{4} = \frac{3}{4}$$

$$b = \frac{\sqrt{3}}{2}$$

$b > 0$ because it is the length of the side of a triangle.

This results in Figure 26(c).

EXAMPLE 6 **Finding the Exact Values of the Trigonometric Functions of $\frac{\pi}{3} = 60°$**

Find the exact values of the six trigonometric functions of $\frac{\pi}{3} = 60°$.

Solution Position the triangle in Figure 26(c) so that the 60° angle is in the standard position. See Figure 27. The point on the unit circle that corresponds to $\theta = \frac{\pi}{3} = 60°$ is $P = \left(\frac{1}{2}, \frac{\sqrt{3}}{2}\right)$. Then

Figure 27

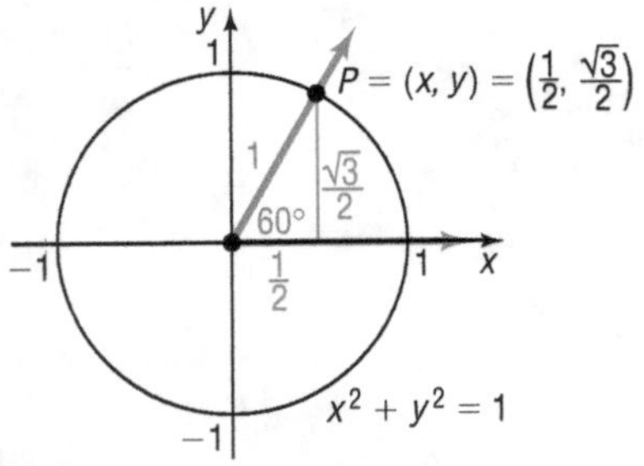

$$\sin\frac{\pi}{3} = \sin 60° = \frac{\sqrt{3}}{2} \qquad \cos\frac{\pi}{3} = \cos 60° = \frac{1}{2}$$

$$\csc\frac{\pi}{3} = \csc 60° = \frac{1}{\frac{\sqrt{3}}{2}} = \frac{2}{\sqrt{3}} = \frac{2\sqrt{3}}{3} \qquad \sec\frac{\pi}{3} = \sec 60° = \frac{1}{\frac{1}{2}} = 2$$

$$\tan\frac{\pi}{3} = \tan 60° = \frac{\frac{\sqrt{3}}{2}}{\frac{1}{2}} = \sqrt{3} \qquad \cot\frac{\pi}{3} = \cot 60° = \frac{\frac{1}{2}}{\frac{\sqrt{3}}{2}} = \frac{1}{\sqrt{3}} = \frac{\sqrt{3}}{3}$$

■

EXAMPLE 7 **Finding the Exact Values of the Trigonometric Functions of $\frac{\pi}{6} = 30°$**

Find the exact values of the trigonometric functions of $\frac{\pi}{6} = 30°$.

Solution Position the triangle in Figure 26(c) so that the 30° angle is in the standard position. See Figure 28. The point on the unit circle that corresponds to $\theta = \frac{\pi}{6} = 30°$ is $P = \left(\frac{\sqrt{3}}{2}, \frac{1}{2}\right)$. Then

Figure 28

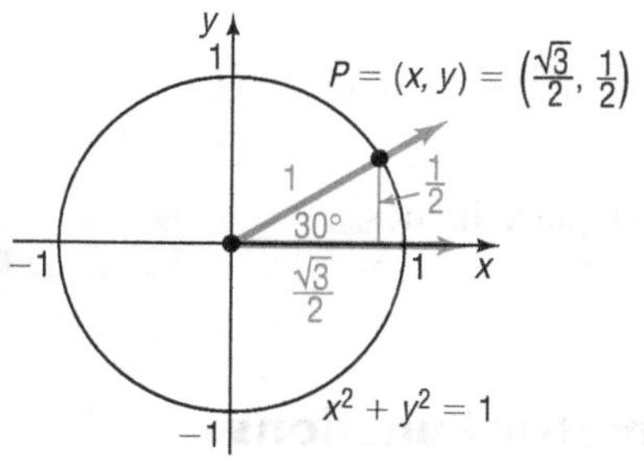

$$\sin\frac{\pi}{6} = \sin 30° = \frac{1}{2} \qquad \cos\frac{\pi}{6} = \cos 30° = \frac{\sqrt{3}}{2}$$

$$\csc\frac{\pi}{6} = \csc 30° = \frac{1}{\frac{1}{2}} = 2 \qquad \sec\frac{\pi}{6} = \sec 30° = \frac{1}{\frac{\sqrt{3}}{2}} = \frac{2}{\sqrt{3}} = \frac{2\sqrt{3}}{3}$$

$$\tan\frac{\pi}{6} = \tan 30° = \frac{\frac{1}{2}}{\frac{\sqrt{3}}{2}} = \frac{1}{\sqrt{3}} = \frac{\sqrt{3}}{3} \qquad \cot\frac{\pi}{6} = \cot 30° = \frac{\frac{\sqrt{3}}{2}}{\frac{1}{2}} = \sqrt{3}$$

Table 3 summarizes the information just derived for $\frac{\pi}{6} = 30°$, $\frac{\pi}{4} = 45°$, and $\frac{\pi}{3} = 60°$. Until you memorize the entries in Table 3, you should draw an appropriate diagram to determine the values given in the table.

Table 3

θ (Radians)	θ (Degrees)	$\sin\theta$	$\cos\theta$	$\tan\theta$	$\csc\theta$	$\sec\theta$	$\cot\theta$
$\frac{\pi}{6}$	30°	$\frac{1}{2}$	$\frac{\sqrt{3}}{2}$	$\frac{\sqrt{3}}{3}$	2	$\frac{2\sqrt{3}}{3}$	$\sqrt{3}$
$\frac{\pi}{4}$	45°	$\frac{\sqrt{2}}{2}$	$\frac{\sqrt{2}}{2}$	1	$\sqrt{2}$	$\sqrt{2}$	1
$\frac{\pi}{3}$	60°	$\frac{\sqrt{3}}{2}$	$\frac{1}{2}$	$\sqrt{3}$	$\frac{2\sqrt{3}}{3}$	2	$\frac{\sqrt{3}}{3}$

Now Work PROBLEM 39

EXAMPLE 8 Constructing a Rain Gutter

A rain gutter is to be constructed of aluminum sheets 12 inches wide. After marking off a length of 4 inches from each edge, this length is bent up at an angle θ. See Figure 29. The area A of the opening may be expressed as a function of θ as

$$A(\theta) = 16 \sin\theta(\cos\theta + 1)$$

Find the area A of the opening for $\theta = 30°$, $\theta = 45°$, and $\theta = 60°$.

Solution For $\theta = 30°$: $A(30°) = 16 \sin 30°(\cos 30° + 1)$

$$= 16\left(\frac{1}{2}\right)\left(\frac{\sqrt{3}}{2} + 1\right) = 4\sqrt{3} + 8 \approx 14.9$$

Figure 29

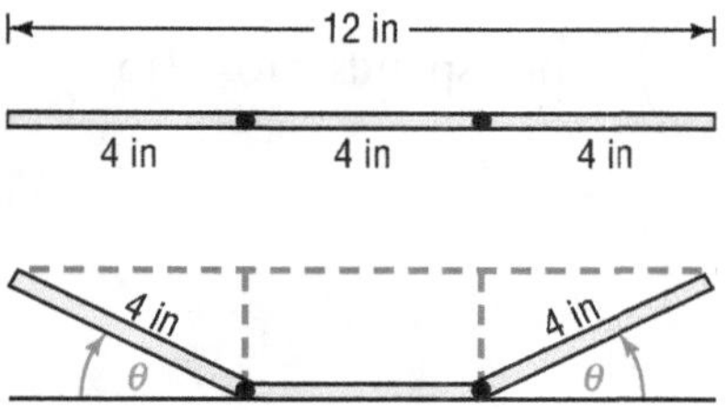

The area of the opening for $\theta = 30°$ is about 14.9 square inches.

For $\theta = 45°$: $A(45°) = 16 \sin 45°(\cos 45° + 1)$

$$= 16\left(\frac{\sqrt{2}}{2}\right)\left(\frac{\sqrt{2}}{2} + 1\right) = 8 + 8\sqrt{2} \approx 19.3$$

The area of the opening for $\theta = 45°$ is about 19.3 square inches.

$$\text{For } \theta = 60°: \quad A(60°) = 16 \sin 60°(\cos 60° + 1)$$
$$= 16\left(\frac{\sqrt{3}}{2}\right)\left(\frac{1}{2} + 1\right) = 12\sqrt{3} \approx 20.8$$

The area of the opening for $\theta = 60°$ is about 20.8 square inches.

5 Find the Exact Values of the Trigonometric Functions for Integer Multiples of $\frac{\pi}{6} = 30°, \frac{\pi}{4} = 45°$, and $\frac{\pi}{3} = 60°$

We know the exact values of the trigonometric functions of $\frac{\pi}{4} = 45°$. Using symmetry, we can find the exact values of the trigonometric functions of $\frac{3\pi}{4} = 135°$, $\frac{5\pi}{4} = 225°$, and $\frac{7\pi}{4} = 315°$.

Figure 30

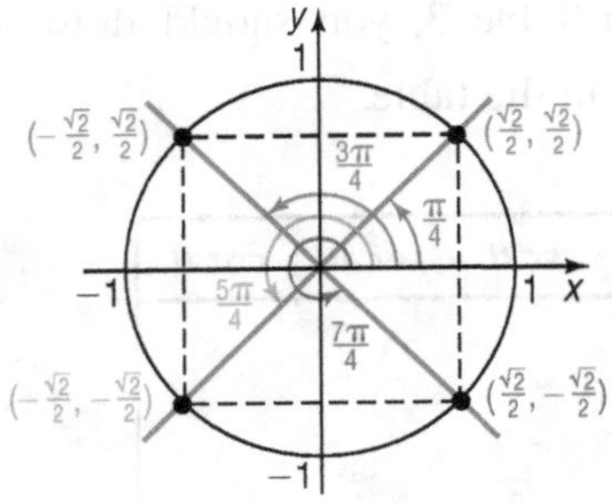

See Figure 30. Using symmetry with respect to the y-axis, the point $\left(-\frac{\sqrt{2}}{2}, \frac{\sqrt{2}}{2}\right)$ is the point on the unit circle that corresponds to the angle $\frac{3\pi}{4} = 135°$. Similarly, using symmetry with respect to the origin, the point $\left(-\frac{\sqrt{2}}{2}, -\frac{\sqrt{2}}{2}\right)$ is the point on the unit circle that corresponds to the angle $\frac{5\pi}{4} = 225°$. Finally, using symmetry with respect to the x-axis, the point $\left(\frac{\sqrt{2}}{2}, -\frac{\sqrt{2}}{2}\right)$ is the point on the unit circle that corresponds to the angle $\frac{7\pi}{4} = 315°$.

EXAMPLE 9 Finding Exact Values for Multiples of $\frac{\pi}{4} = 45°$

Find the exact value of each expression.

(a) $\cos \frac{5\pi}{4}$ (b) $\sin 135°$ (c) $\tan 315°$

Solution (a) From Figure 30, we see the point $\left(-\frac{\sqrt{2}}{2}, -\frac{\sqrt{2}}{2}\right)$ corresponds to $\frac{5\pi}{4}$, so $\cos \frac{5\pi}{4} = x = -\frac{\sqrt{2}}{2}$.

(b) Since $135° = \frac{3\pi}{4}$, the point $\left(-\frac{\sqrt{2}}{2}, \frac{\sqrt{2}}{2}\right)$ corresponds to $135°$, so $\sin 135° = \frac{\sqrt{2}}{2}$.

(c) Since $315° = \frac{7\pi}{4}$, the point $\left(\frac{\sqrt{2}}{2}, -\frac{\sqrt{2}}{2}\right)$ corresponds to $315°$, so

$$\tan 315° = \frac{-\frac{\sqrt{2}}{2}}{\frac{\sqrt{2}}{2}} = -1.$$

Figure 30 can also be used to find exact values for other multiples of $\frac{\pi}{4} = 45°$. For example, the point $\left(\frac{\sqrt{2}}{2}, -\frac{\sqrt{2}}{2}\right)$ is the point on the unit circle that corresponds to the angle $-\frac{\pi}{4} = -45°$; the point $\left(\frac{\sqrt{2}}{2}, \frac{\sqrt{2}}{2}\right)$ is the point on the unit circle that corresponds to the angle $\frac{9\pi}{4} = 405°$.

Now Work PROBLEMS 49 AND 53

The use of symmetry also provides information about certain integer multiples of the angles $\frac{\pi}{6} = 30°$ and $\frac{\pi}{3} = 60°$. See Figures 31 and 32.

Figure 31

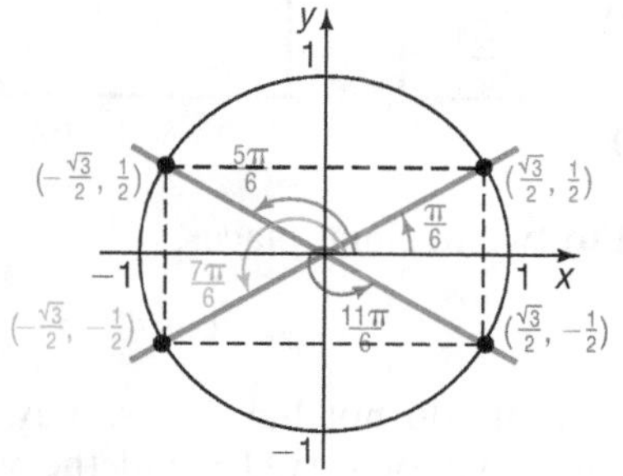

Figure 32

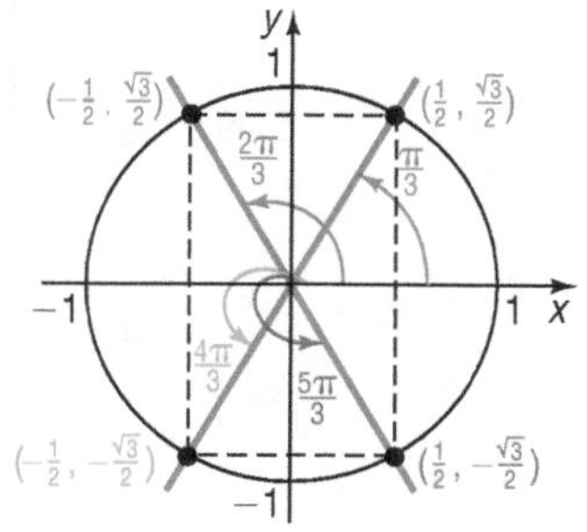

EXAMPLE 10

Finding Exact Values for Multiples of $\frac{\pi}{6} = 30°$ or $\frac{\pi}{3} = 60°$

Based on Figures 31 and 32, we see that

(a) $\cos 210° = \cos \frac{7\pi}{6} = -\frac{\sqrt{3}}{2}$

(b) $\sin(-60°) = \sin\left(-\frac{\pi}{3}\right) = -\frac{\sqrt{3}}{2}$

(c) $\tan \frac{5\pi}{3} = \frac{-\frac{\sqrt{3}}{2}}{\frac{1}{2}} = -\sqrt{3}$

Now Work PROBLEM 45

6 Use a Calculator to Approximate the Value of a Trigonometric Function

Before getting started, you must first decide whether to enter the angle in the calculator using radians or degrees and then set the calculator to the correct MODE. Check your instruction manual to find out how your calculator handles degrees and radians. Your calculator has keys marked [sin], [cos], and [tan]. To find the values of the remaining three trigonometric functions, secant, cosecant, and cotangent, we use the fact that, if $P = (x, y)$ is a point on the unit circle on the terminal side of θ, then

WARNING On your calculator the second functions $\sin^{-1}$, $\cos^{-1}$, and $\tan^{-1}$ do not represent the reciprocal of sin, cos, and tan.

$$\sec \theta = \frac{1}{x} = \frac{1}{\cos \theta} \qquad \csc \theta = \frac{1}{y} = \frac{1}{\sin \theta} \qquad \cot \theta = \frac{x}{y} = \frac{1}{\frac{y}{x}} = \frac{1}{\tan \theta}$$

EXAMPLE 11 Using a Calculator to Approximate the Value of a Trigonometric Function

Use a calculator to find the approximate value of:

(a) $\cos 48°$ (b) $\csc 21°$ (c) $\tan \frac{\pi}{12}$

Express your answer rounded to two decimal places.

Solution (a) First, we set the MODE to receive degrees. See Figure 33(a). Figure 33(b) shows the solution using a TI-84 Plus graphing calculator.

Figure 33

(a) (b)

Rounded to two decimal places,

$$\cos 48° = 0.67$$

(b) Most calculators do not have a csc key. The manufacturers assume the user knows some trigonometry. To find the value of csc 21°, we use the fact that $\csc 21° = \frac{1}{\sin 21°}$. Figure 34 shows the solution using a TI-84 Plus graphing calculator. Rounded to two decimal places,

$$\csc 21° = 2.79$$

(c) Set the MODE to receive radians. Figure 35 shows the solution using a TI-84 Plus graphing calculator. Rounded to two decimal places,

$$\tan \frac{\pi}{12} = 0.27$$

Figure 34

Figure 35

Now Work PROBLEM 63

7 Use a Circle of Radius *r* to Evaluate the Trigonometric Functions

Until now, to find the exact value of a trigonometric function of an angle θ required that we locate the corresponding point $P = (x, y)$ on the unit circle. In fact, though, any circle whose center is at the origin can be used.

Let θ be any nonquadrantal angle placed in standard position. Let $P = (x, y)$ be the point on the circle $x^2 + y^2 = r^2$ that corresponds to θ, and let $P^* = (x^*, y^*)$ be the point on the unit circle that corresponds to θ. See Figure 36, where θ is shown in quadrant II.

Figure 36

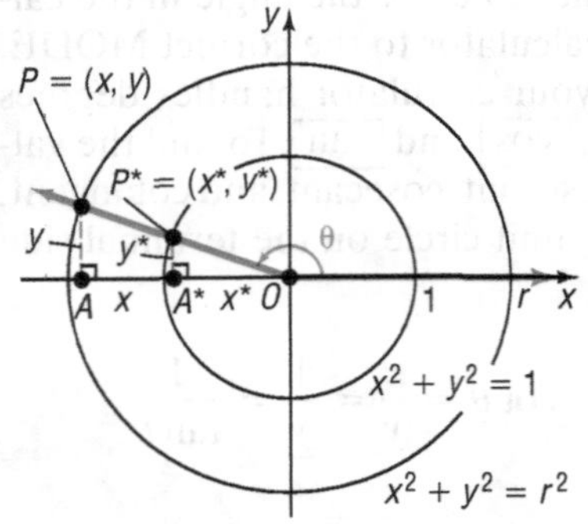

Notice that the triangles OA^*P^* and OAP are similar; as a result, the ratios of corresponding sides are equal.

$$\frac{y^*}{1} = \frac{y}{r} \qquad \frac{x^*}{1} = \frac{x}{r} \qquad \frac{y^*}{x^*} = \frac{y}{x}$$

$$\frac{1}{y^*} = \frac{r}{y} \qquad \frac{1}{x^*} = \frac{r}{x} \qquad \frac{x^*}{y^*} = \frac{x}{y}$$

These results lead us to formulate the following theorem:

THEOREM

For an angle θ in standard position, let $P = (x, y)$ be the point on the terminal side of θ that is also on the circle $x^2 + y^2 = r^2$. Then

$$\sin\theta = \frac{y}{r} \qquad \cos\theta = \frac{x}{r} \qquad \tan\theta = \frac{y}{x} \quad x \neq 0$$

$$\csc\theta = \frac{r}{y} \quad y \neq 0 \qquad \sec\theta = \frac{r}{x} \quad x \neq 0 \qquad \cot\theta = \frac{x}{y} \quad y \neq 0$$

EXAMPLE 12 Finding the Exact Values of the Six Trigonometric Functions

Find the exact values of each of the six trigonometric functions of an angle θ if $(4, -3)$ is a point on its terminal side.

Solution See Figure 37. The point $(4, -3)$ is on a circle of radius $r = \sqrt{4^2 + (-3)^2} = \sqrt{16 + 9} = \sqrt{25} = 5$ with the center at the origin.

For the point $(x, y) = (4, -3)$, we have $x = 4$ and $y = -3$. Since $r = 5$, we find

$$\sin\theta = \frac{y}{r} = -\frac{3}{5} \qquad \cos\theta = \frac{x}{r} = \frac{4}{5} \qquad \tan\theta = \frac{y}{x} = -\frac{3}{4}$$

$$\csc\theta = \frac{r}{y} = -\frac{5}{3} \qquad \sec\theta = \frac{r}{x} = \frac{5}{4} \qquad \cot\theta = \frac{x}{y} = -\frac{4}{3}$$

Figure 37

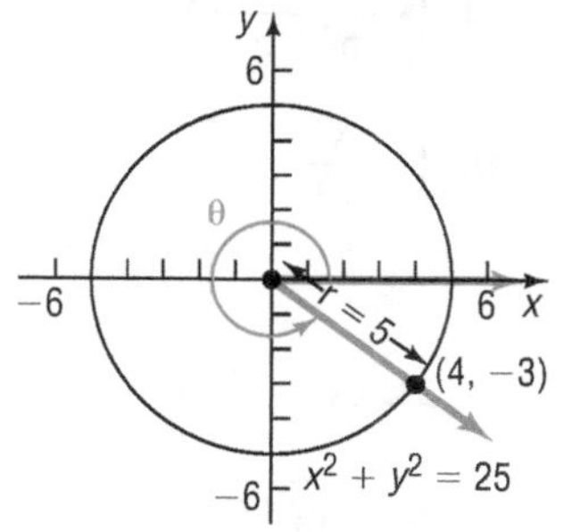

Now Work PROBLEM 75

Historical Feature

The name *sine* for the sine function is due to a medieval confusion. The name comes from the Sanskrit word *jīva* (meaning chord), first used in India by Araybhata the Elder (AD 510). He really meant half-chord, but abbreviated it. This was brought into Arabic as *jība*, which was meaningless. Because the proper Arabic word *jaib* would be written the same way (short vowels are not written out in Arabic), *jība* was pronounced as *jaib*, which meant bosom or hollow, and *jība* remains as the Arabic word for sine to this day. Scholars translating the Arabic works into Latin found that the word *sinus* also meant bosom or hollow, and from *sinus* we get the word *sine*.

The name *tangent*, due to Thomas Finck (1583), can be understood by looking at Figure 38. The line segment $\overline{DC}$ is tangent to the circle at C. If $d(O, B) = d(O, C) = 1$, then the length of the line segment $\overline{DC}$ is

$$d(D, C) = \frac{d(D, C)}{1} = \frac{d(D, C)}{d(O, C)} = \tan\alpha$$

The old name for the tangent is *umbra versa* (meaning turned shadow), referring to the use of the tangent in solving height problems with shadows.

The names of the remaining functions came about as follows. If α and β are complementary angles, then $\cos\alpha = \sin\beta$. Because β is the complement of α, it was natural to write the cosine of α as *sin co* α. Probably for reasons involving ease of pronunciation, the *co* migrated to the front, and then cosine received a three-letter abbreviation to match sin, sec, and tan. The two other cofunctions were similarly treated, except that the long forms *cotan* and *cosec* survive to this day in some countries.

Figure 38

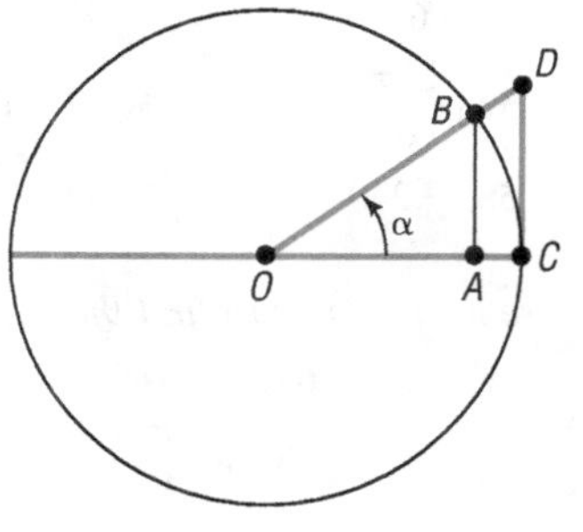

6.2 Assess Your Understanding

'Are You Prepared?' *Answers are given at the end of these exercises. If you get a wrong answer, read the pages listed in red.*

1. In a right triangle, with legs a and b and hypotenuse c, the Pythagorean Theorem states that ________. (p. A14)
2. The value of the function $f(x) = 3x - 7$ at 5 is ________. (pp. 60–62)
3. ***True or False*** For a function $y = f(x)$, for each x in the domain, there is exactly one element y in the range. (pp. 56–60)
4. If two triangles are similar, then corresponding angles are ________ and the lengths of corresponding sides are ________. (p. A17)
5. What point is symmetric with respect to the y-axis to the point $\left(\frac{1}{2}, \frac{\sqrt{3}}{2}\right)$? (pp. 19–20)
6. If (x, y) is a point on the unit circle in quadrant IV and if $x = \frac{\sqrt{3}}{2}$, what is y? (p. 45)

Concepts and Vocabulary

7. $\tan\frac{\pi}{4} + \sin 30° =$ ________.
8. Using a calculator, $\sin 2 =$ ________, rounded to two decimal places.
9. ***True or False*** Exact values can be found for the trigonometric functions of 60°.
10. ***True or False*** Exact values can be found for the sine of any angle.

Skill Building

In Problems 11–18, t is a real number and $P = (x, y)$ is the point on the unit circle that corresponds to t. Find the exact values of the six trigonometric functions of t.

11. $\left(\frac{\sqrt{3}}{2}, \frac{1}{2}\right)$ 12. $\left(\frac{1}{2}, -\frac{\sqrt{3}}{2}\right)$ 13. $\left(-\frac{2}{5}, \frac{\sqrt{21}}{5}\right)$ 14. $\left(-\frac{1}{5}, \frac{2\sqrt{6}}{5}\right)$

15. $\left(-\frac{\sqrt{2}}{2}, \frac{\sqrt{2}}{2}\right)$ 16. $\left(\frac{\sqrt{2}}{2}, \frac{\sqrt{2}}{2}\right)$ 17. $\left(\frac{2\sqrt{2}}{3}, -\frac{1}{3}\right)$ 18. $\left(-\frac{\sqrt{5}}{3}, -\frac{2}{3}\right)$

In Problems 19–28, find the exact value. Do not use a calculator.

19. $\sin\frac{11\pi}{2}$ 20. $\cos(7\pi)$ 21. $\tan(6\pi)$ 22. $\cot\frac{7\pi}{2}$ 23. $\csc\frac{11\pi}{2}$

24. $\sec(8\pi)$ 25. $\cos\left(-\frac{3\pi}{2}\right)$ 26. $\sin(-3\pi)$ 27. $\sec(-\pi)$ 28. $\tan(-5\pi)$

In Problems 29–44, find the exact value of each expression. Do not use a calculator.

29. $\sin 45° + \cos 60°$ 30. $\sin 30° - \cos 45°$ 31. $\sin 90° + \tan 45°$ 32. $\cos 180° - \sin 180°$

33. $\sin 45° \cos 45°$ 34. $\tan 45° \cos 30°$ 35. $\csc 45° \tan 60°$ 36. $\sec 30° \cot 45°$

37. $4 \sin 90° - 3 \tan 180°$ 38. $5 \cos 90° - 8 \sin 270°$ 39. $2 \sin\frac{\pi}{3} - 3 \tan\frac{\pi}{6}$ 40. $2 \sin\frac{\pi}{4} + 3 \tan\frac{\pi}{4}$

41. $2 \sec\frac{\pi}{4} + 4 \cot\frac{\pi}{3}$ 42. $3 \csc\frac{\pi}{3} + \cot\frac{\pi}{4}$ 43. $\csc\frac{\pi}{2} + \cot\frac{\pi}{2}$ 44. $\sec\pi - \csc\frac{\pi}{2}$

In Problems 45–62, find the exact values of the six trigonometric functions of the given angle. If any are not defined, say "not defined." Do not use a calculator.

45. $\frac{2\pi}{3}$ 46. $\frac{5\pi}{6}$ 47. 210° 48. 240° 49. $\frac{3\pi}{4}$ 50. $\frac{11\pi}{4}$

51. $\frac{8\pi}{3}$ 52. $\frac{13\pi}{6}$ 53. 405° 54. 390° 55. $-\frac{\pi}{6}$ 56. $-\frac{\pi}{3}$

57. −135° 58. −240° 59. $\frac{5\pi}{2}$ 60. 5π 61. 720° 62. 630°

In Problems 63–74, use a calculator to find the approximate value of each expression rounded to two decimal places.

63. $\sin 28°$ 64. $\cos 14°$ 65. $\sec 21°$ 66. $\cot 70°$

67. $\tan\frac{\pi}{10}$ 68. $\sin\frac{\pi}{8}$ 69. $\cot\frac{\pi}{12}$ 70. $\csc\frac{5\pi}{13}$

71. $\sin 1$ 72. $\tan 1$ 73. $\sin 1°$ 74. $\tan 1°$

In Problems 75–82, a point on the terminal side of an angle θ in standard position is given. Find the exact values of the six trigonometric functions of θ.

75. $(-3, 4)$
76. $(5, -12)$
77. $(2, -3)$
78. $(-1, -2)$
79. $(-2, -2)$
80. $(-1, 1)$
81. $\left(\frac{1}{3}, \frac{1}{4}\right)$
82. $(0.3, 0.4)$

83. Find the exact value of:
$$\sin 45° + \sin 135° + \sin 225° + \sin 315°$$

84. Find the exact value of:
$$\tan 60° + \tan 150°$$

85. Find the exact value of:
$$\sin 40° + \sin 130° + \sin 220° + \sin 310°$$

86. Find the exact value of:
$$\tan 40° + \tan 140°$$

87. If $f(\theta) = \sin\theta = 0.1$, find $f(\theta + \pi)$.

88. If $f(\theta) = \cos\theta = 0.3$, find $f(\theta + \pi)$.

89. If $f(\theta) = \tan\theta = 3$, find $f(\theta + \pi)$.

90. If $f(\theta) = \cot\theta = -2$, find $f(\theta + \pi)$.

91. If $\sin\theta = \frac{1}{5}$, find $\csc\theta$.

92. If $\cos\theta = \frac{2}{3}$, find $\sec\theta$.

In Problems 93–104, $f(\theta) = \sin\theta$ and $g(\theta) = \cos\theta$. Find the exact value of each function below if $\theta = 60°$. Do not use a calculator.

93. $f(\theta)$
94. $g(\theta)$
95. $f\left(\frac{\theta}{2}\right)$
96. $g\left(\frac{\theta}{2}\right)$
97. $[f(\theta)]^2$
98. $[g(\theta)]^2$
99. $f(2\theta)$
100. $g(2\theta)$
101. $2f(\theta)$
102. $2g(\theta)$
103. $f(-\theta)$
104. $g(-\theta)$

Mixed Practice

In Problems 105–112, $f(x) = \sin x$, $g(x) = \cos x$, $h(x) = 2x$, and $p(x) = \frac{x}{2}$. Find the value of each of the following:

105. $(f + g)(30°)$
106. $(f - g)(60°)$
107. $(f \cdot g)\left(\frac{3\pi}{4}\right)$
108. $(f \cdot g)\left(\frac{4\pi}{3}\right)$
109. $(f \circ h)\left(\frac{\pi}{6}\right)$
110. $(g \circ p)(60°)$
111. $(p \circ g)(315°)$
112. $(h \circ f)\left(\frac{5\pi}{6}\right)$

113. (a) Find $f\left(\frac{\pi}{4}\right)$. What point is on the graph of f?
(b) Using the result of part (a), what point is on the graph of f^{-1}?
(c) What point is on the graph of $y = f\left(x + \frac{\pi}{4}\right) - 3$ if $x = \frac{\pi}{4}$?

114. (a) Find $g\left(\frac{\pi}{6}\right)$. What point is on the graph of g?
(b) Using the result of part (a), what point is on the graph of g^{-1}?
(c) What point is on the graph of $y = 2g\left(x - \frac{\pi}{6}\right)$ if $x = \frac{\pi}{6}$?

Applications and Extensions

115. Use a calculator in radian mode to complete the following table.

What can you conclude about the value of $f(\theta) = \frac{\sin\theta}{\theta}$ as θ approaches 0?

θ	0.5	0.4	0.2	0.1	0.01	0.001	0.0001	0.00001
$\sin\theta$								
$f(\theta) = \frac{\sin\theta}{\theta}$								

116. Use a calculator in radian mode to complete the following table.

What can you conclude about the value of $g(\theta) = \dfrac{\cos\theta - 1}{\theta}$ as θ approaches 0?

θ	0.5	0.4	0.2	0.1	0.01	0.001	0.0001	0.00001
$\cos\theta - 1$								
$g(\theta) = \dfrac{\cos\theta - 1}{\theta}$								

For Problems 117–120, use the following discussion.

Projectile Motion *The path of a projectile fired at an inclination θ to the horizontal with initial speed v_0 is a parabola (see the figure).*

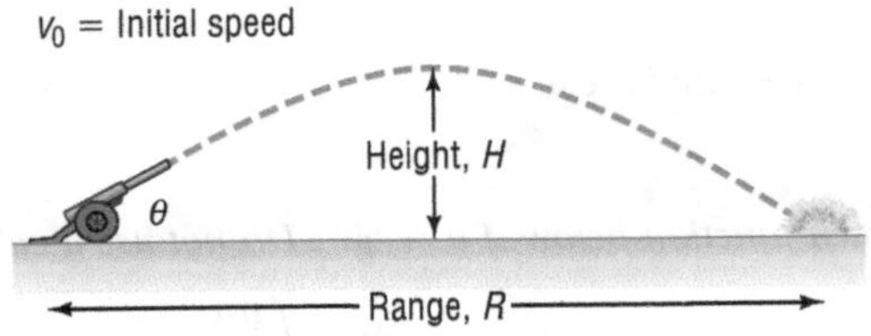

The range R of the projectile, that is, the horizontal distance that the projectile travels, is found by using the function

$$R(\theta) = \frac{v_0^2 \sin(2\theta)}{g}$$

where $g \approx 32.2$ feet per second per second ≈ 9.8 meters per second per second is the acceleration due to gravity. The maximum height H of the projectile is given by the function

$$H(\theta) = \frac{v_0^2 (\sin\theta)^2}{2g}$$

In Problems 117–120, find the range R and maximum height H.

117. The projectile is fired at an angle of 45° to the horizontal with an initial speed of 100 feet per second.

118. The projectile is fired at an angle of 30° to the horizontal with an initial speed of 150 meters per second.

119. The projectile is fired at an angle of 25° to the horizontal with an initial speed of 500 meters per second.

120. The projectile is fired at an angle of 50° to the horizontal with an initial speed of 200 feet per second.

121. Inclined Plane See the figure.

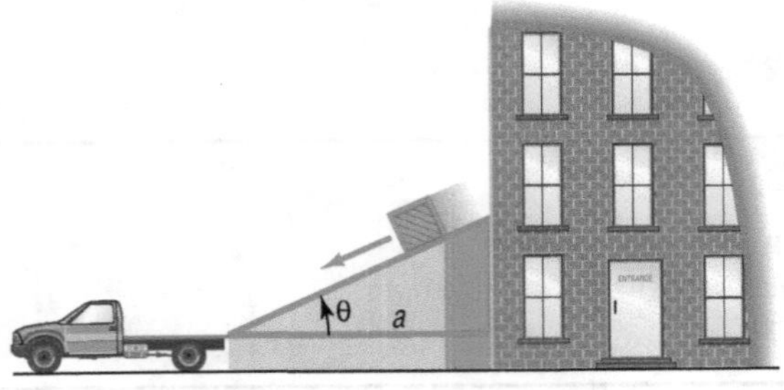

If friction is ignored, the time t (in seconds) required for a block to slide down an inclined plane is given by the function

$$t(\theta) = \sqrt{\frac{2a}{g \sin\theta \cos\theta}}$$

where a is the length (in feet) of the base and $g \approx 32$ feet per second per second is the acceleration due to gravity. How long does it take a block to slide down an inclined plane with base $a = 10$ feet when:
(a) $\theta = 30°$? (b) $\theta = 45°$? (c) $\theta = 60°$?

122. Piston Engines In a certain piston engine, the distance x (in centimeters) from the center of the drive shaft to the head of the piston is given by the function

$$x(\theta) = \cos\theta + \sqrt{16 + 0.5\cos(2\theta)}$$

where θ is the angle between the crank and the path of the piston head. See the figure. Find x when $\theta = 30°$ and when $\theta = 45°$.

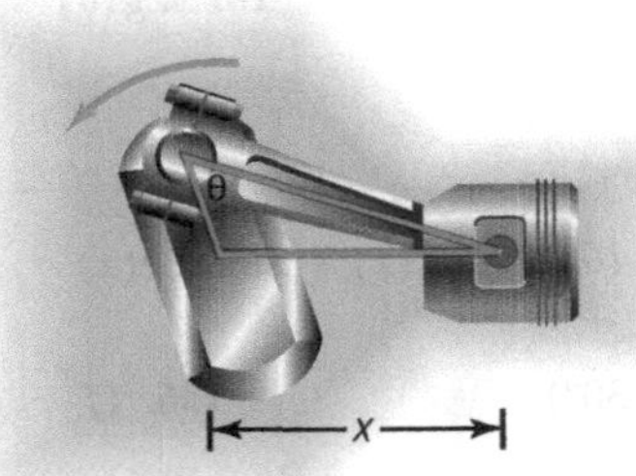

123. Calculating the Time of a Trip Two oceanfront homes are located 8 miles apart on a straight stretch of beach, each a distance of 1 mile from a paved road that parallels the ocean. See the figure.

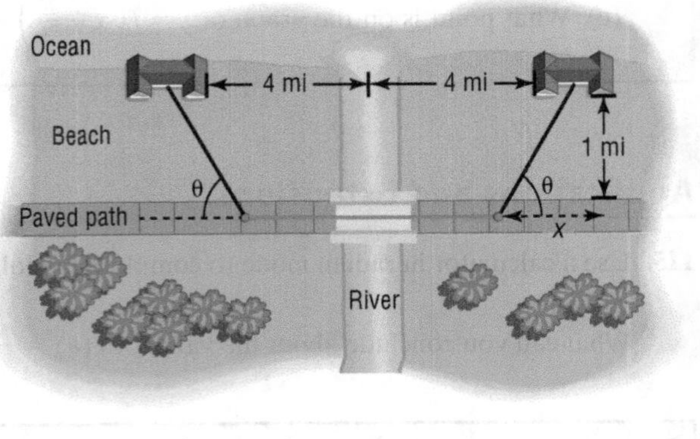

Sally can jog 8 miles per hour along the paved road, but only 3 miles per hour in the sand on the beach. Because of a river directly between the two houses, it is necessary to jog in the sand to the road, continue on the road, and then jog directly back in the sand to get from one house to the other. The time T to get from one house to the other as a function of the angle θ shown in the illustration is

$$T(\theta) = 1 + \frac{2}{3 \sin \theta} - \frac{1}{4 \tan \theta}, \qquad 0° < \theta < 90°$$

(a) Calculate the time T for $\theta = 30°$. How long is Sally on the paved road?
(b) Calculate the time T for $\theta = 45°$. How long is Sally on the paved road?
(c) Calculate the time T for $\theta = 60°$. How long is Sally on the paved road?
(d) Calculate the time T for $\theta = 90°$. Describe the path taken. Why can't the formula for T be used?

124. Designing Fine Decorative Pieces A designer of decorative art plans to market solid gold spheres encased in clear crystal cones. Each sphere is of fixed radius R and will be enclosed in a cone of height h and radius r. See the illustration. Many cones can be used to enclose the sphere, each having a different slant angle θ. The volume V of the cone can be expressed as a function of the slant angle θ of the cone as

$$V(\theta) = \frac{1}{3}\pi R^3 \frac{(1 + \sec \theta)^3}{(\tan \theta)^2} \qquad 0° < \theta < 90°$$

What volume V is required to enclose a sphere of radius 2 centimeters in a cone whose slant angle θ is 30°? 45°? 60°?

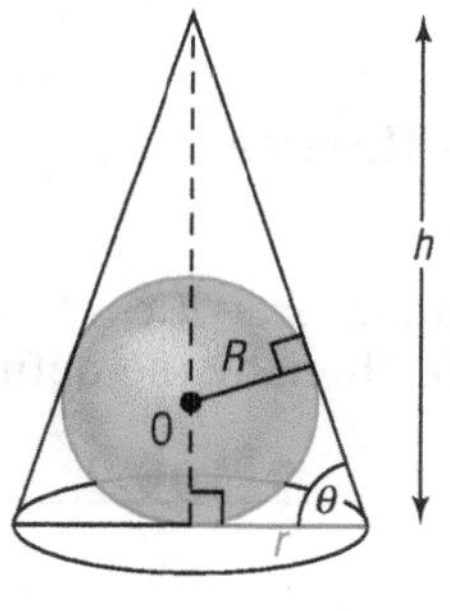

125. Projectile Motion An object is propelled upward at an angle θ, $45° < \theta < 90°$, to the horizontal with an initial velocity of v_0 feet per second from the base of an inclined plane that makes an angle of 45° with the horizontal. See the illustration. If air resistance is ignored, the distance R that it travels up the inclined plane as a function of θ is given by

$$R(\theta) = \frac{v_0^2\sqrt{2}}{32}[\sin(2\theta) - \cos(2\theta) - 1]$$

(a) Find the distance R that the object travels along the inclined plane if the initial velocity is 32 feet per second and $\theta = 60°$.
(b) Graph $R = R(\theta)$ if the initial velocity is 32 feet per second.
(c) What value of θ makes R largest?

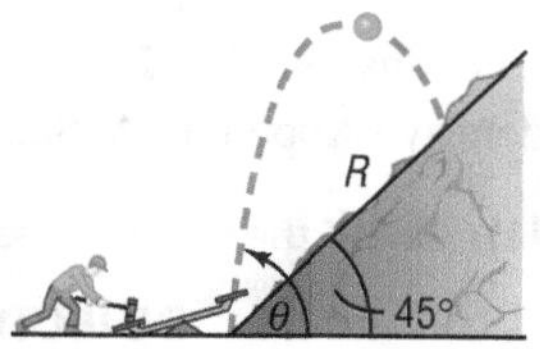

126. If θ, $0 < \theta < \pi$, is the angle between the positive x-axis and a nonhorizontal, nonvertical line L, show that the slope m of L equals $\tan \theta$. The angle θ is called the **inclination** of L.

[**Hint:** See the illustration, where we have drawn the line M parallel to L and passing through the origin. Use the fact that M intersects the unit circle at the point $(\cos \theta, \sin \theta)$.]

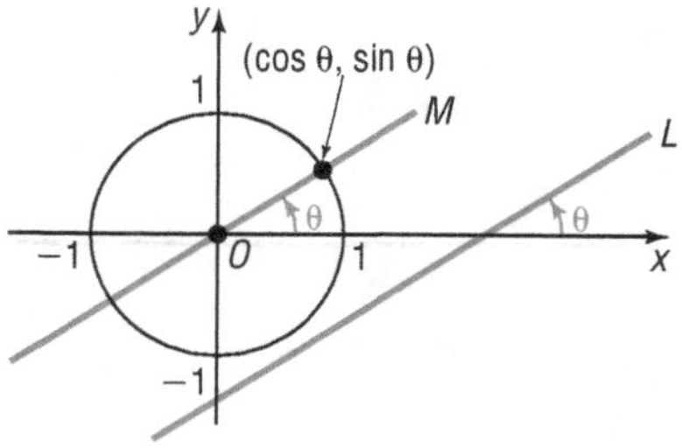

In Problems 127–128, use the figure to approximate the value of the six trigonometric functions at t to the nearest tenth. Then use a calculator to approximate each of the six trigonometric functions at t.

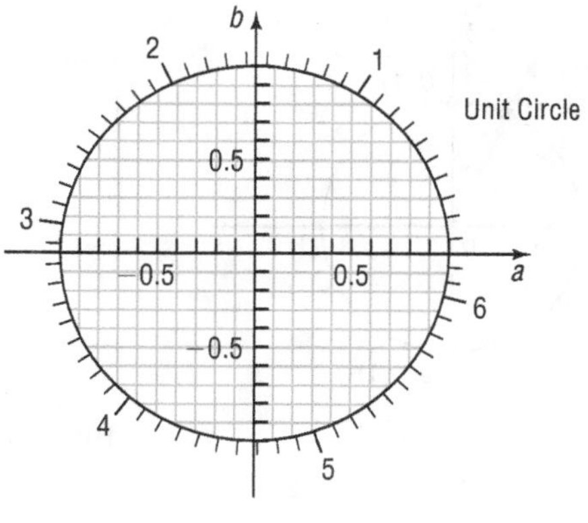

127. (a) $t = 1$ (b) $t = 5.1$

128. (a) $t = 2$ (b) $t = 4$

Discussion and Writing

129. Write a brief paragraph that explains how to quickly compute the trigonometric functions of 30°, 45°, and 60°.

130. Write a brief paragraph that explains how to quickly compute the trigonometric functions of 0°, 90°, 180°, and 270°.

131. How would you explain the meaning of the sine function to a fellow student who has just completed college algebra?

'Are You Prepared?' Answers

1. $c^2 = a^2 + b^2$ **2.** 8 **3.** True **4.** equal; proportional **5.** $\left(-\frac{1}{2}, \frac{\sqrt{3}}{2}\right)$ **6.** $-\frac{1}{2}$

6.3 Properties of the Trigonometric Functions

PREPARING FOR THIS SECTION *Before getting started, review the following:*

- Functions (Section 2.1, pp. 56–64)
- Identity (Appendix A, Section A.6, p. A46)
- Even and Odd Functions (Section 2.3, pp. 79–81)

Now Work the 'Are You Prepared?' problems on page 392.

OBJECTIVES
1. Determine the Domain and the Range of the Trigonometric Functions (p. 382)
2. Determine the Period of the Trigonometric Functions (p. 384)
3. Determine the Signs of the Trigonometric Functions in a Given Quadrant (p. 386)
4. Find the Values of the Trigonometric Functions Using Fundamental Identities (p. 386)
5. Find the Exact Values of the Trigonometric Functions of an Angle Given One of the Functions and the Quadrant of the Angle (p. 389)
6. Use Even–Odd Properties to Find the Exact Values of the Trigonometric Functions (p. 391)

1 Determine the Domain and the Range of the Trigonometric Functions

Let θ be an angle in standard position, and let $P = (x, y)$ be the point on the unit circle that corresponds to θ. See Figure 39. Then, by the definition given earlier,

Figure 39

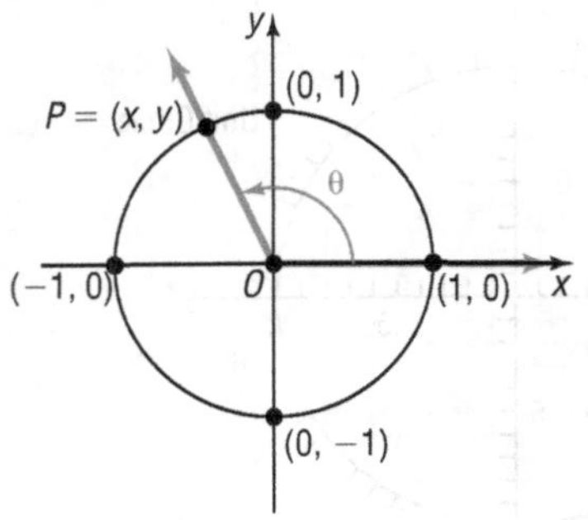

$$\sin\theta = y \qquad \cos\theta = x \qquad \tan\theta = \frac{y}{x} \quad x \neq 0$$
$$\csc\theta = \frac{1}{y} \quad y \neq 0 \qquad \sec\theta = \frac{1}{x} \quad x \neq 0 \qquad \cot\theta = \frac{x}{y} \quad y \neq 0$$

For $\sin\theta$ and $\cos\theta$, θ can be any angle, so it follows that the domain of the sine function and cosine function is the set of all real numbers.

> The domain of the sine function is the set of all real numbers.
> The domain of the cosine function is the set of all real numbers.

If $x = 0$, then the tangent function and the secant function are not defined. That is, for the tangent function and secant function, the x-coordinate of $P = (x, y)$ cannot be 0. See Figure 39. On the unit circle, there are two such points $(0, 1)$ and $(0, -1)$. These two points correspond to the angles $\frac{\pi}{2}(90^\circ)$ and $\frac{3\pi}{2}(270^\circ)$ or, more generally, to any angle that is an odd integer multiple of $\frac{\pi}{2}(90^\circ)$, such as $\pm\frac{\pi}{2}(\pm 90^\circ)$, $\pm\frac{3\pi}{2}(\pm 270^\circ)$, $\pm\frac{5\pi}{2}(\pm 450^\circ)$, and so on. Such angles must therefore be excluded from the domain of the tangent function and secant function.

The domain of the tangent function is the set of all real numbers, except odd integer multiples of $\frac{\pi}{2}(90°)$.

The domain of the secant function is the set of all real numbers, except odd integer multiples of $\frac{\pi}{2}(90°)$.

If $y = 0$, then the cotangent function and the cosecant function are not defined. For the cotangent function and cosecant function, the y-coordinate of $P = (x, y)$ cannot be 0. See Figure 39. On the unit circle, there are two such points, $(1, 0)$ and $(-1, 0)$. These two points correspond to the angles $0(0°)$ and $\pi(180°)$ or, more generally, to any angle that is an integer multiple of $\pi(180°)$, such as $0(0°)$, $\pm\pi(\pm 180°)$, $\pm 2\pi(\pm 360°)$, $\pm 3\pi(\pm 540°)$, and so on. Such angles must therefore be excluded from the domain of the cotangent function and cosecant function.

The domain of the cotangent function is the set of all real numbers, except integer multiples of $\pi(180°)$.

The domain of the cosecant function is the set of all real numbers, except integer multiples of $\pi(180°)$.

Next we determine the range of each of the six trigonometric functions. Refer again to Figure 39. Let $P = (x, y)$ be the point on the unit circle that corresponds to the angle θ. It follows that $-1 \leq x \leq 1$ and $-1 \leq y \leq 1$. Since $\sin\theta = y$ and $\cos\theta = x$, we have

$$-1 \leq \sin\theta \leq 1 \qquad -1 \leq \cos\theta \leq 1$$

The range of both the sine function and the cosine function consists of all real numbers between -1 and 1, inclusive. Using absolute value notation, we have $|\sin\theta| \leq 1$ and $|\cos\theta| \leq 1$.

If θ is not an integer multiple of $\pi(180°)$, then $\csc\theta = \frac{1}{y}$. Since $y = \sin\theta$ and $|y| = |\sin\theta| \leq 1$, it follows that $|\csc\theta| = \frac{1}{|\sin\theta|} = \frac{1}{|y|} \geq 1$. The range of the cosecant function consists of all real numbers less than or equal to -1 or greater than or equal to 1. That is,

$$\csc\theta \leq -1 \quad \text{or} \quad \csc\theta \geq 1$$

NOTE If $|y| \leq 1$, then $\frac{1}{|y|} \geq 1$. For example, $\left|-\frac{1}{2}\right| < 1$ and $\frac{1}{\left|-\frac{1}{2}\right|} = 2 > 1$.

If θ is not an odd integer multiple of $\frac{\pi}{2}(90°)$, then, $\sec\theta = \frac{1}{x}$. Since $x = \cos\theta$ and $|x| = |\cos\theta| \leq 1$, it follows that $|\sec\theta| = \frac{1}{|\cos\theta|} = \frac{1}{|x|} \geq 1$. The range of the secant function consists of all real numbers less than or equal to -1 or greater than or equal to 1. That is,

$$\sec\theta \leq -1 \quad \text{or} \quad \sec\theta \geq 1$$

The range of both the tangent function and the cotangent function is the set of all real numbers.

$$-\infty < \tan\theta < \infty \qquad -\infty < \cot\theta < \infty$$

You are asked to prove this in Problems 121 and 122.

Table 4 summarizes these results.

Table 4

Function	Symbol	Domain	Range
sine	$f(\theta) = \sin\theta$	All real numbers	All real numbers from −1 to 1, inclusive
cosine	$f(\theta) = \cos\theta$	All real numbers	All real numbers from −1 to 1, inclusive
tangent	$f(\theta) = \tan\theta$	All real numbers, except odd integer multiples of $\frac{\pi}{2}$ (90°)	All real numbers
cosecant	$f(\theta) = \csc\theta$	All real numbers, except integer multiples of π (180°)	All real numbers greater than or equal to 1 or less than or equal to −1
secant	$f(\theta) = \sec\theta$	All real numbers, except odd integer multiples of $\frac{\pi}{2}$ (90°)	All real numbers greater than or equal to 1 or less than or equal to −1
cotangent	$f(\theta) = \cot\theta$	All real numbers, except integer multiples of π (180°)	All real numbers

Now Work PROBLEM 97

2 Determine the Period of the Trigonometric Functions

Figure 40

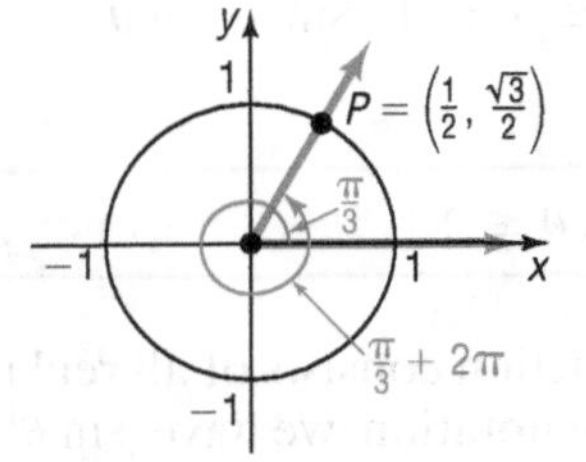

Look at Figure 40. This figure shows that for an angle of $\frac{\pi}{3}$ radians the corresponding point P on the unit circle is $\left(\frac{1}{2}, \frac{\sqrt{3}}{2}\right)$. Notice that, for an angle of $\frac{\pi}{3} + 2\pi$ radians, the corresponding point P on the unit circle is also $\left(\frac{1}{2}, \frac{\sqrt{3}}{2}\right)$. Then

$$\sin\frac{\pi}{3} = \frac{\sqrt{3}}{2} \quad \text{and} \quad \sin\left(\frac{\pi}{3} + 2\pi\right) = \frac{\sqrt{3}}{2}$$

$$\cos\frac{\pi}{3} = \frac{1}{2} \quad \text{and} \quad \cos\left(\frac{\pi}{3} + 2\pi\right) = \frac{1}{2}$$

Figure 41

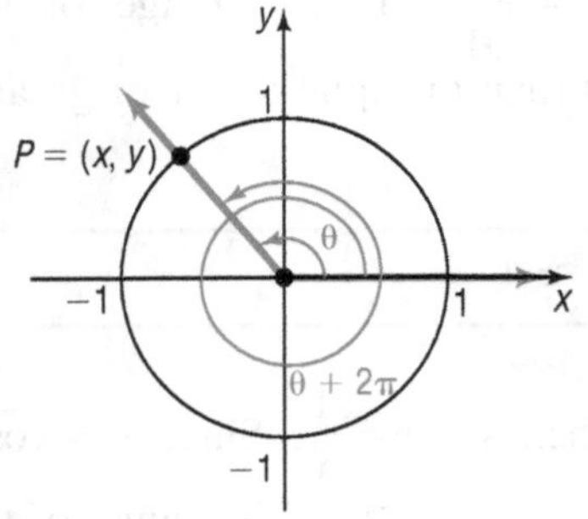

This example illustrates a more general situation. For a given angle θ, measured in radians, suppose that we know the corresponding point $P = (x, y)$ on the unit circle. Now add 2π to θ. The point on the unit circle corresponding to $\theta + 2\pi$ is identical to the point P on the unit circle corresponding to θ. See Figure 41. The values of the trigonometric functions of $\theta + 2\pi$ are equal to the values of the corresponding trigonometric functions of θ.

If we add (or subtract) integer multiples of 2π to θ, the values of the sine and cosine function remain unchanged. That is, for all θ

$$\sin(\theta + 2\pi k) = \sin\theta \qquad \cos(\theta + 2\pi k) = \cos\theta \tag{1}$$
where k is any integer.

Functions that exhibit this kind of behavior are called *periodic functions*.

DEFINITION A function f is called **periodic** if there is a positive number p such that, whenever θ is in the domain of f, so is $\theta + p$, and

$$f(\theta + p) = f(\theta)$$

If there is a smallest such number p, this smallest value is called the **(fundamental) period** of f.

Based on equation (1), the sine and cosine functions are periodic. In fact, the sine and cosine functions have period 2π. You are asked to prove this fact in Problems 123 and 124. The secant and cosecant functions are also periodic with period 2π, and the tangent and cotangent functions are periodic with period π. You are asked to prove these statements in Problems 125 through 128.

These facts are summarized as follows:

In Words

Tangent and cotangent have period π; the others have period 2π.

Periodic Properties

$$\sin(\theta + 2\pi) = \sin\theta \quad \cos(\theta + 2\pi) = \cos\theta \quad \tan(\theta + \pi) = \tan\theta$$
$$\csc(\theta + 2\pi) = \csc\theta \quad \sec(\theta + 2\pi) = \sec\theta \quad \cot(\theta + \pi) = \cot\theta$$

Because the sine, cosine, secant, and cosecant functions have period 2π, once we know their values over an interval of length 2π, we know all their values; similarly, since the tangent and cotangent functions have period π, once we know their values over an interval of length π, we know all their values.

EXAMPLE 1 Finding Exact Values Using Periodic Properties

Find the exact value of:

(a) $\sin\frac{17\pi}{4}$ (b) $\cos(5\pi)$ (c) $\tan\frac{5\pi}{4}$

Solution (a) It is best to sketch the angle first, as shown in Figure 42(a). Since the period of the sine function is 2π, each full revolution can be ignored. This leaves the angle $\frac{\pi}{4}$. Then

$$\sin\frac{17\pi}{4} = \sin\left(\frac{\pi}{4} + 4\pi\right) = \sin\frac{\pi}{4} = \frac{\sqrt{2}}{2}$$

(b) See Figure 42(b). Since the period of the cosine function is 2π, each full revolution can be ignored. This leaves the angle π. Then

$$\cos(5\pi) = \cos(\pi + 4\pi) = \cos\pi = -1$$

(c) See Figure 42(c). Since the period of the tangent function is π, each half-revolution can be ignored. This leaves the angle $\frac{\pi}{4}$. Then

$$\tan\frac{5\pi}{4} = \tan\left(\frac{\pi}{4} + \pi\right) = \tan\frac{\pi}{4} = 1$$

Figure 42

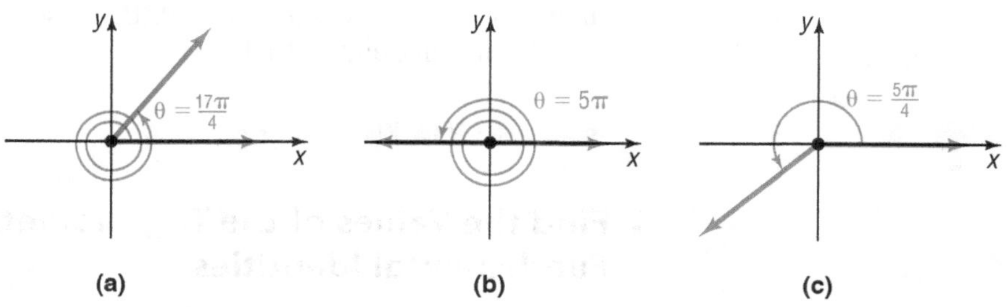

The periodic properties of the trigonometric functions will be very helpful to us when we study their graphs later in the chapter.

Now Work PROBLEM 11

3 Determine the Signs of the Trigonometric Functions in a Given Quadrant

Let $P = (x, y)$ be the point on the unit circle that corresponds to the angle θ. If we know in which quadrant the point P lies, then we can determine the signs of the trigonometric functions of θ. For example, if $P = (x, y)$ lies in quadrant IV, as shown in Figure 43, then we know that $x > 0$ and $y < 0$. Consequently,

Figure 43

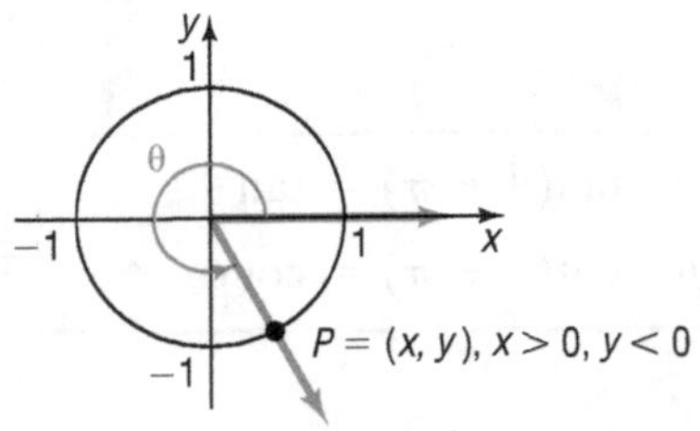

$$\sin\theta = y < 0 \qquad \cos\theta = x > 0 \qquad \tan\theta = \frac{y}{x} < 0$$

$$\csc\theta = \frac{1}{y} < 0 \qquad \sec\theta = \frac{1}{x} > 0 \qquad \cot\theta = \frac{x}{y} < 0$$

Table 5 lists the signs of the six trigonometric functions for each quadrant. See also Figure 44.

Table 5

Quadrant of P	sin θ, csc θ	cos θ, sec θ	tan θ, cot θ
I	Positive	Positive	Positive
II	Positive	Negative	Negative
III	Negative	Negative	Positive
IV	Negative	Positive	Negative

Figure 44

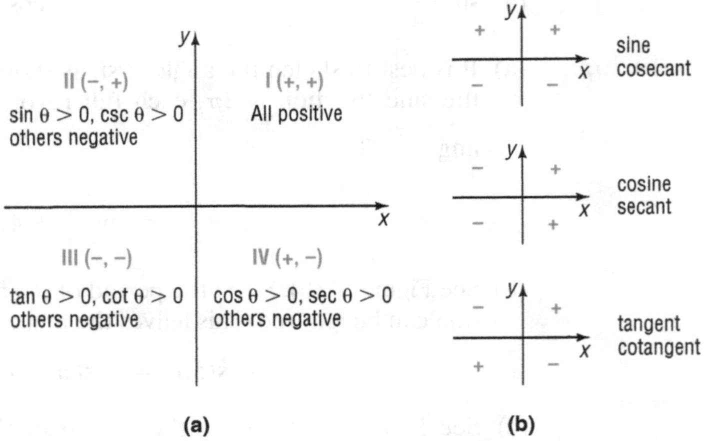

EXAMPLE 2 **Finding the Quadrant in Which an Angle θ Lies**

If $\sin\theta < 0$ and $\cos\theta < 0$, name the quadrant in which the angle θ lies.

Solution Let $P = (x, y)$ be the point on the unit circle corresponding to θ. Then $\sin\theta = y < 0$ and $\cos\theta = x < 0$. Because points in quadrant III have $x < 0$ and $y < 0$, θ lies in quadrant III.

Now Work PROBLEM 27

4 Find the Values of the Trigonometric Functions Using Fundamental Identities

If $P = (x, y)$ is the point on the unit circle corresponding to θ, then

$$\sin\theta = y \qquad \cos\theta = x \qquad \tan\theta = \frac{y}{x} \quad \text{if } x \neq 0$$

$$\csc\theta = \frac{1}{y} \quad \text{if } y \neq 0 \qquad \sec\theta = \frac{1}{x} \quad \text{if } x \neq 0 \qquad \cot\theta = \frac{x}{y} \quad \text{if } y \neq 0$$

Based on these definitions, we have the **reciprocal identities:**

Reciprocal Identities

$$\csc\theta = \frac{1}{\sin\theta} \qquad \sec\theta = \frac{1}{\cos\theta} \qquad \cot\theta = \frac{1}{\tan\theta} \tag{2}$$

Two other fundamental identities are the **quotient identities.**

Quotient Identities

$$\tan\theta = \frac{\sin\theta}{\cos\theta} \qquad \cot\theta = \frac{\cos\theta}{\sin\theta} \tag{3}$$

The proofs of identities (2) and (3) follow from the definitions of the trigonometric functions. (See Problems 129 and 130.)

If $\sin\theta$ and $\cos\theta$ are known, identities (2) and (3) make it easy to find the values of the remaining trigonometric functions.

EXAMPLE 3 Finding Exact Values Using Identities when Sine and Cosine Are Given

Given $\sin\theta = \frac{\sqrt{5}}{5}$ and $\cos\theta = \frac{2\sqrt{5}}{5}$, find the exact values of the four remaining trigonometric functions of θ using identities.

Solution Based on a quotient identity from (3), we have

$$\tan\theta = \frac{\sin\theta}{\cos\theta} = \frac{\frac{\sqrt{5}}{5}}{\frac{2\sqrt{5}}{5}} = \frac{1}{2}$$

Then we use the reciprocal identities from (2) to get

$$\csc\theta = \frac{1}{\sin\theta} = \frac{1}{\frac{\sqrt{5}}{5}} = \frac{5}{\sqrt{5}} = \sqrt{5} \qquad \sec\theta = \frac{1}{\cos\theta} = \frac{1}{\frac{2\sqrt{5}}{5}} = \frac{5}{2\sqrt{5}} = \frac{\sqrt{5}}{2} \qquad \cot\theta = \frac{1}{\tan\theta} = \frac{1}{\frac{1}{2}} = 2$$

Now Work PROBLEM 35

The equation of the unit circle is $x^2 + y^2 = 1$, or equivalently,

$$y^2 + x^2 = 1$$

If $P = (x, y)$ is the point on the unit circle that corresponds to the angle θ, then $y = \sin\theta$ and $x = \cos\theta$, so we have

$$(\sin\theta)^2 + (\cos\theta)^2 = 1 \tag{4}$$

It is customary to write $\sin^2\theta$ instead of $(\sin\theta)^2$, $\cos^2\theta$ instead of $(\cos\theta)^2$, and so on. With this notation, we can rewrite equation (4) as

$$\sin^2\theta + \cos^2\theta = 1 \tag{5}$$

If $\cos\theta \neq 0$, we can divide each side of equation (5) by $\cos^2\theta$.

$$\frac{\sin^2\theta}{\cos^2\theta} + \frac{\cos^2\theta}{\cos^2\theta} = \frac{1}{\cos^2\theta}$$

$$\left(\frac{\sin\theta}{\cos\theta}\right)^2 + 1 = \left(\frac{1}{\cos\theta}\right)^2$$

Now use identities (2) and (3) to get

$$\tan^2\theta + 1 = \sec^2\theta \qquad \textbf{(6)}$$

Similarly, if $\sin\theta \neq 0$, we can divide equation (5) by $\sin^2\theta$ and use identities (2) and (3) to get $1 + \cot^2\theta = \csc^2\theta$, which we write as

$$\cot^2\theta + 1 = \csc^2\theta \qquad \textbf{(7)}$$

Collectively, the identities in (5), (6), and (7) are referred to as the **Pythagorean identities.**

Let's pause here to summarize the fundamental identities.

Fundamental Identities

$$\tan\theta = \frac{\sin\theta}{\cos\theta} \qquad \cot\theta = \frac{\cos\theta}{\sin\theta}$$

$$\csc\theta = \frac{1}{\sin\theta} \qquad \sec\theta = \frac{1}{\cos\theta} \qquad \cot\theta = \frac{1}{\tan\theta}$$

$$\sin^2\theta + \cos^2\theta = 1 \qquad \tan^2\theta + 1 = \sec^2\theta \qquad \cot^2\theta + 1 = \csc^2\theta$$

EXAMPLE 4 Finding the Exact Value of a Trigonometric Expression Using Identities

Find the exact value of each expression. Do not use a calculator.

(a) $\tan 20^\circ - \dfrac{\sin 20^\circ}{\cos 20^\circ}$ (b) $\sin^2\dfrac{\pi}{12} + \dfrac{1}{\sec^2\dfrac{\pi}{12}}$

Solution (a) $\tan 20^\circ - \dfrac{\sin 20^\circ}{\cos 20^\circ} = \tan 20^\circ - \tan 20^\circ = 0$

$\uparrow$ $\dfrac{\sin\theta}{\cos\theta} = \tan\theta$

(b) $\sin^2\dfrac{\pi}{12} + \dfrac{1}{\sec^2\dfrac{\pi}{12}} = \sin^2\dfrac{\pi}{12} + \cos^2\dfrac{\pi}{12} = 1$

$\uparrow$ $\cos\theta = \dfrac{1}{\sec\theta}$ $\uparrow$ $\sin^2\theta + \cos^2\theta = 1$

Now Work PROBLEM 79

5 Find the Exact Values of the Trigonometric Functions of an Angle Given One of the Functions and the Quadrant of the Angle

Many problems require finding the exact values of the remaining trigonometric functions when the value of one of them is known and the quadrant in which θ lies can be found. There are two approaches to solving such problems. One approach uses a circle of radius r; the other uses identities.

When using identities, sometimes a rearrangement is required. For example, the Pythagorean identity

$$\sin^2\theta + \cos^2\theta = 1$$

can be solved for $\sin\theta$ in terms of $\cos\theta$ (or vice versa) as follows:

$$\sin^2\theta = 1 - \cos^2\theta$$
$$\sin\theta = \pm\sqrt{1 - \cos^2\theta}$$

where the + sign is used if $\sin\theta > 0$ and the − sign is used if $\sin\theta < 0$. Similarly, in $\tan^2\theta + 1 = \sec^2\theta$, we can solve for $\tan\theta$ (or $\sec\theta$), and in $\cot^2\theta + 1 = \csc^2\theta$, we can solve for $\cot\theta$ (or $\csc\theta$).

EXAMPLE 5 Given One Value of a Trigonometric Function and the Sign of Another, Find the Remaining Ones

Given that $\sin\theta = \frac{1}{3}$ and $\cos\theta < 0$, find the exact value of each of the remaining five trigonometric functions.

Solution 1 Using a Circle

Suppose that $P = (x, y)$ is the point on a circle that corresponds to θ. Since $\sin\theta = \frac{1}{3} > 0$ and $\cos\theta < 0$, the point $P = (x, y)$ is in quadrant II. Because $\sin\theta = \frac{1}{3} = \frac{y}{r}$, we let $y = 1$ and $r = 3$. The point $P = (x, y) = (x, 1)$ that corresponds to θ lies on the circle of radius 3: $x^2 + y^2 = 9$. See Figure 45.

Figure 45

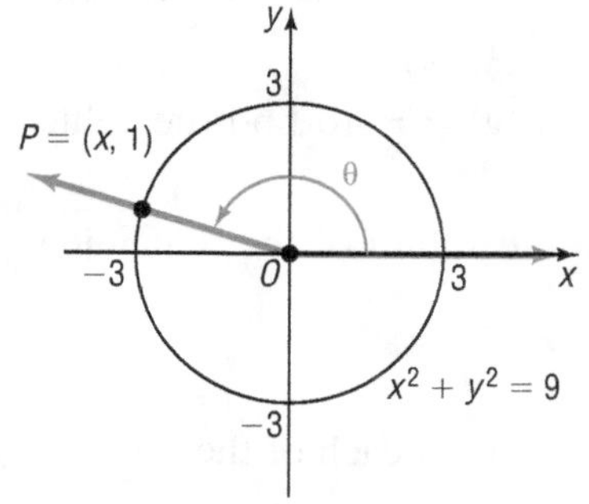

To find x, we use the fact that $x^2 + y^2 = 9$, $y = 1$, and P is in quadrant II (so $x < 0$).

$$x^2 + y^2 = 9$$
$$x^2 + 1^2 = 9 \qquad y = 1$$
$$x^2 = 8$$
$$x = -2\sqrt{2} \qquad x < 0$$

Since $x = -2\sqrt{2}$, $y = 1$, and $r = 3$, we find that

$$\cos\theta = \frac{x}{r} = -\frac{2\sqrt{2}}{3} \qquad \tan\theta = \frac{y}{x} = \frac{1}{-2\sqrt{2}} = -\frac{\sqrt{2}}{4}$$

$$\csc\theta = \frac{r}{y} = \frac{3}{1} = 3 \qquad \sec\theta = \frac{r}{x} = \frac{3}{-2\sqrt{2}} = -\frac{3\sqrt{2}}{4} \qquad \cot\theta = \frac{x}{y} = \frac{-2\sqrt{2}}{1} = -2\sqrt{2}$$

■

Solution 2 Using Identities

First, we solve the identity $\sin^2\theta + \cos^2\theta = 1$ for $\cos\theta$.

$$\sin^2\theta + \cos^2\theta = 1$$
$$\cos^2\theta = 1 - \sin^2\theta$$
$$\cos\theta = \pm\sqrt{1 - \sin^2\theta}$$

Because $\cos\theta < 0$, we choose the minus sign and use the fact that $\sin\theta = \frac{1}{3}$.

$$\cos\theta = -\sqrt{1-\sin^2\theta} = -\sqrt{1-\frac{1}{9}} = -\sqrt{\frac{8}{9}} = -\frac{2\sqrt{2}}{3}$$

$\uparrow$ $\sin\theta = \frac{1}{3}$

Now we know the values of $\sin\theta$ and $\cos\theta$, so we can use quotient and reciprocal identities to get

$$\tan\theta = \frac{\sin\theta}{\cos\theta} = \frac{\frac{1}{3}}{\frac{-2\sqrt{2}}{3}} = \frac{1}{-2\sqrt{2}} = -\frac{\sqrt{2}}{4} \qquad \cot\theta = \frac{1}{\tan\theta} = -2\sqrt{2}$$

$$\sec\theta = \frac{1}{\cos\theta} = \frac{1}{\frac{-2\sqrt{2}}{3}} = \frac{-3}{2\sqrt{2}} = -\frac{3\sqrt{2}}{4} \qquad \csc\theta = \frac{1}{\sin\theta} = \frac{1}{\frac{1}{3}} = 3$$

Finding the Values of the Trigonometric Functions of θ when One Is Known and the Quadrant of θ Is Known

Given the value of one trigonometric function and the quadrant in which θ lies, the exact value of each of the remaining five trigonometric functions can be found in either of two ways.

Method 1 Using a Circle of Radius r

STEP 1: Assign a value to two of the three variables x, y, r based on the value of the given trigonometric function and the location of P.

STEP 2: Draw a circle showing the location of the angle θ and the point $P = (x, y)$ that corresponds to θ. The radius of the circle that contains $P = (x, y)$ is $r = \sqrt{x^2 + y^2}$.

STEP 3: Use the fact that P lies on the circle $x^2 + y^2 = r^2$ to find the value of the missing variable.

STEP 4: Apply the theorem on page 377 to find the values of the remaining trigonometric functions.

Method 2 Using Identities

Use appropriately selected identities to find the value of each of the remaining trigonometric functions.

EXAMPLE 6 Given One Value of a Trigonometric Function and the Sign of Another, Find the Remaining Ones

Given that $\tan\theta = \frac{1}{2}$ and $\sin\theta < 0$, find the exact value of each of the remaining five trigonometric functions of θ.

Solution 1 Using a Circle

STEP 1: Since $\tan\theta = \frac{1}{2} > 0$ and $\sin\theta < 0$, the point $P = (x, y)$ that corresponds to θ lies in quadrant III. Since $\tan\theta = \frac{1}{2} = \frac{y}{x}$ and θ lies in quadrant III, we let $x = -2$ and $y = -1$.

STEP 2: Figure 46 shows a circle with the point $P = (-2, -1)$ and the angle θ labeled.

Figure 46

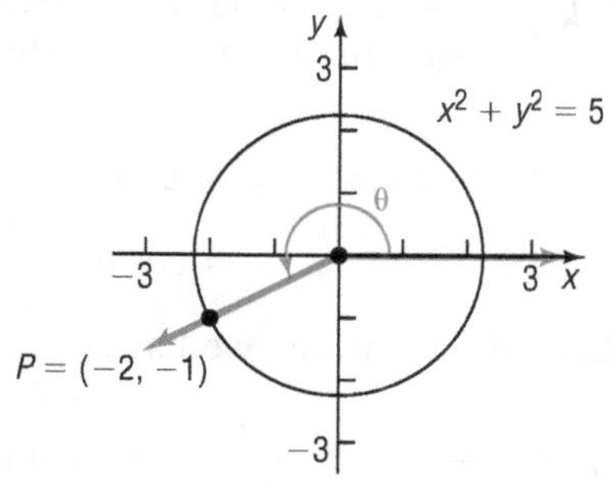

STEP 3: We know $x = -2$ and $y = -1$, so $r = \sqrt{x^2 + y^2} = \sqrt{(-2)^2 + (-1)^2} = \sqrt{5}$, and P lies on the circle $x^2 + y^2 = 5$.

STEP 4: Now apply the theorem on page 377 using $x = -2$, $y = -1$, and $r = \sqrt{5}$.

$$\sin\theta = \frac{y}{r} = \frac{-1}{\sqrt{5}} = -\frac{\sqrt{5}}{5} \qquad \cos\theta = \frac{x}{r} = \frac{-2}{\sqrt{5}} = -\frac{2\sqrt{5}}{5}$$

$$\csc\theta = \frac{r}{y} = \frac{\sqrt{5}}{-1} = -\sqrt{5} \qquad \sec\theta = \frac{r}{x} = \frac{\sqrt{5}}{-2} = -\frac{\sqrt{5}}{2} \qquad \cot\theta = \frac{x}{y} = \frac{-2}{-1} = 2$$

Solution 2 Using Identities

Because we know the value of $\tan\theta$, we use the Pythagorean identity that involves $\tan\theta$, that is, $\tan^2\theta + 1 = \sec^2\theta$. Since $\tan\theta = \frac{1}{2} > 0$ and $\sin\theta < 0$, then θ lies in quadrant III, where $\sec\theta < 0$.

$$\tan^2\theta + 1 = \sec^2\theta \qquad \text{Pythagorean identity}$$

$$\left(\frac{1}{2}\right)^2 + 1 = \sec^2\theta \qquad \tan\theta = \frac{1}{2}$$

$$\sec^2\theta = \frac{1}{4} + 1 = \frac{5}{4} \qquad \text{Proceed to solve for } \sec\theta.$$

$$\sec\theta = -\frac{\sqrt{5}}{2} \qquad \sec\theta < 0$$

Now we know $\tan\theta = \frac{1}{2}$ and $\sec\theta = -\frac{\sqrt{5}}{2}$. Using reciprocal identities, we find

$$\cos\theta = \frac{1}{\sec\theta} = \frac{1}{-\frac{\sqrt{5}}{2}} = -\frac{2}{\sqrt{5}} = -\frac{2\sqrt{5}}{5}$$

$$\cot\theta = \frac{1}{\tan\theta} = \frac{1}{\frac{1}{2}} = 2$$

To find $\sin\theta$, we use the following reasoning:

$$\tan\theta = \frac{\sin\theta}{\cos\theta} \quad \text{so} \quad \sin\theta = \tan\theta \cdot \cos\theta = \left(\frac{1}{2}\right)\cdot\left(-\frac{2\sqrt{5}}{5}\right) = -\frac{\sqrt{5}}{5}$$

$$\csc\theta = \frac{1}{\sin\theta} = \frac{1}{-\frac{\sqrt{5}}{5}} = -\frac{5}{\sqrt{5}} = -\sqrt{5}$$

Now Work PROBLEM 43

6 Use Even–Odd Properties to Find the Exact Values of the Trigonometric Functions

Recall that a function f is even if $f(-\theta) = f(\theta)$ for all θ in the domain of f; a function f is odd if $f(-\theta) = -f(\theta)$ for all θ in the domain of f. We will now show that the trigonometric functions sine, tangent, cotangent, and cosecant are odd functions and the functions cosine and secant are even functions.

In Words

Cosine and secant are even functions; the others are odd functions.

Even–Odd Properties

$$\sin(-\theta) = -\sin\theta \qquad \cos(-\theta) = \cos\theta \qquad \tan(-\theta) = -\tan\theta$$

$$\csc(-\theta) = -\csc\theta \qquad \sec(-\theta) = \sec\theta \qquad \cot(-\theta) = -\cot\theta$$

Figure 47

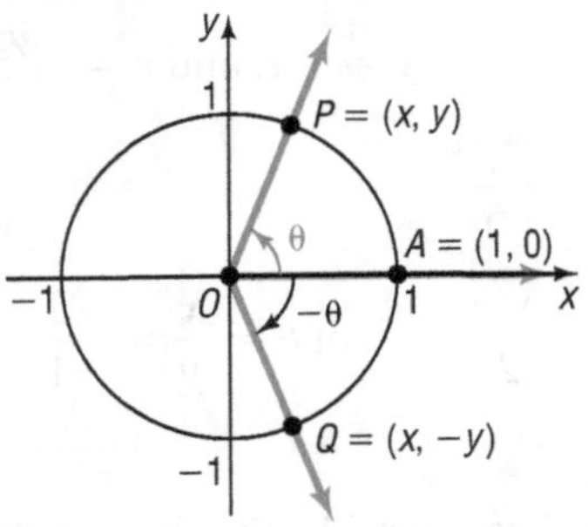

Proof Let $P = (x, y)$ be the point on the unit circle that corresponds to the angle θ. See Figure 47. Using symmetry, the point Q on the unit circle that corresponds to the angle $-\theta$ will have coordinates $(x, -y)$. Using the definition of the trigonometric functions, we have

$$\sin\theta = y \text{ and } \sin(-\theta) = -y = -\sin\theta \qquad \cos\theta = x \text{ and } \cos(-\theta) = x = \cos\theta$$

Now, using these results and some of the fundamental identities, we have

$$\tan(-\theta) = \frac{\sin(-\theta)}{\cos(-\theta)} = \frac{-\sin\theta}{\cos\theta} = -\tan\theta \qquad \cot(-\theta) = \frac{1}{\tan(-\theta)} = \frac{1}{-\tan\theta} = -\cot\theta$$

$$\sec(-\theta) = \frac{1}{\cos(-\theta)} = \frac{1}{\cos\theta} = \sec\theta \qquad \csc(-\theta) = \frac{1}{\sin(-\theta)} = \frac{1}{-\sin\theta} = -\csc\theta$$

■

EXAMPLE 7

Finding Exact Values Using Even–Odd Properties

Find the exact value of:

(a) $\sin(-45°)$ (b) $\cos(-\pi)$ (c) $\cot\left(-\frac{3\pi}{2}\right)$ (d) $\tan\left(-\frac{37\pi}{4}\right)$

Solution

(a) $\sin(-45°) = -\sin 45° = -\frac{\sqrt{2}}{2}$ (Odd function)

(b) $\cos(-\pi) = \cos\pi = -1$ (Even function)

(c) $\cot\left(-\frac{3\pi}{2}\right) = -\cot\frac{3\pi}{2} = 0$ (Odd function)

(d) $\tan\left(-\frac{37\pi}{4}\right) = -\tan\frac{37\pi}{4} = -\tan\left(\frac{\pi}{4} + 9\pi\right) = -\tan\frac{\pi}{4} = -1$ (Odd function; Period is π.)

■

Now Work PROBLEM 59

6.3 Assess Your Understanding

'Are You Prepared?' *Answers are given at the end of these exercises. If you get a wrong answer, read the pages listed in red.*

1. The domain of the function $f(x) = \frac{x+1}{2x+1}$ is ________. (pp. 63–64)
2. A function for which $f(x) = f(-x)$ for all x in the domain of f is called an ________ function. (pp. 79–81)
3. ***True or False*** The function $f(x) = \sqrt{x}$ is even. (pp. 79–81)
4. ***True or False*** The equation $x^2 + 2x = (x + 1)^2 - 1$ is an identity. (p. A46)

Concepts and Vocabulary

5. The sine, cosine, cosecant, and secant functions have period ________; the tangent and cotangent functions have period ________.
6. The domain of the tangent function is ________.
7. The range of the sine function is ________.
8. ***True or False*** The only even trigonometric functions are the cosine and secant functions.
9. ***True or False*** All the trigonometric functions are periodic, with period 2π.
10. ***True or False*** The range of the secant function is the set of positive real numbers.

Skill Building

In Problems 11–26, use the fact that the trigonometric functions are periodic to find the exact value of each expression. Do not use a calculator.

11. $\sin 405°$ **12.** $\cos 420°$ **13.** $\tan 405°$ **14.** $\sin 390°$ **15.** $\csc 450°$ **16.** $\sec 540°$

17. $\cot 390°$ **18.** $\sec 420°$ **19.** $\cos \frac{33\pi}{4}$ **20.** $\sin \frac{9\pi}{4}$ **21.** $\tan(21\pi)$ **22.** $\csc \frac{9\pi}{2}$

23. $\sec \frac{17\pi}{4}$ **24.** $\cot \frac{17\pi}{4}$ **25.** $\tan \frac{19\pi}{6}$ **26.** $\sec \frac{25\pi}{6}$

In Problems 27–34, name the quadrant in which the angle θ lies.

27. $\sin \theta > 0, \quad \cos \theta < 0$ **28.** $\sin \theta < 0, \quad \cos \theta > 0$ **29.** $\sin \theta < 0, \quad \tan \theta < 0$ **30.** $\cos \theta > 0, \quad \tan \theta > 0$

31. $\cos \theta > 0, \quad \tan \theta < 0$ **32.** $\cos \theta < 0, \quad \tan \theta > 0$ **33.** $\sec \theta < 0, \quad \sin \theta > 0$ **34.** $\csc \theta > 0, \quad \cos \theta < 0$

In Problems 35–42, $\sin \theta$ and $\cos \theta$ are given. Find the exact value of each of the four remaining trigonometric functions.

35. $\sin \theta = -\frac{3}{5}, \quad \cos \theta = \frac{4}{5}$ **36.** $\sin \theta = \frac{4}{5}, \quad \cos \theta = -\frac{3}{5}$ **37.** $\sin \theta = \frac{2\sqrt{5}}{5}, \quad \cos \theta = \frac{\sqrt{5}}{5}$

38. $\sin \theta = -\frac{\sqrt{5}}{5}, \quad \cos \theta = -\frac{2\sqrt{5}}{5}$ **39.** $\sin \theta = \frac{1}{2}, \quad \cos \theta = \frac{\sqrt{3}}{2}$ **40.** $\sin \theta = \frac{\sqrt{3}}{2}, \quad \cos \theta = \frac{1}{2}$

41. $\sin \theta = -\frac{1}{3}, \quad \cos \theta = \frac{2\sqrt{2}}{3}$ **42.** $\sin \theta = \frac{2\sqrt{2}}{3}, \quad \cos \theta = -\frac{1}{3}$

In Problems 43–58, find the exact value of each of the remaining trigonometric functions of θ.

43. $\sin \theta = \frac{12}{13}$, θ in quadrant II **44.** $\cos \theta = \frac{3}{5}$, θ in quadrant IV **45.** $\cos \theta = -\frac{4}{5}$, θ in quadrant III

46. $\sin \theta = -\frac{5}{13}$, θ in quadrant III **47.** $\sin \theta = \frac{5}{13}$, $90° < \theta < 180°$ **48.** $\cos \theta = \frac{4}{5}$, $270° < \theta < 360°$

49. $\cos \theta = -\frac{1}{3}, \quad \frac{\pi}{2} < \theta < \pi$ **50.** $\sin \theta = -\frac{2}{3}, \quad \pi < \theta < \frac{3\pi}{2}$ **51.** $\sin \theta = \frac{2}{3}, \quad \tan \theta < 0$

52. $\cos \theta = -\frac{1}{4}, \quad \tan \theta > 0$ **53.** $\sec \theta = 2, \quad \sin \theta < 0$ **54.** $\csc \theta = 3, \quad \cot \theta < 0$

55. $\tan \theta = \frac{3}{4}, \quad \sin \theta < 0$ **56.** $\cot \theta = \frac{4}{3}, \quad \cos \theta < 0$ **57.** $\tan \theta = -\frac{1}{3}, \quad \sin \theta > 0$

58. $\sec \theta = -2, \quad \tan \theta > 0$

In Problems 59–76, use the even–odd properties to find the exact value of each expression. Do not use a calculator.

59. $\sin(-60°)$ **60.** $\cos(-30°)$ **61.** $\tan(-30°)$ **62.** $\sin(-135°)$ **63.** $\sec(-60°)$ **64.** $\csc(-30°)$

65. $\sin(-90°)$ **66.** $\cos(-270°)$ **67.** $\tan\left(-\frac{\pi}{4}\right)$ **68.** $\sin(-\pi)$ **69.** $\cos\left(-\frac{\pi}{4}\right)$ **70.** $\sin\left(-\frac{\pi}{3}\right)$

71. $\tan(-\pi)$ **72.** $\sin\left(-\frac{3\pi}{2}\right)$ **73.** $\csc\left(-\frac{\pi}{4}\right)$ **74.** $\sec(-\pi)$ **75.** $\sec\left(-\frac{\pi}{6}\right)$ **76.** $\csc\left(-\frac{\pi}{3}\right)$

In Problems 77–88, use properties of the trigonometric functions to find the exact value of each expression. Do not use a calculator.

77. $\sin^2 40° + \cos^2 40°$ **78.** $\sec^2 18° - \tan^2 18°$ **79.** $\sin 80° \csc 80°$ **80.** $\tan 10° \cot 10°$

81. $\tan 40° - \frac{\sin 40°}{\cos 40°}$ **82.** $\cot 20° - \frac{\cos 20°}{\sin 20°}$ **83.** $\cos 400° \cdot \sec 40°$ **84.** $\tan 200° \cdot \cot 20°$

85. $\sin\left(-\frac{\pi}{12}\right)\csc \frac{25\pi}{12}$ **86.** $\sec\left(-\frac{\pi}{18}\right) \cdot \cos \frac{37\pi}{18}$ **87.** $\frac{\sin(-20°)}{\cos 380°} + \tan 200°$ **88.** $\frac{\sin 70°}{\cos(-430°)} + \tan(-70°)$

89. If $\sin \theta = 0.3$, find the value of:

$$\sin \theta + \sin(\theta + 2\pi) + \sin(\theta + 4\pi)$$

90. If $\cos \theta = 0.2$, find the value of:

$$\cos \theta + \cos(\theta + 2\pi) + \cos(\theta + 4\pi)$$

91. If $\tan \theta = 3$, find the value of:

$$\tan \theta + \tan(\theta + \pi) + \tan(\theta + 2\pi)$$

92. If $\cot \theta = -2$, find the value of:

$$\cot \theta + \cot(\theta - \pi) + \cot(\theta - 2\pi)$$

93. Find the exact value of:
$\sin 1° + \sin 2° + \sin 3° + \cdots + \sin 358° + \sin 359°$

94. Find the exact value of:
$\cos 1° + \cos 2° + \cos 3° + \cdots + \cos 358° + \cos 359°$

95. What is the domain of the sine function?

96. What is the domain of the cosine function?

97. For what numbers θ is $f(\theta) = \tan\theta$ not defined?

98. For what numbers θ is $f(\theta) = \cot\theta$ not defined?

99. For what numbers θ is $f(\theta) = \sec\theta$ not defined?

100. For what numbers θ is $f(\theta) = \csc\theta$ not defined?

101. What is the range of the sine function?

102. What is the range of the cosine function?

103. What is the range of the tangent function?

104. What is the range of the cotangent function?

105. What is the range of the secant function?

106. What is the range of the cosecant function?

107. Is the sine function even, odd, or neither? Is its graph symmetric? With respect to what?

108. Is the cosine function even, odd, or neither? Is its graph symmetric? With respect to what?

109. Is the tangent function even, odd, or neither? Is its graph symmetric? With respect to what?

110. Is the cotangent function even, odd, or neither? Is its graph symmetric? With respect to what?

111. Is the secant function even, odd, or neither? Is its graph symmetric? With respect to what?

112. Is the cosecant function even, odd, or neither? Is its graph symmetric? With respect to what?

Applications and Extensions

In Problems 113–118, use the periodic and even–odd properties.

113. If $f(\theta) = \sin\theta$ and $f(a) = \frac{1}{3}$, find the exact value of:

(a) $f(-a)$ (b) $f(a) + f(a + 2\pi) + f(a + 4\pi)$

114. If $f(\theta) = \cos\theta$ and $f(a) = \frac{1}{4}$, find the exact value of:

(a) $f(-a)$ (b) $f(a) + f(a + 2\pi) + f(a - 2\pi)$

115. If $f(\theta) = \tan\theta$ and $f(a) = 2$, find the exact value of:

(a) $f(-a)$ (b) $f(a) + f(a + \pi) + f(a + 2\pi)$

116. If $f(\theta) = \cot\theta$ and $f(a) = -3$, find the exact value of:

(a) $f(-a)$ (b) $f(a) + f(a + \pi) + f(a + 4\pi)$

117. If $f(\theta) = \sec\theta$ and $f(a) = -4$, find the exact value of:

(a) $f(-a)$ (b) $f(a) + f(a + 2\pi) + f(a + 4\pi)$

118. If $f(\theta) = \csc\theta$ and $f(a) = 2$, find the exact value of:

(a) $f(-a)$ (b) $f(a) + f(a + 2\pi) + f(a + 4\pi)$

119. Calculating the Time of a Trip From a parking lot, you want to walk to a house on the beach. The house is located 1500 feet down a paved path that parallels the ocean, which is 500 feet away. See the illustration. Along the path you can walk 300 feet per minute, but in the sand on the beach you can only walk 100 feet per minute.

The time T to get from the parking lot to the beach house can be expressed as a function of the angle θ shown in the illustration and is

$$T(\theta) = 5 - \frac{5}{3\tan\theta} + \frac{5}{\sin\theta} \qquad 0 < \theta < \frac{\pi}{2}$$

Calculate the time T if you walk directly from the parking lot to the house.

[**Hint:** $\tan\theta = \frac{500}{1500}$.]

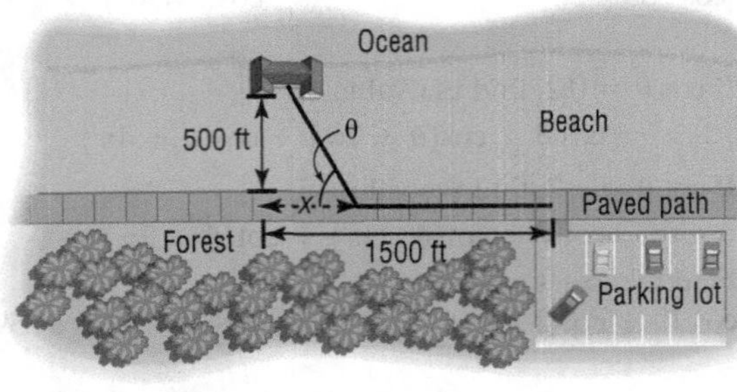

120. Calculating the Time of a Trip Two oceanfront homes are located 8 miles apart on a straight stretch of beach, each a distance of 1 mile from a paved road that parallels the ocean. Sally can jog 8 miles per hour along the paved road, but only 3 miles per hour in the sand on the beach. Because a river flows directly between the two houses, it is necessary to jog in the sand to the road, continue on the road, and then jog directly back in the sand to get from one house to the other. See the illustration. The time T to get from one house to the other as a function of the angle θ shown in the illustration is

$$T(\theta) = 1 + \frac{2}{3\sin\theta} - \frac{1}{4\tan\theta} \qquad 0 < \theta < \frac{\pi}{2}$$

(a) Calculate the time T for $\tan\theta = \frac{1}{4}$.
(b) Describe the path taken.
(c) Explain why θ must be larger than 14°.

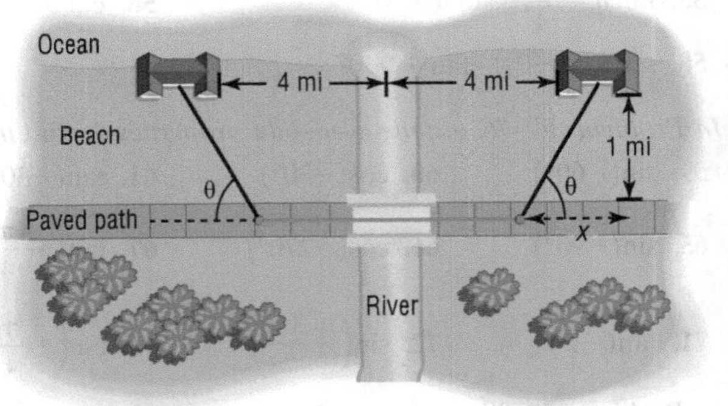

121. Show that the range of the tangent function is the set of all real numbers.

122. Show that the range of the cotangent function is the set of all real numbers.

123. Show that the period of $f(\theta) = \sin\theta$ is 2π.
[**Hint:** Assume that $0 < p < 2\pi$ exists so that $\sin(\theta + p) = \sin\theta$ for all θ. Let $\theta = 0$ to find p. Then let $\theta = \frac{\pi}{2}$ to obtain a contradiction.]

124. Show that the period of $f(\theta) = \cos\theta$ is 2π.

125. Show that the period of $f(\theta) = \sec\theta$ is 2π.

126. Show that the period of $f(\theta) = \csc\theta$ is 2π.

127. Show that the period of $f(\theta) = \tan\theta$ is π.

128. Show that the period of $f(\theta) = \cot\theta$ is π.

129. Prove the reciprocal identities given in formula (2).

130. Prove the quotient identities given in formula (3).

131. Establish the identity:

$$(\sin\theta\cos\phi)^2 + (\sin\theta\sin\phi)^2 + \cos^2\theta = 1$$

Discussion and Writing

132. Write down five properties of the tangent function. Explain the meaning of each.

133. Describe your understanding of the meaning of a periodic function.

134. Explain how to find the value of sin 390° using periodic properties.

135. Explain how to find the value of $\cos(-45°)$ using even–odd properties.

'Are You Prepared?' Answers

1. $\left\{x \middle| x \neq -\frac{1}{2}\right\}$ **2.** Even **3.** False **4.** True

6.4 Graphs of the Sine and Cosine Functions*

PREPARING FOR THIS SECTION *Before getting started, review the following:*

- Graphing Techniques: Transformations (Section 2.5, pp. 100–108)

Now Work the 'Are You Prepared?' problems on page 406.

OBJECTIVES
1. Graph Functions of the Form $y = A\sin(\omega x)$ Using Transformations (p. 397)
2. Graph Functions of the Form $y = A\cos(\omega x)$ Using Transformations (p. 398)
3. Determine the Amplitude and Period of Sinusoidal Functions (p. 400)
4. Graph Sinusoidal Functions Using Key Points (p. 401)
5. Find an Equation for a Sinusoidal Graph (p. 405)

Since we want to graph the trigonometric functions in the *xy*-plane, we shall use the traditional symbols x for the independent variable (or argument) and y for the dependent variable (or value at x) for each function. So we write the six trigonometric functions as

$$y = f(x) = \sin x \qquad y = f(x) = \cos x \qquad y = f(x) = \tan x$$
$$y = f(x) = \csc x \qquad y = f(x) = \sec x \qquad y = f(x) = \cot x$$

Here the independent variable x represents an angle, measured in radians. In calculus, x will usually be treated as a real number. As we said earlier, these are equivalent ways of viewing x.

The Graph of the Sine Function $y = \sin x$

Since the sine function has period 2π, we need to graph $y = \sin x$ only on the interval $[0, 2\pi]$. The remainder of the graph will consist of repetitions of this portion of the graph.

*For those who wish to include phase shifts here, Section 6.6 can be covered immediately after Section 6.4 without loss of continuity.

Table 6

x	$y = \sin x$	(x, y)
0	0	$(0, 0)$
$\frac{\pi}{6}$	$\frac{1}{2}$	$\left(\frac{\pi}{6}, \frac{1}{2}\right)$
$\frac{\pi}{2}$	1	$\left(\frac{\pi}{2}, 1\right)$
$\frac{5\pi}{6}$	$\frac{1}{2}$	$\left(\frac{5\pi}{6}, \frac{1}{2}\right)$
π	0	$(\pi, 0)$
$\frac{7\pi}{6}$	$-\frac{1}{2}$	$\left(\frac{7\pi}{6}, -\frac{1}{2}\right)$
$\frac{3\pi}{2}$	-1	$\left(\frac{3\pi}{2}, -1\right)$
$\frac{11\pi}{6}$	$-\frac{1}{2}$	$\left(\frac{11\pi}{6}, -\frac{1}{2}\right)$
2π	0	$(2\pi, 0)$

We begin by constructing Table 6, which lists some points on the graph of $y = \sin x$, $0 \le x \le 2\pi$. As the table shows, the graph of $y = \sin x$, $0 \le x \le 2\pi$, begins at the origin. As x increases from 0 to $\frac{\pi}{2}$, the value of $y = \sin x$ increases from 0 to 1; as x increases from $\frac{\pi}{2}$ to π to $\frac{3\pi}{2}$, the value of y decreases from 1 to 0 to -1; as x increases from $\frac{3\pi}{2}$ to 2π, the value of y increases from -1 to 0. If we plot the points listed in Table 6 and connect them with a smooth curve, we obtain the graph shown in Figure 48.

Figure 48
$y = \sin x, 0 \le x \le 2\pi$

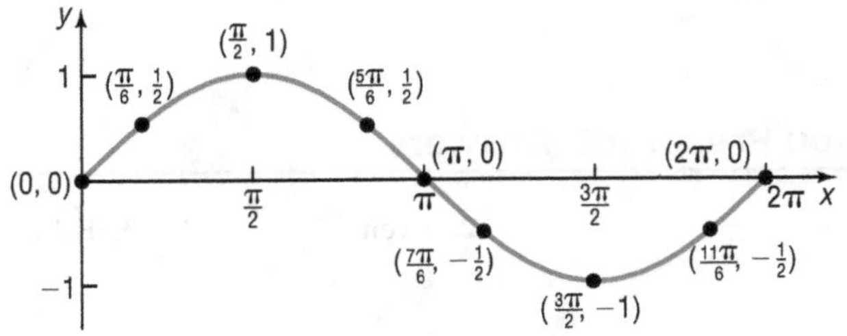

The graph in Figure 48 is one period, or **cycle,** of the graph of $y = \sin x$. To obtain a more complete graph of $y = \sin x$, we continue the graph in each direction, as shown in Figure 49(a). Figure 49(b) shows the graph on a TI-84 Plus graphing calculator.

Figure 49
$y = \sin x, -\infty < x < \infty$

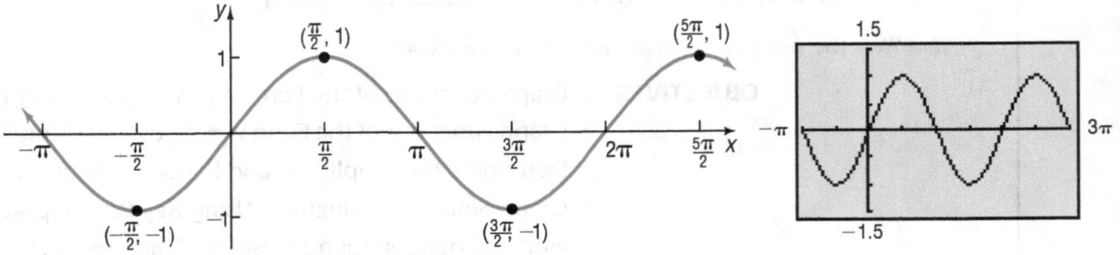

(a) (b)

The graph of $y = \sin x$ illustrates some of the facts that we already know about the sine function.

Properties of the Sine Function $y = \sin x$

1. The domain is the set of all real numbers.
2. The range consists of all real numbers from -1 to 1, inclusive.
3. The sine function is an odd function, as the symmetry of the graph with respect to the origin indicates.
4. The sine function is periodic, with period 2π.
5. The x-intercepts are $\ldots, -2\pi, -\pi, 0, \pi, 2\pi, 3\pi, \ldots$; the y-intercept is 0.
6. The maximum value is 1 and occurs at $x = \ldots, -\frac{3\pi}{2}, \frac{\pi}{2}, \frac{5\pi}{2}, \frac{9\pi}{2}, \ldots$; the minimum value is -1 and occurs at $x = \ldots, -\frac{\pi}{2}, \frac{3\pi}{2}, \frac{7\pi}{2}, \frac{11\pi}{2}, \ldots$.

Now Work PROBLEMS 9, 11, AND 13

1 Graph Functions of the Form $y = A\sin(\omega x)$ Using Transformations

EXAMPLE 1 Graphing Functions of the Form $y = A\sin(\omega x)$ Using Transformations

Graph $y = 3\sin x$ using transformations. Use the graph to determine the domain and the range of $y = 3\sin x$.

Solution Figure 50 illustrates the steps.

Figure 50

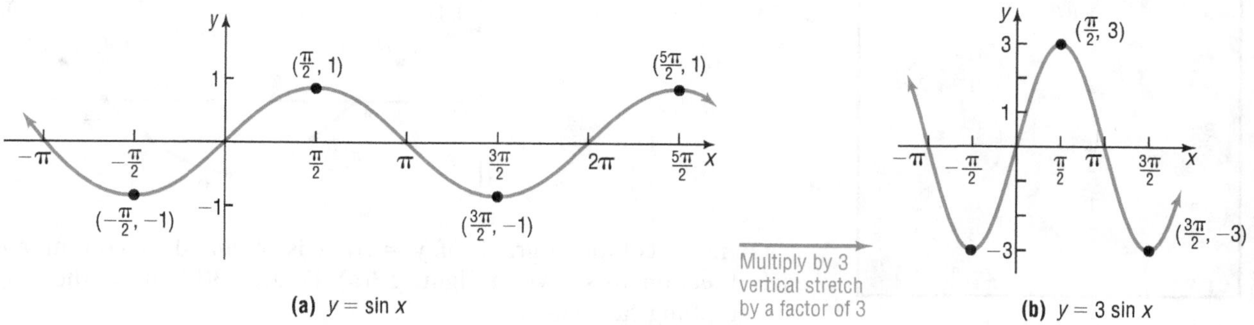

The domain of $y = 3\sin x$ is the set of all real numbers or $(-\infty, \infty)$. The range of $y = 3\sin x$ is $\{y \mid -3 \le y \le 3\}$ or $[-3, 3]$.

Check: Graph $Y_1 = 3\sin x$ to verify the graph shown in Figure 50(b).

EXAMPLE 2 Graphing Functions of the Form $y = A\sin(\omega x)$ Using Transformations

Graph $y = -\sin(2x)$ using transformations. Use the graph to determine the domain and the range of $y = -\sin(2x)$.

Solution Figure 51 illustrates the steps.

Figure 51

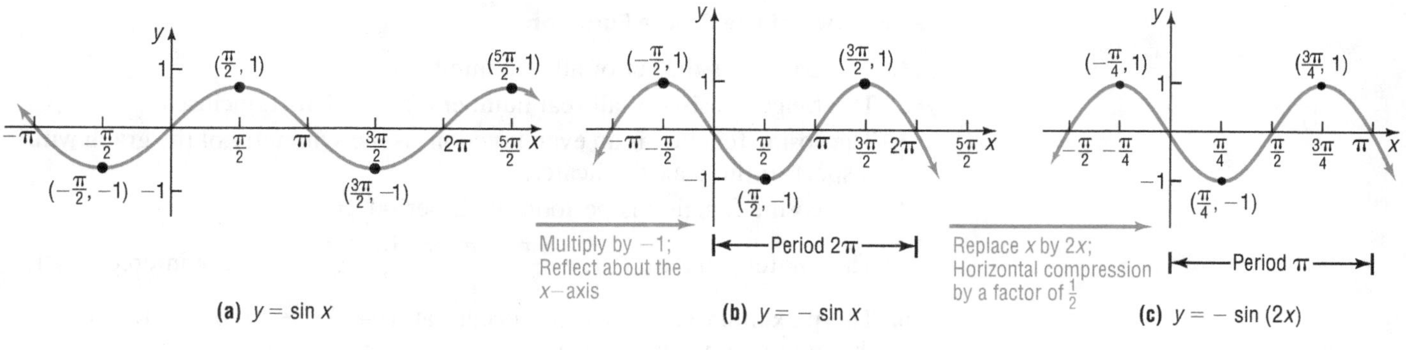

The domain of $y = -\sin(2x)$ is the set of all real numbers. The range of $y = -\sin(2x)$ is $\{y \mid -1 \le y \le 1\}$ or $[-1, 1]$.

Notice in Figure 51(c) that the period of the function $y = -\sin(2x)$ is π due to the horizontal compression of the original period 2π by a factor of $\frac{1}{2}$.

Check: Graph $Y_1 = -\sin(2x)$ to verify the graph shown in Figure 51(c).

Now Work PROBLEM 45 USING TRANSFORMATIONS

Table 7

x	$y = \cos x$	(x, y)
0	1	$(0, 1)$
$\frac{\pi}{3}$	$\frac{1}{2}$	$\left(\frac{\pi}{3}, \frac{1}{2}\right)$
$\frac{\pi}{2}$	0	$\left(\frac{\pi}{2}, 0\right)$
$\frac{2\pi}{3}$	$-\frac{1}{2}$	$\left(\frac{2\pi}{3}, -\frac{1}{2}\right)$
π	-1	$(\pi, -1)$
$\frac{4\pi}{3}$	$-\frac{1}{2}$	$\left(\frac{4\pi}{3}, -\frac{1}{2}\right)$
$\frac{3\pi}{2}$	0	$\left(\frac{3\pi}{2}, 0\right)$
$\frac{5\pi}{3}$	$\frac{1}{2}$	$\left(\frac{5\pi}{3}, \frac{1}{2}\right)$
2π	1	$(2\pi, 1)$

The Graph of the Cosine Function

The cosine function also has period 2π. We proceed as we did with the sine function by constructing Table 7, which lists some points on the graph of $y = \cos x$, $0 \le x \le 2\pi$. As the table shows, the graph of $y = \cos x$, $0 \le x \le 2\pi$, begins at the point $(0, 1)$. As x increases from 0 to $\frac{\pi}{2}$ to π, the value of y decreases from 1 to 0 to -1; as x increases from π to $\frac{3\pi}{2}$ to 2π, the value of y increases from -1 to 0 to 1. As before, we plot the points in Table 7 to get one period or cycle of the graph. See Figure 52.

Figure 52
$y = \cos x, 0 \le x \le 2\pi$

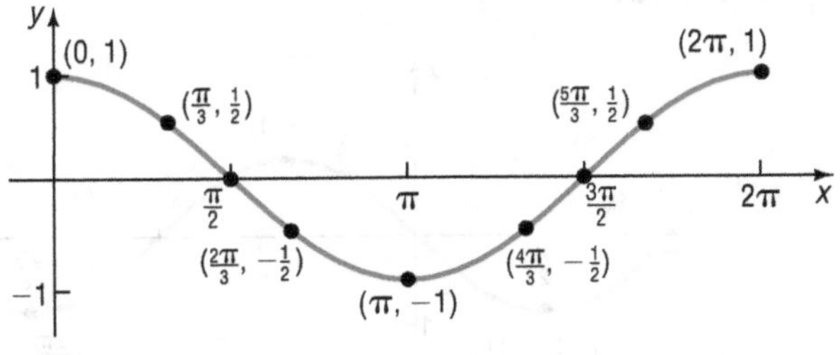

A more complete graph of $y = \cos x$ is obtained by continuing the graph in each direction, as shown in Figure 53(a). Figure 53(b) shows the graph on a TI-84 Plus graphing calculator.

Figure 53
$y = \cos x, -\infty < x < \infty$

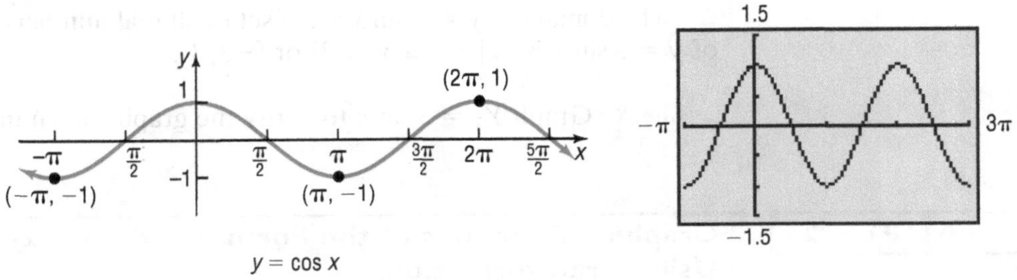

(a) (b)

The graph of $y = \cos x$ illustrates some of the facts that we already know about the cosine function.

Properties of the Cosine Function

1. The domain is the set of all real numbers.
2. The range consists of all real numbers from -1 to 1, inclusive.
3. The cosine function is an even function, as the symmetry of the graph with respect to the y-axis indicates.
4. The cosine function is periodic, with period 2π.
5. The x-intercepts are $\ldots, -\frac{3\pi}{2}, -\frac{\pi}{2}, \frac{\pi}{2}, \frac{3\pi}{2}, \frac{5\pi}{2}, \ldots$; the y-intercept is 1.
6. The maximum value is 1 and occurs at $x = \ldots, -2\pi, 0, 2\pi, 4\pi, 6\pi, \ldots$; the minimum value is -1 and occurs at $x = \ldots, -\pi, \pi, 3\pi, 5\pi, \ldots$.

2 Graph Functions of the Form $y = A\cos(\omega x)$ Using Transformations

EXAMPLE 3 **Graphing Functions of the Form $y = A\cos(\omega x)$ Using Transformations**

Graph $y = 2\cos(3x)$ using transformations. Use the graph to determine the domain and the range of $y = 2\cos(3x)$.

Solution Figure 54 shows the steps.

Figure 54

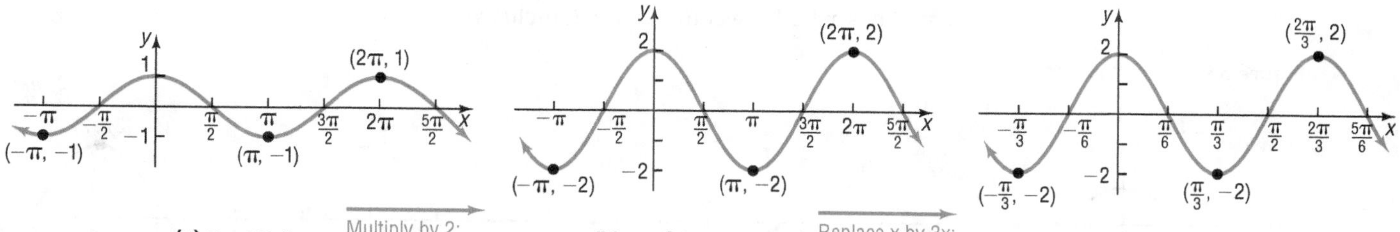

(a) $y = \cos x$ (b) $y = 2\cos x$ (c) $y = 2\cos(3x)$

The domain of $y = 2\cos(3x)$ is the set of all real numbers or $(-\infty, \infty)$. The range of $y = 2\cos(3x)$ is $\{y \mid -2 \le y \le 2\}$ or $[-2, 2]$.

Check: Graph $Y_1 = 2\cos(3x)$ to verify the graph shown in Figure 54(c).

Notice in Figure 54(c) that the period of the function $y = 2\cos(3x)$ is $\frac{2\pi}{3}$ due to the compression of the original period 2π by a factor of $\frac{1}{3}$.

Now Work PROBLEM 53 USING TRANSFORMATIONS

Sinusoidal Graphs

Shift the graph of $y = \cos x$ to the right $\frac{\pi}{2}$ units to obtain the graph of $y = \cos\left(x - \frac{\pi}{2}\right)$. See Figure 55(a). Now look at the graph of $y = \sin x$ in Figure 55(b). We see that the graph of $y = \sin x$ is the same as the graph of $y = \cos\left(x - \frac{\pi}{2}\right)$.

Figure 55

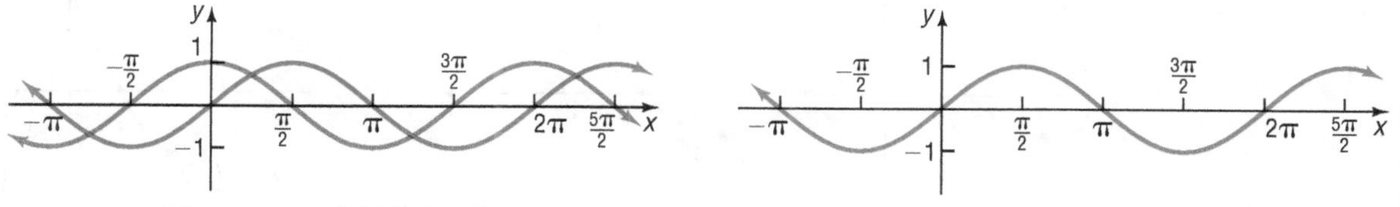

(a) $y = \cos x$ $y = \cos\left(x - \frac{\pi}{2}\right)$ (b) $y = \sin x$

Based on Figure 55, we conjecture that

$$\sin x = \cos\left(x - \frac{\pi}{2}\right)$$

Seeing the Concept

Graph $Y_1 = \sin x$ and $Y_2 = \cos\left(x - \frac{\pi}{2}\right)$. How many graphs do you see?

(We shall prove this fact in Chapter 7.) Because of this relationship, the graphs of functions of the form $y = A\sin(\omega x)$ or $y = A\cos(\omega x)$ are referred to as **sinusoidal graphs.**

Let's look at some general properties of sinusoidal graphs.

3 Determine the Amplitude and Period of Sinusoidal Functions

In Figure 56(b) we show the graph of $y = 2\cos x$. Notice that the values of $y = 2\cos x$ lie between -2 and 2, inclusive.

Figure 56

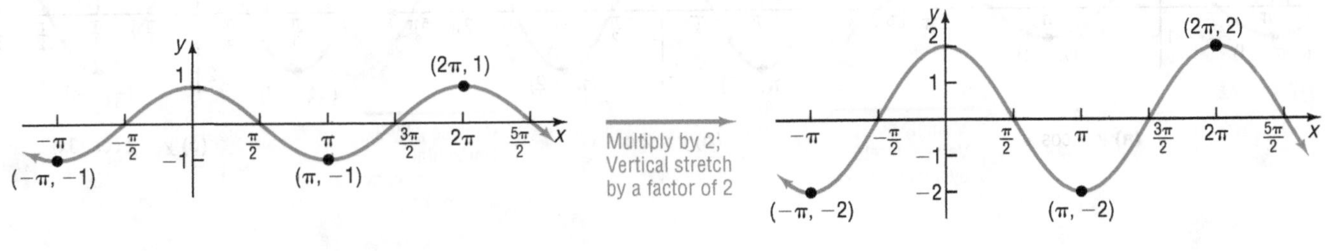

(a) $y = \cos x$ **(b)** $y = 2\cos x$

In general, the values of the functions $y = A\sin x$ and $y = A\cos x$, where $A \neq 0$, will always satisfy the inequalities

$$-|A| \leq A\sin x \leq |A| \quad \text{and} \quad -|A| \leq A\cos x \leq |A|$$

respectively. The number $|A|$ is called the **amplitude** of $y = A\sin x$ or $y = A\cos x$. See Figure 57.

Figure 57

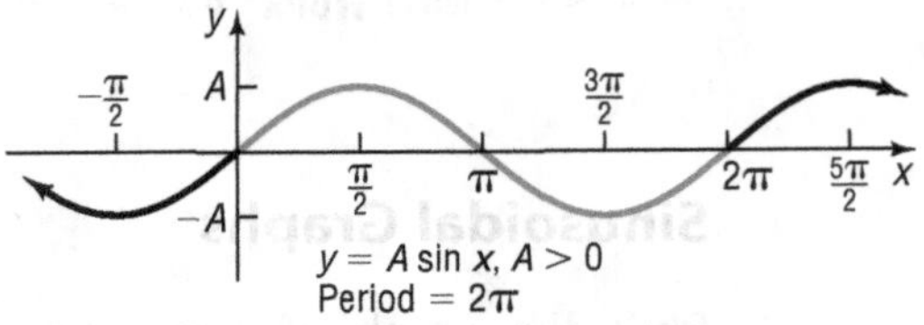

In Figure 58(a), we show the graph of $y = \cos x$. In Figure 58(b), we show the graph of $y = \cos(3x)$. Notice that the period of the function $y = \cos(3x)$ is $\frac{2\pi}{3}$, due to the horizontal compression of the period of $y = \cos x$, 2π, by a factor of $\frac{1}{3}$.

Figure 58

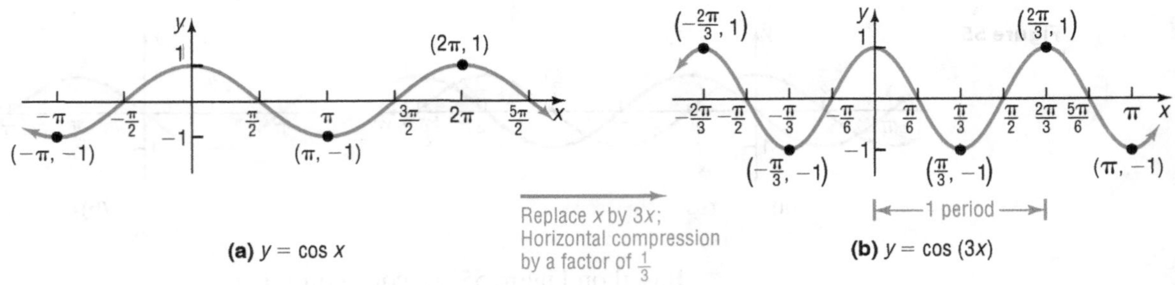

(a) $y = \cos x$ **(b)** $y = \cos(3x)$

In general, if $\omega > 0$, the functions $y = \sin(\omega x)$ and $y = \cos(\omega x)$ will have period $T = \frac{2\pi}{\omega}$. To see why, recall that the graph of $y = \sin(\omega x)$ is obtained from the graph of $y = \sin x$ by performing a horizontal compression or stretch by a factor $\frac{1}{\omega}$. This horizontal compression replaces the interval $[0, 2\pi]$, which contains one period of the graph of $y = \sin x$, by the interval $\left[0, \frac{2\pi}{\omega}\right]$, which contains one period of the graph of $y = \sin(\omega x)$.

For example, for the function $y = \cos(3x)$, graphed in Figure 58(b), $\omega = 3$, so the period is $\dfrac{2\pi}{\omega} = \dfrac{2\pi}{3}$.

One period of the graph of $y = A\sin(\omega x)$ or $y = A\cos(\omega x)$ is called a **cycle.** Figure 59 illustrates the general situation. The blue portion of the graph is one cycle.

Figure 59

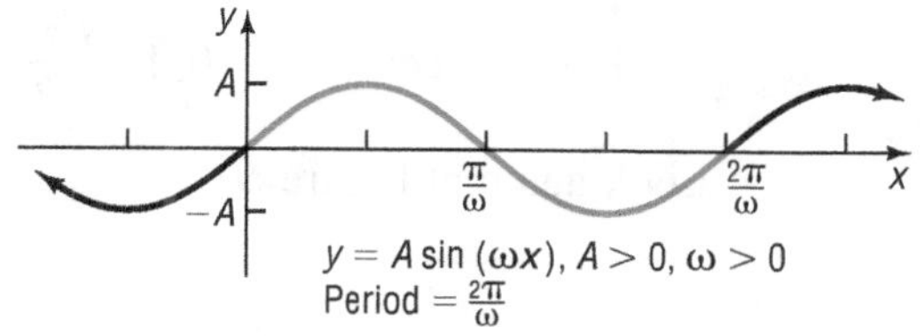

NOTE A function f is even if $f(-x) = f(x)$; a function is odd if $f(-x) = -f(x)$. Since the sine function is odd, $\sin(-\theta) = -\sin\theta$; since the cosine function is even, $\cos(-\theta) = \cos\theta$. ■

If $\omega < 0$ in $y = A\sin(\omega x)$ or $y = A\cos(\omega x)$, we use the Even–Odd Properties of the sine and cosine functions. Since the sine function is an odd function and the cosine function is an even function, we have

$$A\sin(-\omega x) = -A\sin(\omega x) \quad \text{and} \quad A\cos(-\omega x) = A\cos(\omega x)$$

This gives us an equivalent form in which the coefficient of x in the argument is positive. For example,

$$\sin(-2x) = -\sin(2x) \quad \text{and} \quad \cos(-\pi x) = \cos(\pi x)$$

Because of this, we can assume $\omega > 0$.

THEOREM

If $\omega > 0$, the amplitude and period of $y = A\sin(\omega x)$ and $y = A\cos(\omega x)$ are given by

$$\text{Amplitude} = |A| \qquad \text{Period} = T = \frac{2\pi}{\omega} \tag{1}$$

EXAMPLE 4 **Finding the Amplitude and Period of a Sinusoidal Function**

Determine the amplitude and period of $y = 5\sin(-4x)$.

Solution First, we use the fact that the sine function is odd and write $y = 5\sin(-4x)$ as $y = -5\sin(4x)$. Comparing $y = -5\sin(4x)$ to $y = A\sin(\omega x)$, we find that $A = -5$ and $\omega = 4$. From equation (1),

$$\text{Amplitude} = |A| = |-5| = 5 \qquad \text{Period} = T = \frac{2\pi}{\omega} = \frac{2\pi}{4} = \frac{\pi}{2}$$

■

Now Work PROBLEM 23

4 Graph Sinusoidal Functions Using Key Points

So far, we have graphed functions of the form $y = A\sin(\omega x)$ or $y = A\cos(\omega x)$ using transformations. We now introduce another method that can be used to graph these functions.

Figure 60 on page 402 shows one cycle of the graphs of $y = \sin x$ and $y = \cos x$ on the interval $[0, 2\pi]$. Notice that each graph consists of four parts corresponding to the four subintervals:

$$\left[0, \frac{\pi}{2}\right] \quad \left[\frac{\pi}{2}, \pi\right] \quad \left[\pi, \frac{3\pi}{2}\right] \quad \left[\frac{3\pi}{2}, 2\pi\right]$$

Each subinterval is of length $\frac{\pi}{2}$ (the period 2π divided by 4, the number of parts), and the endpoints of these intervals, $x = 0$, $x = \frac{\pi}{2}$, $x = \pi$, $x = \frac{3\pi}{2}$, $x = 2\pi$, give rise to five key points on each graph:

For $y = \sin x$: $\quad (0, 0), \left(\frac{\pi}{2}, 1\right), (\pi, 0), \left(\frac{3\pi}{2}, -1\right), (2\pi, 0)$

For $y = \cos x$: $\quad (0, 1), \left(\frac{\pi}{2}, 0\right), (\pi, -1), \left(\frac{3\pi}{2}, 0\right), (2\pi, 1)$

Look again at Figure 60.

Figure 60

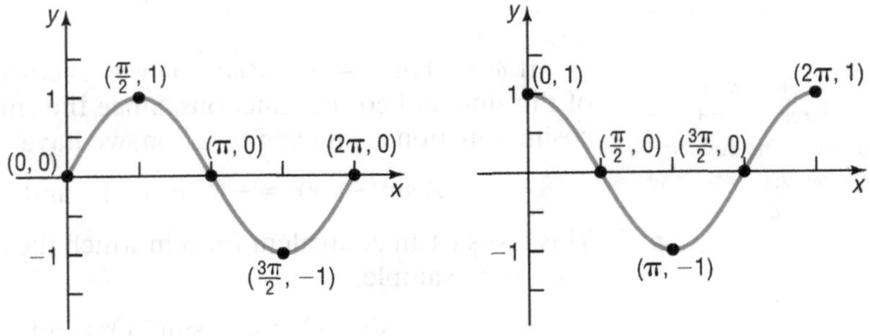

(a) $y = \sin x$ (b) $y = \cos x$

Let's look at an example that illustrates how to graph a sinusoidal function using key points.

EXAMPLE 5

How to Graph a Sinusoidal Function Using Key Points

Graph $y = 3\sin(4x)$ using key points.

Step-by-Step Solution

STEP 1 Determine the amplitude and period of the sinusoidal function.

Comparing $y = 3\sin(4x)$ to $y = A\sin(\omega x)$, we see that $A = 3$ and $\omega = 4$, so the amplitude is $|A| = 3$ and the period is $\frac{2\pi}{\omega} = \frac{2\pi}{4} = \frac{\pi}{2}$. Because the amplitude is 3, the graph of $y = 3\sin(4x)$ will lie between -3 and 3 on the y-axis. Because the period is $\frac{\pi}{2}$, one cycle will begin at $x = 0$ and end at $x = \frac{\pi}{2}$.

STEP 2 Divide the interval $\left[0, \frac{2\pi}{\omega}\right]$ into four subintervals of the same length.

We divide the interval $\left[0, \frac{\pi}{2}\right]$ into four subintervals, each of length $\frac{\pi}{2} \div 4 = \frac{\pi}{8}$, as follows:

$$\left[0, \frac{\pi}{8}\right] \quad \left[\frac{\pi}{8}, \frac{\pi}{8} + \frac{\pi}{8}\right] = \left[\frac{\pi}{8}, \frac{\pi}{4}\right] \quad \left[\frac{\pi}{4}, \frac{\pi}{4} + \frac{\pi}{8}\right] = \left[\frac{\pi}{4}, \frac{3\pi}{8}\right] \quad \left[\frac{3\pi}{8}, \frac{3\pi}{8} + \frac{\pi}{8}\right] = \left[\frac{3\pi}{8}, \frac{\pi}{2}\right]$$

The endpoints of the subintervals are $0, \frac{\pi}{8}, \frac{\pi}{4}, \frac{3\pi}{8}, \frac{\pi}{2}$. These values represent the x-coordinates of the five key points on the graph.

STEP 3 Use the endpoints of these subintervals to obtain five key points on the graph.

To obtain the y-coordinates of the five key points of $y = 3\sin(4x)$, we multiply the y-coordinates of the five key points for $y = \sin x$ in Figure 60(a) by $A = 3$. The five key points are

$$(0, 0) \quad \left(\frac{\pi}{8}, 3\right) \quad \left(\frac{\pi}{4}, 0\right) \quad \left(\frac{3\pi}{8}, -3\right) \quad \left(\frac{\pi}{2}, 0\right)$$

STEP 4 Plot the five key points and draw a sinusoidal graph to obtain the graph of one cycle. Extend the graph in each direction to make it complete.

We plot the five key points obtained in Step 3 and fill in the graph of the sine curve as shown in Figure 61(a). We extend the graph in each direction to obtain the complete graph shown in Figure 61(b). Notice that additional key points appear every $\frac{\pi}{8}$ radian.

Figure 61

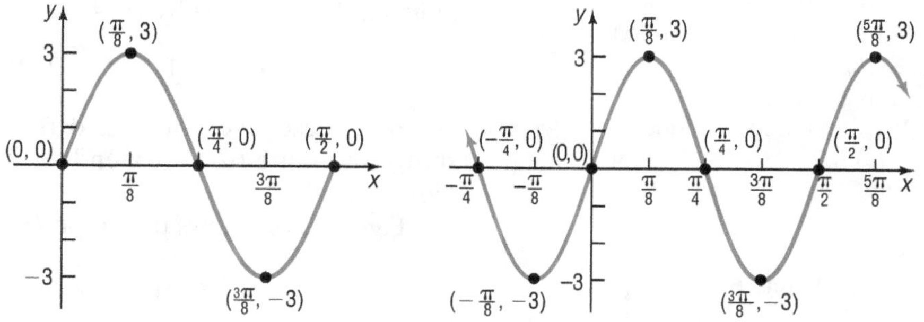

(a) **(b)** $y = 3 \sin(4x)$

NOTE In Step 3 of Example 5, we could also obtain the five key points by evaluating $y = 3\sin(4x)$ at each value of x. ■

Check: Graph $y = 3\sin(4x)$ using transformations. Which graphing method do you prefer?

Now Work PROBLEM 45 USING KEY POINTS

SUMMARY Steps for Graphing a Sinusoidal Function of the Form $y = A\sin(\omega x)$ or $y = A\cos(\omega x)$ Using Key Points

STEP 1: Determine the amplitude and period of the sinusoidal function.

STEP 2: Divide the interval $\left[0, \frac{2\pi}{\omega}\right]$ into four subintervals of the same length.

STEP 3: Use the endpoints of these subintervals to obtain five key points on the graph.

STEP 4: Plot the five key points with a sinusoidal graph to obtain the graph of one cycle. Extend the graph in each direction to make it complete.

EXAMPLE 6 Graphing a Sinusoidal Function Using Key Points

Graph $y = 2\sin\left(-\frac{\pi}{2}x\right)$ using key points.

Solution Since the sine function is odd, we can use the equivalent form:

$$y = -2\sin\left(\frac{\pi}{2}x\right)$$

STEP 1: Comparing $y = -2\sin\left(\frac{\pi}{2}x\right)$ to $y = A\sin(\omega x)$, we find that $A = -2$ and $\omega = \frac{\pi}{2}$. The amplitude is $|A| = |-2| = 2$, and the period is $T = \frac{2\pi}{\omega} = \frac{2\pi}{\frac{\pi}{2}} = 4$.

The graph of $y = -2\sin\left(\frac{\pi}{2}x\right)$ will lie between -2 and 2 on the y-axis. One cycle will begin at $x = 0$ and end at $x = 4$.

STEP 2: We divide the interval $[0, 4]$ into four subintervals, each of length $4 \div 4 = 1$. The x-coordinates of the five key points are:

0	$0 + 1 = 1$	$1 + 1 = 2$	$2 + 1 = 3$	$3 + 1 = 4$
1st x-coordinate	2nd x-coordinate	3rd x-coordinate	4th x-coordinate	5th x-coordinate

STEP 3: Since $y = -2\sin\left(\frac{\pi}{2}x\right)$, we multiply the y-coordinates of the five key points in Figure 60(a) by $A = -2$. The five key points on the graph are

$$(0, 0) \quad (1, -2) \quad (2, 0) \quad (3, 2) \quad (4, 0)$$

STEP 4: We plot these five points and fill in the graph of the sine function as shown in Figure 62(a). Extending the graph in each direction, we obtain Figure 62(b).

Figure 62(c) shows the graph using a graphing utility.

COMMENT To graph a sinusoidal function of the form $y = A\sin(\omega x)$ or $y = A\cos(\omega x)$ using a graphing utility, we use the amplitude to set $Y_{\min}$ and $Y_{\max}$ and use the period to set $X_{\min}$ and $X_{\max}$. ■

Figure 62

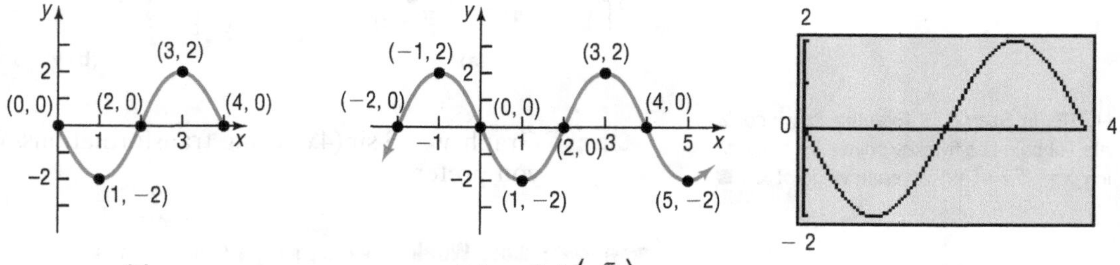

(a) (b) $y = 2\sin\left(-\frac{\pi}{2}x\right)$ (c)

Check: Graph $y = 2\sin\left(-\frac{\pi}{2}x\right)$ using transformations. Which graphing method do you prefer?

Now Work PROBLEM 49 USING KEY POINTS

If the function to be graphed is of the form $y = A\sin(\omega x) + B$ [or $y = A\cos(\omega x) + B$], first graph $y = A\sin(\omega x)$ [or $y = A\cos(\omega x)$] and then use a vertical shift.

EXAMPLE 7 Graphing a Sinusoidal Function Using Key Points

Graph $y = -4\cos(\pi x) - 2$ using key points. Use the graph to determine the domain and the range of $y = -4\cos(\pi x) - 2$.

Solution We begin by graphing the function $y = -4\cos(\pi x)$. Comparing $y = -4\cos(\pi x)$ with $y = A\cos(\omega x)$, we find that $A = -4$ and $\omega = \pi$. The amplitude is $|A| = |-4| = 4$, and the period is $T = \frac{2\pi}{\omega} = \frac{2\pi}{\pi} = 2$.

The graph of $y = -4\cos(\pi x)$ will lie between -4 and 4 on the y-axis. One cycle will begin at $x = 0$ and end at $x = 2$.

We divide the interval $[0, 2]$ into four subintervals, each of length $2 \div 4 = \frac{1}{2}$. The x-coordinates of the five key points are:

0	$0 + \frac{1}{2} = \frac{1}{2}$	$\frac{1}{2} + \frac{1}{2} = 1$	$1 + \frac{1}{2} = \frac{3}{2}$	$\frac{3}{2} + \frac{1}{2} = 2$
1st x-coordinate	2nd x-coordinate	3rd x-coordinate	4th x-coordinate	5th x-coordinate

Since $y = -4\cos(\pi x)$, we multiply the y-coordinates of the five key points of $y = \cos x$ shown in Figure 60(b) by $A = -4$ to obtain the five key points on the graph of $y = -4\cos(\pi x)$:

$$(0, -4) \quad \left(\frac{1}{2}, 0\right) \quad (1, 4) \quad \left(\frac{3}{2}, 0\right) \quad (2, -4)$$

We plot these five points and fill in the graph of the cosine function as shown in Figure 63(a). Extending the graph in each direction, we obtain Figure 63(b), the graph of $y = -4\cos(\pi x)$.

A vertical shift down 2 units gives the graph of $y = -4\cos(\pi x) - 2$, as shown in Figure 63(c).

Figure 63

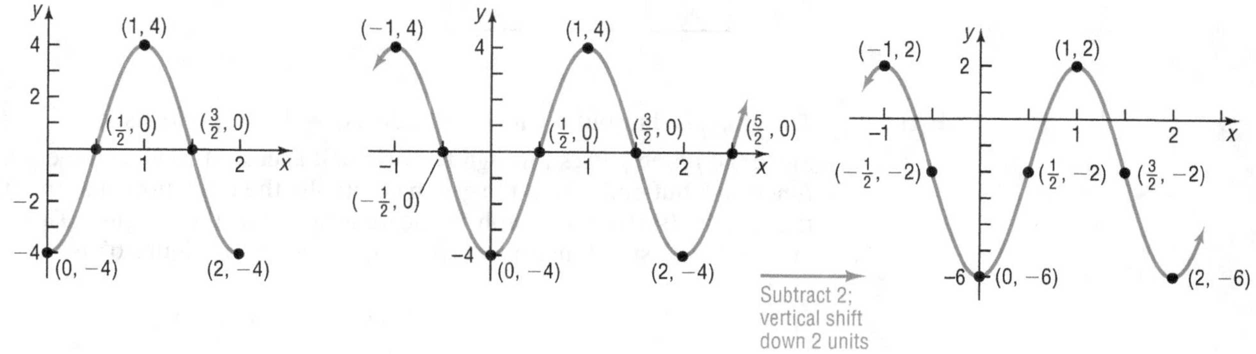

(a) **(b)** $y = -4\cos(\pi x)$ **(c)** $y = -4\cos(\pi x) - 2$

The domain of $y = -4\cos(\pi x) - 2$ is the set of all real numbers or $(-\infty, \infty)$. The range of $y = -4\cos(\pi x) - 2$ is $\{y \mid -6 \le y \le 2\}$ or $[-6, 2]$.

Now Work PROBLEM 59

5 Find an Equation for a Sinusoidal Graph

We can also use the ideas of amplitude and period to identify a sinusoidal function when its graph is given.

EXAMPLE 8 **Finding an Equation for a Sinusoidal Graph**

Find an equation for the graph shown in Figure 64.

Figure 64

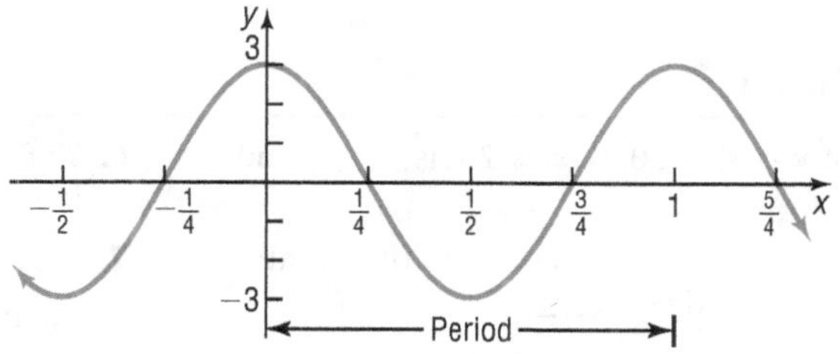

Solution The graph has the characteristics of a cosine function. Do you see why? The maximum value occurs at $x = 0$. So we view the equation as a cosine function $y = A\cos(\omega x)$ with $A = 3$ and period $T = 1$. Then $\frac{2\pi}{\omega} = 1$, so $\omega = 2\pi$. The cosine function whose graph is given in Figure 64 is

$$y = A\cos(\omega x) = 3\cos(2\pi x)$$

Check: Graph $Y_1 = 3\cos(2\pi x)$ and compare the result with Figure 64.

EXAMPLE 9 **Finding an Equation for a Sinusoidal Graph**

Find an equation for the graph shown in Figure 65 on the following page.

Figure 65

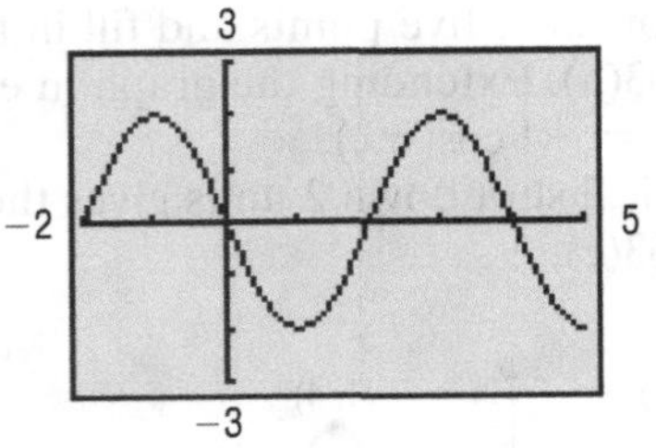

Solution The graph is sinusoidal, with amplitude $|A| = 2$. The period is 4, so $\frac{2\pi}{\omega} = 4$ or $\omega = \frac{\pi}{2}$. Since the graph passes through the origin, it is easiest to view the equation as a sine function,* but notice that the graph is actually the reflection of a sine function about the x-axis (since the graph is decreasing near the origin). This requires that $A = -2$. The sine function whose graph is given in Figure 65 is

$$y = A\sin(\omega x) = -2\sin\left(\frac{\pi}{2}x\right)$$

Check: Graph $Y_1 = -2\sin\left(\frac{\pi}{2}x\right)$ and compare the result with Figure 65. ■

Now Work PROBLEMS 67 AND 71

*The equation could also be viewed as a cosine function with a horizontal shift, but viewing it as a sine function is easier.

6.4 Assess Your Understanding

'Are You Prepared?' *Answers are given at the end of these exercises. If you get a wrong answer, read the pages listed in red.*

1. Use transformations to graph $y = 3x^2$. (pp. 102–104)
2. Use transformations to graph $y = \sqrt{2x}$. (pp. 102–104)

Concepts and Vocabulary

3. The maximum value of $y = \sin x$, $0 \le x \le 2\pi$, is ______ and occurs at $x =$ ______.
4. The function $y = A\sin(\omega x)$, $A > 0$, has amplitude 3 and period 2; then $A =$ ______ and $\omega =$ ______.
5. The function $y = 3\cos(6x)$ has amplitude ______ and period ______.
6. ***True or False*** The graphs of $y = \sin x$ and $y = \cos x$ are identical except for a horizontal shift.
7. ***True or False*** For $y = 2\sin(\pi x)$, the amplitude is 2 and the period is $\frac{\pi}{2}$.
8. ***True or False*** The graph of the sine function has infinitely many x-intercepts.

Skill Building

In Problems 9–18, if necessary, refer to a graph to answer each question.

9. What is the y-intercept of $y = \sin x$?
10. What is the y-intercept of $y = \cos x$?
11. For what numbers x, $-\pi \le x \le \pi$, is the graph of $y = \sin x$ increasing?
12. For what numbers x, $-\pi \le x \le \pi$, is the graph of $y = \cos x$ decreasing?
13. What is the largest value of $y = \sin x$?
14. What is the smallest value of $y = \cos x$?
15. For what numbers x, $0 \le x \le 2\pi$, does $\sin x = 0$?
16. For what numbers x, $0 \le x \le 2\pi$, does $\cos x = 0$?
17. For what numbers x, $-2\pi \le x \le 2\pi$, does $\sin x = 1$? Where does $\sin x = -1$?
18. For what numbers x, $-2\pi \le x \le 2\pi$, does $\cos x = 1$? Where does $\cos x = -1$?

In Problems 19–28, determine the amplitude and period of each function without graphing.

19. $y = 2\sin x$ **20.** $y = 3\cos x$ **21.** $y = -4\cos(2x)$ **22.** $y = -\sin\left(\frac{1}{2}x\right)$

23. $y = 6\sin(\pi x)$ **24.** $y = -3\cos(3x)$ **25.** $y = -\frac{1}{2}\cos\left(\frac{3}{2}x\right)$ **26.** $y = \frac{4}{3}\sin\left(\frac{2}{3}x\right)$

27. $y = \frac{5}{3}\sin\left(-\frac{2\pi}{3}x\right)$ **28.** $y = \frac{9}{5}\cos\left(-\frac{3\pi}{2}x\right)$

In Problems 29–38, match the given function to one of the graphs (A)–(J).

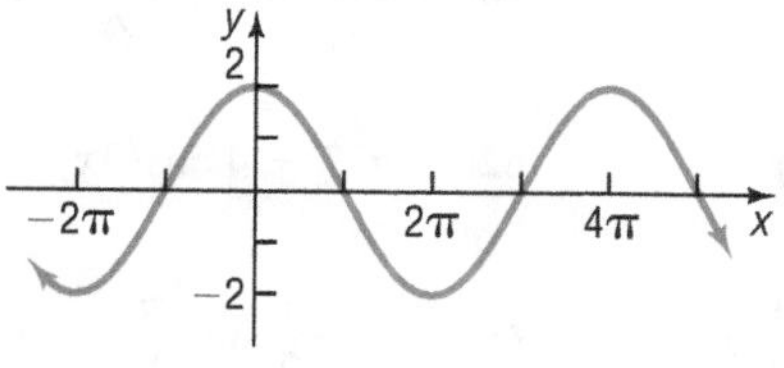

(A)

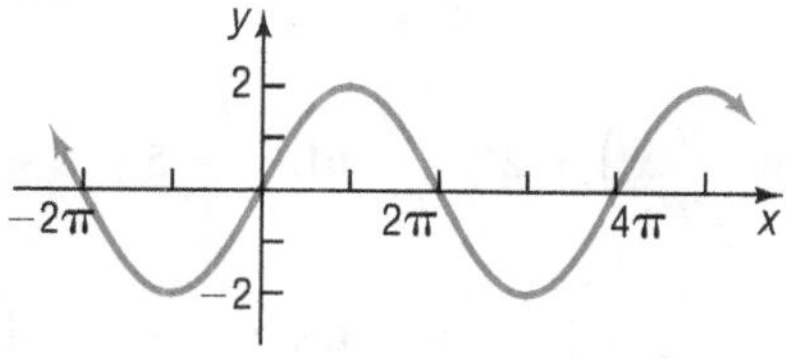

(B)

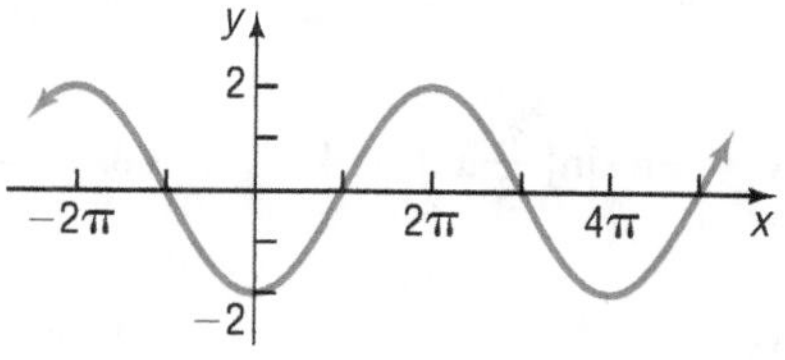

(C)

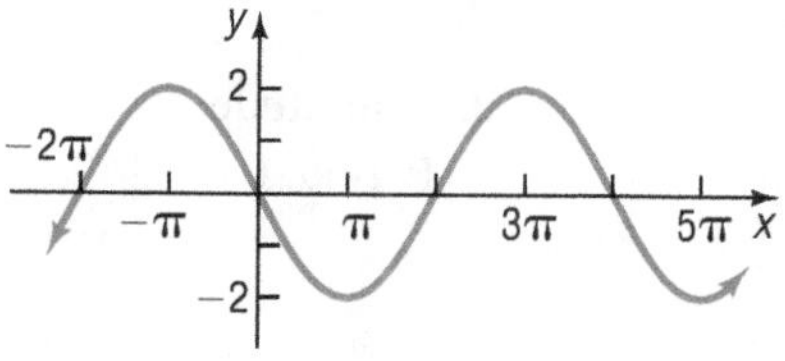

(D)

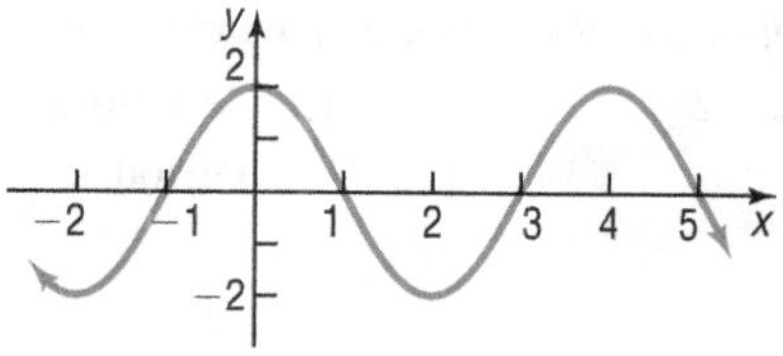

(E)

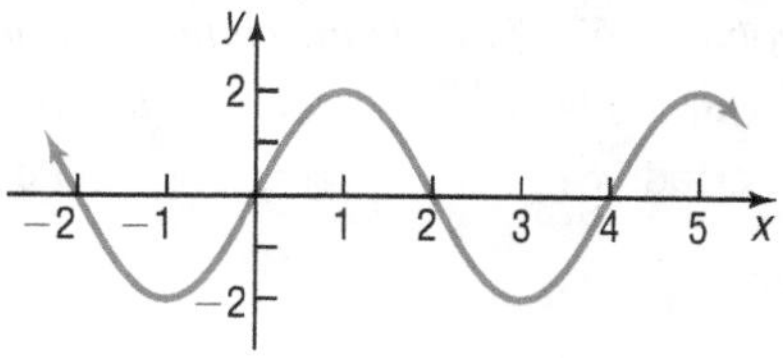

(F)

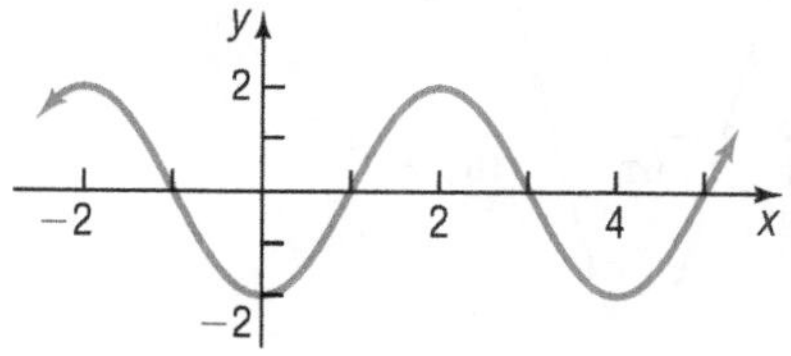

(G)

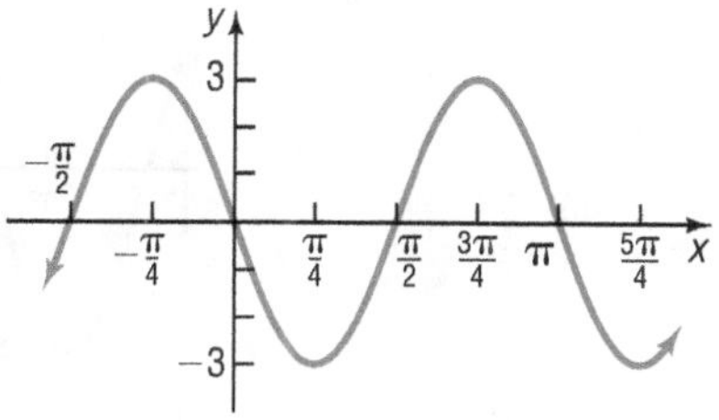

(H)

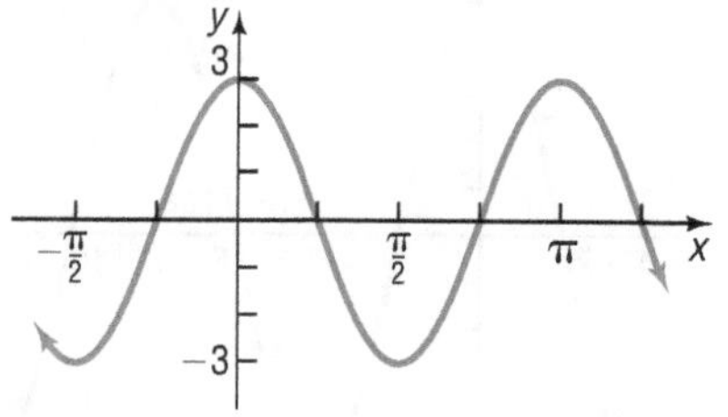

(I)

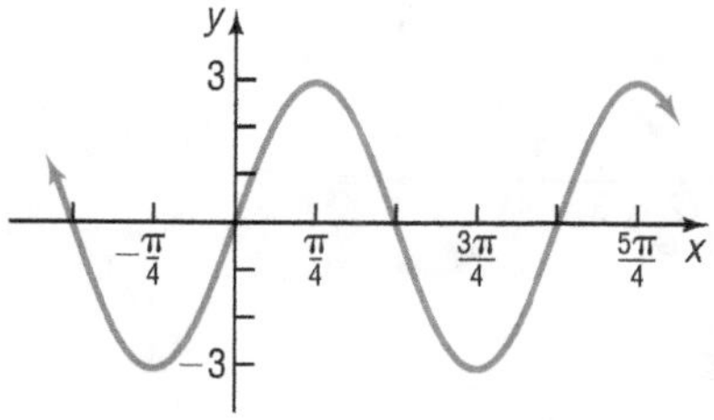

(J)

29. $y = 2\sin\left(\frac{\pi}{2}x\right)$ **30.** $y = 2\cos\left(\frac{\pi}{2}x\right)$ **31.** $y = 2\cos\left(\frac{1}{2}x\right)$

32. $y = 3\cos(2x)$ **33.** $y = -3\sin(2x)$ **34.** $y = 2\sin\left(\frac{1}{2}x\right)$

35. $y = -2\cos\left(\frac{1}{2}x\right)$ **36.** $y = -2\cos\left(\frac{\pi}{2}x\right)$ **37.** $y = 3\sin(2x)$

38. $y = -2\sin\left(\frac{1}{2}x\right)$

In Problems 39–42, match the given function to one of the graphs (A)–(D).

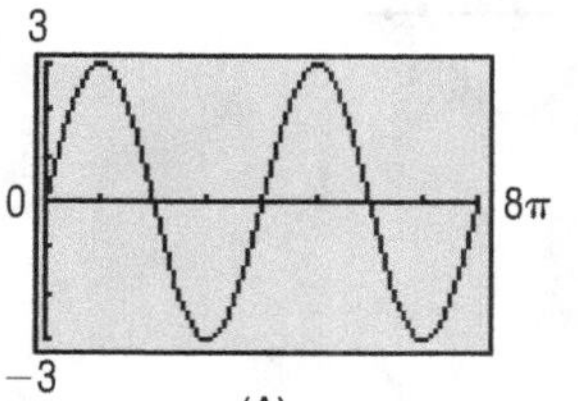

(A)

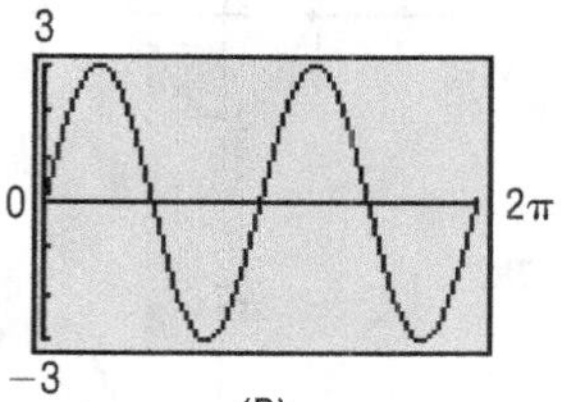

(B)

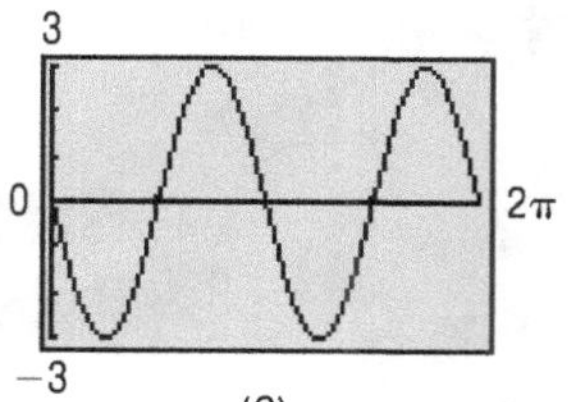

(C)

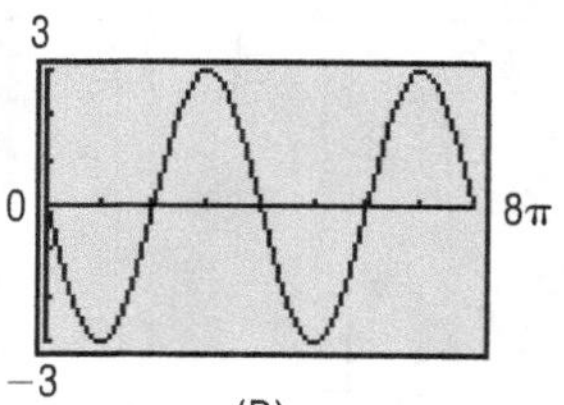

(D)

39. $y = 3\sin\left(\frac{1}{2}x\right)$ **40.** $y = -3\sin(2x)$ **41.** $y = 3\sin(2x)$ **42.** $y = -3\sin\left(\frac{1}{2}x\right)$

In Problems 43–66, graph each function. Be sure to label key points and show at least two cycles. Verify the graph using a graphing utility. Use the graph to determine the domain and the range of each function.

43. $y = 4\cos x$

44. $y = 3\sin x$

45. $y = -4\sin x$

46. $y = -3\cos x$

47. $y = \cos(4x)$

48. $y = \sin(3x)$

49. $y = \sin(-2x)$

50. $y = \cos(-2x)$

51. $y = 2\sin\left(\frac{1}{2}x\right)$

52. $y = 2\cos\left(\frac{1}{4}x\right)$

53. $y = -\frac{1}{2}\cos(2x)$

54. $y = -4\sin\left(\frac{1}{8}x\right)$

55. $y = 2\sin x + 3$

56. $y = 3\cos x + 2$

57. $y = 5\cos(\pi x) - 3$

58. $y = 4\sin\left(\frac{\pi}{2}x\right) - 2$

59. $y = -6\sin\left(\frac{\pi}{3}x\right) + 4$

60. $y = -3\cos\left(\frac{\pi}{4}x\right) + 2$

61. $y = 5 - 3\sin(2x)$

62. $y = 2 - 4\cos(3x)$

63. $y = \frac{5}{3}\sin\left(-\frac{2\pi}{3}x\right)$

64. $y = \frac{9}{5}\cos\left(-\frac{3\pi}{2}x\right)$

65. $y = -\frac{3}{2}\cos\left(\frac{\pi}{4}x\right) + \frac{1}{2}$

66. $y = -\frac{1}{2}\sin\left(\frac{\pi}{8}x\right) + \frac{3}{2}$

In Problems 67–70, write the equation of a sine function that has the given characteristics.

67. Amplitude: 3
Period: π

68. Amplitude: 2
Period: 4π

69. Amplitude: 3
Period: 2

70. Amplitude: 4
Period: 1

In Problems 71–84, find an equation for each graph.

71.

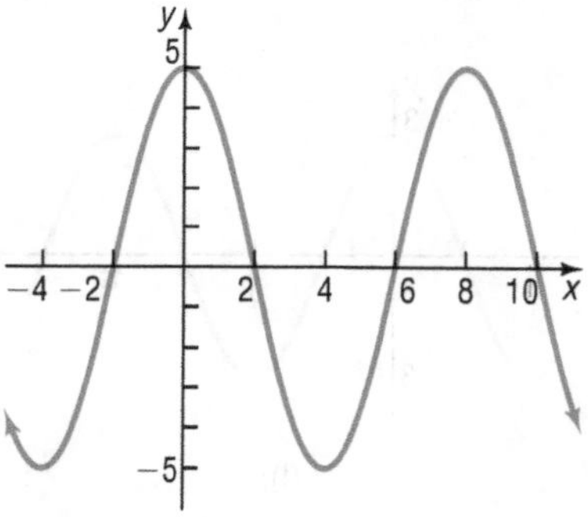

72.

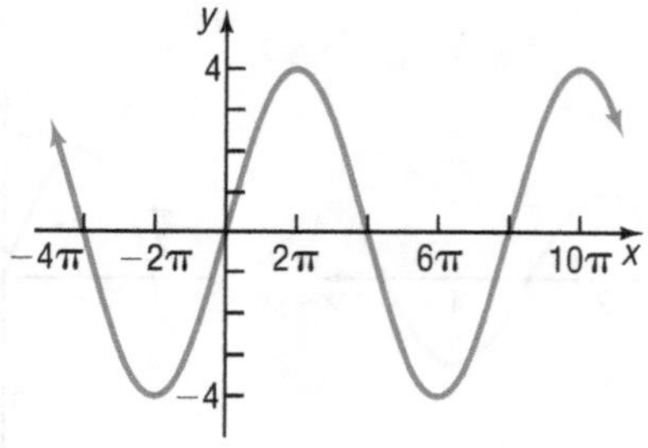

73.

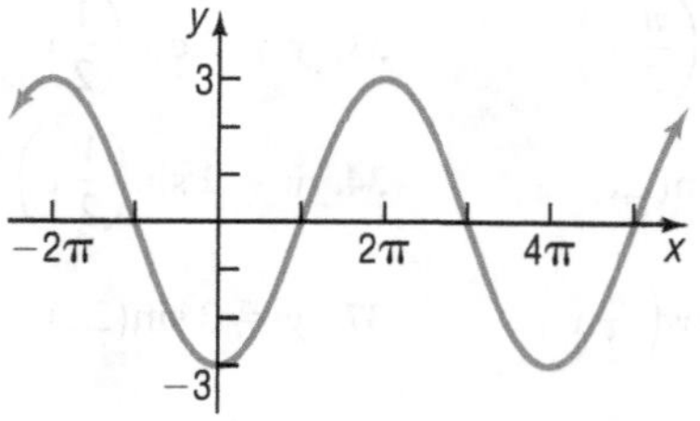

74.

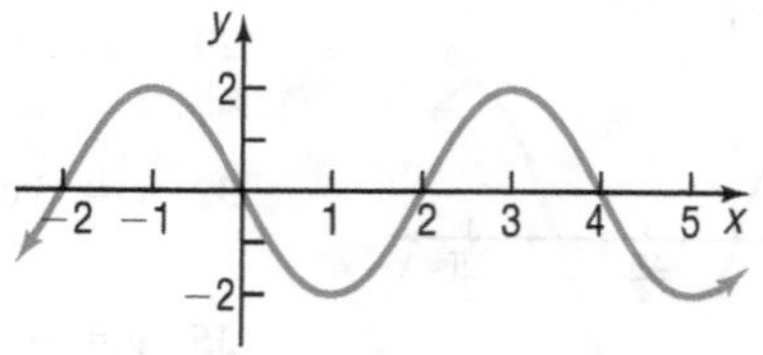

75.

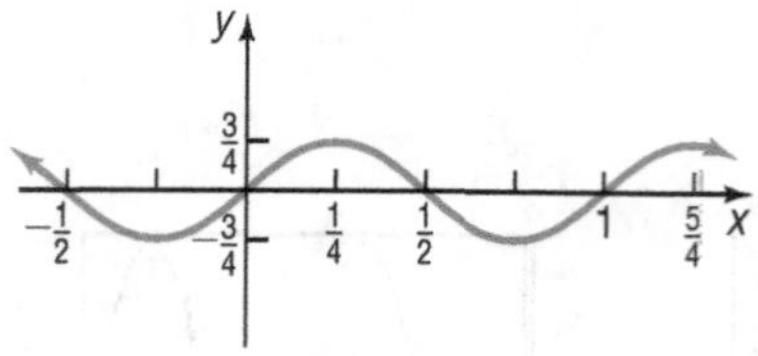

76.

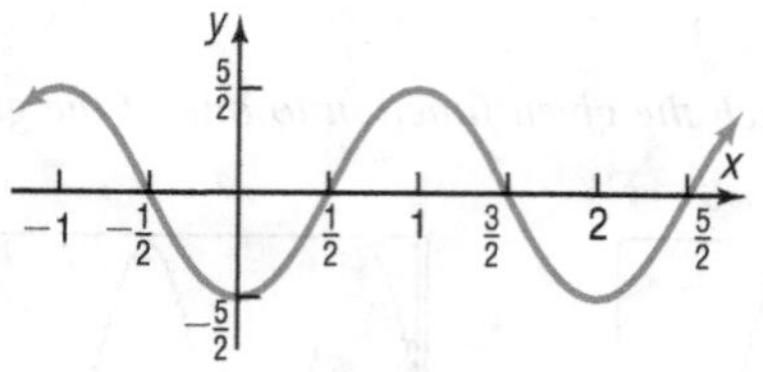

77.

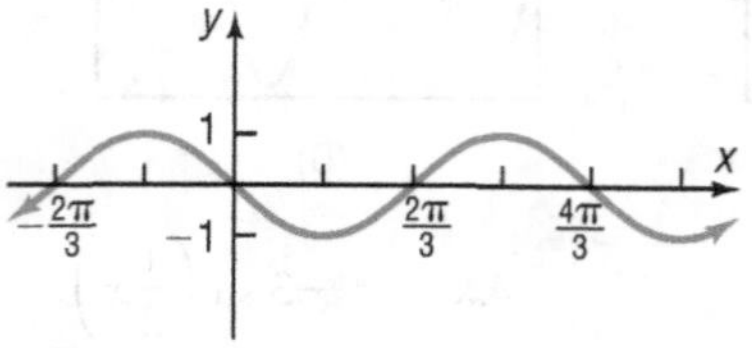

78.

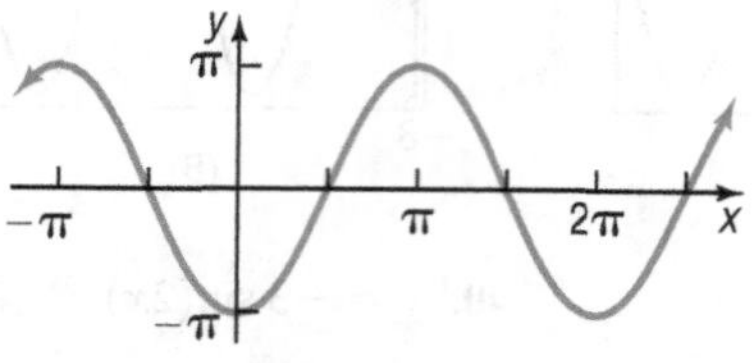

79.

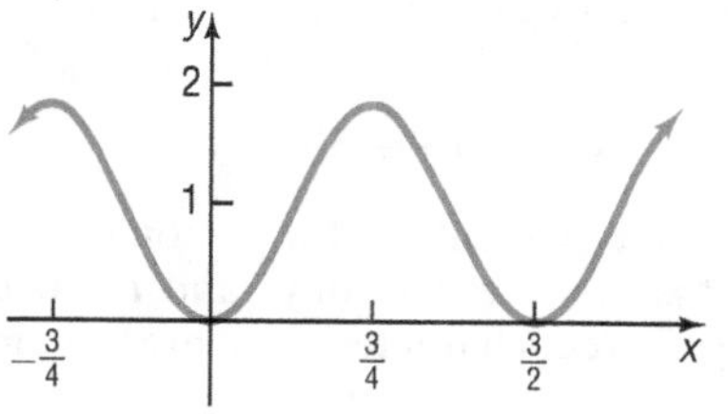

80.

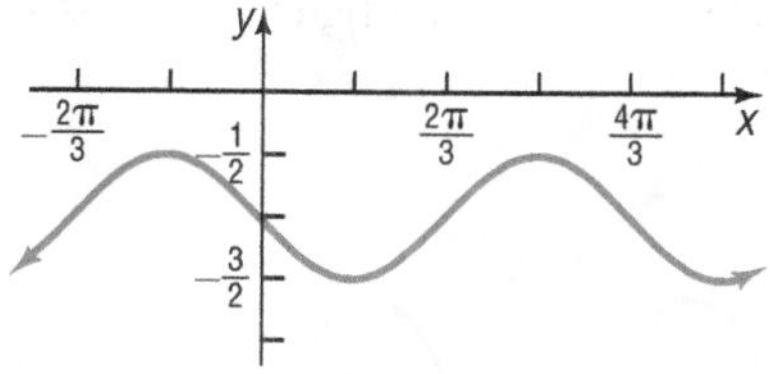

81.

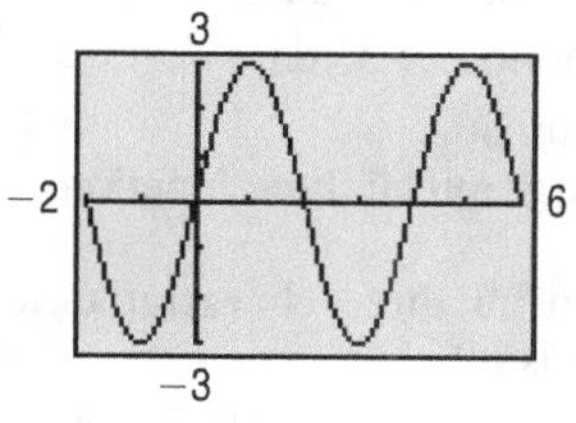

82.

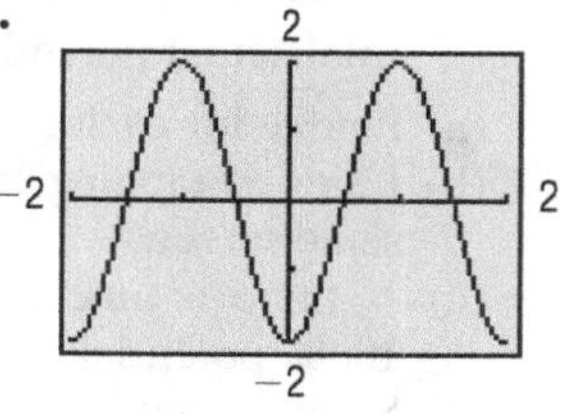

83.

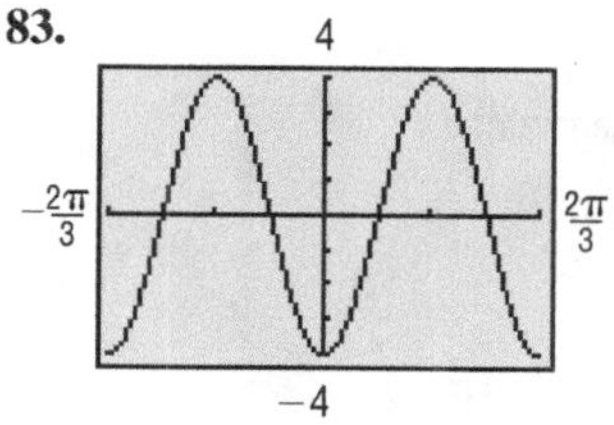

84.

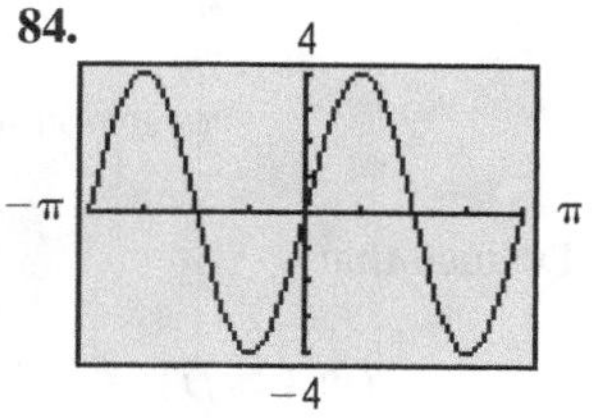

Mixed Practice

In Problems 85–88, find the average rate of change of f from 0 to $\frac{\pi}{2}$.

85. $f(x) = \sin x$

86. $f(x) = \cos x$

87. $f(x) = \sin\left(\frac{x}{2}\right)$

88. $f(x) = \cos(2x)$

In Problems 89–92, find $(f \circ g)(x)$ *and* $(g \circ f)(x)$ *and graph each of these functions.*

89. $f(x) = \sin x$
$g(x) = 4x$

90. $f(x) = \cos x$
$g(x) = \frac{1}{2}x$

91. $f(x) = -2x$
$g(x) = \cos x$

92. $f(x) = -3x$
$g(x) = \sin x$

Applications and Extensions

93. Alternating Current (ac) Circuits The current I, in amperes, flowing through an ac (alternating current) circuit at time t in seconds, is

$$I(t) = 220 \sin(60\pi t) \qquad t \geq 0$$

What is the period? What is the amplitude? Graph this function over two periods.

94. Alternating Current (ac) Circuits The current I, in amperes, flowing through an ac (alternating current) circuit at time t in seconds, is

$$I(t) = 120 \sin(30\pi t) \qquad t \geq 0$$

What is the period? What is the amplitude? Graph this function over two periods.

95. Alternating Current (ac) Generators The voltage V, in volts, produced by an ac generator at time t, in seconds, is

$$V(t) = 220 \sin(120\pi t)$$

(a) What is the amplitude? What is the period?
(b) Graph V over two periods, beginning at $t = 0$.
(c) If a resistance of $R = 10$ ohms is present, what is the current I?
[**Hint:** Use Ohm's Law, $V = IR$.]
(d) What is the amplitude and period of the current I?
(e) Graph I over two periods, beginning at $t = 0$.

96. Alternating Current (ac) Generators The voltage V, in volts, produced by an ac generator at time t, in seconds, is

$$V(t) = 120 \sin(120\pi t)$$

(a) What is the amplitude? What is the period?
(b) Graph V over two periods, beginning at $t = 0$.
(c) If a resistance of $R = 20$ ohms is present, what is the current I?
[**Hint:** Use Ohm's Law, $V = IR$.]
(d) What is the amplitude and period of the current I?
(e) Graph I over two periods, beginning at $t = 0$.

97. Alternating Current (ac) Generators The voltage V produced by an ac generator is sinusoidal. As a function of time, the voltage V is

$$V(t) = V_0 \sin(2\pi f t)$$

where f is the **frequency**, the number of complete oscillations (cycles) per second. [In the United States and Canada, f is 60 hertz (Hz).] The **power** P delivered to a resistance R at any time t is defined as

$$P(t) = \frac{[V(t)]^2}{R}$$

(a) Show that $P(t) = \frac{V_0^2}{R} \sin^2(2\pi f t)$.

(b) The graph of P is shown in the figure. Express P as a sinusoidal function.

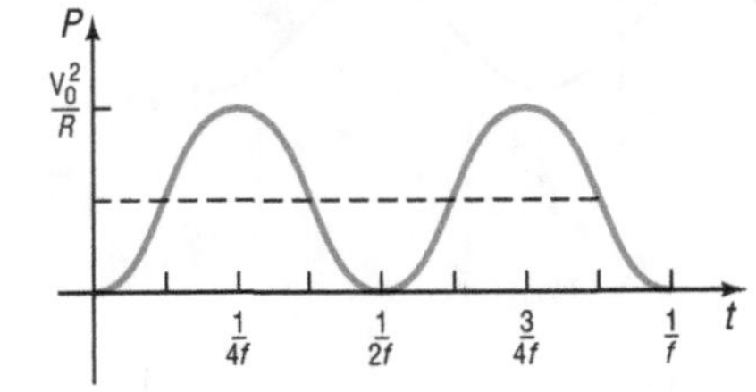

Power in an ac generator

(c) Deduce that

$$\sin^2(2\pi f t) = \frac{1}{2}[1 - \cos(4\pi f t)]$$

98. Bridge Clearance A one-lane highway runs through a tunnel in the shape of one-half a sine curve cycle. The opening is 28 feet wide at road level and is 15 feet tall at its highest point.

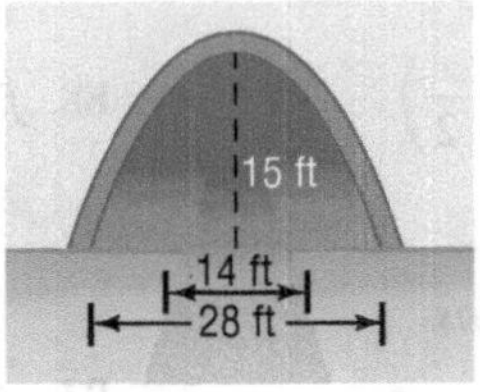

(a) Find an equation for the sine curve that fits the opening. Place the origin at the left end of the sine curve.
(b) If the road is 14 feet wide with 7-foot shoulders on each side, what is the height of the tunnel at the edge of the road?

Source: en.wikipedia.org/wiki/Interstate_Highway_standards and *Ohio Revised Code*

99. Biorhythms In the theory of biorhythms, a sine function of the form

$$P(t) = 50\sin(\omega t) + 50$$

is used to measure the percent P of a person's potential at time t, where t is measured in days and $t = 0$ is the person's birthday. Three characteristics are commonly measured:

Physical potential: period of 23 days
Emotional potential: period of 28 days
Intellectual potential: period of 33 days

(a) Find ω for each characteristic.
(b) Using a graphing utility, graph all three functions on the same screen.
(c) Is there a time t when all three characteristics have 100% potential? When is it?
(d) Suppose that you are 20 years old today ($t = 7305$ days). Describe your physical, emotional, and intellectual potential for the next 30 days.

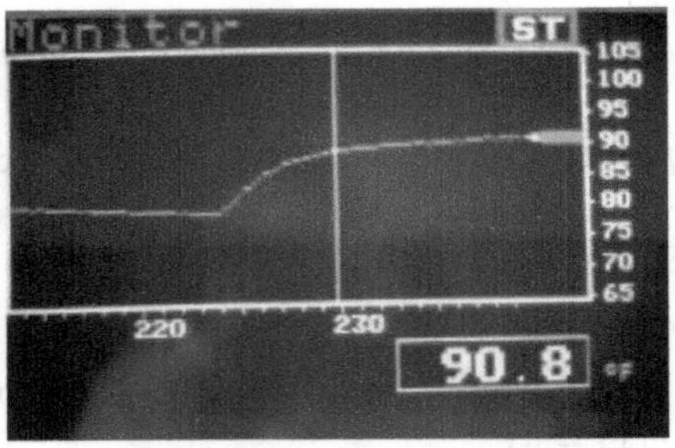

100. Graph $y = |\cos x|$, $-2\pi \leq x \leq 2\pi$.

101. Graph $y = |\sin x|$, $-2\pi \leq x \leq 2\pi$.

Discussion and Writing

102. Explain how you would scale the x-axis and y-axis before graphing $y = 3\cos(\pi x)$.

103. Explain the term *amplitude* as it relates to the graph of a sinusoidal function.

104. Explain how the amplitude and period of a sinusoidal graph are used to establish the scale on each coordinate axis.

105. Find an application in your major field that leads to a sinusoidal graph. Write a paper about your findings.

'Are You Prepared?' Answers

1. Vertical stretch by a factor of 3

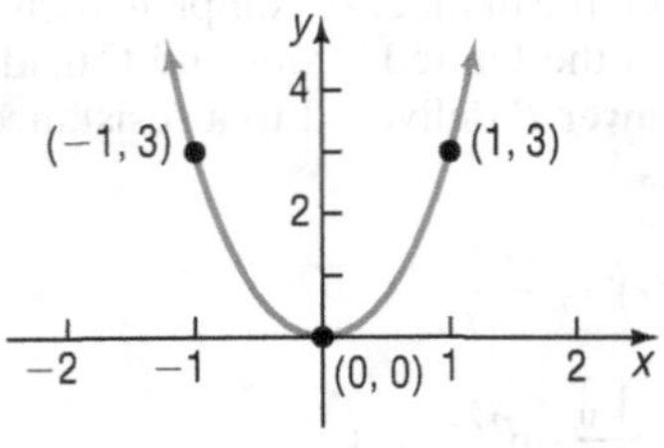

2. Horizontal compression by a factor of $\frac{1}{2}$

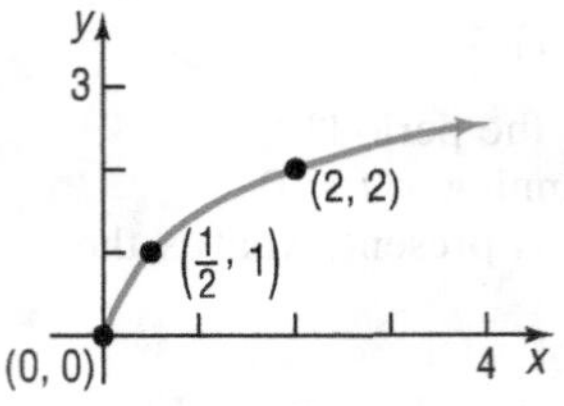

6.5 Graphs of the Tangent, Cotangent, Cosecant, and Secant Functions

PREPARING FOR THIS SECTION *Before getting started, review the following:*

- Vertical Asymptotes (Section 4.2, pp. 194–196)

Now Work the 'Are You Prepared?' problems on page 417.

OBJECTIVES
1. Graph Functions of the Form $y = A\tan(\omega x) + B$ and $y = A\cot(\omega x) + B$ (p. 413)
2. Graph Functions of the Form $y = A\csc(\omega x) + B$ and $y = A\sec(\omega x) + B$ (p. 415)

The Graph of the Tangent Function

Because the tangent function has period π, we only need to determine the graph over some interval of length π. The rest of the graph will consist of repetitions of that graph. Because the tangent function is not defined at $\ldots, -\frac{3\pi}{2}, -\frac{\pi}{2}, \frac{\pi}{2}, \frac{3\pi}{2}, \ldots$, we will concentrate on the interval $\left(-\frac{\pi}{2}, \frac{\pi}{2}\right)$, of length π, and construct Table 8, which lists some points on the graph of $y = \tan x$, $-\frac{\pi}{2} < x < \frac{\pi}{2}$. We plot the points in the table and connect them with a smooth curve. See Figure 66 for a partial graph of $y = \tan x$, where $-\frac{\pi}{3} \le x \le \frac{\pi}{3}$.

Table 8

x	$y = \tan x$	(x, y)
$-\frac{\pi}{3}$	$-\sqrt{3} \approx -1.73$	$\left(-\frac{\pi}{3}, -\sqrt{3}\right)$
$-\frac{\pi}{4}$	-1	$\left(-\frac{\pi}{4}, -1\right)$
$-\frac{\pi}{6}$	$-\frac{\sqrt{3}}{3} \approx -0.58$	$\left(-\frac{\pi}{6}, -\frac{\sqrt{3}}{3}\right)$
0	0	$(0, 0)$
$\frac{\pi}{6}$	$\frac{\sqrt{3}}{3} \approx 0.58$	$\left(\frac{\pi}{6}, \frac{\sqrt{3}}{3}\right)$
$\frac{\pi}{4}$	1	$\left(\frac{\pi}{4}, 1\right)$
$\frac{\pi}{3}$	$\sqrt{3} \approx 1.73$	$\left(\frac{\pi}{3}, \sqrt{3}\right)$

Figure 66 $y = \tan x$, $-\frac{\pi}{3} \le x \le \frac{\pi}{3}$

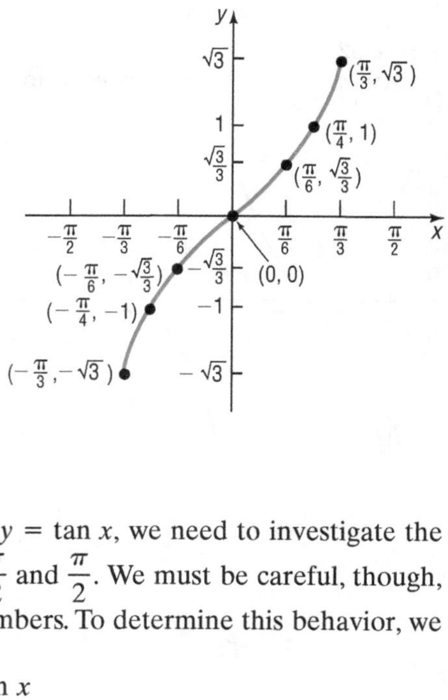

To complete one period of the graph of $y = \tan x$, we need to investigate the behavior of the function as x approaches $-\frac{\pi}{2}$ and $\frac{\pi}{2}$. We must be careful, though, because $y = \tan x$ is not defined at these numbers. To determine this behavior, we use the identity

$$\tan x = \frac{\sin x}{\cos x}$$

See Table 9. If x is close to $\frac{\pi}{2} \approx 1.5708$, but remains less than $\frac{\pi}{2}$, then $\sin x$ will be close to 1 and $\cos x$ will be positive and close to 0. (To see this, refer back to the graphs of the sine function and the cosine function.) So the ratio $\frac{\sin x}{\cos x}$ will be positive and large. In fact, the closer x gets to $\frac{\pi}{2}$, the closer $\sin x$ gets to 1 and $\cos x$ gets to 0, so $\tan x$ approaches $\infty \left(\lim_{x \to \frac{\pi}{2}^-} \tan x = \infty\right)$. In other words, the vertical line $x = \frac{\pi}{2}$ is a vertical asymptote to the graph of $y = \tan x$.

Table 9

x	$\sin x$	$\cos x$	$y = \tan x$
$\frac{\pi}{3} \approx 1.05$	$\frac{\sqrt{3}}{2}$	$\frac{1}{2}$	$\sqrt{3} \approx 1.73$
1.5	0.9975	0.0707	14.1
1.57	0.9999	7.96E−4	1255.8
1.5707	0.9999	9.6E−5	10,381
$\frac{\pi}{2} \approx 1.5708$	1	0	Undefined

If x is close to $-\frac{\pi}{2}$, but remains greater than $-\frac{\pi}{2}$, then $\sin x$ will be close to -1 and $\cos x$ will be positive and close to 0. The ratio $\frac{\sin x}{\cos x}$ approaches $-\infty \left(\lim_{x \to -\frac{\pi}{2}^+} \tan x = -\infty\right)$. In other words, the vertical line $x = -\frac{\pi}{2}$ is also a vertical asymptote to the graph.

With these observations, we can complete one period of the graph. We obtain the complete graph of $y = \tan x$ by repeating this period, as shown in Figure 67.

Figure 68 shows the graph of $y = \tan x, -\infty < x < \infty$, using a graphing utility. Notice we used dot mode when graphing $y = \tan x$. Do you know why?

Figure 67
$y = \tan x, -\infty < x < \infty$, x not equal to odd multiples of $\frac{\pi}{2}$

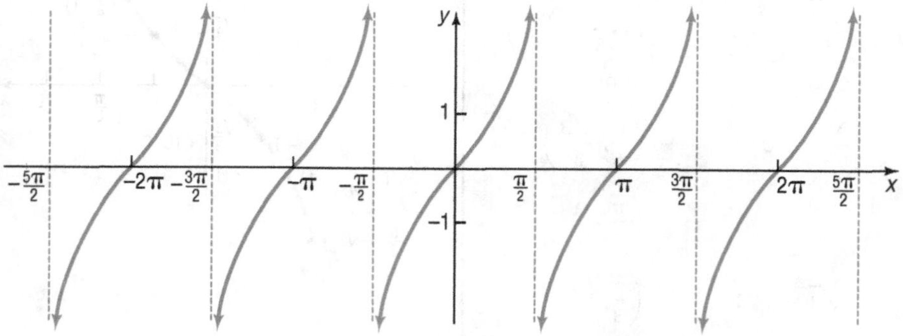

Figure 68

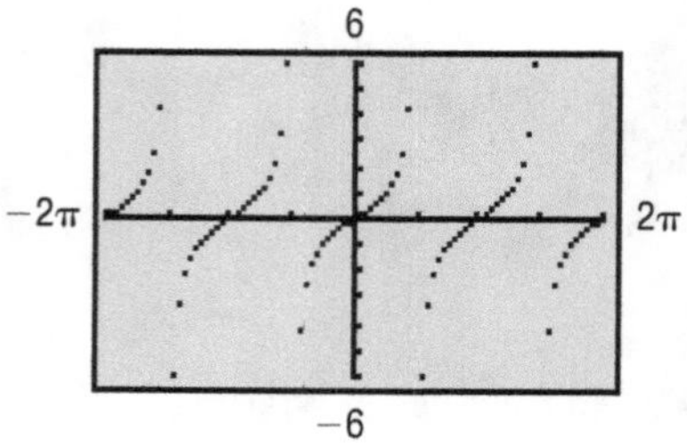

The graph of $y = \tan x$ in Figure 67 illustrates the following properties.

Properties of the Tangent Function

1. The domain is the set of all real numbers, except odd multiples of $\frac{\pi}{2}$.
2. The range is the set of all real numbers.
3. The tangent function is an odd function, as the symmetry of the graph with respect to the origin indicates.

4. The tangent function is periodic, with period π.
5. The x-intercepts are $\ldots, -2\pi, -\pi, 0, \pi, 2\pi, 3\pi, \ldots$; the y-intercept is 0.
6. Vertical asymptotes occur at $x = \ldots, -\frac{3\pi}{2}, -\frac{\pi}{2}, \frac{\pi}{2}, \frac{3\pi}{2}, \ldots$.

Now Work PROBLEMS 7 AND 15

1 Graph Functions of the Form $y = A\tan(\omega x) + B$

For tangent functions, there is no concept of amplitude since the range of the tangent function is $(-\infty, \infty)$. The role of A in $y = A\tan(\omega x) + B$ is to provide the magnitude of the vertical stretch. The period of $y = \tan x$ is π, so the period of $y = A\tan(\omega x) + B$ is $\frac{\pi}{\omega}$, caused by the horizontal compression of the graph by a factor of $\frac{1}{\omega}$. Finally, the presence of B indicates that a vertical shift is required.

EXAMPLE 1 **Graphing Functions of the Form $y = A\tan(\omega x) + B$**

Graph $y = 2\tan x - 1$. Use the graph to determine the domain and the range of $y = 2\tan x - 1$.

Solution Figure 69 shows the steps using transformations.

Figure 69

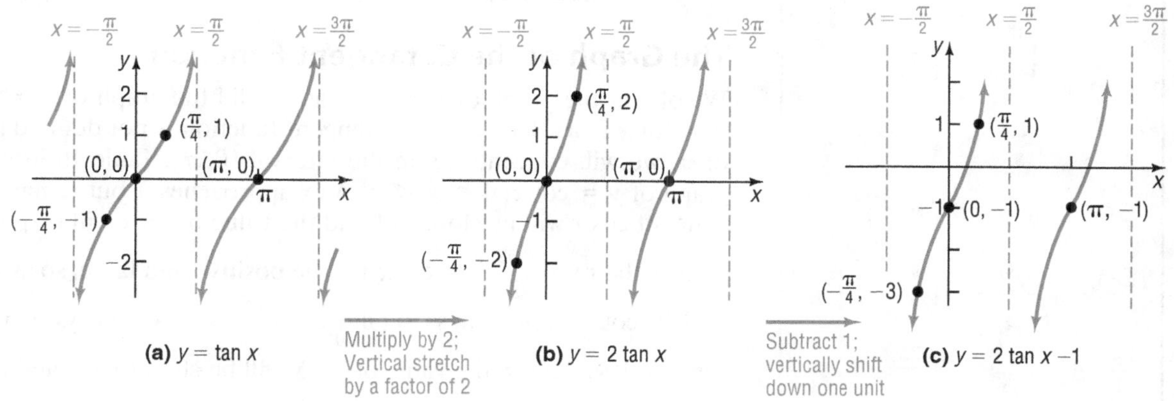

The domain of $y = 2\tan x - 1$ is $\{x \mid x \neq \frac{k\pi}{2}$, k is an odd integer$\}$ and the range is the set of all real numbers or $(-\infty, \infty)$.

Check: Graph $Y_1 = 2\tan x - 1$ to verify the graph shown in Figure 69(c).

EXAMPLE 2 **Graphing Functions of the Form $y = A\tan(\omega x) + B$**

Graph $y = 3\tan(2x)$. Use the graph to determine the domain and the range of $y = 3\tan(2x)$.

Solution Figure 70 shows the steps using transformations.

Figure 70

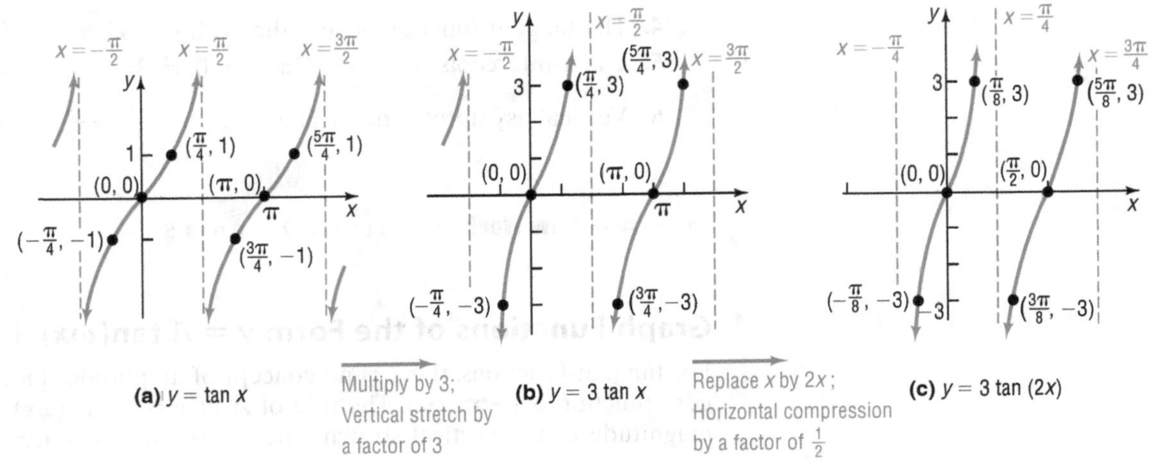

The domain of $y = 3\tan(2x)$ is $\{x \mid x \neq \frac{k\pi}{4}, k \text{ is an odd integer}\}$ and the range is the set of all real numbers or $(-\infty, \infty)$.

Check: Graph $Y_1 = 3\tan(2x)$ to verify the graph in Figure 70(c).

Notice in Figure 70(c) that the period of $y = 3\tan(2x)$ is $\frac{\pi}{2}$ due to the compression of the original period π by a factor of $\frac{1}{2}$. Notice that the asymptotes are $x = -\frac{\pi}{4}, x = \frac{\pi}{4}, x = \frac{3\pi}{4}$, and so on, also due to the compression.

Now Work PROBLEM 21

Table 10

x	$y = \cot x$	(x, y)
$\frac{\pi}{6}$	$\sqrt{3}$	$\left(\frac{\pi}{6}, \sqrt{3}\right)$
$\frac{\pi}{4}$	1	$\left(\frac{\pi}{4}, 1\right)$
$\frac{\pi}{3}$	$\frac{\sqrt{3}}{3}$	$\left(\frac{\pi}{3}, \frac{\sqrt{3}}{3}\right)$
$\frac{\pi}{2}$	0	$\left(\frac{\pi}{2}, 0\right)$
$\frac{2\pi}{3}$	$-\frac{\sqrt{3}}{3}$	$\left(\frac{2\pi}{3}, -\frac{\sqrt{3}}{3}\right)$
$\frac{3\pi}{4}$	-1	$\left(\frac{3\pi}{4}, -1\right)$
$\frac{5\pi}{6}$	$-\sqrt{3}$	$\left(\frac{5\pi}{6}, -\sqrt{3}\right)$

The Graph of the Cotangent Function

We obtain the graph of $y = \cot x$ as we did the graph of $y = \tan x$. The period of $y = \cot x$ is π. Because the cotangent function is not defined for integer multiples of π, we will concentrate on the interval $(0, \pi)$. Table 10 lists some points on the graph of $y = \cot x$, $0 < x < \pi$. As x approaches 0, but remains greater than 0, the value of $\cos x$ will be close to 1 and the value of $\sin x$ will be positive and close to 0. Hence, the ratio $\frac{\cos x}{\sin x} = \cot x$ will be positive and large; so as x approaches 0, with $x > 0$, $\cot x$ approaches ∞ ($\lim_{x\to 0^+} \cot x = \infty$). Similarly, as x approaches π, but remains less than π, the value of $\cos x$ will be close to -1, and the value of $\sin x$ will be positive and close to 0. So the ratio $\frac{\cos x}{\sin x} = \cot x$ will be negative and will approach $-\infty$ as x approaches π ($\lim_{x\to\pi^-} \cot x = -\infty$). Figure 71 shows the graph.

Figure 71
$y = \cot x$, $-\infty < x < \infty$, x not equal to integer multiples of π, $-\infty < y < \infty$

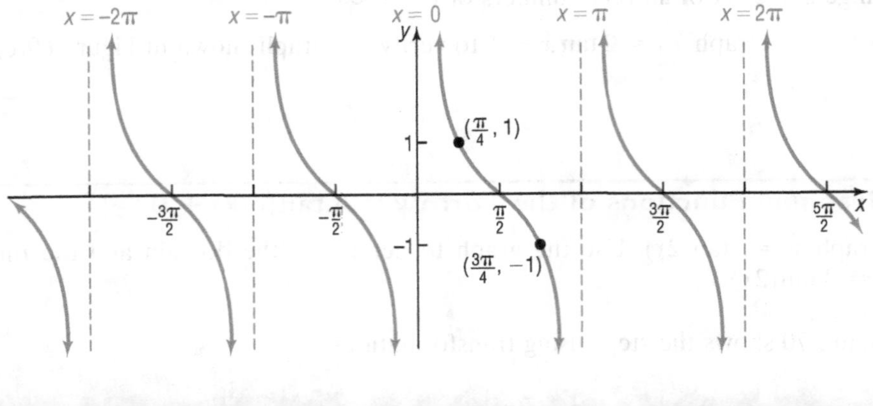

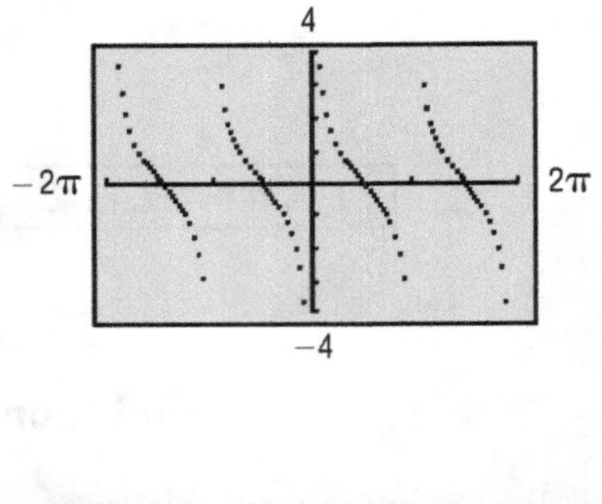

The graph of $y = A\cot(\omega x) + B$ has similar characteristics to those of the tangent function. The cotangent function $y = A\cot(\omega x) + B$ has period $\frac{\pi}{\omega}$. The cotangent function has no amplitude. The role of A is to provide the magnitude of the vertical stretch; the presence of B indicates a vertical shift is required.

Now Work PROBLEM 23

The Graph of the Cosecant Function and the Secant Function

The cosecant and secant functions, sometimes referred to as **reciprocal functions,** are graphed by making use of the reciprocal identities

$$\csc x = \frac{1}{\sin x} \quad \text{and} \quad \sec x = \frac{1}{\cos x}$$

For example, the value of the cosecant function $y = \csc x$ at a given number x equals the reciprocal of the corresponding value of the sine function, provided that the value of the sine function is not 0. If the value of $\sin x$ is 0, then x is an integer multiple of π. At such numbers, the cosecant function is not defined. In fact, the graph of the cosecant function has vertical asymptotes at integer multiples of π. Figure 72 shows the graph.

Figure 72
$y = \csc x$, $-\infty < x < \infty$, x not equal to integer multiples of π, $|y| \geq 1$

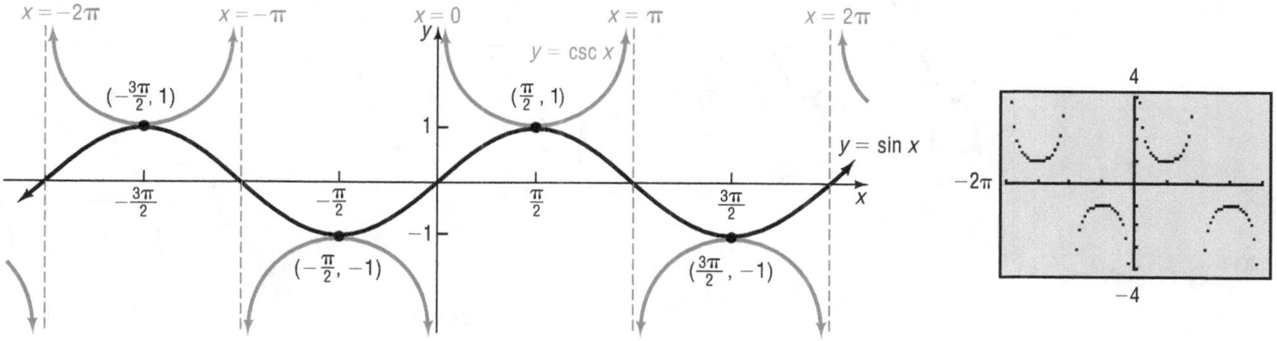

Using the idea of reciprocals, we can similarly obtain the graph of $y = \sec x$. See Figure 73.

Figure 73
$y = \sec x$, $-\infty < x < \infty$, x not equal to odd multiples of $\frac{\pi}{2}$, $|y| \geq 1$

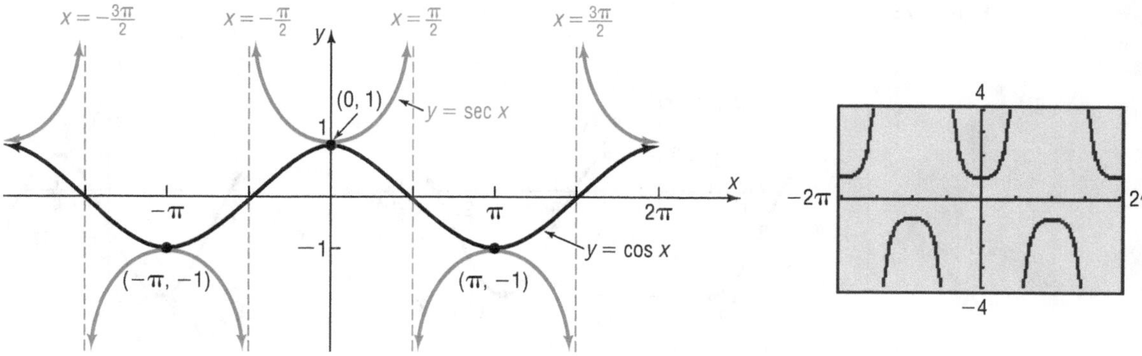

2 Graph Functions of the Form $y = A\csc(\omega x) + B$

The role of A in these functions is to set the range. The range of $y = \csc x$ is $\{y \mid y \leq -1 \text{ or } y \geq 1\}$ or $\{y \mid |y| \geq 1\}$; the range of $y = A\csc x$ is $\{y \mid |y| \geq |A|\}$, due to the vertical stretch of the graph by a factor of $|A|$. Just as with the sine and cosine functions, the period of $y = \csc(\omega x)$ and $y = \sec(\omega x)$ becomes $\frac{2\pi}{\omega}$, due to the horizontal compression of the graph by a factor of $\frac{1}{\omega}$. The presence of B indicates a vertical shift is required.

We shall graph these functions in two ways: using transformations and using the reciprocal function.

EXAMPLE 3 Graphing Functions of the Form $y = A\csc(\omega x) + B$

Graph $y = 2\csc x - 1$. Use the graph to determine the domain and the range of $y = 2\csc x - 1$.

Solution Using Transformations Figure 74 shows the required steps.

Figure 74

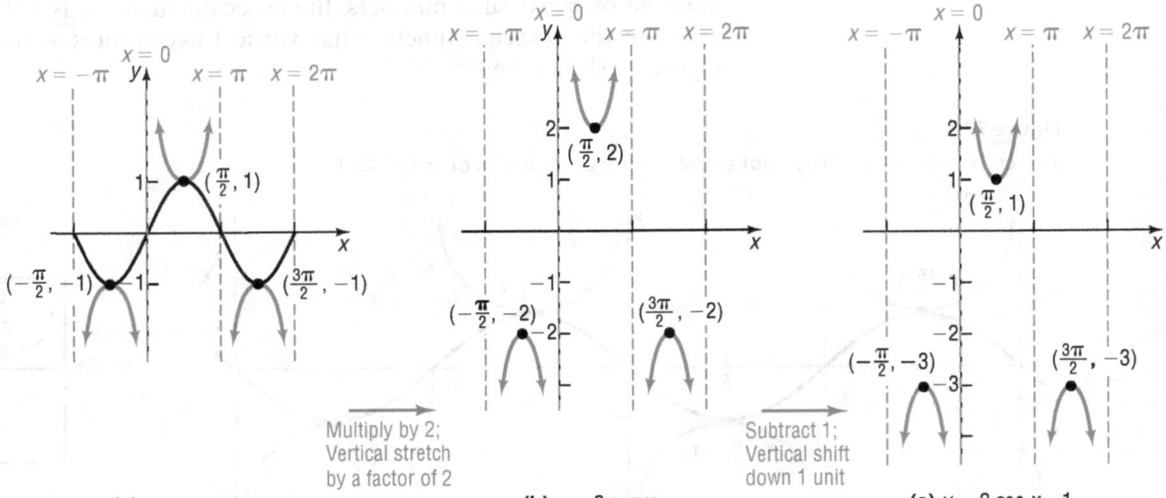

(a) $y = \csc x$ **(b)** $y = 2\csc x$ **(c)** $y = 2\csc x - 1$

Solution Using the Reciprocal Function We graph $y = 2\csc x - 1$ by first graphing the reciprocal function $y = 2\sin x - 1$ and then filling in the graph of $y = 2\csc x - 1$, using the idea of reciprocals. See Figure 75.

Figure 75

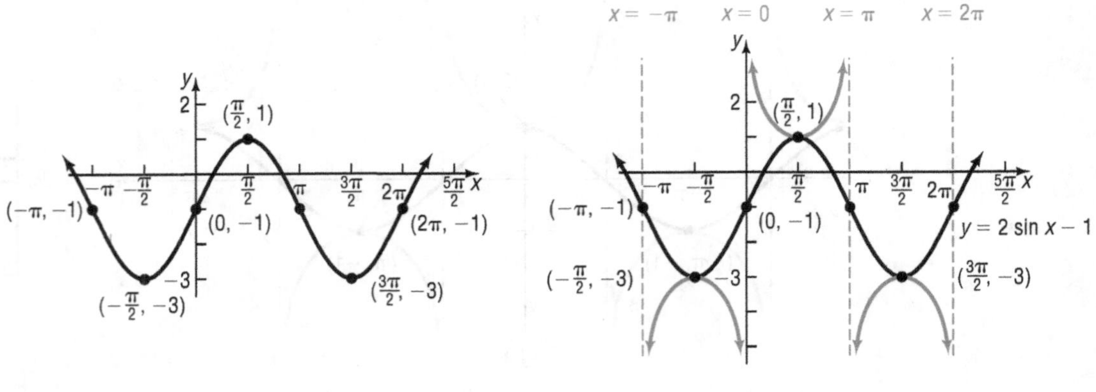

(a) $y = 2\sin x - 1$ **(b)** $y = 2\csc x - 1$

The domain of $y = 2\csc x - 1$ is $\{x \mid x \neq k\pi, k \text{ is an integer}\}$ and the range is $\{y \mid y \leq -3 \text{ or } y \geq 1\}$, or, using interval notation $(-\infty, -3] \cup [1, \infty)$.

Check: Graph $Y_1 = 2\csc x - 1$ to verify the graph shown in Figure 74 (c) or 75 (b).

Now Work PROBLEM 29

6.5 Assess Your Understanding

'Are You Prepared?' *Answers are given at the end of these exercises. If you get a wrong answer, read the pages listed in red.*

1. The graph of $y = \dfrac{3x - 6}{x - 4}$ has a vertical asymptote. What is it? (pp. 195–196)

2. ***True or False*** If $x = 3$ is a vertical asymptote of a function R, then $\lim_{x \to 3} |R(x)| = \infty$. (pp. 194–196)

Concepts and Vocabulary

3. The graph of $y = \tan x$ is symmetric with respect to the _____ and has vertical asymptotes at _____.

4. The graph of $y = \sec x$ is symmetric with respect to the _____ and has vertical asymptotes at _____.

5. It is easiest to graph $y = \sec x$ by first sketching the graph of _____.

6. ***True or False*** The graphs of $y = \tan x$, $y = \cot x$, $y = \sec x$, and $y = \csc x$ each have infinitely many vertical asymptotes.

Skill Building

In Problems 7–16, if necessary, refer to the graphs to answer each question.

7. What is the y-intercept of $y = \tan x$?

8. What is the y-intercept of $y = \cot x$?

9. What is the y-intercept of $y = \sec x$?

10. What is the y-intercept of $y = \csc x$?

11. For what numbers x, $-2\pi \le x \le 2\pi$, does $\sec x = 1$? For what numbers x does $\sec x = -1$?

12. For what numbers x, $-2\pi \le x \le 2\pi$, does $\csc x = 1$? For what numbers x does $\csc x = -1$?

13. For what numbers x, $-2\pi \le x \le 2\pi$, does the graph of $y = \sec x$ have vertical asymptotes?

14. For what numbers x, $-2\pi \le x \le 2\pi$, does the graph of $y = \csc x$ have vertical asymptotes?

15. For what numbers x, $-2\pi \le x \le 2\pi$, does the graph of $y = \tan x$ have vertical asymptotes?

16. For what numbers x, $-2\pi \le x \le 2\pi$, does the graph of $y = \cot x$ have vertical asymptotes?

In Problems 17–40, graph each function. Be sure to label key points and show at least two cycles. Verify the graph using a graphing utility. Use the graph to determine the domain and the range of each function.

17. $y = 3\tan x$

18. $y = -2\tan x$

19. $y = 4\cot x$

20. $y = -3\cot x$

21. $y = \tan\left(\dfrac{\pi}{2}x\right)$

22. $y = \tan\left(\dfrac{1}{2}x\right)$

23. $y = \cot\left(\dfrac{1}{4}x\right)$

24. $y = \cot\left(\dfrac{\pi}{4}x\right)$

25. $y = 2\sec x$

26. $y = \dfrac{1}{2}\csc x$

27. $y = -3\csc x$

28. $y = -4\sec x$

29. $y = 4\sec\left(\dfrac{1}{2}x\right)$

30. $y = \dfrac{1}{2}\csc(2x)$

31. $y = -2\csc(\pi x)$

32. $y = -3\sec\left(\dfrac{\pi}{2}x\right)$

33. $y = \tan\left(\dfrac{1}{4}x\right) + 1$

34. $y = 2\cot x - 1$

35. $y = \sec\left(\dfrac{2\pi}{3}x\right) + 2$

36. $y = \csc\left(\dfrac{3\pi}{2}x\right)$

37. $y = \dfrac{1}{2}\tan\left(\dfrac{1}{4}x\right) - 2$

38. $y = 3\cot\left(\dfrac{1}{2}x\right) - 2$

39. $y = 2\csc\left(\dfrac{1}{3}x\right) - 1$

40. $y = 3\sec\left(\dfrac{1}{4}x\right) + 1$

Mixed Practice

In Problems 41–44, find the average rate of change of f from 0 to $\frac{\pi}{6}$.

41. $f(x) = \tan x$ **42.** $f(x) = \sec x$ **43.** $f(x) = \tan(2x)$ **44.** $f(x) = \sec(2x)$

In Problems 45–48, find $(f \circ g)(x)$ *and* $(g \circ f)(x)$ *and graph each of these functions.*

45. $f(x) = \tan x$, $g(x) = 4x$

46. $f(x) = 2 \sec x$, $g(x) = \frac{1}{2}x$

47. $f(x) = -2x$, $g(x) = \cot x$

48. $f(x) = \frac{1}{2}x$, $g(x) = 2 \csc x$

Applications and Extensions

49. Carrying a Ladder around a Corner Two hallways, one of width 3 feet, the other of width 4 feet, meet at a right angle. See the illustration.

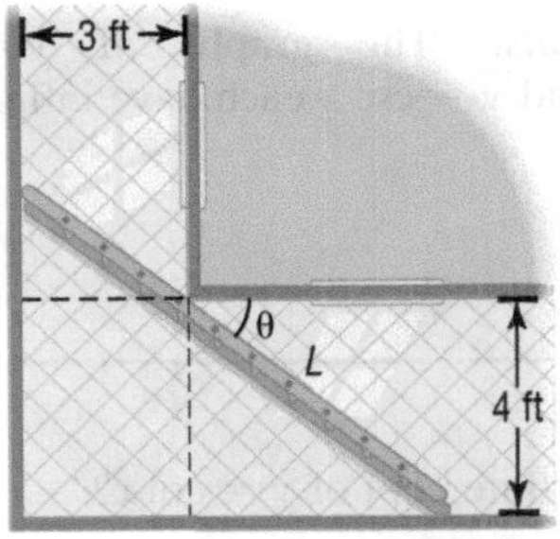

(a) Show that the length L of the line segment shown as a function of the angle θ is

$$L(\theta) = 3 \sec \theta + 4 \csc \theta$$

(b) Graph $L = L(\theta), 0 < \theta < \frac{\pi}{2}$.

(c) For what value of θ is L the least?

(d) What is the length of the longest ladder that can be carried around the corner? Why is this also the least value of L?

50. A Rotating Beacon Suppose that a fire truck is parked in front of a building as shown in the figure.

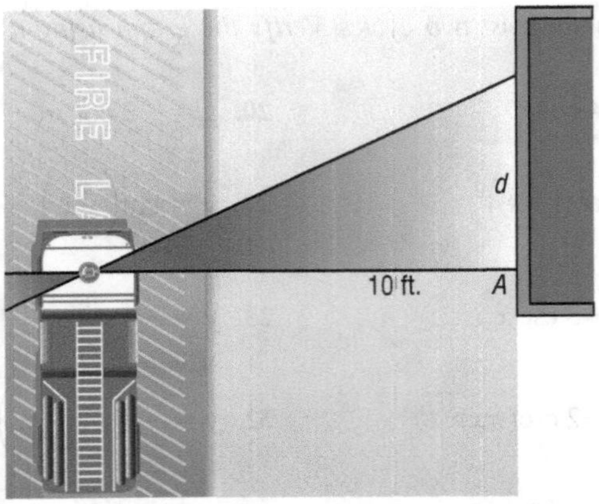

The beacon light on top of the fire truck is located 10 feet from the wall and has a light on each side. If the beacon light rotates 1 revolution every 2 seconds, then a model for determining the distance d, in feet, that the beacon of light is from point A on the wall after t seconds is given by

$$d(t) = |10 \tan(\pi t)|$$

(a) Graph $d(t) = |10 \tan(\pi t)|$ for $0 \le t \le 2$.

(b) For what values of t is the function undefined? Explain what this means in terms of the beam of light on the wall.

(c) Fill in the following table.

t	0	0.1	0.2	0.3	0.4
$d(t) = 10 \tan(\pi t)$					

(d) Compute $\frac{d(0.1) - d(0)}{0.1 - 0}$, $\frac{d(0.2) - d(0.1)}{0.2 - 0.1}$, and so on, for each consecutive value of t. These are called **first differences.**

(e) Interpret the first differences found in part (d). What is happening to the speed of the beam of light as d increases?

51. Exploration Graph

$$y = \tan x \quad \text{and} \quad y = -\cot\left(x + \frac{\pi}{2}\right)$$

Do you think that $\tan x = -\cot\left(x + \frac{\pi}{2}\right)$?

'Are You Prepared?' Answers

1. $x = 4$ **2.** True

6.6 Phase Shift; Sinusoidal Curve Fitting

OBJECTIVES 1 Graph Sinusoidal Functions of the Form $y = A\sin(\omega x - \phi) + B$ (p. 419)
2 Build Sinusoidal Models from Data (p. 423)

1 Graph Sinusoidal Functions of the Form $y = A\sin(\omega x - \phi) + B$

We have seen that the graph of $y = A\sin(\omega x)$, $\omega > 0$, has amplitude $|A|$ and period $T = \dfrac{2\pi}{\omega}$. One cycle can be drawn as x varies from 0 to $\dfrac{2\pi}{\omega}$ or, equivalently, as ωx varies from 0 to 2π. See Figure 76.

Figure 76
One cycle of
$y = A\sin(\omega x)$, $A > 0$, $\omega > 0$

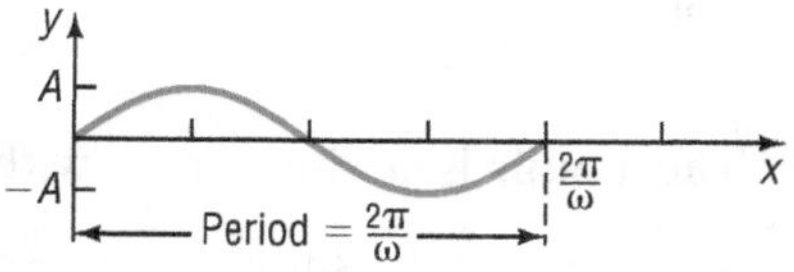

We now want to discuss the graph of

$$y = A\sin(\omega x - \phi)$$

which may also be written as

$$y = A\sin\left[\omega\left(x - \frac{\phi}{\omega}\right)\right]$$

where $\omega > 0$ and ϕ (the Greek letter phi) are real numbers. The graph will be a sine curve with amplitude $|A|$. As $\omega x - \phi$ varies from 0 to 2π, one period will be traced out. This period will begin when

$$\omega x - \phi = 0 \quad \text{or} \quad x = \frac{\phi}{\omega}$$

and will end when

$$\omega x - \phi = 2\pi \quad \text{or} \quad x = \frac{\phi}{\omega} + \frac{2\pi}{\omega}$$

NOTE We can also find the beginning and end of the period by solving the inequality:

$$0 \le \omega x - \phi \le 2\pi$$
$$\phi \le \omega x \le 2\pi + \phi$$
$$\frac{\phi}{\omega} \le x \le \frac{2\pi}{\omega} + \frac{\phi}{\omega}$$

■

See Figure 77.

Figure 77
One cycle of
$y = A\sin(\omega x - \phi)$, $A > 0$, $\omega > 0$, $\phi > 0$

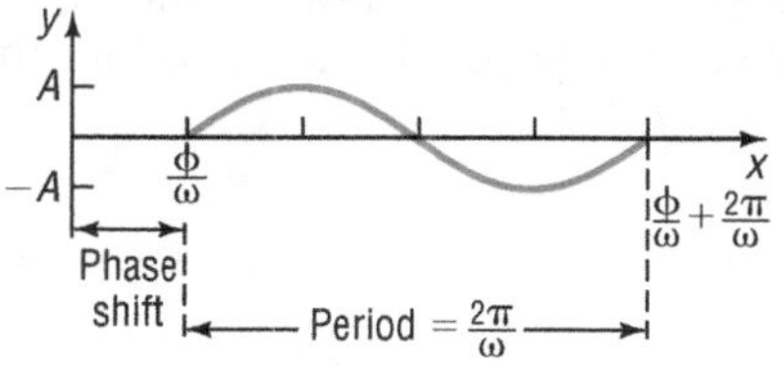

We see that the graph of $y = A\sin(\omega x - \phi) = A\sin\left[\omega\left(x - \dfrac{\phi}{\omega}\right)\right]$ is the same as the graph of $y = A\sin(\omega x)$, except that it has been shifted $\dfrac{\phi}{\omega}$ units (to the right if $\phi > 0$ and to the left if $\phi < 0$). This number $\dfrac{\phi}{\omega}$ is called the **phase shift** of the graph of $y = A\sin(\omega x - \phi)$.

For the graphs of $y = A\sin(\omega x - \phi)$ or $y = A\cos(\omega x - \phi)$, $\omega > 0$,

$$\text{Amplitude} = |A| \qquad \text{Period} = T = \frac{2\pi}{\omega} \qquad \text{Phase shift} = \frac{\phi}{\omega}$$

The phase shift is to the left if $\phi < 0$ and to the right if $\phi > 0$.

EXAMPLE 1 **Finding the Amplitude, Period, and Phase Shift of a Sinusoidal Function and Graphing It**

Find the amplitude, period, and phase shift of $y = 3\sin(2x - \pi)$ and graph the function.

Solution We will use the four steps used to graph sinusoidal functions of the form $y = A\sin(\omega x)$ or $y = A\cos(\omega x)$ given on page 403.

STEP 1: Comparing $y = 3\sin(2x - \pi) = 3\sin\left[2\left(x - \frac{\pi}{2}\right)\right]$

to

$$y = A\sin(\omega x - \phi) = A\sin\left[\omega\left(x - \frac{\phi}{\omega}\right)\right]$$

we find that $A = 3$, $\omega = 2$, and $\phi = \pi$. The graph is a sine curve with amplitude $|A| = 3$, period $T = \frac{2\pi}{\omega} = \frac{2\pi}{2} = \pi$, and phase shift $= \frac{\phi}{\omega} = \frac{\pi}{2}$.

STEP 2: The graph of $y = 3\sin(2x - \pi)$ will lie between -3 and 3 on the y-axis. One cycle will begin at $x = \frac{\phi}{\omega} = \frac{\pi}{2}$ and end at $x = \frac{\phi}{\omega} + \frac{2\pi}{\omega} = \frac{\pi}{2} + \pi = \frac{3\pi}{2}$. To find the five key points, we divide the interval $\left[\frac{\pi}{2}, \frac{3\pi}{2}\right]$ into four subintervals, each of length $\pi \div 4 = \frac{\pi}{4}$, by finding the following values of x:

NOTE We also can find the interval defining one cycle by solving the inequality

$$0 \le 2x - \pi \le 2\pi$$

Then

$$\pi \le 2x \le 3\pi$$

$$\frac{\pi}{2} \le x \le \frac{3\pi}{2}$$

■

$\frac{\pi}{2}$	$\frac{\pi}{2} + \frac{\pi}{4} = \frac{3\pi}{4}$	$\frac{3\pi}{4} + \frac{\pi}{4} = \pi$	$\pi + \frac{\pi}{4} = \frac{5\pi}{4}$	$\frac{5\pi}{4} + \frac{\pi}{4} = \frac{3\pi}{2}$
1st x-coordinate	2nd x-coordinate	3rd x-coordinate	4th x-coordinate	5th x-coordinate

STEP 3: Use these values of x to determine the five key points on the graph:

$$\left(\frac{\pi}{2}, 0\right) \quad \left(\frac{3\pi}{4}, 3\right) \quad (\pi, 0) \quad \left(\frac{5\pi}{4}, -3\right) \quad \left(\frac{3\pi}{2}, 0\right)$$

STEP 4: We plot these five points and fill in the graph of the sine function as shown in Figure 78(a). Extending the graph in each direction, we obtain Figure 78(b).

Figure 78

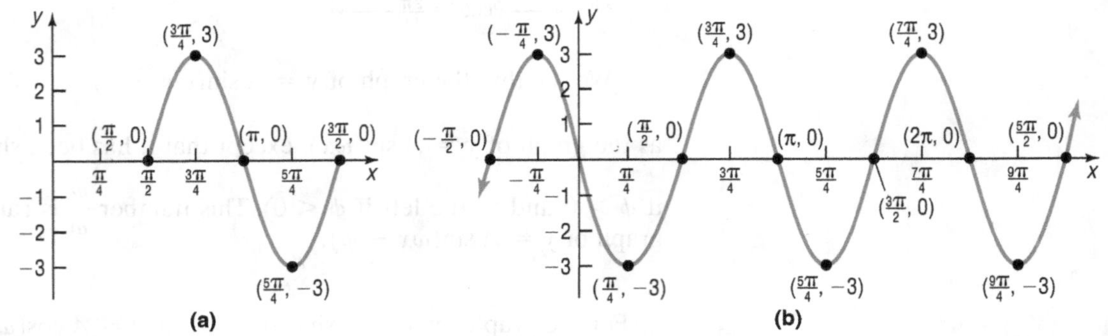

The graph of $y = 3\sin(2x - \pi) = 3\sin\left[2\left(x - \frac{\pi}{2}\right)\right]$ may also be obtained using transformations. See Figure 79.

Figure 79

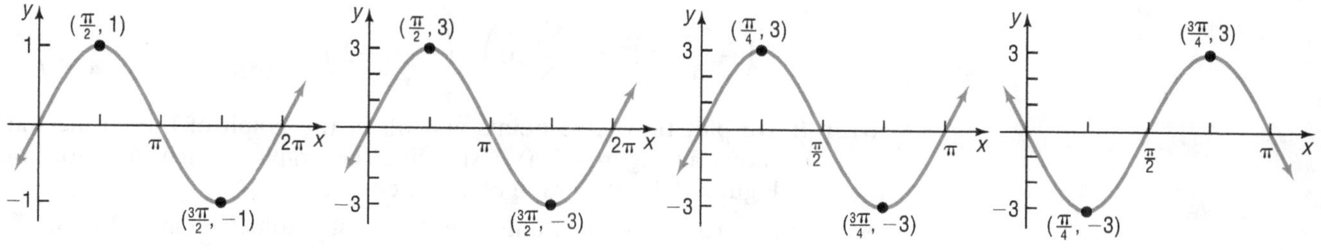

(a) $y = \sin x$ (b) $y = 3 \sin x$ (c) $y = 3 \sin(2x)$ (d) $y = 3 \sin\left[2\left(x - \frac{\pi}{2}\right)\right] = 3 \sin(2x - \pi)$

Figure 80

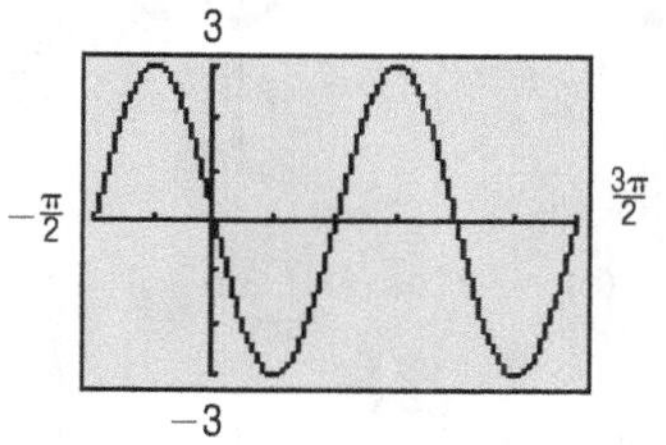

Check: Figure 80 shows the graph of $Y_1 = 3 \sin(2x - \pi)$ using a graphing utility. ■

To graph a sinusoidal function of the form $y = A \sin(\omega x - \phi) + B$, we first graph the function $y = A \sin(\omega x - \phi)$ and then apply a vertical shift.

EXAMPLE 2 Finding the Amplitude, Period, and Phase Shift of a Sinusoidal Function and Graphing It

Find the amplitude, period, and phase shift of $y = 2 \cos(4x + 3\pi) + 1$ and graph the function.

Solution

Step 1: We begin by graphing $y = 2 \cos(4x + 3\pi)$. Comparing

$$y = 2 \cos(4x + 3\pi) = 2 \cos\left[4\left(x + \frac{3\pi}{4}\right)\right]$$

to

$$y = A \cos(\omega x - \phi) = A \cos\left[\omega\left(x - \frac{\phi}{\omega}\right)\right]$$

we see that $A = 2$, $\omega = 4$, and $\phi = -3\pi$. The graph is a cosine curve with amplitude $|A| = 2$, period $T = \frac{2\pi}{\omega} = \frac{2\pi}{4} = \frac{\pi}{2}$, and phase shift $= \frac{\phi}{\omega} = -\frac{3\pi}{4}$.

Step 2: The graph of $y = 2 \cos(4x + 3\pi)$ will lie between -2 and 2 on the y-axis. One cycle will begin at $x = \frac{\phi}{\omega} = -\frac{3\pi}{4}$ and end at $x = \frac{\phi}{\omega} + \frac{2\pi}{\omega} = -\frac{3\pi}{4} + \frac{\pi}{2} = -\frac{\pi}{4}$. To find the five key points, we divide the interval $\left[-\frac{3\pi}{4}, -\frac{\pi}{4}\right]$ into four subintervals, each of the length $\frac{\pi}{2} \div 4 = \frac{\pi}{8}$, by finding the following values.

NOTE We can also find the interval defining one cycle by solving the inequality

$$0 \le 4x + 3\pi \le 2\pi$$

Then

$$-3\pi \le 4x \le -\pi$$

$$-\frac{3\pi}{4} \le x \le -\frac{\pi}{4}$$ ■

$-\frac{3\pi}{4}$	$-\frac{3\pi}{4} + \frac{\pi}{8} = -\frac{5\pi}{8}$	$-\frac{5\pi}{8} + \frac{\pi}{8} = -\frac{\pi}{2}$	$-\frac{\pi}{2} + \frac{\pi}{8} = -\frac{3\pi}{8}$	$-\frac{3\pi}{8} + \frac{\pi}{8} = -\frac{\pi}{4}$
1st x-coordinate	2nd x-coordinate	3rd x-coordinate	4th x-coordinate	5th x-coordinate

STEP 3: The five key points on the graph of $y = 2\cos(4x + 3\pi)$ are

$$\left(-\frac{3\pi}{4}, 2\right) \quad \left(-\frac{5\pi}{8}, 0\right) \quad \left(-\frac{\pi}{2}, -2\right) \quad \left(-\frac{3\pi}{8}, 0\right) \quad \left(-\frac{\pi}{4}, 2\right)$$

STEP 4: We plot these five points and fill in the graph of the cosine function as shown in Figure 81(a). Extending the graph in each direction, we obtain Figure 81(b), the graph of $y = 2\cos(4x + 3\pi)$.

STEP 5: A vertical shift up 1 unit gives the final graph. See Figure 81(c).

Figure 81

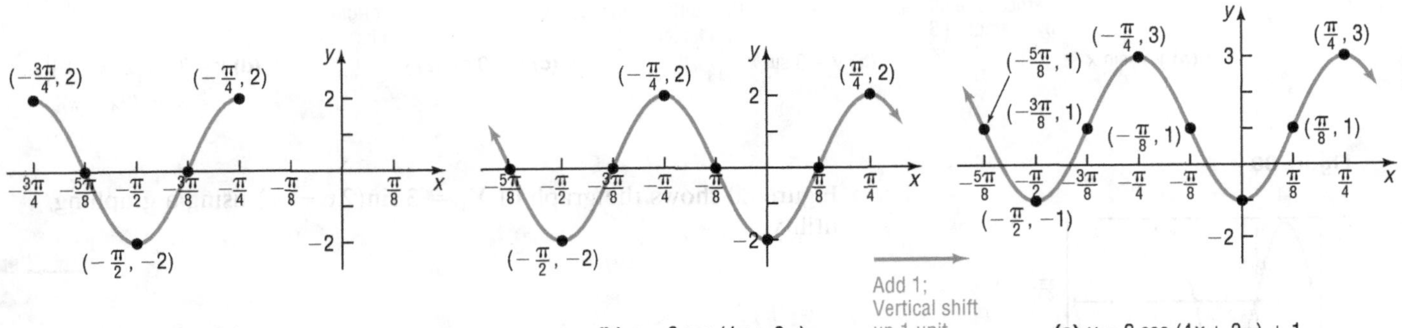

(a) (b) $y = 2\cos(4x + 3\pi)$ (c) $y = 2\cos(4x + 3\pi) + 1$

The graph of $y = 2\cos(4x + 3\pi) + 1 = 2\cos\left[4\left(x + \frac{3\pi}{4}\right)\right] + 1$ may also be obtained using transformations. See Figure 82.

Figure 82

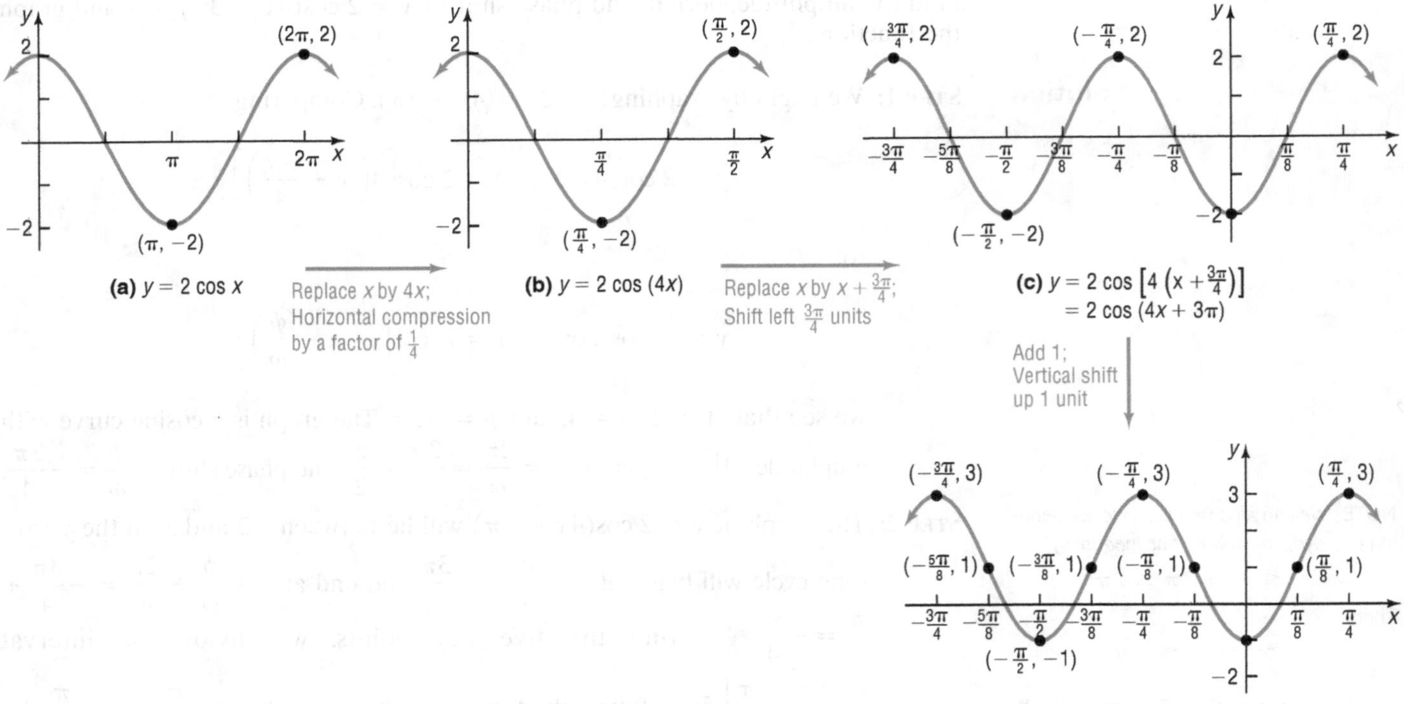

(a) $y = 2\cos x$ (b) $y = 2\cos(4x)$ (c) $y = 2\cos\left[4\left(x + \frac{3\pi}{4}\right)\right] = 2\cos(4x + 3\pi)$ (d) $y = 2\cos(4x + 3\pi) + 1$

Check: Graph $Y_1 = 2\cos(4x + 3\pi) + 1$ to verify the graph in Figure 81(c) or Figure 82(d).

Now Work PROBLEM 3

SUMMARY **Steps for Graphing Sinusoidal Functions $y = A\sin(\omega x - \phi) + B$ or $y = A\cos(\omega x - \phi) + B$**

STEP 1: Determine the amplitude $|A|$ and period $T = \dfrac{2\pi}{\omega}$.

STEP 2: Determine the starting point of one cycle of the graph, $\dfrac{\phi}{\omega}$. Determine the ending point of one cycle of the graph, $\dfrac{\phi}{\omega} + \dfrac{2\pi}{\omega}$. Divide the interval $\left[\dfrac{\phi}{\omega}, \dfrac{\phi}{\omega} + \dfrac{2\pi}{\omega}\right]$ into four subintervals, each of length $\dfrac{2\pi}{\omega} \div 4$.

STEP 3: Use the endpoints of the subintervals to find the five key points on the graph.

STEP 4: Plot the five key points with a sinusoidal graph to obtain one cycle of the graph. Extend the graph in each direction to make it complete.

STEP 5: If $B \neq 0$, apply a vertical shift.

2 Build Sinusoidal Models from Data

Scatter diagrams of data sometimes take the form of a sinusoidal function. Let's look at an example.

The data given in Table 11 represent the average monthly temperatures in Denver, Colorado. Since the data represent *average* monthly temperatures collected over many years, the data will not vary much from year to year and so will essentially repeat each year. In other words, the data are periodic. Figure 83 shows the scatter diagram of these data repeated over 2 years, where $x = 1$ represents January, $x = 2$ represents February, and so on.

Table 11

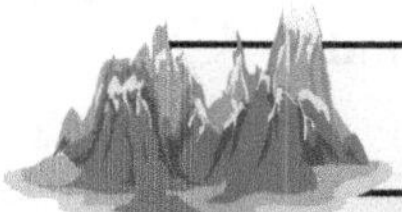

Month, x	Average Monthly Temperature, °F
January, 1	29.7
February, 2	33.4
March, 3	39.0
April, 4	48.2
May, 5	57.2
June, 6	66.9
July, 7	73.5
August, 8	71.4
September, 9	62.3
October, 10	51.4
November, 11	39.0
December, 12	31.0

Source: U.S. National Oceanic and Atmospheric Administration

Figure 83

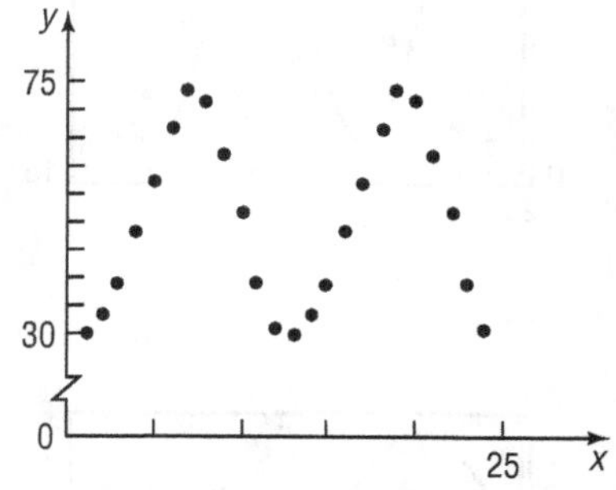

Notice that the scatter diagram looks like the graph of a sinusoidal function. We choose to fit the data to a sine function of the form

$$y = A\sin(\omega x - \phi) + B$$

where A, B, ω, and ϕ are constants.

EXAMPLE 3 Finding a Sinusoidal Function from Temperature Data

Find a sine function that models the data in Table 11.

Solution We begin with a scatter diagram of the data for 1 year. See Figure 84. The data will be fitted to a sine function of the form

$$y = A\sin(\omega x - \phi) + B$$

Figure 84

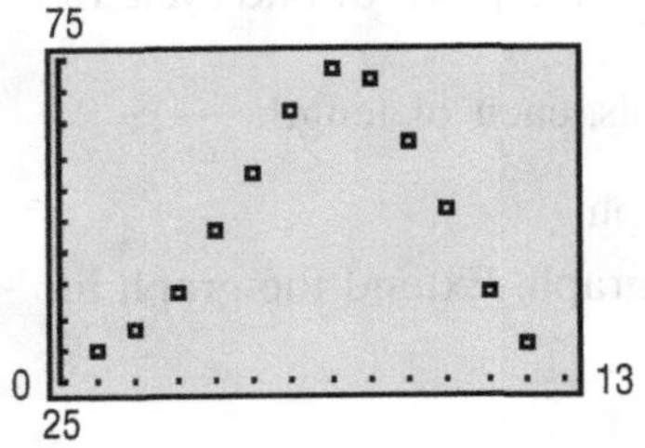

STEP 1: To find the amplitude A, we compute

$$\text{Amplitude} = \frac{\text{largest data value} - \text{smallest data value}}{2}$$

$$= \frac{73.5 - 29.7}{2} = 21.9$$

To see the remaining steps in this process, we superimpose the graph of the function $y = 21.9\sin x$, where x represents months, on the scatter diagram.

Figure 85 shows the two graphs. To fit the data, the graph needs to be shifted vertically, shifted horizontally, and stretched horizontally.

Figure 85

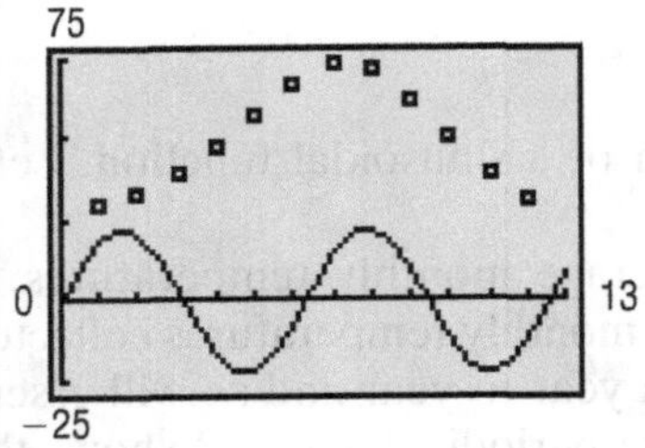

STEP 2: We determine the vertical shift by finding the average of the highest and lowest data values.

$$\text{Vertical shift} = \frac{73.5 + 29.7}{2} = 51.6$$

Now we superimpose the graph of $y = 21.9\sin x + 51.6$ on the scatter diagram. See Figure 86.

We see that the graph needs to be shifted horizontally and stretched horizontally.

Figure 86

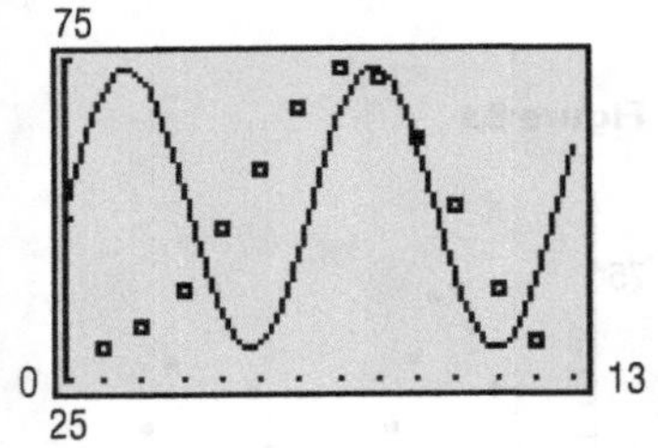

STEP 3: It is easier to find the horizontal stretch factor first. Since the temperatures repeat every 12 months, the period of the function is $T = 12$. Since $T = \frac{2\pi}{\omega} = 12$, we find

$$\omega = \frac{2\pi}{12} = \frac{\pi}{6}$$

Now we superimpose the graph of $y = 21.9\sin\left(\frac{\pi}{6}x\right) + 51.6$ on the scatter diagram. See Figure 87. We see that the graph still needs to be shifted horizontally.

Figure 87

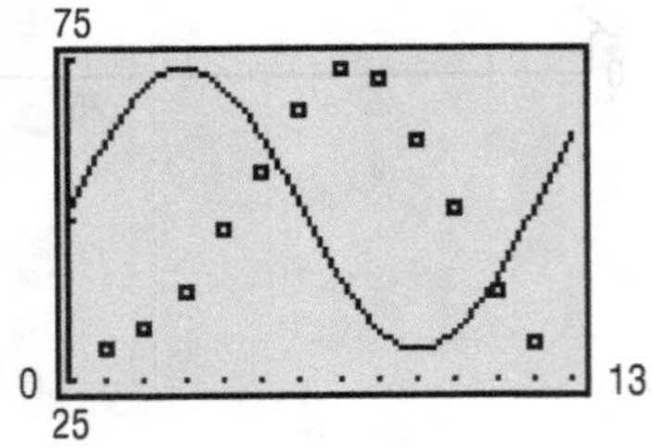

STEP 4: To determine the horizontal shift, we use the period $T = 12$ and divide the interval $[0, 12]$ into four subintervals of length $12 \div 4 = 3$:

$$[0, 3] \quad [3, 6] \quad [6, 9] \quad [9, 12]$$

The sine curve is increasing on the interval $(0, 3)$ and is decreasing on the interval $(3, 9)$, so a local maximum occurs at $x = 3$. The data indicate that a maximum occurs at $x = 7$ (corresponding to July's temperature), so we must shift the graph of the function 4 units to the right by replacing x by $x - 4$. Doing this, we obtain

$$y = 21.9\sin\left(\frac{\pi}{6}(x - 4)\right) + 51.6$$

Multiplying out, we find that a sine function of the form $y = A\sin(\omega x - \phi) + B$ that fits the data is

$$y = 21.9\sin\left(\frac{\pi}{6}x - \frac{2\pi}{3}\right) + 51.6$$

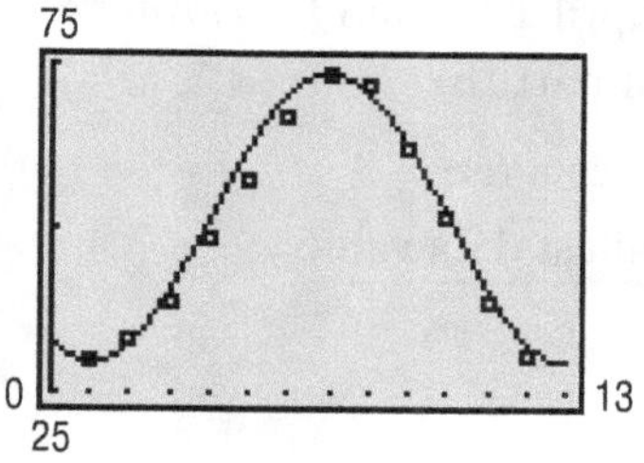

Figure 88

The graph of $y = 21.9 \sin\left(\frac{\pi}{6}x - \frac{2\pi}{3}\right) + 51.6$ and the scatter diagram of the data are shown in Figure 88.

The steps to fit a sine function

$$y = A \sin(\omega x - \phi) + B$$

to sinusoidal data follow:

Steps for Fitting a Sine Function $y = A \sin(\omega x - \phi) + B$ to Data

STEP 1: Determine A, the amplitude of the function.

$$\text{Amplitude} = \frac{\text{largest data value} - \text{smallest data value}}{2}$$

STEP 2: Determine B, the vertical shift of the function.

$$\text{Vertical shift} = \frac{\text{largest data value} + \text{smallest data value}}{2}$$

STEP 3: Determine ω. Since the period T, the time it takes for the data to repeat, is $T = \frac{2\pi}{\omega}$, we have

$$\omega = \frac{2\pi}{T}$$

STEP 4: Determine the horizontal shift of the function by using the period of the data. Divide the period into four subintervals of equal length. Determine the x-coordinate for the maximum of the sine function and the x-coordinate for the maximum value of the data. Use this information to determine the value of the phase shift, $\frac{\phi}{\omega}$.

Now Work PROBLEM 29(a)–(c)

Let's look at another example. Since the number of hours of sunlight in a day cycles annually, the number of hours of sunlight in a day for a given location can be modeled by a sinusoidal function.

The longest day of the year (in terms of hours of sunlight) occurs on the day of the summer solstice. For locations in the northern hemisphere, the summer solstice is the time when the sun is farthest north. In 2007, the summer solstice occurred on June 21 (the 172nd day of the year) at 2:06 PM EDT. The shortest day of the year occurs on the day of the winter solstice. The winter solstice is the time when the Sun is farthest south (again, for locations in the northern hemisphere). In 2007, the winter solstice occurred on December 22 (the 356th day of the year) at 1:08 AM (EST).

EXAMPLE 4 **Finding a Sinusoidal Function for Hours of Daylight**

According to the *Old Farmer's Almanac*, the number of hours of sunlight in Boston on the summer solstice is 15.30 and the number of hours of sunlight on the winter solstice is 9.08.

(a) Find a sinusoidal function of the form $y = A \sin(\omega x - \phi) + B$ that models the data.

(b) Use the function found in part (a) to predict the number of hours of sunlight on April 1, the 91st day of the year.

(c) Draw a graph of the function found in part (a).
(d) Look up the number of hours of sunlight for April 1 in the *Old Farmer's Almanac* and compare it to the results found in part (b).

Source: The *Old Farmer's Almanac,* www.almanac.com/rise

Solution (a) **STEP 1:** Amplitude $= \dfrac{\text{largest data value} - \text{smallest data value}}{2}$

$$= \frac{15.30 - 9.08}{2} = 3.11$$

STEP 2: Vertical shift $= \dfrac{\text{largest data value} + \text{smallest data value}}{2}$

$$= \frac{15.30 + 9.08}{2} = 12.19$$

STEP 3: The data repeat every 365 days. Since $T = \dfrac{2\pi}{\omega} = 365$, we find

$$\omega = \frac{2\pi}{365}$$

So far we have $y = 3.11 \sin\left(\dfrac{2\pi}{365}x - \phi\right) + 12.19$.

STEP 4: To determine the horizontal shift, we use the period $T = 365$ and divide the interval $[0, 365]$ into four subintervals of length $365 \div 4 = 91.25$:

$$[0, 91.25] \quad [91.25, 182.5] \quad [182.5, 273.75] \quad [273.75, 365]$$

The sine curve is increasing on the interval $(0, 91.25)$ and is decreasing on the interval $(91.25, 273.75)$, so a local maximum occurs at $x = 91.25$. Since the maximum occurs on the summer solstice at $x = 172$, we must shift the graph of the function $172 - 91.25 = 80.75$ units to the right by replacing x by $x - 80.75$. Doing this, we obtain

$$y = 3.11 \sin\left(\frac{2\pi}{365}(x - 80.75)\right) + 12.19$$

Multiplying out, we find that a sine function of the form $y = A \sin(\omega x - \phi) + B$ that models the data is

$$y = 3.11 \sin\left(\frac{2\pi}{365}x - \frac{323\pi}{730}\right) + 12.19$$

(b) To predict the number of hours of daylight on April 1, we let $x = 91$ in the function found in part (a) and obtain

$$y = 3.11 \sin\left(\frac{2\pi}{365} \cdot 91 - \frac{323}{730}\pi\right) + 12.19$$
$$\approx 12.74$$

So we predict that there will be about 12.74 hours = 12 hours, 44 minutes of sunlight on April 1 in Boston.

(c) The graph of the function found in part (a) is given in Figure 89.

Figure 89

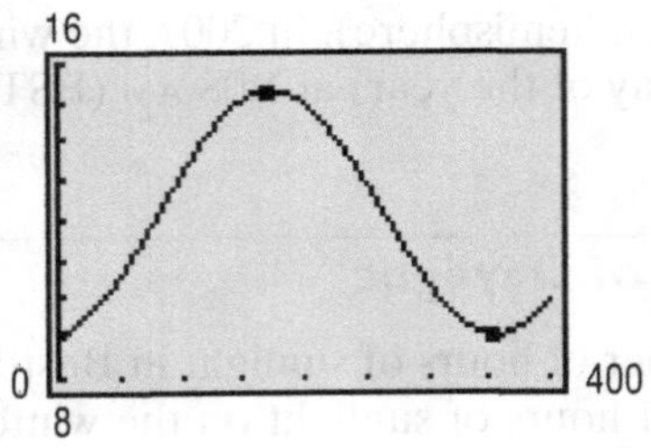

(d) According to the *Old Farmer's Almanac,* there will be 12 hours 43 minutes of sunlight on April 1 in Boston.

Now Work PROBLEM 35

Certain graphing utilities (such as a TI-83, TI-84 Plus, and TI-86) have the capability of finding the sine function of best fit for sinusoidal data. At least four data points are required for this process.

EXAMPLE 5 Finding the Sine Function of Best Fit

Use a graphing utility to find the sine function of best fit that models the data in Table 11. Graph this function with the scatter diagram of the data.

Solution Enter the data from Table 11 and execute the SINe REGression program. The result is shown in Figure 90.

The output that the utility provides shows the equation

$$y = a\sin(bx + c) + d$$

The sinusoidal function of best fit is

$$y = 21.15\sin(0.55x - 2.35) + 51.19$$

where x represents the month and y represents the average temperature.

Figure 91 shows the graph of the sinusoidal function of best fit on the scatter diagram.

Figure 90

Figure 91

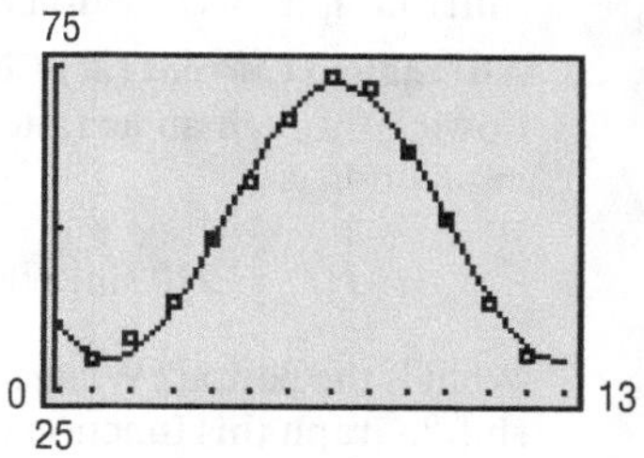

Now Work PROBLEMS 29(d) AND (e)

6.6 Assess Your Understanding

Concepts and Vocabulary

1. For the graph of $y = A\sin(\omega x - \phi)$, the number $\frac{\phi}{\omega}$ is called the _____.

2. ***True or False*** Only two data points are required by a graphing utility to find the sine function of best fit.

Skill Building

In Problems 3–14, find the amplitude, period, and phase shift of each function. Graph each function. Be sure to label key points. Show at least two periods. Verify your graph using a graphing utility.

3. $y = 4\sin(2x - \pi)$
4. $y = 3\sin(3x - \pi)$
5. $y = 2\cos\left(3x + \frac{\pi}{2}\right)$
6. $y = 3\cos(2x + \pi)$
7. $y = -3\sin\left(2x + \frac{\pi}{2}\right)$
8. $y = -2\cos\left(2x - \frac{\pi}{2}\right)$
9. $y = 4\sin(\pi x + 2) - 5$
10. $y = 2\cos(2\pi x + 4) + 4$
11. $y = 3\cos(\pi x - 2) + 5$
12. $y = 2\cos(2\pi x - 4) - 1$
13. $y = -3\sin\left(-2x + \frac{\pi}{2}\right)$
14. $y = -3\cos\left(-2x + \frac{\pi}{2}\right)$

In Problems 15–18, write the equation of a sine function that has the given characteristics.

15. Amplitude: 2
Period: π
Phase shift: $\frac{1}{2}$

16. Amplitude: 3
Period: $\frac{\pi}{2}$
Phase shift: 2

17. Amplitude: 3
Period: 3π
Phase shift: $-\frac{1}{3}$

18. Amplitude: 2
Period: π
Phase shift: -2

Mixed Practice

In Problems 19–26, apply the methods of this and the previous section to graph each function. Be sure to label key points and show at least two periods. Verify your graph using a graphing utility.

19. $y = 2\tan(4x - \pi)$

20. $y = \frac{1}{2}\cot(2x - \pi)$

21. $y = 3\csc\left(2x - \frac{\pi}{4}\right)$

22. $y = \frac{1}{2}\sec(3x - \pi)$

23. $y = -\cot\left(2x + \frac{\pi}{2}\right)$

24. $y = -\tan\left(3x + \frac{\pi}{2}\right)$

25. $y = -\sec(2\pi x + \pi)$

26. $y = -\csc\left(-\frac{1}{2}\pi x + \frac{\pi}{4}\right)$

Applications and Extensions

27. Alternating Current (ac) Circuits The current I, in amperes, flowing through an ac (alternating current) circuit at time t, in seconds, is

$$I(t) = 120\sin\left(30\pi t - \frac{\pi}{3}\right) \qquad t \geq 0$$

What is the period? What is the amplitude? What is the phase shift? Graph this function over two periods.

28. Alternating Current (ac) Circuits The current I, in amperes, flowing through an ac (alternating current) circuit at time t, in seconds, is

$$I(t) = 220\sin\left(60\pi t - \frac{\pi}{6}\right) \qquad t \geq 0$$

What is the period? What is the amplitude? What is the phase shift? Graph this function over two periods.

29. Monthly Temperature The following data represent the average monthly temperatures for Juneau, Alaska.

Month, x	Average Monthly Temperature, °F
January, 1	24.2
February, 2	28.4
March, 3	32.7
April, 4	39.7
May, 5	47.0
June, 6	53.0
July, 7	56.0
August, 8	55.0
September, 9	49.4
October, 10	42.2
November, 11	32.0
December, 12	27.1

Source: U.S. National Oceanic and Atmospheric Administration

(a) Draw a scatter diagram of the data for one period.
(b) Find a sinusoidal function of the form $y = A\sin(\omega x - \phi) + B$ that models the data.
(c) Draw the sinusoidal function found in part (b) on the scatter diagram.
(d) Use a graphing utility to find the sinusoidal function of best fit.
(e) Draw the sinusoidal function of best fit on a scatter diagram of the data.

30. Monthly Temperature The following data represent the average monthly temperatures for Washington, D.C.
(a) Draw a scatter diagram of the data for one period.
(b) Find a sinusoidal function of the form $y = A\sin(\omega x - \phi) + B$ that models the data.
(c) Draw the sinusoidal function found in part (b) on the scatter diagram.
(d) Use a graphing utility to find the sinusoidal function of best fit.
(e) Graph the sinusoidal function of best fit on a scatter diagram of the data.

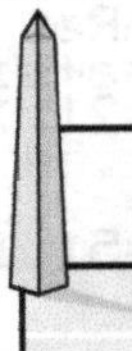

Month, x	Average Monthly Temperature, °F
January, 1	34.6
February, 2	37.5
March, 3	47.2
April, 4	56.5
May, 5	66.4
June, 6	75.6
July, 7	80.0
August, 8	78.5
September, 9	71.3
October, 10	59.7
November, 11	49.8
December, 12	39.4

Source: U.S. National Oceanic and Atmospheric Administration

31. Monthly Temperature The following data represent the average monthly temperatures for Indianapolis, Indiana.

Month, x	Average Monthly Temperature, °F
January, 1	25.5
February, 2	29.6
March, 3	41.4
April, 4	52.4
May, 5	62.8
June, 6	71.9
July, 7	75.4
August, 8	73.2
September, 9	66.6
October, 10	54.7
November, 11	43.0
December, 12	30.9

Source: U.S. National Oceanic and Atmospheric Administration

(a) Draw a scatter diagram of the data for one period.
(b) Find a sinusoidal function of the form $y = A\sin(\omega x - \phi) + B$ that models the data.
(c) Draw the sinusoidal function found in part (b) on the scatter diagram.
(d) Use a graphing utility to find the sinusoidal function of best fit.
(e) Graph the sinusoidal function of best fit on a scatter diagram of the data.

32. Monthly Temperature The following data represent the average monthly temperatures for Baltimore, Maryland.
(a) Draw a scatter diagram of the data for one period.
(b) Find a sinusoidal function of the form $y = A\sin(\omega x - \phi) + B$ that models the data.
(c) Draw the sinusoidal function found in part (b) on the scatter diagram.
(d) Use a graphing utility to find the sinusoidal function of best fit.
(e) Graph the sinusoidal function of best fit on a scatter diagram of the data.

Month, x	Average Monthly Temperature, °F
January, 1	31.8
February, 2	34.8
March, 3	44.1
April, 4	53.4
May, 5	63.4
June, 6	72.5
July, 7	77.0
August, 8	75.6
September, 9	68.5
October, 10	56.6
November, 11	46.8
December, 12	36.7

Source: U.S. National Oceanic and Atmospheric Administration

33. Tides Suppose that the length of time between consecutive high tides is approximately 12.5 hours. According to the National Oceanic and Atmospheric Administration, on Saturday, August 7, 2007, in Savannah, Georgia, high tide occurred at 3:38 AM (3.6333 hours) and low tide occurred at 10:08 AM (10.1333 hours). Water heights are measured as the amounts above or below the mean lower low water. The height of the water at high tide was 8.2 feet, and the height of the water at low tide was −0.6 foot.
(a) Approximately when will the next high tide occur?
(b) Find a sinusoidal function of the form $y = A\sin(\omega x - \phi) + B$ that models the data.
(c) Draw a graph of the function found in part (b).
(d) Use the function found in part (b) to predict the height of the water at the next high tide.

34. Tides Suppose that the length of time between consecutive high tides is approximately 12.5 hours. According to the National Oceanic and Atmospheric Administration, on Saturday, August 7, 2007, in Juneau, Alaska, high tide occurred at 8:11 AM (8.1833 hours) and low tide occurred at 2:14 PM (14.2333 hours). Water heights are measured as the amounts above or below the mean lower low water. The height of the water at high tide was 13.2 feet, and the height of the water at low tide was 2.2 feet.
(a) Approximately when will the next high tide occur?
(b) Find a sinusoidal function of the form $y = A\sin(\omega x - \phi) + B$ that models the data.
(c) Draw a graph of the function found in part (b).
(d) Use the function found in part (b) to predict the height of the water at the next high tide.

35. Hours of Daylight According to the *Old Farmer's Almanac*, in Miami, Florida, the number of hours of sunlight on the summer solstice of 2007 was 13.75, and the number of hours of sunlight on the winter solstice was 10.55.
(a) Find a sinusoidal function of the form $y = A\sin(\omega x - \phi) + B$ that models the data.
(b) Use the function found in part (a) to predict the number of hours of sunlight on April 1, the 91st day of the year.
(c) Draw a graph of the function found in part (a).
(d) Look up the number of hours of sunlight for April 1 in the *Old Farmer's Almanac*, and compare the actual hours of daylight to the results found in part (c).

36. Hours of Daylight According to the *Old Farmer's Almanac*, in Detroit, Michigan, the number of hours of sunlight on the summer solstice of 2007 was 15.30, and the number of hours of sunlight on the winter solstice was 9.10.
(a) Find a sinusoidal function of the form $y = A\sin(\omega x - \phi) + B$ that models the data.
(b) Use the function found in part (a) to predict the number of hours of sunlight on April 1, the 91st day of the year.
(c) Draw a graph of the function found in part (a).
(d) Look up the number of hours of sunlight for April 1 in the *Old Farmer's Almanac*, and compare the actual hours of daylight to the results found in part (c).

37. Hours of Daylight According to the *Old Farmer's Almanac*, in Anchorage, Alaska, the number of hours of sunlight on the summer solstice of 2007 was 19.42 and the number of hours of sunlight on the winter solstice was 5.48.
(a) Find a sinusoidal function of the form $y = A\sin(\omega x - \phi) + B$ that models the data.
(b) Use the function found in part (a) to predict the number of hours of sunlight on April 1, the 91st day of the year.
(c) Draw a graph of the function found in part (a).
(d) Look up the number of hours of sunlight for April 1 in the *Old Farmer's Almanac*, and compare the actual hours of daylight to the results found in part (c).

38. Hours of Daylight According to the *Old Farmer's Almanac*, in Honolulu, Hawaii, the number of hours of sunlight on the summer solstice of 2007 was 13.43 and the number of hours of sunlight on the winter solstice was 10.85.
(a) Find a sinusoidal function of the form $y = A\sin(\omega x - \phi) + B$ that models the data.
(b) Use the function found in part (a) to predict the number of hours of sunlight on April 1, the 91st day of the year.
(c) Draw a graph of the function found in part (a).
(d) Look up the number of hours of sunlight for April 1 in the *Old Farmer's Almanac*, and compare the actual hours of daylight to the results found in part (c).

Discussion and Writing

39. Explain how the amplitude and period of a sinusoidal graph are used to establish the scale on each coordinate axis.

40. Find an application in your major field that leads to a sinusoidal graph. Write a paper about your findings.

CHAPTER REVIEW

Things to Know

Definitions

Angle in standard position (p. 352) — Vertex is at the origin; initial side is along the positive x-axis.

1 Degree (1°) (p. 353) — $1° = \frac{1}{360}$ revolution

1 Radian (p. 355) — The measure of a central angle of a circle whose rays subtend an arc whose length is the radius of the circle

Trigonometric functions (pp. 366–368) — $P = (x, y)$ is the point on the unit circle corresponding to $\theta = t$ radians.

$\sin t = \sin\theta = y$ $\quad \cos t = \cos\theta = x$ $\quad \tan t = \tan\theta = \frac{y}{x}\quad x \neq 0$

$\csc t = \csc\theta = \frac{1}{y}\quad y \neq 0$ $\quad \sec t = \sec\theta = \frac{1}{x}\quad x \neq 0$ $\quad \cot t = \cot\theta = \frac{x}{y}\quad y \neq 0$

Trigonometric functions using a circle of radius r (p. 377) — For an angle θ in standard position $P = (x, y)$ is the point on the terminal side of θ that is also on the circle $x^2 + y^2 = r^2$.

$\sin\theta = \frac{y}{r}$ $\quad \cos\theta = \frac{x}{r}$ $\quad \tan\theta = \frac{y}{x}\quad x \neq 0$

$\csc\theta = \frac{r}{y}\quad y \neq 0$ $\quad \sec\theta = \frac{r}{x}\quad x \neq 0$ $\quad \cot\theta = \frac{x}{y}\quad y \neq 0$

Periodic function (p. 384) — $f(\theta + p) = f(\theta)$, for all θ, $p > 0$, where the smallest such p is the fundamental period

Formulas

1 revolution = 360° (p. 354) = 2π radians (p. 357) — $1° = \frac{\pi}{180}$ radians (p. 357) $\quad$ 1 radian $= \frac{180}{\pi}$ degrees (p. 357)

$s = r\,\theta$ (p. 356) — θ is measured in radians; s is the length of arc subtended by the central angle θ of the circle of radius r.

$A = \frac{1}{2}r^2\,\theta$ (p. 359) — A is the area of the sector of a circle of radius r formed by a central angle of θ radians.

$v = r\omega$ (p. 360) — v is the linear speed along the circle of radius r; ω is the angular speed (measured in radians per unit time).

Table of Values (pp. 370 and 373)

θ (Radians)	θ (Degrees)	$\sin\theta$	$\cos\theta$	$\tan\theta$	$\csc\theta$	$\sec\theta$	$\cot\theta$
0	0°	0	1	0	Not defined	1	Not defined
$\frac{\pi}{6}$	30°	$\frac{1}{2}$	$\frac{\sqrt{3}}{2}$	$\frac{\sqrt{3}}{3}$	2	$\frac{2\sqrt{3}}{3}$	$\sqrt{3}$
$\frac{\pi}{4}$	45°	$\frac{\sqrt{2}}{2}$	$\frac{\sqrt{2}}{2}$	1	$\sqrt{2}$	$\sqrt{2}$	1
$\frac{\pi}{3}$	60°	$\frac{\sqrt{3}}{2}$	$\frac{1}{2}$	$\sqrt{3}$	$\frac{2\sqrt{3}}{3}$	2	$\frac{\sqrt{3}}{3}$
$\frac{\pi}{2}$	90°	1	0	Not defined	1	Not defined	0
π	180°	0	−1	0	Not defined	−1	Not defined
$\frac{3\pi}{2}$	270°	−1	0	Not defined	−1	Not defined	0

The Unit Circle (p. 374–375)

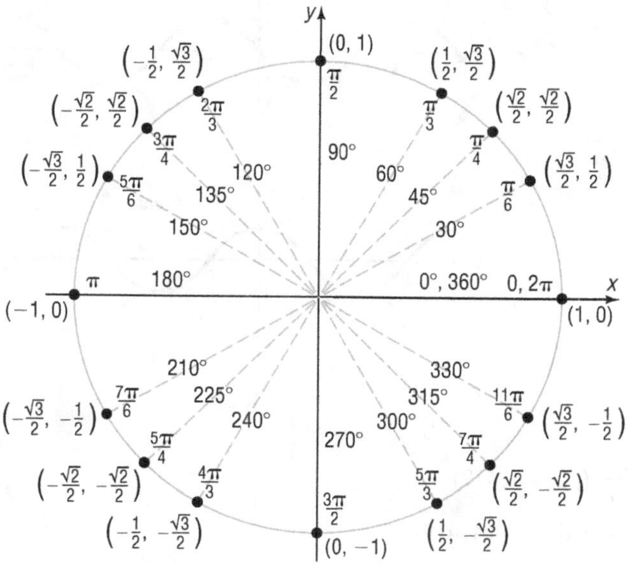

Fundamental identities (p. 388)

$$\tan\theta = \frac{\sin\theta}{\cos\theta} \qquad \cot\theta = \frac{\cos\theta}{\sin\theta}$$

$$\csc\theta = \frac{1}{\sin\theta} \qquad \sec\theta = \frac{1}{\cos\theta} \qquad \cot\theta = \frac{1}{\tan\theta}$$

$$\sin^2\theta + \cos^2\theta = 1 \qquad \tan^2\theta + 1 = \sec^2\theta \qquad \cot^2\theta + 1 = \csc^2\theta$$

Properties of the trigonometric functions

$y = \sin x$ (p. 396)
Domain: $-\infty < x < \infty$
Range: $-1 \leq y \leq 1$
Periodic: period $= 2\pi$ (360°)
Odd function

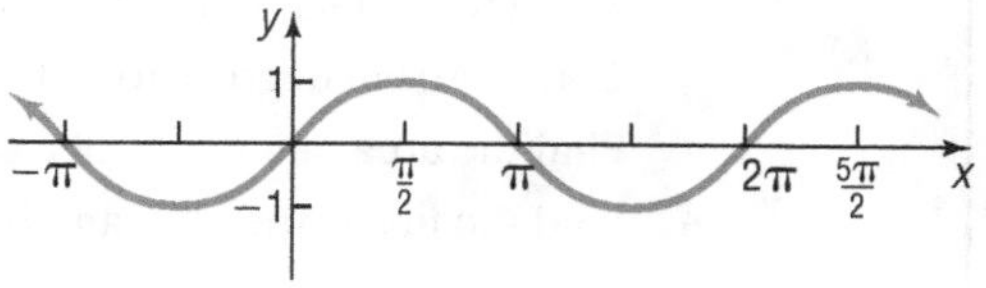

$y = \cos x$ (p. 398)
Domain: $-\infty < x < \infty$
Range: $-1 \leq y \leq 1$
Periodic: period $= 2\pi$ (360°)
Even function

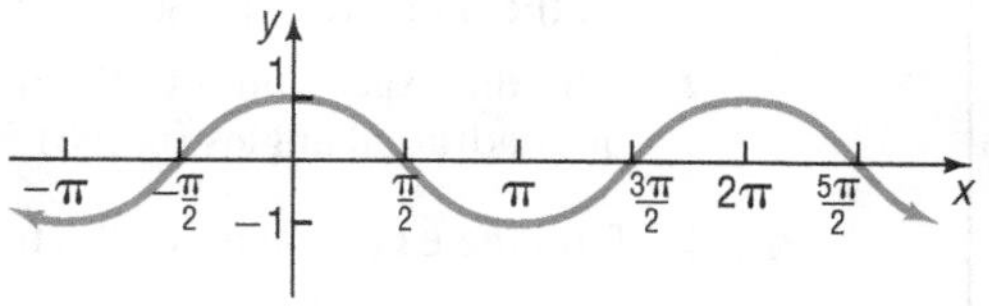

$y = \tan x$ (pp. 412–413)
Domain: $-\infty < x < \infty$, except odd integer multiples of $\frac{\pi}{2}$ (90°)
Range: $-\infty < y < \infty$
Periodic: period $= \pi$ (180°)
Odd function
Vertical asymptotes at odd integer multiples of $\frac{\pi}{2}$

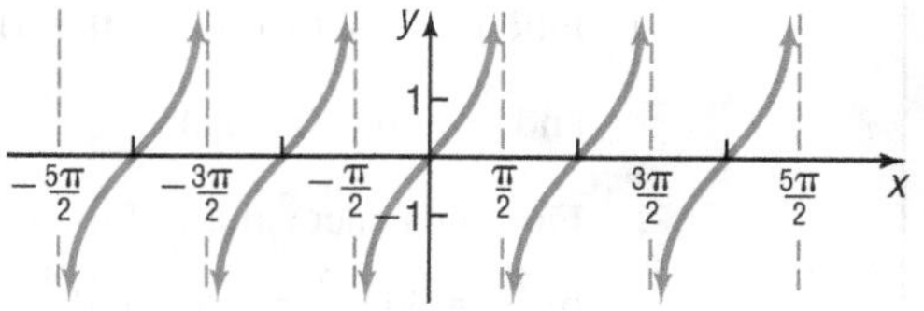

$y = \cot x$ (p. 414)
Domain: $-\infty < x < \infty$, except integer multiples of π (180°)
Range: $-\infty < y < \infty$
Periodic: period $= \pi$ (180°)
Odd function
Vertical asymptotes at integer multiples of π

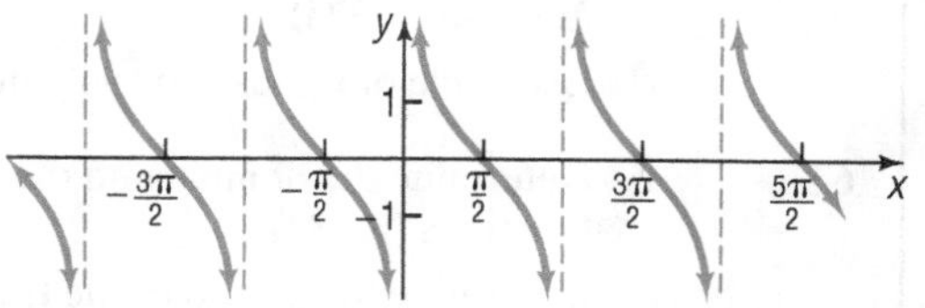

$y = \csc x$ (p. 415)

Domain: $-\infty < x < \infty$, except integer multiples of π (180°)
Range: $|y| \geq 1$
Periodic: period $= 2\pi$ (360°)
Odd function
Vertical asymptotes at integer multiples of π

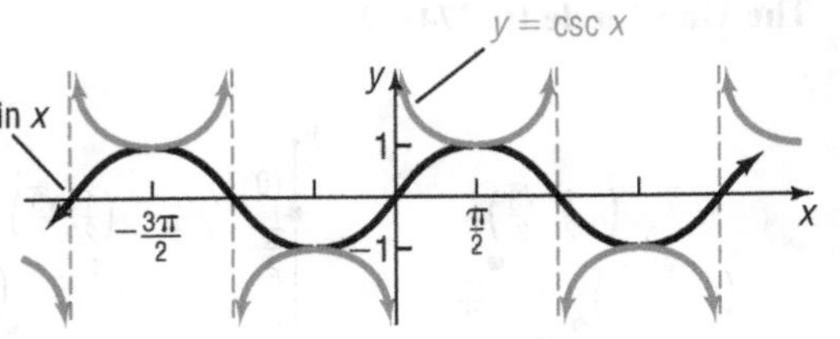

$y = \sec x$ (p. 415)

Domain: $-\infty < x < \infty$, except odd integer multiples of $\frac{\pi}{2}$ (90°)
Range: $|y| \geq 1$
Periodic: period $= 2\pi$ (360°)
Even function
Vertical asymptotes at odd integer multiples of $\frac{\pi}{2}$

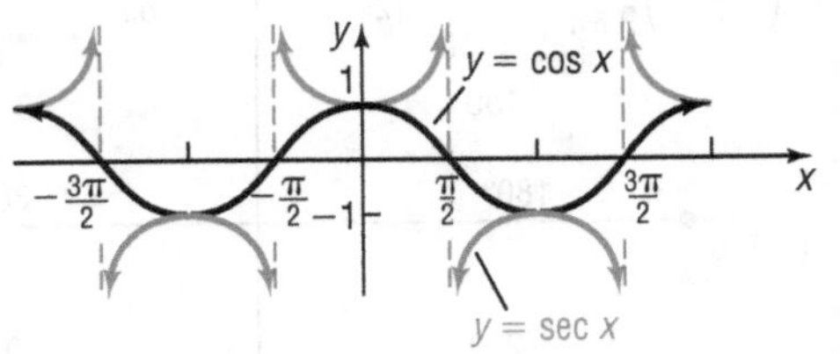

Sinusoidal graphs

$y = A\sin(\omega x) + B, \quad \omega > 0$ Period $= \dfrac{2\pi}{\omega}$ (pp. 401, 419)

$y = A\cos(\omega x) + B, \quad \omega > 0$ Amplitude $= |A|$ (pp. 401, 419)

$y = A\sin(\omega x - \phi) + B = A\sin\left[\omega\left(x - \dfrac{\phi}{\omega}\right)\right] + B$ Phase shift $= \dfrac{\phi}{\omega}$ (p. 419)

$y = A\cos(\omega x - \phi) + B = A\cos\left[\omega\left(x - \dfrac{\phi}{\omega}\right)\right] + B$

Objectives

Section		You should be able to:	Example(s)	Review Exercises
6.1	1	Convert between decimals and degrees, minutes, seconds forms for angles (p. 354)	2	86
	2	Find the arc length of a circle (p. 356)	3	87, 88
	3	Convert from degrees to radians and from radians to degrees (p. 356)	4–6	1–8
	4	Find the area of a sector of a circle (p. 359)	7	87
	5	Find the linear speed of an object traveling in circular motion (p. 360)	8	89–92
6.2	1	Find the exact values of the trigonometric functions using a point on the unit circle (p. 367)	1	83, 97
	2	Find the exact values of the trigonometric functions of quadrantal angles (p. 368)	2, 3	10, 17, 18, 20, 97
	3	Find the exact values of the trigonometric functions of $\frac{\pi}{4} = 45°$ (p. 370)	4, 5	9, 11, 13, 15, 16
	4	Find the exact values of the trigonometric functions of $\frac{\pi}{6} = 30°$ and $\frac{\pi}{3} = 60°$ (p. 371)	6–8	9–15
	5	Find the exact values of the trigonometric functions for integer multiples of $\frac{\pi}{6} = 30°$, $\frac{\pi}{4} = 45°$, and $\frac{\pi}{3} = 60°$ (p. 374)	9, 10	13–16, 19, 97
	6	Use a calculator to approximate the value of a trigonometric function (p. 375)	11	79, 80
	7	Use circle of radius r to evaluate the trigonometric functions (p. 376)	12	84
6.3	1	Determine the domain and the range of the trigonometric functions (p. 382)	pp. 382–384	85
	2	Determine the period of the trigonometric functions (p. 384)	1	85
	3	Determine the signs of the trigonometric functions in a given quadrant (p. 386)	2	81, 82

Section		You should be able to:	Example(s)	Review Exercises
	4	Find the values of the trigonometric functions using fundamental identities (p. 386)	3, 4	21–30
	5	Find the exact values of the trigonometric functions of an angle given one of the functions and the quadrant of the angle (p. 389)	5, 6	31–46
	6	Use even–odd properties to find the exact values of the trigonometric functions (p. 391)	7	27–30
6.4	1	Graph functions of the form $y = A\sin(\omega x)$ using transformations (p. 397)	1, 2	47
	2	Graph functions of the form $y = A\cos(\omega x)$ using transformations (p. 398)	3	48
	3	Determine the amplitude and period of sinusoidal functions (p. 400)	4	63–68
	4	Graph sinusoidal functions using key points (p. 401)	5–7	47, 48, 67, 68, 93
	5	Find an equation for a sinusoidal graph (p. 405)	8, 9	75–78
6.5	1	Graph functions of the form $y = A\tan(\omega x) + B$ and $y = A\cot(\omega x) + B$ (p. 413)	1, 2	53, 54, 56
	2	Graph functions of the form $y = A\csc(\omega x) + B$ and $y = A\sec(\omega x) + B$ (p. 415)	3	57
6.6	1	Graph sinusoidal functions of the form $y = A\sin(\omega x - \phi) + B$ (p. 419)	1, 2	49, 50, 59, 60, 69–74, 94
	2	Build sinusoidal models from data (p. 423)	3	95, 96

Review Exercises

In Problems 1–4, convert each angle in degrees to radians. Express your answer as a multiple of π.

1. $135°$ **2.** $210°$ **3.** $18°$ **4.** $15°$

In Problems 5–8, convert each angle in radians to degrees.

5. $\frac{3\pi}{4}$ **6.** $\frac{2\pi}{3}$ **7.** $-\frac{5\pi}{2}$ **8.** $-\frac{3\pi}{2}$

In Problems 9–30, find the exact value of each expression. Do not use a calculator.

9. $\tan\frac{\pi}{4} - \sin\frac{\pi}{6}$ **10.** $\cos\frac{\pi}{3} + \sin\frac{\pi}{2}$ **11.** $3\sin 45° - 4\tan\frac{\pi}{6}$

12. $4\cos 60° + 3\tan\frac{\pi}{3}$ **13.** $6\cos\frac{3\pi}{4} + 2\tan\left(-\frac{\pi}{3}\right)$ **14.** $3\sin\frac{2\pi}{3} - 4\cos\frac{5\pi}{2}$

15. $\sec\left(-\frac{\pi}{3}\right) - \cot\left(-\frac{5\pi}{4}\right)$ **16.** $4\csc\frac{3\pi}{4} - \cot\left(-\frac{\pi}{4}\right)$ **17.** $\tan\pi + \sin\pi$

18. $\cos\frac{\pi}{2} - \csc\left(-\frac{\pi}{2}\right)$ **19.** $\cos 540° - \tan(-405°)$ **20.** $\sin 270° + \cos(-180°)$

21. $\sin^2 20° + \frac{1}{\sec^2 20°}$ **22.** $\frac{1}{\cos^2 40°} - \frac{1}{\cot^2 40°}$ **23.** $\sec 50° \cos 50°$

24. $\tan 10° \cot 10°$ **25.** $\frac{\sin 50°}{\cos 40°}$ **26.** $\frac{\tan 20°}{\cot 70°}$

27. $\frac{\sin(-40°)}{\cos 50°}$ **28.** $\tan(-20°)\cot 20°$ **29.** $\sin 400° \sec(-50°)$ **30.** $\cot 200° \cot(-70°)$

In Problems 31–46, find the exact value of each of the remaining trigonometric functions.

31. $\sin\theta = \frac{4}{5}$, θ is acute **32.** $\tan\theta = \frac{1}{4}$, θ is acute **33.** $\tan\theta = \frac{12}{5}$, $\sin\theta < 0$

34. $\cot\theta = \frac{12}{5}$, $\cos\theta < 0$ **35.** $\sec\theta = -\frac{5}{4}$, $\tan\theta < 0$ **36.** $\csc\theta = -\frac{5}{3}$, $\cot\theta < 0$

37. $\sin\theta = \frac{12}{13}$, θ in quadrant II
38. $\cos\theta = -\frac{3}{5}$, θ in quadrant III
39. $\sin\theta = -\frac{5}{13}$, $\frac{3\pi}{2} < \theta < 2\pi$
40. $\cos\theta = \frac{12}{13}$, $\frac{3\pi}{2} < \theta < 2\pi$
41. $\tan\theta = \frac{1}{3}$, $180° < \theta < 270°$
42. $\tan\theta = -\frac{2}{3}$, $90° < \theta < 180°$
43. $\sec\theta = 3$, $\frac{3\pi}{2} < \theta < 2\pi$
44. $\csc\theta = -4$, $\pi < \theta < \frac{3\pi}{2}$
45. $\cot\theta = -2$, $\frac{\pi}{2} < \theta < \pi$
46. $\tan\theta = -2$, $\frac{3\pi}{2} < \theta < 2\pi$

In Problems 47–62, graph each function. Each graph should contain at least two periods. Verify the graph using a graphing utility. Use the graph to determine the domain and the range of each function.

47. $y = 2\sin(4x)$
48. $y = -3\cos(2x)$
49. $y = -2\cos\left(x + \frac{\pi}{2}\right)$
50. $y = 3\sin(x - \pi)$
51. $y = \tan(x + \pi)$
52. $y = -\tan\left(x - \frac{\pi}{2}\right)$
53. $y = -2\tan(3x)$
54. $y = 4\tan(2x)$
55. $y = \cot\left(x + \frac{\pi}{4}\right)$
56. $y = -4\cot(2x)$
57. $y = 4\sec(2x)$
58. $y = \csc\left(x + \frac{\pi}{4}\right)$
59. $y = 4\sin(2x + 4) - 2$
60. $y = 3\cos(4x + 2) + 1$
61. $y = 4\tan\left(\frac{x}{2} + \frac{\pi}{4}\right)$
62. $y = 5\cot\left(\frac{x}{3} - \frac{\pi}{4}\right)$

In Problems 63–66, determine the amplitude and period of each function without graphing.

63. $y = 4\cos x$
64. $y = \sin(2x)$
65. $y = -8\sin\left(\frac{\pi}{2}x\right)$
66. $y = -2\cos(3\pi x)$

In Problems 67–74, find the amplitude, period, and phase shift of each function. Graph each function. Show at least two periods. Verify the graph using a graphing utility.

67. $y = 4\sin(3x)$
68. $y = 2\cos\left(\frac{1}{3}x\right)$
69. $y = 2\sin(2x - \pi)$
70. $y = -\cos\left(\frac{1}{2}x + \frac{\pi}{2}\right)$
71. $y = \frac{1}{2}\sin\left(\frac{3}{2}x - \pi\right)$
72. $y = \frac{3}{2}\cos(6x + 3\pi)$
73. $y = -\frac{2}{3}\cos(\pi x - 6)$
74. $y = -7\sin\left(\frac{\pi}{3}x - \frac{4}{3}\right)$

In Problems 75–78, find a function whose graph is given.

75.

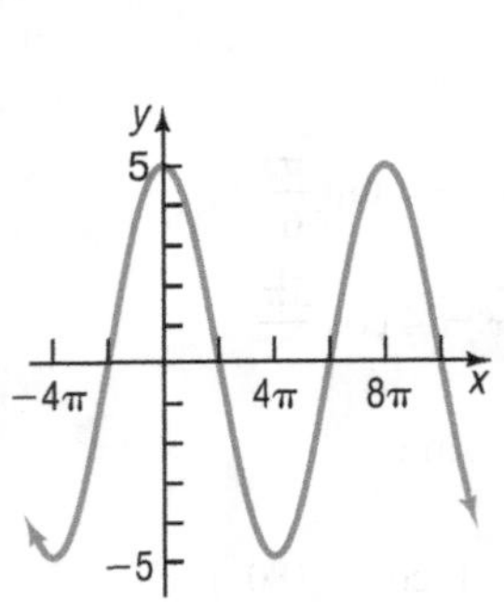

76.

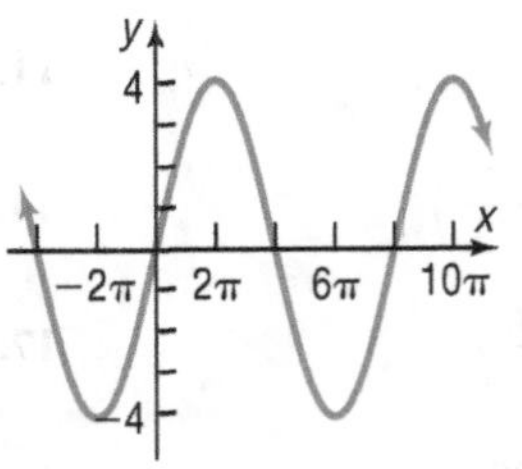

77.

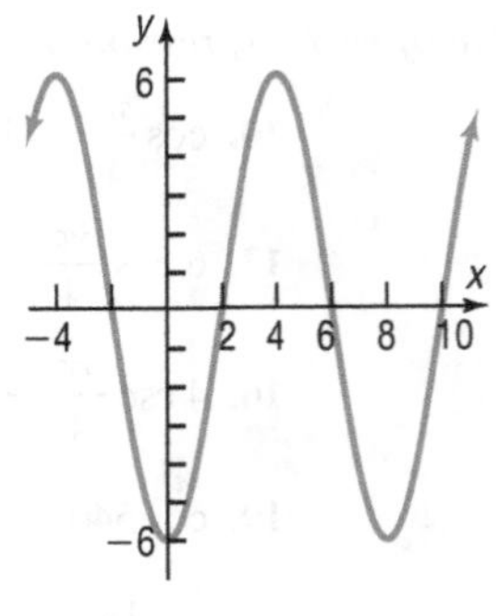

78.

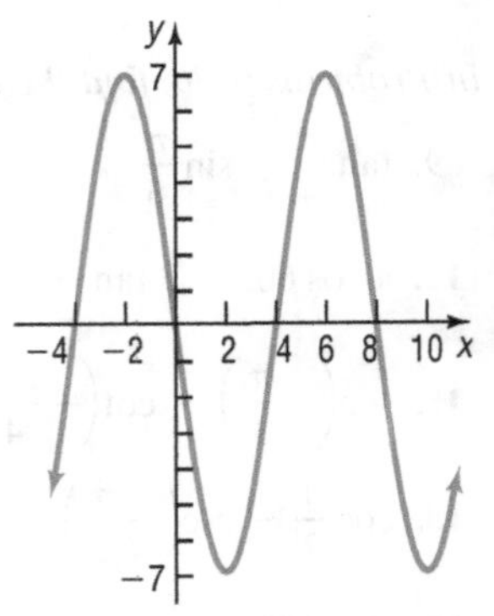

79. Use a calculator to approximate $\sin\frac{\pi}{8}$. Round the answer to two decimal places.

80. Use a calculator to approximate sec 10°. Round the answer to two decimal places.

81. Determine the signs of the six trigonometric functions of an angle θ whose terminal side is in quadrant III.

82. Name the quadrant θ lies in if $\cos\theta > 0$ and $\tan\theta < 0$.

83. Find the exact values of the six trigonometric functions of t if $P = \left(-\frac{1}{3}, \frac{2\sqrt{2}}{3}\right)$ is the point on the unit circle that corresponds to t.

84. Find the exact value of $\sin t$, $\cos t$, and $\tan t$ if $P = (-2, 5)$ is the point on the circle that corresponds to t.

85. What is the domain and the range of the secant function? What is the period?

86. (a) Convert the angle 32°20′35″ to a decimal in degrees. Round the answer to two decimal places.
(b) Convert the angle 63.18° to D°M′S″ form. Express the answer to the nearest second.

87. Find the length of the arc subtended by a central angle of 30° on a circle of radius 2 feet. What is the area of the sector?

88. The minute hand of a clock is 8 inches long. How far does the tip of the minute hand move in 30 minutes? How far does it move in 20 minutes?

89. Angular Speed of a Race Car A race car is driven around a circular track at a constant speed of 180 miles per hour. If the diameter of the track is $\frac{1}{2}$ mile, what is the angular speed of the car? Express your answer in revolutions per hour (which is equivalent to laps per hour).

90. Merry-Go-Rounds A neighborhood carnival has a merry-go-round whose radius is 25 feet. If the time for one revolution is 30 seconds, how fast is the merry-go-round going?

91. Lighthouse Beacons The Montauk Point Lighthouse on Long Island has dual beams (two light sources opposite each other). Ships at sea observe a blinking light every 5 seconds. What rotation speed is required to do this?

92. Spin Balancing Tires The radius of each wheel of a car is 16 inches. At how many revolutions per minute should a spin balancer be set to balance the tires at a speed of 90 miles per hour? Is the setting different for a wheel of radius 14 inches? If so, what is this setting?

93. Alternating Voltage The electromotive force E, in volts, in a certain ac (alternating circuit) circuit obeys the function

$$E(t) = 120\sin(120\pi t), \qquad t \ge 0$$

where t is measured in seconds.

(a) What is the maximum value of E?
(b) What is the period?
(c) Graph this function over two periods.

94. Alternating Current The current I, in amperes, flowing through an ac (alternating current) circuit at time t is

$$I(t) = 220\sin\left(30\pi t + \frac{\pi}{6}\right), \qquad t \ge 0$$

(a) What is the period?
(b) What is the amplitude?
(c) What is the phase shift?
(d) Graph this function over two periods.

95. Monthly Temperature The following data represent the average monthly temperatures for Phoenix, Arizona.

Month, m	Average Monthly Temperature, T
January, 1	51
February, 2	55
March, 3	63
April, 4	67
May, 5	77
June, 6	86
July, 7	90
August, 8	90
September, 9	84
October, 10	71
November, 11	59
December, 12	52

SOURCE: U.S. National Oceanic and Atmospheric Administration

(a) Draw a scatter diagram of the data for one period.
(b) Find a sinusoidal function of the form $y = A\sin(\omega x - \phi) + B$ that fits the data.
(c) Draw the sinusoidal function found in part (b) on the scatter diagram.
(d) Use a graphing utility to find the sinusoidal function of best fit.
(e) Graph the sinusoidal function of best fit on the scatter diagram.

96. Hours of Daylight According to the *Old Farmer's Almanac,* in Las Vegas, Nevada, the number of hours of sunlight on the summer solstice is 14.63 and the number of hours of sunlight on the winter solstice is 9.72.

(a) Find a sinusoidal function of the form $y = A\sin(\omega x - \phi) + B$ that fits the data.
(b) Use the function found in part (a) to predict the number of hours of sunlight on April 1, the 91st day of the year.
(c) Draw a graph of the function found in part (a).
(d) Look up the number of hours of sunlight for April 1 in the *Old Farmer's Almanac* and compare the actual hours of daylight to the results found in part (c).

97. Unit Circle On the unit circle below, fill in the missing angles (in radians) and the corresponding terminal points P of each angle.

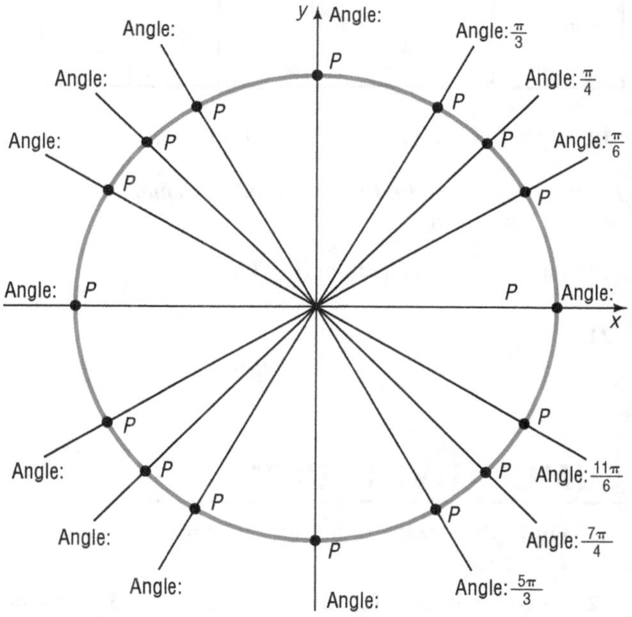

CHAPTER TEST

In Problems 1–3, convert each angle in degrees to radians. Express your answer as a multiple of π.

1. $260°$ **2.** $-400°$ **3.** $13°$

In Problems 4–6 convert each angle in radians to degrees.

4. $-\frac{\pi}{8}$ **5.** $\frac{9\pi}{2}$ **6.** $\frac{3\pi}{4}$

In Problems 7–12, find the exact value of each expression.

7. $\sin\frac{\pi}{6}$ **8.** $\cos\left(-\frac{5\pi}{4}\right) - \cos\frac{3\pi}{4}$

9. $\cos(-120°)$ **10.** $\tan 330°$

11. $\sin\frac{\pi}{2} - \tan\frac{19\pi}{4}$ **12.** $2\sin^2 60° - 3\cos 45°$

In Problems 13–16, use a calculator to evaluate each expression. Round your answer to three decimal places.

13. $\sin 17°$ **14.** $\cos\frac{2\pi}{5}$ **15.** $\sec 229°$ **16.** $\cot\frac{28\pi}{9}$

17. Fill in each table entry with the sign of each function.

	$\sin\theta$	$\cos\theta$	$\tan\theta$	$\sec\theta$	$\csc\theta$	$\cot\theta$
θ in QI						
θ in QII						
θ in QIII						
θ in QIV						

18. If $f(x) = \sin x$ and $f(a) = \frac{3}{5}$, find $f(-a)$.

In Problems 19–21 find the value of the remaining five trigonometric functions of θ.

19. $\sin\theta = \frac{5}{7}$, θ in quadrant II **20.** $\cos\theta = \frac{2}{3}$, $\frac{3\pi}{2} < \theta < 2\pi$

21. $\tan\theta = -\frac{12}{5}$, $\frac{\pi}{2} < \theta < \pi$

In Problems 22–24, the point (x, y) is on the terminal side of angle θ in standard position. Find the exact value of the given trigonometric function.

22. $(2, 7)$, $\sin\theta$ **23.** $(-5, 11)$, $\cos\theta$

24. $(6, -3)$, $\tan\theta$

In Problems 25 and 26, graph the function.

25. $y = 2\sin\left(\frac{x}{3} - \frac{\pi}{6}\right)$ **26.** $y = \tan\left(-x + \frac{\pi}{4}\right) + 2$

27. Write an equation for a sinusoidal graph with the following properties:

$$A = -3 \quad \text{period} = \frac{2\pi}{3} \quad \text{phase shift} = -\frac{\pi}{4}$$

28. Logan has a garden in the shape of a sector of a circle; the outer rim of the garden is 25 feet long and the central angle of the sector is 50°. She wants to add a 3-foot wide walk to the outer rim; how many square feet of paving blocks will she need to build the walk?

29. Hungarian Adrian Annus won the gold medal for the hammer throw at the 2004 Olympics in Athens with a winning distance of 83.19 meters.* The event consists of swinging a 16-pound weight attached to a wire 190 centimeters long—in a circle and then releasing it. Assuming his release is at a 45° angle to the ground, the hammer will travel a distance of $\frac{v_0^2}{g}$ meters, where $g = 9.8$ meters/second^2 and v_0 is the linear speed of the hammer when released. At what rate (rpm) was he swinging the hammer upon release?

* Annus was stripped of his medal after refusing to cooperate with postmedal drug testing.

CUMULATIVE REVIEW

1. Find the real solutions, if any, of the equation $2x^2 + x - 1 = 0$.

2. Find an equation for the line with slope -3 containing the point $(-2, 5)$.

3. Find an equation for a circle of radius 4 and center at the point $(0, -2)$.

4. Discuss the equation $2x - 3y = 12$. Graph it.

5. Discuss the equation $x^2 + y^2 - 2x + 4y - 4 = 0$. Graph it.

6. Use transformations to graph the function $y = (x - 3)^2 + 2$.

7. Sketch a graph of each of the following functions. Label at least three points on each graph.

(a) $y = x^2$ (b) $y = x^3$ (c) $y = e^x$

(d) $y = \ln x$ (e) $y = \sin x$ (f) $y = \tan x$

8. Find the inverse function of $f(x) = 3x - 2$.

9. Find the exact value of $(\sin 14°)^2 + (\cos 14°)^2 - 3$.

10. Graph $y = 3\sin(2x)$.

11. Find the exact value of $\tan\frac{\pi}{4} - 3\cos\frac{\pi}{6} + \csc\frac{\pi}{6}$.

12. Find an exponential function for the following graph. Express your answer in the form $y = Ab^x$.

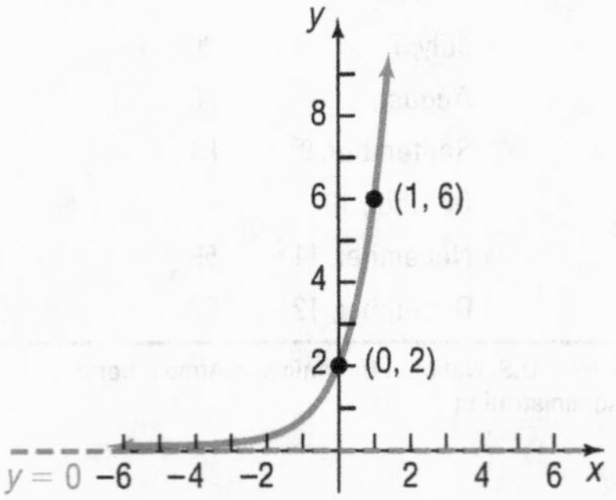

13. Find a sinusoidal function for the following graph.

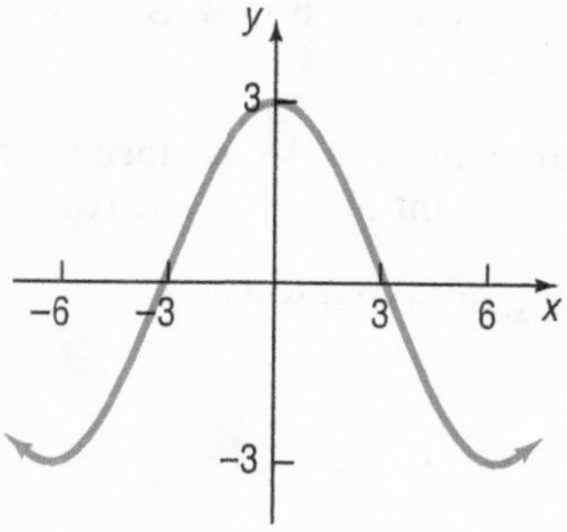

14. (a) Find a linear function that contains the points $(-2, 3)$ and $(1, -6)$. What is the slope? What are the intercepts of the function? Graph the function. Be sure to label the intercepts.

(b) Find a quadratic function that contains the point $(-2, 3)$ with vertex $(1, -6)$. What are the intercepts of the function? Graph the function.

(c) Show that there is no exponential function of the form $f(x) = ae^x$ that contains the points $(-2, 3)$ and $(1, -6)$.

15. (a) Find a polynomial function of degree 3 whose y-intercept is 5 and whose x-intercepts are -2, 3, and 5. Graph the function.

(b) Find a rational function whose y-intercept is 5 and whose x-intercepts are $-2, 3$, and 5 that has the line $x = 2$ as a vertical asymptote. Graph the function.

CHAPTER PROJECTS

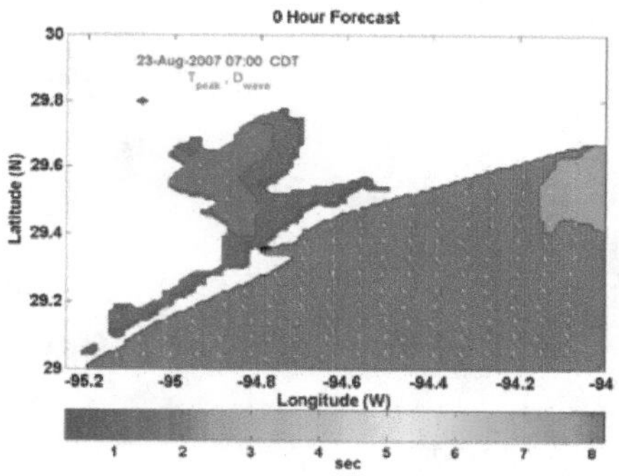

I. Tides The given table is a partial tide table for November 2006 for the Sabine Bank Lighthouse, a shoal located offshore from Texas where the Sabine River empties into the Gulf of Mexico.

1. On November 15, when was the tide high? This is called *high tide*. On November 19, when was the tide low? This is called *low tide*. Most days will have two high tides and two low tides.
2. Why do you think there is a negative height for the low tide on November 20? What is the height measured against?
3. On your graphing utility, draw a scatter diagram for the data in the table. Let t (time, in hours) be the independent variable, with $t = 0$ being 12:00 AM on November 14, $t = 24$ being 12:00 AM on November 15, and so on. Let h be the height in feet. Remember that there are 60 minutes in an hour. Also, make sure your graphing utility is in radian mode.
4. What shape does the data take? What is the period of the data? What is the amplitude? Is the amplitude constant? Explain.
5. Find a sine curve that models the data. Is there a vertical shift? Is there a phase shift?
6. Using your graphing utility, find the sinusoidal function of best fit. How does this model compare to the model from part 5?
7. Using the model found in part (5) and the sinusoidal equation of best fit found in part (6), predict the high tides and the low tides on November 21.
8. Looking at the times of day that the low tides occur, what do you think causes the low tides to vary so much each day? Explain. Does this seem to have the same type of effect on the high tides? Explain.

	Low Tide		Low Tide		High Tide		High Tide		Sun/Moon Phase	
Nov	**Time**	**Ht (ft)**	**Time**	**Ht (ft)**	**Time**	**Ht (ft)**	**Time**	**Ht (ft)**	**Sunrise/set**	**Moonrise/set**
14	6:26a	2.0	4:38p	1.4	9:29a	2.2	11:14p	2.8	6:40a/5:20p	1:05a/2:02p
15	6:22a	1.6	5:34p	1.8	11:18a	2.4	11:15p	2.6	6:41a/5:20p	1:58a/2:27p
16	6:28a	1.2	6:25p	2.0	12:37p	2.6	11:16p	2.6	6:41a/5:19p	2:50a/2:52p
17	6:40a	0.8	7:12p	2.4	1:38p	2.8	11:16p	2.6	6:42a/5:19p	3:43a/3:19p
18	6:56a	0.4	7:57p	2.6	2:27p	3.0	11:14p	2.8	6:43a/5:19p	4:38a/3:47p
19	7:17a	0.0	8:38p	2.6	3:10p	3.2	11:05p	2.8	6:44a/5:18p	5:35a/4:20p
20	7:43a	−0.2			3:52p	3.4			6:45a/5:18p	6:34a/4:57p

[**Note:** a, AM; p, PM.]

Sources: *National Oceanic and Atmospheric Administration (http://tidesandcurrents.noaa.gov)* and *U.S. Naval Observatory (http://aa.usno.navy.mil)*

The following projects are available on the Instructor's Resource Center (IRC):

II. Project at Motorola *Digital Transmission over the Air* Learn how Motorola Corporation transmits digital sequences by modulating the phase of the carrier waves.

III. Identifying Mountain Peaks in Hawaii The visibility of a mountain is affected by its altitude, distance from the viewer, and the curvature of Earth's surface. Trigonometry can be used to determine whether a distant object can be seen.

IV. CBL Experiment Technology is used to model and study the effects of damping on sound waves.

Analytic Trigonometry

7

In an Instant, the Land Merged with the Sea

John Lancaster and Peter S. Goodman—Washington Post Foreign Service—Sunday, January 2, 2005—Although the tsunami would have been barely perceptible to passengers on a ship at sea, it rolled outward from the fault zone at about 420 miles per hour, roughly the speed of a commercial jetliner. Even at that speed, however, the surge took about two hours to travel to the Indian mainland.

The tsunami hit coastal areas in different ways. In some places, the first event was the recession of water; in others, it was a flood. The difference was determined at the origin of the tsunami: Along the fault line, the sea floor rose in some places and fell in others. Some coastal areas felt the effect of the sinking first and saw the water recede before it returned, often with a vengeance; elsewhere, the opposite happened. Places farther from the origin of the tsunami, such as Sri Lanka, experienced more waves than did closer areas, such as Sumatra.

As the tsunami approached shallower water near land, its behavior began to change. Its velocity slowed and the distance between its crests, known as wavelength, shortened. The stored energy in the wave was partly transformed into an increase in wave height. What happened next varied widely according to local bottom contours. In some areas, the tsunami broke like a massive beach wave; in others, it caused a sudden, rapid increase in sea level, like water pouring over the edge of a tub.

"The ocean turns into a river," explained Steven N. Ward, a geophysicist and tsunami expert at the University of California at Santa Cruz. "It comes in for about 10 minutes, and it flows back out for 10 minutes. You can't duck under it, you can't stand up in it, and you can't outrun it."

—See Chapter Project I—

A Look Back

In Chapter 5, we defined inverse functions and developed their properties, particularly the relationship between the domain and range of a function and its inverse. We learned that the graphs of a function and its inverse are symmetric with respect to the line $y = x$.

We continued in Chapter 5 by defining the exponential function and the inverse of the exponential function, the logarithmic function. In Chapter 6, we defined the six trigonometric functions and looked at their properties.

A Look Ahead

In the first two sections of this chapter, we define the six inverse trigonometric functions and investigate their properties. In Sections 7.3 through 7.6 of this chapter, we continue the derivation of identities. These identities play an important role in calculus, the physical and life sciences, and economics, where they are used to simplify complicated expressions. The last two sections of this chapter deal with equations that contain trigonometric functions.

Outline

7.1 The Inverse Sine, Cosine, and Tangent Functions

PREPARING FOR THIS SECTION *Before getting started, review the following:*

- Inverse Functions (Section 5.2, pp. 255–265)
- Values of the Trigonometric Functions (Section 6.2, pp. 365–377)
- Properties of the Sine, Cosine, and Tangent Functions (Section 6.3, pp. 382–392)
- Graphs of the Sine, Cosine, and Tangent Functions (Section 6.4, pp. 395–399, and Section 6.5, pp. 411–415)

Now Work the 'Are You Prepared?' problems on page 450.

OBJECTIVES
1. Find the Exact Value of an Inverse Sine, Cosine, or Tangent Function (p. 441)
2. Find an Approximate Value of an Inverse Sine Function (p. 443)
3. Use Properties of Inverse Functions to Find Exact Values of Certain Composite Functions (p. 443)
4. Find the Inverse Function of a Trigonometric Function (p. 449)
5. Solve Equations Involving Inverse Trigonometric Functions (p. 450)

In Section 5.2 we discussed inverse functions, and we noted that if a function is one-to-one it will have an inverse function. We also observed that if a function is not one-to-one it may be possible to restrict its domain in some suitable manner so that the restricted function is one-to-one. For example, the function $y = x^2$ is not one-to-one; however, if we restrict the domain to $x \geq 0$, the function is one-to-one.

Other properties of a one-to-one function f and its inverse function f^{-1} that we discussed in Section 5.2 are summarized next.

1. $f^{-1}(f(x)) = x$ for every x in the domain of f and $f(f^{-1}(x)) = x$ for every x in the domain of f^{-1}.
2. Domain of f = range of f^{-1} and range of f = domain of f^{-1}.
3. The graph of f and the graph of f^{-1} are symmetric with respect to the line $y = x$.
4. If a function $y = f(x)$ has an inverse function, the implicit equation of the inverse function is $x = f(y)$. If we solve this equation for y, we obtain the explicit equation $y = f^{-1}(x)$.

The Inverse Sine Function

In Figure 1, we show the graph of $y = \sin x$. Because every horizontal line $y = b$, where b is between -1 and 1, intersects the graph of $y = \sin x$ infinitely many times, it follows from the horizontal-line test that the function $y = \sin x$ is not one-to-one.

Figure 1
$y = \sin x, -\infty < x < \infty, -1 \leq y \leq 1$

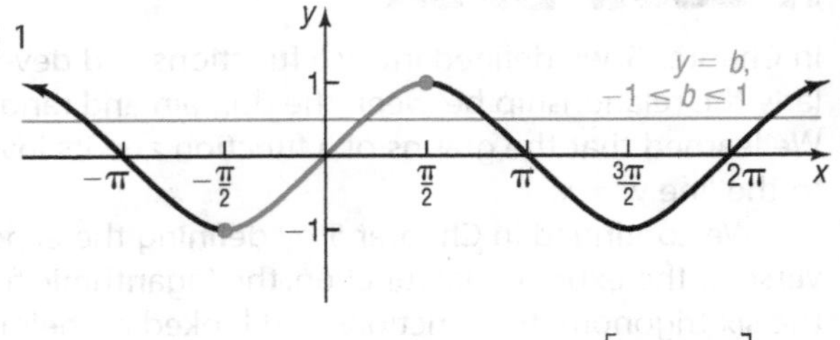

However, if we restrict the domain of $y = \sin x$ to the interval $\left[-\frac{\pi}{2}, \frac{\pi}{2}\right]$, the restricted function

$$y = \sin x \qquad -\frac{\pi}{2} \leq x \leq \frac{\pi}{2}$$

is one-to-one and so will have an inverse function.* See Figure 2.

Figure 2
$y = \sin x, -\frac{\pi}{2} \leq x \leq \frac{\pi}{2}, -1 \leq y \leq 1$

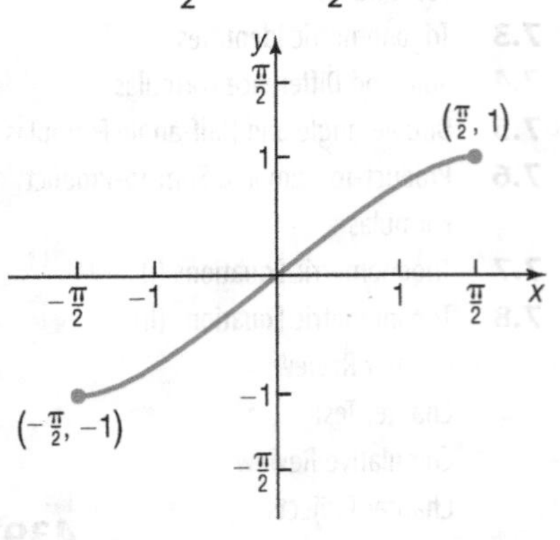

*Although there are many other ways to restrict the domain and obtain a one-to-one function, mathematicians have agreed to use the interval $\left[-\frac{\pi}{2}, \frac{\pi}{2}\right]$ to define the inverse of $y = \sin x$.

An equation for the inverse of $y = f(x) = \sin x$ is obtained by interchanging x and y. The implicit form of the inverse function is $x = \sin y, -\frac{\pi}{2} \leq y \leq \frac{\pi}{2}$. The explicit form is called the **inverse sine** of x and is symbolized by $y = f^{-1}(x) = \sin^{-1} x$.

DEFINITION

$$y = \sin^{-1} x \quad \text{means} \quad x = \sin y$$
$$\text{where} \quad -1 \leq x \leq 1 \quad \text{and} \quad -\frac{\pi}{2} \leq y \leq \frac{\pi}{2} \qquad \textbf{(1)}$$

NOTE Remember, the domain of a function f equals the range of its inverse, f^{-1}, and the range of a function f equals the domain of its inverse, f^{-1}. Because the restricted domain of the sine function is $\left[-\frac{\pi}{2}, \frac{\pi}{2}\right]$, the range of the inverse sine function is $\left[-\frac{\pi}{2}, \frac{\pi}{2}\right]$; because the range of the sine function is $[-1, 1]$, the domain of the inverse sine function is $[-1, 1]$. ■

Because $y = \sin^{-1} x$ means $x = \sin y$, we read $y = \sin^{-1} x$ as "y is the angle or real number whose sine equals x." Alternatively, we can say that "y is the inverse sine of x." Be careful about the notation used. The superscript -1 that appears in $y = \sin^{-1} x$ is not an exponent, but is reminiscent of the symbolism f^{-1} used to denote the inverse function of f. (To avoid this notation, some books use the notation $y = \text{Arcsin } x$ instead of $y = \sin^{-1} x$.)

The inverse of a function f receives as input an element from the range of f and returns as output an element in the domain of f. The restricted sine function, $y = f(x) = \sin x$, receives as input an angle or real number x in the interval $\left[-\frac{\pi}{2}, \frac{\pi}{2}\right]$ and outputs a real number in the interval $[-1, 1]$. Therefore, the inverse sine function $y = \sin^{-1} x$ receives as input a real number in the interval $[-1, 1]$ or $-1 \leq x \leq 1$, its domain, and outputs an angle or real number in the interval $\left[-\frac{\pi}{2}, \frac{\pi}{2}\right]$ or $-\frac{\pi}{2} \leq y \leq \frac{\pi}{2}$, its range.

The graph of the inverse sine function can be obtained by reflecting the restricted portion of the graph of $y = f(x) = \sin x$ about the line $y = x$, as shown in Figure 3(a). Figure 3(b) shows the graph using a graphing utility.

Figure 3
$y = \sin^{-1} x, -1 \leq x \leq 1, -\frac{\pi}{2} \leq y \leq \frac{\pi}{2}$

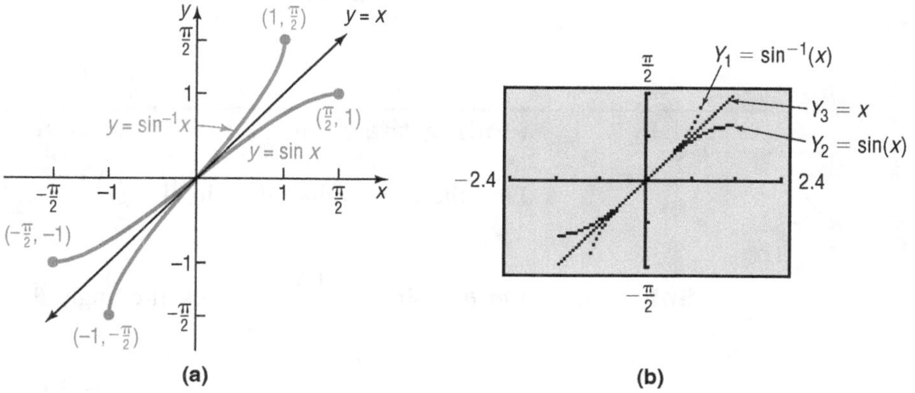

1 Find the Exact Value of an Inverse Sine Function

For some numbers x, it is possible to find the exact value of $y = \sin^{-1} x$.

EXAMPLE 1 **Finding the Exact Value of an Inverse Sine Function**

Find the exact value of: $\sin^{-1} 1$

Solution Let $\theta = \sin^{-1} 1$. We seek the angle $\theta, -\frac{\pi}{2} \leq \theta \leq \frac{\pi}{2}$, whose sine equals 1.

$$\theta = \sin^{-1} 1 \qquad -\frac{\pi}{2} \leq \theta \leq \frac{\pi}{2}$$
$$\sin \theta = 1 \qquad -\frac{\pi}{2} \leq \theta \leq \frac{\pi}{2} \qquad \text{By definition of } y = \sin^{-1} x$$

Now look at Table 1 and Figure 4.

Table 1

θ	$-\frac{\pi}{2}$	$-\frac{\pi}{3}$	$-\frac{\pi}{4}$	$-\frac{\pi}{6}$	0	$\frac{\pi}{6}$	$\frac{\pi}{4}$	$\frac{\pi}{3}$	$\frac{\pi}{2}$
$\sin\theta$	-1	$-\frac{\sqrt{3}}{2}$	$-\frac{\sqrt{2}}{2}$	$-\frac{1}{2}$	0	$\frac{1}{2}$	$\frac{\sqrt{2}}{2}$	$\frac{\sqrt{3}}{2}$	1

Figure 4

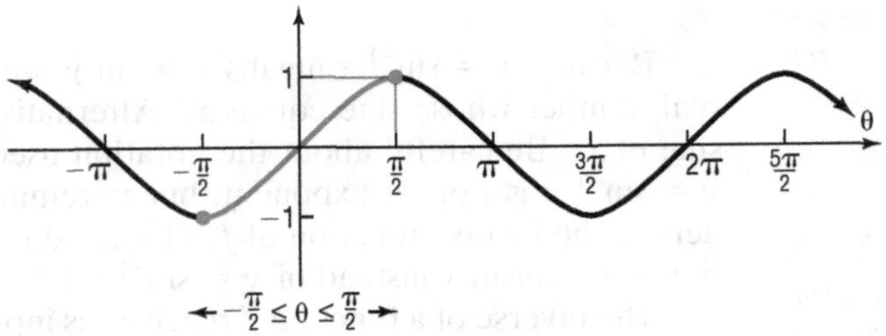

We see that the only angle θ within the interval $\left[-\frac{\pi}{2}, \frac{\pi}{2}\right]$ whose sine is 1 is $\frac{\pi}{2}$. (Note that $\sin\frac{5\pi}{2}$ also equals 1, but $\frac{5\pi}{2}$ lies outside the interval $\left[-\frac{\pi}{2}, \frac{\pi}{2}\right]$ and hence is not admissible.) So, since $\sin\frac{\pi}{2} = 1$ and $\frac{\pi}{2}$ is in $\left[-\frac{\pi}{2}, \frac{\pi}{2}\right]$, we conclude that

$$\sin^{-1} 1 = \frac{\pi}{2}$$

Now Work PROBLEM 13

EXAMPLE 2 Finding the Exact Value of an Inverse Sine Function

Find the exact value of: $\sin^{-1}\left(-\frac{1}{2}\right)$

Solution Let $\theta = \sin^{-1}\left(-\frac{1}{2}\right)$. We seek the angle θ, $-\frac{\pi}{2} \le \theta \le \frac{\pi}{2}$, whose sine equals $-\frac{1}{2}$.

$$\theta = \sin^{-1}\left(-\frac{1}{2}\right) \qquad -\frac{\pi}{2} \le \theta \le \frac{\pi}{2}$$

$$\sin\theta = -\frac{1}{2} \qquad -\frac{\pi}{2} \le \theta \le \frac{\pi}{2}$$

(Refer to Table 1 and Figure 4, if necessary.) The only angle within the interval $\left[-\frac{\pi}{2}, \frac{\pi}{2}\right]$ whose sine is $-\frac{1}{2}$ is $-\frac{\pi}{6}$. So, since $\sin\left(-\frac{\pi}{6}\right) = -\frac{1}{2}$ and $-\frac{\pi}{6}$ is in the interval $\left[-\frac{\pi}{2}, \frac{\pi}{2}\right]$, we conclude that

$$\sin^{-1}\left(-\frac{1}{2}\right) = -\frac{\pi}{6}$$

Now Work PROBLEM 19

2 Find an Approximate Value of an Inverse Sine Function

For most numbers x, the value $y = \sin^{-1} x$ must be approximated.

EXAMPLE 3 **Finding an Approximate Value of an Inverse Sine Function**

Find an approximate value of:

(a) $\sin^{-1}\dfrac{1}{3}$ (b) $\sin^{-1}\left(-\dfrac{1}{4}\right)$

Express the answer in radians rounded to two decimal places.

Solution Because we want the angle measured in radians, we first set the mode to radians.

(a) Figure 5(a) shows the solution using a TI-84 Plus graphing calculator.

Figure 5a

We have $\sin^{-1}\dfrac{1}{3} = 0.34$, rounded to two decimal places.

(b) Figure 5(b) shows the solution using a TI-84 Plus graphing calculator.

Figure 5b

We have $\sin^{-1}\left(-\dfrac{1}{4}\right) = -0.25$, rounded to two decimal places.

Now Work PROBLEM 25

3 Use Properties of Inverse Functions to Find Exact Values of Certain Composite Functions

When we discussed functions and their inverses in Section 5.2, we found that $f^{-1}(f(x)) = x$ for all x in the domain of f and $f(f^{-1}(x)) = x$ for all x in the domain of f^{-1}. In terms of the sine function and its inverse, these properties are of the form

$$f^{-1}(f(x)) = \sin^{-1}(\sin x) = x \quad \text{where } -\frac{\pi}{2} \le x \le \frac{\pi}{2} \quad \textbf{(2a)}$$

$$f(f^{-1}(x)) = \sin(\sin^{-1} x) = x \quad \text{where } -1 \le x \le 1 \quad \textbf{(2b)}$$

EXAMPLE 4 **Finding the Exact Value of Certain Composite Functions**

Find the exact value of each of the following composite functions:

(a) $\sin^{-1}\left(\sin\dfrac{\pi}{8}\right)$ (b) $\sin^{-1}\left(\sin\dfrac{5\pi}{8}\right)$

Solution (a) The composite function $\sin^{-1}\left(\sin\dfrac{\pi}{8}\right)$ follows the form of equation (2a).

Because $\dfrac{\pi}{8}$ is in the interval $\left[-\dfrac{\pi}{2}, \dfrac{\pi}{2}\right]$, we can use (2a). Then

$$\sin^{-1}\left(\sin\frac{\pi}{8}\right) = \frac{\pi}{8}$$

Figure 6 shows the calculation using a graphing calculator.

Figure 6

(b) The composite function $\sin^{-1}\left(\sin \frac{5\pi}{8}\right)$ follows the form of equation (2a), but $\frac{5\pi}{8}$ is not in the interval $\left[-\frac{\pi}{2}, \frac{\pi}{2}\right]$. To use (2a) we need to find an angle θ in the interval $\left[-\frac{\pi}{2}, \frac{\pi}{2}\right]$ for which $\sin \theta = \sin \frac{5\pi}{8}$. Then, using (2a), $\sin^{-1}\left(\sin \frac{5\pi}{8}\right) = \sin^{-1}(\sin \theta) = \theta$, and we are finished.

Look at Figure 7. We see that $\sin\frac{5\pi}{8} = y = \sin\frac{3\pi}{8}$. Since $\frac{3\pi}{8}$ is in the interval $\left[-\frac{\pi}{2}, \frac{\pi}{2}\right]$, we have

$$\sin^{-1}\left(\sin \frac{5\pi}{8}\right) = \sin^{-1}\left(\sin \frac{3\pi}{8}\right) = \frac{3\pi}{8}$$

↑ Apply (2a).

Figure 7

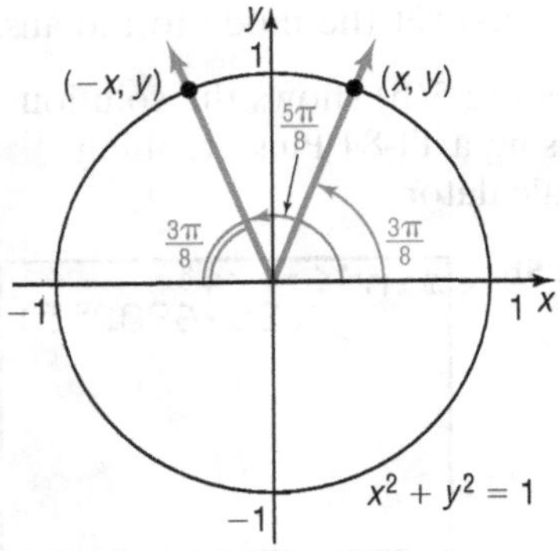

We can verify the results using a graphing calculator. Figure 8(a) shows that $\sin^{-1}\left(\sin \frac{5\pi}{8}\right) \neq \frac{5\pi}{8}$. In Figure 8(b), we see that

$$\sin^{-1}\left(\sin \frac{5\pi}{8}\right) = \sin^{-1}\left(\sin \frac{3\pi}{8}\right) = \frac{3\pi}{8}$$

Figure 8

(a) (b)

Now Work PROBLEM 41

EXAMPLE 5 **Finding the Exact Value of Certain Composite Functions**

Find the exact value, if any, of each composite function.

(a) $\sin(\sin^{-1} 0.8)$ (b) $\sin(\sin^{-1} 1.8)$

Solution (a) The composite function $\sin(\sin^{-1} 0.8)$ follows the form of equation (2b) and 0.8 is in the interval $[-1, 1]$. So we use (2b):

$$\sin(\sin^{-1} 0.8) = 0.8$$

Figure 9

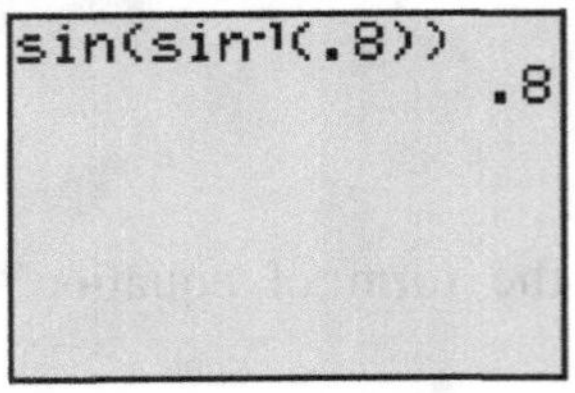

Figure 9 verifies the result.

(b) The composite function $\sin(\sin^{-1} 1.8)$ follows the form of equation (2b), but 1.8 is not in the domain of the inverse sine function. This composite function is not defined. See Figure 10. Can you explain why the error occurs?

Figure 10

Now Work PROBLEM 45

The Inverse Cosine Function

In Figure 11 we show the graph of $y = \cos x$. Because every horizontal line $y = b$, where b is between -1 and 1, intersects the graph of $y = \cos x$ infinitely many times, it follows that the cosine function is not one-to-one.

Figure 11
$y = \cos x, -\infty < x < \infty, -1 \le y \le 1.$

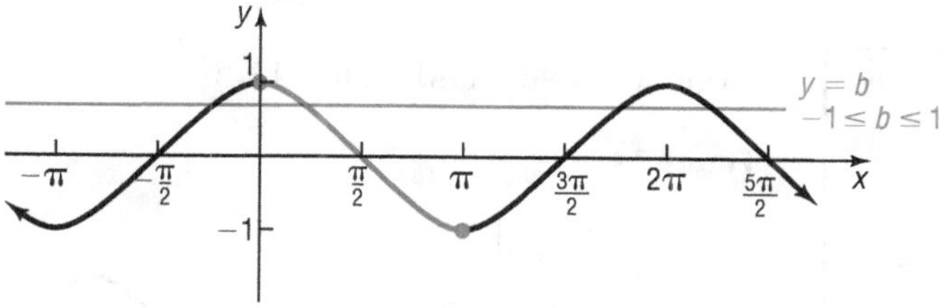

Figure 12
$y = \cos x, 0 \le x \le \pi, -1 \le y \le 1$

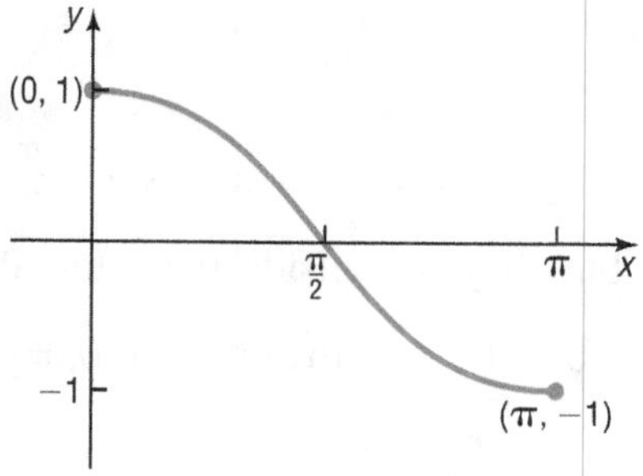

However, if we restrict the domain of $y = \cos x$ to the interval $[0, \pi]$, the restricted function

$$y = \cos x \qquad 0 \le x \le \pi$$

is one-to-one and hence will have an inverse function.* See Figure 12.

An equation for the inverse of $y = f(x) = \cos x$ is obtained by interchanging x and y. The implicit form of the inverse function is $x = \cos y, 0 \le y \le \pi$. The explicit form is called the **inverse cosine** of x and is symbolized by $y = f^{-1}(x) = \cos^{-1} x$ (or by $y = \text{Arccos}\, x$).

DEFINITION

$$y = \cos^{-1} x \quad \text{means} \quad x = \cos y$$
$$\text{where} \quad -1 \le x \le 1 \quad \text{and} \quad 0 \le y \le \pi \qquad \textbf{(3)}$$

Here y is the angle whose cosine is x. Because the range of the cosine function, $y = \cos x$, is $-1 \le y \le 1$, the domain of the inverse function $y = \cos^{-1} x$ is $-1 \le x \le 1$. Because the restricted domain of the cosine function, $y = \cos x$, is $0 \le x \le \pi$, the range of the inverse function $y = \cos^{-1} x$ is $0 \le y \le \pi$.

The graph of $y = \cos^{-1} x$ can be obtained by reflecting the restricted portion of the graph of $y = \cos x$ about the line $y = x$, as shown in Figure 13.

Figure 13
$y = \cos^{-1} x, -1 \le x \le 1, 0 \le y \le \pi$

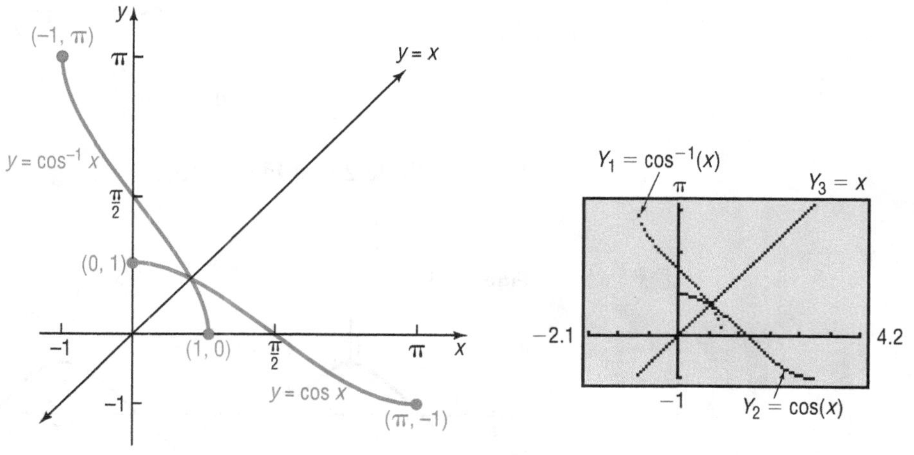

(a) (b)

*This is the generally accepted restriction to define the inverse cosine function.

EXAMPLE 6

Finding the Exact Value of an Inverse Cosine Function

Find the exact value of: $\cos^{-1} 0$

Solution Let $\theta = \cos^{-1} 0$. We seek the angle $\theta, 0 \le \theta \le \pi$, whose cosine equals 0.

$$\theta = \cos^{-1} 0 \qquad 0 \le \theta \le \pi$$
$$\cos\theta = 0 \qquad 0 \le \theta \le \pi$$

Table 2

θ	$\cos\theta$
0	1
$\frac{\pi}{6}$	$\frac{\sqrt{3}}{2}$
$\frac{\pi}{4}$	$\frac{\sqrt{2}}{2}$
$\frac{\pi}{3}$	$\frac{1}{2}$
$\frac{\pi}{2}$	0
$\frac{2\pi}{3}$	$-\frac{1}{2}$
$\frac{3\pi}{4}$	$-\frac{\sqrt{2}}{2}$
$\frac{5\pi}{6}$	$-\frac{\sqrt{3}}{2}$
π	-1

Look at Table 2 and Figure 14.

Figure 14

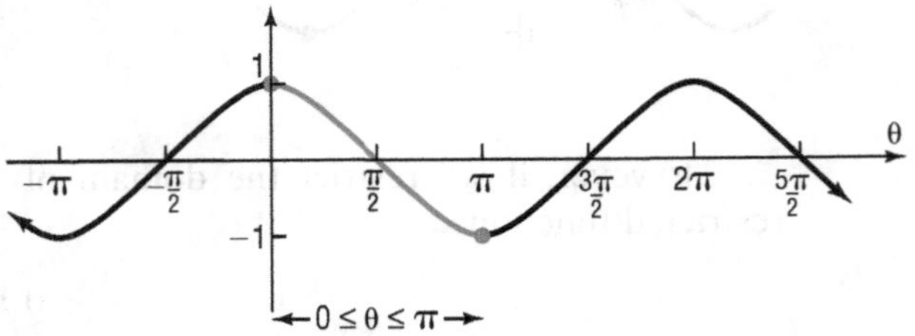

We see that the only angle θ within the interval $[0, \pi]$ whose cosine is 0 is $\frac{\pi}{2}$. [Note that $\cos\frac{3\pi}{2}$ and $\cos\left(-\frac{\pi}{2}\right)$ also equal 0, but they lie outside the interval $[0, \pi]$ and hence are not admissible.] Since $\cos\frac{\pi}{2} = 0$ and $\frac{\pi}{2}$ is in the interval $[0, \pi]$, we conclude that

$$\cos^{-1} 0 = \frac{\pi}{2}$$

EXAMPLE 7

Finding the Exact Value of an Inverse Cosine Function

Find the exact value of: $\cos^{-1}\left(-\frac{\sqrt{2}}{2}\right)$

Solution Let $\theta = \cos^{-1}\left(-\frac{\sqrt{2}}{2}\right)$. We seek the angle θ, $0 \le \theta \le \pi$, whose cosine equals $-\frac{\sqrt{2}}{2}$.

$$\theta = \cos^{-1}\left(-\frac{\sqrt{2}}{2}\right) \qquad 0 \le \theta \le \pi$$
$$\cos\theta = -\frac{\sqrt{2}}{2} \qquad 0 \le \theta \le \pi$$

Look at Table 2 and Figure 15.

Figure 15

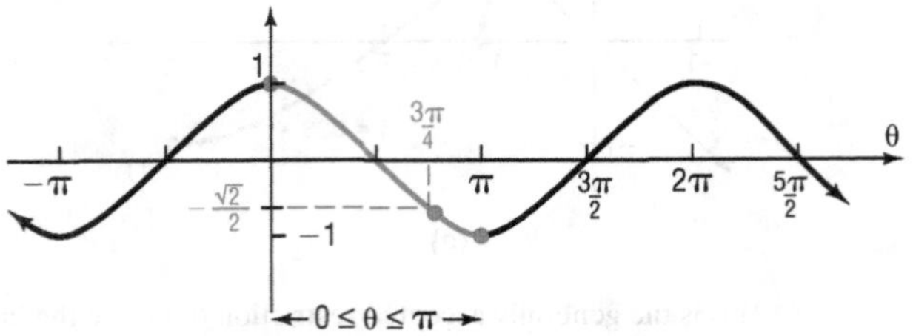

We see that the only angle θ within the interval $[0, \pi]$ whose cosine is $-\frac{\sqrt{2}}{2}$ is $\frac{3\pi}{4}$. So, since $\cos\frac{3\pi}{4} = -\frac{\sqrt{2}}{2}$ and $\frac{3\pi}{4}$ is in the interval $[0, \pi]$, we conclude that

$$\cos^{-1}\left(-\frac{\sqrt{2}}{2}\right) = \frac{3\pi}{4}$$

Now Work PROBLEM 23

For the cosine function and its inverse, the following properties hold:

$f^{-1}(f(x)) = \cos^{-1}(\cos x) = x$	where $0 \le x \le \pi$	**(4a)**
$f(f^{-1}(x)) = \cos(\cos^{-1} x) = x$	where $-1 \le x \le 1$	**(4b)**

EXAMPLE 8 **Using Properties of Inverse Functions to Find the Exact Value of Certain Composite Functions**

Find the exact value of:

(a) $\cos^{-1}\left(\cos\frac{\pi}{12}\right)$ (b) $\cos[\cos^{-1}(-0.4)]$ (c) $\cos^{-1}\left[\cos\left(-\frac{2\pi}{3}\right)\right]$ (d) $\cos(\cos^{-1}\pi)$

Solution (a) $\cos^{-1}\left(\cos\frac{\pi}{12}\right) = \frac{\pi}{12}$ $\frac{\pi}{12}$ is in the interval $[0, \pi]$; use Property (4a).

(b) $\cos[\cos^{-1}(-0.4)] = -0.4$ -0.4 is in the interval $[-1, 1]$; use Property (4b).

(c) The angle $-\frac{2\pi}{3}$ is not in the interval $[0, \pi]$, so we cannot use (4a). However, because the cosine function is even, $\cos\left(-\frac{2\pi}{3}\right) = \cos\frac{2\pi}{3}$. Since $\frac{2\pi}{3}$ is in the interval $[0, \pi]$, we have

$$\cos^{-1}\left[\cos\left(-\frac{2\pi}{3}\right)\right] = \cos^{-1}\left(\cos\frac{2\pi}{3}\right) = \frac{2\pi}{3}$$ $\frac{2\pi}{3}$ is in the interval $[0, \pi]$; apply (4a).

(d) Because π is not in the interval $[-1, 1]$, the domain of the inverse cosine function, $\cos^{-1}\pi$ is not defined. This means the composite function $\cos(\cos^{-1}\pi)$ is also not defined.

Now Work PROBLEMS 37 AND 49

The Inverse Tangent Function

In Figure 16 on page 448 we show the graph of $y = \tan x$. Because every horizontal line intersects the graph infinitely many times, it follows that the tangent function is not one-to-one.

However, if we restrict the domain of $y = \tan x$ to the interval $\left(-\frac{\pi}{2}, \frac{\pi}{2}\right)$, the restricted function

$$y = \tan x \qquad -\frac{\pi}{2} < x < \frac{\pi}{2}$$

is one-to-one and hence has an inverse function.* See Figure 17.

*This is the generally accepted restriction.

Figure 16

$y = \tan x, -\infty < x < \infty$, x not equal to odd multiples of $\frac{\pi}{2}$, $-\infty < y < \infty$

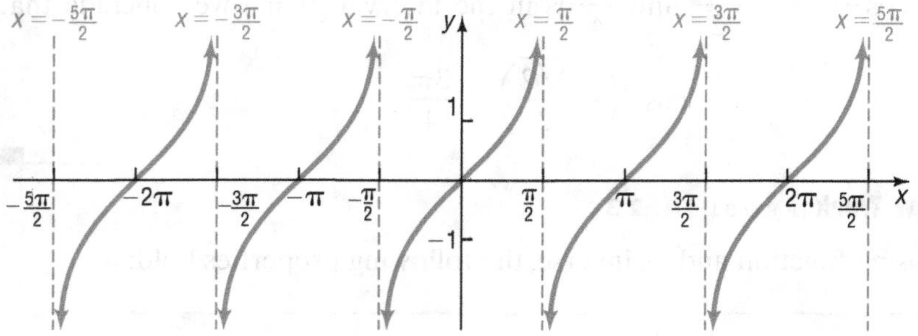

Figure 17

$y = \tan x, -\frac{\pi}{2} < x < \frac{\pi}{2}, -\infty < y < \infty$

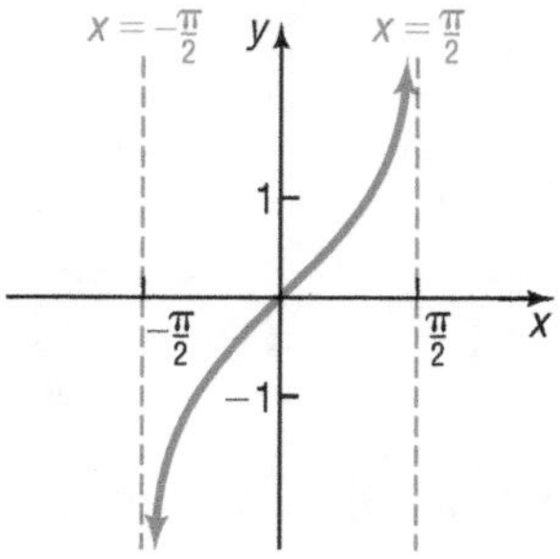

An equation for the inverse of $y = f(x) = \tan x$ is obtained by interchanging x and y. The implicit form of the inverse function is $x = \tan y$, $-\frac{\pi}{2} < y < \frac{\pi}{2}$. The explicit form is called the **inverse tangent** of x and is symbolized by $y = f^{-1}(x) = \tan^{-1} x$ (or by $y = \text{Arctan}\, x$).

DEFINITION

$$y = \tan^{-1} x \quad \text{means} \quad x = \tan y$$
$$\text{where} \quad -\infty < x < \infty \quad \text{and} \quad -\frac{\pi}{2} < y < \frac{\pi}{2} \qquad \textbf{(5)}$$

Here y is the angle whose tangent is x. The domain of the function $y = \tan^{-1} x$ is $-\infty < x < \infty$, and its range is $-\frac{\pi}{2} < y < \frac{\pi}{2}$. The graph of $y = \tan^{-1} x$ can be obtained by reflecting the restricted portion of the graph of $y = \tan x$ about the line $y = x$, as shown in Figure 18.

Figure 18

$y = \tan^{-1} x$,
$-\infty < x < \infty$,
$-\frac{\pi}{2} < y < \frac{\pi}{2}$

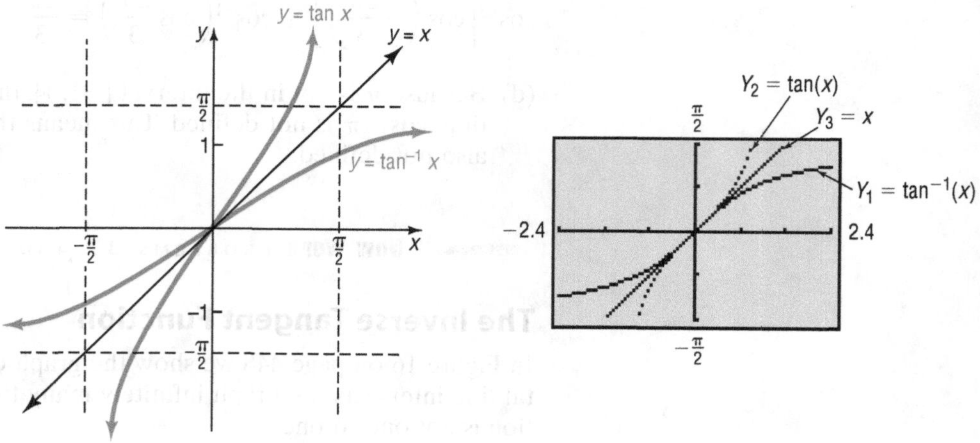

(a) (b)

EXAMPLE 9	Finding the Exact Value of an Inverse Tangent Function

Find the exact value of:

(a) $\tan^{-1} 1$ (b) $\tan^{-1}(-\sqrt{3})$

Solution (a) Let $\theta = \tan^{-1} 1$. We seek the angle $\theta, -\frac{\pi}{2} < \theta < \frac{\pi}{2}$, whose tangent equals 1.

$$\theta = \tan^{-1} 1 \qquad -\frac{\pi}{2} < \theta < \frac{\pi}{2}$$
$$\tan\theta = 1 \qquad -\frac{\pi}{2} < \theta < \frac{\pi}{2}$$

Table 3

θ	$\tan\theta$
$-\frac{\pi}{2}$	Undefined
$-\frac{\pi}{3}$	$-\sqrt{3}$
$-\frac{\pi}{4}$	-1
$-\frac{\pi}{6}$	$-\frac{\sqrt{3}}{3}$
0	0
$\frac{\pi}{6}$	$\frac{\sqrt{3}}{3}$
$\frac{\pi}{4}$	1
$\frac{\pi}{3}$	$\sqrt{3}$
$\frac{\pi}{2}$	Undefined

Look at Table 3. The only angle θ within the interval $\left(-\frac{\pi}{2}, \frac{\pi}{2}\right)$ whose tangent is 1 is $\frac{\pi}{4}$. Since $\tan\frac{\pi}{4} = 1$ and $\frac{\pi}{4}$ is in the interval $\left(-\frac{\pi}{2}, \frac{\pi}{2}\right)$, we conclude that

$$\tan^{-1} 1 = \frac{\pi}{4}$$

(b) Let $\theta = \tan^{-1}(-\sqrt{3})$. We seek the angle $\theta, -\frac{\pi}{2} < \theta < \frac{\pi}{2}$, whose tangent equals $-\sqrt{3}$.

$$\theta = \tan^{-1}(-\sqrt{3}) \qquad -\frac{\pi}{2} < \theta < \frac{\pi}{2}$$
$$\tan\theta = -\sqrt{3} \qquad -\frac{\pi}{2} < \theta < \frac{\pi}{2}$$

Look at Table 3. The only angle θ within the interval $\left(-\frac{\pi}{2}, \frac{\pi}{2}\right)$ whose tangent is $-\sqrt{3}$ is $-\frac{\pi}{3}$. Since $\tan\left(-\frac{\pi}{3}\right) = -\sqrt{3}$ and $-\frac{\pi}{3}$ is in the interval $\left(-\frac{\pi}{2}, \frac{\pi}{2}\right)$, we conclude that

$$\tan^{-1}(-\sqrt{3}) = -\frac{\pi}{3}$$

Now Work PROBLEM 17

For the tangent function and its inverse, the following properties hold:

$$f^{-1}(f(x)) = \tan^{-1}(\tan x) = x \quad \text{where } -\frac{\pi}{2} < x < \frac{\pi}{2}$$
$$f(f^{-1}(x)) = \tan(\tan^{-1} x) = x \quad \text{where } -\infty < x < \infty$$

Now Work PROBLEM 43

4 Find the Inverse Function of a Trigonometric Function

EXAMPLE 10 **Finding the Inverse Function of a Trigonometric Function**

Find the inverse function f^{-1} of $f(x) = 2\sin x - 1$. State the domain and the range of f and f^{-1}.

Solution We follow the steps on page 263 for finding the inverse function.

$$y = 2\sin x - 1$$
$$x = 2\sin y - 1 \quad \text{Interchange } x \text{ and } y.$$
$$x + 1 = 2\sin y \quad \text{Proceed to solve for } y.$$
$$\sin y = \frac{x+1}{2}$$
$$y = \sin^{-1}\frac{x+1}{2} \quad \text{Apply the definition (1).}$$

The inverse function is $f^{-1}(x) = \sin^{-1}\frac{x+1}{2}$.

The domain of $f(x) = 2\sin x - 1$ is the set of all real numbers. Therefore, the range of f^{-1} is the set of all real numbers.

The graph of $f(x) = 2\sin x - 1$ can be obtained by vertically stretching $y = \sin x$ by a factor of 2 and then shifting the resulting graph down 1 unit. So the range of $f(x) = 2\sin x - 1$ is $[-3, 1]$. Therefore, the domain of f^{-1} is $[-3, 1]$.

We could also find the domain of f^{-1} by noting that the argument of the inverse sine function is $\frac{x+1}{2}$ and that it must lie in the interval $[-1, 1]$. That is,

$$-1 \le \frac{x+1}{2} \le 1$$

$$-2 \le x + 1 \le 2 \quad \text{Multiply each part by 2.}$$

$$-3 \le x \le 1 \quad \text{Add } -1 \text{ to each part.}$$

The domain of f^{-1} is $\{x \mid -3 \le x \le 1\}$.

Now Work PROBLEM 55

5 Solve Equations Involving Inverse Trigonometric Functions

Equations that contain inverse trigonometric functions are called **inverse trigonometric equations.**

EXAMPLE 11 Solving an Equation Involving an Inverse Trigonometric Function

Solve the equation: $3\sin^{-1}x = \pi$

Solution To solve an equation involving a single inverse trigonometric function, first isolate the inverse trigonometric function.

$$3\sin^{-1}x = \pi$$

$$\sin^{-1}x = \frac{\pi}{3} \quad \text{Divide both sides by 3.}$$

$$x = \sin\frac{\pi}{3} \quad y = \sin^{-1}x \text{ means } x = \sin y.$$

$$x = \frac{\sqrt{3}}{2}$$

The solution set is $\left\{\frac{\sqrt{3}}{2}\right\}$.

Now Work PROBLEM 61

7.1 Assess Your Understanding

'Are You Prepared?' *Answers are given at the end of these exercises. If you get a wrong answer, read the pages listed in red.*

1. What is the domain and the range of $y = \sin x$? (pp. 382–384)
2. A suitable restriction on the domain of the function $f(x) = (x-1)^2$ to make it one-to-one would be _____. (pp. 257–258, 264)
3. If the domain of a one-to-one function is $[3, \infty)$, the range of its inverse is _____. (pp. 258–259)
4. True or False The graph of $y = \cos x$ is decreasing on the interval $[0, \pi]$. (p. 398)
5. $\tan\frac{\pi}{4} =$ _____; $\sin\frac{\pi}{3} =$ _____ (pp. 370–374)
6. $\sin\left(-\frac{\pi}{6}\right) =$ _____; $\cos\pi =$ _____ (pp. 369–375)

Concepts and Vocabulary

7. $y = \sin^{-1}x$ means _____, where $-1 \le x \le 1$ and $-\frac{\pi}{2} \le y \le \frac{\pi}{2}$.
8. The value of $\sin^{-1}\left[\sin\frac{\pi}{2}\right]$ is _____.

9. $\cos^{-1}\left[\cos\dfrac{\pi}{5}\right] = $ _____.

10. True or False The domain of $y = \sin^{-1} x$ is $-\dfrac{\pi}{2} \le x \le \dfrac{\pi}{2}$.

11. True or False $\sin(\sin^{-1} 0) = 0$ and $\cos(\cos^{-1} 0) = 0$.

12. True or False $y = \tan^{-1} x$ means $x = \tan y$, where $-\infty < x < \infty$ and $-\dfrac{\pi}{2} < y < \dfrac{\pi}{2}$.

Skill Building

In Problems 13–24, find the exact value of each expression.

13. $\sin^{-1} 0$ **14.** $\cos^{-1} 1$ **15.** $\sin^{-1}(-1)$ **16.** $\cos^{-1}(-1)$

17. $\tan^{-1} 0$ **18.** $\tan^{-1}(-1)$ **19.** $\sin^{-1}\dfrac{\sqrt{2}}{2}$ **20.** $\tan^{-1}\dfrac{\sqrt{3}}{3}$

21. $\tan^{-1}\sqrt{3}$ **22.** $\sin^{-1}\left(-\dfrac{\sqrt{3}}{2}\right)$ **23.** $\cos^{-1}\left(-\dfrac{\sqrt{3}}{2}\right)$ **24.** $\sin^{-1}\left(-\dfrac{\sqrt{2}}{2}\right)$

In Problems 25–36, use a calculator to find the value of each expression rounded to two decimal places.

25. $\sin^{-1} 0.1$ **26.** $\cos^{-1} 0.6$ **27.** $\tan^{-1} 5$ **28.** $\tan^{-1} 0.2$

29. $\cos^{-1}\dfrac{7}{8}$ **30.** $\sin^{-1}\dfrac{1}{8}$ **31.** $\tan^{-1}(-0.4)$ **32.** $\tan^{-1}(-3)$

33. $\sin^{-1}(-0.12)$ **34.** $\cos^{-1}(-0.44)$ **35.** $\cos^{-1}\dfrac{\sqrt{2}}{3}$ **36.** $\sin^{-1}\dfrac{\sqrt{3}}{5}$

In Problems 37–44, find the exact value of each expression. Do not use a calculator.

37. $\cos^{-1}\left(\cos\dfrac{4\pi}{5}\right)$ **38.** $\sin^{-1}\left[\sin\left(-\dfrac{\pi}{10}\right)\right]$ **39.** $\tan^{-1}\left[\tan\left(-\dfrac{3\pi}{8}\right)\right]$ **40.** $\sin^{-1}\left[\sin\left(-\dfrac{3\pi}{7}\right)\right]$

41. $\sin^{-1}\left(\sin\dfrac{9\pi}{8}\right)$ **42.** $\cos^{-1}\left[\cos\left(-\dfrac{5\pi}{3}\right)\right]$ **43.** $\tan^{-1}\left(\tan\dfrac{4\pi}{5}\right)$ **44.** $\tan^{-1}\left[\tan\left(-\dfrac{2\pi}{3}\right)\right]$

In Problems 45–52, find the exact value, if any, of each composite function. If there is no value, say it is "not defined." Do not use a calculator.

45. $\sin\left(\sin^{-1}\dfrac{1}{4}\right)$ **46.** $\cos\left[\cos^{-1}\left(-\dfrac{2}{3}\right)\right]$ **47.** $\tan\left(\tan^{-1} 4\right)$ **48.** $\tan\left[\tan^{-1}(-2)\right]$

49. $\cos\left(\cos^{-1} 1.2\right)$ **50.** $\sin\left[\sin^{-1}(-2)\right]$ **51.** $\tan\left(\tan^{-1} \pi\right)$ **52.** $\sin\left[\sin^{-1}(-1.5)\right]$

In Problems 53–60, find the inverse function f^{-1} of each function f. State the domain and the range of f and f^{-1}.

53. $f(x) = 5 \sin x + 2$ **54.** $f(x) = 2 \tan x - 3$ **55.** $f(x) = -2 \cos(3x)$ **56.** $f(x) = 3 \sin(2x)$

57. $f(x) = -\tan(x + 1) - 3$ **58.** $f(x) = \cos(x + 2) + 1$ **59.** $f(x) = 3 \sin(2x + 1)$ **60.** $f(x) = 2 \cos(3x + 2)$

In Problems 61–68, find the exact solution of each equation.

61. $4 \sin^{-1}(x) = \pi$ **62.** $2 \cos^{-1} x = \pi$ **63.** $3 \cos^{-1}(2x) = 2\pi$

64. $-6 \sin^{-1}(3x) = \pi$ **65.** $3 \tan^{-1} x = \pi$ **66.** $-4 \tan^{-1} x = \pi$

67. $4 \cos^{-1} x - 2\pi = 2 \cos^{-1} x$ **68.** $5 \sin^{-1} x - 2\pi = 2 \sin^{-1} x - 3\pi$

Applications and Extensions

In Problems 69–74, use the following discussion. The formula

$$D = 24\left[1 - \frac{\cos^{-1}(\tan i \tan \theta)}{\pi}\right]$$

can be used to approximate the number of hours of daylight D when the declination of the Sun is $i°$ at a location $\theta°$ north latitude for any date between the vernal equinox and autumnal equinox. The declination of the Sun is defined as the angle i between the equatorial plane and any ray of light from the Sun. The latitude of

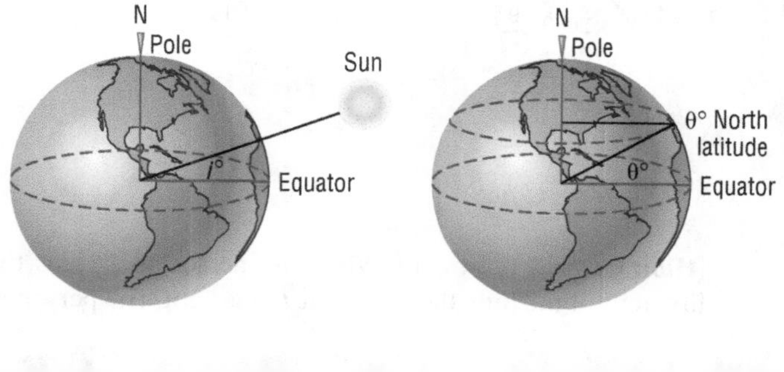

a location is the angle θ between the Equator and the location on the surface of Earth, with the vertex of the angle located at the center of Earth. See the figure. To use the formula, $\cos^{-1}(\tan i \tan \theta)$ must be expressed in radians.

69. Approximate the number of hours of daylight in Houston, Texas (29°45′ north latitude), for the following dates:
(a) Summer solstice ($i = 23.5°$)
(b) Vernal equinox ($i = 0°$)
(c) July 4 ($i = 22°48'$)

70. Approximate the number of hours of daylight in New York, New York (40°45′ north latitude), for the following dates:
(a) Summer solstice ($i = 23.5°$)
(b) Vernal equinox ($i = 0°$)
(c) July 4 ($i = 22°48'$)

71. Approximate the number of hours of daylight in Honolulu, Hawaii (21°18′ north latitude), for the following dates:
(a) Summer solstice ($i = 23.5°$)
(b) Vernal equinox ($i = 0°$)
(c) July 4 ($i = 22°48'$)

72. Approximate the number of hours of daylight in Anchorage, Alaska (61°10′ north latitude), for the following dates:
(a) Summer solstice ($i = 23.5°$)
(b) Vernal equinox ($i = 0°$)
(c) July 4 ($i = 22°48'$)

73. Approximate the number of hours of daylight at the Equator (0° north latitude) for the following dates:
(a) Summer solstice ($i = 23.5°$)
(b) Vernal equinox ($i = 0°$)
(c) July 4 ($i = 22°48'$)
(d) What do you conclude about the number of hours of daylight throughout the year for a location at the Equator?

74. Approximate the number of hours of daylight for any location that is 66°30′ north latitude for the following dates:
(a) Summer solstice ($i = 23.5°$)
(b) Vernal equinox ($i = 0°$)
(c) July 4 ($i = 22°48'$)
(d) The number of hours of daylight on the winter solstice may be found by computing the number of hours of daylight on the summer solstice and subtracting this result from 24 hours, due to the symmetry of the orbital path of Earth around the Sun. Compute the number of hours of daylight for this location on the winter solstice. What do you conclude about daylight for a location at 66°30′ north latitude?

75. Being the First to See the Rising Sun Cadillac Mountain, elevation 1530 feet, is located in Acadia National Park, Maine, and is the highest peak on the east coast of the United States. It is said that a person standing on the summit will be the first person in the United States to see the rays of the rising Sun. How much sooner would a person atop Cadillac Mountain see the first rays than a person standing below at sea level?

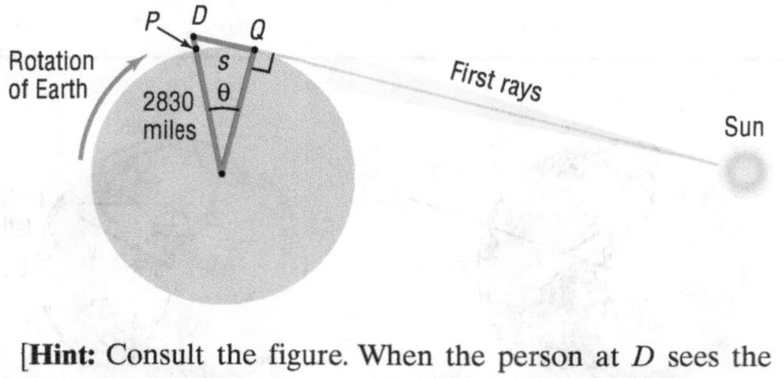

[**Hint:** Consult the figure. When the person at D sees the first rays of the Sun, the person at P does not. The person at P sees the first rays of the Sun only after Earth has rotated so that P is at location Q. Compute the length of the arc subtended by the central angle θ. Then use the fact that, at the latitude of Cadillac Mountain, in 24 hours a length of $2\pi(2830) \approx 17{,}781.4$ miles is subtended, and find the time that it takes to subtend this length.]

76. Movie Theater Screens Suppose that a movie theater has a screen that is 28 feet tall. When you sit down, the bottom of the screen is 6 feet above your eye level. The angle formed by drawing a line from your eye to the bottom of the screen and from your eye to the top of the screen is called the **viewing angle.** In the figure, θ is the viewing angle. Suppose that you sit x feet from the screen. The viewing angle θ is given by the function

$$\theta(x) = \tan^{-1}\left(\frac{34}{x}\right) - \tan^{-1}\left(\frac{6}{x}\right)$$

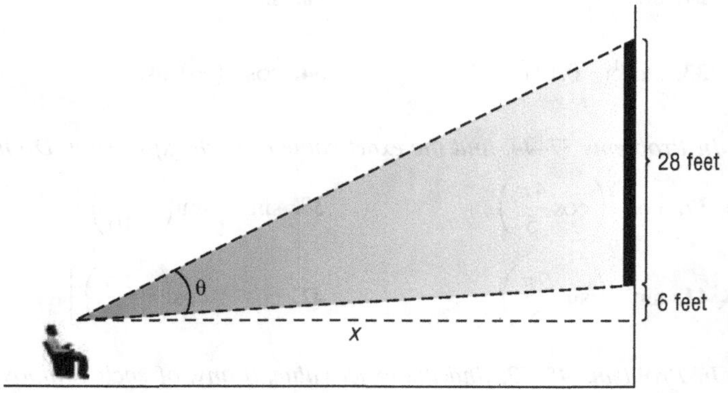

(a) What is your viewing angle if you sit 10 feet from the screen? 15 feet? 20 feet?
(b) If there is 5 feet between the screen and the first row of seats and there is 3 feet between each row, which row results in the largest viewing angle?
(c) Using a graphing utility, graph

$$\theta(x) = \tan^{-1}\left(\frac{34}{x}\right) - \tan^{-1}\left(\frac{6}{x}\right)$$

What value of x results in the largest viewing angle?

77. Area under a Curve The area under the graph of $y = \dfrac{1}{1 + x^2}$ and above the x-axis between $x = a$ and $x = b$ is given by

$$\tan^{-1} b - \tan^{-1} a$$

See the figure.

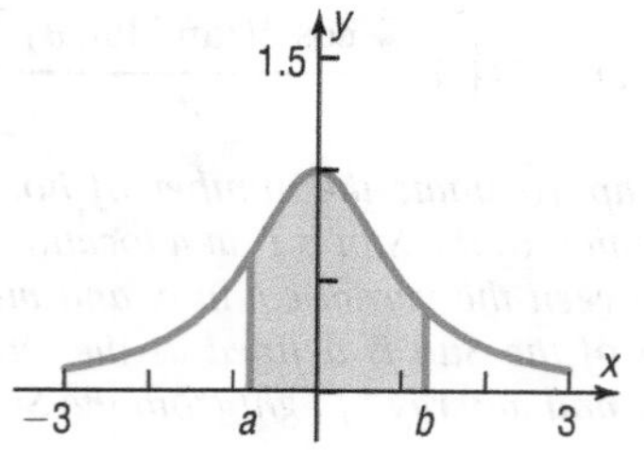

(a) Find the exact area under the graph of $y = \dfrac{1}{1 + x^2}$ and above the x-axis between $x = 0$ and $x = \sqrt{3}$.

(b) Find the exact area under the graph of $y = \dfrac{1}{1 + x^2}$ and above the x-axis between $x = -\dfrac{\sqrt{3}}{3}$ and $x = 1$.

78. Area under a Curve The area under the graph of $y = \dfrac{1}{\sqrt{1 - x^2}}$ and above the x-axis between $x = a$ and $x = b$ is given by

$$\sin^{-1} b - \sin^{-1} a$$

See the figure.

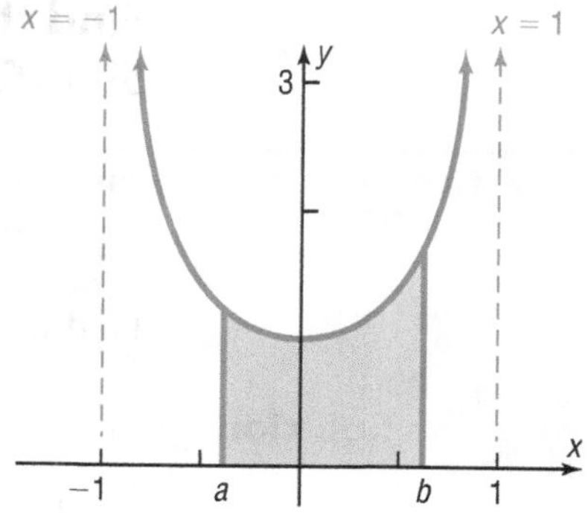

(a) Find the exact area under the graph of $y = \dfrac{1}{\sqrt{1 - x^2}}$ and above the x-axis between $x = 0$ and $x = \dfrac{\sqrt{3}}{2}$.

(b) Find the exact area under the graph of $y = \dfrac{1}{\sqrt{1 - x^2}}$ and above the x-axis between $x = -\dfrac{1}{2}$ and $x = \dfrac{1}{2}$.

Problems 79 and 80 require the following discussion:
The shortest distance between two points on Earth's surface can be determined from the latitude and longitude of the two locations. For example, if location 1 has (lat, lon) $= (\alpha_1, \beta_1)$ *and location 2 has* (lat, lon) $= (\alpha_2, \beta_2)$, *the shortest distance between the two locations is approximately*

$$d = \frac{2\pi}{360} r \cos^{-1}[(\cos \alpha_1 \cos \beta_1 \cos \alpha_2 \cos \beta_2) + (\cos \alpha_1 \sin \beta_1 \cos \alpha_2 \sin \beta_2) + (\sin \alpha_1 \sin \alpha_2)]$$

where r = radius of Earth $\approx$ 3960 miles and the inverse cosine function is expressed in radians. Also N *latitude and* E *longitude are positive angles while* S *latitude and* W *longitude are negative angles.*

City	Latitude	Longitude
Chicago, IL	41°50′N	87°37′W
Honolulu, HI	21°18′N	157°50′W
Melbourne, Australia	37°47′S	144°58′E

Source: *www.infoplease.com*

79. Shortest Distance from Chicago to Honolulu Find the shortest distance from Chicago, latitude 41°50′N, longitude 87°37′W to Honolulu, latitude 21°18′N, longitude 157°50′W. Round your answer to the nearest mile.

80. Shortest Distance from Honolulu to Melbourne, Australia Find the shortest distance from Honolulu to Melbourne, Australia, latitude 37°47′S, longitude 144°58′E. Round your answer to the nearest mile.

'Are You Prepared?' Answers

1. Domain: the set of all real numbers; range: $-1 \le y \le 1$

2. Two answers are possible: $x \le 1$ or $x \ge 1$

3. $[3, \infty)$

4. True

5. $1; \dfrac{\sqrt{3}}{2}$

6. $-\dfrac{1}{2}; -1$

7.2 The Inverse Trigonometric Functions (Continued)

PREPARING FOR THIS SECTION *Before getting started, review the following concepts:*

- Finding Exact Values Given the Value of a Trigonometric Function and the Quadrant of the Angle (Section 6.3, pp. 389–391)
- Graphs of the Secant, Cosecant, and Cotangent Functions (Section 6.5, pp. 414–417)
- Domain and Range of the Secant, Cosecant, and Cotangent Functions (Section 6.3, pp. 382–384)

Now Work the 'Are You Prepared?' problems on page 457.

OBJECTIVES
1. Find the Exact Value of Expressions Involving the Inverse Sine, Cosine, and Tangent Functions (p. 454)
2. Know the Definitions of the Inverse Secant, Cosecant, and Cotangent Functions (p. 455)
3. Use a Calculator to Evaluate $\sec^{-1} x$, $\csc^{-1} x$, and $\cot^{-1} x$ (p. 456)
4. Write a Trigonometric Expression as an Algebraic Expression (p. 456)

1 Find the Exact Value of Expressions Involving the Inverse Sine, Cosine, and Tangent Functions

EXAMPLE 1 Finding the Exact Value of Expressions Involving Inverse Trigonometric Functions

Find the exact value of: $\sin\left(\tan^{-1}\frac{1}{2}\right)$

Figure 19

$\tan\theta = \frac{1}{2}$

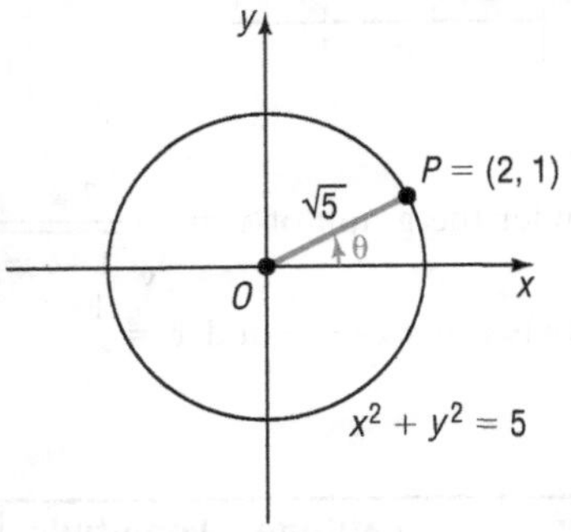

Solution Let $\theta = \tan^{-1}\frac{1}{2}$. Then $\tan\theta = \frac{1}{2}$, where $-\frac{\pi}{2} < \theta < \frac{\pi}{2}$. We seek $\sin\theta$. Because $\tan\theta > 0$, it follows that $0 < \theta < \frac{\pi}{2}$, so θ lies in quadrant I. Since $\tan\theta = \frac{1}{2} = \frac{y}{x}$, we let $x = 2$ and $y = 1$. Since $r = d(O, P) = \sqrt{2^2 + 1^2} = \sqrt{5}$, the point $P = (x, y) = (2, 1)$ is on the circle $x^2 + y^2 = 5$. See Figure 19. Then, with $x = 2$, $y = 1$, and $r = \sqrt{5}$, we have

$$\sin\left(\tan^{-1}\frac{1}{2}\right) = \sin\theta = \frac{1}{\sqrt{5}} = \frac{\sqrt{5}}{5}$$

$\uparrow$ $\sin\theta = \frac{y}{r}$

EXAMPLE 2 Finding the Exact Value of Expressions Involving Inverse Trigonometric Functions

Find the exact value of: $\cos\left[\sin^{-1}\left(-\frac{1}{3}\right)\right]$

Figure 20

$\sin\theta = -\frac{1}{3}$

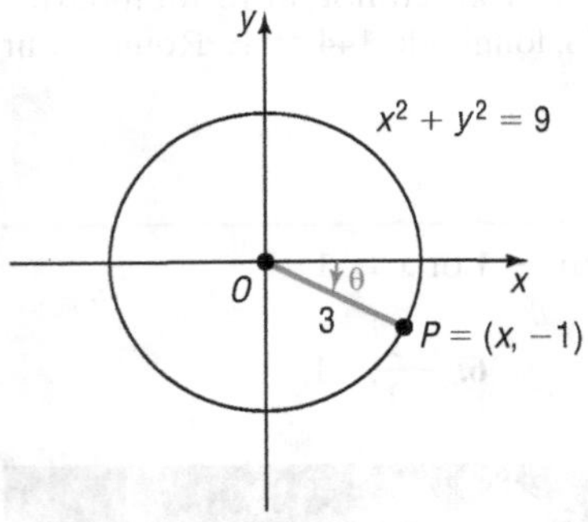

Solution Let $\theta = \sin^{-1}\left(-\frac{1}{3}\right)$. Then $\sin\theta = -\frac{1}{3}$ and $-\frac{\pi}{2} \le \theta \le \frac{\pi}{2}$. We seek $\cos\theta$. Because $\sin\theta < 0$, it follows that $-\frac{\pi}{2} \le \theta < 0$, so θ lies in quadrant IV. Since $\sin\theta = \frac{-1}{3} = \frac{y}{r}$, we let $y = -1$ and $r = 3$. The point $P = (x, y) = (x, -1)$, $x > 0$, is on a circle of radius 3, $x^2 + y^2 = 9$. See Figure 20. Then

$$x^2 + y^2 = 9$$
$$x^2 + (-1)^2 = 9 \qquad y = -1$$
$$x^2 = 8$$
$$x = 2\sqrt{2} \qquad x > 0$$

Then we have $x = 2\sqrt{2}$, $y = -1$, and $r = 3$, so

$$\cos\left[\sin^{-1}\left(-\frac{1}{3}\right)\right] = \cos\theta = \frac{2\sqrt{2}}{3}$$

$\uparrow$ $\cos\theta = \frac{x}{r}$

EXAMPLE 3 Finding the Exact Value of Expressions Involving Inverse Trigonometric Functions

Find the exact value of: $\tan\left[\cos^{-1}\left(-\frac{1}{3}\right)\right]$

Solution Let $\theta = \cos^{-1}\left(-\frac{1}{3}\right)$. Then $\cos\theta = -\frac{1}{3}$ and $0 \le \theta \le \pi$. We seek $\tan\theta$. Because $\cos\theta < 0$, it follows that $\frac{\pi}{2} < \theta \le \pi$, so θ lies in quadrant II. Since $\cos\theta = \frac{-1}{3} = \frac{x}{r}$, we let $x = -1$ and $r = 3$. The point $P = (x, y) = (-1, y)$, $y > 0$, is on a circle of radius $r = 3$, $x^2 + y^2 = 9$. See Figure 21. Then

$$x^2 + y^2 = 9$$
$$(-1)^2 + y^2 = 9 \qquad x = -1$$

Figure 21

$\cos\theta = -\frac{1}{3}$

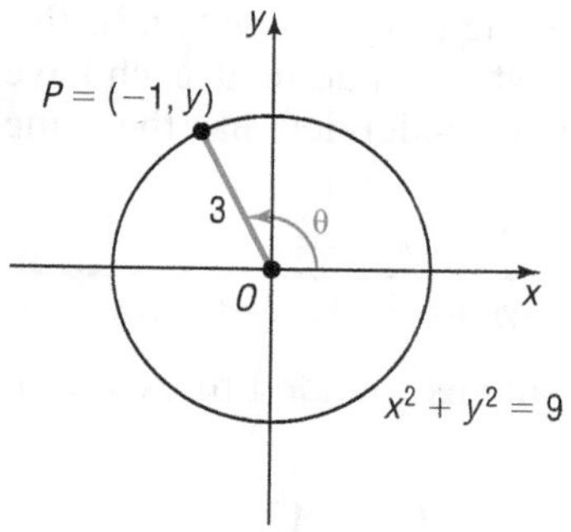

$$y^2 = 8$$
$$y = 2\sqrt{2} \qquad y > 0$$

Then, we have $x = -1$, $y = 2\sqrt{2}$, and $r = 3$, so

$$\tan\left[\cos^{-1}\left(-\frac{1}{3}\right)\right] = \tan\theta = \frac{2\sqrt{2}}{-1} = -2\sqrt{2}$$

$\uparrow \tan\theta = \frac{y}{x}$

Now Work PROBLEMS 9 AND 27

2 Know the Definitions of the Inverse Secant, Cosecant, and Cotangent Functions

The inverse secant, inverse cosecant, and inverse cotangent functions are defined as follows:

DEFINITION

$$y = \sec^{-1} x \quad \text{means} \quad x = \sec y \qquad \textbf{(1)}$$
$$\text{where} \quad |x| \ge 1 \quad \text{and} \quad 0 \le y \le \pi, \quad y \ne \frac{\pi}{2}^{*}$$

$$y = \csc^{-1} x \quad \text{means} \quad x = \csc y \qquad \textbf{(2)}$$
$$\text{where} \quad |x| \ge 1 \quad \text{and} \quad -\frac{\pi}{2} \le y \le \frac{\pi}{2}, \quad y \ne 0^{\dagger}$$

$$y = \cot^{-1} x \quad \text{means} \quad x = \cot y \qquad \textbf{(3)}$$
$$\text{where} \quad -\infty < x < \infty \quad \text{and} \quad 0 < y < \pi$$

You are encouraged to review the graphs of the cotangent, cosecant, and secant functions in Figures 71, 72, and 73 in Section 6.5 to help you to see the basis for these definitions.

EXAMPLE 4 **Finding the Exact Value of an Inverse Cosecant Function**

Find the exact value of: $\csc^{-1} 2$

Solution Let $\theta = \csc^{-1} 2$. We seek the angle θ, $-\frac{\pi}{2} \le \theta \le \frac{\pi}{2}$, $\theta \ne 0$, whose cosecant equals 2 $\left(\text{or, equivalently, whose sine equals } \frac{1}{2}\right)$.

$$\theta = \csc^{-1} 2 \qquad -\frac{\pi}{2} \le \theta \le \frac{\pi}{2}, \quad \theta \ne 0$$
$$\csc\theta = 2 \qquad -\frac{\pi}{2} \le \theta \le \frac{\pi}{2}, \quad \theta \ne 0 \qquad \sin\theta = \frac{1}{2}$$

The only angle θ in the interval $-\frac{\pi}{2} \le \theta \le \frac{\pi}{2}$, $\theta \ne 0$, whose cosecant is 2 $\left[\sin\theta = \frac{1}{2}\right]$ is $\frac{\pi}{6}$, so $\csc^{-1} 2 = \frac{\pi}{6}$.

Now Work PROBLEM 39

*Most books use this definition. A few use the restriction $0 \le y < \frac{\pi}{2}, \pi \le y < \frac{3\pi}{2}$.

†Most books use this definition. A few use the restriction $-\pi < y \le -\frac{\pi}{2}, 0 < y \le \frac{\pi}{2}$.

3 Use a Calculator to Evaluate $\sec^{-1} x$, $\csc^{-1} x$, and $\cot^{-1} x$

Most calculators do not have keys for evaluating the inverse cotangent, cosecant, and secant functions. The easiest way to evaluate them is to convert to an inverse trigonometric function whose range is the same as the one to be evaluated. In this regard, notice that $y = \cot^{-1} x$ and $y = \sec^{-1} x$, except where undefined, each have the same range as $y = \cos^{-1} x$; $y = \csc^{-1} x$, except where undefined, has the same range as $y = \sin^{-1} x$.

NOTE Remember, the range of $y = \sin^{-1} x$ is $\left[-\frac{\pi}{2}, \frac{\pi}{2}\right]$; the range of $y = \cos^{-1} x$ is $[0, \pi]$. ■

EXAMPLE 5 **Approximating the Value of Inverse Trigonometric Functions**

Use a calculator to approximate each expression in radians rounded to two decimal places.

(a) $\sec^{-1} 3$ (b) $\csc^{-1}(-4)$ (c) $\cot^{-1} \frac{1}{2}$ (d) $\cot^{-1}(-2)$

Solution First, set your calculator to radian mode.

(a) Let $\theta = \sec^{-1} 3$. Then $\sec \theta = 3$ and $0 \le \theta \le \pi, \theta \ne \frac{\pi}{2}$. We seek $\cos \theta$ because $y = \cos^{-1} x$ has the same range as $y = \sec^{-1} x$, except where undefined. Since $\sec \theta = \frac{1}{\cos \theta} = 3$, we have $\cos \theta = \frac{1}{3}$. Then $\theta = \cos^{-1} \frac{1}{3}$ and

$$\sec^{-1} 3 = \theta = \cos^{-1} \frac{1}{3} \approx 1.23$$

↑ Use a calculator.

Figure 22
$\cot \theta = \frac{1}{2}, 0 < \theta < \pi$

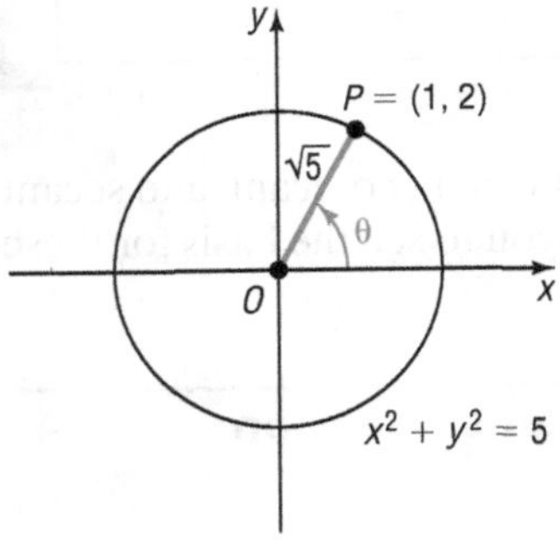

(b) Let $\theta = \csc^{-1}(-4)$. Then $\csc \theta = -4, -\frac{\pi}{2} \le \theta \le \frac{\pi}{2}, \theta \ne 0$. We seek $\sin \theta$ because $y = \sin^{-1} x$ has the same range as $y = \csc^{-1} x$, except where undefined. Since $\csc \theta = \frac{1}{\sin \theta} = -4$, we have $\sin \theta = -\frac{1}{4}$. Then $\theta = \sin^{-1}\left(-\frac{1}{4}\right)$, and

$$\csc^{-1}(-4) = \theta = \sin^{-1}\left(-\frac{1}{4}\right) \approx -0.25$$

(c) We proceed as before. Let $\theta = \cot^{-1} \frac{1}{2}$. Then $\cot \theta = \frac{1}{2}, 0 < \theta < \pi$. From these facts we know that θ lies in quadrant I. We seek $\cos \theta$ because $y = \cos^{-1} x$ has the same range as $y = \cot^{-1} x$, except where undefined. To find $\cos \theta$, we use Figure 22. Then $\cos \theta = \frac{1}{\sqrt{5}}$, $0 < \theta < \frac{\pi}{2}$, $\theta = \cos^{-1}\left(\frac{1}{\sqrt{5}}\right)$, and

$$\cot^{-1} \frac{1}{2} = \theta = \cos^{-1}\left(\frac{1}{\sqrt{5}}\right) \approx 1.11$$

Figure 23
$\cot \theta = -2, 0 < \theta < \pi$

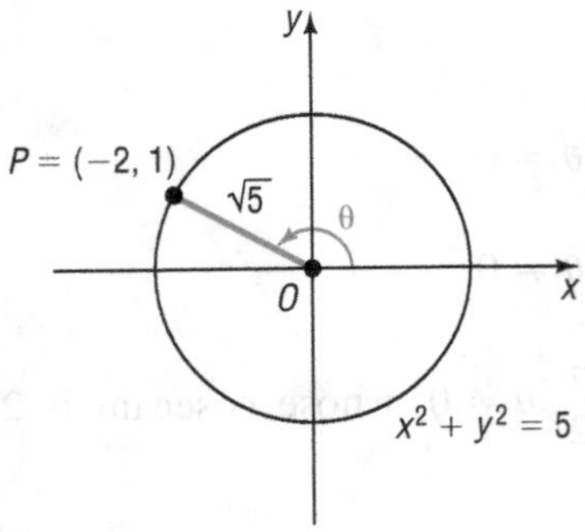

(d) Let $\theta = \cot^{-1}(-2)$. Then $\cot \theta = -2, 0 < \theta < \pi$. From these facts we know that θ lies in quadrant II. We seek $\cos \theta$. To find it, we use Figure 23. Then $\cos \theta = -\frac{2}{\sqrt{5}}$, $\frac{\pi}{2} < \theta < \pi$, $\theta = \cos^{-1}\left(-\frac{2}{\sqrt{5}}\right)$, and

$$\cot^{-1}(-2) = \theta = \cos^{-1}\left(-\frac{2}{\sqrt{5}}\right) \approx 2.68$$

■

Now Work PROBLEM 45

4 Write a Trigonometric Expression as an Algebraic Expression

EXAMPLE 6 **Writing a Trigonometric Expression as an Algebraic Expression**

Write $\sin(\tan^{-1} u)$ as an algebraic expression containing u.

Solution Let $\theta = \tan^{-1} u$ so that $\tan\theta = u$, $-\dfrac{\pi}{2} < \theta < \dfrac{\pi}{2}$, $-\infty < u < \infty$. As a result, we know that $\sec\theta > 0$. Then

$$\sin(\tan^{-1} u) = \underset{\substack{\uparrow\\ \text{Multiply by 1: } \frac{\cos\theta}{\cos\theta}}}{\sin\theta = \sin\theta\cdot\frac{\cos\theta}{\cos\theta}} = \underset{\substack{\uparrow\\ \frac{\sin\theta}{\cos\theta} = \tan\theta}}{\tan\theta\cos\theta} = \frac{\tan\theta}{\sec\theta} = \underset{\substack{\uparrow\\ \sec^2\theta = 1+\tan^2\theta\\ \sec\theta > 0}}{\frac{\tan\theta}{\sqrt{1+\tan^2\theta}}} = \frac{u}{\sqrt{1+u^2}}$$

Now Work PROBLEM 57

7.2 Assess Your Understanding

'Are You Prepared?' *Answers are given at the end of these exercises. If you get a wrong answer, read the pages listed in red.*

1. What is the domain and the range of $y = \sec x$? (pp. 382–384)
2. True or False The graph of $y = \sec x$ is increasing on the interval $\left[0, \dfrac{\pi}{2}\right)$ and on the interval $\left(\dfrac{\pi}{2}, \pi\right]$. (p. 415)
3. If $\cot\theta = -2$ and $0 < \theta < \pi$, then $\cos\theta =$ ______. (pp. 389–391)

Concepts and Vocabulary

4. $y = \sec^{-1} x$ means ______, where $|x|$ ______ and ______ $\le y \le$ ______, $y \ne \dfrac{\pi}{2}$.
5. $\cos(\tan^{-1} 1) =$ ______.
6. True or False It is impossible to obtain exact values for the inverse secant function.
7. True or False $\csc^{-1} 0.5$ is not defined.
8. True or False The domain of the inverse cotangent function is the set of real numbers.

Skill Building

In Problems 9–36, find the exact value of each expression.

9. $\cos\left(\sin^{-1}\dfrac{\sqrt{2}}{2}\right)$
10. $\sin\left(\cos^{-1}\dfrac{1}{2}\right)$
11. $\tan\left[\cos^{-1}\left(-\dfrac{\sqrt{3}}{2}\right)\right]$
12. $\tan\left[\sin^{-1}\left(-\dfrac{1}{2}\right)\right]$
13. $\sec\left(\cos^{-1}\dfrac{1}{2}\right)$
14. $\cot\left[\sin^{-1}\left(-\dfrac{1}{2}\right)\right]$
15. $\csc(\tan^{-1} 1)$
16. $\sec(\tan^{-1}\sqrt{3})$
17. $\sin[\tan^{-1}(-1)]$
18. $\cos\left[\sin^{-1}\left(-\dfrac{\sqrt{3}}{2}\right)\right]$
19. $\sec\left[\sin^{-1}\left(-\dfrac{1}{2}\right)\right]$
20. $\csc\left[\cos^{-1}\left(-\dfrac{\sqrt{3}}{2}\right)\right]$
21. $\cos^{-1}\left(\cos\dfrac{5\pi}{4}\right)$
22. $\tan^{-1}\left(\tan\dfrac{2\pi}{3}\right)$
23. $\sin^{-1}\left[\sin\left(-\dfrac{7\pi}{6}\right)\right]$
24. $\cos^{-1}\left[\cos\left(-\dfrac{\pi}{3}\right)\right]$
25. $\tan\left(\sin^{-1}\dfrac{1}{3}\right)$
26. $\tan\left(\cos^{-1}\dfrac{1}{3}\right)$
27. $\sec\left(\tan^{-1}\dfrac{1}{2}\right)$
28. $\cos\left(\sin^{-1}\dfrac{\sqrt{2}}{3}\right)$
29. $\cot\left[\sin^{-1}\left(-\dfrac{\sqrt{2}}{3}\right)\right]$
30. $\csc[\tan^{-1}(-2)]$
31. $\sin[\tan^{-1}(-3)]$
32. $\cot\left[\cos^{-1}\left(-\dfrac{\sqrt{3}}{3}\right)\right]$
33. $\sec\left(\sin^{-1}\dfrac{2\sqrt{5}}{5}\right)$
34. $\csc\left(\tan^{-1}\dfrac{1}{2}\right)$
35. $\sin^{-1}\left(\cos\dfrac{3\pi}{4}\right)$
36. $\cos^{-1}\left(\sin\dfrac{7\pi}{6}\right)$

In Problems 37–44, find the exact value of each expression.

37. $\cot^{-1}\sqrt{3}$
38. $\cot^{-1} 1$
39. $\csc^{-1}(-1)$
40. $\csc^{-1}\sqrt{2}$
41. $\sec^{-1}\dfrac{2\sqrt{3}}{3}$
42. $\sec^{-1}(-2)$
43. $\cot^{-1}\left(-\dfrac{\sqrt{3}}{3}\right)$
44. $\csc^{-1}\left(-\dfrac{2\sqrt{3}}{3}\right)$

In Problems 45–56, use a calculator to find the value of each expression rounded to two decimal places.

45. $\sec^{-1} 4$
46. $\csc^{-1} 5$
47. $\cot^{-1} 2$
48. $\sec^{-1}(-3)$
49. $\csc^{-1}(-3)$
50. $\cot^{-1}\left(-\dfrac{1}{2}\right)$
51. $\cot^{-1}(-\sqrt{5})$
52. $\cot^{-1}(-8.1)$
53. $\csc^{-1}\left(-\dfrac{3}{2}\right)$
54. $\sec^{-1}\left(-\dfrac{4}{3}\right)$
55. $\cot^{-1}\left(-\dfrac{3}{2}\right)$
56. $\cot^{-1}(-\sqrt{10})$

In Problems 57–66, write each trigonometric expression as an algebraic expression in u.

57. $\cos(\tan^{-1}u)$
58. $\sin(\cos^{-1}u)$
59. $\tan(\sin^{-1}u)$
60. $\tan(\cos^{-1}u)$
61. $\sin(\sec^{-1}u)$
62. $\sin(\cot^{-1}u)$
63. $\cos(\csc^{-1}u)$
64. $\cos(\sec^{-1}u)$
65. $\tan(\cot^{-1}u)$
66. $\tan(\sec^{-1}u)$

Mixed Practice

In Problems 67–78, $f(x) = \sin x$, $g(x) = \cos x$, and $h(x) = \tan x$. Find the exact value of each composite function.

67. $g\left(f^{-1}\left(\frac{12}{13}\right)\right)$
68. $f\left(g^{-1}\left(\frac{5}{13}\right)\right)$
69. $g^{-1}\left(f\left(\frac{7\pi}{4}\right)\right)$
70. $f^{-1}\left(g\left(\frac{5\pi}{6}\right)\right)$
71. $h\left(f^{-1}\left(-\frac{3}{5}\right)\right)$
72. $h\left(g^{-1}\left(-\frac{4}{5}\right)\right)$
73. $g\left(h^{-1}\left(\frac{12}{5}\right)\right)$
74. $f\left(h^{-1}\left(\frac{5}{12}\right)\right)$
75. $g^{-1}\left(f\left(-\frac{4\pi}{3}\right)\right)$
76. $g^{-1}\left(f\left(-\frac{5\pi}{6}\right)\right)$
77. $h\left(g^{-1}\left(-\frac{1}{4}\right)\right)$
78. $h\left(f^{-1}\left(-\frac{2}{5}\right)\right)$

Applications and Extensions

Problems 79 and 80 require the following discussion: When granular materials are allowed to fall freely, they form conical (cone-shaped) piles. The naturally occurring angle of slope, measured from the horizontal, at which the loose material comes to rest is called the angle of repose and varies for different materials. The angle of repose θ is related to the height h and base radius r of the conical pile by the equation $\theta = \cot^{-1}\frac{r}{h}$. See the illustration.

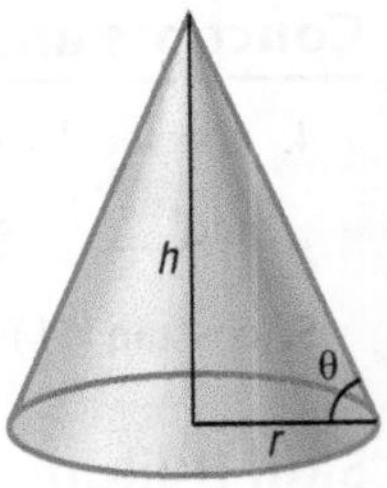

79. **Angle of Repose: Deicing Salt** Because of potential transportation issues (for example, frozen waterways), the deicing salt used by highway departments in the Midwest must be ordered early and stored for future use. When deicing salt is stored in a pile 14 feet high, the diameter of the base of the pile is 45 feet.
(a) Find the angle of repose for deicing salt.
(b) What is the base diameter of a pile that is 17 feet high?
(c) What is the height of a pile that has a base diameter of approximately 122 feet?
Source: *Salt Institute, The Salt Storage Handbook,* 2006

80. **Angle of Repose: Bunker Sand** The steepness of sand bunkers on a golf course is affected by the angle of repose of the sand (a larger angle of repose allows for steeper bunkers). A freestanding pile of loose sand from a United States Golf Association (USGA) bunker had a height of 4 feet and a base diameter of approximately 6.68 feet.
(a) Find the angle of repose for USGA bunker sand.
(b) What is the height of such a pile if the diameter of the base is 8 feet?
(c) A 6-foot high pile of loose Tour Grade 50/50 sand has a base diameter of approximately 8.44 feet. Which type of sand (USGA or Tour Grade 50/50) would be better suited for steep bunkers?
Source: 2004 *Annual Report, Purdue University Turfgrass Science Program*

81. **Artillery** A projectile fired into the first quadrant from the origin of a coordinate system will pass through the point (x, y) at time t according to the relationship $\cot\theta = \frac{2x}{2y + gt^2}$ where θ = the angle of elevation of the launcher and g = the acceleration due to gravity = 32.2 feet/second^2. An artilleryman is firing at an enemy bunker located 2450 feet up the side of a hill that is 6175 feet away. He fires a round, and exactly 2.27 seconds later he scores a direct hit.
(a) What angle of elevation did he use?
(b) If the angle of elevation is also given by $\sec\theta = \frac{v_0 t}{x}$, where v_0 is the muzzle velocity of the weapon, find the muzzle velocity of the artillery piece he used.
Source: *www.egwald.com/geometry/projectile3d.php*

82. Using a graphing utility, graph $y = \cot^{-1}x$.
83. Using a graphing utility, graph $y = \sec^{-1}x$.
84. Using a graphing utility, graph $y = \csc^{-1}x$.

Discussion and Writing

85. Explain in your own words how you would use your calculator to find the value of $\cot^{-1} 10$.

86. Consult three books on calculus and write down the definition in each of $y = \sec^{-1} x$ and $y = \csc^{-1} x$. Compare these with the definitions given in this book.

'Are You Prepared?' Answers

1. Domain: $\left\{x \middle| x \neq \text{odd integer multiples of } \frac{\pi}{2}\right\}$; range: $\{y \leq -1 \text{ or } y \geq 1\}$
2. True
3. $\frac{-2\sqrt{5}}{5}$

7.3 Trigonometric Identities

PREPARING FOR THIS SECTION *Before getting started, review the following:*

- Fundamental Identities (Section 6.3, p. 388)
- Even–Odd Properties (Section 6.3, p. 391)

Now Work the 'Are You Prepared?' problems on page 463.

OBJECTIVES 1 Use Algebra to Simplify Trigonometric Expressions (p. 460)
2 Establish Identities (p. 461)

We saw in the previous chapter that the trigonometric functions lend themselves to a wide variety of identities. Before establishing some additional identities, let's review the definition of an *identity*.

DEFINITION Two functions f and g are said to be **identically equal** if

$$f(x) = g(x)$$

for every value of x for which both functions are defined. Such an equation is referred to as an **identity.** An equation that is not an identity is called a **conditional equation.**

For example, the following are identities:

$$(x + 1)^2 = x^2 + 2x + 1 \qquad \sin^2 x + \cos^2 x = 1 \qquad \csc x = \frac{1}{\sin x}$$

The following are conditional equations:

$2x + 5 = 0$ True only if $x = -\frac{5}{2}$

$\sin x = 0$ True only if $x = k\pi$, k an integer

$\sin x = \cos x$ True only if $x = \frac{\pi}{4} + 2k\pi$ or $x = \frac{5\pi}{4} + 2k\pi$, k an integer

The following summarizes the trigonometric identities that we have established thus far.

Quotient Identities

$$\tan\theta = \frac{\sin\theta}{\cos\theta} \qquad \cot\theta = \frac{\cos\theta}{\sin\theta}$$

Reciprocal Identities

$$\csc\theta = \frac{1}{\sin\theta} \qquad \sec\theta = \frac{1}{\cos\theta} \qquad \cot\theta = \frac{1}{\tan\theta}$$

Pythagorean Identities

$$\sin^2\theta + \cos^2\theta = 1 \qquad \tan^2\theta + 1 = \sec^2\theta$$
$$\cot^2\theta + 1 = \csc^2\theta$$

Even–Odd Identities

$$\sin(-\theta) = -\sin\theta \qquad \cos(-\theta) = \cos\theta \qquad \tan(-\theta) = -\tan\theta$$
$$\csc(-\theta) = -\csc\theta \qquad \sec(-\theta) = \sec\theta \qquad \cot(-\theta) = -\cot\theta$$

This list of identities comprises what we shall refer to as the **basic trigonometric identities.** These identities should not merely be memorized, but should be *known* (just as you know your name rather than have it memorized). In fact, minor variations of a basic identity are often used. For example, we might want to use

$$\sin^2\theta = 1 - \cos^2\theta \quad \text{or} \quad \cos^2\theta = 1 - \sin^2\theta$$

instead of $\sin^2\theta + \cos^2\theta = 1$. For this reason, among others, you need to know these relationships and be very comfortable with variations of them.

1 Use Algebra to Simplify Trigonometric Expressions

The ability to use algebra to manipulate trigonometric expressions is a key skill that one must have to establish identities. Some of the techniques used in establishing identities are multiplying by a "well-chosen 1," writing a trigonometric expression over a common denominator, rewriting a trigonometric expression in terms of sine and cosine only, and factoring.

EXAMPLE 1 Using Algebraic Techniques to Simplify Trigonometric Expressions

(a) Simplify $\dfrac{\cot\theta}{\csc\theta}$ by rewriting each trigonometric function in terms of sine and cosine functions.

(b) Show that $\dfrac{\cos\theta}{1+\sin\theta} = \dfrac{1-\sin\theta}{\cos\theta}$ by multiplying the numerator and denominator by $1 - \sin\theta$.

(c) Simplify $\dfrac{1+\sin u}{\sin u} + \dfrac{\cot u - \cos u}{\cos u}$ by rewriting the expression over a common denominator.

(d) Simplify $\dfrac{\sin^2 v - 1}{\tan v \sin v - \tan v}$ by factoring.

Solution

(a) $$\frac{\cot\theta}{\csc\theta} = \frac{\dfrac{\cos\theta}{\sin\theta}}{\dfrac{1}{\sin\theta}} = \frac{\cos\theta}{\sin\theta}\cdot\frac{\sin\theta}{1} = \cos\theta$$

(b) $$\frac{\cos\theta}{1+\sin\theta} = \frac{\cos\theta}{1+\sin\theta}\cdot\frac{1-\sin\theta}{1-\sin\theta} = \frac{\cos\theta(1-\sin\theta)}{1-\sin^2\theta}$$

Multiply by a well-chosen 1: $\dfrac{1-\sin\theta}{1-\sin\theta}$.

$$= \frac{\cos\theta(1-\sin\theta)}{\cos^2\theta} = \frac{1-\sin\theta}{\cos\theta}$$

(c) $$\frac{1+\sin u}{\sin u} + \frac{\cot u - \cos u}{\cos u} = \frac{1+\sin u}{\sin u}\cdot\frac{\cos u}{\cos u} + \frac{\cot u - \cos u}{\cos u}\cdot\frac{\sin u}{\sin u}$$

$$= \frac{\cos u + \sin u\cos u + \cot u \sin u - \cos u \sin u}{\sin u \cos u} = \frac{\cos u + \dfrac{\cos u}{\sin u}\cdot\sin u}{\sin u\cos u}$$

$\cot u = \dfrac{\cos u}{\sin u}$

$$= \frac{\cos u + \cos u}{\sin u\cos u} = \frac{2\cos u}{\sin u \cos u} = \frac{2}{\sin u}$$

(d) $$\frac{\sin^2 v - 1}{\tan v\sin v - \tan v} = \frac{(\sin v + 1)(\sin v - 1)}{\tan v(\sin v - 1)} = \frac{\sin v + 1}{\tan v}$$

■

Now Work PROBLEMS 9, 11, AND 13

2 Establish Identities

In the examples that follow, the directions will read "Establish the identity. . . . " As you will see, this is accomplished by starting with one side of the given equation (usually the one containing the more complicated expression) and, using appropriate basic identities and algebraic manipulations, arriving at the other side. The selection of appropriate basic identities to obtain the desired result is learned only through experience and lots of practice.

EXAMPLE 2 Establishing an Identity

Establish the identity: $\csc\theta \cdot \tan\theta = \sec\theta$

Solution We start with the left side, because it contains the more complicated expression, and apply a reciprocal identity and a quotient identity.

$$\csc\theta \cdot \tan\theta = \frac{1}{\cancel{\sin\theta}} \cdot \frac{\cancel{\sin\theta}}{\cos\theta} = \frac{1}{\cos\theta} = \sec\theta$$

Having arrived at the right side, the identity is established.

NOTE A graphing utility can be used to provide evidence of an identity. For example, if we graph $Y_1 = \csc x \cdot \tan x$ and $Y_2 = \sec x$, the graphs appear to be the same. This provides evidence that $Y_1 = Y_2$. However, it does not prove their equality. *A graphing utility cannot be used to establish an identity—identities must be established algebraically.* ■

Now Work PROBLEM 19

EXAMPLE 3 Establishing an Identity

Establish the identity: $\sin^2(-\theta) + \cos^2(-\theta) = 1$

Solution We begin with the left side and, because the arguments are $-\theta$, apply Even–Odd Identities.

$$\begin{aligned}\sin^2(-\theta) + \cos^2(-\theta) &= [\sin(-\theta)]^2 + [\cos(-\theta)]^2 \\ &= (-\sin\theta)^2 + (\cos\theta)^2 && \text{Even–Odd Identities} \\ &= (\sin\theta)^2 + (\cos\theta)^2 \\ &= 1 && \text{Pythagorean Identity}\end{aligned}$$

EXAMPLE 4 Establishing an Identity

Establish the identity: $\dfrac{\sin^2(-\theta) - \cos^2(-\theta)}{\sin(-\theta) - \cos(-\theta)} = \cos\theta - \sin\theta$

Solution We begin with two observations: The left side contains the more complicated expression. Also, the left side contains expressions with the argument $-\theta$, whereas the right side contains expressions with the argument θ. We decide, therefore, to start with the left side and apply Even–Odd Identities.

$$\begin{aligned}\frac{\sin^2(-\theta) - \cos^2(-\theta)}{\sin(-\theta) - \cos(-\theta)} &= \frac{[\sin(-\theta)]^2 - [\cos(-\theta)]^2}{\sin(-\theta) - \cos(-\theta)} \\ &= \frac{(-\sin\theta)^2 - (\cos\theta)^2}{-\sin\theta - \cos\theta} && \text{Even–Odd Identities} \\ &= \frac{(\sin\theta)^2 - (\cos\theta)^2}{-\sin\theta - \cos\theta} && \text{Simplify.} \\ &= \frac{(\sin\theta - \cos\theta)\cancel{(\sin\theta + \cos\theta)}}{-\cancel{(\sin\theta + \cos\theta)}} && \text{Factor.} \\ &= \frac{\sin\theta - \cos\theta}{-1} = -(\sin\theta - \cos\theta) = -\sin\theta + \cos\theta \\ &= \cos\theta - \sin\theta && \text{Cancel and simplify.}\end{aligned}$$

EXAMPLE 5 **Establishing an Identity**

Establish the identity: $\dfrac{1 + \tan u}{1 + \cot u} = \tan u$

Solution

$$\frac{1 + \tan u}{1 + \cot u} = \frac{1 + \tan u}{1 + \dfrac{1}{\tan u}} = \frac{1 + \tan u}{\dfrac{\tan u + 1}{\tan u}}$$

$$= \frac{\tan u(1 + \tan u)}{\tan u + 1} = \tan u$$

Now Work PROBLEMS 23 AND 27

When sums or differences of quotients appear, it is usually best to rewrite them as a single quotient, especially if the other side of the identity consists of only one term.

EXAMPLE 6 **Establishing an Identity**

Establish the identity: $\dfrac{\sin\theta}{1 + \cos\theta} + \dfrac{1 + \cos\theta}{\sin\theta} = 2\csc\theta$

Solution The left side is more complicated, so we start with it and proceed to add.

$$\frac{\sin\theta}{1 + \cos\theta} + \frac{1 + \cos\theta}{\sin\theta} = \frac{\sin^2\theta + (1 + \cos\theta)^2}{(1 + \cos\theta)(\sin\theta)}$$ Add the quotients.

$$= \frac{\sin^2\theta + 1 + 2\cos\theta + \cos^2\theta}{(1 + \cos\theta)(\sin\theta)}$$ Remove parentheses in the numerator.

$$= \frac{(\sin^2\theta + \cos^2\theta) + 1 + 2\cos\theta}{(1 + \cos\theta)(\sin\theta)}$$ Regroup.

$$= \frac{2 + 2\cos\theta}{(1 + \cos\theta)(\sin\theta)}$$ Pythagorean Identity

$$= \frac{2(1 + \cos\theta)}{(1 + \cos\theta)(\sin\theta)}$$ Factor and cancel.

$$= \frac{2}{\sin\theta}$$

$$= 2\csc\theta$$ Reciprocal Identity

Now Work PROBLEM 49

Sometimes it helps to write one side in terms of sine and cosine functions only.

EXAMPLE 7 **Establishing an Identity**

Establish the identity: $\dfrac{\tan v + \cot v}{\sec v \csc v} = 1$

Solution

$$\frac{\tan v + \cot v}{\sec v \csc v} = \frac{\dfrac{\sin v}{\cos v} + \dfrac{\cos v}{\sin v}}{\dfrac{1}{\cos v} \cdot \dfrac{1}{\sin v}} = \frac{\dfrac{\sin^2 v + \cos^2 v}{\cos v \sin v}}{\dfrac{1}{\cos v \sin v}}$$

Change to sines and cosines. Add the quotients in the numerator.

$$= \frac{1}{\cos v \sin v} \cdot \frac{\cos v \sin v}{1} = 1$$

Divide the quotients; $\sin^2 v + \cos^2 v = 1$.

Now Work PROBLEM 69

Sometimes, multiplying the numerator and denominator by an appropriate factor will result in a simplification.

EXAMPLE 8 Establishing an Identity

Establish the identity: $\dfrac{1 - \sin\theta}{\cos\theta} = \dfrac{\cos\theta}{1 + \sin\theta}$

Solution We start with the left side and multiply the numerator and the denominator by $1 + \sin\theta$. (Alternatively, we could multiply the numerator and denominator of the right side by $1 - \sin\theta$.)

$$\frac{1 - \sin\theta}{\cos\theta} = \frac{1 - \sin\theta}{\cos\theta} \cdot \frac{1 + \sin\theta}{1 + \sin\theta}$$ Multiply the numerator and denominator by $1 + \sin\theta$.

$$= \frac{1 - \sin^2\theta}{\cos\theta(1 + \sin\theta)}$$

$$= \frac{\cos^2\theta}{\cos\theta(1 + \sin\theta)}$$ $1 - \sin^2\theta = \cos^2\theta$

$$= \frac{\cos\theta}{1 + \sin\theta}$$ Cancel.

Now Work PROBLEM 53

Although a lot of practice is the only real way to learn how to establish identities, the following guidelines should prove helpful.

WARNING Be careful not to handle identities to be established as if they were conditional equations. You *cannot* establish an identity by such methods as adding the same expression to each side and obtaining a true statement. This practice is not allowed, because the original statement is precisely the one that you are trying to establish. You do not know until it has been established that it is, in fact, true.

Guidelines for Establishing Identities

1. It is almost always preferable to start with the side containing the more complicated expression.
2. Rewrite sums or differences of quotients as a single quotient.
3. Sometimes rewriting one side in terms of sine and cosine functions only will help.
4. Always keep your goal in mind. As you manipulate one side of the expression, you must keep in mind the form of the expression on the other side.

7.3 Assess Your Understanding

'Are You Prepared?' *Answers are given at the end of these exercises. If you get a wrong answer, read the pages listed in red.*

1. True or False $\sin^2\theta = 1 - \cos^2\theta$. (p. 388)

2. True or False $\sin(-\theta) + \cos(-\theta) = \cos\theta - \sin\theta$. (p. 391)

Concepts and Vocabulary

3. Suppose that f and g are two functions with the same domain. If $f(x) = g(x)$ for every x in the domain, the equation is called a(n) _____. Otherwise, it is called a(n) _____ equation.

4. $\tan^2\theta - \sec^2\theta =$ _____.

5. $\cos(-\theta) - \cos\theta =$ _____.

6. True or False $\sin(-\theta) + \sin\theta = 0$ for any value of θ.

7. True or False In establishing an identity, it is often easiest to just multiply both sides by a well-chosen nonzero expression involving the variable.

8. True or False $\tan\theta \cdot \cos\theta = \sin\theta$ for any $\theta \neq (2k+1)\frac{\pi}{2}$.

Skill Building

In Problems 9–18, simplify each trigonometric expression by following the indicated direction.

9. Rewrite in terms of sine and cosine functions: $\tan\theta \cdot \csc\theta$

10. Rewrite in terms of sine and cosine functions: $\cot\theta \cdot \sec\theta$

11. Multiply $\dfrac{\cos\theta}{1-\sin\theta}$ by $\dfrac{1+\sin\theta}{1+\sin\theta}$.

12. Multiply $\dfrac{\sin\theta}{1+\cos\theta}$ by $\dfrac{1-\cos\theta}{1-\cos\theta}$.

13. Rewrite over a common denominator:
$$\frac{\sin\theta+\cos\theta}{\cos\theta}+\frac{\cos\theta-\sin\theta}{\sin\theta}$$

14. Rewrite over a common denominator:
$$\frac{1}{1-\cos v}+\frac{1}{1+\cos v}$$

15. Multiply and simplify: $\dfrac{(\sin\theta+\cos\theta)(\sin\theta+\cos\theta)-1}{\sin\theta\cos\theta}$

16. Multiply and simplify: $\dfrac{(\tan\theta+1)(\tan\theta+1)-\sec^2\theta}{\tan\theta}$

17. Factor and simplify: $\dfrac{3\sin^2\theta+4\sin\theta+1}{\sin^2\theta+2\sin\theta+1}$

18. Factor and simplify: $\dfrac{\cos^2\theta-1}{\cos^2\theta-\cos\theta}$

In Problems 19–98, establish each identity.

19. $\csc\theta\cdot\cos\theta = \cot\theta$

20. $\sec\theta\cdot\sin\theta = \tan\theta$

21. $1+\tan^2(-\theta) = \sec^2\theta$

22. $1+\cot^2(-\theta) = \csc^2\theta$

23. $\cos\theta(\tan\theta+\cot\theta) = \csc\theta$

24. $\sin\theta(\cot\theta+\tan\theta) = \sec\theta$

25. $\tan u\cot u - \cos^2 u = \sin^2 u$

26. $\sin u\csc u - \cos^2 u = \sin^2 u$

27. $(\sec\theta-1)(\sec\theta+1) = \tan^2\theta$

28. $(\csc\theta-1)(\csc\theta+1) = \cot^2\theta$

29. $(\sec\theta+\tan\theta)(\sec\theta-\tan\theta) = 1$

30. $(\csc\theta+\cot\theta)(\csc\theta-\cot\theta) = 1$

31. $\cos^2\theta(1+\tan^2\theta) = 1$

32. $(1-\cos^2\theta)(1+\cot^2\theta) = 1$

33. $(\sin\theta+\cos\theta)^2+(\sin\theta-\cos\theta)^2 = 2$

34. $\tan^2\theta\cos^2\theta+\cot^2\theta\sin^2\theta = 1$

35. $\sec^4\theta-\sec^2\theta = \tan^4\theta+\tan^2\theta$

36. $\csc^4\theta-\csc^2\theta = \cot^4\theta+\cot^2\theta$

37. $\sec u - \tan u = \dfrac{\cos u}{1+\sin u}$

38. $\csc u - \cot u = \dfrac{\sin u}{1+\cos u}$

39. $3\sin^2\theta+4\cos^2\theta = 3+\cos^2\theta$

40. $9\sec^2\theta-5\tan^2\theta = 5+4\sec^2\theta$

41. $1-\dfrac{\cos^2\theta}{1+\sin\theta} = \sin\theta$

42. $1-\dfrac{\sin^2\theta}{1-\cos\theta} = -\cos\theta$

43. $\dfrac{1+\tan v}{1-\tan v} = \dfrac{\cot v+1}{\cot v-1}$

44. $\dfrac{\csc v-1}{\csc v+1} = \dfrac{1-\sin v}{1+\sin v}$

45. $\dfrac{\sec\theta}{\csc\theta}+\dfrac{\sin\theta}{\cos\theta} = 2\tan\theta$

46. $\dfrac{\csc\theta-1}{\cot\theta} = \dfrac{\cot\theta}{\csc\theta+1}$

47. $\dfrac{1+\sin\theta}{1-\sin\theta} = \dfrac{\csc\theta+1}{\csc\theta-1}$

48. $\dfrac{\cos\theta+1}{\cos\theta-1} = \dfrac{1+\sec\theta}{1-\sec\theta}$

49. $\dfrac{1-\sin v}{\cos v}+\dfrac{\cos v}{1-\sin v} = 2\sec v$

50. $\dfrac{\cos v}{1+\sin v}+\dfrac{1+\sin v}{\cos v} = 2\sec v$

51. $\dfrac{\sin\theta}{\sin\theta-\cos\theta} = \dfrac{1}{1-\cot\theta}$

52. $1-\dfrac{\sin^2\theta}{1+\cos\theta} = \cos\theta$

53. $\dfrac{1-\sin\theta}{1+\sin\theta} = (\sec\theta-\tan\theta)^2$

54. $\dfrac{1-\cos\theta}{1+\cos\theta} = (\csc\theta-\cot\theta)^2$

55. $\dfrac{\cos\theta}{1-\tan\theta}+\dfrac{\sin\theta}{1-\cot\theta} = \sin\theta+\cos\theta$

56. $\dfrac{\cot\theta}{1-\tan\theta}+\dfrac{\tan\theta}{1-\cot\theta} = 1+\tan\theta+\cot\theta$

57. $\tan\theta + \dfrac{\cos\theta}{1+\sin\theta} = \sec\theta$

58. $\dfrac{\sin\theta\cos\theta}{\cos^2\theta - \sin^2\theta} = \dfrac{\tan\theta}{1-\tan^2\theta}$

59. $\dfrac{\tan\theta + \sec\theta - 1}{\tan\theta - \sec\theta + 1} = \tan\theta + \sec\theta$

60. $\dfrac{\sin\theta - \cos\theta + 1}{\sin\theta + \cos\theta - 1} = \dfrac{\sin\theta + 1}{\cos\theta}$

61. $\dfrac{\tan\theta - \cot\theta}{\tan\theta + \cot\theta} = \sin^2\theta - \cos^2\theta$

62. $\dfrac{\sec\theta - \cos\theta}{\sec\theta + \cos\theta} = \dfrac{\sin^2\theta}{1+\cos^2\theta}$

63. $\dfrac{\tan u - \cot u}{\tan u + \cot u} + 1 = 2\sin^2 u$

64. $\dfrac{\tan u - \cot u}{\tan u + \cot u} + 2\cos^2 u = 1$

65. $\dfrac{\sec\theta + \tan\theta}{\cot\theta + \cos\theta} = \tan\theta\sec\theta$

66. $\dfrac{\sec\theta}{1+\sec\theta} = \dfrac{1-\cos\theta}{\sin^2\theta}$

67. $\dfrac{1-\tan^2\theta}{1+\tan^2\theta} + 1 = 2\cos^2\theta$

68. $\dfrac{1-\cot^2\theta}{1+\cot^2\theta} + 2\cos^2\theta = 1$

69. $\dfrac{\sec\theta - \csc\theta}{\sec\theta\csc\theta} = \sin\theta - \cos\theta$

70. $\dfrac{\sin^2\theta - \tan\theta}{\cos^2\theta - \cot\theta} = \tan^2\theta$

71. $\sec\theta - \cos\theta = \sin\theta\tan\theta$

72. $\tan\theta + \cot\theta = \sec\theta\csc\theta$

73. $\dfrac{1}{1-\sin\theta} + \dfrac{1}{1+\sin\theta} = 2\sec^2\theta$

74. $\dfrac{1+\sin\theta}{1-\sin\theta} - \dfrac{1-\sin\theta}{1+\sin\theta} = 4\tan\theta\sec\theta$

75. $\dfrac{\sec\theta}{1-\sin\theta} = \dfrac{1+\sin\theta}{\cos^3\theta}$

76. $\dfrac{1+\sin\theta}{1-\sin\theta} = (\sec\theta + \tan\theta)^2$

77. $\dfrac{(\sec v - \tan v)^2 + 1}{\csc v(\sec v - \tan v)} = 2\tan v$

78. $\dfrac{\sec^2 v - \tan^2 v + \tan v}{\sec v} = \sin v + \cos v$

79. $\dfrac{\sin\theta + \cos\theta}{\cos\theta} - \dfrac{\sin\theta - \cos\theta}{\sin\theta} = \sec\theta\csc\theta$

80. $\dfrac{\sin\theta + \cos\theta}{\sin\theta} - \dfrac{\cos\theta - \sin\theta}{\cos\theta} = \sec\theta\csc\theta$

81. $\dfrac{\sin^3\theta + \cos^3\theta}{\sin\theta + \cos\theta} = 1 - \sin\theta\cos\theta$

82. $\dfrac{\sin^3\theta + \cos^3\theta}{1 - 2\cos^2\theta} = \dfrac{\sec\theta - \sin\theta}{\tan\theta - 1}$

83. $\dfrac{\cos^2\theta - \sin^2\theta}{1 - \tan^2\theta} = \cos^2\theta$

84. $\dfrac{\cos\theta + \sin\theta - \sin^3\theta}{\sin\theta} = \cot\theta + \cos^2\theta$

85. $\dfrac{(2\cos^2\theta - 1)^2}{\cos^4\theta - \sin^4\theta} = 1 - 2\sin^2\theta$

86. $\dfrac{1 - 2\cos^2\theta}{\sin\theta\cos\theta} = \tan\theta - \cot\theta$

87. $\dfrac{1 + \sin\theta + \cos\theta}{1 + \sin\theta - \cos\theta} = \dfrac{1+\cos\theta}{\sin\theta}$

88. $\dfrac{1 + \cos\theta + \sin\theta}{1 + \cos\theta - \sin\theta} = \sec\theta + \tan\theta$

89. $(a\sin\theta + b\cos\theta)^2 + (a\cos\theta - b\sin\theta)^2 = a^2 + b^2$

90. $(2a\sin\theta\cos\theta)^2 + a^2(\cos^2\theta - \sin^2\theta)^2 = a^2$

91. $\dfrac{\tan\alpha + \tan\beta}{\cot\alpha + \cot\beta} = \tan\alpha\tan\beta$

92. $(\tan\alpha + \tan\beta)(1 - \cot\alpha\cot\beta) + (\cot\alpha + \cot\beta)(1 - \tan\alpha\tan\beta) = 0$

93. $(\sin\alpha + \cos\beta)^2 + (\cos\beta + \sin\alpha)(\cos\beta - \sin\alpha) = 2\cos\beta(\sin\alpha + \cos\beta)$

94. $(\sin\alpha - \cos\beta)^2 + (\cos\beta + \sin\alpha)(\cos\beta - \sin\alpha) = -2\cos\beta(\sin\alpha - \cos\beta)$

95. $\ln|\sec\theta| = -\ln|\cos\theta|$

96. $\ln|\tan\theta| = \ln|\sin\theta| - \ln|\cos\theta|$

97. $\ln|1 + \cos\theta| + \ln|1 - \cos\theta| = 2\ln|\sin\theta|$

98. $\ln|\sec\theta + \tan\theta| + \ln|\sec\theta - \tan\theta| = 0$

In Problems 99–102, show that the functions f and g are identically equal.

99. $f(x) = \sin x \cdot \tan x, \quad g(x) = \sec x - \cos x$

100. $f(x) = \cos x \cdot \cot x, \quad g(x) = \csc x - \sin x$

101. $f(\theta) = \dfrac{1-\sin\theta}{\cos\theta} - \dfrac{\cos\theta}{1+\sin\theta}, \quad g(\theta) = 0$

102. $f(\theta) = \tan\theta + \sec\theta, \quad g(\theta) = \dfrac{\cos\theta}{1-\sin\theta}$

Applications and Extensions

103. Searchlights A searchlight at the grand opening of a new car dealership casts a spot of light on a wall located 75 meters from the searchlight. The acceleration $\ddot{r}$ of the spot of light is found to be $\ddot{r} = 1200 \sec \theta (2 \sec^2 \theta - 1)$. Show that this is equivalent to $\ddot{r} = 1200\left(\dfrac{1 + \sin^2 \theta}{\cos^3 \theta}\right)$.

Source: Adapted from Hibbeler, *Engineering Mechanics: Dynamics,* 10th ed. © 2004.

104. Optical Measurement Optical methods of measurement often rely on the interference of two light waves. If two light waves, identical except for a phase lag, are mixed together, the resulting intensity, or irradiance, is given by $I_t = 4A^2 \dfrac{(\csc \theta - 1)(\sec \theta + \tan \theta)}{\csc \theta \sec \theta}$. Show that this is equivalent to $I_t = (2A \cos \theta)^2$.

Source: *Experimental Techniques,* July/August 2002.

Discussion and Writing

105. Write a few paragraphs outlining your strategy for establishing identities.

106. Write down the three Pythagorean Identities.

107. Why do you think it is usually preferable to start with the side containing the more complicated expression when establishing an identity?

108. Make up an identity that is not a Fundamental Identity.

'Are You Prepared?' Answers

1. True **2.** True

7.4 Sum and Difference Formulas

PREPARING FOR THIS SECTION *Before getting started, review the following:*

- Distance Formula (Section 1.1, pp. 4–6)
- Values of the Trigonometric Functions (Section 6.2, pp. 365–377)
- Finding Exact Values Given the Value of a Trigonometric Function and the Quadrant of the Angle (Section 6.3, pp. 389–391)

Now Work the 'Are You Prepared?' problems on page 473.

OBJECTIVES
1. Use Sum and Difference Formulas to Find Exact Values (p. 467)
2. Use Sum and Difference Formulas to Establish Identities (p. 468)
3. Use Sum and Difference Formulas Involving Inverse Trigonometric Functions (p. 472)

In this section, we continue our derivation of trigonometric identities by obtaining formulas that involve the sum or difference of two angles, such as $\cos(\alpha + \beta)$, $\cos(\alpha - \beta)$, or $\sin(\alpha + \beta)$. These formulas are referred to as the **sum and difference formulas.** We begin with the formulas for $\cos(\alpha + \beta)$ and $\cos(\alpha - \beta)$.

THEOREM

Sum and Difference Formulas for the Cosine Function

$$\cos(\alpha + \beta) = \cos \alpha \cos \beta - \sin \alpha \sin \beta \quad (1)$$

$$\cos(\alpha - \beta) = \cos \alpha \cos \beta + \sin \alpha \sin \beta \quad (2)$$

In Words

Formula (1) states that the cosine of the sum of two angles equals the cosine of the first angle times the cosine of the second angle minus the sine of the first angle times the sine of the second angle.

Proof We will prove formula (2) first. Although this formula is true for all numbers α and β, we shall assume in our proof that $0 < \beta < \alpha < 2\pi$. We begin with the unit circle and place the angles α and β in standard position, as shown in Figure 24(a). The point P_1 lies on the terminal side of β, so its coordinates are $(\cos \beta, \sin \beta)$; and the point P_2 lies on the terminal side of α, so its coordinates are $(\cos \alpha, \sin \alpha)$.

Now place the angle $\alpha - \beta$ in standard position, as shown in Figure 24(b). The point A has coordinates $(1, 0)$, and the point P_3 is on the terminal side of the angle $\alpha - \beta$, so its coordinates are $(\cos(\alpha - \beta), \sin(\alpha - \beta))$.

Figure 24

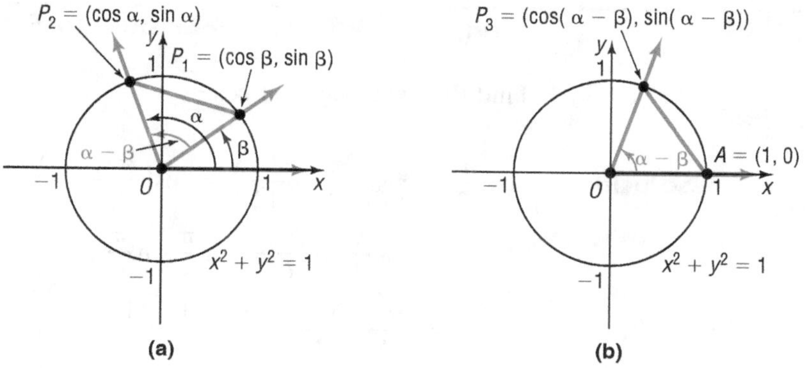

Looking at triangle OP_1P_2 in Figure 24(a) and triangle OAP_3 in Figure 24(b), we see that these triangles are congruent. (Do you see why? We have SAS: two sides and the included angle, $\alpha - \beta$, are equal.) As a result, the unknown side of each triangle must be equal; that is,

$$d(A, P_3) = d(P_1, P_2)$$

Using the distance formula, we find that

$$\sqrt{[\cos(\alpha - \beta) - 1]^2 + [\sin(\alpha - \beta) - 0]^2} = \sqrt{(\cos \alpha - \cos \beta)^2 + (\sin \alpha - \sin \beta)^2} \quad d(A, P_3) = d(P_1, P_2)$$

$$[\cos(\alpha - \beta) - 1]^2 + \sin^2(\alpha - \beta) = (\cos \alpha - \cos \beta)^2 + (\sin \alpha - \sin \beta)^2 \quad \text{Square both sides.}$$

$$\cos^2(\alpha - \beta) - 2\cos(\alpha - \beta) + 1 + \sin^2(\alpha - \beta) = \cos^2 \alpha - 2 \cos \alpha \cos \beta + \cos^2 \beta + \sin^2 \alpha - 2 \sin \alpha \sin \beta + \sin^2 \beta \quad \text{Multiply out the squared terms.}$$

$$2 - 2\cos(\alpha - \beta) = 2 - 2 \cos \alpha \cos \beta - 2 \sin \alpha \sin \beta \quad \text{Apply a Pythagorean Identity (3 times).}$$

$$-2\cos(\alpha - \beta) = -2 \cos \alpha \cos \beta - 2 \sin \alpha \sin \beta \quad \text{Subtract 2 from each side.}$$

$$\cos(\alpha - \beta) = \cos \alpha \cos \beta + \sin \alpha \sin \beta \quad \text{Divide each side by } -2.$$

This is formula (2). ■

The proof of formula (1) follows from formula (2) and the Even–Odd Identities. We use the fact that $\alpha + \beta = \alpha - (-\beta)$. Then

$$\begin{aligned} \cos(\alpha + \beta) &= \cos[\alpha - (-\beta)] \\ &= \cos \alpha \cos(-\beta) + \sin \alpha \sin(-\beta) && \text{Use formula (2).} \\ &= \cos \alpha \cos \beta - \sin \alpha \sin \beta && \text{Even–Odd Identities} \end{aligned}$$

1 Use Sum and Difference Formulas to Find Exact Values

One use of formulas (1) and (2) is to obtain the exact value of the cosine of an angle that can be expressed as the sum or difference of angles whose sine and cosine are known exactly.

EXAMPLE 1 Using the Sum Formula to Find Exact Values

Find the exact value of $\cos 75°$.

Solution Since $75° = 45° + 30°$, we use formula (1) to obtain

$$\cos 75° = \cos(45° + 30°) \underset{\text{Formula (1)}}{=} \cos 45° \cos 30° - \sin 45° \sin 30°$$

$$= \frac{\sqrt{2}}{2} \cdot \frac{\sqrt{3}}{2} - \frac{\sqrt{2}}{2} \cdot \frac{1}{2} = \frac{1}{4}\left(\sqrt{6} - \sqrt{2}\right)$$

■

EXAMPLE 2 **Using the Difference Formula to Find Exact Values**

Find the exact value of $\cos \frac{\pi}{12}$.

Solution

$$\cos \frac{\pi}{12} = \cos\left(\frac{3\pi}{12} - \frac{2\pi}{12}\right) = \cos\left(\frac{\pi}{4} - \frac{\pi}{6}\right)$$

$$= \cos \frac{\pi}{4} \cos \frac{\pi}{6} + \sin \frac{\pi}{4} \sin \frac{\pi}{6} \quad \text{Use formula (2).}$$

$$= \frac{\sqrt{2}}{2} \cdot \frac{\sqrt{3}}{2} + \frac{\sqrt{2}}{2} \cdot \frac{1}{2} = \frac{1}{4}(\sqrt{6} + \sqrt{2})$$

Now Work PROBLEM 11

2 Use Sum and Difference Formulas to Establish Identities

Another use of formulas (1) and (2) is to establish other identities. Two important identities are given next.

Seeing the Concept

Graph $Y_1 = \cos\left(\frac{\pi}{2} - \theta\right)$ and $Y_2 = \sin \theta$ on the same screen. Does this demonstrate the result 3(a)? How would you demonstrate the result 3(b)?

$$\cos\left(\frac{\pi}{2} - \theta\right) = \sin \theta \quad \textbf{(3a)}$$

$$\sin\left(\frac{\pi}{2} - \theta\right) = \cos \theta \quad \textbf{(3b)}$$

Proof To prove formula (3a), we use the formula for $\cos(\alpha - \beta)$ with $\alpha = \frac{\pi}{2}$ and $\beta = \theta$.

$$\cos\left(\frac{\pi}{2} - \theta\right) = \cos \frac{\pi}{2} \cos \theta + \sin \frac{\pi}{2} \sin \theta$$

$$= 0 \cdot \cos \theta + 1 \cdot \sin \theta$$

$$= \sin \theta$$

To prove formula (3b), we make use of the identity (3a) just established.

$$\sin\left(\frac{\pi}{2} - \theta\right) \underset{\text{Use (3a)}}{=} \cos\left[\frac{\pi}{2} - \left(\frac{\pi}{2} - \theta\right)\right] = \cos \theta$$

■

Formulas (3a) and (3b) should look familiar. They are the basis for the theorem stated in Chapter 6: Cofunctions of complementary angles are equal. Also, since

$$\cos\left(\frac{\pi}{2} - \theta\right) = \cos\left[-\left(\theta - \frac{\pi}{2}\right)\right] \underset{\text{Even property of cosine}}{=} \cos\left(\theta - \frac{\pi}{2}\right)$$

and since

$$\cos\left(\frac{\pi}{2} - \theta\right) \underset{\text{3(a)}}{=} \sin \theta$$

it follows that $\cos\left(\theta - \frac{\pi}{2}\right) = \sin \theta$. The graphs of $y = \cos\left(\theta - \frac{\pi}{2}\right)$ and $y = \sin \theta$ are identical.

Having established the identities in formulas (3a) and (3b), we now can derive the sum and difference formulas for $\sin(\alpha + \beta)$ and $\sin(\alpha - \beta)$.

Proof

$$\sin(\alpha+\beta) = \cos\left[\frac{\pi}{2} - (\alpha+\beta)\right] \quad \text{Formula (3a)}$$
$$= \cos\left[\left(\frac{\pi}{2} - \alpha\right) - \beta\right]$$
$$= \cos\left(\frac{\pi}{2} - \alpha\right)\cos\beta + \sin\left(\frac{\pi}{2} - \alpha\right)\sin\beta \quad \text{Formula (2)}$$
$$= \sin\alpha\cos\beta + \cos\alpha\sin\beta \quad \text{Formulas (3a) and (3b)}$$
$$\sin(\alpha-\beta) = \sin[\alpha + (-\beta)]$$
$$= \sin\alpha\cos(-\beta) + \cos\alpha\sin(-\beta) \quad \text{Use the sum formula for the sine just obtained.}$$
$$= \sin\alpha\cos\beta + \cos\alpha(-\sin\beta) \quad \text{Even–Odd Identities}$$
$$= \sin\alpha\cos\beta - \cos\alpha\sin\beta$$

■

In Words

Formula (4) states that the sine of the sum of two angles equals the sine of the first angle times the cosine of the second angle plus the cosine of the first angle times the sine of the second angle.

THEOREM

Sum and Difference Formulas for the Sine Function

$$\sin(\alpha+\beta) = \sin\alpha\cos\beta + \cos\alpha\sin\beta \quad \textbf{(4)}$$
$$\sin(\alpha-\beta) = \sin\alpha\cos\beta - \cos\alpha\sin\beta \quad \textbf{(5)}$$

EXAMPLE 3 Using the Sum Formula to Find Exact Values

Find the exact value of $\sin\frac{7\pi}{12}$.

Solution

$$\sin\frac{7\pi}{12} = \sin\left(\frac{3\pi}{12} + \frac{4\pi}{12}\right) = \sin\left(\frac{\pi}{4} + \frac{\pi}{3}\right)$$
$$= \sin\frac{\pi}{4}\cos\frac{\pi}{3} + \cos\frac{\pi}{4}\sin\frac{\pi}{3} \quad \text{Formula (4)}$$
$$= \frac{\sqrt{2}}{2}\cdot\frac{1}{2} + \frac{\sqrt{2}}{2}\cdot\frac{\sqrt{3}}{2} = \frac{1}{4}\left(\sqrt{2} + \sqrt{6}\right)$$

Now Work PROBLEM 17

EXAMPLE 4 Using the Difference Formula to Find Exact Values

Find the exact value of $\sin 80^\circ \cos 20^\circ - \cos 80^\circ \sin 20^\circ$.

Solution The form of the expression $\sin 80^\circ \cos 20^\circ - \cos 80^\circ \sin 20^\circ$ is that of the right side of formula (5) for $\sin(\alpha - \beta)$ with $\alpha = 80^\circ$ and $\beta = 20^\circ$. That is,

$$\sin 80^\circ \cos 20^\circ - \cos 80^\circ \sin 20^\circ = \sin(80^\circ - 20^\circ) = \sin 60^\circ = \frac{\sqrt{3}}{2}$$

Now Work PROBLEMS 23 AND 27

EXAMPLE 5 Finding Exact Values

If it is known that $\sin\alpha = \frac{4}{5}$, $\frac{\pi}{2} < \alpha < \pi$, and that $\sin\beta = -\frac{2}{\sqrt{5}} = -\frac{2\sqrt{5}}{5}$, $\pi < \beta < \frac{3\pi}{2}$, find the exact value of

(a) $\cos\alpha$ (b) $\cos\beta$ (c) $\cos(\alpha+\beta)$ (d) $\sin(\alpha+\beta)$

Solution (a) Since $\sin\alpha = \frac{4}{5} = \frac{y}{r}$ and $\frac{\pi}{2} < \alpha < \pi$, we let $y = 4$ and $r = 5$ and place α in quadrant II. The point $P = (x, y) = (x, 4)$, $x < 0$, is on a circle of radius 5, that is, $x^2 + y^2 = 25$. See Figure 25. Then

Figure 25

$\sin\alpha = \frac{4}{5}, \frac{\pi}{2} < \alpha < \pi$

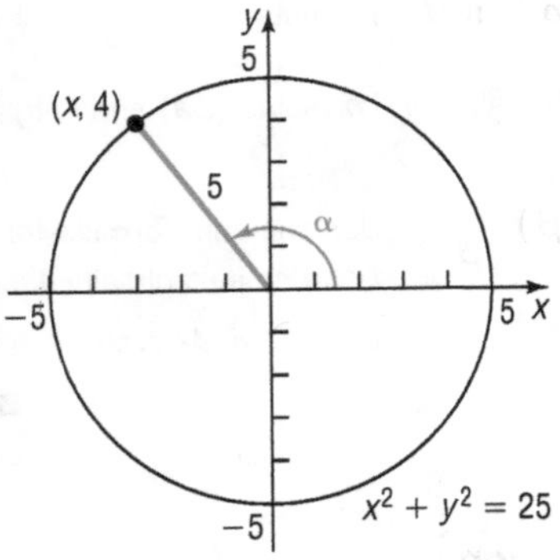

$$\begin{aligned} x^2 + y^2 &= 25 \\ x^2 + 16 &= 25 \quad && y = 4 \\ x^2 &= 25 - 16 = 9 \\ x &= -3 && x < 0 \end{aligned}$$

Then

$$\cos\alpha = \frac{x}{r} = -\frac{3}{5}$$

Alternatively, we can find $\cos\alpha$ using identities, as follows:

$$\cos\alpha = -\sqrt{1 - \sin^2\alpha} = -\sqrt{1 - \frac{16}{25}} = -\sqrt{\frac{9}{25}} = -\frac{3}{5}$$

$\uparrow$ α in quadrant II, $\cos\alpha < 0$

(b) Since $\sin\beta = \frac{-2}{\sqrt{5}} = \frac{y}{r}$ and $\pi < \beta < \frac{3\pi}{2}$, we let $y = -2$ and $r = \sqrt{5}$ and place β in quadrant III. The point $P = (x, y) = (x, -2)$, $x < 0$, is on a circle of radius $\sqrt{5}$, that is, $x^2 + y^2 = 5$. See Figure 26. Then,

Figure 26

$\sin\beta = \frac{-2}{\sqrt{5}}, \pi < \beta < \frac{3\pi}{2}$

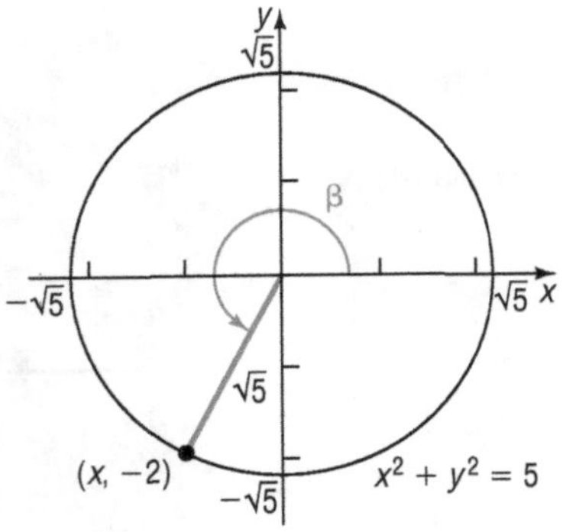

$$\begin{aligned} x^2 + y^2 &= 5 \\ x^2 + 4 &= 5 \quad && y = -2 \\ x^2 &= 1 \\ x &= -1 && x < 0 \end{aligned}$$

Then

$$\cos\beta = \frac{x}{r} = \frac{-1}{\sqrt{5}} = -\frac{\sqrt{5}}{5}$$

Alternatively, we can find $\cos\beta$ using identities, as follows:

$$\cos\beta = -\sqrt{1 - \sin^2\beta} = -\sqrt{1 - \frac{4}{5}} = -\sqrt{\frac{1}{5}} = -\frac{\sqrt{5}}{5}$$

(c) Using the results found in parts (a) and (b) and formula (1), we have

$$\begin{aligned} \cos(\alpha + \beta) &= \cos\alpha\cos\beta - \sin\alpha\sin\beta \\ &= -\frac{3}{5}\left(-\frac{\sqrt{5}}{5}\right) - \frac{4}{5}\left(-\frac{2\sqrt{5}}{5}\right) = \frac{11\sqrt{5}}{25} \end{aligned}$$

(d)
$$\begin{aligned} \sin(\alpha + \beta) &= \sin\alpha\cos\beta + \cos\alpha\sin\beta \\ &= \frac{4}{5}\left(-\frac{\sqrt{5}}{5}\right) + \left(-\frac{3}{5}\right)\left(-\frac{2\sqrt{5}}{5}\right) = \frac{2\sqrt{5}}{25} \end{aligned}$$

Now Work PROBLEMS 31(a), (b), AND (c)

EXAMPLE 6 Establishing an Identity

Establish the identity: $\dfrac{\cos(\alpha - \beta)}{\sin\alpha\sin\beta} = \cot\alpha\cot\beta + 1$

Solution

$$\frac{\cos(\alpha-\beta)}{\sin\alpha\sin\beta} = \frac{\cos\alpha\cos\beta+\sin\alpha\sin\beta}{\sin\alpha\sin\beta} = \frac{\cos\alpha\cos\beta}{\sin\alpha\sin\beta}+\frac{\sin\alpha\sin\beta}{\sin\alpha\sin\beta} = \frac{\cos\alpha}{\sin\alpha}\cdot\frac{\cos\beta}{\sin\beta}+1 = \cot\alpha\cot\beta+1$$

Now Work PROBLEMS 45 AND 57

We use the identity $\tan\theta = \frac{\sin\theta}{\cos\theta}$ and the sum formulas for $\sin(\alpha+\beta)$ and $\cos(\alpha+\beta)$ to derive a formula for $\tan(\alpha+\beta)$.

Proof $\tan(\alpha+\beta) = \frac{\sin(\alpha+\beta)}{\cos(\alpha+\beta)} = \frac{\sin\alpha\cos\beta+\cos\alpha\sin\beta}{\cos\alpha\cos\beta-\sin\alpha\sin\beta}$

Now we divide the numerator and denominator by $\cos\alpha\cos\beta$.

$$\tan(\alpha+\beta) = \frac{\frac{\sin\alpha\cos\beta+\cos\alpha\sin\beta}{\cos\alpha\cos\beta}}{\frac{\cos\alpha\cos\beta-\sin\alpha\sin\beta}{\cos\alpha\cos\beta}} = \frac{\frac{\sin\alpha\cancel{\cos\beta}}{\cos\alpha\cancel{\cos\beta}}+\frac{\cancel{\cos\alpha}\sin\beta}{\cancel{\cos\alpha}\cos\beta}}{\frac{\cancel{\cos\alpha\cos\beta}}{\cancel{\cos\alpha\cos\beta}}-\frac{\sin\alpha\sin\beta}{\cos\alpha\cos\beta}}$$

$$= \frac{\frac{\sin\alpha}{\cos\alpha}+\frac{\sin\beta}{\cos\beta}}{1-\frac{\sin\alpha}{\cos\alpha}\cdot\frac{\sin\beta}{\cos\beta}} = \frac{\tan\alpha+\tan\beta}{1-\tan\alpha\tan\beta}$$ ■

Proof We use the sum formula for $\tan(\alpha+\beta)$ and Even–Odd Properties to get the difference formula.

$$\tan(\alpha-\beta) = \tan[\alpha+(-\beta)] = \frac{\tan\alpha+\tan(-\beta)}{1-\tan\alpha\tan(-\beta)} = \frac{\tan\alpha-\tan\beta}{1+\tan\alpha\tan\beta}$$ ■

We have proved the following results:

THEOREM

Sum and Difference Formulas for the Tangent Function

$$\tan(\alpha+\beta) = \frac{\tan\alpha+\tan\beta}{1-\tan\alpha\tan\beta} \quad (6)$$

$$\tan(\alpha-\beta) = \frac{\tan\alpha-\tan\beta}{1+\tan\alpha\tan\beta} \quad (7)$$

In Words

Formula (6) states that the tangent of the sum of two angles equals the tangent of the first angle plus the tangent of the second angle, all divided by 1 minus their product.

Now Work PROBLEM 31(d)

EXAMPLE 7 Establishing an Identity

Prove the identity: $\tan(\theta+\pi) = \tan\theta$

Solution

$$\tan(\theta+\pi) = \frac{\tan\theta+\tan\pi}{1-\tan\theta\tan\pi} = \frac{\tan\theta+0}{1-\tan\theta\cdot 0} = \tan\theta$$

The result obtained in Example 7 verifies that the tangent function is periodic with period π, a fact that we discussed earlier.

EXAMPLE 8 **Establishing an Identity**

Prove the identity: $\tan\left(\theta + \frac{\pi}{2}\right) = -\cot\theta$

Solution We cannot use formula (6), since $\tan\frac{\pi}{2}$ is not defined. Instead, we proceed as follows:

$$\tan\left(\theta + \frac{\pi}{2}\right) = \frac{\sin\left(\theta + \frac{\pi}{2}\right)}{\cos\left(\theta + \frac{\pi}{2}\right)} = \frac{\sin\theta\cos\frac{\pi}{2} + \cos\theta\sin\frac{\pi}{2}}{\cos\theta\cos\frac{\pi}{2} - \sin\theta\sin\frac{\pi}{2}}$$

$$= \frac{(\sin\theta)(0) + (\cos\theta)(1)}{(\cos\theta)(0) - (\sin\theta)(1)} = \frac{\cos\theta}{-\sin\theta} = -\cot\theta$$

WARNING Be careful when using formulas (6) and (7). These formulas can be used only for angles α and β for which $\tan\alpha$ and $\tan\beta$ are defined, that is, all angles except odd integer multiples of $\frac{\pi}{2}$. ■

3 Use Sum and Difference Formulas Involving Inverse Trigonometric Functions

EXAMPLE 9 **Finding the Exact Value of an Expression Involving Inverse Trigonometric Functions**

Find the exact value of: $\sin\left(\cos^{-1}\frac{1}{2} + \sin^{-1}\frac{3}{5}\right)$

Solution We seek the sine of the sum of two angles, $\alpha = \cos^{-1}\frac{1}{2}$ and $\beta = \sin^{-1}\frac{3}{5}$. Then

$$\cos\alpha = \frac{1}{2} \quad 0 \le \alpha \le \pi \quad \text{and} \quad \sin\beta = \frac{3}{5} \quad -\frac{\pi}{2} \le \beta \le \frac{\pi}{2}$$

We use Pythagorean Identities to obtain $\sin\alpha$ and $\cos\beta$. Since $\sin\alpha \ge 0$ and $\cos\beta \ge 0$ (do you know why?), we find

$$\sin\alpha = \sqrt{1 - \cos^2\alpha} = \sqrt{1 - \frac{1}{4}} = \sqrt{\frac{3}{4}} = \frac{\sqrt{3}}{2}$$

$$\cos\beta = \sqrt{1 - \sin^2\beta} = \sqrt{1 - \frac{9}{25}} = \sqrt{\frac{16}{25}} = \frac{4}{5}$$

NOTE In Example 9, we could also find $\sin\alpha$ by using $\cos\alpha = \frac{1}{2} = \frac{x}{r}$, so $x = 1$ and $r = 2$. Then $b = \sqrt{3}$ and $\sin\alpha = \frac{y}{r} = \frac{\sqrt{3}}{2}$. We could find $\cos\beta$ in a similar fashion. ■

As a result,

$$\sin\left(\cos^{-1}\frac{1}{2} + \sin^{-1}\frac{3}{5}\right) = \sin(\alpha + \beta) = \sin\alpha\cos\beta + \cos\alpha\sin\beta$$

$$= \frac{\sqrt{3}}{2}\cdot\frac{4}{5} + \frac{1}{2}\cdot\frac{3}{5} = \frac{4\sqrt{3} + 3}{10}$$

Now Work PROBLEM 73

EXAMPLE 10 **Writing a Trigonometric Expression as an Algebraic Expression**

Write $\sin(\sin^{-1}u + \cos^{-1}v)$ as an algebraic expression containing u and v (that is, without any trigonometric functions). Give the restrictions on u and v.

Solution First, for $\sin^{-1}u$, we have $-1 \le u \le 1$ and for $\cos^{-1}v$, we have $-1 \le v \le 1$. Now let $\alpha = \sin^{-1}u$ and $\beta = \cos^{-1}v$. Then

$$\sin\alpha = u \quad -\frac{\pi}{2} \le \alpha \le \frac{\pi}{2} \quad -1 \le u \le 1$$

$$\cos\beta = v \quad 0 \le \beta \le \pi \quad -1 \le v \le 1$$

Since $-\frac{\pi}{2} \le \alpha \le \frac{\pi}{2}$, we know that $\cos\alpha \ge 0$. As a result,

$$\cos\alpha = \sqrt{1-\sin^2\alpha} = \sqrt{1-u^2}$$

Similarly, since $0 \le \beta \le \pi$, we know that $\sin\beta \ge 0$. Then

$$\sin\beta = \sqrt{1-\cos^2\beta} = \sqrt{1-v^2}$$

As a result,

$$\sin(\sin^{-1}u + \cos^{-1}v) = \sin(\alpha+\beta) = \sin\alpha\cos\beta + \cos\alpha\sin\beta$$
$$= uv + \sqrt{1-u^2}\sqrt{1-v^2}$$

Now Work PROBLEM 83

SUMMARY Sum and Difference Formulas

$$\cos(\alpha+\beta) = \cos\alpha\cos\beta - \sin\alpha\sin\beta \qquad \cos(\alpha-\beta) = \cos\alpha\cos\beta + \sin\alpha\sin\beta$$
$$\sin(\alpha+\beta) = \sin\alpha\cos\beta + \cos\alpha\sin\beta \qquad \sin(\alpha-\beta) = \sin\alpha\cos\beta - \cos\alpha\sin\beta$$
$$\tan(\alpha+\beta) = \frac{\tan\alpha+\tan\beta}{1-\tan\alpha\tan\beta} \qquad \tan(\alpha-\beta) = \frac{\tan\alpha-\tan\beta}{1+\tan\alpha\tan\beta}$$

7.4 Assess Your Understanding

'Are You Prepared?' *Answers are given at the end of these exercises. If you get a wrong answer, read the pages listed in red.*

1. The distance d from the point $(2, -3)$ to the point $(5, 1)$ is ______. (pp. 4–6)

2. If $\sin\theta = \frac{4}{5}$ and θ is in quadrant II, then $\cos\theta =$ ______. (pp. 389–391)

3. (a) $\sin\frac{\pi}{4}\cdot\cos\frac{\pi}{3} =$ ______. (pp. 370–374)
(b) $\tan\frac{\pi}{4} - \sin\frac{\pi}{6} =$ ______. (pp. 370–374)

Concepts and Vocabulary

4. $\cos(\alpha+\beta) = \cos\alpha\cos\beta$ ____ $\sin\alpha\sin\beta$

5. $\sin(\alpha-\beta) = \sin\alpha\cos\beta$ ____ $\cos\alpha\sin\beta$

6. True or False $\sin(\alpha+\beta) = \sin\alpha + \sin\beta + 2\sin\alpha\sin\beta$

7. True or False $\tan 75^\circ = \tan 30^\circ + \tan 45^\circ$

8. True or False $\cos\left(\frac{\pi}{2}-\theta\right) = \cos\theta$

Skill Building

In Problems 9–20, find the exact value of each expression.

9. $\sin\frac{5\pi}{12}$ **10.** $\sin\frac{\pi}{12}$ **11.** $\cos\frac{7\pi}{12}$ **12.** $\tan\frac{7\pi}{12}$ **13.** $\cos 165^\circ$ **14.** $\sin 105^\circ$

15. $\tan 15^\circ$ **16.** $\tan 195^\circ$ **17.** $\sin\frac{17\pi}{12}$ **18.** $\tan\frac{19\pi}{12}$ **19.** $\sec\left(-\frac{\pi}{12}\right)$ **20.** $\cot\left(-\frac{5\pi}{12}\right)$

In Problems 21–30, find the exact value of each expression.

21. $\sin 20^\circ\cos 10^\circ + \cos 20^\circ\sin 10^\circ$

22. $\sin 20^\circ\cos 80^\circ - \cos 20^\circ\sin 80^\circ$

23. $\cos 70^\circ\cos 20^\circ - \sin 70^\circ\sin 20^\circ$

24. $\cos 40^\circ\cos 10^\circ + \sin 40^\circ\sin 10^\circ$

25. $\dfrac{\tan 20^\circ + \tan 25^\circ}{1 - \tan 20^\circ\tan 25^\circ}$

26. $\dfrac{\tan 40^\circ - \tan 10^\circ}{1 + \tan 40^\circ\tan 10^\circ}$

27. $\sin\frac{\pi}{12}\cos\frac{7\pi}{12} - \cos\frac{\pi}{12}\sin\frac{7\pi}{12}$

28. $\cos\frac{5\pi}{12}\cos\frac{7\pi}{12} - \sin\frac{5\pi}{12}\sin\frac{7\pi}{12}$

29. $\cos\frac{\pi}{12}\cos\frac{5\pi}{12} + \sin\frac{5\pi}{12}\sin\frac{\pi}{12}$

30. $\sin\frac{\pi}{18}\cos\frac{5\pi}{18} + \cos\frac{\pi}{18}\sin\frac{5\pi}{18}$

In Problems 31–36, find the exact value of each of the following under the given conditions:

(a) $\sin(\alpha + \beta)$ (b) $\cos(\alpha + \beta)$ (c) $\sin(\alpha - \beta)$ (d) $\tan(\alpha - \beta)$

31. $\sin \alpha = \frac{3}{5}, 0 < \alpha < \frac{\pi}{2}$; $\cos \beta = \frac{2\sqrt{5}}{5}, -\frac{\pi}{2} < \beta < 0$

32. $\cos \alpha = \frac{\sqrt{5}}{5}, 0 < \alpha < \frac{\pi}{2}$; $\sin \beta = -\frac{4}{5}, -\frac{\pi}{2} < \beta < 0$

33. $\tan \alpha = -\frac{4}{3}, \frac{\pi}{2} < \alpha < \pi$; $\cos \beta = \frac{1}{2}, 0 < \beta < \frac{\pi}{2}$

34. $\tan \alpha = \frac{5}{12}, \pi < \alpha < \frac{3\pi}{2}$; $\sin \beta = -\frac{1}{2}, \pi < \beta < \frac{3\pi}{2}$

35. $\sin \alpha = \frac{5}{13}, -\frac{3\pi}{2} < \alpha < -\pi$; $\tan \beta = -\sqrt{3}, \frac{\pi}{2} < \beta < \pi$

36. $\cos \alpha = \frac{1}{2}, -\frac{\pi}{2} < \alpha < 0$; $\sin \beta = \frac{1}{3}, 0 < \beta < \frac{\pi}{2}$

37. If $\sin \theta = \frac{1}{3}$, θ in quadrant II, find the exact value of:

(a) $\cos \theta$ (b) $\sin\left(\theta + \frac{\pi}{6}\right)$

(c) $\cos\left(\theta - \frac{\pi}{3}\right)$ (d) $\tan\left(\theta + \frac{\pi}{4}\right)$

38. If $\cos \theta = \frac{1}{4}$, θ in quadrant IV, find the exact value of:

(a) $\sin \theta$ (b) $\sin\left(\theta - \frac{\pi}{6}\right)$

(c) $\cos\left(\theta + \frac{\pi}{3}\right)$ (d) $\tan\left(\theta - \frac{\pi}{4}\right)$

In Problems 39–44, use the figures to evaluate each function if $f(x) = \sin x$, $g(x) = \cos x$, and $h(x) = \tan x$.

39. $f(\alpha + \beta)$ 40. $g(\alpha + \beta)$ 41. $g(\alpha - \beta)$

42. $f(\alpha - \beta)$ 43. $h(\alpha + \beta)$ 44. $h(\alpha - \beta)$

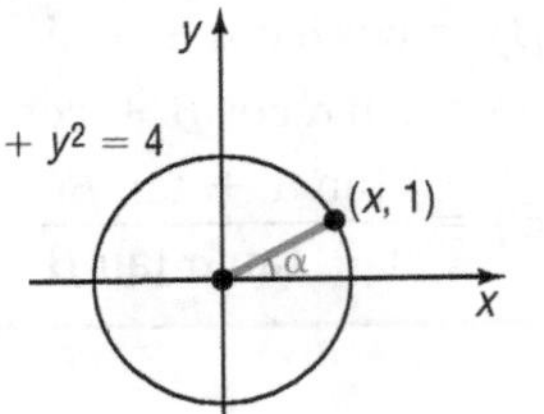

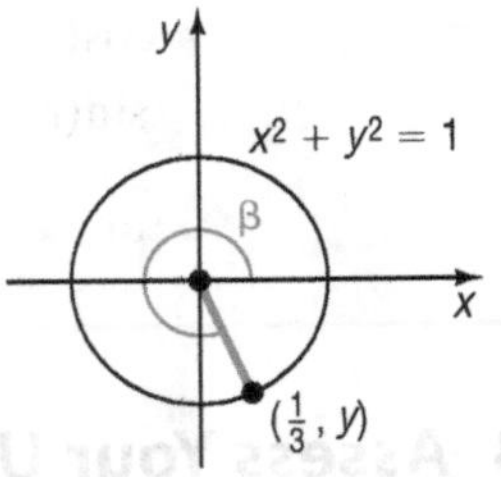

In Problems 45–70, establish each identity.

45. $\sin\left(\frac{\pi}{2} + \theta\right) = \cos \theta$

46. $\cos\left(\frac{\pi}{2} + \theta\right) = -\sin \theta$

47. $\sin(\pi - \theta) = \sin \theta$

48. $\cos(\pi - \theta) = -\cos \theta$

49. $\sin(\pi + \theta) = -\sin \theta$

50. $\cos(\pi + \theta) = -\cos \theta$

51. $\tan(\pi - \theta) = -\tan \theta$

52. $\tan(2\pi - \theta) = -\tan \theta$

53. $\sin\left(\frac{3\pi}{2} + \theta\right) = -\cos \theta$

54. $\cos\left(\frac{3\pi}{2} + \theta\right) = \sin \theta$

55. $\sin(\alpha + \beta) + \sin(\alpha - \beta) = 2 \sin \alpha \cos \beta$

56. $\cos(\alpha + \beta) + \cos(\alpha - \beta) = 2 \cos \alpha \cos \beta$

57. $\frac{\sin(\alpha + \beta)}{\sin \alpha \cos \beta} = 1 + \cot \alpha \tan \beta$

58. $\frac{\sin(\alpha + \beta)}{\cos \alpha \cos \beta} = \tan \alpha + \tan \beta$

59. $\frac{\cos(\alpha + \beta)}{\cos \alpha \cos \beta} = 1 - \tan \alpha \tan \beta$

60. $\frac{\cos(\alpha - \beta)}{\sin \alpha \cos \beta} = \cot \alpha + \tan \beta$

61. $\frac{\sin(\alpha + \beta)}{\sin(\alpha - \beta)} = \frac{\tan \alpha + \tan \beta}{\tan \alpha - \tan \beta}$

62. $\frac{\cos(\alpha + \beta)}{\cos(\alpha - \beta)} = \frac{1 - \tan \alpha \tan \beta}{1 + \tan \alpha \tan \beta}$

63. $\cot(\alpha + \beta) = \frac{\cot \alpha \cot \beta - 1}{\cot \beta + \cot \alpha}$

64. $\cot(\alpha - \beta) = \frac{\cot \alpha \cot \beta + 1}{\cot \beta - \cot \alpha}$

65. $\sec(\alpha + \beta) = \frac{\csc \alpha \csc \beta}{\cot \alpha \cot \beta - 1}$

66. $\sec(\alpha - \beta) = \frac{\sec \alpha \sec \beta}{1 + \tan \alpha \tan \beta}$

67. $\sin(\alpha - \beta) \sin(\alpha + \beta) = \sin^2 \alpha - \sin^2 \beta$

68. $\cos(\alpha - \beta) \cos(\alpha + \beta) = \cos^2 \alpha - \sin^2 \beta$

69. $\sin(\theta + k\pi) = (-1)^k \sin \theta$, k any integer

70. $\cos(\theta + k\pi) = (-1)^k \cos \theta$, k any integer

In Problems 71–82, find the exact value of each expression.

71. $\sin\left(\sin^{-1} \frac{1}{2} + \cos^{-1} 0\right)$

72. $\sin\left(\sin^{-1} \frac{\sqrt{3}}{2} + \cos^{-1} 1\right)$

73. $\sin\left[\sin^{-1} \frac{3}{5} - \cos^{-1}\left(-\frac{4}{5}\right)\right]$

74. $\sin\left[\sin^{-1}\left(-\frac{4}{5}\right) - \tan^{-1} \frac{3}{4}\right]$

75. $\cos\left(\tan^{-1} \frac{4}{3} + \cos^{-1} \frac{5}{13}\right)$

76. $\cos\left[\tan^{-1} \frac{5}{12} - \sin^{-1}\left(-\frac{3}{5}\right)\right]$

77. $\cos\left(\sin^{-1} \frac{5}{13} - \tan^{-1} \frac{3}{4}\right)$

78. $\cos\left(\tan^{-1} \frac{4}{3} + \cos^{-1} \frac{12}{13}\right)$

79. $\tan\left(\sin^{-1} \frac{3}{5} + \frac{\pi}{6}\right)$

80. $\tan\left(\frac{\pi}{4} - \cos^{-1} \frac{3}{5}\right)$

81. $\tan\left(\sin^{-1} \frac{4}{5} + \cos^{-1} 1\right)$

82. $\tan\left(\cos^{-1} \frac{4}{5} + \sin^{-1} 1\right)$

In Problems 83–88, write each trigonometric expression as an algebraic expression containing u and v. Give the restrictions required on u and v.

83. $\cos(\cos^{-1} u + \sin^{-1} v)$

84. $\sin(\sin^{-1} u - \cos^{-1} v)$

85. $\sin(\tan^{-1} u - \sin^{-1} v)$

86. $\cos(\tan^{-1} u + \tan^{-1} v)$

87. $\tan(\sin^{-1} u - \cos^{-1} v)$

88. $\sec(\tan^{-1} u + \cos^{-1} v)$

Applications and Extensions

89. Show that $\sin^{-1} v + \cos^{-1} v = \dfrac{\pi}{2}$.

90. Show that $\tan^{-1} v + \cot^{-1} v = \dfrac{\pi}{2}$.

91. Show that $\tan^{-1}\left(\dfrac{1}{v}\right) = \dfrac{\pi}{2} - \tan^{-1} v$, if $v > 0$.

92. Show that $\cot^{-1} e^{v} = \tan^{-1} e^{-v}$.

93. Show that $\sin(\sin^{-1} v + \cos^{-1} v) = 1$.

94. Show that $\cos(\sin^{-1} v + \cos^{-1} v) = 0$.

95. Calculus Show that the difference quotient for $f(x) = \sin x$ is given by

$$\frac{f(x+h) - f(x)}{h} = \frac{\sin(x+h) - \sin x}{h} = \cos x \cdot \frac{\sin h}{h} - \sin x \cdot \frac{1 - \cos h}{h}$$

96. Calculus Show that the difference quotient for $f(x) = \cos x$ is given by

$$\frac{f(x+h) - f(x)}{h} = \frac{\cos(x+h) - \cos x}{h} = -\sin x \cdot \frac{\sin h}{h} - \cos x \cdot \frac{1 - \cos h}{h}$$

97. One, Two, Three
(a) Show that $\tan(\tan^{-1} 1 + \tan^{-1} 2 + \tan^{-1} 3) = 0$.
(b) Conclude from part (a) that

$$\tan^{-1} 1 + \tan^{-1} 2 + \tan^{-1} 3 = \pi$$

Source: *College Mathematics Journal*, Vol. 37, No. 3, May 2006

98. Electric Power In an alternating current (ac) circuit, the instantaneous power p at time t is given by

$$p(t) = V_m I_m \cos\phi \sin^2(\omega t) - V_m I_m \sin\phi \sin(\omega t)\cos(\omega t)$$

Show that this is equivalent to

$$p(t) = V_m I_m \sin(\omega t)\sin(\omega t - \phi)$$

Source: *HyperPhysics, hosted by Georgia State University*

99. Geometry: Angle Between Two Lines Let L_1 and L_2 denote two nonvertical intersecting lines, and let θ denote the acute angle between L_1 and L_2 (see the figure). Show that

$$\tan\theta = \frac{m_2 - m_1}{1 + m_1 m_2}$$

where m_1 and m_2 are the slopes of L_1 and L_2, respectively. [**Hint:** Use the facts that $\tan\theta_1 = m_1$ and $\tan\theta_2 = m_2$.]

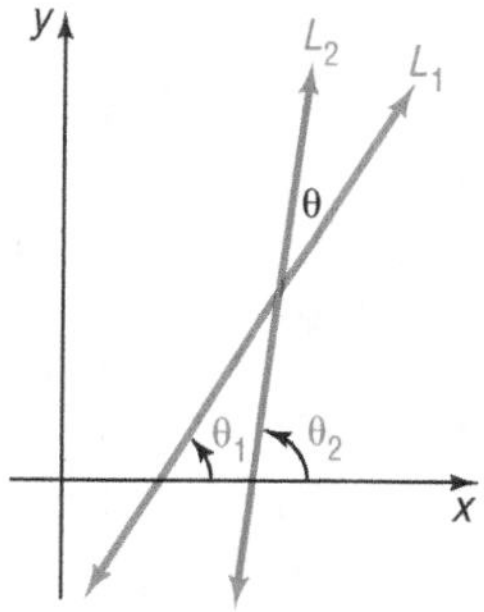

100. If $\alpha + \beta + \gamma = 180°$ and

$$\cot\theta = \cot\alpha + \cot\beta + \cot\gamma, \quad 0 < \theta < 90°$$

show that

$$\sin^3\theta = \sin(\alpha - \theta)\sin(\beta - \theta)\sin(\gamma - \theta)$$

101. If $\tan\alpha = x + 1$ and $\tan\beta = x - 1$, show that

$$2\cot(\alpha - \beta) = x^2$$

Discussion and Writing

102. Discuss the following derivation:

$$\tan\left(\theta + \frac{\pi}{2}\right) = \frac{\tan\theta + \tan\frac{\pi}{2}}{1 - \tan\theta\tan\frac{\pi}{2}} = \frac{\dfrac{\tan\theta}{\tan\frac{\pi}{2}} + 1}{\dfrac{1}{\tan\frac{\pi}{2}} - \tan\theta} = \frac{0 + 1}{0 - \tan\theta} = \frac{1}{-\tan\theta} = -\cot\theta$$

Can you justify each step?

103. Explain why formula (7) cannot be used to show that

$$\tan\left(\frac{\pi}{2} - \theta\right) = \cot\theta$$

Establish this identity by using formulas (3a) and (3b).

'Are You Prepared?' Answers

1. 5 **2.** $-\dfrac{3}{5}$ **3.** (a) $\dfrac{\sqrt{2}}{4}$ (b) $\dfrac{1}{2}$

7.5 Double-angle and Half-angle Formulas

OBJECTIVES
1 Use Double-angle Formulas to Find Exact Values (p. 476)
2 Use Double-angle Formulas to Establish Identities (p. 477)
3 Use Half-angle Formulas to Find Exact Values (p. 479)

In this section we derive formulas for $\sin(2\theta)$, $\cos(2\theta)$, $\sin\left(\frac{1}{2}\theta\right)$, and $\cos\left(\frac{1}{2}\theta\right)$ in terms of $\sin\theta$ and $\cos\theta$. They are derived using the sum formulas.

In the sum formulas for $\sin(\alpha+\beta)$ and $\cos(\alpha+\beta)$, let $\alpha = \beta = \theta$. Then

$$\begin{aligned}\sin(\alpha+\beta) &= \sin\alpha\cos\beta + \cos\alpha\sin\beta\\ \sin(\theta+\theta) &= \sin\theta\cos\theta + \cos\theta\sin\theta\\ \sin(2\theta) &= 2\sin\theta\cos\theta\end{aligned}$$

and

$$\begin{aligned}\cos(\alpha+\beta) &= \cos\alpha\cos\beta - \sin\alpha\sin\beta\\ \cos(\theta+\theta) &= \cos\theta\cos\theta - \sin\theta\sin\theta\\ \cos(2\theta) &= \cos^2\theta - \sin^2\theta\end{aligned}$$

An application of the Pythagorean Identity $\sin^2\theta + \cos^2\theta = 1$ results in two other ways to express $\cos(2\theta)$.

$$\cos(2\theta) = \cos^2\theta - \sin^2\theta = (1-\sin^2\theta) - \sin^2\theta = 1 - 2\sin^2\theta$$

and

$$\cos(2\theta) = \cos^2\theta - \sin^2\theta = \cos^2\theta - (1-\cos^2\theta) = 2\cos^2\theta - 1$$

We have established the following **Double-angle Formulas:**

THEOREM **Double-angle Formulas**

$$\sin(2\theta) = 2\sin\theta\cos\theta \quad \textbf{(1)}$$

$$\cos(2\theta) = \cos^2\theta - \sin^2\theta \quad \textbf{(2)}$$

$$\cos(2\theta) = 1 - 2\sin^2\theta \quad \textbf{(3)}$$

$$\cos(2\theta) = 2\cos^2\theta - 1 \quad \textbf{(4)}$$

1 Use Double-angle Formulas to Find Exact Values

EXAMPLE 1 Finding Exact Values Using the Double-angle Formula

If $\sin\theta = \frac{3}{5}$, $\frac{\pi}{2} < \theta < \pi$, find the exact value of:

(a) $\sin(2\theta)$ (b) $\cos(2\theta)$

Solution (a) Because $\sin(2\theta) = 2\sin\theta\cos\theta$ and we already know that $\sin\theta = \frac{3}{5}$, we only need to find $\cos\theta$. Since $\sin\theta = \frac{3}{5} = \frac{y}{r}$, $\frac{\pi}{2} < \theta < \pi$, we let $y = 3$ and $r = 5$

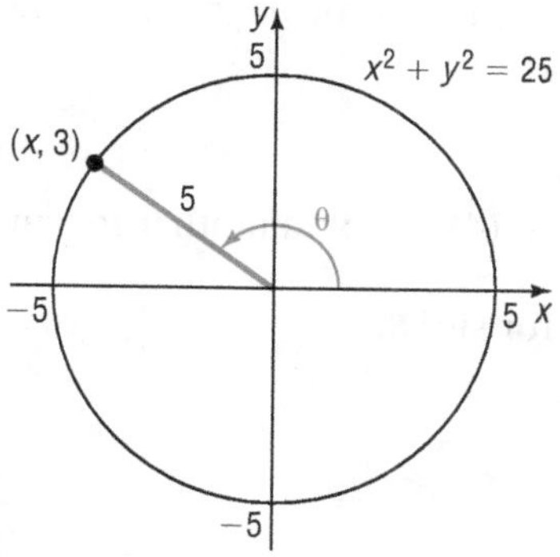

Figure 27

and place θ in quadrant II. The point $P = (x, y) = (x, 3)$, $x < 0$, is on a circle of radius 5, that is, $x^2 + y^2 = 25$. See Figure 27. Then

$$\begin{aligned} x^2 + y^2 &= 25 \\ x^2 + 9 &= 25 \qquad y = 3 \\ x^2 &= 25 - 9 = 16 \\ x &= -4 \qquad x < 0 \end{aligned}$$

We find that $\cos\theta = \frac{x}{r} = \frac{-4}{5}$. Now we use formula (1) to obtain

$$\sin(2\theta) = 2\sin\theta\cos\theta = 2\left(\frac{3}{5}\right)\left(-\frac{4}{5}\right) = -\frac{24}{25}$$

(b) Because we are given $\sin\theta = \frac{3}{5}$, it is easiest to use formula (3) to get $\cos(2\theta)$.

$$\cos(2\theta) = 1 - 2\sin^2\theta = 1 - 2\left(\frac{9}{25}\right) = 1 - \frac{18}{25} = \frac{7}{25}$$

■

WARNING In finding $\cos(2\theta)$ in Example 1(b), we chose to use a version of the Double-angle Formula, formula (3). Note that we are unable to use the Pythagorean Identity $\cos(2\theta) = \pm\sqrt{1 - \sin^2(2\theta)}$, with $\sin(2\theta) = -\frac{24}{25}$, because we have no way of knowing which sign to choose. ■

Now Work PROBLEMS 7(a) AND (b)

2 Use Double-angle Formulas to Establish Identities

EXAMPLE 2 **Establishing Identities**

(a) Develop a formula for $\tan(2\theta)$ in terms of $\tan\theta$.
(b) Develop a formula for $\sin(3\theta)$ in terms of $\sin\theta$ and $\cos\theta$.

Solution (a) In the sum formula for $\tan(\alpha + \beta)$, let $\alpha = \beta = \theta$. Then

$$\tan(\alpha + \beta) = \frac{\tan\alpha + \tan\beta}{1 - \tan\alpha\tan\beta}$$

$$\tan(\theta + \theta) = \frac{\tan\theta + \tan\theta}{1 - \tan\theta\tan\theta}$$

$$\tan(2\theta) = \frac{2\tan\theta}{1 - \tan^2\theta} \qquad \textbf{(5)}$$

(b) To get a formula for $\sin(3\theta)$, we use the sum formula and write 3θ as $2\theta + \theta$.

$$\sin(3\theta) = \sin(2\theta + \theta) = \sin(2\theta)\cos\theta + \cos(2\theta)\sin\theta$$

Now use the Double-angle Formulas to get

$$\begin{aligned} \sin(3\theta) &= (2\sin\theta\cos\theta)(\cos\theta) + (\cos^2\theta - \sin^2\theta)(\sin\theta) \\ &= 2\sin\theta\cos^2\theta + \sin\theta\cos^2\theta - \sin^3\theta \\ &= 3\sin\theta\cos^2\theta - \sin^3\theta \end{aligned}$$

■

The formula obtained in Example 2(b) can also be written as

$$\begin{aligned} \sin(3\theta) = 3\sin\theta\cos^2\theta - \sin^3\theta &= 3\sin\theta(1 - \sin^2\theta) - \sin^3\theta \\ &= 3\sin\theta - 4\sin^3\theta \end{aligned}$$

That is, $\sin(3\theta)$ is a third-degree polynomial in the variable $\sin \theta$. In fact, $\sin(n\theta)$, n a positive odd integer, can always be written as a polynomial of degree n in the variable $\sin \theta$.*

Now Work PROBLEM 65

By rearranging the Double-angle Formulas (3) and (4), we obtain other formulas that we will use later in this section.

We begin with formula (3) and proceed to solve for $\sin^2 \theta$.

$$\cos(2\theta) = 1 - 2\sin^2 \theta$$
$$2\sin^2 \theta = 1 - \cos(2\theta)$$

$$\sin^2 \theta = \frac{1 - \cos(2\theta)}{2} \qquad \textbf{(6)}$$

Similarly, using formula (4), we proceed to solve for $\cos^2 \theta$.

$$\cos(2\theta) = 2\cos^2 \theta - 1$$
$$2\cos^2 \theta = 1 + \cos(2\theta)$$

$$\cos^2 \theta = \frac{1 + \cos(2\theta)}{2} \qquad \textbf{(7)}$$

Formulas (6) and (7) can be used to develop a formula for $\tan^2 \theta$.

$$\tan^2 \theta = \frac{\sin^2 \theta}{\cos^2 \theta} = \frac{\dfrac{1 - \cos(2\theta)}{2}}{\dfrac{1 + \cos(2\theta)}{2}}$$

$$\tan^2 \theta = \frac{1 - \cos(2\theta)}{1 + \cos(2\theta)} \qquad \textbf{(8)}$$

Formulas (6) through (8) do not have to be memorized since their derivations are so straightforward.

Formulas (6) and (7) are important in calculus. The next example illustrates a problem that arises in calculus requiring the use of formula (7).

EXAMPLE 3 Establishing an Identity

Write an equivalent expression for $\cos^4 \theta$ that does not involve any powers of sine or cosine greater than 1.

Solution The idea here is to apply formula (7) twice.

$$\cos^4 \theta = (\cos^2 \theta)^2 = \left(\frac{1 + \cos(2\theta)}{2}\right)^2 \qquad \text{Formula (7)}$$

$$= \frac{1}{4}[1 + 2\cos(2\theta) + \cos^2(2\theta)]$$

*Because of the work done by P. L. Chebyshëv, these polynomials are sometimes called *Chebyshëv polynomials*.

$$= \frac{1}{4} + \frac{1}{2}\cos(2\theta) + \frac{1}{4}\cos^2(2\theta)$$

$$= \frac{1}{4} + \frac{1}{2}\cos(2\theta) + \frac{1}{4}\left\{\frac{1 + \cos[2(2\theta)]}{2}\right\} \quad \text{Formula (7)}$$

$$= \frac{1}{4} + \frac{1}{2}\cos(2\theta) + \frac{1}{8}[1 + \cos(4\theta)]$$

$$= \frac{3}{8} + \frac{1}{2}\cos(2\theta) + \frac{1}{8}\cos(4\theta)$$

Now Work PROBLEM 41

Identities, such as the Double-angle Formulas, can sometimes be used to rewrite expressions in a more suitable form. Let's look at an example.

EXAMPLE 4 Projectile Motion

Figure 28

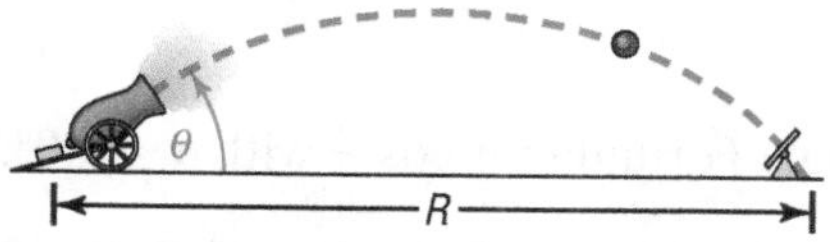

An object is propelled upward at an angle θ to the horizontal with an initial velocity of v_0 feet per second. See Figure 28. If air resistance is ignored, the **range** R, the horizontal distance that the object travels, is given by the function

$$R(\theta) = \frac{1}{16}v_0^2 \sin\theta\cos\theta$$

(a) Show that $R(\theta) = \frac{1}{32}v_0^2\sin(2\theta)$.

(b) Find the angle θ for which R is a maximum.

Solution (a) We rewrite the given expression for the range using the Double-angle Formula $\sin(2\theta) = 2\sin\theta\cos\theta$. Then

$$R(\theta) = \frac{1}{16}v_0^2\sin\theta\cos\theta = \frac{1}{16}v_0^2\frac{2\sin\theta\cos\theta}{2} = \frac{1}{32}v_0^2\sin(2\theta)$$

(b) In this form, the largest value for the range R can be found. For a fixed initial speed v_0, the angle θ of inclination to the horizontal determines the value of R. Since the largest value of a sine function is 1, occurring when the argument 2θ is 90°, it follows that for maximum R we must have

$$2\theta = 90°$$
$$\theta = 45°$$

An inclination to the horizontal of 45° results in the maximum range.

3 Use Half-angle Formulas to Find Exact Values

Another important use of formulas (6) through (8) is to prove the *Half-angle Formulas*. In formulas (6) through (8), let $\theta = \frac{\alpha}{2}$. Then

$$\sin^2\frac{\alpha}{2} = \frac{1 - \cos\alpha}{2} \qquad \cos^2\frac{\alpha}{2} = \frac{1 + \cos\alpha}{2} \qquad \tan^2\frac{\alpha}{2} = \frac{1 - \cos\alpha}{1 + \cos\alpha} \quad \textbf{(9)}$$

COMMENT The identities in box (9) will prove useful in integral calculus. ■

If we solve for the trigonometric functions on the left sides of equations (9), we obtain the Half-angle Formulas.

THEOREM **Half-angle Formulas**

$$\sin\frac{\alpha}{2} = \pm\sqrt{\frac{1-\cos\alpha}{2}} \qquad \textbf{(10a)}$$

$$\cos\frac{\alpha}{2} = \pm\sqrt{\frac{1+\cos\alpha}{2}} \qquad \textbf{(10b)}$$

$$\tan\frac{\alpha}{2} = \pm\sqrt{\frac{1-\cos\alpha}{1+\cos\alpha}} \qquad \textbf{(10c)}$$

where the + or − sign is determined by the quadrant of the angle $\frac{\alpha}{2}$.

EXAMPLE 5 Finding Exact Values Using Half-angle Formulas

Use a Half-angle Formula to find the exact value of:
(a) $\cos 15°$ (b) $\sin(-15°)$

Solution (a) Because $15° = \frac{30°}{2}$, we can use the Half-angle Formula for $\cos\frac{\alpha}{2}$ with $\alpha = 30°$. Also, because $15°$ is in quadrant I, $\cos 15° > 0$, we choose the + sign in using formula (10b):

$$\cos 15° = \cos\frac{30°}{2} = \sqrt{\frac{1+\cos 30°}{2}}$$

$$= \sqrt{\frac{1+\sqrt{3}/2}{2}} = \sqrt{\frac{2+\sqrt{3}}{4}} = \frac{\sqrt{2+\sqrt{3}}}{2}$$

(b) We use the fact that $\sin(-15°) = -\sin 15°$ and then apply formula (10a).

$$\sin(-15°) = -\sin\frac{30°}{2} = -\sqrt{\frac{1-\cos 30°}{2}}$$

$$= -\sqrt{\frac{1-\sqrt{3}/2}{2}} = -\sqrt{\frac{2-\sqrt{3}}{4}} = -\frac{\sqrt{2-\sqrt{3}}}{2}$$

It is interesting to compare the answer found in Example 5(a) with the answer to Example 2 of Section 7.4. There we calculated

$$\cos\frac{\pi}{12} = \cos 15° = \frac{1}{4}\left(\sqrt{6}+\sqrt{2}\right)$$

Based on this and the result of Example 5(a), we conclude that

$$\frac{1}{4}\left(\sqrt{6}+\sqrt{2}\right) \quad \text{and} \quad \frac{\sqrt{2+\sqrt{3}}}{2}$$

are equal. (Since each expression is positive, you can verify this equality by squaring each expression.) Two very different looking, yet correct, answers can be obtained, depending on the approach taken to solve a problem.

Now Work PROBLEM 19

EXAMPLE 6 Finding Exact Values Using Half-angle Formulas

If $\cos\alpha = -\frac{3}{5}$, $\pi < \alpha < \frac{3\pi}{2}$, find the exact value of:

(a) $\sin\frac{\alpha}{2}$ (b) $\cos\frac{\alpha}{2}$ (c) $\tan\frac{\alpha}{2}$

Solution First, we observe that if $\pi < \alpha < \frac{3\pi}{2}$ then $\frac{\pi}{2} < \frac{\alpha}{2} < \frac{3\pi}{4}$. As a result, $\frac{\alpha}{2}$ lies in quadrant II.

(a) Because $\frac{\alpha}{2}$ lies in quadrant II, $\sin\frac{\alpha}{2} > 0$, so we use the + sign in formula (10a) to get

$$\sin\frac{\alpha}{2} = \sqrt{\frac{1-\cos\alpha}{2}} = \sqrt{\frac{1-\left(-\frac{3}{5}\right)}{2}}$$
$$= \sqrt{\frac{\frac{8}{5}}{2}} = \sqrt{\frac{4}{5}} = \frac{2}{\sqrt{5}} = \frac{2\sqrt{5}}{5}$$

(b) Because $\frac{\alpha}{2}$ lies in quadrant II, $\cos\frac{\alpha}{2} < 0$, so we use the − sign in formula (10b) to get

$$\cos\frac{\alpha}{2} = -\sqrt{\frac{1+\cos\alpha}{2}} = -\sqrt{\frac{1+\left(-\frac{3}{5}\right)}{2}}$$
$$= -\sqrt{\frac{\frac{2}{5}}{2}} = -\frac{1}{\sqrt{5}} = -\frac{\sqrt{5}}{5}$$

(c) Because $\frac{\alpha}{2}$ lies in quadrant II, $\tan\frac{\alpha}{2} < 0$, so we use the − sign in formula (10c) to get

$$\tan\frac{\alpha}{2} = -\sqrt{\frac{1-\cos\alpha}{1+\cos\alpha}} = -\sqrt{\frac{1-\left(-\frac{3}{5}\right)}{1+\left(-\frac{3}{5}\right)}} = -\sqrt{\frac{\frac{8}{5}}{\frac{2}{5}}} = -2$$

Another way to solve Example 6(c) is to use the solutions found in parts (a) and (b).

$$\tan\frac{\alpha}{2} = \frac{\sin\frac{\alpha}{2}}{\cos\frac{\alpha}{2}} = \frac{\frac{2\sqrt{5}}{5}}{-\frac{\sqrt{5}}{5}} = -2$$

Now Work PROBLEMS 7(c) AND (d)

There is a formula for $\tan\frac{\alpha}{2}$ that does not contain + and − signs, making it more useful than Formula 10(c). To derive it, we use the formulas

$$1 - \cos\alpha = 2\sin^2\frac{\alpha}{2} \qquad \text{Formula (9)}$$

and

$$\sin \alpha = \sin\left[2\left(\frac{\alpha}{2}\right)\right] = 2 \sin \frac{\alpha}{2} \cos \frac{\alpha}{2} \quad \text{Double-angle Formula}$$

Then

$$\frac{1 - \cos \alpha}{\sin \alpha} = \frac{2 \sin^2 \frac{\alpha}{2}}{2 \sin \frac{\alpha}{2} \cos \frac{\alpha}{2}} = \frac{\sin \frac{\alpha}{2}}{\cos \frac{\alpha}{2}} = \tan \frac{\alpha}{2}$$

Since it also can be shown that

$$\frac{1 - \cos \alpha}{\sin \alpha} = \frac{\sin \alpha}{1 + \cos \alpha}$$

we have the following two Half-angle Formulas:

Half-angle Formulas for $\tan \frac{\alpha}{2}$

$$\tan \frac{\alpha}{2} = \frac{1 - \cos \alpha}{\sin \alpha} = \frac{\sin \alpha}{1 + \cos \alpha} \qquad \textbf{(11)}$$

With this formula, the solution to Example 6(c) can be obtained as follows:

$$\cos \alpha = -\frac{3}{5} \quad \pi < \alpha < \frac{3\pi}{2}$$

$$\sin \alpha = -\sqrt{1 - \cos^2 \alpha} = -\sqrt{1 - \frac{9}{25}} = -\sqrt{\frac{16}{25}} = -\frac{4}{5}$$

Then, by equation (11),

$$\tan \frac{\alpha}{2} = \frac{1 - \cos \alpha}{\sin \alpha} = \frac{1 - \left(-\frac{3}{5}\right)}{-\frac{4}{5}} = \frac{\frac{8}{5}}{-\frac{4}{5}} = -2$$

7.5 Assess Your Understanding

Concepts and Vocabulary

1. $\cos(2\theta) = \cos^2 \theta -$ ____ $=$ ____ $- 1 = 1 -$ ____.
2. $\sin^2 \frac{\theta}{2} = \frac{—}{2}$.
3. $\tan \frac{\theta}{2} = \frac{1 - \cos \theta}{—}$.
4. True or False $\cos(2\theta)$ has three equivalent forms: $\cos^2 \theta - \sin^2 \theta$, $1 - 2 \sin^2 \theta$, $2 \cos^2 \theta - 1$
5. True or False $\sin(2\theta)$ has two equivalent forms: $2 \sin \theta \cos \theta$ and $\sin^2 \theta - \cos^2 \theta$
6. True or False $\tan(2\theta) + \tan(2\theta) = \tan(4\theta)$

Skill Building

In Problems 7–18, use the information given about the angle θ, $0 \le \theta < 2\pi$, to find the exact value of

(a) $\sin(2\theta)$ (b) $\cos(2\theta)$ (c) $\sin \frac{\theta}{2}$ (d) $\cos \frac{\theta}{2}$

7. $\sin \theta = \frac{3}{5} \quad 0 < \theta < \frac{\pi}{2}$
8. $\cos \theta = \frac{3}{5} \quad 0 < \theta < \frac{\pi}{2}$
9. $\tan \theta = \frac{4}{3} \quad \pi < \theta < \frac{3\pi}{2}$
10. $\tan \theta = \frac{1}{2} \quad \pi < \theta < \frac{3\pi}{2}$
11. $\cos \theta = -\frac{\sqrt{6}}{3} \quad \frac{\pi}{2} < \theta < \pi$
12. $\sin \theta = -\frac{\sqrt{3}}{3} \quad \frac{3\pi}{2} < \theta < 2\pi$

13. $\sec\theta = 3 \quad \sin\theta > 0$
14. $\csc\theta = -\sqrt{5} \quad \cos\theta < 0$
15. $\cot\theta = -2 \quad \sec\theta < 0$
16. $\sec\theta = 2 \quad \csc\theta < 0$
17. $\tan\theta = -3 \quad \sin\theta < 0$
18. $\cot\theta = 3 \quad \cos\theta < 0$

In Problems 19–28, use the Half-angle Formulas to find the exact value of each expression.

19. $\sin 22.5°$
20. $\cos 22.5°$
21. $\tan \frac{7\pi}{8}$
22. $\tan \frac{9\pi}{8}$
23. $\cos 165°$
24. $\sin 195°$
25. $\sec \frac{15\pi}{8}$
26. $\csc \frac{7\pi}{8}$
27. $\sin\left(-\frac{\pi}{8}\right)$
28. $\cos\left(-\frac{3\pi}{8}\right)$

In Problems 29–40, use the figures to evaluate each function given that $f(x) = \sin x$, $g(x) = \cos x$, and $h(x) = \tan x$.

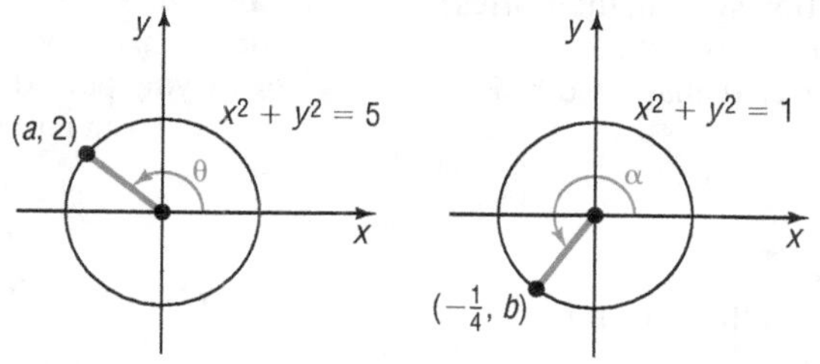

29. $f(2\theta)$
30. $g(2\theta)$
31. $g\left(\frac{\theta}{2}\right)$
32. $f\left(\frac{\theta}{2}\right)$
33. $h(2\theta)$
34. $h\left(\frac{\theta}{2}\right)$
35. $g(2\alpha)$
36. $f(2\alpha)$
37. $f\left(\frac{\alpha}{2}\right)$
38. $g\left(\frac{\alpha}{2}\right)$
39. $h\left(\frac{\alpha}{2}\right)$
40. $h(2\alpha)$

41. Show that $\sin^4\theta = \frac{3}{8} - \frac{1}{2}\cos(2\theta) + \frac{1}{8}\cos(4\theta)$.

42. Show that $\sin(4\theta) = (\cos\theta)(4\sin\theta - 8\sin^3\theta)$.

43. Develop a formula for $\cos(3\theta)$ as a third-degree polynomial in the variable $\cos\theta$.

44. Develop a formula for $\cos(4\theta)$ as a fourth-degree polynomial in the variable $\cos\theta$.

45. Find an expression for $\sin(5\theta)$ as a fifth-degree polynomial in the variable $\sin\theta$.

46. Find an expression for $\cos(5\theta)$ as a fifth-degree polynomial in the variable $\cos\theta$.

In Problems 47–68, establish each identity.

47. $\cos^4\theta - \sin^4\theta = \cos(2\theta)$

48. $\frac{\cot\theta - \tan\theta}{\cot\theta + \tan\theta} = \cos(2\theta)$

49. $\cot(2\theta) = \frac{\cot^2\theta - 1}{2\cot\theta}$

50. $\cot(2\theta) = \frac{1}{2}(\cot\theta - \tan\theta)$

51. $\sec(2\theta) = \frac{\sec^2\theta}{2 - \sec^2\theta}$

52. $\csc(2\theta) = \frac{1}{2}\sec\theta\csc\theta$

53. $\cos^2(2u) - \sin^2(2u) = \cos(4u)$

54. $(4\sin u\cos u)(1 - 2\sin^2 u) = \sin(4u)$

55. $\frac{\cos(2\theta)}{1 + \sin(2\theta)} = \frac{\cot\theta - 1}{\cot\theta + 1}$

56. $\sin^2\theta\cos^2\theta = \frac{1}{8}[1 - \cos(4\theta)]$

57. $\sec^2\frac{\theta}{2} = \frac{2}{1 + \cos\theta}$

58. $\csc^2\frac{\theta}{2} = \frac{2}{1 - \cos\theta}$

59. $\cot^2\frac{v}{2} = \frac{\sec v + 1}{\sec v - 1}$

60. $\tan\frac{v}{2} = \csc v - \cot v$

61. $\cos\theta = \frac{1 - \tan^2\frac{\theta}{2}}{1 + \tan^2\frac{\theta}{2}}$

62. $1 - \frac{1}{2}\sin(2\theta) = \frac{\sin^3\theta + \cos^3\theta}{\sin\theta + \cos\theta}$

63. $\frac{\sin(3\theta)}{\sin\theta} - \frac{\cos(3\theta)}{\cos\theta} = 2$

64. $\frac{\cos\theta + \sin\theta}{\cos\theta - \sin\theta} - \frac{\cos\theta - \sin\theta}{\cos\theta + \sin\theta} = 2\tan(2\theta)$

65. $\tan(3\theta) = \frac{3\tan\theta - \tan^3\theta}{1 - 3\tan^2\theta}$

66. $\tan\theta + \tan(\theta + 120°) + \tan(\theta + 240°) = 3\tan(3\theta)$

67. $\ln|\sin\theta| = \frac{1}{2}(\ln|1 - \cos(2\theta)| - \ln 2)$

68. $\ln|\cos\theta| = \frac{1}{2}(\ln|1 + \cos(2\theta)| - \ln 2)$

Mixed Practice

In Problems 69–80, find the exact value of each expression.

69. $\sin\left(2\sin^{-1}\frac{1}{2}\right)$ **70.** $\sin\left[2\sin^{-1}\frac{\sqrt{3}}{2}\right]$ **71.** $\cos\left(2\sin^{-1}\frac{3}{5}\right)$ **72.** $\cos\left(2\cos^{-1}\frac{4}{5}\right)$

73. $\tan\left[2\cos^{-1}\left(-\frac{3}{5}\right)\right]$ **74.** $\tan\left(2\tan^{-1}\frac{3}{4}\right)$ **75.** $\sin\left(2\cos^{-1}\frac{4}{5}\right)$ **76.** $\cos\left[2\tan^{-1}\left(-\frac{4}{3}\right)\right]$

77. $\sin^2\left(\frac{1}{2}\cos^{-1}\frac{3}{5}\right)$ **78.** $\cos^2\left(\frac{1}{2}\sin^{-1}\frac{3}{5}\right)$ **79.** $\sec\left(2\tan^{-1}\frac{3}{4}\right)$ **80.** $\csc\left[2\sin^{-1}\left(-\frac{3}{5}\right)\right]$

Applications and Extensions

81. Laser Projection In a laser projection system, the **optical** or **scanning angle** θ is related to the throw distance D from the scanner to the screen and the projected image width W by the equation

$$D = \frac{\frac{1}{2}W}{\csc\theta - \cot\theta}$$

(a) Show that the projected image width is given by

$$W = 2D\tan\frac{\theta}{2}$$

(b) Find the optical angle if the throw distance is 15 feet and the projected image width is 6.5 feet.

Source: *Pangolin Laser Systems, Inc.*

82. Product of Inertia The **product of inertia** for an area about inclined axes is given by the formula

$$I_{uv} = I_x\sin\theta\cos\theta - I_y\sin\theta\cos\theta + I_{xy}(\cos^2\theta - \sin^2\theta)$$

Show that this is equivalent to

$$I_{uv} = \frac{I_x - I_y}{2}\sin(2\theta) + I_{xy}\cos(2\theta)$$

Source: Adapted from Hibbeler, *Engineering Mechanics: Statics*, 10th ed., Prentice Hall © 2004.

83. Projectile Motion An object is propelled upward at an angle θ, $45° < \theta < 90°$, to the horizontal with an initial velocity of v_0 feet per second from the base of a plane that makes an angle of 45° with the horizontal. See the illustration. If air resistance is ignored, the distance R that it travels up the inclined plane is given by the function

$$R(\theta) = \frac{v_0^2\sqrt{2}}{16}\cos\theta(\sin\theta - \cos\theta)$$

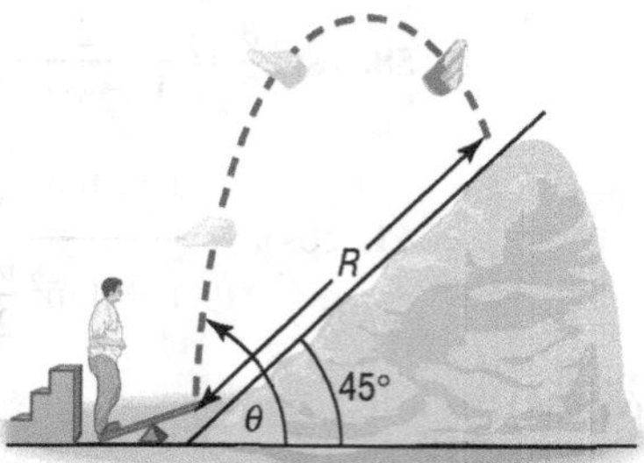

(a) Show that

$$R(\theta) = \frac{v_0^2\sqrt{2}}{32}[\sin(2\theta) - \cos(2\theta) - 1]$$

(b) Graph $R = R(\theta)$. (Use $v_0 = 32$ feet per second.)

(c) What value of θ makes R the largest? (Use $v_0 = 32$ feet per second.)

84. Sawtooth Curve An oscilloscope often displays a sawtooth curve. This curve can be approximated by sinusoidal curves of varying periods and amplitudes. A first approximation to the sawtooth curve is given by

$$y = \frac{1}{2}\sin(2\pi x) + \frac{1}{4}\sin(4\pi x)$$

Show that $y = \sin(2\pi x)\cos^2(\pi x)$.

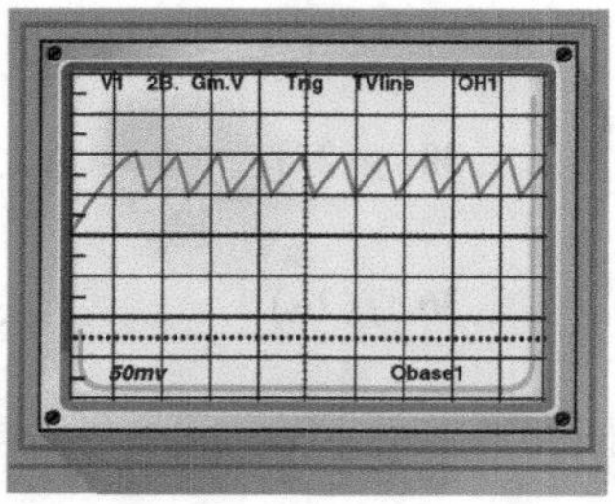

85. Area of an Isosceles Triangle Show that the area A of an isosceles triangle whose equal sides are of length s and θ is the angle between them is

$$A = \frac{1}{2}s^2\sin\theta$$

[**Hint:** See the illustration. The height h bisects the angle θ and is the perpendicular bisector of the base.]

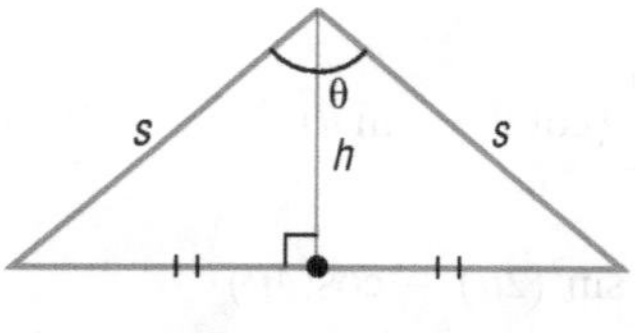

86. Geometry A rectangle is inscribed in a semicircle of radius 1. See the illustration.

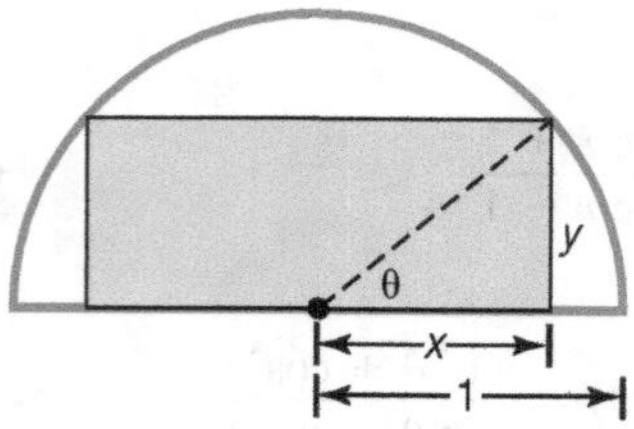

(a) Express the area A of the rectangle as a function of the angle θ shown in the illustration.

(b) Show that $A(\theta) = \sin(2\theta)$.

(c) Find the angle θ that results in the largest area A.

(d) Find the dimensions of this largest rectangle.

87. If $x = 2\tan\theta$, express $\sin(2\theta)$ as a function of x.

88. If $x = 2\tan\theta$, express $\cos(2\theta)$ as a function of x.

89. Find the value of the number C:

$$\frac{1}{2}\sin^2 x + C = -\frac{1}{4}\cos(2x)$$

90. Find the value of the number C:

$$\frac{1}{2}\cos^2 x + C = \frac{1}{4}\cos(2x)$$

91. If $z = \tan\frac{\alpha}{2}$, show that $\sin\alpha = \frac{2z}{1 + z^2}$.

92. If $z = \tan\frac{\alpha}{2}$, show that $\cos\alpha = \frac{1 - z^2}{1 + z^2}$.

93. Graph $f(x) = \sin^2 x = \frac{1 - \cos(2x)}{2}$ for $0 \le x \le 2\pi$ by using transformations.

94. Repeat Problem 93 for $g(x) = \cos^2 x$.

95. Use the fact that

$$\cos\frac{\pi}{12} = \frac{1}{4}\left(\sqrt{6} + \sqrt{2}\right)$$

to find $\sin\frac{\pi}{24}$ and $\cos\frac{\pi}{24}$.

96. Show that

$$\cos\frac{\pi}{8} = \frac{\sqrt{2 + \sqrt{2}}}{2}$$

and use it to find $\sin\frac{\pi}{16}$ and $\cos\frac{\pi}{16}$.

97. Show that

$$\sin^3\theta + \sin^3(\theta + 120°) + \sin^3(\theta + 240°) = -\frac{3}{4}\sin(3\theta)$$

98. If $\tan\theta = a\tan\frac{\theta}{3}$, express $\tan\frac{\theta}{3}$ in terms of a.

Discussion and Writing

99. Research Chebyshëv polynomials. Write a report on your findings.

7.6 Product-to-Sum and Sum-to-Product Formulas

OBJECTIVES
1 Express Products as Sums (p. 485)
2 Express Sums as Products (p. 486)

1 Express Products as Sums

Sum and difference formulas can be used to derive formulas for writing the products of sines and/or cosines as sums or differences. These identities are usually called the **Product-to-Sum Formulas.**

THEOREM

Product-to-Sum Formulas

$$\sin\alpha\sin\beta = \frac{1}{2}[\cos(\alpha - \beta) - \cos(\alpha + \beta)] \quad (1)$$

$$\cos\alpha\cos\beta = \frac{1}{2}[\cos(\alpha - \beta) + \cos(\alpha + \beta)] \quad (2)$$

$$\sin\alpha\cos\beta = \frac{1}{2}[\sin(\alpha + \beta) + \sin(\alpha - \beta)] \quad (3)$$

These formulas do not have to be memorized. Instead, you should remember how they are derived. Then, when you want to use them, either look them up or derive them, as needed.

To derive formulas (1) and (2), write down the sum and difference formulas for the cosine:

$$\cos(\alpha - \beta) = \cos\alpha\cos\beta + \sin\alpha\sin\beta \quad (4)$$

$$\cos(\alpha + \beta) = \cos\alpha\cos\beta - \sin\alpha\sin\beta \quad (5)$$

Subtract equation (5) from equation (4) to get

$$\cos(\alpha - \beta) - \cos(\alpha + \beta) = 2\sin\alpha\sin\beta$$

from which

$$\sin\alpha\sin\beta = \frac{1}{2}[\cos(\alpha - \beta) - \cos(\alpha + \beta)]$$

Now add equations (4) and (5) to get

$$\cos(\alpha - \beta) + \cos(\alpha + \beta) = 2 \cos \alpha \cos \beta$$

from which

$$\cos \alpha \cos \beta = \frac{1}{2}[\cos(\alpha - \beta) + \cos(\alpha + \beta)]$$

To derive Product-to-Sum Formula (3), use the sum and difference formulas for sine in a similar way. (You are asked to do this in Problem 43.)

EXAMPLE 1 **Expressing Products as Sums**

Express each of the following products as a sum containing only sines or only cosines.

(a) $\sin(6\theta) \sin(4\theta)$ (b) $\cos(3\theta) \cos \theta$ (c) $\sin(3\theta) \cos(5\theta)$

Solution (a) We use formula (1) to get

$$\sin(6\theta) \sin(4\theta) = \frac{1}{2}[\cos(6\theta - 4\theta) - \cos(6\theta + 4\theta)] = \frac{1}{2}[\cos(2\theta) - \cos(10\theta)]$$

(b) We use formula (2) to get

$$\cos(3\theta) \cos \theta = \frac{1}{2}[\cos(3\theta - \theta) + \cos(3\theta + \theta)] = \frac{1}{2}[\cos(2\theta) + \cos(4\theta)]$$

(c) We use formula (3) to get

$$\sin(3\theta) \cos(5\theta) = \frac{1}{2}[\sin(3\theta + 5\theta) + \sin(3\theta - 5\theta)] = \frac{1}{2}[\sin(8\theta) + \sin(-2\theta)] = \frac{1}{2}[\sin(8\theta) - \sin(2\theta)]$$

Now Work PROBLEM 1

2 Express Sums as Products

The **Sum-to-Product Formulas** are given next.

THEOREM **Sum-to-Product Formulas**

$$\sin \alpha + \sin \beta = 2 \sin \frac{\alpha + \beta}{2} \cos \frac{\alpha - \beta}{2} \quad (6)$$

$$\sin \alpha - \sin \beta = 2 \sin \frac{\alpha - \beta}{2} \cos \frac{\alpha + \beta}{2} \quad (7)$$

$$\cos \alpha + \cos \beta = 2 \cos \frac{\alpha + \beta}{2} \cos \frac{\alpha - \beta}{2} \quad (8)$$

$$\cos \alpha - \cos \beta = -2 \sin \frac{\alpha + \beta}{2} \sin \frac{\alpha - \beta}{2} \quad (9)$$

We will derive formula (6) and leave the derivations of formulas (7) through (9) as exercises (see Problems 44 through 46).

Proof

$$2\sin\frac{\alpha+\beta}{2}\cos\frac{\alpha-\beta}{2} = 2\cdot\frac{1}{2}\left[\sin\left(\frac{\alpha+\beta}{2}+\frac{\alpha-\beta}{2}\right)+\sin\left(\frac{\alpha+\beta}{2}-\frac{\alpha-\beta}{2}\right)\right]$$

Product-to-Sum Formula (3)

$$= \sin\frac{2\alpha}{2}+\sin\frac{2\beta}{2} = \sin\alpha+\sin\beta$$

■

EXAMPLE 2 **Expressing Sums (or Differences) as a Product**

Express each sum or difference as a product of sines and/or cosines.

(a) $\sin(5\theta) - \sin(3\theta)$ (b) $\cos(3\theta) + \cos(2\theta)$

Solution (a) We use formula (7) to get

$$\sin(5\theta) - \sin(3\theta) = 2\sin\frac{5\theta-3\theta}{2}\cos\frac{5\theta+3\theta}{2}$$
$$= 2\sin\theta\cos(4\theta)$$

(b) $$\cos(3\theta)+\cos(2\theta) = 2\cos\frac{3\theta+2\theta}{2}\cos\frac{3\theta-2\theta}{2}$$ Formula (8)
$$= 2\cos\frac{5\theta}{2}\cos\frac{\theta}{2}$$

■

Now Work PROBLEM 11

7.6 Assess Your Understanding

Skill Building

In Problems 1–10, express each product as a sum containing only sines or only cosines.

1. $\sin(4\theta)\sin(2\theta)$
2. $\cos(4\theta)\cos(2\theta)$
3. $\sin(4\theta)\cos(2\theta)$
4. $\sin(3\theta)\sin(5\theta)$
5. $\cos(3\theta)\cos(5\theta)$
6. $\sin(4\theta)\cos(6\theta)$
7. $\sin\theta\sin(2\theta)$
8. $\cos(3\theta)\cos(4\theta)$
9. $\sin\frac{3\theta}{2}\cos\frac{\theta}{2}$
10. $\sin\frac{\theta}{2}\cos\frac{5\theta}{2}$

In Problems 11–18, express each sum or difference as a product of sines and/or cosines.

11. $\sin(4\theta) - \sin(2\theta)$
12. $\sin(4\theta) + \sin(2\theta)$
13. $\cos(2\theta) + \cos(4\theta)$
14. $\cos(5\theta) - \cos(3\theta)$
15. $\sin\theta + \sin(3\theta)$
16. $\cos\theta + \cos(3\theta)$
17. $\cos\frac{\theta}{2} - \cos\frac{3\theta}{2}$
18. $\sin\frac{\theta}{2} - \sin\frac{3\theta}{2}$

In Problems 19–36, establish each identity.

19. $\dfrac{\sin\theta + \sin(3\theta)}{2\sin(2\theta)} = \cos\theta$
20. $\dfrac{\cos\theta + \cos(3\theta)}{2\cos(2\theta)} = \cos\theta$
21. $\dfrac{\sin(4\theta) + \sin(2\theta)}{\cos(4\theta) + \cos(2\theta)} = \tan(3\theta)$
22. $\dfrac{\cos\theta - \cos(3\theta)}{\sin(3\theta) - \sin\theta} = \tan(2\theta)$
23. $\dfrac{\cos\theta - \cos(3\theta)}{\sin\theta + \sin(3\theta)} = \tan\theta$
24. $\dfrac{\cos\theta - \cos(5\theta)}{\sin\theta + \sin(5\theta)} = \tan(2\theta)$
25. $\sin\theta[\sin\theta + \sin(3\theta)] = \cos\theta[\cos\theta - \cos(3\theta)]$
26. $\sin\theta[\sin(3\theta) + \sin(5\theta)] = \cos\theta[\cos(3\theta) - \cos(5\theta)]$
27. $\dfrac{\sin(4\theta) + \sin(8\theta)}{\cos(4\theta) + \cos(8\theta)} = \tan(6\theta)$
28. $\dfrac{\sin(4\theta) - \sin(8\theta)}{\cos(4\theta) - \cos(8\theta)} = -\cot(6\theta)$
29. $\dfrac{\sin(4\theta) + \sin(8\theta)}{\sin(4\theta) - \sin(8\theta)} = -\dfrac{\tan(6\theta)}{\tan(2\theta)}$
30. $\dfrac{\cos(4\theta) - \cos(8\theta)}{\cos(4\theta) + \cos(8\theta)} = \tan(2\theta)\tan(6\theta)$
31. $\dfrac{\sin\alpha + \sin\beta}{\sin\alpha - \sin\beta} = \tan\dfrac{\alpha+\beta}{2}\cot\dfrac{\alpha-\beta}{2}$
32. $\dfrac{\cos\alpha + \cos\beta}{\cos\alpha - \cos\beta} = -\cot\dfrac{\alpha+\beta}{2}\cot\dfrac{\alpha-\beta}{2}$

33. $\dfrac{\sin\alpha + \sin\beta}{\cos\alpha + \cos\beta} = \tan\dfrac{\alpha+\beta}{2}$

34. $\dfrac{\sin\alpha - \sin\beta}{\cos\alpha - \cos\beta} = -\cot\dfrac{\alpha+\beta}{2}$

35. $1 + \cos(2\theta) + \cos(4\theta) + \cos(6\theta) = 4\cos\theta\cos(2\theta)\cos(3\theta)$

36. $1 - \cos(2\theta) + \cos(4\theta) - \cos(6\theta) = 4\sin\theta\cos(2\theta)\sin(3\theta)$

Applications and Extensions

37. Touch-Tone Phones On a Touch-Tone phone, each button produces a unique sound. The sound produced is the sum of two tones, given by

$$y = \sin(2\pi lt) \quad \text{and} \quad y = \sin(2\pi ht)$$

where l and h are the low and high frequencies (cycles per second) shown on the illustration. For example, if you touch 7, the low frequency is $l = 852$ cycles per second and the high frequency is $h = 1209$ cycles per second. The sound emitted by touching 7 is

$$y = \sin[2\pi(852)t] + \sin[2\pi(1209)t]$$

Touch-Tone phone

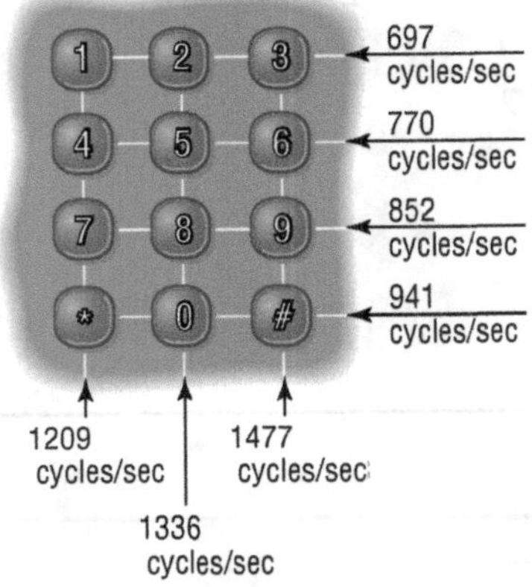

(a) Write this sound as a product of sines and/or cosines.
(b) Determine the maximum value of y.
(c) Graph the sound emitted by touching 7.

38. Touch-Tone Phones
(a) Write the sound emitted by touching the # key as a product of sines and/or cosines.
(b) Determine the maximum value of y.
(c) Graph the sound emitted by touching the # key.

39. Moment of Inertia The moment of inertia I of an object is a measure of how easy it is to rotate the object about some fixed point. In engineering mechanics, it is sometimes necessary to compute moments of inertia with respect to a set of rotated axes. These moments are given by the equations

$$I_u = I_x\cos^2\theta + I_y\sin^2\theta - 2I_{xy}\sin\theta\cos\theta$$
$$I_v = I_x\sin^2\theta + I_y\cos^2\theta + 2I_{xy}\sin\theta\cos\theta$$

Use Product-to-Sum Formulas to show that

$$I_u = \frac{I_x + I_y}{2} + \frac{I_x - I_y}{2}\cos(2\theta) - I_{xy}\sin(2\theta)$$

and

$$I_v = \frac{I_x + I_y}{2} - \frac{I_x - I_y}{2}\cos(2\theta) + I_{xy}\sin(2\theta)$$

Source: Adapted from Hibbeler, *Engineering Mechanics: Statics*, 10th ed., Prentice Hall © 2004.

40. Projectile Motion The range R of a projectile propelled downward from the top of an inclined plane at an angle θ to the inclined plane is given by

$$R(\theta) = \frac{2v_0^2\sin\theta\cos(\theta - \phi)}{g\cos^2\phi}$$

where v_0 is the initial velocity of the projectile, ϕ is the angle the plane makes with respect to the horizontal, and g is acceleration due to gravity.

(a) Show that for fixed v_0 and ϕ the maximum range down the incline is given by $R_{max} = \dfrac{v_0^2}{g(1 - \sin\phi)}$.
(b) Determine the maximum range if the projectile has an initial velocity of 50 meters/second, the angle of the plane is $\phi = 35°$, and $g = 9.8$ meters/second^2.

41. If $\alpha + \beta + \gamma = \pi$, show that

$$\sin(2\alpha) + \sin(2\beta) + \sin(2\gamma) = 4\sin\alpha\sin\beta\sin\gamma$$

42. If $\alpha + \beta + \gamma = \pi$, show that

$$\tan\alpha + \tan\beta + \tan\gamma = \tan\alpha\tan\beta\tan\gamma$$

43. Derive formula (3).

44. Derive formula (7).

45. Derive formula (8).

46. Derive formula (9).

7.7 Trigonometric Equations (I)

PREPARING FOR THIS SECTION *Before getting started, review the following:*

- Solving Equations (Appendix A, Section A.6, pp. A46–A57)
- Values of the Trigonometric Functions (Section 6.2, pp. 368–376)

Now Work the 'Are You Prepared?' problems on page 492.

OBJECTIVE 1 Solve Equations Involving a Single Trigonometric Function (p. 489)

1 Solve Equations Involving a Single Trigonometric Function

The previous four sections of this chapter were devoted to trigonometric identities, that is, equations involving trigonometric functions that are satisfied by every value in the domain of the variable. In the remaining two sections, we discuss **trigonometric equations,** that is, equations involving trigonometric functions that are satisfied only by some values of the variable (or, possibly, are not satisfied by any values of the variable). The values that satisfy the equation are called **solutions** of the equation.

EXAMPLE 1 Checking Whether a Given Number Is a Solution of a Trigonometric Equation

Determine whether $\theta = \frac{\pi}{4}$ is a solution of the equation $2\sin\theta - 1 = 0$. Is $\theta = \frac{\pi}{6}$ a solution?

Solution Replace θ by $\frac{\pi}{4}$ in the given equation. The result is

$$2\sin\frac{\pi}{4} - 1 = 2\cdot\frac{\sqrt{2}}{2} - 1 = \sqrt{2} - 1 \neq 0$$

We conclude that $\frac{\pi}{4}$ is not a solution.

Next replace θ by $\frac{\pi}{6}$ in the equation. The result is

$$2\sin\frac{\pi}{6} - 1 = 2\cdot\frac{1}{2} - 1 = 1 - 1 = 0$$

We conclude that $\frac{\pi}{6}$ is a solution of the given equation.

The equation given in Example 1 has other solutions besides $\theta = \frac{\pi}{6}$. For example, $\theta = \frac{5\pi}{6}$ is also a solution, as is $\theta = \frac{13\pi}{6}$. (You should check this for yourself.) In fact, the equation has an infinite number of solutions due to the periodicity of the sine function, as can be seen in Figure 29, which shows the graph of $Y_1 = 2\sin x - 1$. Each x-intercept represents a solution of the equation $2\sin x - 1 = 0$.

Figure 29

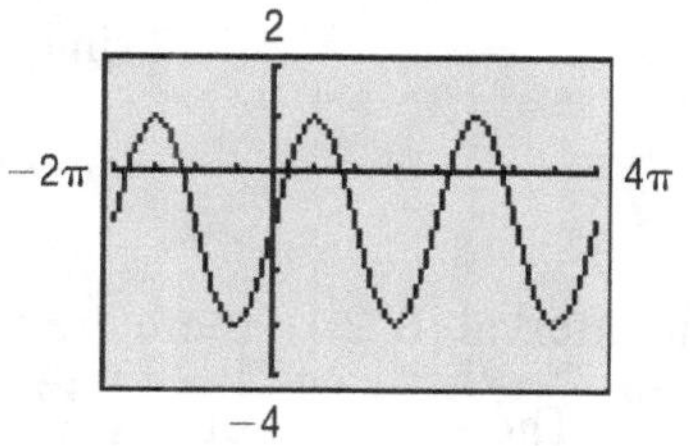

Unless the domain of the variable is restricted, we need to find *all* the solutions of a trigonometric equation. As the next example illustrates, finding all the solutions can be accomplished by first finding solutions over an interval whose length equals the period of the function and then adding multiples of that period to the solutions found. Let's look at some examples.

EXAMPLE 2 Finding All the Solutions of a Trigonometric Equation

Solve the equation: $\cos\theta = \frac{1}{2}$

Give a general formula for all the solutions. List eight of the solutions.

Solution The period of the cosine function is 2π. In the interval $[0, 2\pi)$, there are two angles θ for which $\cos\theta = \frac{1}{2}$: $\theta = \frac{\pi}{3}$ and $\theta = \frac{5\pi}{3}$. See Figure 30. Because the cosine function has period 2π, all the solutions of $\cos\theta = \frac{1}{2}$ may be given by the general formula

Figure 30

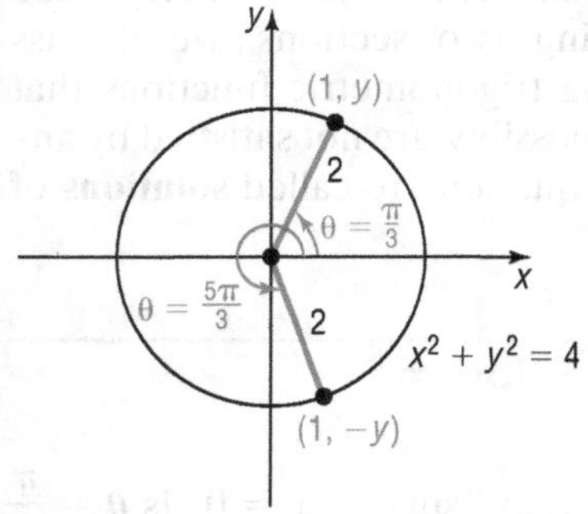

$$\theta = \frac{\pi}{3} + 2k\pi \quad \text{or} \quad \theta = \frac{5\pi}{3} + 2k\pi \qquad k \text{ any integer}$$

Eight of the solutions are

$$\underbrace{-\frac{5\pi}{3}, -\frac{\pi}{3}}_{k=-1}, \underbrace{\frac{\pi}{3}, \frac{5\pi}{3}}_{k=0}, \underbrace{\frac{7\pi}{3}, \frac{11\pi}{3}}_{k=1}, \underbrace{\frac{13\pi}{3}, \frac{17\pi}{3}}_{k=2}$$

Figure 31

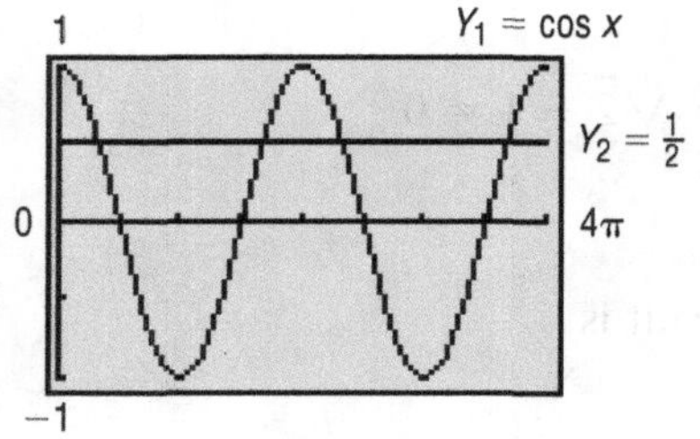

Check: We can verify the solutions by graphing $Y_1 = \cos x$ and $Y_2 = \frac{1}{2}$ to determine where the graphs intersect. (Be sure to graph in radian mode.) See Figure 31. The graph of Y_1 intersects the graph of Y_2 at $x = 1.05\left(\approx\frac{\pi}{3}\right)$, $5.24\left(\approx\frac{5\pi}{3}\right)$, $7.33\left(\approx\frac{7\pi}{3}\right)$, and $11.52\left(\approx\frac{11\pi}{3}\right)$, rounded to two decimal places.

Now Work PROBLEM 31

In most of our work, we shall be interested only in finding solutions of trigonometric equations for $0 \le \theta < 2\pi$.

EXAMPLE 3 Solving a Linear Trigonometric Equation

Solve the equation: $2\sin\theta + \sqrt{3} = 0, \quad 0 \le \theta < 2\pi$

Solution We solve the equation for $\sin\theta$.

$$2\sin\theta + \sqrt{3} = 0$$

$$2\sin\theta = -\sqrt{3} \qquad \text{Subtract } \sqrt{3} \text{ from both sides.}$$

$$\sin\theta = -\frac{\sqrt{3}}{2} \qquad \text{Divide both sides by 2.}$$

In the interval $[0, 2\pi)$, there are two angles θ for which $\sin\theta = -\frac{\sqrt{3}}{2}$: $\theta = \frac{4\pi}{3}$ and $\theta = \frac{5\pi}{3}$. The solution set is $\left\{\frac{4\pi}{3}, \frac{5\pi}{3}\right\}$.

Now Work PROBLEM 7

When the argument of the trigonometric function in an equation is a multiple of θ, the general formula must be used to solve the equation.

EXAMPLE 4 Solving a Trigonometric Equation

Solve the equation: $\sin(2\theta) = \frac{1}{2}, \quad 0 \le \theta < 2\pi$

Solution In the interval $[0, 2\pi)$, the sine function has a value $\frac{1}{2}$ at $\frac{\pi}{6}$ and $\frac{5\pi}{6}$. See Figure 32. Since the period of the sine function is 2π and the argument is 2θ in the equation $\sin(2\theta) = \frac{1}{2}$, we write the general formula that gives all the solutions.

Figure 32

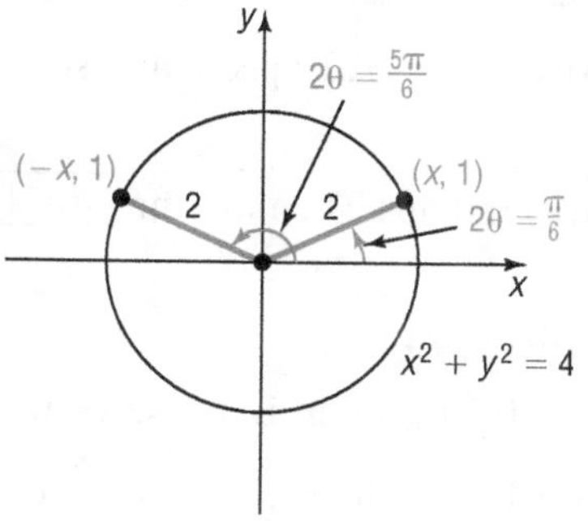

$$2\theta = \frac{\pi}{6} + 2k\pi \quad \text{or} \quad 2\theta = \frac{5\pi}{6} + 2k\pi \qquad k \text{ any integer}$$

$$\theta = \frac{\pi}{12} + k\pi \quad \text{or} \quad \theta = \frac{5\pi}{12} + k\pi \qquad \text{Divide by 2.}$$

Then

$$\theta = \frac{\pi}{12} + (-1)\pi = \frac{-11\pi}{12} \qquad k = -1 \qquad \theta = \frac{5\pi}{12} + (-1)\pi = \frac{-7\pi}{12}$$

$$\theta = \frac{\pi}{12} + (0)\pi = \frac{\pi}{12} \qquad k = 0 \qquad \theta = \frac{5\pi}{12} + (0)\pi = \frac{5\pi}{12}$$

$$\theta = \frac{\pi}{12} + (1)\pi = \frac{13\pi}{12} \qquad k = 1 \qquad \theta = \frac{5\pi}{12} + (1)\pi = \frac{17\pi}{12}$$

$$\theta = \frac{\pi}{12} + (2)\pi = \frac{25\pi}{12} \qquad k = 2 \qquad \theta = \frac{5\pi}{12} + (2)\pi = \frac{29\pi}{12}$$

In the interval $[0, 2\pi)$, the solutions of $\sin(2\theta) = \frac{1}{2}$ are $\theta = \frac{\pi}{12}$, $\theta = \frac{5\pi}{12}$, $\theta = \frac{13\pi}{12}$, and $\theta = \frac{17\pi}{12}$. The solution set is $\left\{\frac{\pi}{12}, \frac{5\pi}{12}, \frac{13\pi}{12}, \frac{17\pi}{12}\right\}$.

Check: Verify these solutions by graphing $Y_1 = \sin(2x)$ and $Y_2 = \frac{1}{2}$ for $0 \le x \le 2\pi$.

WARNING In solving a trigonometric equation for θ, $0 \le \theta < 2\pi$, in which the argument is not θ (as in Example 4), you must write down all the solutions first and then list those that are in the interval $[0, 2\pi)$. Otherwise, solutions may be lost. For example, in solving $\sin(2\theta) = \frac{1}{2}$, if you write the solutions $2\theta = \frac{\pi}{6}$ and $2\theta = \frac{5\pi}{6}$, you will find only $\theta = \frac{\pi}{12}$ and $\theta = \frac{5\pi}{12}$ and miss the other solutions.

Now Work PROBLEM 13

EXAMPLE 5 Solving a Trigonometric Equation

Solve the equation: $\tan\left(\theta - \frac{\pi}{2}\right) = 1, \quad 0 \le \theta < 2\pi$

Solution The period of the tangent function is π. In the interval $[0, \pi)$, the tangent function has the value 1 when the argument is $\frac{\pi}{4}$. Because the argument is $\theta - \frac{\pi}{2}$ in the given equation, we write the general formula that gives all the solutions.

$$\theta - \frac{\pi}{2} = \frac{\pi}{4} + k\pi \qquad k \text{ any integer}$$

$$\theta = \frac{3\pi}{4} + k\pi$$

In the interval $[0, 2\pi)$, $\theta = \frac{3\pi}{4}$ and $\theta = \frac{3\pi}{4} + \pi = \frac{7\pi}{4}$ are the only solutions. The solution set is $\left\{\frac{3\pi}{4}, \frac{7\pi}{4}\right\}$.

The next example illustrates how to solve trigonometric equations using a calculator.

EXAMPLE 6 **Solving a Trigonometric Equation with a Calculator**

Use a calculator to solve the equation $\sin\theta = 0.3$, $0 \le \theta < 2\pi$. Express any solutions in radians, rounded to two decimal places.

Solution To solve $\sin\theta = 0.3$ on a calculator, first set the mode to radians. Then use the $\boxed{\sin^{-1}}$ key to obtain

$$\theta = \sin^{-1}(0.3) \approx 0.3046927$$

Rounded to two decimal places, $\theta = \sin^{-1}(0.3) = 0.30$ radian. Because of the definition of $y = \sin^{-1} x$, the angle θ that we obtain is the angle $-\frac{\pi}{2} \le \theta \le \frac{\pi}{2}$ for which $\sin\theta = 0.3$. Another angle for which $\sin\theta = 0.3$ is $\pi - 0.30$. See Figure 33. The angle $\pi - 0.30$ is the angle in quadrant II, where $\sin\theta = 0.3$. The solutions for $\sin\theta = 0.3$, $0 \le \theta < 2\pi$, are

$$\theta = 0.30 \text{ radian} \quad \text{and} \quad \theta = \pi - 0.30 \approx 2.84 \text{ radians}$$

The solution set is $\{0.30, 2.84\}$.

Figure 33

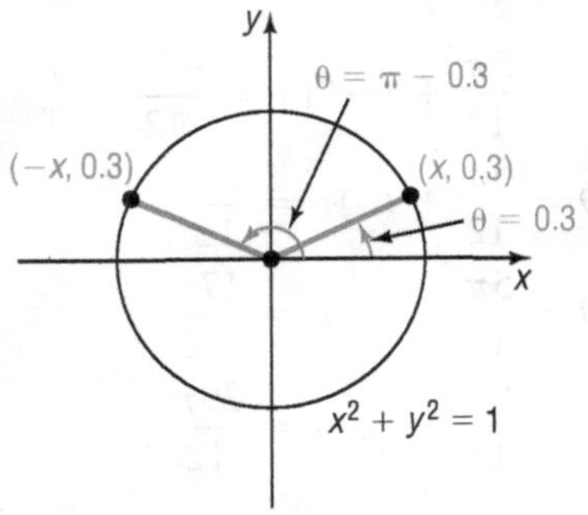

WARNING Example 6 illustrates that caution must be exercised when solving trigonometric equations on a calculator. Remember that the calculator supplies an angle only within the restrictions of the definition of the inverse trigonometric function. To find the remaining solutions, you must identify other quadrants, if any, in which a solution may be located. ■

Now Work PROBLEM 41

7.7 Assess Your Understanding

'Are You Prepared?' *Answers are given at the end of these exercises. If you get a wrong answer, read the pages listed in red.*

1. Solve: $3x - 5 = -x + 1$ (pp. A47–A49)
2. $\sin\left(\frac{\pi}{4}\right) =$ ______; $\cos\left(\frac{8\pi}{3}\right) =$ ______ (pp. 370–371 and 374–375)

Concepts and Vocabulary

3. Two solutions of the equation $\sin\theta = \frac{1}{2}$ are ______ and ______.
4. All the solutions of the equation $\sin\theta = \frac{1}{2}$ are ______.
5. True or False Most trigonometric equations have unique solutions.
6. True or False The equation $\sin\theta = 2$ has a real solution that can be found using a calculator.

Skill Building

In Problems 7–30, solve each equation on the interval $0 \le \theta < 2\pi$.

7. $2\sin\theta + 3 = 2$
8. $1 - \cos\theta = \frac{1}{2}$
9. $4\cos^2\theta = 1$
10. $\tan^2\theta = \frac{1}{3}$
11. $2\sin^2\theta - 1 = 0$
12. $4\cos^2\theta - 3 = 0$
13. $\sin(3\theta) = -1$
14. $\tan\frac{\theta}{2} = \sqrt{3}$
15. $\cos(2\theta) = -\frac{1}{2}$
16. $\tan(2\theta) = -1$
17. $\sec\frac{3\theta}{2} = -2$
18. $\cot\frac{2\theta}{3} = -\sqrt{3}$
19. $2\sin\theta + 1 = 0$
20. $\cos\theta + 1 = 0$
21. $\tan\theta + 1 = 0$
22. $\sqrt{3}\cot\theta + 1 = 0$
23. $4\sec\theta + 6 = -2$
24. $5\csc\theta - 3 = 2$
25. $3\sqrt{2}\cos\theta + 2 = -1$
26. $4\sin\theta + 3\sqrt{3} = \sqrt{3}$
27. $\cos\left(2\theta - \frac{\pi}{2}\right) = -1$
28. $\sin\left(3\theta + \frac{\pi}{18}\right) = 1$
29. $\tan\left(\frac{\theta}{2} + \frac{\pi}{3}\right) = 1$
30. $\cos\left(\frac{\theta}{3} - \frac{\pi}{4}\right) = \frac{1}{2}$

In Problems 31–40, solve each equation. Give a general formula for all the solutions. List six solutions.

31. $\sin\theta = \frac{1}{2}$ **32.** $\tan\theta = 1$ **33.** $\tan\theta = -\frac{\sqrt{3}}{3}$ **34.** $\cos\theta = -\frac{\sqrt{3}}{2}$ **35.** $\cos\theta = 0$

36. $\sin\theta = \frac{\sqrt{2}}{2}$ **37.** $\cos(2\theta) = -\frac{1}{2}$ **38.** $\sin(2\theta) = -1$ **39.** $\sin\frac{\theta}{2} = -\frac{\sqrt{3}}{2}$ **40.** $\tan\frac{\theta}{2} = -1$

In Problems 41–52, use a calculator to solve each equation on the interval $0 \le \theta < 2\pi$. Round answers to two decimal places.

41. $\sin\theta = 0.4$ **42.** $\cos\theta = 0.6$ **43.** $\tan\theta = 5$ **44.** $\cot\theta = 2$

45. $\cos\theta = -0.9$ **46.** $\sin\theta = -0.2$ **47.** $\sec\theta = -4$ **48.** $\csc\theta = -3$

49. $5\tan\theta + 9 = 0$ **50.** $4\cot\theta = -5$ **51.** $3\sin\theta - 2 = 0$ **52.** $4\cos\theta + 3 = 0$

Mixed Practice

53. What are the zeros of $f(x) = 4\sin^2 x - 3$ on the interval $[0, 2\pi]$?

54. What are the zeros of $f(x) = 2\cos(3x) + 1$ on the interval $[0, \pi]$?

55. $f(x) = 3\sin x$.
(a) Find the zeros of f on the interval $[-2\pi, 4\pi]$.
(b) Graph $f(x) = 3\sin x$ on the interval $[-2\pi, 4\pi]$.
(c) Solve $f(x) = \frac{3}{2}$ on the interval $[-2\pi, 4\pi]$. What points are on the graph of f? Label these points on the graph drawn in part (b).
(d) Use the graph drawn in part (b) along with the results of part (c) to determine the values of x such that $f(x) > \frac{3}{2}$ on the interval $[-2\pi, 4\pi]$.

56. $f(x) = 2\cos x$.
(a) Find the zeros of f on the interval $[-2\pi, 4\pi]$.
(b) Graph $f(x) = 2\cos x$ on the interval $[-2\pi, 4\pi]$.
(c) Solve $f(x) = -\sqrt{3}$ on the interval $[-2\pi, 4\pi]$. What points are on the graph of f? Label these points on the graph drawn in part (b).
(d) Use the graph drawn in part (b) along with the results of part (c) to determine the values of x such that $f(x) < -\sqrt{3}$ on the interval $[-2\pi, 4\pi]$.

57. $f(x) = 4\tan x$.
(a) Solve $f(x) = -4$.
(b) For what values of x is $f(x) < -4$ on the interval $\left(-\frac{\pi}{2}, \frac{\pi}{2}\right)$?

58. $f(x) = \cot x$.
(a) Solve $f(x) = -\sqrt{3}$.
(b) For what values of x is $f(x) > -\sqrt{3}$ on the interval $(0, \pi)$?

59. (a) Graph $f(x) = 3\sin(2x) + 2$ and $g(x) = \frac{7}{2}$ on the same Cartesian plane for the interval $[0, \pi]$.
(b) Solve $f(x) = g(x)$ on the interval $[0, \pi]$ and label the points of intersection on the graph drawn in part (b).
(c) Solve $f(x) > g(x)$ on the interval $[0, \pi]$.
(d) Shade the region bounded by $f(x) = 3\sin(2x) + 2$ and $g(x) = \frac{7}{2}$ between the two points found in part (b) on the graph drawn in part (a).

60. (a) Graph $f(x) = 2\cos\frac{x}{2} + 3$ and $g(x) = 4$ on the same Cartesian plane for the interval $[0, 4\pi]$.
(b) Solve $f(x) = g(x)$ on the interval $[0, 4\pi]$ and label the points of intersection on the graph drawn in part (b).
(c) Solve $f(x) < g(x)$ on the interval $[0, 4\pi]$.
(d) Shade the region bounded by $f(x) = 2\cos\frac{x}{2} + 3$ and $g(x) = 4$ between the two points found in part (b) on the graph drawn in part (a).

61. (a) Graph $f(x) = -4\cos x$ and $g(x) = 2\cos x + 3$ on the same Cartesian plane for the interval $[0, 2\pi]$.
(b) Solve $f(x) = g(x)$ on the interval $[0, 2\pi]$ and label the points of intersection on the graph drawn in part (b).
(c) Solve $f(x) > g(x)$ on the interval $[0, 2\pi]$.
(d) Shade the region bounded by $f(x) = -4\cos x$ and $g(x) = 2\cos x + 3$ between the two points found in part (b) on the graph drawn in part (a).

62. (a) Graph $f(x) = 2\sin x$ and $g(x) = -2\sin x + 2$ on the same Cartesian plane for the interval $[0, 2\pi]$.
(b) Solve $f(x) = g(x)$ on the interval $[0, 2\pi]$ and label the points of intersection on the graph drawn in part (b).
(c) Solve $f(x) > g(x)$ on the interval $[0, 2\pi]$.
(d) Shade the region bounded by $f(x) = 2\sin x$ and $g(x) = -2\sin x + 2$ between the two points found in part (b) on the graph drawn in part (a).

Applications and Extensions

63. Blood Pressure Blood pressure is a way of measuring the amount of force exerted on the walls of blood vessels. It is measured using two numbers: systolic (as the heart beats) blood pressure and diastolic (as the heart rests) blood pressure. Blood pressures vary substantially from person to person, but a typical blood pressure is 120/80, which means the systolic blood pressure is 120 mm Hg and the diastolic blood pressure is 80 mmHg. Assuming that a person's heart beats 70 times per minute, the blood pressure of an individual P after t seconds can be modeled by the function

$$P(t) = 100 + 20\sin\left(\frac{7\pi}{3}t\right)$$

(a) In the interval $[0, 1]$, determine the times at which the blood pressure is 100 mmHg.

(b) In the interval [0, 1], determine the times at which the blood pressure is 120 mmHg.

(c) In the interval [0, 1], determine the times at which the blood pressures is between 100 and 105 mmHg.

64. The Ferris Wheel In 1893, George Ferris engineered the Ferris Wheel. It was 250 feet in diameter. If the wheel makes 1 revolution every 40 seconds, then the function

$$h(t) = 125 \sin\left(0.157t - \frac{\pi}{2}\right) + 125$$

represents the height h, in feet, of a seat on the wheel as a function of time t, where t is measured in seconds. The ride begins when $t = 0$.

(a) During the first 40 seconds of the ride, at what time t is an individual on the Ferris Wheel exactly 125 feet above the ground?

(b) During the first 80 seconds of the ride, at what time t is an individual on the Ferris Wheel exactly 250 feet above the ground?

(c) During the first 40 seconds of the ride, over what interval of time t is an individual on the Ferris Wheel more than 125 feet above the ground?

65. Holding Pattern An airplane is asked to stay within a holding pattern near Chicago's O'Hare International Airport. The function $d(x) = 70 \sin(0.65x) + 150$ represents the distance d, in miles, that the airplane is from the airport at time x, in minutes.

(a) When the plane enters the holding pattern, $x = 0$, how far is it from O'Hare?

(b) During the first 20 minutes after the plane enters the holding pattern, at what time x is the plane exactly 100 miles from the airport?

(c) During the first 20 minutes after the plane enters the holding pattern, at what time x is the plane more than 100 miles from the airport?

(d) While the plane is in the holding pattern, will it ever be within 70 miles of the airport? Why?

66. Projectile Motion A golfer hits a golf ball with an initial velocity of 100 miles per hour. The range R of the ball as a function of the angle θ to the horizontal is given by $R(\theta) = 672 \sin(2\theta)$, where R is measured in feet.

(a) At what angle θ should the ball be hit if the golfer wants the ball to travel 450 feet (150 yards)?

(b) At what angle θ should the ball be hit if the golfer wants the ball to travel 540 feet (180 yards)?

(c) At what angle θ should the ball be hit if the golfer wants the ball to travel at least 480 feet (160 yards)?

(d) Can the golfer hit the ball 720 feet (240 yards)?

The following discussion of Snell's Law of Refraction (named after Willebrord Snell, 1580–1626) is needed for Problems 67–73. Light, sound, and other waves travel at different speeds, depending on the media (air, water, wood, and so on) through which they pass. Suppose that light travels from a point A in one medium, where its speed is v_1, to a point B in another medium, where its speed is v_2. Refer to the figure, where the angle θ_1 is called the* angle of incidence *and the angle θ_2 is the* angle of refraction. *Snell's Law, which can be proved using calculus, states that*

$$\frac{\sin \theta_1}{\sin \theta_2} = \frac{v_1}{v_2}$$

The ratio $\frac{v_1}{v_2}$ *is called the* index of refraction. *Some values are given in the following table.*

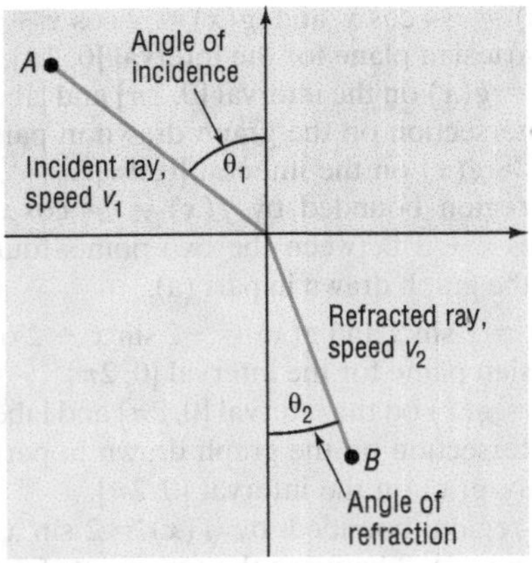

Some Indexes of Refraction

Medium	Index of Refraction†
Water	1.33
Ethyl alcohol (20°C)	1.36
Carbon disulfide	1.63
Air (1 atm and 0°C)	1.00029
Diamond	2.42
Fused quartz	1.46
Glass, crown	1.52
Glass, dense flint	1.66
Sodium chloride	1.54

67. The index of refraction of light in passing from a vacuum into water is 1.33. If the angle of incidence is 40°, determine the angle of refraction.

68. The index of refraction of light in passing from a vacuum into dense flint glass is 1.66. If the angle of incidence is 50°, determine the angle of refraction.

69. Ptolemy, who lived in the city of Alexandria in Egypt during the second century AD, gave the measured values in the following table for the angle of incidence θ_1 and the angle of refraction θ_2 for a light beam passing from air into water. Do these values agree with Snell's Law? If so, what index of refraction results? (These data are of interest as the oldest recorded physical measurements.)†

θ_1	θ_2	θ_1	θ_2
10°	8°	50°	35°0′
20°	15°30′	60°	40°30′
30°	22°30′	70°	45°30′
40°	29°0′	80°	50°0′

*Because this law was also deduced by René Descartes in France, it is also known as Descartes's Law.

†For light of wavelength 589 nanometers, measured with respect to a vacuum. The index with respect to air is negligibly different in most cases.

70. Bending Light The speed of yellow sodium light (wavelength, 589 nanometers) in a certain liquid is measured to be 1.92×10^8 meters per second. What is the index of refraction of this liquid, with respect to air, for sodium light?*
[**Hint:** The speed of light in air is approximately 2.998×10^8 meters per second.]

71. Bending Light A beam of light with a wavelength of 589 nanometers traveling in air makes an angle of incidence of 40° on a slab of transparent material, and the refracted beam makes an angle of refraction of 26°. Find the index of refraction of the material.*

72. Bending Light A light ray with a wavelength of 589 nanometers (produced by a sodium lamp) traveling through air makes an angle of incidence of 30° on a smooth, flat slab of crown glass. Find the angle of refraction.*

73. A light beam passes through a thick slab of material whose index of refraction is n_2. Show that the emerging beam is parallel to the incident beam.*

74. Brewster's Law If the angle of incidence and the angle of refraction are complementary angles, the angle of incidence is referred to as the Brewster angle θ_B. The Brewster angle is related to the index of refractions of the two media, n_1 and n_2, by the equation $n_1 \sin \theta_B = n_2 \cos \theta_B$, where n_1 is the index of refraction of the incident medium and n_2 is the index of refraction of the refractive medium. Determine the Brewster angle for a light beam traveling through water (at 20°C) that makes an angle of incidence with a smooth, flat slab of crown glass.

*Adapted from Halliday and Resnick, *Fundamentals of Physics,* 7th ed., 2005, John Wiley & Sons.

Discussion and Writing

75. Explain in your own words how you would use your calculator to solve the equation $\cos x = -0.6, 0 \le x < 2\pi$. How would you modify your approach to solve the equation $\cot x = 5, 0 < x < 2\pi$?

'Are You Prepared?' Answers

1. $\left\{\frac{3}{2}\right\}$ **2.** $\frac{\sqrt{2}}{2}; -\frac{1}{2}$

7.8 Trigonometric Equations (II)

PREPARING FOR THIS SECTION *Before getting started, review the following:*

- Solving Quadratic Equations by Factoring (Appendix A, Section A.6, pp. A50–A51)
- The Quadratic Formula (Appendix A, Section A.6, pp. A53–A55)
- Solving Equations Quadratic in Form (Appendix A, Section A.6, pp. A55–A56)
- Using a Graphing Utility to Solve Equations (Section 1.3, pp. 26–28)

Now Work the 'Are You Prepared?' problems on page 500.

OBJECTIVES
1 Solve Trigonometric Equations Quadratic in Form (p. 495)
2 Solve Trigonometric Equations Using Identities (p. 496)
3 Solve Trigonometric Equations Linear in Sine and Cosine (p. 498)
4 Solve Trigonometric Equations Using a Graphing Utility (p. 500)

1 Solve Trigonometric Equations Quadratic in Form

In this section we continue our study of trigonometric equations. Many trigonometric equations can be solved by applying techniques that we already know, such as applying the quadratic formula (if the equation is a second-degree polynomial) or factoring.

EXAMPLE 1 **Solving a Trigonometric Equation Quadratic in Form**

Solve the equation: $2\sin^2\theta - 3\sin\theta + 1 = 0, \quad 0 \le \theta < 2\pi$

Solution This equation is a quadratic equation (in $\sin\theta$) that can be factored.

$$2\sin^2\theta - 3\sin\theta + 1 = 0 \qquad 2x^2 - 3x + 1 = 0, \quad x = \sin\theta$$
$$(2\sin\theta - 1)(\sin\theta - 1) = 0 \qquad (2x - 1)(x - 1) = 0$$

$$2\sin\theta - 1 = 0 \quad \text{or} \quad \sin\theta - 1 = 0 \qquad \text{Use the Zero-Product Property.}$$

$$\sin\theta = \frac{1}{2} \quad \text{or} \quad \sin\theta = 1$$

Solving each equation in the interval $[0, 2\pi)$, we obtain

$$\theta = \frac{\pi}{6} \qquad \theta = \frac{5\pi}{6} \qquad \theta = \frac{\pi}{2}$$

The solution set is $\left\{\frac{\pi}{6}, \frac{5\pi}{6}, \frac{\pi}{2}\right\}$.

Now Work PROBLEM 7

2 Solve Trigonometric Equations Using Identities

When a trigonometric equation contains more than one trigonometric function, identities sometimes can be used to obtain an equivalent equation that contains only one trigonometric function.

EXAMPLE 2 **Solving a Trigonometric Equation Using Identities**

Solve the equation: $3\cos\theta + 3 = 2\sin^2\theta, \quad 0 \le \theta < 2\pi$

Solution The equation in its present form contains a sine and a cosine. However, a form of the Pythagorean Identity can be used to transform the equation into an equivalent expression containing only cosines.

$$3\cos\theta + 3 = 2\sin^2\theta$$

$$3\cos\theta + 3 = 2(1 - \cos^2\theta) \qquad \sin^2\theta = 1 - \cos^2\theta$$

$$3\cos\theta + 3 = 2 - 2\cos^2\theta$$

$$2\cos^2\theta + 3\cos\theta + 1 = 0 \qquad \text{Quadratic in } \cos\theta$$

$$(2\cos\theta + 1)(\cos\theta + 1) = 0 \qquad \text{Factor.}$$

$$2\cos\theta + 1 = 0 \quad \text{or} \quad \cos\theta + 1 = 0 \qquad \text{Use the Zero-Product Property.}$$

$$\cos\theta = -\frac{1}{2} \quad \text{or} \quad \cos\theta = -1$$

Solving each equation in the interval $[0, 2\pi)$, we obtain

$$\theta = \frac{2\pi}{3} \qquad \theta = \frac{4\pi}{3} \qquad \theta = \pi$$

The solution set is $\left\{\frac{2\pi}{3}, \pi, \frac{4\pi}{3}\right\}$.

Check: Graph $Y_1 = 3\cos x + 3$ and $Y_2 = 2\sin^2 x, 0 \le x \le 2\pi$, and approximate the points of intersection.

When a trigonometric equation contains trigonometric functions with different arguments, identities can sometimes be used to obtain an equivalent equation with the same argument.

EXAMPLE 3 **Solving a Trigonometric Equation Using Identities**

Solve the equation: $\cos(2\theta) + 3 = 5\cos\theta, \quad 0 \le \theta < 2\pi$

Solution First, we observe that the given equation contains two cosine functions, but with different arguments, θ and 2θ. We use the Double-angle Formula $\cos(2\theta) = 2\cos^2\theta - 1$ to obtain an equivalent equation containing only $\cos\theta$.

$$\cos(2\theta) + 3 = 5\cos\theta$$

$$(2\cos^2\theta - 1) + 3 = 5\cos\theta \qquad \cos(2\theta) = 2\cos^2\theta - 1$$

$$2\cos^2\theta - 5\cos\theta + 2 = 0 \qquad \text{Place in standard form.}$$

$$(\cos\theta - 2)(2\cos\theta - 1) = 0 \quad \text{Factor.}$$

$$\cos\theta = 2 \quad \text{or} \quad \cos\theta = \frac{1}{2} \quad \text{Solve by using the Zero-Product property.}$$

For any angle θ, $-1 \le \cos\theta \le 1$; therefore, the equation $\cos\theta = 2$ has no solution. The solutions of $\cos\theta = \frac{1}{2}$, $0 \le \theta < 2\pi$, are

$$\theta = \frac{\pi}{3} \qquad \theta = \frac{5\pi}{3}$$

The solution set is $\left\{\frac{\pi}{3}, \frac{5\pi}{3}\right\}$.

Check: Graph $Y_1 = \cos(2x) + 3$ and $Y_2 = 5\cos x$, $0 \le x \le 2\pi$, and approximate the points of intersection.

Now Work PROBLEM 23

EXAMPLE 4

Solving a Trigonometric Equation Using Identities

Solve the equation: $\cos^2\theta + \sin\theta = 2, \quad 0 \le \theta < 2\pi$

Solution This equation involves two trigonometric functions, sine and cosine. We use a form of the Pythagorean Identity, $\sin^2\theta + \cos^2\theta = 1$, to rewrite the equation in terms of $\sin\theta$.

$$\cos^2\theta + \sin\theta = 2$$

$$(1 - \sin^2\theta) + \sin\theta = 2 \quad \cos^2\theta = 1 - \sin^2\theta$$

$$\sin^2\theta - \sin\theta + 1 = 0$$

This is a quadratic equation in $\sin\theta$. The discriminant is $b^2 - 4ac = (-1)^2 - 4\cdot1\cdot1 = -3 < 0$. Therefore, the equation has no real solution. The solution set is the empty set, $\varnothing$.

Check: Graph $Y_1 = \cos^2 x + \sin x$ and $Y_2 = 2$. See Figure 34. The two graphs never intersect, so the equation $Y_1 = Y_2$ has no real solution.

Figure 34

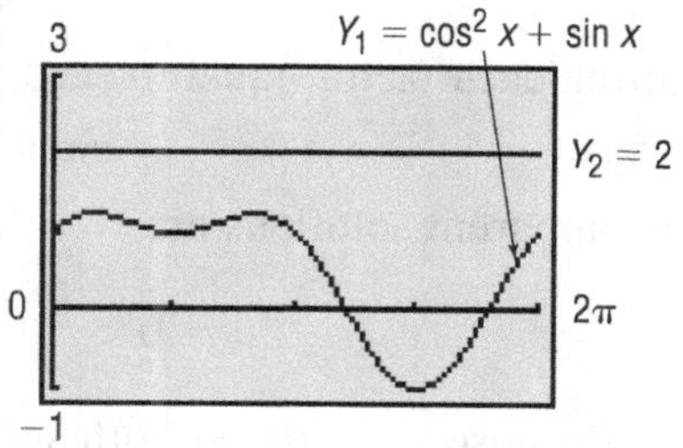

EXAMPLE 5

Solving a Trigonometric Equation Using Identities

Solve the equation: $\sin\theta\cos\theta = -\frac{1}{2}, \quad 0 \le \theta < 2\pi$

Solution The left side of the given equation is in the form of the Double-angle Formula $2\sin\theta\cos\theta = \sin(2\theta)$, except for a factor of 2. We multiply each side by 2.

$$\sin\theta\cos\theta = -\frac{1}{2}$$

$$2\sin\theta\cos\theta = -1 \quad \text{Multiply each side by 2.}$$

$$\sin(2\theta) = -1 \quad \text{Double-angle Formula}$$

The argument here is 2θ. So we need to write all the solutions of this equation and then list those that are in the interval $[0, 2\pi)$. Because $\sin\left(\frac{3\pi}{2} + 2\pi k\right) = -1$ for any integer k, we have

$$2\theta = \frac{3\pi}{2} + 2k\pi \quad \text{k any integer}$$
$$\theta = \frac{3\pi}{4} + k\pi$$

$$\underset{k=-1}{\theta = \frac{3\pi}{4} + (-1)\pi = -\frac{\pi}{4}}, \quad \underset{k=0}{\theta = \frac{3\pi}{4} + (0)\pi = \frac{3\pi}{4}}, \quad \underset{k=1}{\theta = \frac{3\pi}{4} + (1)\pi = \frac{7\pi}{4}}, \quad \underset{k=2}{\theta = \frac{3\pi}{4} + (2)\pi = \frac{11\pi}{4}}$$

The solutions in the interval $[0, 2\pi)$ are

$$\theta = \frac{3\pi}{4} \qquad \theta = \frac{7\pi}{4}$$

The solution set is $\left\{\frac{3\pi}{4}, \frac{7\pi}{4}\right\}$.

3 Solve Trigonometric Equations Linear in Sine and Cosine

Sometimes it is necessary to square both sides of an equation to obtain expressions that allow the use of identities. Remember, squaring both sides of an equation may introduce extraneous solutions. As a result, apparent solutions must be checked.

EXAMPLE 6 Solving a Trigonometric Equation Linear in Sine and Cosine

Solve the equation: $\sin\theta + \cos\theta = 1, \quad 0 \le \theta < 2\pi$

Solution A Attempts to use available identities do not lead to equations that are easy to solve. (Try it yourself.) Given the form of this equation, we decide to square each side.

$$\sin\theta + \cos\theta = 1$$
$$(\sin\theta + \cos\theta)^2 = 1 \quad \text{Square each side.}$$
$$\sin^2\theta + 2\sin\theta\cos\theta + \cos^2\theta = 1 \quad \text{Remove parentheses.}$$
$$2\sin\theta\cos\theta = 0 \quad \sin^2\theta + \cos^2\theta = 1$$
$$\sin\theta\cos\theta = 0$$

Setting each factor equal to zero, we obtain

$$\sin\theta = 0 \quad \text{or} \quad \cos\theta = 0$$

The apparent solutions are

$$\theta = 0 \qquad \theta = \pi \qquad \theta = \frac{\pi}{2} \qquad \theta = \frac{3\pi}{2}$$

Because we squared both sides of the original equation, we must check these apparent solutions to see if any are extraneous.

$$\theta = 0: \quad \sin 0 + \cos 0 = 0 + 1 = 1 \quad \text{A solution}$$
$$\theta = \pi: \quad \sin\pi + \cos\pi = 0 + (-1) = -1 \quad \text{Not a solution}$$
$$\theta = \frac{\pi}{2}: \quad \sin\frac{\pi}{2} + \cos\frac{\pi}{2} = 1 + 0 = 1 \quad \text{A solution}$$
$$\theta = \frac{3\pi}{2}: \quad \sin\frac{3\pi}{2} + \cos\frac{3\pi}{2} = -1 + 0 = -1 \quad \text{Not a solution}$$

The values $\theta = \pi$ and $\theta = \frac{3\pi}{2}$ are extraneous. The solution set is $\left\{0, \frac{\pi}{2}\right\}$.

Solution B We start with the equation

$$\sin\theta + \cos\theta = 1$$

and divide each side by $\sqrt{2}$. (The reason for this choice will become apparent shortly.) Then

$$\frac{1}{\sqrt{2}}\sin\theta + \frac{1}{\sqrt{2}}\cos\theta = \frac{1}{\sqrt{2}}$$

The left side now resembles the formula for the sine of the sum of two angles, one of which is θ. The other angle is unknown (call it ϕ.) Then

$$\sin(\theta + \phi) = \sin\theta\cos\phi + \cos\theta\sin\phi = \frac{1}{\sqrt{2}} = \frac{\sqrt{2}}{2} \qquad \textbf{(1)}$$

where

$$\cos\phi = \frac{1}{\sqrt{2}} = \frac{\sqrt{2}}{2}, \qquad \sin\phi = \frac{1}{\sqrt{2}} = \frac{\sqrt{2}}{2}, \qquad 0 \le \phi < 2\pi$$

The angle ϕ is therefore $\frac{\pi}{4}$. As a result, equation (1) becomes

$$\sin\left(\theta + \frac{\pi}{4}\right) = \frac{\sqrt{2}}{2}$$

Figure 35

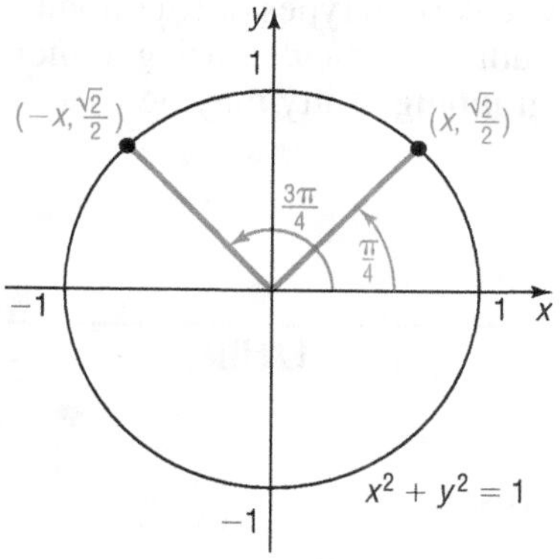

In the interval $[0, 2\pi)$, there are two angles whose sine is $\frac{\sqrt{2}}{2}$: $\frac{\pi}{4}$ and $\frac{3\pi}{4}$. See Figure 35. As a result,

$$\theta + \frac{\pi}{4} = \frac{\pi}{4} \quad \text{or} \quad \theta + \frac{\pi}{4} = \frac{3\pi}{4}$$

$$\theta = 0 \quad \text{or} \quad \theta = \frac{\pi}{2}$$

The solution set is $\left\{0, \frac{\pi}{2}\right\}$.

This second method of solution can be used to solve any linear equation in the variables $\sin\theta$ and $\cos\theta$. Let's look at an example.

EXAMPLE 7 Solving a Trigonometric Equation Linear in $\sin\theta$ and $\cos\theta$

Solve:

$$a\sin\theta + b\cos\theta = c \qquad \textbf{(2)}$$

where a, b, and c are constants and either $a \ne 0$ or $b \ne 0$.

Solution We divide each side of equation (2) by $\sqrt{a^2 + b^2}$. Then

$$\frac{a}{\sqrt{a^2+b^2}}\sin\theta + \frac{b}{\sqrt{a^2+b^2}}\cos\theta = \frac{c}{\sqrt{a^2+b^2}} \qquad \textbf{(3)}$$

There is a unique angle ϕ, $0 \le \phi < 2\pi$, for which

$$\cos\phi = \frac{a}{\sqrt{a^2+b^2}} \quad \text{and} \quad \sin\phi = \frac{b}{\sqrt{a^2+b^2}} \qquad \textbf{(4)}$$

Figure 36

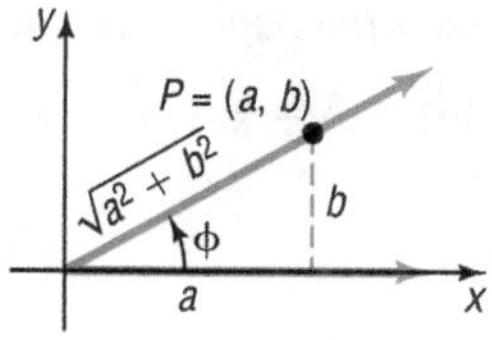

Figure 36 shows the situation for $a > 0$ and $b > 0$. Equation (3) may be written as

$$\sin\theta\cos\phi + \cos\theta\sin\phi = \frac{c}{\sqrt{a^2+b^2}}$$

or, equivalently,

$$\sin(\theta + \phi) = \frac{c}{\sqrt{a^2 + b^2}} \qquad (5)$$

where ϕ satisfies the equations in (4).

If $|c| > \sqrt{a^2 + b^2}$, then $\sin(\theta + \phi) > 1$ or $\sin(\theta + \phi) < -1$, and equation (5) has no solution.

If $|c| \leq \sqrt{a^2 + b^2}$, then all the solutions of equation (5) are

$$\theta + \phi = \sin^{-1}\frac{c}{\sqrt{a^2 + b^2}} + 2k\pi \quad \text{or} \quad \theta + \phi = \pi - \sin^{-1}\frac{c}{\sqrt{a^2 + b^2}} + 2k\pi$$

Because the angle ϕ is determined by the equations in (4), these provide the solutions to equation (2).

Now Work PROBLEM 41

4 Solve Trigonometric Equations Using a Graphing Utility

The techniques introduced in this section apply only to certain types of trigonometric equations. Solutions for other types are usually studied in calculus, using numerical methods. In the next example, we show how a graphing utility may be used to obtain solutions.

EXAMPLE 8 Solving Trigonometric Equations Using a Graphing Utility

Solve: $5 \sin x + x = 3$

Express the solution(s) rounded to two decimal places.

Solution This type of trigonometric equation cannot be solved by previous methods. A graphing utility, though, can be used here. The solution(s) of this equation is the same as the points of intersection of the graphs of $Y_1 = 5 \sin x + x$ and $Y_2 = 3$. See Figure 37.

Figure 37

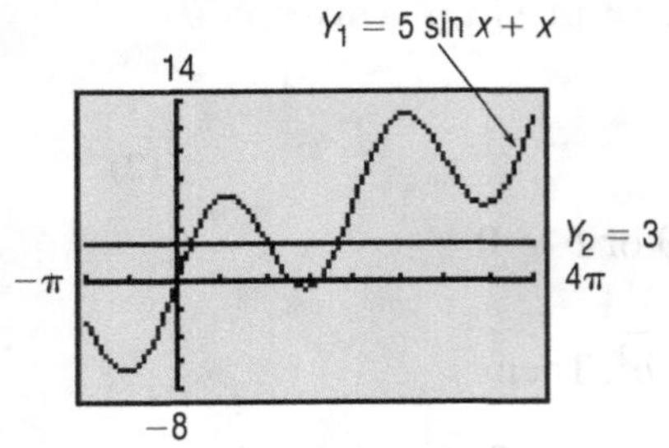

There are three points of intersection; the x-coordinates are the solutions that we seek. Using INTERSECT, we find

$$x = 0.52 \qquad x = 3.18 \qquad x = 5.71$$

The solution set is $\{0.52, 3.18, 5.71\}$.

Now Work PROBLEM 47

7.8 Assess Your Understanding

'Are You Prepared?' *Answers are given at the end of these exercises. If you get a wrong answer, read the pages listed in red.*

1. Find the real solutions of $4x^2 - x - 5 = 0$. (pp. A50–A51)
2. Find the real solutions of $x^2 - x - 1 = 0$. (pp. A53–A55)
3. Find the real solutions of $(2x - 1)^2 - 3(2x - 1) - 4 = 0$. (pp. A55–A56)
4. Use a graphing utility to solve $5x^3 - 2 = x - x^2$. Round answers to two decimal places. (pp. 26–27)

Skill Building

In Problems 5–46, solve each equation on the interval $0 \le \theta < 2\pi$. Verify your results using a graphing utility.

5. $2\cos^2\theta + \cos\theta = 0$
6. $\sin^2\theta - 1 = 0$
7. $2\sin^2\theta - \sin\theta - 1 = 0$
8. $2\cos^2\theta + \cos\theta - 1 = 0$
9. $(\tan\theta - 1)(\sec\theta - 1) = 0$
10. $(\cot\theta + 1)\left(\csc\theta - \frac{1}{2}\right) = 0$
11. $\sin^2\theta - \cos^2\theta = 1 + \cos\theta$
12. $\cos^2\theta - \sin^2\theta + \sin\theta = 0$
13. $\sin^2\theta = 6(\cos\theta + 1)$
14. $2\sin^2\theta = 3(1 - \cos\theta)$
15. $\cos(2\theta) + 6\sin^2\theta = 4$
16. $\cos(2\theta) = 2 - 2\sin^2\theta$
17. $\cos\theta = \sin\theta$
18. $\cos\theta + \sin\theta = 0$
19. $\tan\theta = 2\sin\theta$
20. $\sin(2\theta) = \cos\theta$
21. $\sin\theta = \csc\theta$
22. $\tan\theta = \cot\theta$
23. $\cos(2\theta) = \cos\theta$
24. $\sin(2\theta)\sin\theta = \cos\theta$
25. $\sin(2\theta) + \sin(4\theta) = 0$
26. $\cos(2\theta) + \cos(4\theta) = 0$
27. $\cos(4\theta) - \cos(6\theta) = 0$
28. $\sin(4\theta) - \sin(6\theta) = 0$
29. $1 + \sin\theta = 2\cos^2\theta$
30. $\sin^2\theta = 2\cos\theta + 2$
31. $2\sin^2\theta - 5\sin\theta + 3 = 0$
32. $2\cos^2\theta - 7\cos\theta - 4 = 0$
33. $3(1 - \cos\theta) = \sin^2\theta$
34. $4(1 + \sin\theta) = \cos^2\theta$
35. $\tan^2\theta = \frac{3}{2}\sec\theta$
36. $\csc^2\theta = \cot\theta + 1$
37. $3 - \sin\theta = \cos(2\theta)$
38. $\cos(2\theta) + 5\cos\theta + 3 = 0$
39. $\sec^2\theta + \tan\theta = 0$
40. $\sec\theta = \tan\theta + \cot\theta$
41. $\sin\theta - \sqrt{3}\cos\theta = 1$
42. $\sqrt{3}\sin\theta + \cos\theta = 1$
43. $\tan(2\theta) + 2\sin\theta = 0$
44. $\tan(2\theta) + 2\cos\theta = 0$
45. $\sin\theta + \cos\theta = \sqrt{2}$
46. $\sin\theta + \cos\theta = -\sqrt{2}$

In Problems 47–58, use a graphing utility to solve each equation. Express the solution(s) rounded to two decimal places.

47. $x + 5\cos x = 0$
48. $x - 4\sin x = 0$
49. $22x - 17\sin x = 3$
50. $19x + 8\cos x = 2$
51. $\sin x + \cos x = x$
52. $\sin x - \cos x = x$
53. $x^2 - 2\cos x = 0$
54. $x^2 + 3\sin x = 0$
55. $x^2 - 2\sin(2x) = 3x$
56. $x^2 = x + 3\cos(2x)$
57. $6\sin x - e^x = 2, \quad x > 0$
58. $4\cos(3x) - e^x = 1, \quad x > 0$

Mixed Practice

In Problems 59–64, find the real zeros of each trigonometric function on the interval $0 \le x < 2\pi$.

59. $f(x) = 4\cos^2 x - 1$
60. $f(x) = 4\sin^2 x - 3$
61. $f(x) = \sin(2x) - \sin x$
62. $f(x) = \cos(2x) + \cos x$
63. $f(x) = \sin^2 x + 2\cos x + 2$
64. $f(x) = \cos(2x) + \sin^2 x$

Applications and Extensions

65. Constructing a Rain Gutter A rain gutter is to be constructed of aluminum sheets 12 inches wide. After marking off a length of 4 inches from each edge, this length is bent up at an angle θ. See the illustration. The area A of the opening as a function of θ is given by

$$A(\theta) = 16\sin\theta(\cos\theta + 1) \quad 0^\circ < \theta < 90^\circ$$

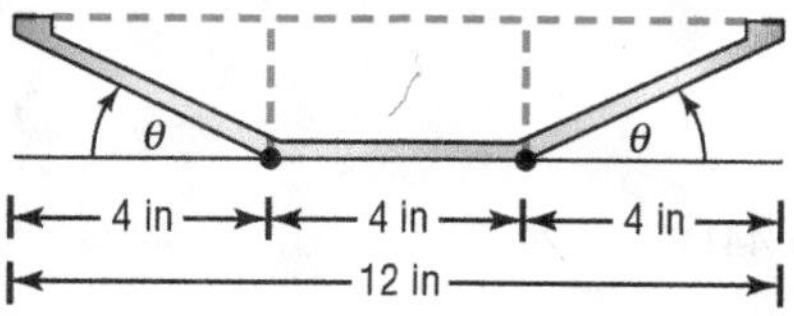

(a) In calculus, you will be asked to find the angle θ that maximizes A by solving the equation

$$\cos(2\theta) + \cos\theta = 0, \quad 0^\circ < \theta < 90^\circ$$

Solve this equation for θ by using the Double-angle Formula.

(b) Solve the equation in part (a) for θ by writing the sum of the two cosines as a product.

(c) What is the maximum area A of the opening?

(d) Graph $A = A(\theta)$, $0^\circ \le \theta \le 90^\circ$, and find the angle θ that maximizes the area A. Also find the maximum area. Compare the results to the answers found earlier.

66. Projectile Motion An object is propelled upward at an angle θ, $45^\circ < \theta < 90^\circ$, to the horizontal with an initial velocity of v_0 feet per second from the base of an inclined plane that makes an angle of 45° with the horizontal. See the illustration. If air resistance is ignored, the distance R that the object travels up the inclined plane is given by

$$R(\theta) = \frac{v_0^2\sqrt{2}}{32}[\sin(2\theta) - \cos(2\theta) - 1]$$

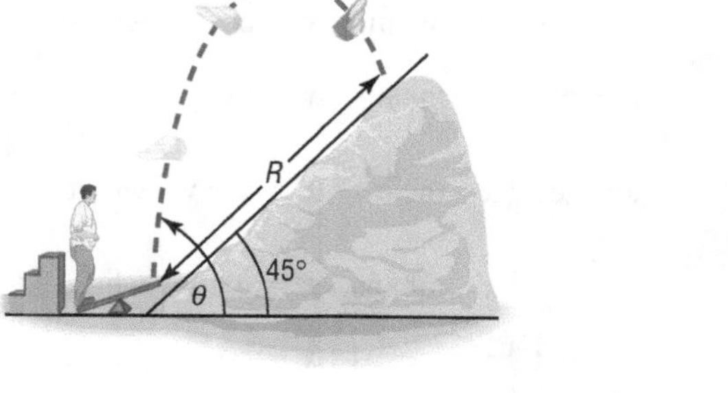

(a) In calculus, you will be asked to find the angle θ that maximizes R by solving the equation

$$\sin(2\theta) + \cos(2\theta) = 0$$

Solve this equation for θ using the method of Example 7.
(b) Solve this equation for θ by dividing each side by $\cos(2\theta)$.
(c) What is the maximum distance R if $v_0 = 32$ feet per second?
(d) Graph $R = R(\theta)$, $45° \le \theta \le 90°$, and find the angle θ that maximizes the distance R. Also find the maximum distance. Use $v_0 = 32$ feet per second. Compare the results with the answers found earlier.

67. **Heat Transfer** In the study of heat transfer, the equation $x + \tan x = 0$ occurs. Graph $Y_1 = -x$ and $Y_2 = \tan x$ for $x \ge 0$. Conclude that there are an infinite number of points of intersection of these two graphs. Now find the first two positive solutions of $x + \tan x = 0$ rounded to two decimal places.

68. **Carrying a Ladder Around a Corner** Two hallways, one of width 3 feet, the other of width 4 feet, meet at a right angle. See the illustration.

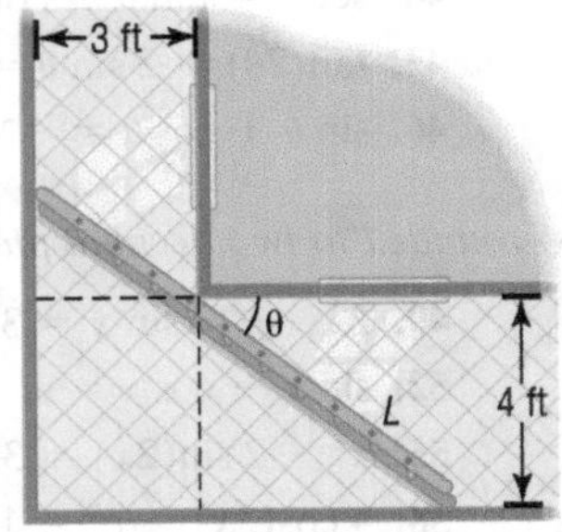

(a) Show that the length L as a function of θ is

$$L(\theta) = 4 \csc \theta + 3 \sec \theta$$

(b) In calculus, you will be asked to find the length of the longest ladder that can turn the corner by solving the equation

$$3 \sec \theta \tan \theta - 4 \csc \theta \cot \theta = 0, \quad 0° < \theta < 90°$$

Solve this equation for θ.
(c) What is the length of the longest ladder that can be carried around the corner?
(d) Graph $L = L(\theta)$, $0° \le \theta \le 90°$, and find the angle θ that minimizes the length L.
(e) Compare the result with the one found in part (b). Explain why the two answers are the same.

69. **Projectile Motion** The horizontal distance that a projectile will travel in the air (ignoring air resistance) is given by the equation

$$R(\theta) = \frac{v_0^2 \sin(2\theta)}{g}$$

where v_0 is the initial velocity of the projectile, θ is the angle of elevation, and g is acceleration due to gravity (9.8 meters per second squared).
(a) If you can throw a baseball with an initial speed of 34.8 meters per second, at what angle of elevation θ should you direct the throw so that the ball travels a distance of 107 meters before striking the ground?
(b) Determine the maximum distance that you can throw the ball.
(c) Graph $R = R(\theta)$, with $v_0 = 34.8$ meters per second.
(d) Verify the results obtained in parts (a) and (b) using a graphing utility.

70. **Projectile Motion** Refer to Problem 69.
(a) If you can throw a baseball with an initial speed of 40 meters per second, at what angle of elevation θ should you direct the throw so that the ball travels a distance of 110 meters before striking the ground?
(b) Determine the maximum distance that you can throw the ball.
(c) Graph $R = R(\theta)$, with $v_0 = 40$ meters per second.
(d) Verify the results obtained in parts (a) and (b) using a graphing utility.

'Are You Prepared?' Answers

1. $\left\{-1, \frac{5}{4}\right\}$ 2. $\left\{\frac{1-\sqrt{5}}{2}, \frac{1+\sqrt{5}}{2}\right\}$ 3. $\left\{0, \frac{5}{2}\right\}$ 4. $\{0.76\}$

CHAPTER REVIEW

Things to Know

Definitions of the six inverse trigonometric functions

$y = \sin^{-1} x$ means $x = \sin y$ where $-1 \le x \le 1$, $-\frac{\pi}{2} \le y \le \frac{\pi}{2}$ (p. 441)

$y = \cos^{-1} x$ means $x = \cos y$ where $-1 \le x \le 1$, $0 \le y \le \pi$ (p. 445)

$y = \tan^{-1} x$ means $x = \tan y$ where $-\infty < x < \infty$, $-\frac{\pi}{2} < y < \frac{\pi}{2}$ (p. 448)

$y = \sec^{-1} x$ means $x = \sec y$ where $|x| \ge 1$, $0 \le y \le \pi$, $y \ne \frac{\pi}{2}$ (p. 455)

$y = \csc^{-1} x$ means $x = \csc y$ where $|x| \ge 1$, $-\frac{\pi}{2} \le y \le \frac{\pi}{2}$, $y \ne 0$ (p. 455)

$y = \cot^{-1} x$ means $x = \cot y$ where $-\infty < x < \infty$, $0 < y < \pi$ (p. 455)

Sum and difference formulas (pp. 466, 469, and 471)

$\cos(\alpha + \beta) = \cos\alpha\cos\beta - \sin\alpha\sin\beta$ $\qquad$ $\cos(\alpha - \beta) = \cos\alpha\cos\beta + \sin\alpha\sin\beta$

$\sin(\alpha + \beta) = \sin\alpha\cos\beta + \cos\alpha\sin\beta$ $\qquad$ $\sin(\alpha - \beta) = \sin\alpha\cos\beta - \cos\alpha\sin\beta$

$\tan(\alpha + \beta) = \dfrac{\tan\alpha + \tan\beta}{1 - \tan\alpha\tan\beta}$ $\qquad$ $\tan(\alpha - \beta) = \dfrac{\tan\alpha - \tan\beta}{1 + \tan\alpha\tan\beta}$

Double-angle Formulas (pp. 476 and 477)

$\sin(2\theta) = 2\sin\theta\cos\theta$ $\qquad$ $\cos(2\theta) = \cos^2\theta - \sin^2\theta$ $\qquad$ $\tan(2\theta) = \dfrac{2\tan\theta}{1 - \tan^2\theta}$

$\cos(2\theta) = 2\cos^2\theta - 1$ $\qquad$ $\cos(2\theta) = 1 - 2\sin^2\theta$

Half-angle Formulas (pp. 479, 480, and 482)

$\sin^2\dfrac{\alpha}{2} = \dfrac{1 - \cos\alpha}{2}$ $\qquad$ $\cos^2\dfrac{\alpha}{2} = \dfrac{1 + \cos\alpha}{2}$ $\qquad$ $\tan^2\dfrac{\alpha}{2} = \dfrac{1 - \cos\alpha}{1 + \cos\alpha}$

$\sin\dfrac{\alpha}{2} = \pm\sqrt{\dfrac{1 - \cos\alpha}{2}}$ $\qquad$ $\cos\dfrac{\alpha}{2} = \pm\sqrt{\dfrac{1 + \cos\alpha}{2}}$ $\qquad$ $\tan\dfrac{\alpha}{2} = \pm\sqrt{\dfrac{1 - \cos\alpha}{1 + \cos\alpha}} = \dfrac{1 - \cos\alpha}{\sin\alpha} = \dfrac{\sin\alpha}{1 + \cos\alpha}$

where the + or − is determined by the quadrant of $\dfrac{\alpha}{2}$.

Product-to-Sum Formulas (p. 485)

$\sin\alpha\sin\beta = \dfrac{1}{2}[\cos(\alpha - \beta) - \cos(\alpha + \beta)]$

$\cos\alpha\cos\beta = \dfrac{1}{2}[\cos(\alpha - \beta) + \cos(\alpha + \beta)]$

$\sin\alpha\cos\beta = \dfrac{1}{2}[\sin(\alpha + \beta) + \sin(\alpha - \beta)]$

Sum-to-Product Formulas (p. 486)

$\sin\alpha + \sin\beta = 2\sin\dfrac{\alpha + \beta}{2}\cos\dfrac{\alpha - \beta}{2}$ $\qquad$ $\sin\alpha - \sin\beta = 2\sin\dfrac{\alpha - \beta}{2}\cos\dfrac{\alpha + \beta}{2}$

$\cos\alpha + \cos\beta = 2\cos\dfrac{\alpha + \beta}{2}\cos\dfrac{\alpha - \beta}{2}$ $\qquad$ $\cos\alpha - \cos\beta = -2\sin\dfrac{\alpha + \beta}{2}\sin\dfrac{\alpha - \beta}{2}$

Objectives

Section		You should be able to ...	Example(s)	Review Exercises
7.1	1	Find the exact value of an inverse sine, cosine, or tangent function (p. 441)	1, 2, 6, 7, 9	1–6
	2	Find an approximate value of an inverse sine function (p. 443)	3	121–124
	3	Use properties of inverse functions to find exact values of certain composite functions (p. 443)	4, 5, 8	9–20
	4	Find the inverse function of a trigonometric function (p. 449)	10	33–36
	5	Solve equations involving inverse trigonometric functions (p. 450)	11	133, 134
7.2	1	Find the exact value of expressions involving the inverse sine, cosine, and tangent functions (p. 454)	1–3	21–32
	2	Know the definitions of the inverse secant, cosecant, and cotangent functions (p. 455)	4	7, 8, 29, 30
	3	Use a calculator to evaluate $\sec^{-1} x$, $\csc^{-1} x$, and $\cot^{-1} x$ (p. 456)	5	125, 126
	4	Write a trigonometric expression as an algebraic expression (p. 456)	6	37–40
7.3	1	Use algebra to simplify trigonometric expressions (p. 460)	1	41–72
	2	Establish identities (p. 461)	2–8	41–58
7.4	1	Use sum and difference formulas to find exact values (p. 467)	1, 2	73–80, 81–90(a)–(d), 135
	2	Use sum and difference formulas to establish identities (p. 468)	3–8	59–62
	3	Use sum and difference formulas involving inverse trigonometric functions (p. 472)	9, 10	91–94

7.5	1	Use double-angle formulas to find exact values (p. 476)	1	81–90(e), (f), 95, 96
	2	Use double-angle formulas to establish identities (p. 477)	2–4	65–67
	3	Use half-angle formulas to find exact values (p. 479)	5, 6	81–90(g), (h), 135
7.6	1	Express products as sums (p. 485)	1	68
	2	Express sums as products (p. 486)	2	69–72
7.7	1	Solve equations involving a single trigonometric function (p. 489)	1–6	97–106
7.8	1	Solve trigonometric equations quadratic in form (p. 495)	1	113, 114
	2	Solve trigonometric equations using identities (p. 496)	2–5	97–112, 115–118
	3	Solve trigonometric equations linear in sine and cosine (p. 498)	6, 7	119, 120
	4	Solve trigonometric equations using a graphing utility (p. 500)	8	127–132

Review Exercises

In Problems 1–8, find the exact value of each expression. Do not use a calculator.

1. $\sin^{-1} 1$ **2.** $\cos^{-1} 0$ **3.** $\tan^{-1} 1$ **4.** $\sin^{-1}\left(-\frac{1}{2}\right)$

5. $\cos^{-1}\left(-\frac{\sqrt{3}}{2}\right)$ **6.** $\tan^{-1}(-\sqrt{3})$ **7.** $\sec^{-1}\sqrt{2}$ **8.** $\cot^{-1}(-1)$

In Problems 9–32, find the exact value, if any, of each composite function. If there is no value, say it is "not defined." Do not use a calculator.

9. $\sin^{-1}\left(\sin\frac{3\pi}{8}\right)$ **10.** $\cos^{-1}\left(\cos\frac{3\pi}{4}\right)$ **11.** $\tan^{-1}\left(\tan\frac{2\pi}{3}\right)$ **12.** $\sin^{-1}\left[\sin\left(-\frac{\pi}{8}\right)\right]$

13. $\cos^{-1}\left(\cos\frac{15\pi}{7}\right)$ **14.** $\sin^{-1}\left[\sin\left(-\frac{8\pi}{9}\right)\right]$ **15.** $\sin(\sin^{-1} 0.9)$ **16.** $\cos(\cos^{-1} 0.6)$

17. $\cos[\cos^{-1}(-0.3)]$ **18.** $\tan[\tan^{-1} 5]$ **19.** $\cos[\cos^{-1}(-1.6)]$ **20.** $\sin(\sin^{-1} 1.6)$

21. $\sin^{-1}\left(\cos\frac{2\pi}{3}\right)$ **22.** $\cos^{-1}\left(\tan\frac{3\pi}{4}\right)$ **23.** $\tan^{-1}\left(\tan\frac{7\pi}{4}\right)$ **24.** $\cos^{-1}\left(\cos\frac{7\pi}{6}\right)$

25. $\tan\left[\sin^{-1}\left(-\frac{\sqrt{3}}{2}\right)\right]$ **26.** $\tan\left[\cos^{-1}\left(-\frac{1}{2}\right)\right]$ **27.** $\sec\left(\tan^{-1}\frac{\sqrt{3}}{3}\right)$ **28.** $\csc\left(\sin^{-1}\frac{\sqrt{3}}{2}\right)$

29. $\sin\left(\cot^{-1}\frac{3}{4}\right)$ **30.** $\cos\left(\csc^{-1}\frac{5}{3}\right)$ **31.** $\tan\left[\sin^{-1}\left(-\frac{4}{5}\right)\right]$ **32.** $\tan\left[\cos^{-1}\left(-\frac{3}{5}\right)\right]$

In Problems 33–36, find the inverse function f^{-1} of each function f. State the domain and the range of f^{-1} and f.

33. $f(x) = 2\sin(3x)$ **34.** $f(x) = \tan(2x+3) - 1$ **35.** $f(x) = -\cos x + 3$ **36.** $f(x) = 2\sin(-x+1)$

In Problems 37–40, write each trigonometric expression as an algebraic expression in u.

37. $\cos(\sin^{-1} u)$ **38.** $\cos(\csc^{-1} u)$ **39.** $\sin(\csc^{-1} u)$ **40.** $\tan(\csc^{-1} u)$

In Problems 41–72, establish each identity.

41. $\tan\theta\cot\theta - \sin^2\theta = \cos^2\theta$ **42.** $\sin\theta\csc\theta - \sin^2\theta = \cos^2\theta$ **43.** $\sin^2\theta(1+\cot^2\theta) = 1$

44. $(1-\sin^2\theta)(1+\tan^2\theta) = 1$ **45.** $5\cos^2\theta + 3\sin^2\theta = 3 + 2\cos^2\theta$ **46.** $4\sin^2\theta + 2\cos^2\theta = 4 - 2\cos^2\theta$

47. $\frac{1-\cos\theta}{\sin\theta} + \frac{\sin\theta}{1-\cos\theta} = 2\csc\theta$ **48.** $\frac{\sin\theta}{1+\cos\theta} + \frac{1+\cos\theta}{\sin\theta} = 2\csc\theta$ **49.** $\frac{\cos\theta}{\cos\theta - \sin\theta} = \frac{1}{1-\tan\theta}$

50. $1 - \frac{\sin^2\theta}{1+\cos\theta} = \cos\theta$ **51.** $\frac{\csc\theta}{1+\csc\theta} = \frac{1-\sin\theta}{\cos^2\theta}$ **52.** $\frac{1+\sec\theta}{\sec\theta} = \frac{\sin^2\theta}{1-\cos\theta}$

53. $\csc\theta - \sin\theta = \cos\theta\cot\theta$ **54.** $\frac{\csc\theta}{1-\cos\theta} = \frac{1+\cos\theta}{\sin^3\theta}$ **55.** $\frac{1-\sin\theta}{\sec\theta} = \frac{\cos^3\theta}{1+\sin\theta}$

56. $\frac{1-\cos\theta}{1+\cos\theta} = (\csc\theta - \cot\theta)^2$ **57.** $\frac{1-2\sin^2\theta}{\sin\theta\cos\theta} = \cot\theta - \tan\theta$ **58.** $\frac{(2\sin^2\theta - 1)^2}{\sin^4\theta - \cos^4\theta} = 1 - 2\cos^2\theta$

59. $\frac{\cos(\alpha+\beta)}{\cos\alpha\sin\beta} = \cot\beta - \tan\alpha$ **60.** $\frac{\sin(\alpha-\beta)}{\sin\alpha\cos\beta} = 1 - \cot\alpha\tan\beta$ **61.** $\frac{\cos(\alpha-\beta)}{\cos\alpha\cos\beta} = 1 + \tan\alpha\tan\beta$

62. $\frac{\cos(\alpha+\beta)}{\sin\alpha\cos\beta} = \cot\alpha - \tan\beta$ **63.** $(1+\cos\theta)\tan\frac{\theta}{2} = \sin\theta$ **64.** $\sin\theta\tan\frac{\theta}{2} = 1 - \cos\theta$

65. $2\cot\theta\cot(2\theta) = \cot^2\theta - 1$

66. $2\sin(2\theta)(1 - 2\sin^2\theta) = \sin(4\theta)$

67. $1 - 8\sin^2\theta\cos^2\theta = \cos(4\theta)$

68. $\dfrac{\sin(3\theta)\cos\theta - \sin\theta\cos(3\theta)}{\sin(2\theta)} = 1$

69. $\dfrac{\sin(2\theta) + \sin(4\theta)}{\cos(2\theta) + \cos(4\theta)} = \tan(3\theta)$

70. $\dfrac{\sin(2\theta) + \sin(4\theta)}{\sin(2\theta) - \sin(4\theta)} + \dfrac{\tan(3\theta)}{\tan\theta} = 0$

71. $\dfrac{\cos(2\theta) - \cos(4\theta)}{\cos(2\theta) + \cos(4\theta)} - \tan\theta\tan(3\theta) = 0$

72. $\cos(2\theta) - \cos(10\theta) = \tan(4\theta)[\sin(2\theta) + \sin(10\theta)]$

In Problems 73–80, find the exact value of each expression.

73. $\sin 165°$

74. $\tan 105°$

75. $\cos\dfrac{5\pi}{12}$

76. $\sin\left(-\dfrac{\pi}{12}\right)$

77. $\cos 80°\cos 20° + \sin 80°\sin 20°$

78. $\sin 70°\cos 40° - \cos 70°\sin 40°$

79. $\tan\dfrac{\pi}{8}$

80. $\sin\dfrac{5\pi}{8}$

In Problems 81–90, use the information given about the angles α and β to find the exact value of:

(a) $\sin(\alpha + \beta)$ (b) $\cos(\alpha + \beta)$ (c) $\sin(\alpha - \beta)$ (d) $\tan(\alpha + \beta)$

(e) $\sin(2\alpha)$ (f) $\cos(2\beta)$ (g) $\sin\dfrac{\beta}{2}$ (h) $\cos\dfrac{\alpha}{2}$

81. $\sin\alpha = \dfrac{4}{5}, 0 < \alpha < \dfrac{\pi}{2}; \sin\beta = \dfrac{5}{13}, \dfrac{\pi}{2} < \beta < \pi$

82. $\cos\alpha = \dfrac{4}{5}, 0 < \alpha < \dfrac{\pi}{2}; \cos\beta = \dfrac{5}{13}, -\dfrac{\pi}{2} < \beta < 0$

83. $\sin\alpha = -\dfrac{3}{5}, \pi < \alpha < \dfrac{3\pi}{2}; \cos\beta = \dfrac{12}{13}, \dfrac{3\pi}{2} < \beta < 2\pi$

84. $\sin\alpha = -\dfrac{4}{5}, -\dfrac{\pi}{2} < \alpha < 0; \cos\beta = -\dfrac{5}{13}, \dfrac{\pi}{2} < \beta < \pi$

85. $\tan\alpha = \dfrac{3}{4}, \pi < \alpha < \dfrac{3\pi}{2}; \tan\beta = \dfrac{12}{5}, 0 < \beta < \dfrac{\pi}{2}$

86. $\tan\alpha = -\dfrac{4}{3}, \dfrac{\pi}{2} < \alpha < \pi; \cot\beta = \dfrac{12}{5}, \pi < \beta < \dfrac{3\pi}{2}$

87. $\sec\alpha = 2, -\dfrac{\pi}{2} < \alpha < 0; \sec\beta = 3, \dfrac{3\pi}{2} < \beta < 2\pi$

88. $\csc\alpha = 2, \dfrac{\pi}{2} < \alpha < \pi; \sec\beta = -3, \dfrac{\pi}{2} < \beta < \pi$

89. $\sin\alpha = -\dfrac{2}{3}, \pi < \alpha < \dfrac{3\pi}{2}; \cos\beta = -\dfrac{2}{3}, \pi < \beta < \dfrac{3\pi}{2}$

90. $\tan\alpha = -2, \dfrac{\pi}{2} < \alpha < \pi; \cot\beta = -2, \dfrac{\pi}{2} < \beta < \pi$

In Problems 91–96, find the exact value of each expression.

91. $\cos\left(\sin^{-1}\dfrac{3}{5} - \cos^{-1}\dfrac{1}{2}\right)$

92. $\sin\left(\cos^{-1}\dfrac{5}{13} - \cos^{-1}\dfrac{4}{5}\right)$

93. $\tan\left[\sin^{-1}\left(-\dfrac{1}{2}\right) - \tan^{-1}\dfrac{3}{4}\right]$

94. $\cos\left[\tan^{-1}(-1) + \cos^{-1}\left(-\dfrac{4}{5}\right)\right]$

95. $\sin\left[2\cos^{-1}\left(-\dfrac{3}{5}\right)\right]$

96. $\cos\left(2\tan^{-1}\dfrac{4}{3}\right)$

In Problems 97–120, solve each equation on the interval $0 \le \theta < 2\pi$. Verify your results using a graphing utility.

97. $\cos\theta = \dfrac{1}{2}$

98. $\sin\theta = -\dfrac{\sqrt{3}}{2}$

99. $2\cos\theta + \sqrt{2} = 0$

100. $\tan\theta + \sqrt{3} = 0$

101. $\sin(2\theta) + 1 = 0$

102. $\cos(2\theta) = 0$

103. $\tan(2\theta) = 0$

104. $\sin(3\theta) = 1$

105. $\sec^2\theta = 4$

106. $\csc^2\theta = 1$

107. $\sin\theta = \tan\theta$

108. $\cos\theta = \sec\theta$

109. $\sin\theta + \sin(2\theta) = 0$

110. $\cos(2\theta) = \sin\theta$

111. $\sin(2\theta) - \cos\theta - 2\sin\theta + 1 = 0$

112. $\sin(2\theta) - \sin\theta - 2\cos\theta + 1 = 0$

113. $2\sin^2\theta - 3\sin\theta + 1 = 0$

114. $2\cos^2\theta + \cos\theta - 1 = 0$

115. $4\sin^2\theta = 1 + 4\cos\theta$

116. $8 - 12\sin^2\theta = 4\cos^2\theta$

117. $\sin(2\theta) = \sqrt{2}\cos\theta$

118. $1 + \sqrt{3}\cos\theta + \cos(2\theta) = 0$

119. $\sin\theta - \cos\theta = 1$

120. $\sin\theta - \sqrt{3}\cos\theta = 2$

In Problems 121–126, use a calculator to find an approximate value for each expression, rounded to two decimal places.

121. $\sin^{-1} 0.7$

122. $\cos^{-1}\dfrac{4}{5}$

123. $\tan^{-1}(-2)$

124. $\cos^{-1}(-0.2)$

125. $\sec^{-1} 3$

126. $\cot^{-1}(-4)$

In Problems 127–132, use a graphing utility to solve each equation on the interval $0 \le x < 2\pi$. Approximate any solutions rounded to two decimal places.

127. $2x = 5\cos x$

128. $2x = 5\sin x$

129. $2\sin x + 3\cos x = 4x$

130. $3\cos x + x = \sin x$

131. $\sin x = \ln x$

132. $\sin x = e^{-x}$

In Problems 133 and 134, find the exact solution of each equation.

133. $-3\sin^{-1} x = \pi$

134. $2\cos^{-1} x + \pi = 4\cos^{-1} x$

135. Use a Half-angle Formula to find the exact value of $\sin 15°$. Then use a difference formula to find the exact value of $\sin 15°$. Show that the answers found are the same.

136. If you are given the value of $\cos\theta$ and want the exact value of $\cos(2\theta)$, what form of the Double-angle Formula for $\cos(2\theta)$ is most efficient to use?

CHAPTER TEST

In Problems 1–6, find the exact value of each expression. Express angles in radians.

1. $\sec^{-1}\left(\frac{2}{\sqrt{3}}\right)$

2. $\sin^{-1}\left(-\frac{\sqrt{2}}{2}\right)$

3. $\sin^{-1}\left(\sin\frac{11\pi}{5}\right)$

4. $\tan\left(\tan^{-1}\frac{7}{3}\right)$

5. $\cot\left(\csc^{-1}\sqrt{10}\right)$

6. $\sec\left(\cos^{-1}\left(-\frac{3}{4}\right)\right)$

In Problems 7–10, use a calculator to evaluate each expression. Express angles in radians rounded to two decimal places.

7. $\sin^{-1}0.382$

8. $\sec^{-1}1.4$

9. $\tan^{-1}3$

10. $\cot^{-1}5$

In Problems 11–16 establish each identity.

11. $\frac{\csc\theta + \cot\theta}{\sec\theta + \tan\theta} = \frac{\sec\theta - \tan\theta}{\csc\theta - \cot\theta}$

12. $\sin\theta\tan\theta + \cos\theta = \sec\theta$

13. $\tan\theta + \cot\theta = 2\csc(2\theta)$

14. $\frac{\sin(\alpha + \beta)}{\tan\alpha + \tan\beta} = \cos\alpha\cos\beta$

15. $\sin(3\theta) = 3\sin\theta - 4\sin^3\theta$

16. $\frac{\tan\theta - \cot\theta}{\tan\theta + \cot\theta} = 1 - 2\cos^2\theta$

In Problems 17–24 use sum, difference, product, or half-angle formulas to find the exact value of each expression.

17. $\cos 15°$

18. $\tan 75°$

19. $\sin\left(\frac{1}{2}\cos^{-1}\frac{3}{5}\right)$

20. $\tan\left(2\sin^{-1}\frac{6}{11}\right)$

21. $\cos\left(\sin^{-1}\frac{2}{3} + \tan^{-1}\frac{3}{2}\right)$

22. $\sin 75°\cos 15°$

23. $\sin 75° + \sin 15°$

24. $\cos 65°\cos 20° + \sin 65°\sin 20°$

In Problems 25–29, solve each equation on $0 \le \theta < 2\pi$.

25. $4\sin^2\theta - 3 = 0$

26. $-3\cos\left(\frac{\pi}{2} - \theta\right) = \tan\theta$

27. $\cos^2\theta + 2\sin\theta\cos\theta - \sin^2\theta = 0$

28. $\sin(\theta + 1) = \cos\theta$

29. $4\sin^2\theta + 7\sin\theta = 2$

30. Stage 16 of the 2004 Tour de France was a time trial from Bourg d'Oisans to L'Alpe d'Huez. The average grade (slope as a percent) for most of the 15-kilometer mountainous trek was 7.9%. What was the change in elevation from the beginning to the end of the route?

CUMULATIVE REVIEW

1. Find the real solutions, if any, of the equation $3x^2 + x - 1 = 0$.

2. Find an equation for the line containing the points $(-2, 5)$ and $(4, -1)$. What is the distance between these points? What is their midpoint?

3. Test the equation $3x + y^2 = 9$ for symmetry with respect to the x-axis, y-axis, and origin. List the intercepts.

4. Use transformations to graph the equation $y = |x - 3| + 2$.

5. Use transformations to graph the equation $y = 3e^x - 2$.

6. Use transformations to graph the equation

$$y = \cos\left(x - \frac{\pi}{2}\right) - 1.$$

7. Sketch a graph of each of the following functions. Label at least three points on each graph. Name the inverse function of each and show its graph.

(a) $y = x^3$ (b) $y = e^x$

(c) $y = \sin x,\quad -\frac{\pi}{2} \le x \le \frac{\pi}{2}$

(d) $y = \cos x,\quad 0 \le x \le \pi$

8. If $\sin\theta = -\frac{1}{3}$ and $\pi < \theta < \frac{3\pi}{2}$, find the exact value of:

(a) $\cos\theta$ (b) $\tan\theta$ (c) $\sin(2\theta)$

(d) $\cos(2\theta)$ (e) $\sin\left(\frac{1}{2}\theta\right)$ (f) $\cos\left(\frac{1}{2}\theta\right)$

9. Find the exact value of $\cos(\tan^{-1}2)$.

10. If $\sin\alpha = \frac{1}{3}, \frac{\pi}{2} < \alpha < \pi$, and $\cos\beta = -\frac{1}{3}, \pi < \beta < \frac{3\pi}{2}$, find the exact value of:

(a) $\cos\alpha$ (b) $\sin\beta$ (c) $\cos(2\alpha)$

(d) $\cos(\alpha + \beta)$ (e) $\sin\frac{\beta}{2}$

11. For the function

$$f(x) = 2x^5 - x^4 - 4x^3 + 2x^2 + 2x - 1:$$

(a) Find the real zeros and their multiplicity.
(b) Find the intercepts.
(c) Find the power function that the graph of f resembles for large $|x|$.
(d) Graph f using a graphing utility.
(e) Approximate the turning points, if any exist.
(f) Use the information obtained in parts (a)–(e) to sketch a graph of f by hand.
(g) Identify the intervals on which f is increasing, decreasing, or constant.

12. If $f(x) = 2x^2 + 3x + 1$ and $g(x) = x^2 + 3x + 2$, solve:

(a) $f(x) = 0$ (b) $f(x) = g(x)$

(c) $f(x) > 0$ (d) $f(x) \ge g(x)$

CHAPTER PROJECTS

I. Waves A stretched string that is attached at both ends, pulled in a direction perpendicular to the string, and released has motion that is described as wave motion. If we assume no friction and a length such that there are no "echoes" (that is, the wave does not bounce back), the transverse motion (motion perpendicular to the string) can be modeled by the equation

$$y = y_m \sin(kx - \omega t)$$

where y_m is the amplitude measured in meters and k and ω are constants. The height of the wave depends on the distance x from one endpoint of the string and on the time t, so a typical wave has horizontal and vertical motion over time.

(a) What is the amplitude of the wave

$$y = 0.00421 \sin(68.3x - 2.68t)?$$

(b) The value of ω is the angular frequency measured in radians per second. What is the angular frequency of the wave given in part (a)?

(c) The frequency f is the number of vibrations per second (hertz) made by the wave as it passes a certain point. Its value is found using the formula $f = \frac{\omega}{2\pi}$. What is the frequency of the wave given in part (a)?

(d) The wavelength, λ, of a wave is the shortest distance at which the wave pattern repeats itself for a constant t. Thus, $\lambda = \frac{2\pi}{k}$. What is the wavelength of the wave given in part (a)?

(e) Graph the height of the string a distance $x = 1$ meter from an endpoint.

(f) If two waves travel simultaneously along the same stretched string, the vertical displacement of the string when both waves act is $y = y_1 + y_2$, where y_1 is the vertical displacement of the first wave and y_2 is the vertical displacement of the second wave. This result is called the Principle of Superposition and was analyzed by the French mathematician Jean Baptiste Fourier (1768–1830). When two waves travel along the same string, one wave will differ from the other wave by a phase constant ϕ. That is,

$$y_1 = y_m \sin(kx - \omega t)$$
$$y_2 = y_m \sin(kx - \omega t + \phi)$$

assuming that each wave has the same amplitude. Write $y_1 + y_2$ as a product using the Sum-to-Product Formulas.

(g) Suppose that two waves are moving in the same direction along a stretched string. The amplitude of each wave is 0.0045 meter, and the phase difference between them is 2.5 radians. The wavelength, λ, of each wave is 0.09 meter, and the frequency, f, is 2.3 hertz. Find y_1, y_2, and $y_1 + y_2$.

(h) Using a graphing utility, graph y_1, y_2, and $y_1 + y_2$ on the same viewing window.

(i) Redo parts (g) and (h) with the phase difference between the waves being 0.4 radian.

(j) What effect does the phase difference have on the amplitude of $y_1 + y_2$?

The following projects are available on the Instructor's Resource Center (IRC):

II. Project at Motorola Sending Pictures Wirelessly The electronic transmission of pictures is made practical by image compression, mathematical methods that greatly reduce the number of bits of data used to compose the picture.

III. Calculus of Differences Finding consecutive difference quotients is called finding finite differences and is used to analyze the graph of an unknown function.

Applications of Trigonometric Functions

8

From Lewis and Clark to Landsat

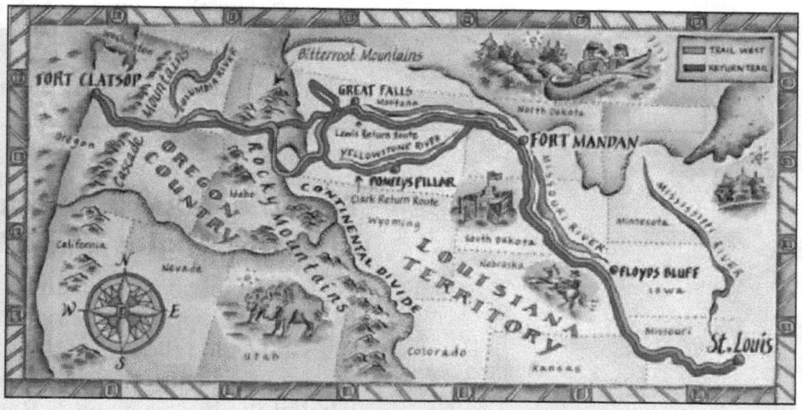

For \$140, you can buy a handheld Global Positioning System receiver that will gauge your latitude and longitude to within a couple of meters. But in 1804, when Meriwether Lewis and William Clark ventured across the Louisiana Territory, a state of the art positioning system consisted of an octant, a pocket chronometer, and a surveyor's compass.

But somehow, Clark—the cartographer in the group—made do. When San Francisco map collector David Rumsey took his copy of Lewis and Clark's published map of their journey, scanned it into a computer, and matched landmarks such as river junctions against corresponding features on today's maps, he found that it took only a slight amount of digital stretching and twisting to make Clark's map conform to modern coordinates. In fact, Rumsey was able to combine Clark's depiction of his party's route to the Pacific with pages from government atlases from the 1870s and 1970s and photos from NASA Landsat satellites, creating a digital composite that documents not only a historic adventure, but also the history of mapmaking itself.

Source: Wade Roush, "From Lewis and Clark to Landsat: David Rumsey's Digital Maps Marry Past and Present," *Technology Review*, 108, no. 7 (July 2005): 26–27.

—See Chapter Project I—

A Look Back

In Chapter 6 we defined the six trigonometric functions using the unit circle and then extended this definition to include general angles. In particular, we learned to evaluate the trigonometric functions. We also learned how to graph sinusoidal functions. In Chapter 7, we defined the inverse trigonometric functions and solved equations involving the trigonometric functions.

A Look Ahead

In this chapter, we define the trigonometric functions using right triangles and then use the trigonometric functions to solve applied problems. The first four sections deal with applications involving right triangles and *oblique triangles*, triangles that do not have a right angle. To solve problems involving oblique triangles, we will develop the Law of Sines and the Law of Cosines. We will also develop formulas for finding the area of a triangle.

The final section deals with applications of sinusoidal functions involving simple harmonic motion and damped motion.

Outline

8.1 Right Triangle Trigonometry; Applications

PREPARING FOR THIS SECTION *Before getting started, review the following:*

- Pythagorean Theorem (Appendix A, Section A.2, pp. A14–A15)
- Trigonometric Equations (I) (Section 7.7, pp. 488–492)

Now Work the 'Are You Prepared?' problems on page 517.

OBJECTIVES
1 Find the Value of Trigonometric Functions of Acute Angles Using Right Triangles (p. 510)
2 Use the Complementary Angle Theorem (p. 512)
3 Solve Right Triangles (p. 512)
4 Solve Applied Problems (p. 513)

1 Find the Value of Trigonometric Functions of Acute Angles Using Right Triangles

A triangle in which one angle is a right angle (90°) is called a **right triangle.** Recall that the side opposite the right angle is called the **hypotenuse,** and the remaining two sides are called the **legs** of the triangle. In Figure 1(a), we have labeled the hypotenuse as c to indicate that its length is c units, and, in a like manner, we have labeled the legs as a and b. Because the triangle is a right triangle, the Pythagorean Theorem tells us that

$$a^2 + b^2 = c^2$$

In Figure 1(a), we also show the angle θ. The angle θ is an **acute angle:** that is, $0° < \theta < 90°$ for θ measured in degrees and $0 < \theta < \frac{\pi}{2}$ for θ measured in radians.

Place θ in standard position, as shown in Figure 1(b). Then the coordinates of the point P are (a, b). Also, P is a point on the terminal side of θ that is on the circle $x^2 + y^2 = c^2$. (Do you see why?)

Figure 1

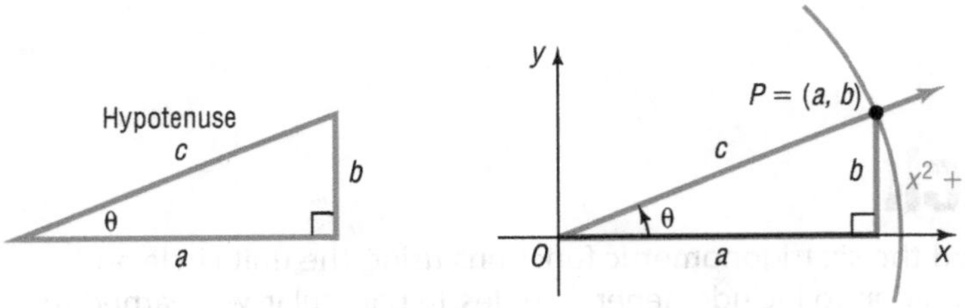

(a) (b)

Now use the theorem on page 377 with a circle of radius c, $x^2 + y^2 = c^2$. By referring to the lengths of the sides of the triangle by the names hypotenuse (c), opposite (b), and adjacent (a), as indicated in Figure 2, we can express the trigonometric functions of θ as ratios of the sides of a right triangle.

Figure 2

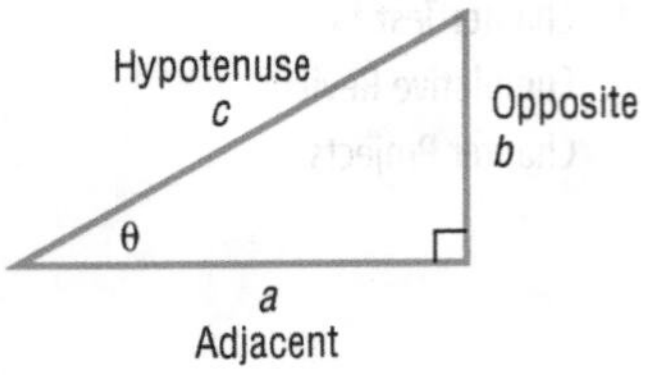

$$\sin\theta = \frac{\text{Opposite}}{\text{Hypotenuse}} = \frac{b}{c} \qquad \csc\theta = \frac{\text{Hypotenuse}}{\text{Opposite}} = \frac{c}{b}$$

$$\cos\theta = \frac{\text{Adjacent}}{\text{Hypotenuse}} = \frac{a}{c} \qquad \sec\theta = \frac{\text{Hypotenuse}}{\text{Adjacent}} = \frac{c}{a} \qquad (1)$$

$$\tan\theta = \frac{\text{Opposite}}{\text{Adjacent}} = \frac{b}{a} \qquad \cot\theta = \frac{\text{Adjacent}}{\text{Opposite}} = \frac{a}{b}$$

Notice that each trigonometric function of the acute angle θ is positive.

EXAMPLE 1 Finding the Value of Trigonometric Functions from a Right Triangle

Find the exact value of the six trigonometric functions of the angle θ in Figure 3.

Solution We see in Figure 3 that the two given sides of the triangle are

$$c = \text{Hypotenuse} = 5, \quad a = \text{Adjacent} = 3$$

Figure 3

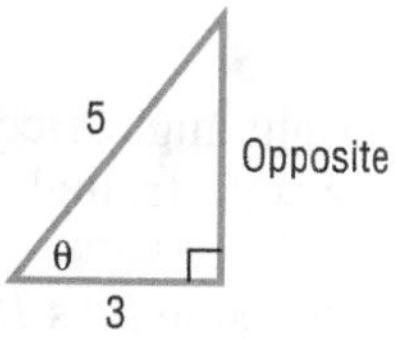

To find the length of the opposite side, we use the Pythagorean Theorem.

$$(\text{Adjacent})^2 + (\text{Opposite})^2 = (\text{Hypotenuse})^2$$
$$3^2 + (\text{Opposite})^2 = 5^2$$
$$(\text{Opposite})^2 = 25 - 9 = 16$$
$$\text{Opposite} = 4$$

Now that we know the lengths of the three sides, we use the ratios in equations (1) to find the value of each of the six trigonometric functions.

$$\sin\theta = \frac{\text{Opposite}}{\text{Hypotenuse}} = \frac{4}{5} \quad \cos\theta = \frac{\text{Adjacent}}{\text{Hypotenuse}} = \frac{3}{5} \quad \tan\theta = \frac{\text{Opposite}}{\text{Adjacent}} = \frac{4}{3}$$

$$\csc\theta = \frac{\text{Hypotenuse}}{\text{Opposite}} = \frac{5}{4} \quad \sec\theta = \frac{\text{Hypotenuse}}{\text{Adjacent}} = \frac{5}{3} \quad \cot\theta = \frac{\text{Adjacent}}{\text{Opposite}} = \frac{3}{4}$$

Now Work PROBLEM 9

The values of the trigonometric functions of an acute angle are ratios of the lengths of the sides of a right triangle. This way of viewing the trigonometric functions leads to many applications and, in fact, was the point of view used by early mathematicians (before calculus) in studying the subject of trigonometry.

We look at one such application next.

EXAMPLE 2 Constructing a Rain Gutter

A rain gutter is to be constructed of aluminum sheets 12 inches wide. See Figure 4(a). After marking off a length of 4 inches from each edge, this length is bent up at an angle θ. See Figure 4(b).

(a) Express the area A of the opening as a function of θ.
[**Hint:** Let b denote the vertical height of the bend.]

(b) Graph $A = A(\theta)$. Find the angle θ that makes A largest. (This bend will allow the most water to flow through the gutter.)

Figure 4

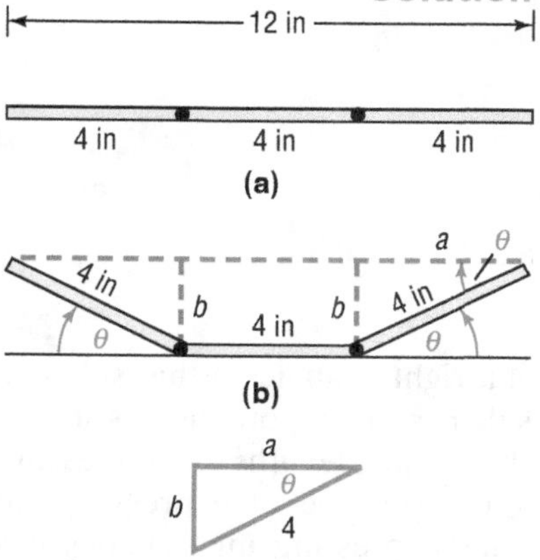

Solution (a) Look again at Figure 4(b). The area A of the opening is the sum of the areas of two congruent right triangles and one rectangle. Look at Figure 4(c), which shows one of the triangles in Figure 4(b) redrawn. We see that

$$\cos\theta = \frac{a}{4} \quad \text{so} \quad a = 4\cos\theta \qquad \sin\theta = \frac{b}{4} \quad \text{so} \quad b = 4\sin\theta$$

The area of the triangle is

$$\text{area} = \frac{1}{2}(\text{base})(\text{height}) = \frac{1}{2}ab = \frac{1}{2}(4\cos\theta)(4\sin\theta) = 8\sin\theta\cos\theta$$

So the area of the two congruent triangles is $16\sin\theta\cos\theta$.

The rectangle has length 4 and height b, so its area is

$$4b = 4(4\sin\theta) = 16\sin\theta$$

Figure 5

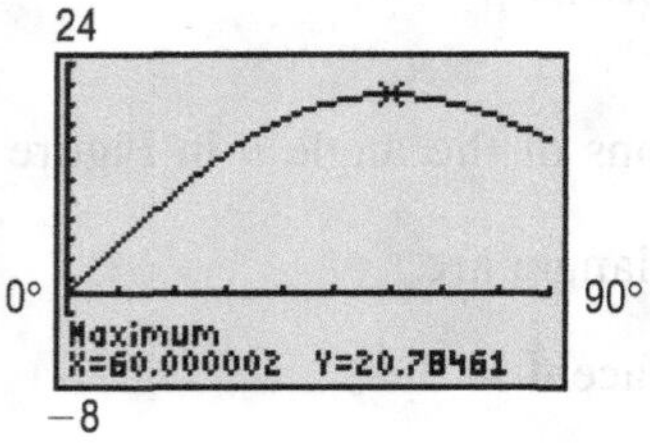

The area A of the opening is

$$A = \text{area of the two triangles} + \text{area of the rectangle}$$
$$A(\theta) = 16\sin\theta\cos\theta + 16\sin\theta = 16\sin\theta(\cos\theta + 1)$$

(b) Figure 5 shows the graph of $A = A(\theta)$. Using MAXIMUM, the angle θ that makes A largest is 60°.

2 Use the Complementary Angle Theorem

Two acute angles are called **complementary** if their sum is a right angle. Because the sum of the angles of any triangle is 180°, it follows that, for a right triangle, the two acute angles are complementary.

Figure 6

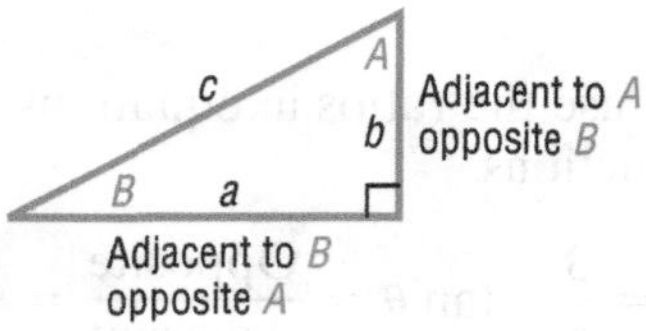

Refer now to Figure 6. We have labeled the angle opposite side b as B and the angle opposite side a as A. Notice that side b is adjacent to angle A and side a is adjacent to angle B. As a result,

$$\sin B = \frac{b}{c} = \cos A \qquad \cos B = \frac{a}{c} = \sin A \qquad \tan B = \frac{b}{a} = \cot A$$
$$\csc B = \frac{c}{b} = \sec A \qquad \sec B = \frac{c}{a} = \csc A \qquad \cot B = \frac{a}{b} = \tan A \tag{2}$$

Because of these relationships, the functions sine and cosine, tangent and cotangent, and secant and cosecant are called **cofunctions** of each other. The identities (2) may be expressed in words as follows:

THEOREM **Complementary Angle Theorem**

Cofunctions of complementary angles are equal.

Examples of this theorem are given next:

Complementary angles: $\sin 30° = \cos 60°$ (Cofunctions)

Complementary angles: $\tan 40° = \cot 50°$ (Cofunctions)

Complementary angles: $\sec 80° = \csc 10°$ (Cofunctions)

EXAMPLE 3 Using the Complementary Angle Theorem

(a) $\sin 62° = \cos(90° - 62°) = \cos 28°$

(b) $\tan\dfrac{\pi}{12} = \cot\left(\dfrac{\pi}{2} - \dfrac{\pi}{12}\right) = \cot\dfrac{5\pi}{12}$

(c) $\sin^2 40° + \sin^2 50° = \sin^2 40° + \cos^2 40° = 1$

↑ $\sin 50° = \cos 40°$

Now Work PROBLEM 19

3 Solve Right Triangles

Figure 7

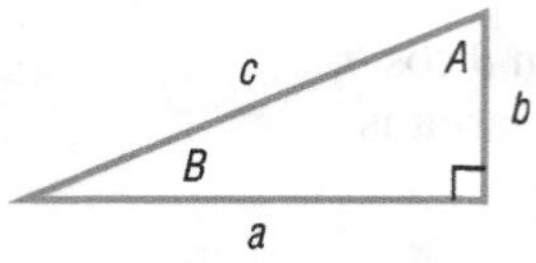

In the discussion that follows, we will always label a right triangle so that side a is opposite angle A, side b is opposite angle B, and side c is the hypotenuse, as shown in Figure 7. **To solve a right triangle** means to find the missing lengths of its sides and the measurements of its angles. We shall follow the practice of expressing the lengths of the sides rounded to two decimal places and expressing angles in degrees rounded to one decimal place. (Be sure that your calculator is in degree mode.)

To solve a right triangle, we need to know one of the acute angles A or B and a side, or else two sides. Then we make use of the Pythagorean Theorem and the fact that the sum of the angles of a triangle is 180°. The sum of the angles A and B in a right triangle is therefore 90°.

THEOREM For the right triangle shown in Figure 7, we have

$$c^2 = a^2 + b^2 \qquad A + B = 90^\circ$$

EXAMPLE 4 Solving a Right Triangle

Use Figure 8. If $b = 2$ and $A = 40^\circ$, find a, c, and B.

Figure 8

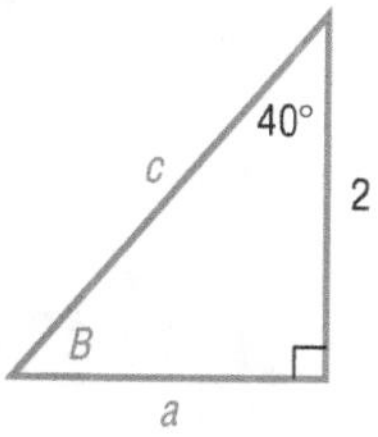

Solution Since $A = 40^\circ$ and $A + B = 90^\circ$, we find that $B = 50^\circ$. To find the sides a and c, we use the facts that

$$\tan 40^\circ = \frac{a}{2} \quad \text{and} \quad \cos 40^\circ = \frac{2}{c}$$

Now solve for a and c.

$$a = 2\tan 40^\circ \approx 1.68 \quad \text{and} \quad c = \frac{2}{\cos 40^\circ} \approx 2.61$$

Now Work PROBLEM 29

EXAMPLE 5 Solving a Right Triangle

Use Figure 9. If $a = 3$ and $b = 2$, find c, A, and B.

Figure 9

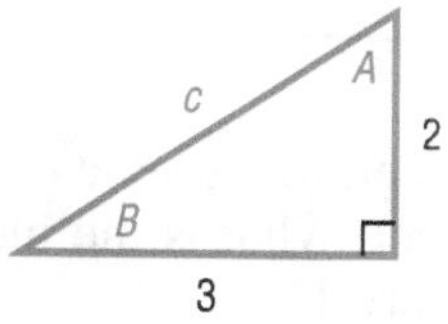

Solution Since $a = 3$ and $b = 2$, then, by the Pythagorean Theorem, we have

$$c^2 = a^2 + b^2 = 3^2 + 2^2 = 9 + 4 = 13$$
$$c = \sqrt{13} \approx 3.61$$

To find angle A, we use the fact that

$$\tan A = \frac{3}{2} \quad \text{so} \quad A = \tan^{-1}\frac{3}{2}$$

Set the mode on your calculator to degrees. Then, rounded to one decimal place, we find that $A = 56.3^\circ$. Since $A + B = 90^\circ$, we find that $B = 33.7^\circ$.

NOTE To avoid round-off errors when using a calculator, we will store unrounded values in memory for use in subsequent calculations.

Now Work PROBLEM 39

4 Solve Applied Problems*

In addition to developing models using right triangles, we can use right triangle trigonometry to measure heights and distances that are either awkward or impossible to measure by ordinary means. When using right triangles to solve these problems, pay attention to the known measures. This will indicate what trigonometric function to use. For example, if we know the measure of an angle and the length of the side adjacent to the angle, and wish to find the length of the opposite side, we would use the tangent function. Do you know why?

*In applied problems, it is important that answers be reported with both justifiable accuracy and appropriate significant figures. In this chapter we shall assume that the problem data are accurate to the number of significant digits, resulting in sides being rounded to two decimal places and angles being rounded to one decimal place.

EXAMPLE 6 Finding the Width of a River

A surveyor can measure the width of a river by setting up a transit* at a point C on one side of the river and taking a sighting of a point A on the other side. Refer to Figure 10. After turning through an angle of 90° at C, the surveyor walks a distance of 200 meters to point B. Using the transit at B, the angle θ is measured and found to be 20°. What is the width of the river rounded to the nearest meter?

Figure 10

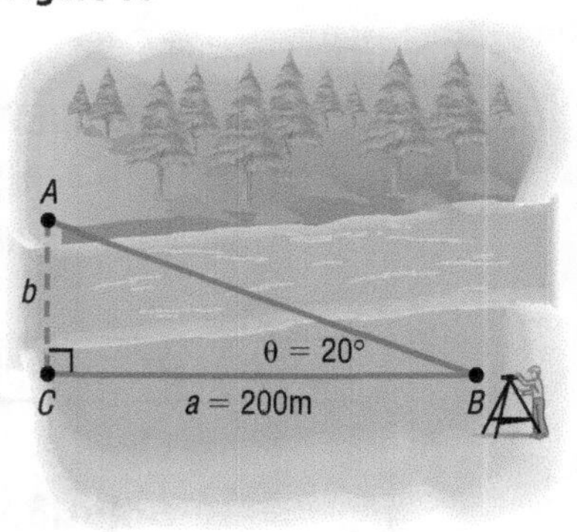

Solution We seek the length of side b. We know a and θ. So we use the fact that b is opposite θ and a is adjacent to θ and write

$$\tan\theta = \frac{b}{a}$$

which leads to

$$\tan 20° = \frac{b}{200}$$

$$b = 200\tan 20° \approx 72.79 \text{ meters}$$

The width of the river is 73 meters, rounded to the nearest meter.

Now Work PROBLEM 49

EXAMPLE 7 Finding the Inclination of a Mountain Trail

A straight trail leads from the Alpine Hotel, elevation 8000 feet, to a scenic overlook, elevation 11,100 feet. The length of the trail is 14,100 feet. What is the inclination (grade) of the trail? That is, what is the angle B in Figure 11?

Figure 11

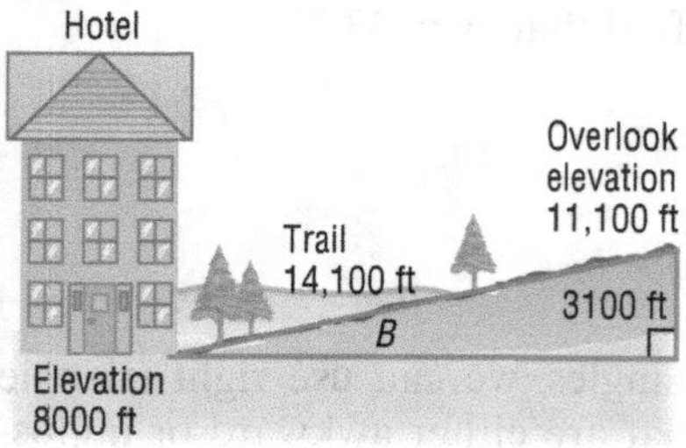

Solution As we can see in Figure 11, we know the length of the side opposite angle B and the length of the hypotenuse. The angle B obeys the equation

$$\sin B = \frac{3100}{14{,}100}$$

Using a calculator,

$$B = \sin^{-1}\frac{3100}{14{,}100} \approx 12.7°$$

The inclination (grade) of the trail is approximately 12.7°.

Now Work PROBLEM 55

Vertical heights can sometimes be measured using either the *angle of elevation* or the *angle of depression.* If a person is looking up at an object, the acute angle measured from the horizontal to a line of sight to the object is called the **angle of elevation.** See Figure 12(a).

* An instrument used in surveying to measure angles.

Figure 12

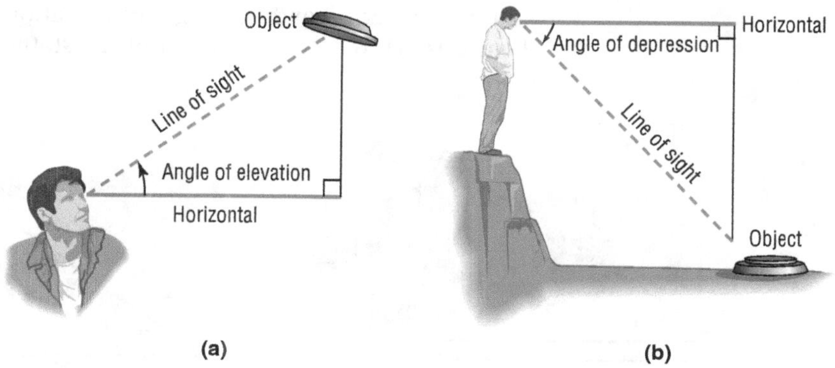

If a person is standing on a cliff looking down at an object, the acute angle made by the line of sight to the object and the horizontal is called the **angle of depression.** See Figure 12(b).

EXAMPLE 8 Finding the Height of a Cloud

Meteorologists find the height of a cloud using an instrument called a **ceilometer.** A ceilometer consists of a **light projector** that directs a vertical light beam up to the cloud base and a **light detector** that scans the cloud to detect the light beam. See Figure 13(a). On December 1, 2006, at Midway Airport in Chicago, a ceilometer was employed to find the height of the cloud cover. It was set up with its light detector 300 feet from its light projector. If the angle of elevation from the light detector to the base of the cloud is 75°, what is the height of the cloud cover?

Figure 13

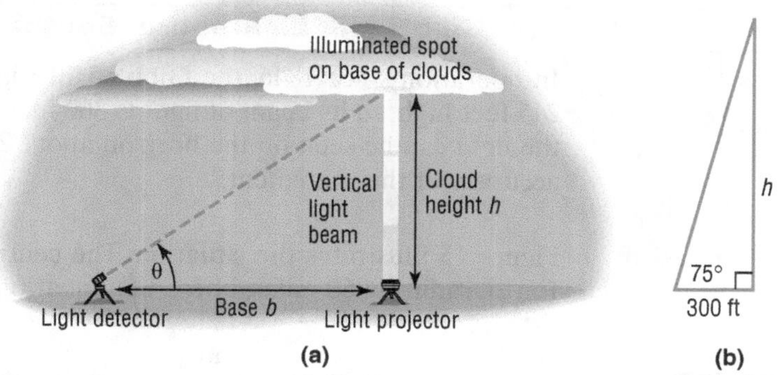

Solution Figure 13(b) illustrates the situation. To find the height h, we use the fact that $\tan 75° = \dfrac{h}{300}$, so

$$h = 300 \tan 75° \approx 1120 \text{ feet}$$

The ceiling (height to the base of the cloud cover) is approximately 1120 feet.

■

Now Work PROBLEM 51

The idea behind Example 8 can also be used to find the height of an object with a base that is not accessible to the horizontal.

EXAMPLE 9 Finding the Height of a Statue on a Building

Adorning the top of the Board of Trade building in Chicago is a statue of Ceres, the Roman goddess of wheat. From street level, two observations are taken 400 feet from the center of the building. The angle of elevation to the base of the statue is found to be 55.1° and the angle of elevation to the top of the statue is 56.5°. See Figure 14(a). What is the height of the statue?

Figure 14

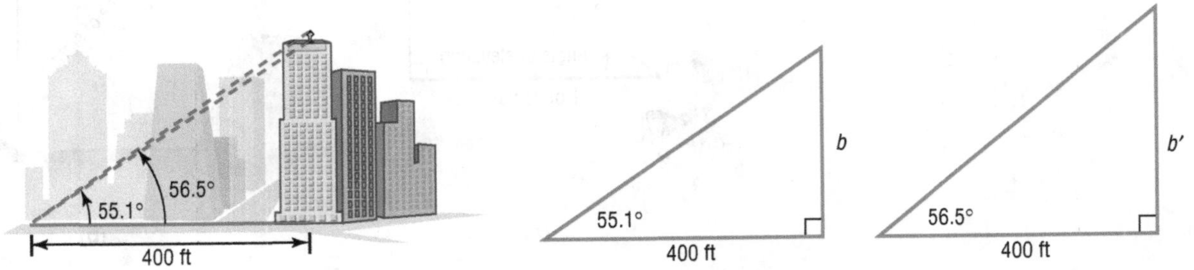

(a) (b)

Solution Figure 14(b) shows two triangles that replicate Figure 14(a). The height of the statue of Ceres will be $b' - b$. To find b and b', we refer to Figure 14(b).

$$\tan 55.1° = \frac{b}{400} \qquad \tan 56.5° = \frac{b'}{400}$$

$$b = 400 \tan 55.1° \approx 573.39 \qquad b' = 400 \tan 56.5° \approx 604.33$$

The height of the statue is approximately $604.33 - 573.39 = 30.94$ feet ≈ 31 feet.

Now Work PROBLEM 71

EXAMPLE 10 The Gibb's Hill Lighthouse, Southampton, Bermuda

In operation since 1846, the Gibb's Hill Lighthouse stands 117 feet high on a hill 245 feet high, so its beam of light is 362 feet above sea level. A brochure states that the light can be seen on the horizon about 26 miles from the lighthouse. Verify the accuracy of this statement.

Solution Figure 15 illustrates the situation. The central angle θ, positioned at the center of Earth, radius 3960 miles, obeys the equation

Figure 15

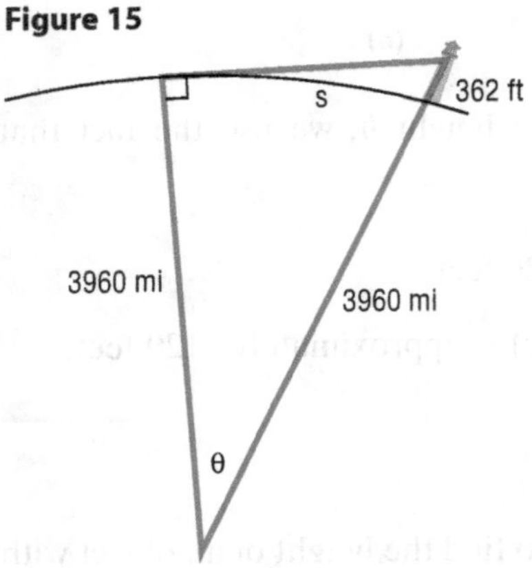

$$\cos\theta = \frac{3960}{3960 + \frac{362}{5280}} \approx 0.999982687 \qquad \text{1 mile} = 5280 \text{ feet}$$

Solving for θ, we find

$$\theta \approx 0.33715° \approx 20.23'$$

The brochure does not indicate whether the distance is measured in nautical miles or statute miles. Let's calculate both distances.

The distance s in nautical miles (refer to Problem 114, p. 364) is the measure of the angle θ in minutes, so $s \approx 20.23$ nautical miles.

The distance s in statute miles is given by the formula $s = r\theta$, where θ is measured in radians. Then, since

$$\theta \approx 20.23' \underset{1' = \frac{1°}{60}}{\approx} 0.33715° \underset{1° = \frac{\pi}{180}\text{ radian}}{\approx} 0.00588 \text{ radian}$$

Figure 16

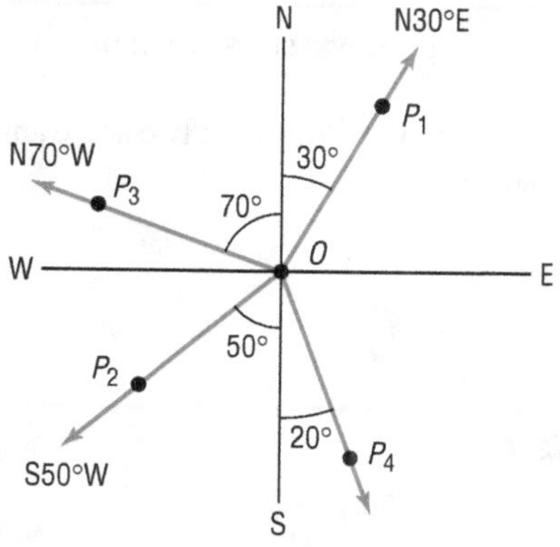

we find that

$$s = r\theta \approx (3960)(0.00588) \approx 23.3 \text{ miles}$$

In either case, it would seem that the brochure overstated the distance somewhat.

In navigation and surveying, the **direction** or **bearing** from a point O to a point P equals the acute angle θ between the ray OP and the vertical line through O, the north–south line.

Figure 16 illustrates some bearings. Notice that the bearing from O to P_1 is denoted by the symbolism N30°E, indicating that the bearing is 30° east of north. In writing the bearing from O to P, the direction north or south always appears first, followed by an acute angle, followed by east or west. In Figure 16, the bearing from O to P_2 is S50°W, and from O to P_3 it is N70°W.

EXAMPLE 11 **Finding the Bearing of an Object**

In Figure 16, what is the bearing from O to an object at P_4?

Solution The acute angle between the ray OP_4 and the north–south line through O is given as 20°. The bearing from O to P_4 is S20°E.

EXAMPLE 12 **Finding the Bearing of an Airplane**

A Boeing 777 aircraft takes off from O'Hare Airport on runway 2 LEFT, which has a bearing of N20°E.* After flying for 1 mile, the pilot of the aircraft requests permission to turn 90° and head toward the northwest. The request is granted. After the plane goes 2 miles in this direction, what bearing should the control tower use to locate the aircraft?

Solution Figure 17 illustrates the situation. After flying 1 mile from the airport O (the control tower), the aircraft is at P. After turning 90° toward the northwest and flying 2 miles, the aircraft is at the point Q. In triangle OPQ, the angle θ obeys the equation

Figure 17

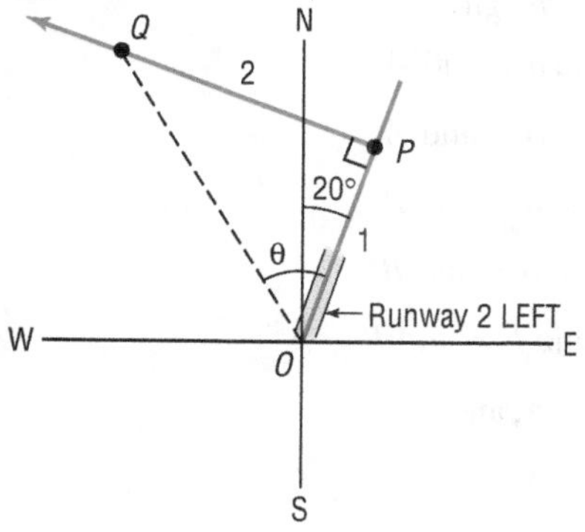

$$\tan\theta = \frac{2}{1} = 2 \quad \text{so} \quad \theta = \tan^{-1} 2 \approx 63.4°$$

The acute angle between north and the ray OQ is 63.4° − 20° = 43.4°. The bearing of the aircraft from O to Q is N43.4°W.

Now Work PROBLEM 63

* In air navigation, the term **azimuth** denotes the positive angle measured clockwise from the north (N) to a ray OP. In Figure 16, the azimuth from O to P_1 is 30°; the azimuth from O to P_2 is 230°; the azimuth from O to P_3 is 290°. In naming runways, the units digit is left off the azimuth. Runway 2 LEFT means the left runway with a direction of azimuth 20° (bearing N20°E). Runway 23 is the runway with azimuth 230° and bearing S50°W.

8.1 Assess Your Understanding

'Are You Prepared?' *Answers are given at the end of these exercises. If you get a wrong answer, read the pages listed in red.*

1. In a right triangle, if the length of the hypotenuse is 5 and the length of one of the other sides is 3, what is the length of the third side? (pp. A14–A15)

2. If θ is an acute angle, solve the equation $\tan\theta = \frac{1}{2}$. Express your answer in degrees, rounded to one decimal place. (pp. 488–492)

3. If θ is an acute angle, solve the equation $\sin\theta = \frac{1}{2}$. (pp. 488–492)

Concepts and Vocabulary

4. ***True or False*** $\sin 52° = \cos 48°$.

5. ***True or False*** In a right triangle, one of the angles is 90° and the sum of the other two angles is 90°.

6. When you look up at an object, the acute angle measured from the horizontal to a line-of-sight observation of the object is called the ______ ______ ______.

7. ***True or False*** In a right triangle, if two sides are known, we can solve the triangle.

8. ***True or False*** In a right triangle, if we know the two acute angles, we can solve the triangle.

Skill Building

In Problems 9–18, find the exact value of the six trigonometric functions of the angle θ in each figure.

9.
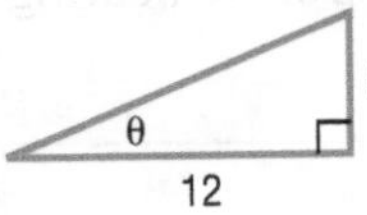

10.
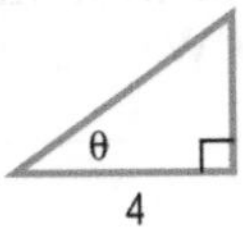

11.

12.
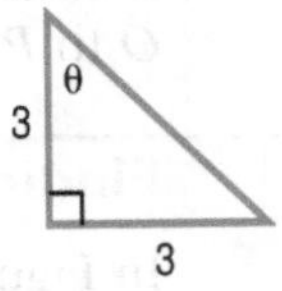

13.
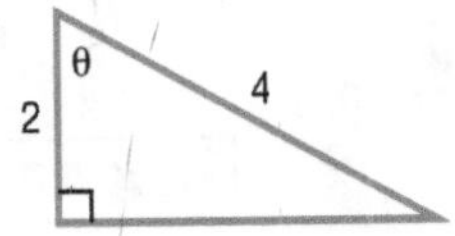

14.
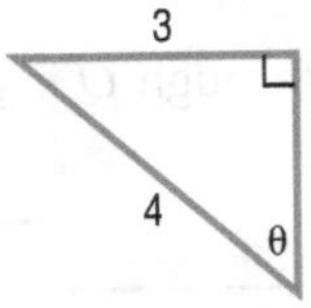

15.
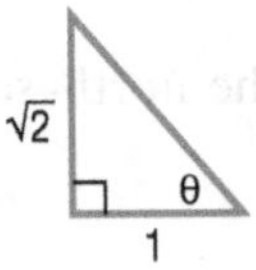

16.
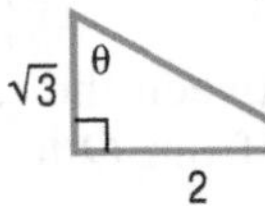

17.
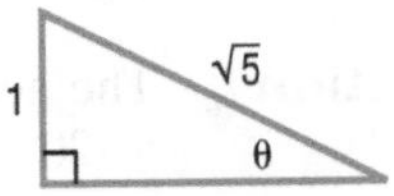

18.
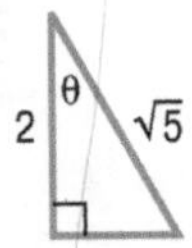

In Problems 19–28, find the exact value of each expression. Do not use a calculator.

19. $\sin 38° - \cos 52°$

20. $\tan 12° - \cot 78°$

21. $\dfrac{\cos 10°}{\sin 80°}$

22. $\dfrac{\cos 40°}{\sin 50°}$

23. $1 - \cos^2 20° - \cos^2 70°$

24. $1 + \tan^2 5° - \csc^2 85°$

25. $\tan 20° - \dfrac{\cos 70°}{\cos 20°}$

26. $\cot 40° - \dfrac{\sin 50°}{\sin 40°}$

27. $\cos 35° \sin 55° + \sin 35° \cos 55°$

28. $\sec 35° \csc 55° - \tan 35° \cot 55°$

In Problems 29–42, use the right triangle shown below. Then, using the given information, solve the triangle.

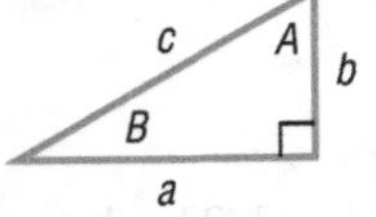

29. $b = 5$, $B = 20°$; find a, c, and A

30. $b = 4$, $B = 10°$; find a, c, and A

31. $a = 6$, $B = 40°$; find b, c, and A

32. $a = 7$, $B = 50°$; find b, c, and A

33. $b = 4$, $A = 10°$; find a, c, and B

34. $b = 6$, $A = 20°$; find a, c, and B

35. $a = 5$, $A = 25°$; find b, c, and B

36. $a = 6$, $A = 40°$; find b, c, and B

37. $c = 9$, $B = 20°$; find b, a, and A

38. $c = 10$, $A = 40°$; find b, a, and B

39. $a = 5$, $b = 3$; find c, A, and B

40. $a = 2$, $b = 8$; find c, A, and B

41. $a = 2$, $c = 5$; find b, A, and B

42. $b = 4$, $c = 6$; find a, A, and B

Applications and Extensions

43. **Geometry** The hypotenuse of a right triangle is 5 inches. If one leg is 2 inches, find the degree measure of each angle.

44. **Geometry** The hypotenuse of a right triangle is 3 feet. If one leg is 1 foot, find the degree measure of each angle.

45. **Geometry** A right triangle has a hypotenuse of length 8 inches. If one angle is 35°, find the length of each leg.

46. **Geometry** A right triangle has a hypotenuse of length 10 centimeters. If one angle is 40°, find the length of each leg.

47. **Geometry** A right triangle contains a 25° angle.
(a) If one leg is of length 5 inches, what is the length of the hypotenuse?
(b) There are two answers. How is this possible?

48. **Geometry** A right triangle contains an angle of $\dfrac{\pi}{8}$ radian.
(a) If one leg is of length 3 meters, what is the length of the hypotenuse?
(b) There are two answers. How is this possible?

49. **Finding the Width of a Gorge** Find the distance from A to C across the gorge illustrated in the figure.

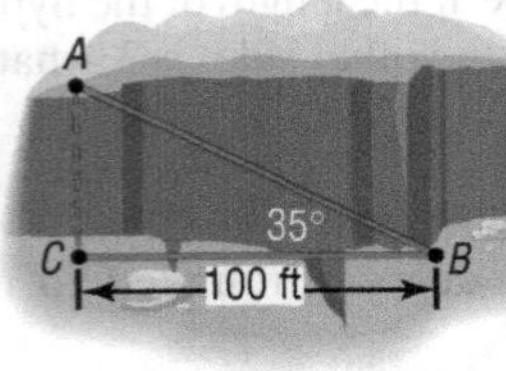

50. Finding the Distance across a Pond Find the distance from A to C across the pond illustrated in the figure.

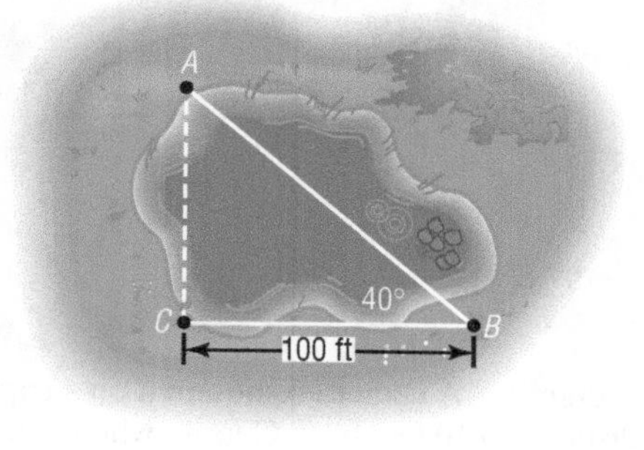

51. The Eiffel Tower The tallest tower built before the era of television masts, the Eiffel Tower was completed on March 31, 1889. Find the height of the Eiffel Tower (before a television mast was added to the top) using the information given in the illustration.

52. Finding the Distance of a Ship from Shore A person in a small boat, offshore from a vertical cliff known to be 100 feet in height, takes a sighting of the top of the cliff. If the angle of elevation is found to be 25°, how far offshore is the boat?

53. Finding the Distance to a Plateau Suppose that you are headed toward a plateau 50 meters high. If the angle of elevation to the top of the plateau is 20°, how far are you from the base of the plateau?

54. Finding the Reach of a Ladder A 22-foot extension ladder leaning against a building makes a 70° angle with the ground. How far up the building does the ladder touch?

55. Finding the Angle of Elevation of the Sun At 10 AM on April 26, 2007, a building 300 feet high casts a shadow 50 feet long. What is the angle of elevation of the Sun?

56. Directing a Laser Beam A laser beam is to be directed through a small hole in the center of a circle of radius 10 feet. The origin of the beam is 35 feet from the circle (see the figure). At what angle of elevation should the beam be aimed to ensure that it goes through the hole?

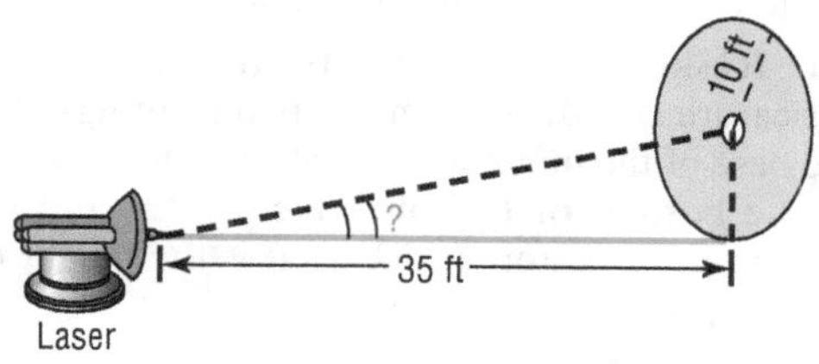

57. Finding the Speed of a Truck A state trooper is hidden 30 feet from a highway. One second after a truck passes, the angle θ between the highway and the line of observation from the patrol car to the truck is measured. See the illustration.

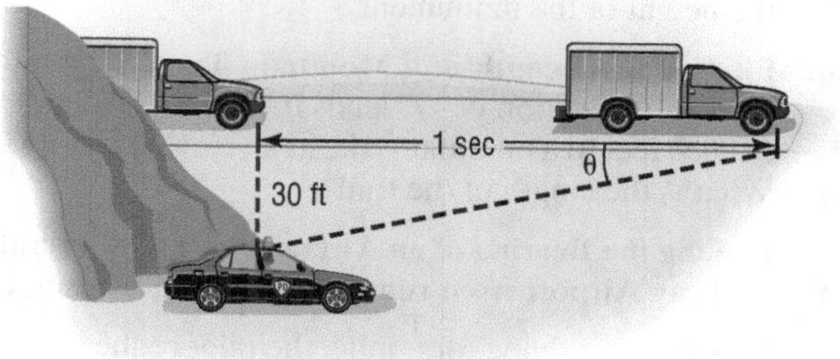

(a) If the angle measures 15°, how fast is the truck traveling? Express the answer in feet per second and in miles per hour.

(b) If the angle measures 20°, how fast is the truck traveling? Express the answer in feet per second and in miles per hour.

(c) If the speed limit is 55 miles per hour and a speeding ticket is issued for speeds of 5 miles per hour or more over the limit, for what angles should the trooper issue a ticket?

58. Security A security camera in a neighborhood bank is mounted on a wall 9 feet above the floor. What angle of depression should be used if the camera is to be directed to a spot 6 feet above the floor and 12 feet from the wall?

59. Parallax One method of measuring the distance from Earth to a star is the parallax method. The idea behind computing this distance is to measure the angle formed between the Earth and the star at two different points in time. Typically, the measurements are taken so that the side opposite the angle is as large as possible. Therefore, the optimal approach is to measure the angle when Earth is on opposite sides of the Sun, as shown in the figure.

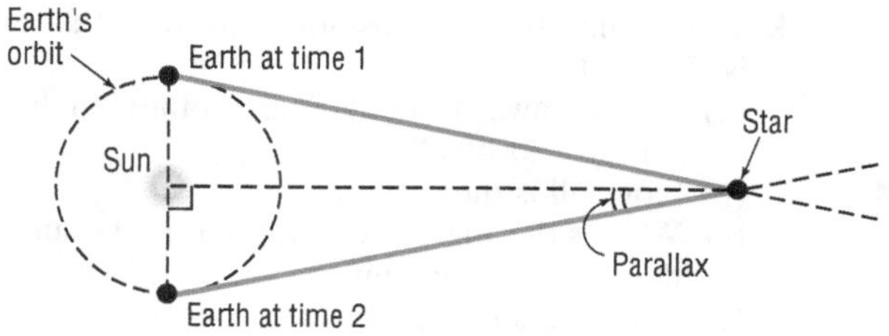

(a) Proxima Centauri is 4.22 light-years from Earth. If 1 light-year is about 5.9 trillion miles, how many miles is Proxima Centauri from Earth?

(b) The mean distance from Earth to the Sun is 93,000,000 miles. What is the parallax of Proxima Centauri?

60. Parallax See Problem 59. 61 Cygni, sometimes called Bessel's Star (after Friedrich Bessel, who measured the distance from Earth to the star in 1838), is a star in the constellation Cygnus.

(a) 61 Cygni is 11.14 light-years from Earth. If 1 light-year is about 5.9 trillion miles, how many miles is 61 Cygni from Earth?

(b) The mean distance from Earth to the Sun is 93,000,000 miles. What is the parallax of 61 Cygni?

61. **Washington Monument** The angle of elevation of the Sun is 35.1° at the instant the shadow cast by the Washington Monument is 789 feet long. Use this information to calculate the height of the monument.

62. **Finding the Length of a Mountain Trail** A straight trail with an inclination of 17° leads from a hotel at an elevation of 9000 feet to a mountain lake at an elevation of 11,200 feet. What is the length of the trail?

63. **Finding the Bearing of an Aircraft** A DC-9 aircraft leaves Midway Airport from runway 4 RIGHT, whose bearing is N40°E. After flying for $\frac{1}{2}$ mile, the pilot requests permission to turn 90° and head toward the southeast. The permission is granted. After the airplane goes 1 mile in this direction, what bearing should the control tower use to locate the aircraft?

64. **Finding the Bearing of a Ship** A ship leaves the port of Miami with a bearing of S80°E and a speed of 15 knots. After 1 hour, the ship turns 90° toward the south. After 2 hours, maintaining the same speed, what is the bearing to the ship from port?

65. **Niagara Falls Incline Railway** Situated between Portage Road and the Niagara Parkway directly across from the Canadian Horseshoe Falls, the Falls Incline Railway is a funicular that carries passengers up an embankment to Table Rock Observation Point. If the length of the track is 51.8 meters and the angle of inclination is 36°2′, determine the height of the embankment.

Source: www.niagaraparks.com

66. **Sears Tower** The Sears Tower in Chicago is the third tallest building in the world and is topped by a high antenna. A surveyor on the ground makes the following measurement:

1. The angle of elevation from his position to the top of the building is 34°.

2. The distance from his position to the top of the building is 2593 feet.

3. The distance from his position to the top of the antenna is 2743 feet.

(a) How far away from the (base of the) building is the surveyor located?

(b) How tall is the building?

(c) What is the angle of elevation from the surveyor to the top of the antenna?

(d) How tall is the antenna?

Source: www.infoplease.com/ce6/us/A0844218.html

67. **Constructing a Highway** A highway whose primary directions are north–south is being constructed along the west coast of Florida. Near Naples, a bay obstructs the straight path of the road. Since the cost of a bridge is prohibitive, engineers decide to go around the bay. The illustration shows the path that they decide on and the measurements taken. What is the length of highway needed to go around the bay?

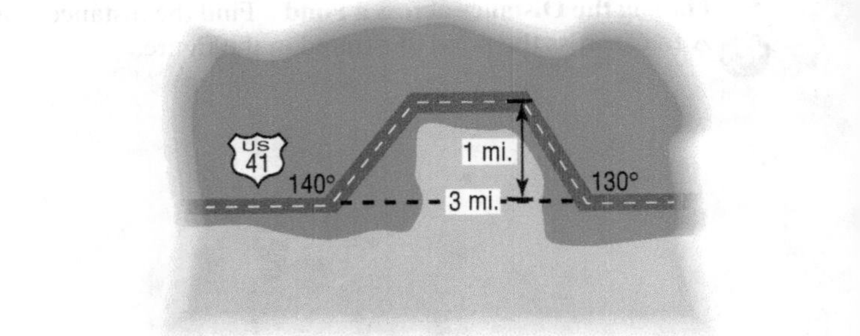

68. **Photography** A camera is mounted on a tripod 4 feet high at a distance of 10 feet from George, who is 6 feet tall. See the illustration. If the camera lens has angles of depression and elevation of 20°, will George's feet and head be seen by the lens? If not, how far back will the camera need to be moved to include George's feet and head?

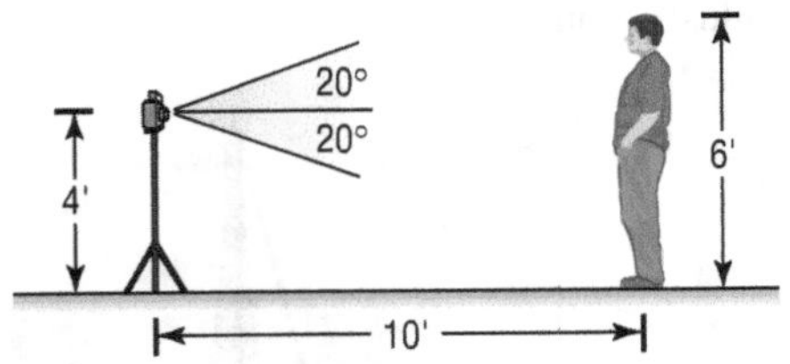

69. **Finding the Distance between Two Objects** A blimp, suspended in the air at a height of 500 feet, lies directly over a line from Soldier Field to the Adler Planetarium on Lake Michigan (see the figure). If the angle of depression from the blimp to the stadium is 32° and from the blimp to the planetarium is 23°, find the distance between Soldier Field and the Adler Planetarium.

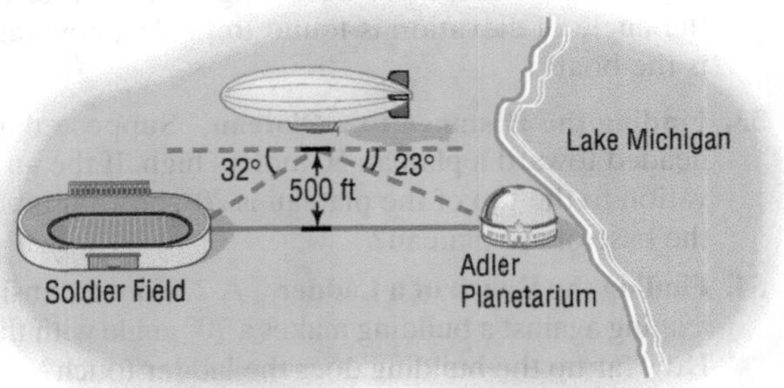

70. **Hot-Air Balloon** While taking a ride in a hot-air balloon in Napa Valley, Francisco wonders how high he is. To find out, he chooses a landmark that is to the east of the balloon and measures the angle of depression to be 54°. A few minutes later, after traveling 100 feet east, the angle of depression to the same landmark is determined to be 61°. Use this information to determine the height of the balloon.

71. **Mt. Rushmore** To measure the height of Lincoln's caricature on Mt. Rushmore, two sightings 800 feet from the base of the mountain are taken. If the angle of elevation to the bottom of Lincoln's face is 32° and the angle of elevation to the top is 35°, what is the height of Lincoln's face?

72. The CN Tower The CN Tower, located in Toronto, Canada, is the tallest structure in the world. While visiting Toronto, a tourist wondered what the height of the tower above the top of the Sky Pod is. While standing 4000 feet from the tower, she measured the angle to the top of the Sky Pod to be 20.1°. At this same distance, the angle of elevation to the top of the tower was found to be 24.4°. Use this information to determine the height of the tower above the Sky Pod.

73. Chicago Skyscrapers The angle of inclination from the base of the John Hancock Center to the top of the main structure of the Sears Tower is approximately 10.3°. If the main structure of the Sears Tower is 1451 feet tall, how far apart are the two skyscrapers? Assume the bases of the two buildings are at the same elevation.

Source: www.emporis.com

74. Estimating the Width of the Mississippi River A tourist at the top of the Gateway Arch (height, 630 feet) in St. Louis, Missouri observes a boat moored on the Illinois side of the Mississippi River 2070 feet directly across from the Arch. She also observes a boat moored on the Missouri side directly across from the first boat (see diagram). Given that $B = \cot^{-1}\frac{67}{55}$, estimate the width of the Mississippi River at the St. Louis riverfront.

Source: U.S. Army Corps of Engineers

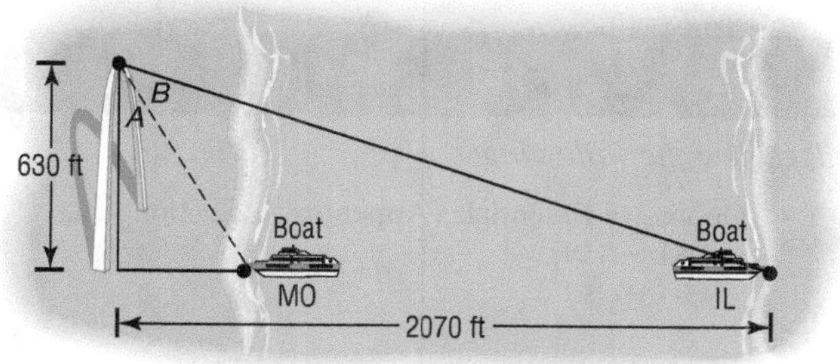

75. Finding the Pitch of a Roof A carpenter is preparing to put a roof on a garage that is 20 feet by 40 feet by 20 feet. A steel support beam 46 feet in length is positioned in the center of the garage. To support the roof, another beam will be attached to the top of the center beam (see the figure). At what angle of elevation is the new beam? In other words, what is the pitch of the roof?

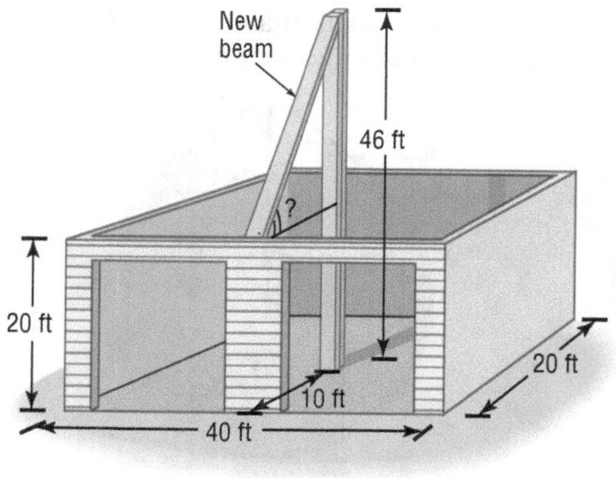

76. Shooting Free Throws in Basketball The eyes of a basketball player are 6 feet above the floor. The player is at the free-throw line, which is 15 feet from the center of the basket rim (see the figure). What is the angle of elevation from the player's eyes to the center of the rim?

[**Hint:** The rim is 10 feet above the floor.]

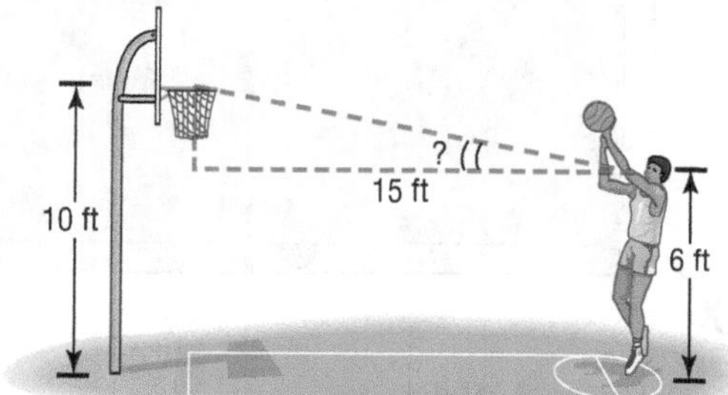

77. Geometry Find the value of the angle θ in degrees rounded to the nearest tenth of a degree.

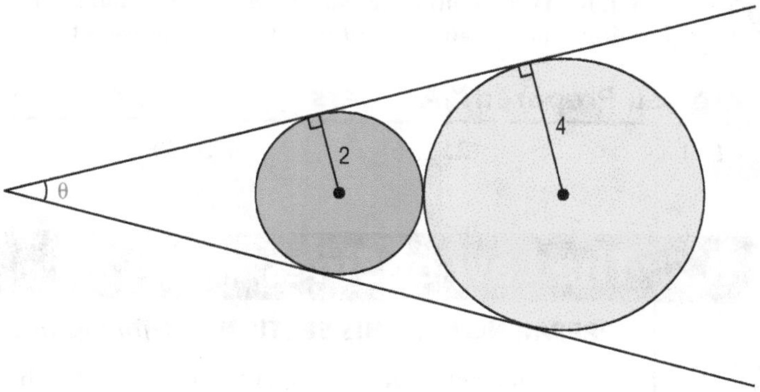

78. Surveillance Satellites A surveillance satellite circles Earth at a height of h miles above the surface. Suppose that d is the distance, in miles, on the surface of Earth that can be observed from the satellite. See the illustration on page 522.

(a) Find an equation that relates the central angle θ to the height h.

(b) Find an equation that relates the observable distance d and θ.

(c) Find an equation that relates d and h.

(d) If d is to be 2500 miles, how high must the satellite orbit above Earth?

(e) If the satellite orbits at a height of 300 miles, what distance d on the surface can be observed?

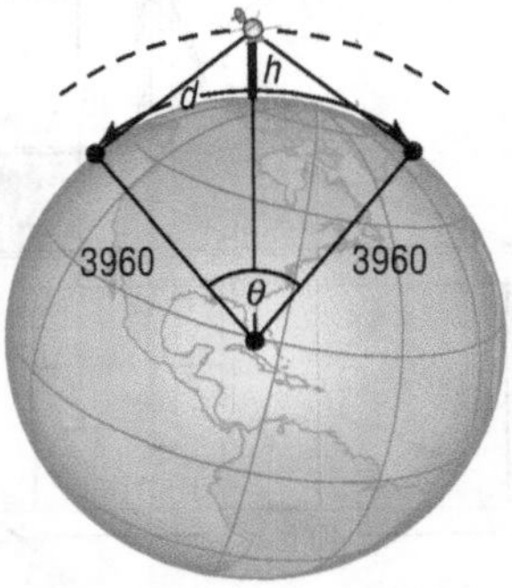

79. Calculating Pool Shots A pool player located at **X** wants to shoot the white ball off the top cushion and hit the red ball dead center. He knows from physics that the white ball will come off a cushion at the same angle as it hits a cushion. Where on the top cushion should he hit the white ball?

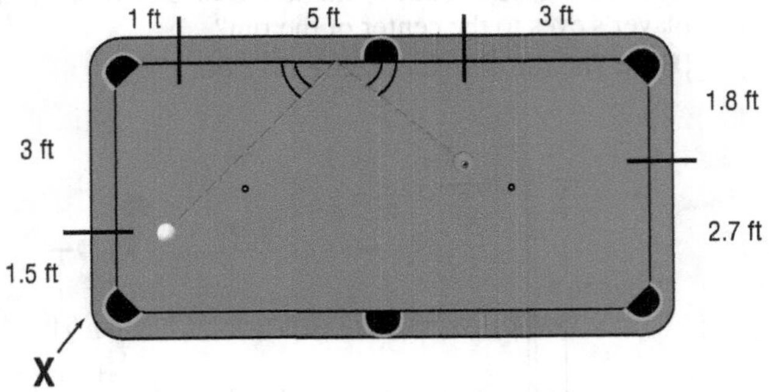

80. The Freedom Tower The Freedom Tower is to be the centerpiece of the rebuilding of the World Trade Center in New York City. The tower will be 1776 feet tall (not including a broadcast antenna). The angle of elevation from the base of an office building to the top of the tower is 34°. The angle of elevation from the helipad on the roof of the office building to the top of the tower is 20°.

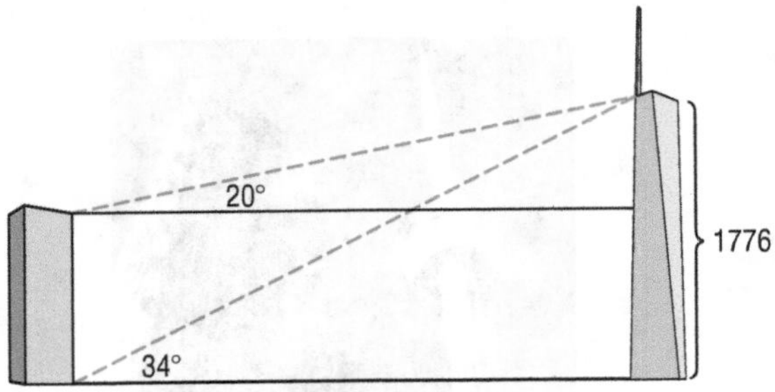

(a) How far away is the office building from the Freedom Tower? Assume the side of the tower is vertical. Round to the nearest foot.

(b) How tall is the office building? Round to the nearest foot.

Discussion and Writing

81. Explain how you would measure the width of the Grand Canyon from a point on its ridge.

82. Explain how you would measure the height of a TV tower that is on the roof of a tall building.

83. **The Gibb's Hill Lighthouse. Southampton, Bermuda** In operation since 1846, the Gibb's Hill Lighthouse stands 117 feet high on a hill 245 feet high, so its beam of light is 362 feet above sea level. A brochure states that ships 40 miles away can see the light and planes flying at 10,000 feet can see it 120 miles away. Verify the accuracy of these statements. What assumption did the brochure make about the height of the ship?

'Are You Prepared?' Answers

1. 4 **2.** 26.6° **3.** 30°

8.2 The Law of Sines

PREPARING FOR THIS SECTION *Before getting started, review the following:*

- Trigonometric Equations (I) (Section 7.7, pp. 488–492)
- Difference Formula for the Sine Function (Section 7.4, p. 469)
- Geometry Essentials (Appendix A, Section A.2, pp. A14–A19)

Now Work the 'Are You Prepared?' problems on page 529.

OBJECTIVES
1 Solve SAA or ASA Triangles (p. 524)
2 Solve SSA Triangles (p. 525)
3 Solve Applied Problems (p. 527)

If none of the angles of a triangle is a right angle, the triangle is called **oblique.** An oblique triangle will have either three acute angles or two acute angles and one obtuse angle (an angle between 90° and 180°). See Figure 18.

Figure 18

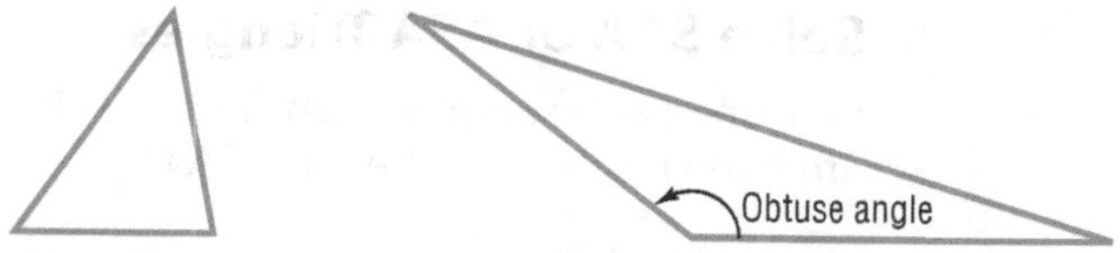

(a) All angles are acute (b) Two acute angles and one obtuse angle

Figure 19

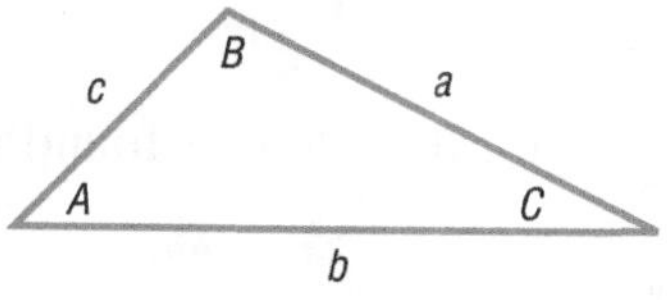

In the discussion that follows, we will always label an oblique triangle so that side a is opposite angle A, side b is opposite angle B, and side c is opposite angle C, as shown in Figure 19.

To **solve an oblique triangle** means to find the lengths of its sides and the measurements of its angles. To do this, we shall need to know the length of one side* along with (i) two angles; (ii) one angle and one other side; or (iii) the other two sides. There are four possibilities to consider:

Case 1: One side and two angles are known (ASA or SAA).
Case 2: Two sides and the angle opposite one of them are known (SSA).
Case 3: Two sides and the included angle are known (SAS).
Case 4: Three sides are known (SSS).

Figure 20 illustrates the four cases.

Figure 20

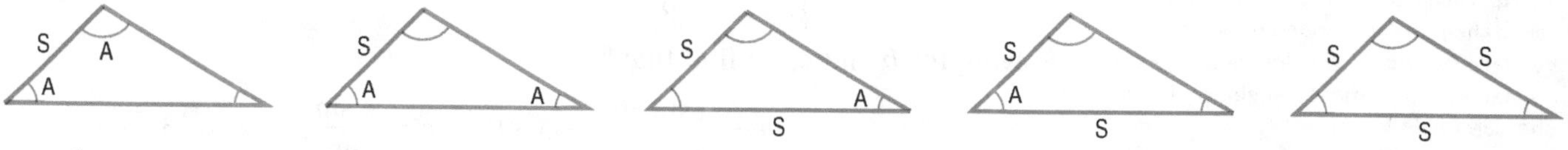

Case 1: ASA Case 1: SAA Case 2: SSA Case 3: SAS Case 4: SSS

WARNING Oblique triangles cannot be solved using the methods of Section 8.1. Do you know why? ■

The **Law of Sines** is used to solve triangles for which Case 1 or 2 holds. Cases 3 and 4 are considered when we study the Law of Cosines in the next section.

THEOREM

Law of Sines

For a triangle with sides a, b, c and opposite angles A, B, C, respectively,

$$\frac{\sin A}{a} = \frac{\sin B}{b} = \frac{\sin C}{c} \tag{1}$$

A proof of the Law of Sines is given at the end of this section. The Law of Sines actually consists of three equalities:

$$\frac{\sin A}{a} = \frac{\sin B}{b} \qquad \frac{\sin A}{a} = \frac{\sin C}{c} \qquad \frac{\sin B}{b} = \frac{\sin C}{c}$$

Formula (1) is a compact way to write these three equations.

In applying the Law of Sines to solve triangles, we use the fact that the sum of the angles of any triangle equals 180°; that is,

$$A + B + C = 180° \tag{2}$$

*The reason we need to know the length of one side is that, if we only know the angles, this will result in a family of *similar triangles*.

1 Solve SAA or ASA Triangles

Our first two examples show how to solve a triangle when one side and two angles are known (Case 1: SAA or ASA).

EXAMPLE 1 Using the Law of Sines to Solve an SAA Triangle

Solve the triangle: $A = 40°, B = 60°, a = 4$

Solution Figure 21 shows the triangle that we want to solve. The third angle C is found using equation (2).

Figure 21

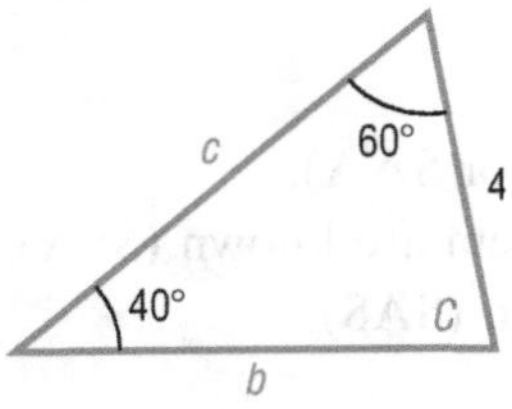

$$A + B + C = 180°$$
$$40° + 60° + C = 180°$$
$$C = 80°$$

Now we use the Law of Sines (twice) to find the unknown sides b and c.

$$\frac{\sin A}{a} = \frac{\sin B}{b} \qquad \frac{\sin A}{a} = \frac{\sin C}{c}$$

Because $a = 4$, $A = 40°$, $B = 60°$, and $C = 80°$, we have

$$\frac{\sin 40°}{4} = \frac{\sin 60°}{b} \qquad \frac{\sin 40°}{4} = \frac{\sin 80°}{c}$$

Solving for b and c, we find that

$$b = \frac{4 \sin 60°}{\sin 40°} \approx 5.39 \qquad c = \frac{4 \sin 80°}{\sin 40°} \approx 6.13$$

NOTE Although not a check, we can verify the reasonableness of our answer by determining if the longest side is opposite the largest angle and the shortest side is opposite the smallest angle. ■

Notice in Example 1 that we found b and c by working with the given side a. This is better than finding b first and working with a rounded value of b to find c.

Now Work PROBLEM 9

EXAMPLE 2 Using the Law of Sines to Solve an ASA Triangle

Solve the triangle: $A = 35°, B = 15°, c = 5$

Solution Figure 22 illustrates the triangle that we want to solve. Because we know two angles ($A = 35°$ and $B = 15°$), we find the third angle using equation (2).

Figure 22

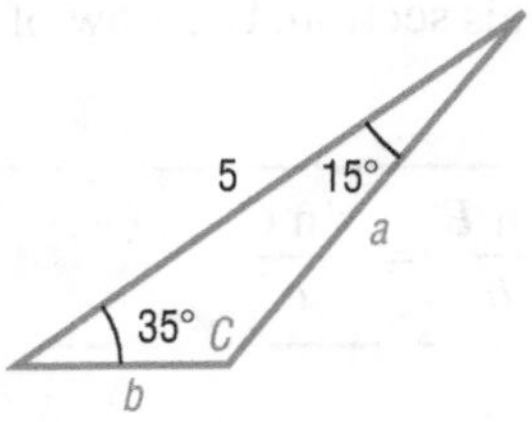

$$A + B + C = 180°$$
$$35° + 15° + C = 180°$$
$$C = 130°$$

Now we know the three angles and one side ($c = 5$) of the triangle. To find the remaining two sides a and b, we use the Law of Sines (twice).

$$\frac{\sin A}{a} = \frac{\sin C}{c} \qquad \frac{\sin B}{b} = \frac{\sin C}{c}$$

$$\frac{\sin 35°}{a} = \frac{\sin 130°}{5} \qquad \frac{\sin 15°}{b} = \frac{\sin 130°}{5}$$

$$a = \frac{5 \sin 35°}{\sin 130°} \approx 3.74 \qquad b = \frac{5 \sin 15°}{\sin 130°} \approx 1.69$$

Now Work PROBLEM 23

2 Solve SSA Triangles

Figure 23

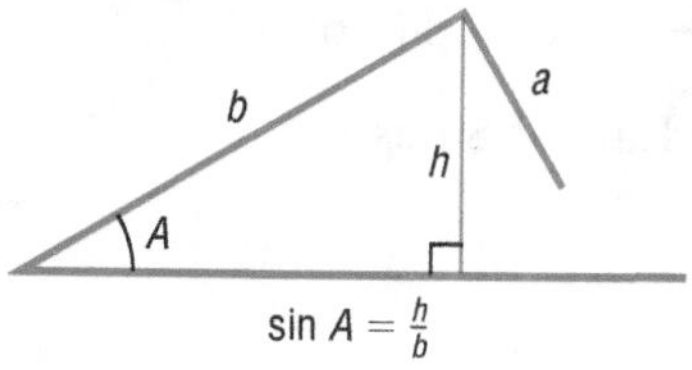

Case 2 (SSA), which applies to triangles for which two sides and the angle opposite one of them are known, is referred to as the **ambiguous case,** because the known information may result in one triangle, two triangles, or no triangle at all. Suppose that we are given sides a and b and angle A, as illustrated in Figure 23. The key to determining the possible triangles, if any, that may be formed from the given information lies primarily with the relative size of side a, the height h, and the fact that $h = b \sin A$.

No Triangle If $a < h = b \sin A$, then side a is not sufficiently long to form a triangle. See Figure 24.

Figure 24
$a < h = b \sin A$

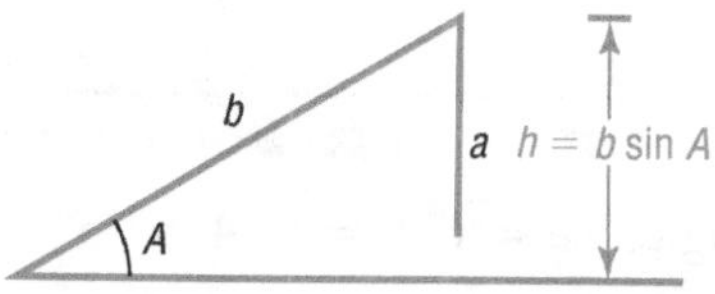

One Right Triangle If $a = h = b \sin A$, then side a is just long enough to form a right triangle. See Figure 25.

Figure 25
$a = h = b \sin A$

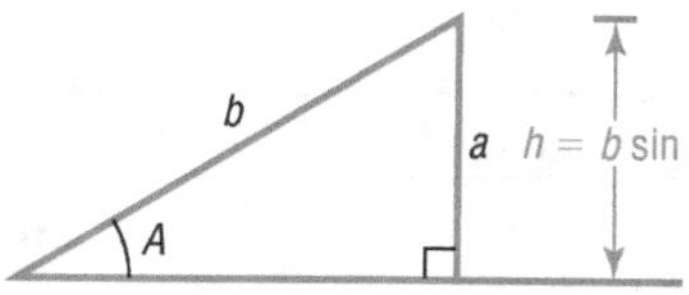

Two Triangles If $h = b \sin A < a$, and $a < b$, two distinct triangles can be formed from the given information. See Figure 26.

Figure 26
$b \sin A < a$ and $a < b$

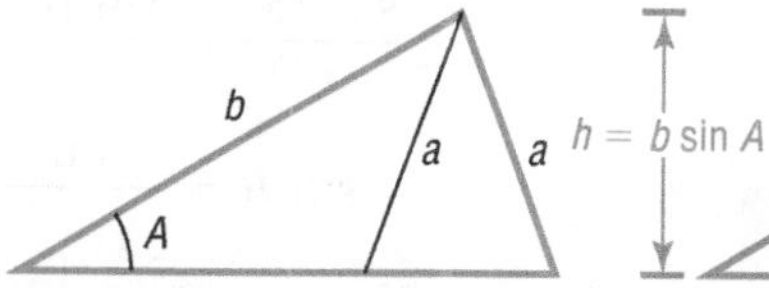

One Triangle If $a \geq b$, only one triangle can be formed. See Figure 27.

Figure 27
$a \geq b$

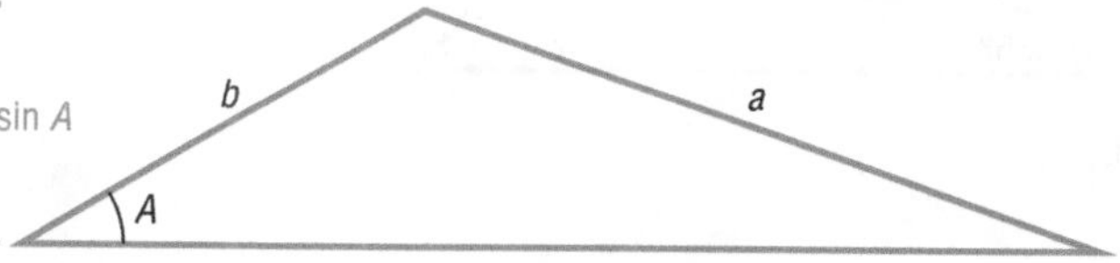

Fortunately, we do not have to rely on an illustration or complicated relationships to draw the correct conclusion in the ambiguous case. The Law of Sines will lead us to the correct determination. Let's see how.

EXAMPLE 3 **Using the Law of Sines to Solve an SSA Triangle (One Solution)**

Solve the triangle: $a = 3, b = 2, A = 40°$

Solution See Figure 28(a). Because we know an angle ($A = 40°$), the side opposite the known angle ($a = 3$), and the side opposite angle B ($b = 2$), we use the Law of Sines to find the angle B.

Figure 28(a)

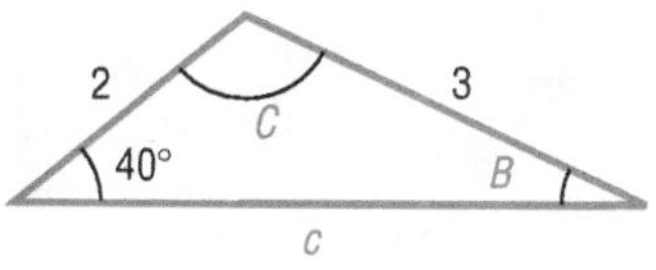

$$\frac{\sin A}{a} = \frac{\sin B}{b}$$

Then

$$\frac{\sin 40°}{3} = \frac{\sin B}{2}$$

$$\sin B = \frac{2 \sin 40°}{3} \approx 0.43$$

There are two angles B, $0° < B < 180°$, for which $\sin B \approx 0.43$.

$$B_1 \approx 25.4° \quad \text{and} \quad B_2 \approx 180° - 25.4° = 154.6°$$

NOTE Here we computed B_1 by determining the value of $\sin^{-1}\left(\frac{2 \sin 40°}{3}\right)$. If you use the rounded value and evaluate $\sin^{-1}(0.43)$, you will obtain a slightly different result. ■

The second possibility, $B_2 \approx 154.6°$, is ruled out, because $A = 40°$, making $A + B_2 \approx 194.6° > 180°$. Now, using $B_1 \approx 25.4°$, we find that

$$C = 180° - A - B_1 \approx 180° - 40° - 25.4° = 114.6°$$

The third side c may now be determined using the Law of Sines.

$$\frac{\sin A}{a} = \frac{\sin C}{c}$$

$$\frac{\sin 40°}{3} = \frac{\sin 114.6°}{c}$$

$$c = \frac{3 \sin 114.6°}{\sin 40°} \approx 4.24$$

Figure 28(b)

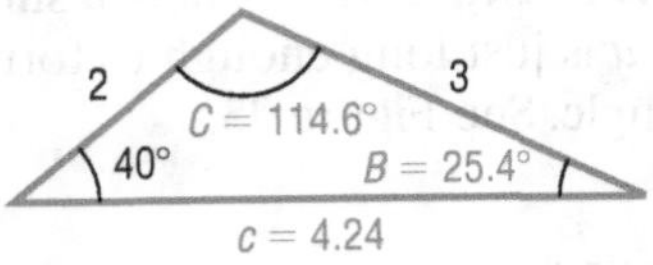

Figure 28(b) illustrates the solved triangle.

EXAMPLE 4 Using the Law of Sines to Solve an SSA Triangle (Two Solutions)

Solve the triangle: $a = 6, b = 8, A = 35°$

Solution See Figure 29(a). Because $a = 6$, $b = 8$, and $A = 35°$ are known, we use the Law of Sines to find the angle B.

Figure 29(a)

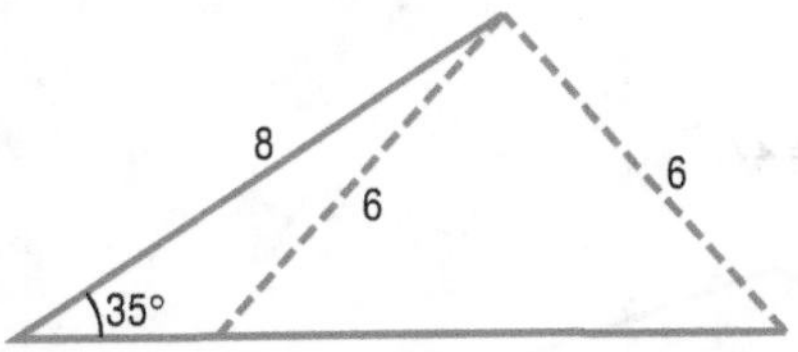

$$\frac{\sin A}{a} = \frac{\sin B}{b}$$

Then

$$\frac{\sin 35°}{6} = \frac{\sin B}{8}$$

$$\sin B = \frac{8 \sin 35°}{6} \approx 0.76$$

$$B_1 \approx 49.9° \quad \text{or} \quad B_2 \approx 180° - 49.9° = 130.1°$$

For both choices of B, we have $A + B < 180°$. There are two triangles, one containing the angle $B_1 \approx 49.9°$ and the other containing the angle $B_2 \approx 130.1°$. The third angle C is either

$$C_1 = 180° - \underset{\substack{\uparrow \\ A = 35° \\ B_1 = 49.9°}}{A - B_1} \approx 95.1° \quad \text{or} \quad C_2 = 180° - \underset{\substack{\uparrow \\ A = 35° \\ B_2 = 130.1°}}{A - B_2} \approx 14.9°$$

The third side c obeys the Law of Sines, so we have

Figure 29(b)

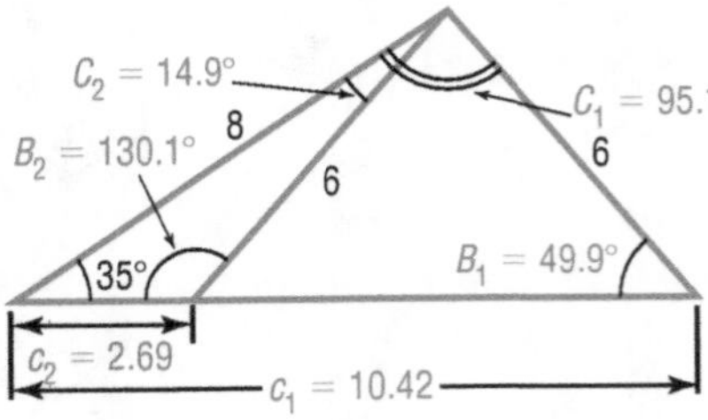

$$\frac{\sin A}{a} = \frac{\sin C_1}{c_1} \qquad \frac{\sin A}{a} = \frac{\sin C_2}{c_2}$$

$$\frac{\sin 35°}{6} = \frac{\sin 95.1°}{c_1} \qquad \frac{\sin 35°}{6} = \frac{\sin 14.9°}{c_2}$$

$$c_1 = \frac{6 \sin 95.1°}{\sin 35°} \approx 10.42 \qquad c_2 = \frac{6 \sin 14.9°}{\sin 35°} \approx 2.69$$

The two solved triangles are illustrated in Figure 29(b).

EXAMPLE 5 Using the Law of Sines to Solve a SSA Triangle (No Solution)

Solve the triangle: $a = 2, c = 1, C = 50°$

Solution Because $a = 2$, $c = 1$, and $C = 50°$ are known, we use the Law of Sines to find the angle A.

$$\frac{\sin A}{a} = \frac{\sin C}{c}$$

$$\frac{\sin A}{2} = \frac{\sin 50°}{1}$$

$$\sin A = 2 \sin 50° \approx 1.53$$

Figure 30

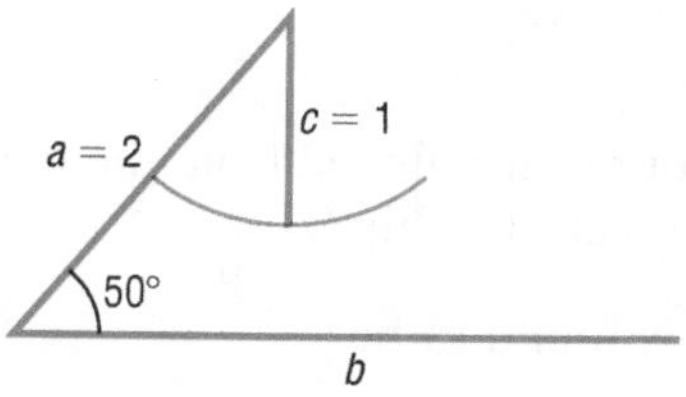

Since there is no angle A for which $\sin A > 1$, there can be no triangle with the given measurements. Figure 30 illustrates the measurements given. Notice that, no matter how we attempt to position side c, it will never touch side b to form a triangle.

Now Work PROBLEMS 25 AND 31

3 Solve Applied Problems

The Law of Sines is particularly useful for solving certain applied problems.

EXAMPLE 6 Finding the Height of a Mountain

To measure the height of a mountain, a surveyor takes two sightings of the peak at a distance 900 meters apart on a direct line to the mountain.* See Figure 31(a). The first observation results in an angle of elevation of 47°, and the second results in an angle of elevation of 35°. If the transit is 2 meters high, what is the height h of the mountain?

Figure 31

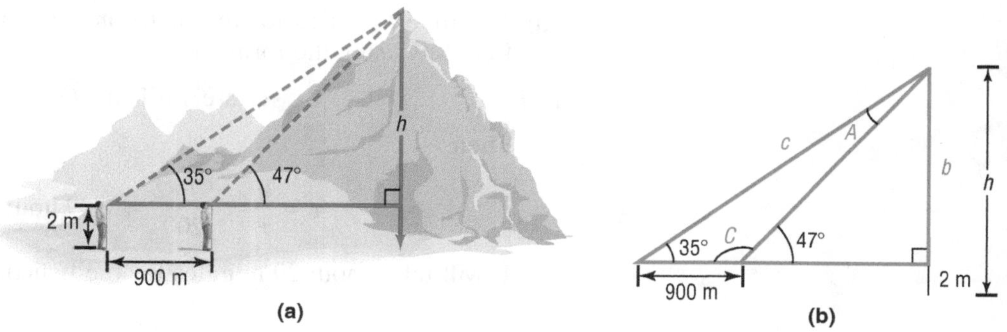

Solution Figure 31(b) shows the triangles that replicate the illustration in Figure 31(a). Since $C + 47° = 180°$, we find that $C = 133°$. Also, since $A + C + 35° = 180°$, we find that $A = 180° - 35° - C = 145° - 133° = 12°$. We use the Law of Sines to find c.

$$\frac{\sin A}{a} = \frac{\sin C}{c} \quad A = 12°, C = 133°, a = 900$$

$$c = \frac{900 \sin 133°}{\sin 12°} \approx 3165.86$$

Using the larger right triangle, we have

$$\sin 35° = \frac{b}{c} \quad c = 3165.86$$

$$b = 3165.86 \sin 35° \approx 1815.86 \approx 1816 \text{ meters}$$

The height of the peak from ground level is approximately $1816 + 2 = 1818$ meters.

Now Work PROBLEM 39

*For simplicity, we assume that these sightings are at the same level.

EXAMPLE 7 Rescue at Sea

Coast Guard Station Zulu is located 120 miles due west of Station X-ray. A ship at sea sends an SOS call that is received by each station. The call to Station Zulu indicates that the bearing of the ship from Zulu is N40°E (40° east of north). The call to Station X-ray indicates that the bearing of the ship from X-ray is N30°W (30° west of north).

(a) How far is each station from the ship?

(b) If a helicopter capable of flying 200 miles per hour is dispatched from the nearest station to the ship, how long will it take to reach the ship?

Solution (a) Figure 32 illustrates the situation. The angle C is found to be

$$C = 180° - 50° - 60° = 70°$$

The Law of Sines can now be used to find the two distances a and b that we seek.

Figure 32

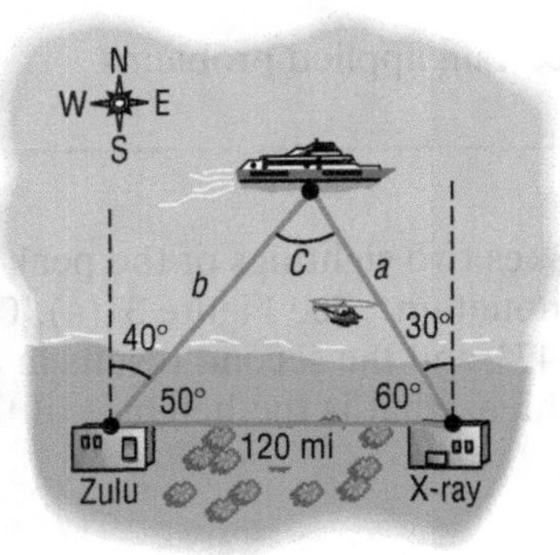

$$\frac{\sin 50°}{a} = \frac{\sin 70°}{120}$$

$$a = \frac{120 \sin 50°}{\sin 70°} \approx 97.82 \text{ miles}$$

$$\frac{\sin 60°}{b} = \frac{\sin 70°}{120}$$

$$b = \frac{120 \sin 60°}{\sin 70°} \approx 110.59 \text{ miles}$$

Station Zulu is about 111 miles from the ship, and Station X-ray is about 98 miles from the ship.

(b) The time t needed for the helicopter to reach the ship from Station X-ray is found by using the formula

$$(\text{Rate}, r)(\text{Time}, t) = \text{Distance}, a$$

Then

$$t = \frac{a}{r} = \frac{97.82}{200} \approx 0.49 \text{ hour} \approx 29 \text{ minutes}$$

It will take about 29 minutes for the helicopter to reach the ship.

Now Work PROBLEM 37

Proof of the Law of Sines To prove the Law of Sines, we construct an altitude of length h from one of the vertices of a triangle. Figure 33(a) shows h for a triangle with three acute angles, and Figure 33(b) shows h for a triangle with an obtuse angle. In each case, the altitude is drawn from the vertex at B. Using either illustration, we have

Figure 33

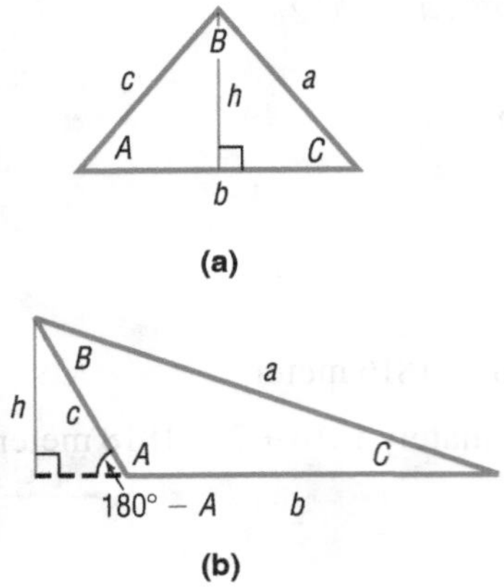

$$\sin C = \frac{h}{a}$$

from which

$$h = a \sin C \qquad (3)$$

From Figure 33(a), it also follows that

$$\sin A = \frac{h}{c}$$

from which

$$h = c \sin A \qquad (4)$$

From Figure 33(b), it follows that

$$\sin(180° - A) = \sin A = \frac{h}{c}$$

$$\uparrow$$

$$\sin(180° - A) = \sin 180° \cos A - \cos 180° \sin A = \sin A$$

which again gives

$$h = c \sin A$$

So, whether the triangle has three acute angles or has two acute angles and one obtuse angle, equations (3) and (4) hold. As a result, we may equate the expressions for h in equations (3) and (4) to get

$$a \sin C = c \sin A$$

from which

$$\frac{\sin A}{a} = \frac{\sin C}{c} \tag{5}$$

Figure 34

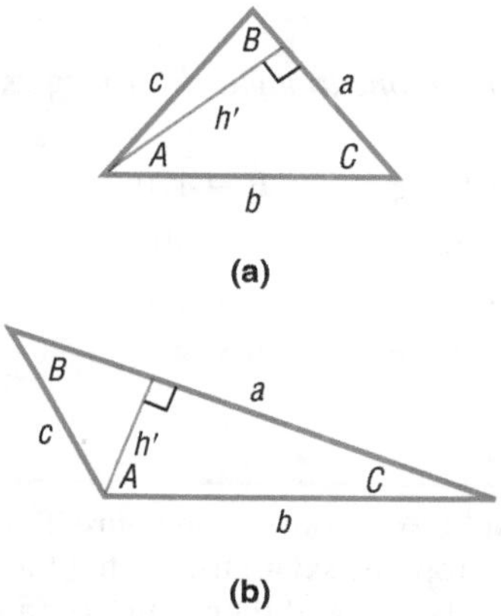

In a similar manner, by constructing the altitude h' from the vertex of angle A as shown in Figure 34, we can show that

$$\sin B = \frac{h'}{c} \quad \text{and} \quad \sin C = \frac{h'}{b}$$

Equating the expressions for h', we find that

$$h' = c \sin B = b \sin C$$

from which

$$\frac{\sin B}{b} = \frac{\sin C}{c} \tag{6}$$

When equations (5) and (6) are combined, we have equation (1), the Law of Sines. ■

8.2 Assess Your Understanding

'Are You Prepared?' *Answers are given at the end of these exercises. If you get a wrong answer, read the pages listed in red.*

1. The difference formula for the sine function is $\sin(A - B) =$ _____. (p. 469)

2. If θ is an acute angle, solve the equation $\cos\theta = \frac{\sqrt{3}}{2}$. (pp. 488–492)

3. The two triangles shown are similar. Find the missing length. (pp. A16–A19)

Concepts and Vocabulary

4. If none of the angles of a triangle is a right angle, the triangle is called _____.

5. For a triangle with sides a, b, c and opposite angles A, B, C, the Law of Sines states that _____.

6. ***True or False*** An oblique triangle in which two sides and an angle are given always results in at least one triangle.

7. ***True or False*** The sum of the angles of any triangle equals 180°.

8. ***True or False*** The ambiguous case refers to the fact that, when two sides and the angle opposite one of them are given, sometimes the Law of Sines cannot be used.

Skill Building

In Problems 9–16, solve each triangle.

9.
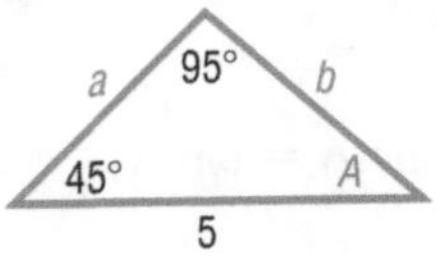

10.
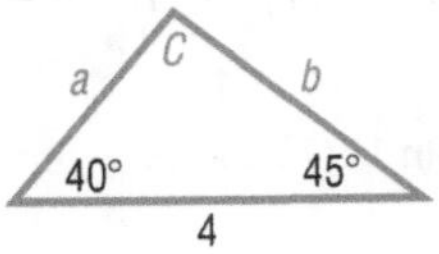

11.
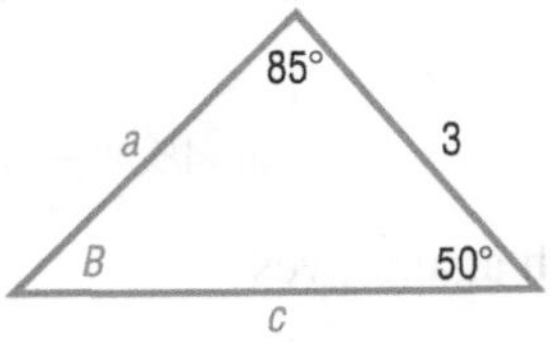

12.
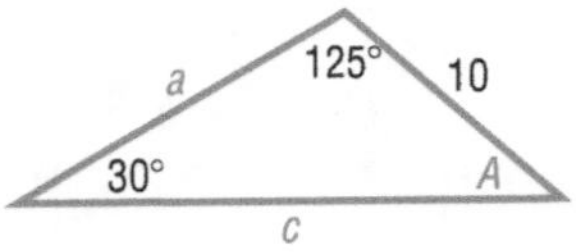

13.
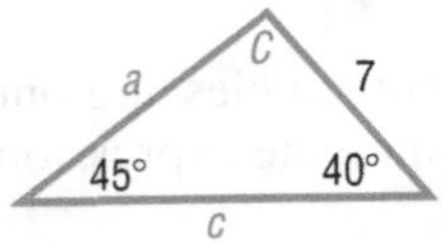

14.
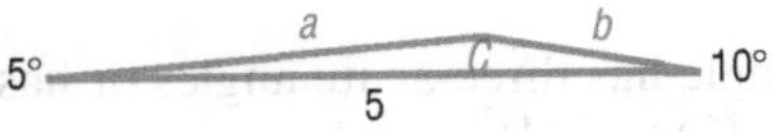

15.
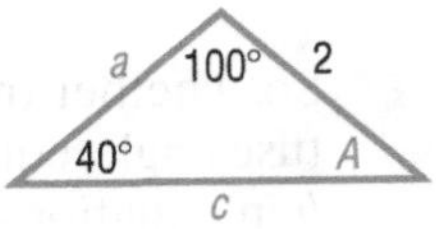

16.
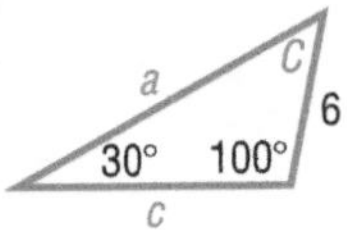

In Problems 17–24, solve each triangle.

17. $A = 40°$, $B = 20°$, $a = 2$

18. $A = 50°$, $C = 20°$, $a = 3$

19. $B = 70°$, $C = 10°$, $b = 5$

20. $A = 70°$, $B = 60°$, $c = 4$

21. $A = 110°$, $C = 30°$, $c = 3$

22. $B = 10°$, $C = 100°$, $b = 2$

23. $A = 40°$, $B = 40°$, $c = 2$

24. $B = 20°$, $C = 70°$, $a = 1$

In Problems 25–36, two sides and an angle are given. Determine whether the given information results in one triangle, two triangles, or no triangle at all. Solve any triangle(s) that results.

25. $a = 3$, $b = 2$, $A = 50°$

26. $b = 4$, $c = 3$, $B = 40°$

27. $b = 5$, $c = 3$, $B = 100°$

28. $a = 2$, $c = 1$, $A = 120°$

29. $a = 4$, $b = 5$, $A = 60°$

30. $b = 2$, $c = 3$, $B = 40°$

31. $b = 4$, $c = 6$, $B = 20°$

32. $a = 3$, $b = 7$, $A = 70°$

33. $a = 2$, $c = 1$, $C = 100°$

34. $b = 4$, $c = 5$, $B = 95°$

35. $a = 2$, $c = 1$, $C = 25°$

36. $b = 4$, $c = 5$, $B = 40°$

Applications and Extensions

37. Rescue at Sea Coast Guard Station Able is located 150 miles due south of Station Baker. A ship at sea sends an SOS call that is received by each station. The call to Station Able indicates that the ship is located N55°E; the call to Station Baker indicates that the ship is located S60°E.

(a) How far is each station from the ship?

(b) If a helicopter capable of flying 200 miles per hour is dispatched from the station nearest the ship, how long will it take to reach the ship?

38. Distance to the Moon At exactly the same time, Tom and Alice measured the angle of elevation to the moon while standing exactly 300 km apart. The angle of elevation to the moon for Tom was 49.8974° and the angle of elevation to the moon for Alice was 49.9312°. See the figure. To the nearest 1000 km, how far was the moon from Earth when the measurement was obtained?

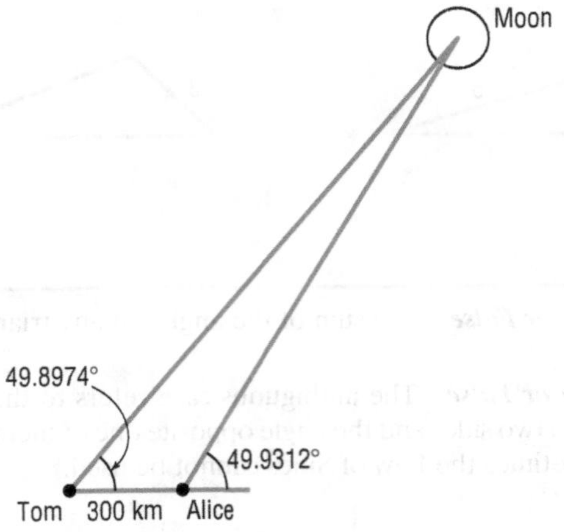

39. Finding the Length of a Ski Lift Consult the figure. To find the length of the span of a proposed ski lift from P to Q, a surveyor measures $\angle DPQ$ to be 25° and then walks off a distance of 1000 feet to R and measures $\angle PRQ$ to be 15°. What is the distance from P to Q?

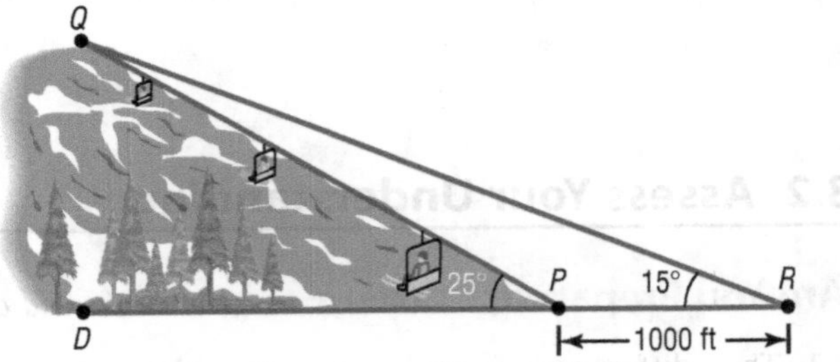

40. Finding the Height of a Mountain Use the illustration in Problem 39 to find the height QD of the mountain.

41. Finding the Height of an Airplane An aircraft is spotted by two observers who are 1000 feet apart. As the airplane passes over the line joining them, each observer takes a sighting of the angle of elevation to the plane, as indicated in the figure. How high is the airplane?

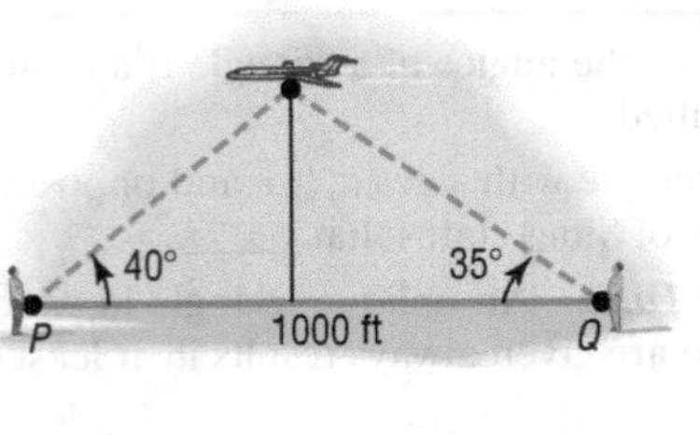

42. Finding the Height of the Bridge over the Royal Gorge The highest bridge in the world is the bridge over the Royal Gorge of the Arkansas River in Colorado. Sightings to the same point at water level directly under the bridge are taken from each side of the 880-foot-long bridge, as indicated in the figure. How high is the bridge?

Source: Guinness Book of World Records

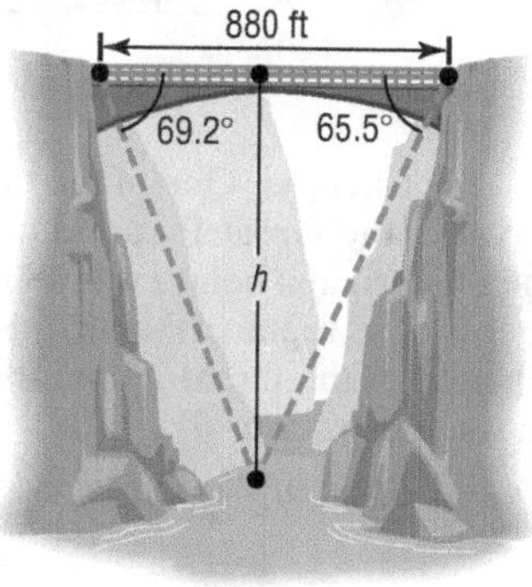

43. Landscaping Pat needs to determine the height of a tree before cutting it down to be sure that it will not fall on a nearby fence. The angle of elevation of the tree from one position on a flat path from the tree is 30°, and from a second position 40 feet farther along this path it is 20°. What is the height of the tree?

44. Construction A loading ramp 10 feet long that makes an angle of 18° with the horizontal is to be replaced by one that makes an angle of 12° with the horizontal. How long is the new ramp?

45. Commercial Navigation Adam must fly home to St. Louis from a business meeting in Oklahoma City. One flight option flies directly to St. Louis, a distance of about 461.1 miles. A second flight option flies first to Kansas City and then connects to St. Louis. The bearing from Oklahoma City to Kansas City is N29.6°E, and the bearing from Oklahoma City to St. Louis is N57.7°E. The bearing from St. Louis to Oklahoma City is S62.1°W, and the bearing from St. Louis to Kansas City is N79.4°W. How many more frequent flyer miles will Adam receive if he takes the connecting flight rather than the direct flight?

Source: www.landings.com

46. Time Lost due to a Navigation Error In attempting to fly from city P to city Q, an aircraft followed a course that was 10° in error, as indicated in the figure. After flying a distance of 50 miles, the pilot corrected the course by turning at point R and flying 70 miles farther. If the constant speed of the aircraft was 250 miles per hour, how much time was lost due to the error?

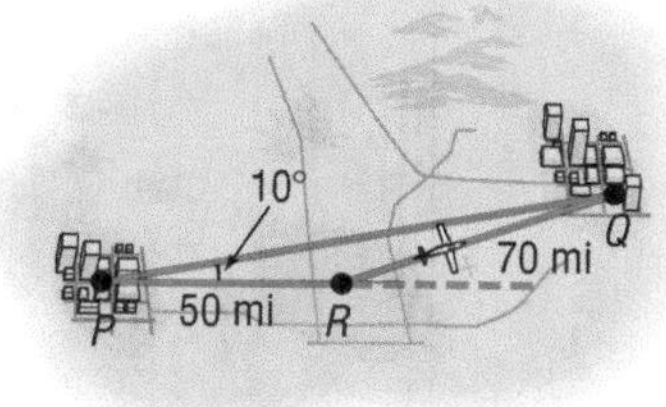

47. Finding the Lean of the Leaning Tower of Pisa The famous Leaning Tower of Pisa was originally 184.5 feet high.* At a distance of 123 feet from the base of the tower, the angle of elevation to the top of the tower is found to be 60°. Find $\angle RPQ$ indicated in the figure. Also, find the perpendicular distance from R to PQ.

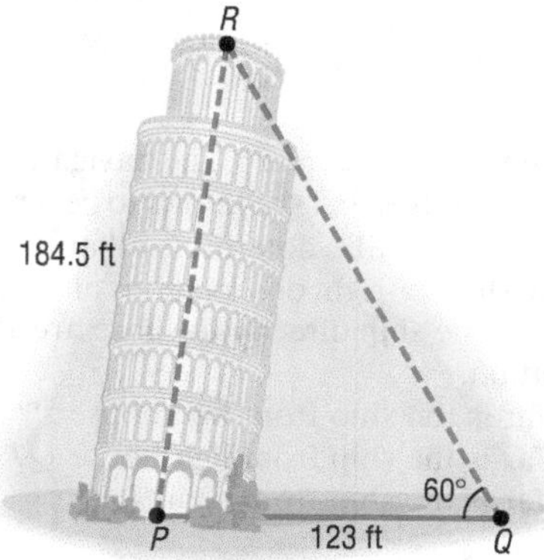

48. Crankshafts on Cars On a certain automobile, the crankshaft is 3 inches long and the connecting rod is 9 inches long (see the figure). At the time when $\angle OPQ$ is 15°, how far is the piston (P) from the center (O) of the crankshaft?

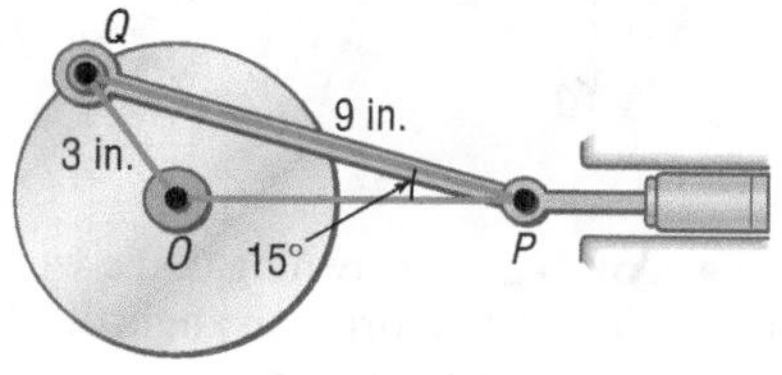

49. Constructing a Highway U.S. 41, a highway whose primary directions are north–south, is being constructed along the west coast of Florida. Near Naples, a bay obstructs the straight

*On February 27, 1964, the government of Italy requested aid in preventing the tower from toppling. A multinational task force of engineers, mathematicians, and historians was assigned and met on the Azores islands to discuss stabilization methods. After over two decades of work on the subject, the tower was closed to the public in January 1990. During the time that the tower was closed, the bells were removed to relieve some weight, and cables were cinched around the third level and anchored several hundred meters away. Apartments and houses in the path of the tower were vacated for safety concerns. After a decade of corrective reconstruction and stabilization efforts, the tower was reopened to the public on December 15, 2001. Many methods were proposed to stabilize the tower, including the addition of 800 metric tons of lead counterweights to the raised end of the base. The final solution to correcting the lean was to remove 38 cubic meters of soil from underneath the raised end. The tower has been declared stable for at least another 300 years.

Source: http://en.wikipedia.org/wiki/Leaning_Tower_of_Pisa, page last modified June 28, 2006

path of the road. Since the cost of a bridge is prohibitive, engineers decide to go around the bay. The illustration shows the path that they decide on and the measurements taken. What is the length of highway needed to go around the bay?

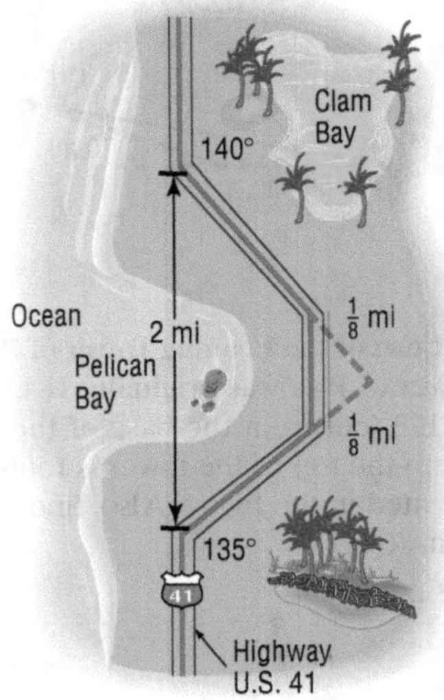

50. Calculating Distances at Sea The navigator of a ship at sea spots two lighthouses that she knows to be 3 miles apart along a straight seashore. She determines that the angles formed between two line-of-sight observations of the lighthouses and the line from the ship directly to shore are 15° and 35°. See the illustration.

(a) How far is the ship from lighthouse P?
(b) How far is the ship from lighthouse Q?
(c) How far is the ship from shore?

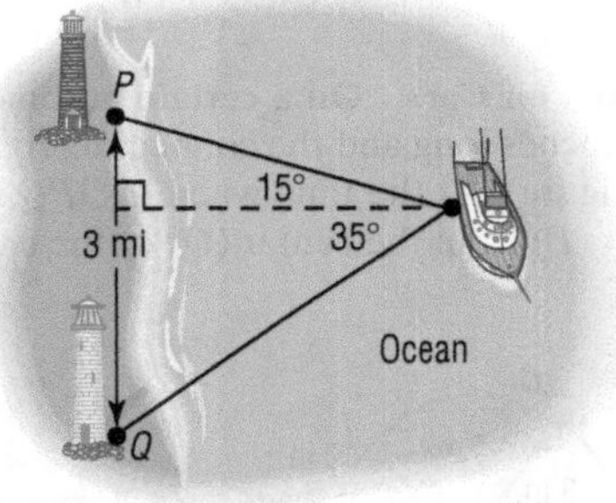

51. Designing an Awning An awning that covers a sliding glass door that is 88 inches tall forms an angle of 50° with the wall. The purpose of the awning is to prevent sunlight from entering the house when the angle of elevation of the Sun is more than 65°. See the figure. Find the length L of the awning.

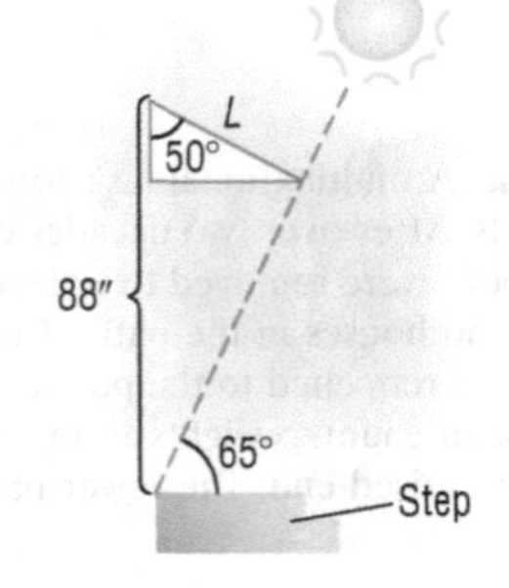

52. Finding Distances A forest ranger is walking on a path inclined at 5° to the horizontal directly toward a 100-foot-tall fire observation tower. The angle of elevation from the path to the top of the tower is 40°. How far is the ranger from the tower at this time?

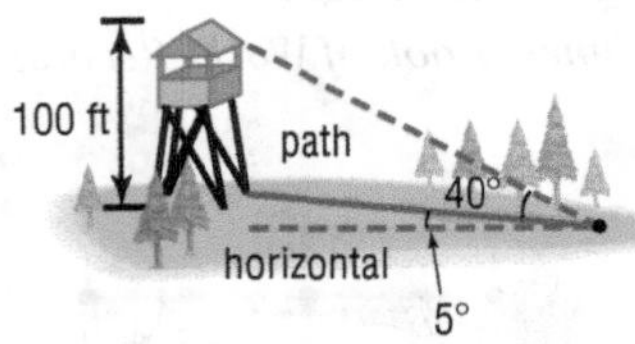

53. Great Pyramid of Cheops One of the original Seven Wonders of the World, the Great Pyramid of Cheops was built about 2580 BC. Its original height was 480 feet 11 inches, but owing to the loss of its topmost stones, it is now shorter. Find the current height of the Great Pyramid using the information given in the illustration.

Source: Guinness Book of World Records

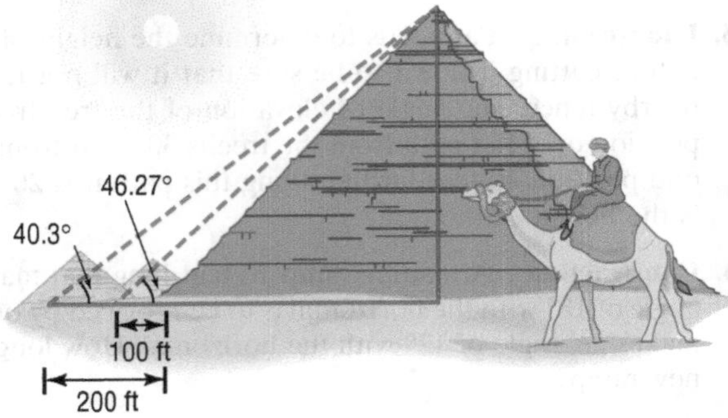

54. Determining the Height of an Aircraft Two sensors are spaced 700 feet apart along the approach to a small airport. When an aircraft is nearing the airport, the angle of elevation from the first sensor to the aircraft is 20°, and from the second sensor to the aircraft it is 15°. Determine how high the aircraft is at this time.

55. Mercury The distance from the Sun to Earth is approximately 149,600,000 kilometers (km). The distance from the Sun to Mercury is approximately 57,910,000 km. The **elongation angle** α is the angle formed between the line of sight from Earth to the Sun and the line of sight from Earth to Mercury. See the figure. Suppose that the elongation angle for Mercury is 15°. Use this information to find the possible distances between Earth and Mercury.

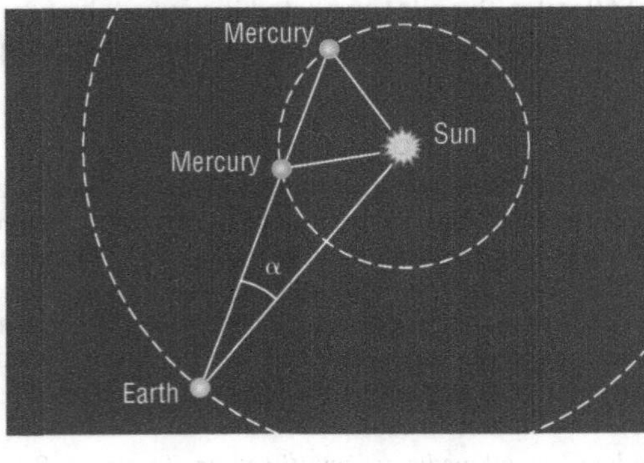

56. **Venus** The distance from the Sun to Earth is approximately 149,600,000 km. The distance from the Sun to Venus is approximately 108,200,000 km. The elongation angle α is the angle formed between the line of sight from Earth to the Sun and the line of sight from Earth to Venus. Suppose that the elongation angle for Venus is 10°. Use this information to find the possible distances between Earth and Venus.

57. **The Original Ferris Wheel** George Washington Gale Ferris, Jr., designed the original Ferris wheel for the 1893 World's Columbian Exposition in Chicago, Illinois. The wheel had 36 equally spaced cars each the size of a school bus. The distance between adjacent cars was approximately 22 feet. Determine the diameter of the wheel to the nearest foot.

Source: Carnegie Library of Pittsburgh, www.clpgh.org

58. **Mollweide's Formula** For any triangle, Mollweide's Formula (named after Karl Mollweide, 1774–1825) states that

$$\frac{a+b}{c} = \frac{\cos\left[\frac{1}{2}(A-B)\right]}{\sin\left(\frac{1}{2}C\right)}$$

Derive it.

[**Hint:** Use the Law of Sines and then a Sum-to-Product Formula. Notice that this formula involves all six parts of a triangle. As a result, it is sometimes used to check the solution of a triangle.]

59. **Mollweide's Formula** Another form of Mollweide's Formula is

$$\frac{a-b}{c} = \frac{\sin\left[\frac{1}{2}(A-B)\right]}{\cos\left(\frac{1}{2}C\right)}$$

Derive it.

60. For any triangle, derive the formula

$$a = b\cos C + c\cos B$$

[**Hint:** Use the fact that $\sin A = \sin(180° - B - C)$.]

61. **Law of Tangents** For any triangle, derive the Law of Tangents.

$$\frac{a-b}{a+b} = \frac{\tan\left[\frac{1}{2}(A-B)\right]}{\tan\left[\frac{1}{2}(A+B)\right]}$$

[**Hint:** Use Mollweide's Formula.]

62. **Circumscribing a Triangle** Show that

$$\frac{\sin A}{a} = \frac{\sin B}{b} = \frac{\sin C}{c} = \frac{1}{2r}$$

where r is the radius of the circle circumscribing the triangle PQR whose sides are a, b, and c, as shown in the figure.

[**Hint:** Draw the diameter PP'. Then $B = \angle PQR = \angle PP'R$, and angle $\angle PRP' = 90°$.]

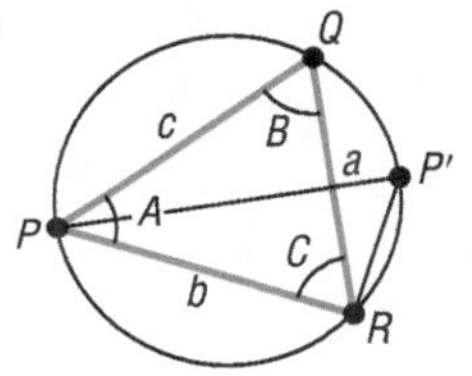

Discussion and Writing

63. Make up three problems involving oblique triangles. One should result in one triangle, the second in two triangles, and the third in no triangle.

64. What do you do first if you are asked to solve a triangle and are given one side and two angles?

65. What do you do first if you are asked to solve a triangle and are given two sides and the angle opposite one of them?

'Are You Prepared?' Answers

1. $\sin A\cos B - \cos A\sin B$ **2.** 30° **3.** $\frac{15}{2}$

8.3 The Law of Cosines

PREPARING FOR THIS SECTION *Before getting started, review the following:*

- Trigonometric Equations (I) (Section 7.7, pp. 488–492)
- Distance Formula (Section 1.1, p. 5)

Now Work the 'Are You Prepared?' problems on page 537.

OBJECTIVES
1 Solve SAS Triangles (p. 534)
2 Solve SSS Triangles (p. 535)
3 Solve Applied Problems (p. 536)

In the previous section, we used the Law of Sines to solve Case 1 (SAA or ASA) and Case 2 (SSA) of an oblique triangle. In this section, we derive the Law of Cosines and use it to solve the remaining cases, 3 and 4.

Case 3: Two sides and the included angle are known (SAS).
Case 4: Three sides are known (SSS).

THEOREM **Law of Cosines**

For a triangle with sides a, b, c and opposite angles A, B, C, respectively,

$$c^2 = a^2 + b^2 - 2ab\cos C \qquad (1)$$
$$b^2 = a^2 + c^2 - 2ac\cos B \qquad (2)$$
$$a^2 = b^2 + c^2 - 2bc\cos A \qquad (3)$$

Figure 35

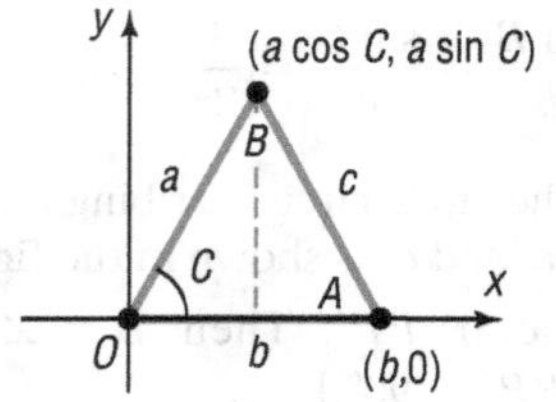

(a) Angle C is acute

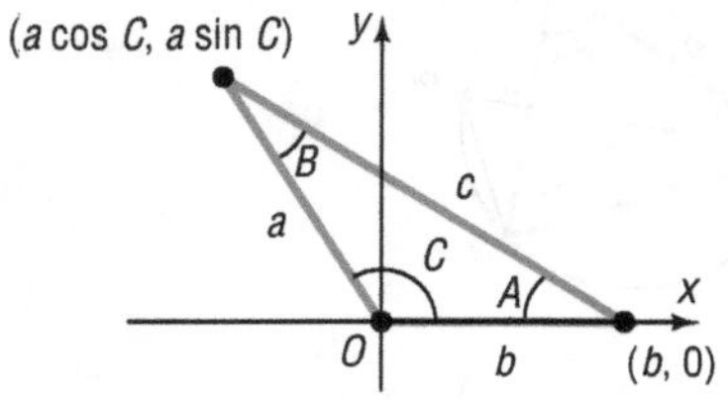

(b) Angle C is obtuse

Proof We will prove only formula (1) here. Formulas (2) and (3) may be proved using the same argument.

We begin by strategically placing a triangle on a rectangular coordinate system so that the vertex of angle C is at the origin and side b lies along the positive x-axis. Regardless of whether C is acute, as in Figure 35(a), or obtuse, as in Figure 35(b), the vertex of angle B has coordinates $(a\cos C, a\sin C)$. The vertex of angle A has coordinates $(b, 0)$.

We can now use the distance formula to compute c^2.

$$\begin{aligned} c^2 &= (b - a\cos C)^2 + (0 - a\sin C)^2 \\ &= b^2 - 2ab\cos C + a^2\cos^2 C + a^2\sin^2 C \\ &= b^2 - 2ab\cos C + a^2(\cos^2 C + \sin^2 C) \\ &= a^2 + b^2 - 2ab\cos C \end{aligned}$$ ■

Each of formulas (1), (2), and (3) may be stated in words as follows:

THEOREM **Law of Cosines**

The square of one side of a triangle equals the sum of the squares of the other two sides minus twice their product times the cosine of their included angle.

Observe that if the triangle is a right triangle (so that, say, $C = 90°$), formula (1) becomes the familiar Pythagorean Theorem: $c^2 = a^2 + b^2$. The Pythagorean Theorem is a special case of the Law of Cosines!

1 Solve SAS Triangles

Let's see how to use the Law of Cosines to solve Case 3 (SAS), which applies to triangles for which two sides and the included angle are known.

EXAMPLE 1 Using the Law of Cosines to Solve an SAS Triangle

Solve the triangle: $a = 2, \quad b = 3, \quad C = 60°$

Solution See Figure 36. Because we know two sides, a and b, and the included angle, $C = 60°$, the Law of Cosines makes it easy to find the third side, c.

Figure 36

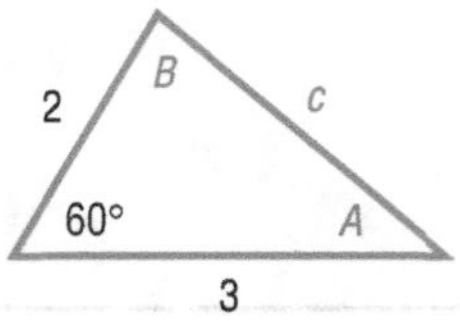

$$\begin{aligned} c^2 &= a^2 + b^2 - 2ab\cos C \\ &= 2^2 + 3^2 - 2\cdot 2\cdot 3\cdot \cos 60° \quad a = 2, b = 3, C = 60° \\ &= 13 - \left(12\cdot\frac{1}{2}\right) = 7 \\ c &= \sqrt{7} \end{aligned}$$

Side c is of length $\sqrt{7}$. To find the angles A and B, we may use either the Law of Sines or the Law of Cosines. It is preferable to use the Law of Cosines, since it will lead to an equation with one solution. Using the Law of Sines would lead to an equation with two solutions that would need to be checked to determine which solution fits the given data. We choose to use formulas (2) and (3) of the Law of Cosines to find A and B.

For A:

$$a^2 = b^2 + c^2 - 2bc \cos A$$
$$2bc \cos A = b^2 + c^2 - a^2$$
$$\cos A = \frac{b^2 + c^2 - a^2}{2bc} = \frac{9 + 7 - 4}{2 \cdot 3\sqrt{7}} = \frac{12}{6\sqrt{7}} = \frac{2\sqrt{7}}{7}$$
$$A = \cos^{-1} \frac{2\sqrt{7}}{7} \approx 40.9°$$

For B:

$$b^2 = a^2 + c^2 - 2ac \cos B$$
$$\cos B = \frac{a^2 + c^2 - b^2}{2ac} = \frac{4 + 7 - 9}{4\sqrt{7}} = \frac{2}{4\sqrt{7}} = \frac{\sqrt{7}}{14}$$
$$B = \cos^{-1} \frac{\sqrt{7}}{14} \approx 79.1°$$

Notice that $A + B + C = 40.9° + 79.1° + 60° = 180°$, as required.

Now Work PROBLEM 9

2 Solve SSS Triangles

The next example illustrates how the Law of Cosines is used when three sides of a triangle are known, Case 4 (SSS).

EXAMPLE 2 Using the Law of Cosines to Solve an SSS Triangle

Solve the triangle: $a = 4, b = 3, c = 6$

Solution See Figure 37. To find the angles A, B, and C, we proceed as we did in the latter part of the solution to Example 1.

Figure 37

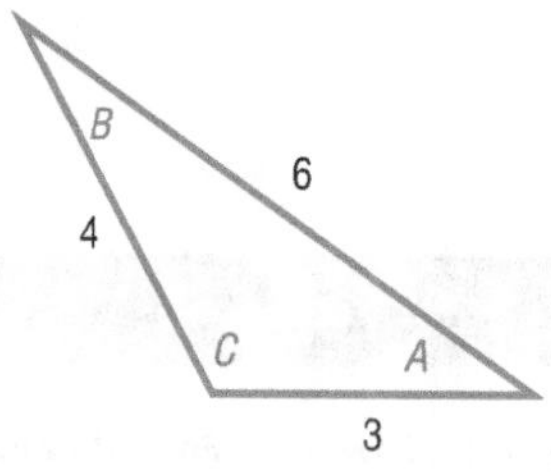

For A:

$$\cos A = \frac{b^2 + c^2 - a^2}{2bc} = \frac{9 + 36 - 16}{2 \cdot 3 \cdot 6} = \frac{29}{36}$$
$$A = \cos^{-1} \frac{29}{36} \approx 36.3°$$

For B:

$$\cos B = \frac{a^2 + c^2 - b^2}{2ac} = \frac{16 + 36 - 9}{2 \cdot 4 \cdot 6} = \frac{43}{48}$$
$$B = \cos^{-1} \frac{43}{48} \approx 26.4°$$

Since we know A and B,

$$C = 180° - A - B \approx 180° - 36.3° - 26.4° = 117.3°$$

Now Work PROBLEM 15

3 Solve Applied Problems

EXAMPLE 3 **Correcting a Navigational Error**

A motorized sailboat leaves Naples, Florida, bound for Key West, 150 miles away. Maintaining a constant speed of 15 miles per hour, but encountering heavy cross-winds and strong currents, the crew finds, after 4 hours, that the sailboat is off course by 20°.

(a) How far is the sailboat from Key West at this time?
(b) Through what angle should the sailboat turn to correct its course?
(c) How much time has been added to the trip because of this? (Assume that the speed remains at 15 miles per hour.)

Solution See Figure 38. With a speed of 15 miles per hour, the sailboat has gone 60 miles after 4 hours. We seek the distance x of the sailboat from Key West. We also seek the angle θ that the sailboat should turn through to correct its course.

Figure 38

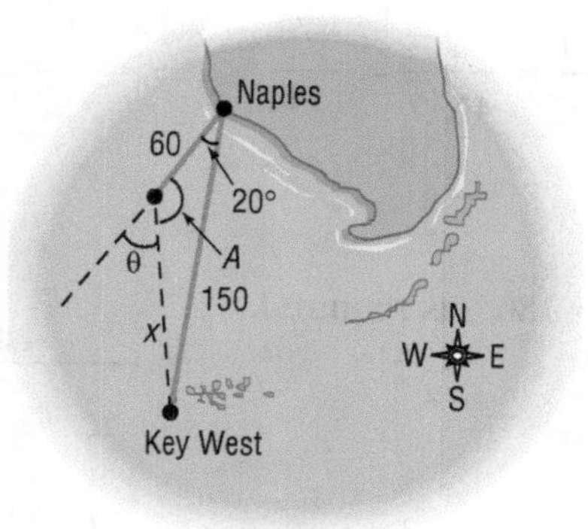

(a) To find x, we use the Law of Cosines, since we know two sides and the included angle.

$$x^2 = 150^2 + 60^2 - 2(150)(60)\cos 20^\circ \approx 9186.53$$

$$x \approx 95.8$$

The sailboat is about 96 miles from Key West.

(b) We now know three sides of the triangle, so we can use the Law of Cosines again to find the angle A opposite the side of length 150 miles.

$$150^2 = 96^2 + 60^2 - 2(96)(60)\cos A$$

$$9684 = -11{,}520 \cos A$$

$$\cos A \approx -0.8406$$

$$A \approx 147.2^\circ$$

The sailboat should turn through an angle of

$$\theta = 180^\circ - A \approx 180^\circ - 147.2^\circ = 32.8^\circ$$

The sailboat should turn through an angle of about 33° to correct its course.

(c) The total length of the trip is now $60 + 96 = 156$ miles. The extra 6 miles will only require about 0.4 hour or 24 minutes more if the speed of 15 miles per hour is maintained.

Now Work PROBLEM 45

Historical Feature

The Law of Sines was known vaguely long before it was explicitly stated by Nasir Eddin (about AD 1250). Ptolemy (about AD 150) was aware of it in a form using a chord function instead of the sine function. But it was first clearly stated in Europe by Regiomontanus, writing in 1464.

The Law of Cosines appears first in Euclid's *Elements* (Book II), but in a well-disguised form in which squares built on the sides of triangles are added and a rectangle representing the cosine term is subtracted. It was thus known to all mathematicians because of their familiarity with Euclid's work. An early modern form of the Law of Cosines, that for finding the angle when the sides are known, was stated by François Viète (in 1593).

The Law of Tangents (see Problem 61 of Exercise 8.2) has become obsolete. In the past it was used in place of the Law of Cosines, because the Law of Cosines was very inconvenient for calculation with logarithms or slide rules. Mixing of addition and multiplication is now very easy on a calculator, however, and the Law of Tangents has been shelved along with the slide rule.

8.3 Assess Your Understanding

'Are You Prepared?' *Answers are given at the end of these exercises. If you get a wrong answer, read the pages listed in red.*

1. Write the formula for the distance d from $P_1 = (x_1, y_1)$ to $P_2 = (x_2, y_2)$. (p. 5)

2. If θ is an acute angle, solve the equation $\cos\theta = \frac{\sqrt{2}}{2}$. (pp. 488–492)

Concepts and Vocabulary

3. If three sides of a triangle are given, the Law of ______ is used to solve the triangle.

4. If one side and two angles of a triangle are given, the Law of ______ is used to solve the triangle.

5. If two sides and the included angle of a triangle are given, the Law of ______ is used to solve the triangle.

6. ***True or False*** Given only the three sides of a triangle, there is insufficient information to solve the triangle.

7. ***True or False*** Given two sides and the included angle, the first thing to do to solve the triangle is to use the Law of Sines.

8. ***True or False*** A special case of the Law of Cosines is the Pythagorean Theorem.

Skill Building

In Problems 9–16, solve each triangle.

9.

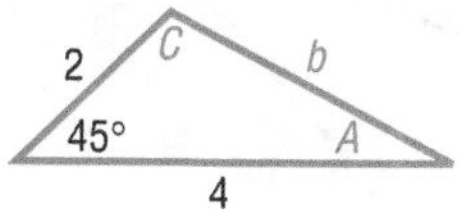

10.

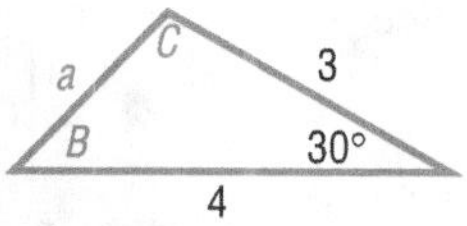

11.

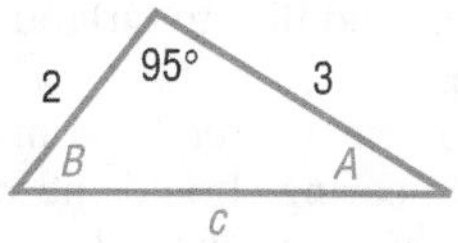

12.

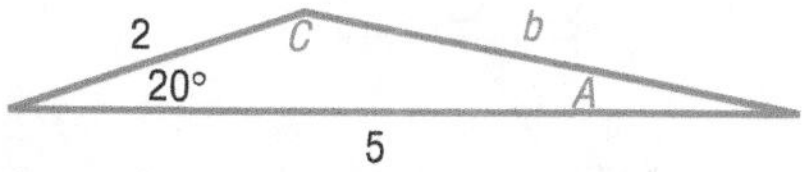

13.

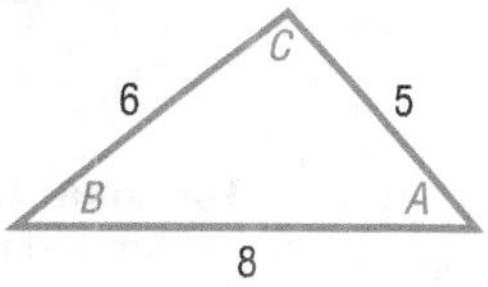

14.

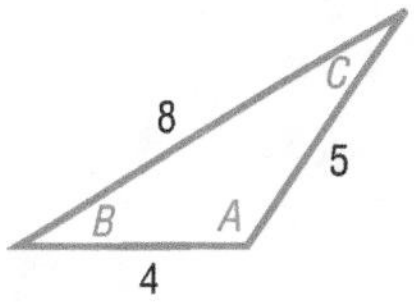

15.

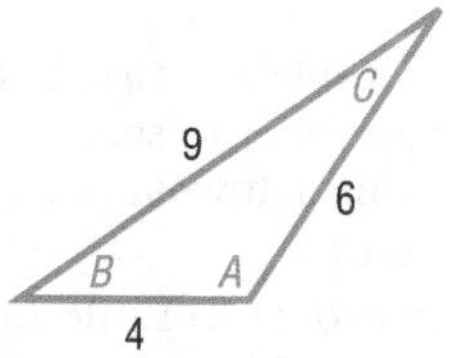

16.

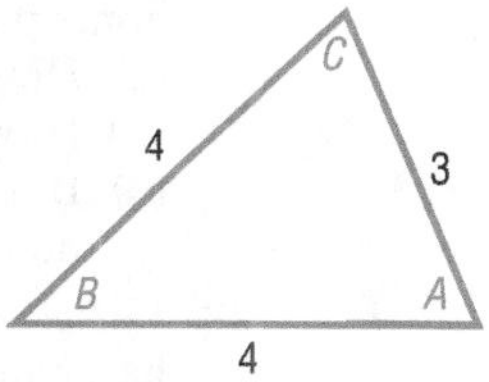

In Problems 17–32, solve each triangle.

17. $a = 3, \quad b = 4, \quad C = 40°$

18. $a = 2, \quad c = 1, \quad B = 10°$

19. $b = 1, \quad c = 3, \quad A = 80°$

20. $a = 6, \quad b = 4, \quad C = 60°$

21. $a = 3, \quad c = 2, \quad B = 110°$

22. $b = 4, \quad c = 1, \quad A = 120°$

23. $a = 2, \quad b = 2, \quad C = 50°$

24. $a = 3, \quad c = 2, \quad B = 90°$

25. $a = 12, \quad b = 13, \quad c = 5$

26. $a = 4, \quad b = 5, \quad c = 3$

27. $a = 2, \quad b = 2, \quad c = 2$

28. $a = 3, \quad b = 3, \quad c = 2$

29. $a = 5, \quad b = 8, \quad c = 9$

30. $a = 4, \quad b = 3, \quad c = 6$

31. $a = 10, \quad b = 8, \quad c = 5$

32. $a = 9, \quad b = 7, \quad c = 10$

Mixed Practice

In Problems 33–42, solve each triangle using either the Law of Sines or the Law of Cosines.

33. $B = 20°, \quad C = 75°, \quad b = 5$

34. $A = 50°, \quad B = 55°, \quad c = 9$

35. $a = 6, \quad b = 8, \quad c = 9$

36. $a = 14, \quad b = 7, \quad A = 85°$

37. $B = 35°, \quad C = 65°, \quad a = 15$

38. $a = 4, \quad c = 5, \quad B = 55°$

39. $A = 10°, \quad a = 3, \quad b = 10$

40. $A = 65°, \quad B = 72°, \quad b = 7$

41. $b = 5, \quad c = 12, \quad A = 60°$

42. $a = 10, \quad b = 10, \quad c = 15$

Applications and Extensions

43. **Distance to the Green** A golfer hits an errant tee shot that lands in the rough. A marker in the center of the fairway is 150 yards from the center of the green. While standing on the marker and facing the green, the golfer turns 110° toward his ball. He then paces off 35 yards to his ball. See the figure. How far is the ball from the center of the green?

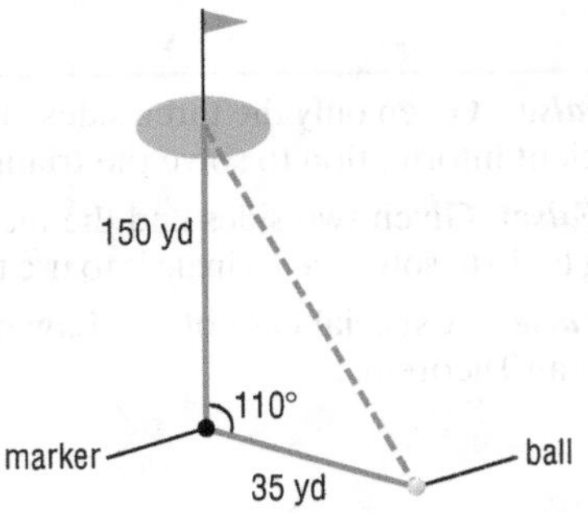

44. **Navigation** An airplane flies due north from Ft. Myers to Sarasota, a distance of 150 miles, and then turns through an angle of 50° and flies to Orlando, a distance of 100 miles. See the figure.
(a) How far is it directly from Ft. Myers to Orlando?
(b) What bearing should the pilot use to fly directly from Ft. Myers to Orlando?

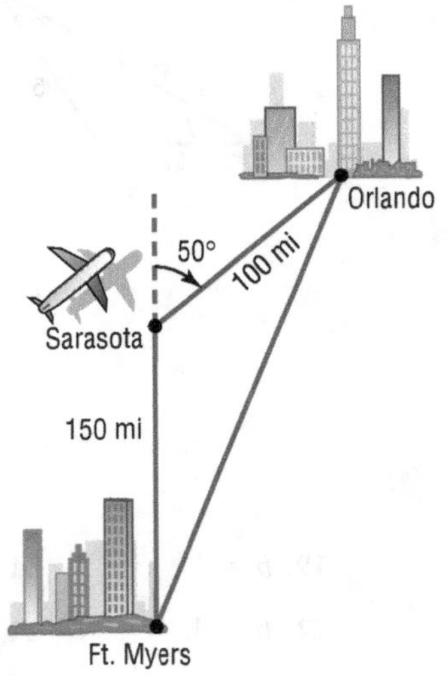

45. **Avoiding a Tropical Storm** A cruise ship maintains an average speed of 15 knots in going from San Juan, Puerto Rico, to Barbados, West Indies, a distance of 600 nautical miles. To avoid a tropical storm, the captain heads out of San Juan in a direction of 20° off a direct heading to Barbados. The captain maintains the 15-knot speed for 10 hours, after which time the path to Barbados becomes clear of storms.

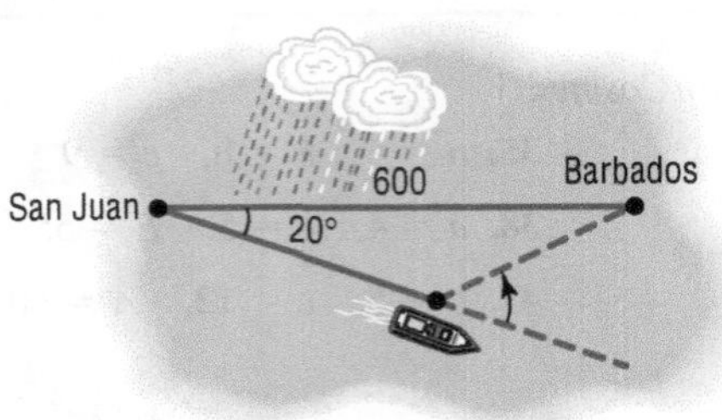

(a) Through what angle should the captain turn to head directly to Barbados?
(b) Once the turn is made, how long will it be before the ship reaches Barbados if the same 15-knot speed is maintained?

46. **Revising a Flight Plan** In attempting to fly from Chicago to Louisville, a distance of 330 miles, a pilot inadvertently took a course that was 10° in error, as indicated in the figure.
(a) If the aircraft maintains an average speed of 220 miles per hour and if the error in direction is discovered after 15 minutes, through what angle should the pilot turn to head toward Louisville?
(b) What new average speed should the pilot maintain so that the total time of the trip is 90 minutes?

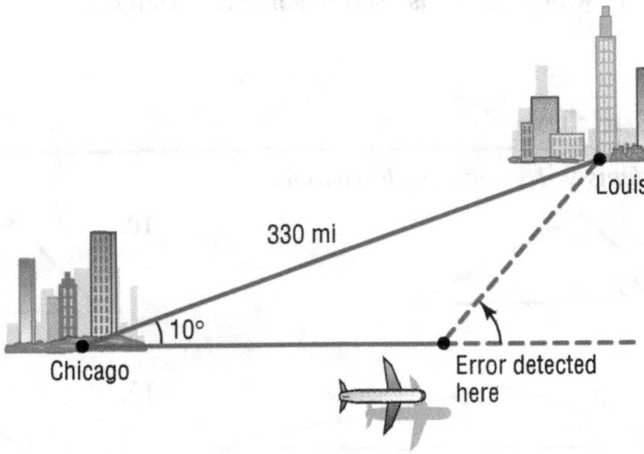

47. **Major League Baseball Field** A Major League baseball diamond is actually a square 90 feet on a side. The pitching rubber is located 60.5 feet from home plate on a line joining home plate and second base.
(a) How far is it from the pitching rubber to first base?
(b) How far is it from the pitching rubber to second base?
(c) If a pitcher faces home plate, through what angle does he need to turn to face first base?

48. **Little League Baseball Field** According to Little League baseball official regulations, the diamond is a square 60 feet on a side. The pitching rubber is located 46 feet from home plate on a line joining home plate and second base.
(a) How far is it from the pitching rubber to first base?
(b) How far is it from the pitching rubber to second base?
(c) If a pitcher faces home plate, through what angle does he need to turn to face first base?

49. **Finding the Length of a Guy Wire** The height of a radio tower is 500 feet, and the ground on one side of the tower slopes upward at an angle of 10° (see the figure).

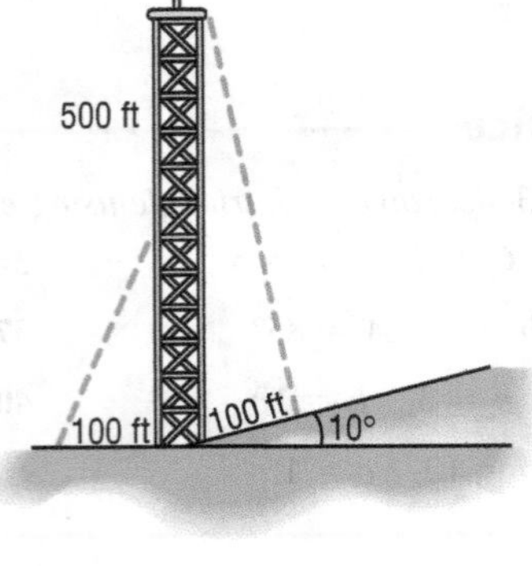

(a) How long should a guy wire be if it is to connect to the top of the tower and be secured at a point on the sloped side 100 feet from the base of the tower?

(b) How long should a second guy wire be if it is to connect to the middle of the tower and be secured at a point 100 feet from the base on the flat side?

50. Finding the Length of a Guy Wire A radio tower 500 feet high is located on the side of a hill with an inclination to the horizontal of 5°. See the figure. How long should two guy wires be if they are to connect to the top of the tower and be secured at two points 100 feet directly above and directly below the base of the tower?

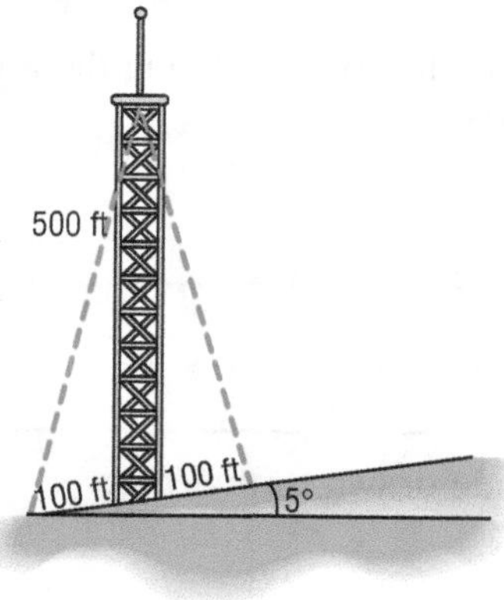

51. Wrigley Field, Home of the Chicago Cubs The distance from home plate to the fence in dead center in Wrigley Field is 400 feet (see the figure). How far is it from the fence in dead center to third base?

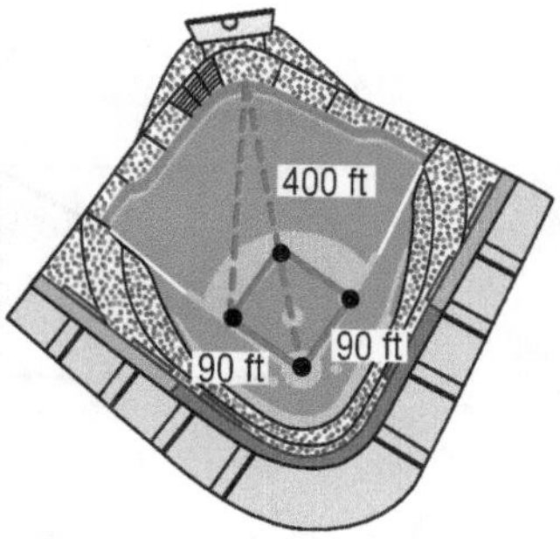

52. Little League Baseball The distance from home plate to the fence in dead center at the Oak Lawn Little League field is 280 feet. How far is it from the fence in dead center to third base?

[**Hint:** The distance between the bases in Little League is 60 feet.]

53. Building a Swing Set Clint is building a wooden swing set for his children. Each supporting end of the swing set is to be an A-frame constructed with two 10-foot-long 4 by 4s joined at a 45° angle. To prevent the swing set from tipping over, Clint wants to secure the base of each A-frame to concrete footings. How far apart should the footings for each A-frame be?

54. Rods and Pistons Rod OA rotates about the fixed point O so that point A travels on a circle of radius r. Connected to point A is another rod AB of length $L > 2r$, and point B is connected to a piston. See the figure. Show that the distance x between point O and point B is given by

$$x = r\cos\theta + \sqrt{r^2\cos^2\theta + L^2 - r^2}$$

where θ is the angle of rotation of rod OA.

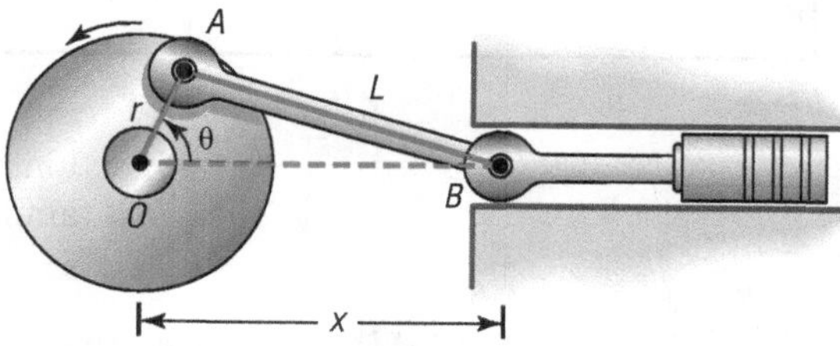

55. Geometry Show that the length d of a chord of a circle of radius r is given by the formula

$$d = 2r\sin\frac{\theta}{2}$$

where θ is the central angle formed by the radii to the ends of the chord. See the figure. Use this result to derive the fact that $\sin\theta < \theta$, where $\theta > 0$ is measured in radians.

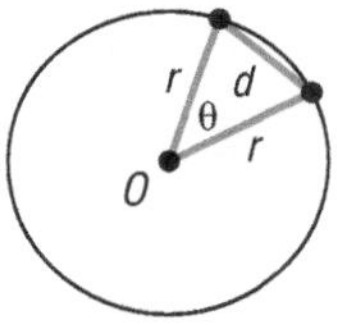

56. For any triangle, show that

$$\cos\frac{C}{2} = \sqrt{\frac{s(s-c)}{ab}}$$

where $s = \frac{1}{2}(a + b + c)$.

[**Hint:** Use a Half-angle Formula and the Law of Cosines.]

57. For any triangle show that

$$\sin\frac{C}{2} = \sqrt{\frac{(s-a)(s-b)}{ab}}$$

where $s = \frac{1}{2}(a + b + c)$.

58. Use the Law of Cosines to prove the identity

$$\frac{\cos A}{a} + \frac{\cos B}{b} + \frac{\cos C}{c} = \frac{a^2 + b^2 + c^2}{2abc}$$

Discussion and Writing

59. What do you do first if you are asked to solve a triangle and are given two sides and the included angle?

60. What do you do first if you are asked to solve a triangle and are given three sides?

61. Make up an applied problem that requires using the Law of Cosines.

62. Write down your strategy for solving an oblique triangle.

'Are You Prepared?' Answers

1. $d = \sqrt{(x_2 - x_1)^2 + (y_2 - y_1)^2}$ **2.** $\theta = 45°$

8.4 Area of a Triangle

PREPARING FOR THIS SECTION *Before getting started, review the following:*

- Geometry Essentials (Appendix A, Section A.2, pp. A15–A16)

Now Work the 'Are You Prepared?' problems on page 542.

OBJECTIVES
1 Find the Area of SAS Triangles (p. 540)
2 Find the Area of SSS Triangles (p. 541)

In this section, we will derive several formulas for calculating the area of a triangle. The most familiar of these is the following:

THEOREM The area K of a triangle is

$$K = \frac{1}{2}bh \qquad (1)$$

where b is the base and h is an altitude drawn to that base.

Proof The derivation of this formula is rather easy once a rectangle of base b and height h is constructed around the triangle. See Figures 39 and 40.

Triangles 1 and 2 in Figure 40 are equal in area, as are triangles 3 and 4. Consequently, the area of the triangle with base b and altitude h is exactly half the area of the rectangle, which is bh.

Figure 39

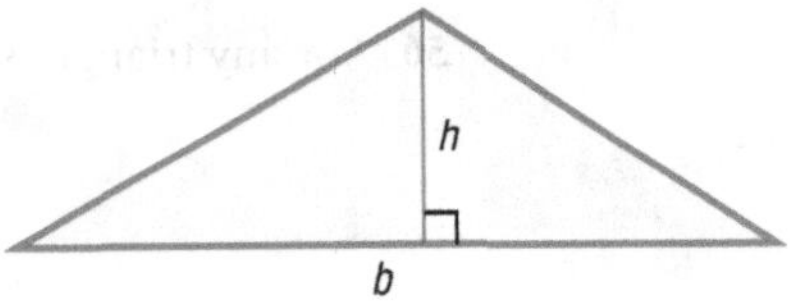

Figure 40

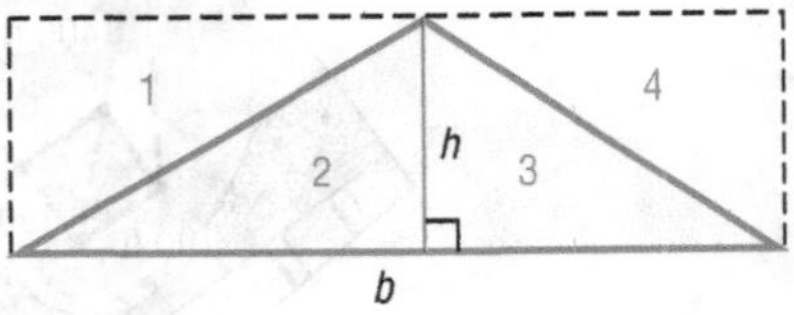

■

1 Find the Area of SAS Triangles

Figure 41

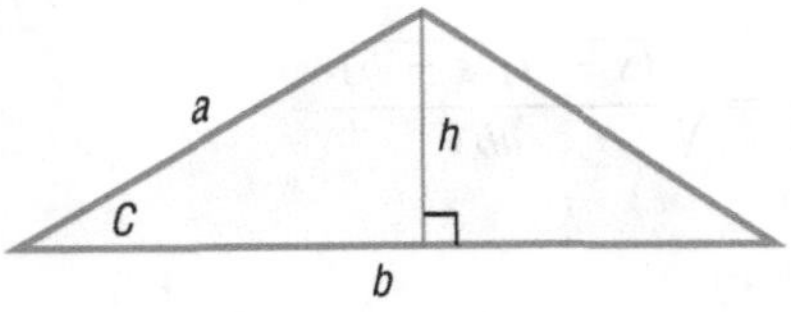

If the base b and altitude h to that base are known, then we can find the area of such a triangle using formula (1). Usually, though, the information required to use formula (1) is not given. Suppose, for example, that we know two sides a and b and the included angle C. See Figure 41. Then the altitude h can be found by noting that

$$\frac{h}{a} = \sin C$$

so that

$$h = a \sin C$$

Using this fact in formula (1) produces

$$K = \frac{1}{2}bh = \frac{1}{2}b(a \sin C) = \frac{1}{2}ab \sin C$$

We now have the formula

$$K = \frac{1}{2}ab \sin C \qquad (2)$$

By dropping altitudes from the other two vertices of the triangle, we obtain the following corresponding formulas:

$$K = \frac{1}{2}bc \sin A \quad (3)$$

$$K = \frac{1}{2}ac \sin B \quad (4)$$

It is easiest to remember these formulas using the following wording:

THEOREM The area K of a triangle equals one-half the product of two of its sides times the sine of their included angle.

EXAMPLE 1 **Finding the Area of an SAS Triangle**

Find the area K of the triangle for which $a = 8$, $b = 6$, and $C = 30°$.

Solution See Figure 42. We use formula (2) to get

Figure 42

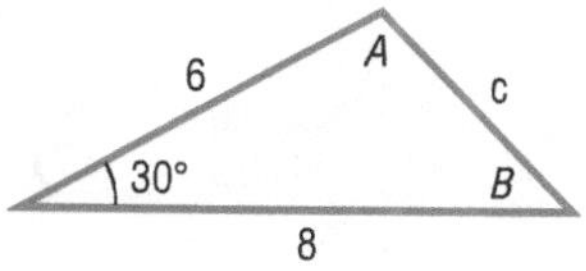

$$K = \frac{1}{2}ab \sin C = \frac{1}{2} \cdot 8 \cdot 6 \cdot \sin 30° = 12 \text{ square units}$$

Now Work PROBLEM 5

2 Find the Area of SSS Triangles

If the three sides of a triangle are known, another formula, called **Heron's Formula** (named after Heron of Alexandria), can be used to find the area of a triangle.

THEOREM **Heron's Formula**

The area K of a triangle with sides a, b, and c is

$$K = \sqrt{s(s-a)(s-b)(s-c)} \quad (5)$$

where $s = \frac{1}{2}(a + b + c)$.

A proof of Heron's Formula is given at the end of this section.

EXAMPLE 2 **Finding the Area of an SSS Triangle**

Find the area of a triangle whose sides are 4, 5, and 7.

Solution We let $a = 4$, $b = 5$, and $c = 7$. Then

$$s = \frac{1}{2}(a + b + c) = \frac{1}{2}(4 + 5 + 7) = 8$$

Heron's Formula then gives the area K as

$$K = \sqrt{s(s-a)(s-b)(s-c)} = \sqrt{8 \cdot 4 \cdot 3 \cdot 1} = \sqrt{96} = 4\sqrt{6} \text{ square units}$$

Now Work PROBLEM 11

Proof of Heron's Formula The proof that we shall give uses the Law of Cosines and is quite different from the proof given by Heron.

From the Law of Cosines,

$$c^2 = a^2 + b^2 - 2ab\cos C$$

and the Half-angle Formula

$$\cos^2\frac{C}{2} = \frac{1+\cos C}{2}$$

we find that

$$\begin{aligned}\cos^2\frac{C}{2} &= \frac{1+\cos C}{2} = \frac{1 + \dfrac{a^2+b^2-c^2}{2ab}}{2}\\ &= \frac{a^2+2ab+b^2-c^2}{4ab} = \frac{(a+b)^2-c^2}{4ab}\\ &= \frac{(a+b-c)(a+b+c)}{4ab} = \frac{2(s-c)\cdot 2s}{4ab} = \frac{s(s-c)}{ab}\end{aligned} \qquad \textbf{(6)}$$

↑ Factor ↑ $a+b-c = a+b+c-2c = 2s-2c = 2(s-c)$

Similarly, using $\sin^2\frac{C}{2} = \frac{1-\cos C}{2}$, we find that

$$\sin^2\frac{C}{2} = \frac{(s-a)(s-b)}{ab} \qquad \textbf{(7)}$$

Now we use formula (2) for the area.

$$\begin{aligned}K &= \frac{1}{2}ab\sin C\\ &= \frac{1}{2}ab\cdot 2\sin\frac{C}{2}\cos\frac{C}{2} && \sin C = \sin\left[2\left(\frac{C}{2}\right)\right] = 2\sin\frac{C}{2}\cos\frac{C}{2}\\ &= ab\sqrt{\frac{(s-a)(s-b)}{ab}}\sqrt{\frac{s(s-c)}{ab}} && \text{Use equations (6) and (7).}\\ &= \sqrt{s(s-a)(s-b)(s-c)}\end{aligned}$$

■

Historical Feature

Heron's Formula (also known as *Hero's Formula*) is due to Heron of Alexandria (first century AD), who had, besides his mathematical talents, a good deal of engineering skills. In various temples his mechanical devices produced effects that seemed supernatural, and visitors presumably were thus influenced to generosity. Heron's book *Metrica*, on making such devices, has survived and was discovered in 1896 in the city of Constantinople.

Heron's Formulas for the area of a triangle caused some mild discomfort in Greek mathematics, because a product with two factors was an area, while one with three factors was a volume, but four factors seemed contradictory in Heron's time.

8.4 Assess Your Understanding

'Are You Prepared?' *Answer is given at the end of these exercises. If you get the wrong answer, read the page listed in red.*

1. The area of a triangle whose base is b and whose height is h is _____ (p. A15)

Concepts and Vocabulary

2. If three sides of a triangle are given, _______ Formula is used to find the area of the triangle.

3. ***True or False*** No formula exists for finding the area of a triangle when only three sides are given.

4. ***True or False*** Given two sides and the included angle, there is a formula that can be used to find the area of the triangle.

Skill Building

In Problems 5–12, find the area of each triangle. Round answers to two decimal places.

5.
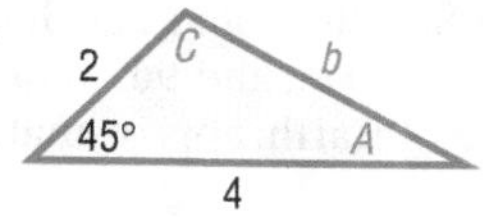

6.
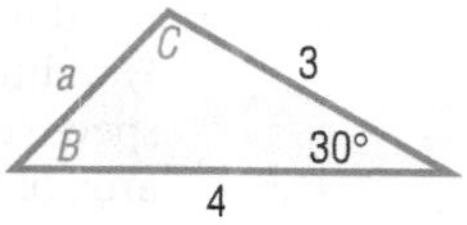

7.
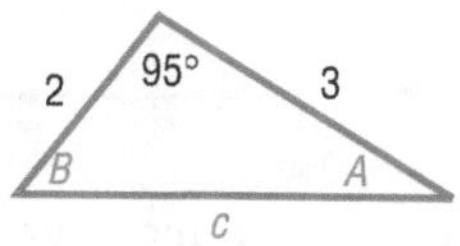

8.
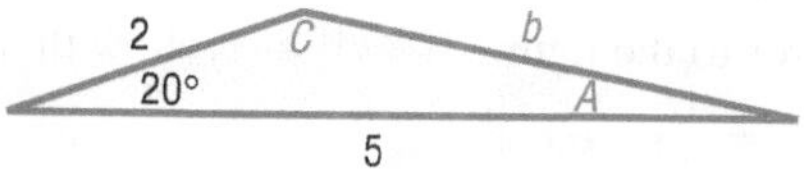

9.
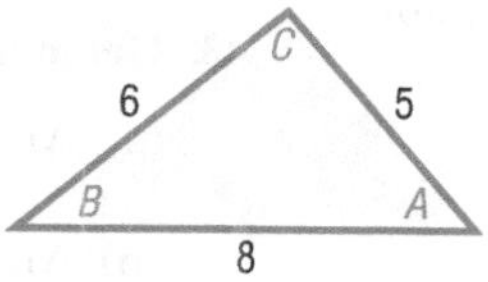

10.
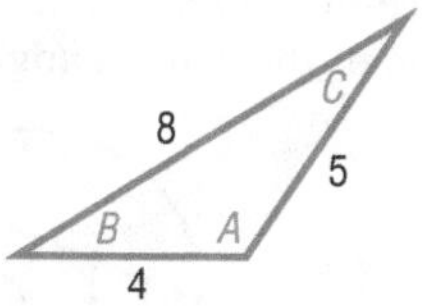

11.
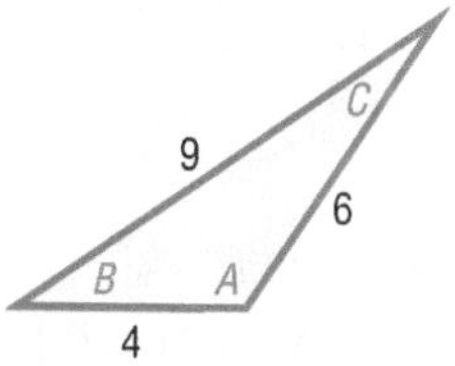

12.
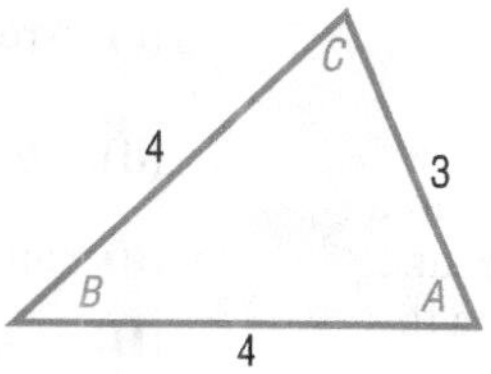

In Problems 13–24, find the area of each triangle. Round answers to two decimal places.

13. $a = 3, \quad b = 4, \quad C = 40°$

14. $a = 2, \quad c = 1, \quad B = 10°$

15. $b = 1, \quad c = 3, \quad A = 80°$

16. $a = 6, \quad b = 4, \quad C = 60°$

17. $a = 3, \quad c = 2, \quad B = 110°$

18. $b = 4, \quad c = 1, \quad A = 120°$

19. $a = 12, \quad b = 13, \quad c = 5$

20. $a = 4, \quad b = 5, \quad c = 3$

21. $a = 2, \quad b = 2, \quad c = 2$

22. $a = 3, \quad b = 3, \quad c = 2$

23. $a = 5, \quad b = 8, \quad c = 9$

24. $a = 4, \quad b = 3, \quad c = 6$

Applications and Extensions

25. Area of an ASA Triangle If two angles and the included side are given, the third angle is easy to find. Use the Law of Sines to show that the area K of a triangle with side a and angles A, B, and C is

$$K = \frac{a^2 \sin B \sin C}{2 \sin A}$$

26. Area of a Triangle Prove the two other forms of the formula given in Problem 25.

$$K = \frac{b^2 \sin A \sin C}{2 \sin B} \quad \text{and} \quad K = \frac{c^2 \sin A \sin B}{2 \sin C}$$

In Problems 27–32, use the results of Problem 25 or 26 to find the area of each triangle. Round answers to two decimal places.

27. $A = 40°, \quad B = 20°, \quad a = 2$

28. $A = 50°, \quad C = 20°, \quad a = 3$

29. $B = 70°, \quad C = 10°, \quad b = 5$

30. $A = 70°, \quad B = 60°, \quad c = 4$

31. $A = 110°, \quad C = 30°, \quad c = 3$

32. $B = 10°, \quad C = 100°, \quad b = 2$

33. Area of a Segment Find the area of the segment (shaded in blue in the figure) of a circle whose radius is 8 feet, formed by a central angle of 70°.

[**Hint:** Subtract the area of the triangle from the area of the sector to obtain the area of the segment.]

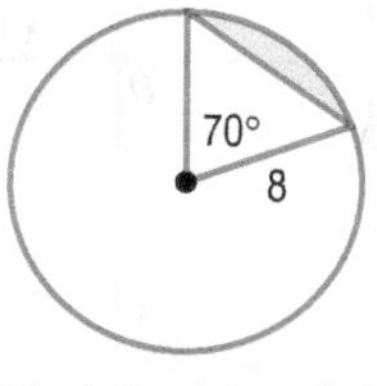

34. Area of a Segment Find the area of the segment of a circle whose radius is 5 inches, formed by a central angle of 40°.

35. Cost of a Triangular Lot The dimensions of a triangular lot are 100 feet by 50 feet by 75 feet. If the price of such land is $3 per square foot, how much does the lot cost?

36. Amount of Material to Make a Tent A cone-shaped tent is made from a circular piece of canvas 24 feet in diameter by removing a sector with central angle 100° and connecting the ends. What is the surface area of the tent?

37. Dimensions of Home Plate The dimensions of home plate at any major league baseball stadium are shown. Find the area of home plate.

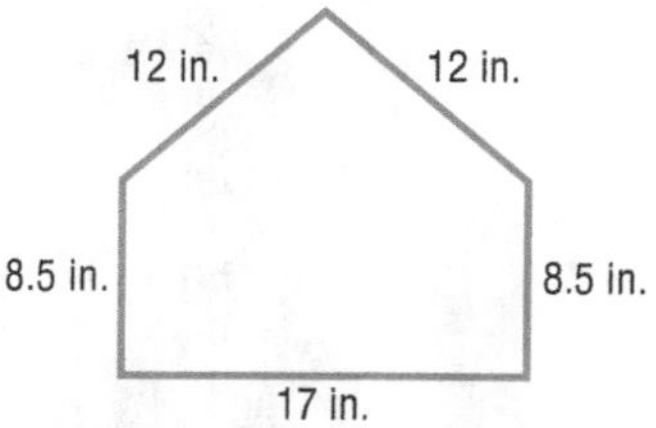

38. Computing Areas Find the area of the shaded region enclosed in a semicircle of diameter 10 inches. The length of the chord PQ is 8 inches.

[**Hint:** Triangle PQR is a right triangle.]

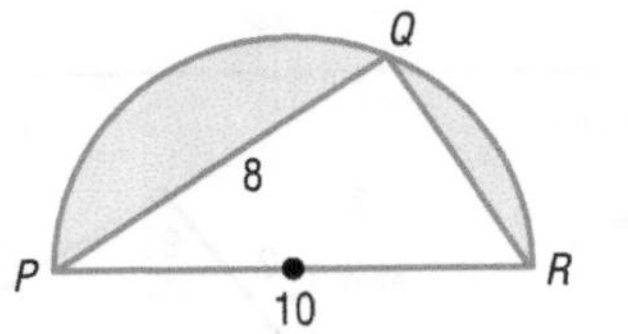

39. Geometry Consult the figure, which shows a circle of radius r with center at O. Find the area K of the shaded region as a function of the central angle θ.

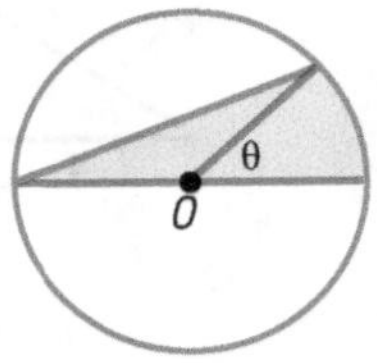

40. Approximating the Area of a Lake To approximate the area of a lake, a surveyor walks around the perimeter of the lake, taking the measurements shown in the illustration. Using this technique, what is the approximate area of the lake?

[**Hint:** Use the Law of Cosines on the three triangles shown and then find the sum of their areas.]

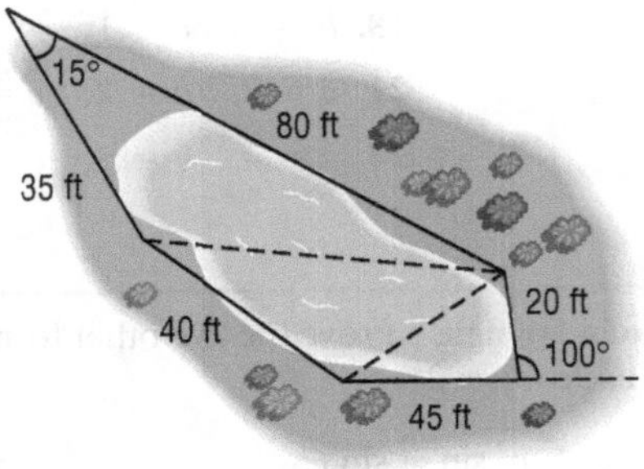

41. The Flatiron Building Completed in 1902 in New York City, the Flatiron Building is triangular shaped and bounded by 22nd Street, Broadway, and 5th Avenue. The building measures approximately 87 feet on the 22nd Street side, 190 feet on the Broadway side, and 173 feet on the 5th Avenue side. Approximate the ground area covered by the building.

Source: Sarah Bradford Landau and Carl W. Condit, *Rise of the New York Skyscraper: 1865–1913*. New Haven, CT: Yale University Press, 1996

42. Bermuda Triangle The Bermuda Triangle is roughly defined by Hamilton, Bermuda; San Juan, Puerto Rico; and Fort Lauderdale, Florida. The distances from Hamilton to Fort Lauderdale, Fort Lauderdale to San Juan, and San Juan to Hamilton are approximately 1028, 1046, and 965 miles respectively. Ignoring the curvature of Earth, approximate the area of the Bermuda Triangle.

Source: www.worldatlas.com

43. Geometry Refer to the figure. If $|OA| = 1$, show that:

(a) Area $\Delta OAC = \frac{1}{2}\sin\alpha\cos\alpha$

(b) Area $\Delta OCB = \frac{1}{2}|OB|^2\sin\beta\cos\beta$

(c) Area $\Delta OAB = \frac{1}{2}|OB|\sin(\alpha+\beta)$

(d) $|OB| = \dfrac{\cos\alpha}{\cos\beta}$

(e) $\sin(\alpha+\beta) = \sin\alpha\cos\beta + \cos\alpha\sin\beta$

[**Hint:** Area ΔOAB = Area ΔOAC + Area ΔOCB.]

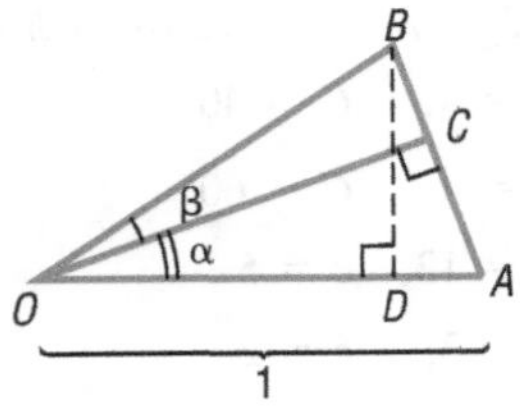

44. Geometry Refer to the figure, in which a unit circle is drawn. The line segment DB is tangent to the circle and θ is acute.

(a) Express the area of ΔOBC in terms of $\sin\theta$ and $\cos\theta$.

(b) Express the area of ΔOBD in terms of $\sin\theta$ and $\cos\theta$.

(c) The area of the sector $\overset{\frown}{OBC}$ of the circle is $\frac{1}{2}\theta$, where θ is measured in radians. Use the results of parts (a) and (b) and the fact that

$$\text{Area } \Delta OBC < \text{Area } \overset{\frown}{OBC} < \text{Area } \Delta OBD$$

to show that

$$1 < \frac{\theta}{\sin\theta} < \frac{1}{\cos\theta}$$

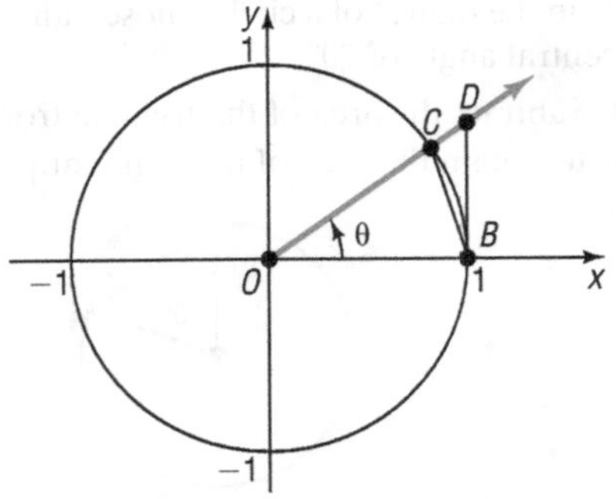

45. The Cow Problem* A cow is tethered to one corner of a square barn, 10 feet by 10 feet, with a rope 100 feet long. What is the maximum grazing area for the cow?

[**Hint:** See the illustration on page 545.]

*Suggested by Professor Teddy Koukounas of Suffolk Community College, who learned of it from an old farmer in Virginia. Solution provided by Professor Kathleen Miranda of SUNY at Old Westbury.

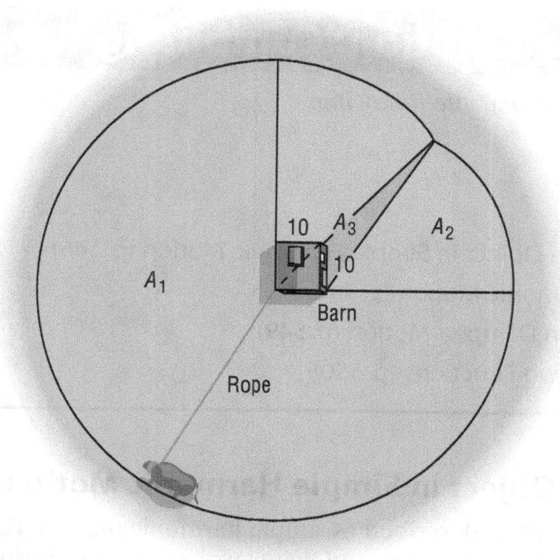

46. Another Cow Problem If the barn in Problem 45 is rectangular, 10 feet by 20 feet, what is the maximum grazing area for the cow?

47. Perfect Triangles A *perfect triangle* is one having natural number sides for which the area is numerically equal to the perimeter. Show that the triangles with the given side lengths are perfect.

(a) 9, 10, 17 (b) 6, 25, 29

Source: M.V. Bonsangue, G. E. Gannon, E. Buchman, and N. Gross, "In Search of Perfect Triangles," *Mathematics Teacher,* Vol. 92, No. 1, 1999: 56–61

48. If h_1, h_2, and h_3 are the altitudes dropped from P, Q, and R, respectively, in a triangle (see the figure), show that

$$\frac{1}{h_1} + \frac{1}{h_2} + \frac{1}{h_3} = \frac{s}{K}$$

where K is the area of the triangle and $s = \frac{1}{2}(a + b + c)$. [**Hint:** $h_1 = \frac{2K}{a}$.]

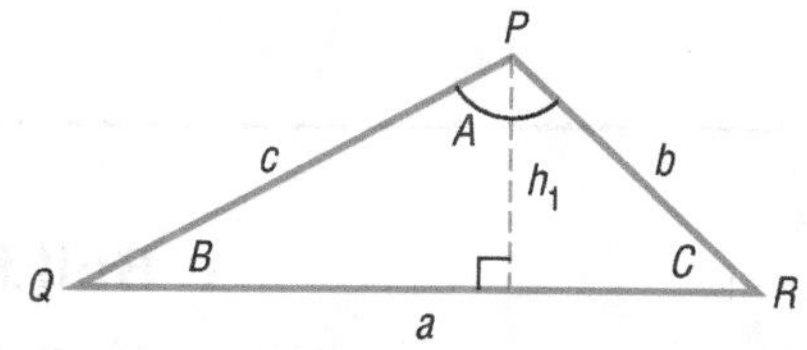

49. Show that a formula for the altitude h from a vertex to the opposite side a of a triangle is

$$h = \frac{a \sin B \sin C}{\sin A}$$

Inscribed Circle *For Problems 50–53, the lines that bisect each angle of a triangle meet in a single point O, and the perpendicular distance r from O to each side of the triangle is the same. The circle with center at O and radius r is called the* **inscribed circle** *of the triangle (see the figure).*

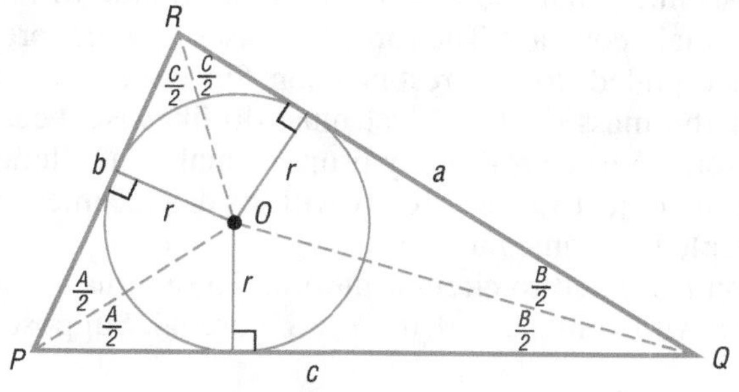

50. Apply the formula from Problem 49 to triangle OPQ to show that

$$r = \frac{c \sin \frac{A}{2} \sin \frac{B}{2}}{\cos \frac{C}{2}}$$

51. Use the result of Problem 50 and the result of Problems 56 and 57 in Section 8.3 to show that

$$\cot \frac{C}{2} = \frac{s - c}{r}$$

where $s = \frac{1}{2}(a + b + c)$.

52. Show that

$$\cot \frac{A}{2} + \cot \frac{B}{2} + \cot \frac{C}{2} = \frac{s}{r}$$

53. Show that the area K of triangle PQR is $K = rs$, where $s = \frac{1}{2}(a + b + c)$. Then show that

$$r = \sqrt{\frac{(s - a)(s - b)(s - c)}{s}}$$

Discussion and Writing

54. What do you do first if you are asked to find the area of a triangle and are given two sides and the included angle?

55. What do you do first if you are asked to find the area of a triangle and are given three sides?

'Are You Prepared?' Answer

1. $K = \frac{1}{2}bh$

8.5 Simple Harmonic Motion; Damped Motion; Combining Waves

PREPARING FOR THIS SECTION *Before getting started, review the following:*

- Sinusoidal Graphs (Section 6.4, pp. 399–406)

Now Work the 'Are You Prepared?' problem on page 552.

OBJECTIVES
1. Build a Model for an Object in Simple Harmonic Motion (p. 546)
2. Analyze Simple Harmonic Motion (p. 548)
3. Analyze an Object in Damped Motion (p. 549)
4. Graph the Sum of Two Functions (p. 550)

1 Build a Model for an Object in Simple Harmonic Motion

Many physical phenomena can be described as simple harmonic motion. Radio and television waves, light waves, sound waves, and water waves exhibit motion that is simple harmonic.

Vibrating tuning fork

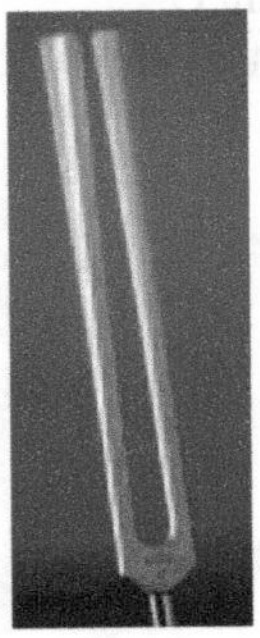

The swinging of a pendulum, the vibrations of a tuning fork, and the bobbing of a weight attached to a coiled spring are examples of vibrational motion. In this type of motion, an object swings back and forth over the same path. In Figure 43, the point B is the **equilibrium (rest) position** of the vibrating object. The **amplitude** is the distance from the object's rest position to its point of greatest displacement (either point A or point C in Figure 43). The **period** is the time required to complete one vibration, that is, the time it takes to go from, say, point A through B to C and back to A.

> **Simple harmonic motion** is a special kind of vibrational motion in which the acceleration a of the object is directly proportional to the negative of its displacement d from its rest position. That is, $a = -kd, k > 0$.

For example, when the mass hanging from the spring in Figure 43 is pulled down from its rest position B to the point C, the force of the spring tries to restore the mass to its rest position. Assuming that there is no frictional force* to retard the motion, the amplitude will remain constant. The force increases in direct proportion to the distance that the mass is pulled from its rest position. Since the force increases directly, the acceleration of the mass of the object must do likewise, because (by Newton's Second Law of Motion) force is directly proportional to acceleration. As a result, the acceleration of the object varies directly with its displacement, and the motion is an example of simple harmonic motion.

Figure 43

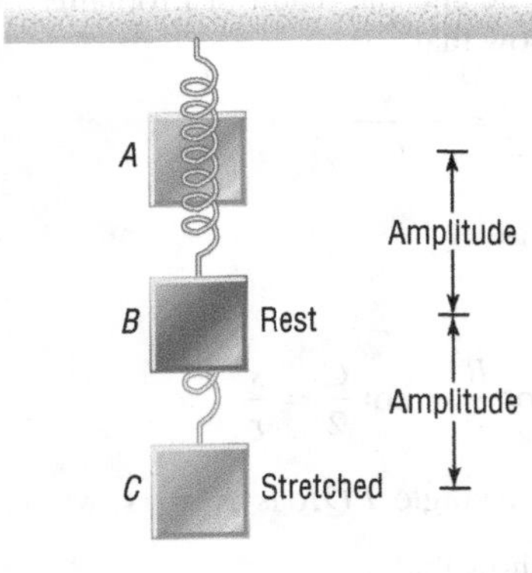

Coiled spring

Simple harmonic motion is related to circular motion. To see this relationship, consider a circle of radius a, with center at $(0, 0)$. See Figure 44. Suppose that an

Figure 44

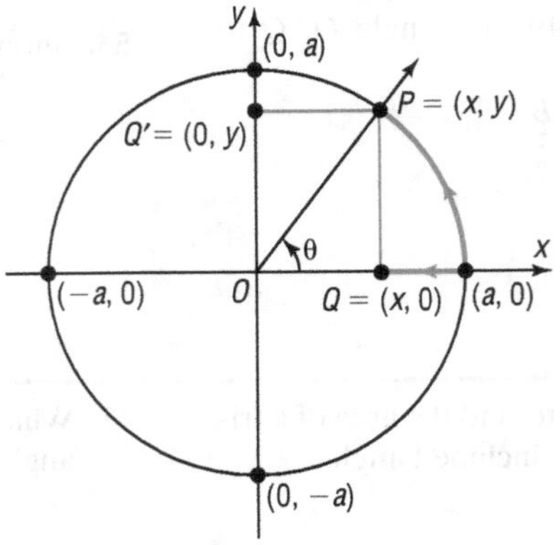

*If friction is present, the amplitude will decrease with time to 0. This type of motion is an example of **damped motion,** which is discussed later in this section.

object initially placed at $(a, 0)$ moves counterclockwise around the circle at a constant angular speed ω. Suppose further that after time t has elapsed the object is at the point $P = (x, y)$ on the circle. The angle θ, in radians, swept out by the ray $\overrightarrow{OP}$ in this time t is

$$\theta = \omega t$$

The coordinates of the point P at time t are

$$x = a\cos\theta = a\cos(\omega t)$$
$$y = a\sin\theta = a\sin(\omega t)$$

Corresponding to each position $P = (x, y)$ of the object moving about the circle, there is the point $Q = (x, 0)$, called the **projection of P on the x-axis.** As P moves around the circle at a constant rate, the point Q moves back and forth between the points $(a, 0)$ and $(-a, 0)$ along the x-axis with a motion that is simple harmonic. Similarly, for each point P there is a point $Q' = (0, y)$, called the **projection of P on the y-axis.** As P moves around the circle, the point Q' moves back and forth between the points $(0, a)$ and $(0, -a)$ on the y-axis with a motion that is simple harmonic. Simple harmonic motion can be described as the projection of constant circular motion on a coordinate axis.

To put it another way, again consider a mass hanging from a spring where the mass is pulled down from its rest position to the point C and then released. See Figure 45(a). The graph shown in Figure 45(b) describes the displacement d of the object from its rest position as a function of time t, assuming that no frictional force is present.

Figure 45

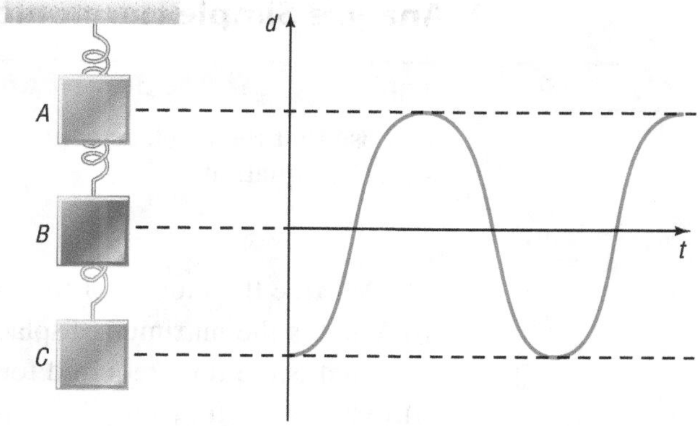

THEOREM

Simple Harmonic Motion

An object that moves on a coordinate axis so that the distance d from its rest position at time t is given by either

$$d = a\cos(\omega t) \quad \text{or} \quad d = a\sin(\omega t)$$

where a and $\omega > 0$ are constants, moves with simple harmonic motion. The motion has amplitude $|a|$ and period $\frac{2\pi}{\omega}$.

The **frequency** f of an object in simple harmonic motion is the number of oscillations per unit time. Since the period is the time required for one oscillation, it follows that the frequency is the reciprocal of the period; that is,

$$f = \frac{\omega}{2\pi} \qquad \omega > 0$$

EXAMPLE 1 **Build a Model for an Object in Harmonic Motion**

Suppose that an object attached to a coiled spring is pulled down a distance of 5 inches from its rest position and then released. If the time for one oscillation is 3 seconds, develop a model that relates the displacement d of the object from its rest position after time t (in seconds). Assume no friction.

Figure 46

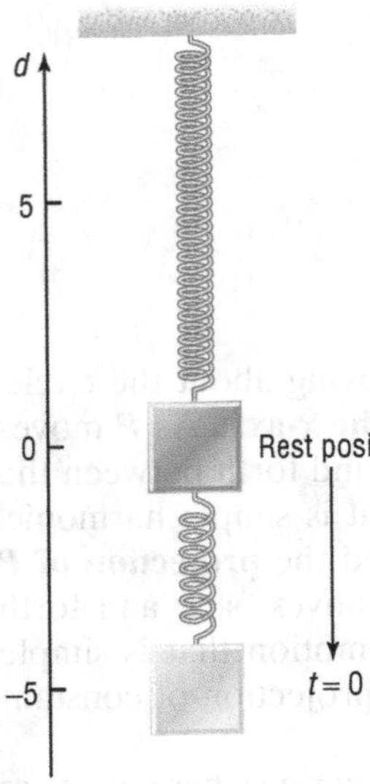

Solution The motion of the object is simple harmonic. See Figure 46. When the object is released ($t = 0$), the displacement of the object from the rest position is -5 units (since the object was pulled down). Because $d = -5$ when $t = 0$, it is easier to use the cosine function*

$$d = a\cos(\omega t)$$

to describe the motion. Now the amplitude is $|-5| = 5$ and the period is 3, so

$$a = -5 \quad \text{and} \quad \frac{2\pi}{\omega} = \text{period} = 3, \quad \omega = \frac{2\pi}{3}$$

An equation that models the motion of the object is

$$d = -5\cos\left[\frac{2\pi}{3}t\right]$$

NOTE In the solution to Example 1, we let $a = -5$, since the initial motion is down. If the initial direction were up, we would let $a = 5$.

Now Work PROBLEM 5

2 Analyze Simple Harmonic Motion

EXAMPLE 2 **Analyzing the Motion of an Object**

Suppose that the displacement d (in meters) of an object at time t (in seconds) satisfies the equation

$$d = 10\sin(5t)$$

(a) Describe the motion of the object.
(b) What is the maximum displacement from its resting position?
(c) What is the time required for one oscillation?
(d) What is the frequency?

Solution We observe that the given equation is of the form

$$d = a\sin(\omega t) \qquad d = 10\sin(5t)$$

where $a = 10$ and $\omega = 5$.

(a) The motion is simple harmonic.
(b) The maximum displacement of the object from its resting position is the amplitude: $|a| = 10$ meters.
(c) The time required for one oscillation is the period:

$$\text{Period} = \frac{2\pi}{\omega} = \frac{2\pi}{5} \text{ seconds}$$

(d) The frequency is the reciprocal of the period. Thus,

$$\text{Frequency} = f = \frac{5}{2\pi} \text{ oscillations per second}$$

Now Work PROBLEM 13

*No phase shift is required if a cosine function is used.

3 Analyze an Object in Damped Motion

Most physical phenomena are affected by friction or other resistive forces. These forces remove energy from a moving system and thereby damp its motion. For example, when a mass hanging from a spring is pulled down a distance a and released, the friction in the spring causes the distance that the mass moves from its at-rest position to decrease over time. As a result, the amplitude of any real oscillating spring or swinging pendulum decreases with time due to air resistance, friction, and so forth. See Figure 47.

Figure 47

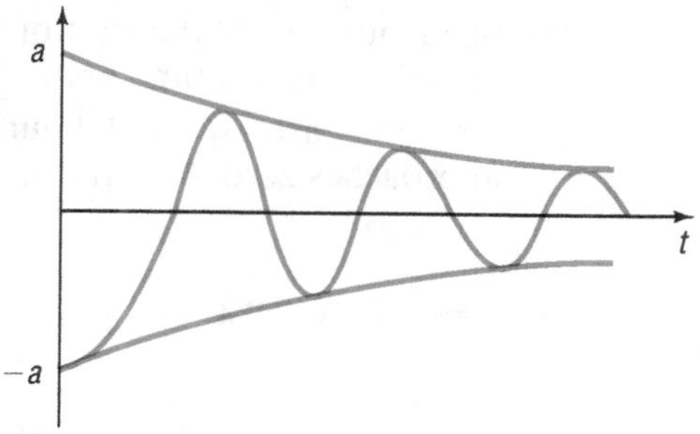

A model that describes this phenomenon maintains a sinusoidal component, but the amplitude of this component will decrease with time to account for the damping effect. In addition, the period of the oscillating component will be affected by the damping. The next result, from physics, describes damped motion.

THEOREM

Damped Motion

The displacement d of an oscillating object from its at-rest position at time t is given by

$$d(t) = ae^{-bt/(2m)} \cos\left(\sqrt{\omega^2 - \frac{b^2}{4m^2}}\, t\right)$$

where b is the **damping factor** or **damping coefficient** and m is the mass of the oscillating object. Here $|a|$ is the displacement at $t = 0$, and $\frac{2\pi}{\omega}$ is the period under simple harmonic motion (no damping).

Notice for $b = 0$ (zero damping) that we have the formula for simple harmonic motion with amplitude $|a|$ and period $\frac{2\pi}{\omega}$.

EXAMPLE 3 Analyzing the Motion of a Pendulum with Damped Motion

Figure 48

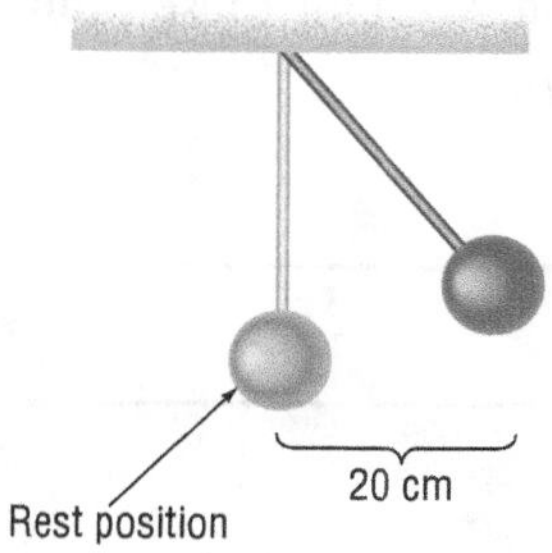

Suppose that a simple pendulum with a bob of mass 10 grams and a damping factor of 0.8 gram/second is pulled 20 centimeters from its at-rest position and released. See Figure 48. The period of the pendulum without the damping effect is 4 seconds.

(a) Develop a model that describes the position of the pendulum bob.

(b) Using a graphing utility, graph the function found in part (a).

(c) What is the displacement of the bob at the start of the second oscillation?

(d) What happens to the displacement of the bob as time increases without bound?

Solution

(a) We have $m = 10$, $a = 20$, and $b = 0.8$. Since the period of the pendulum under simple harmonic motion is 4 seconds, we have

$$4 = \frac{2\pi}{\omega}$$

$$\omega = \frac{2\pi}{4} = \frac{\pi}{2}$$

Figure 49

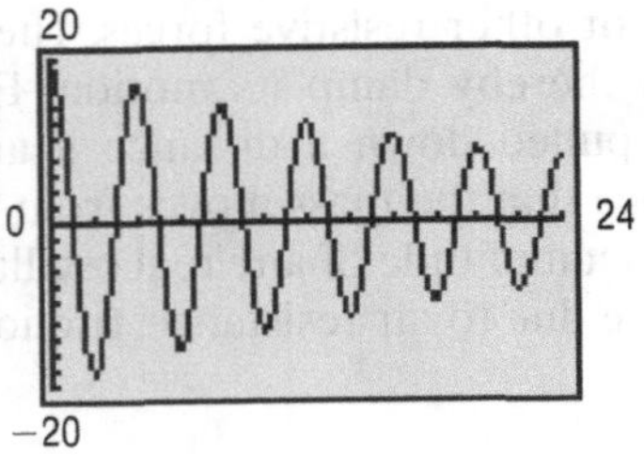

Figure 50

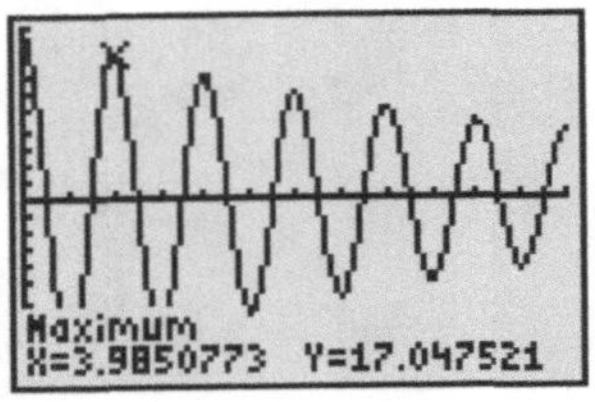

Substituting these values into the equation for damped motion, we obtain

$$d(t) = 20e^{-0.8t/2(10)} \cos\left(\sqrt{\left(\frac{\pi}{2}\right)^2 - \frac{0.8^2}{4(10)^2}}\, t\right)$$

$$= 20e^{-0.8t/20} \cos\left(\sqrt{\frac{\pi^2}{4} - \frac{0.64}{400}}\, t\right)$$

(b) See Figure 49 for the graph of $d = d(t)$.

(c) See Figure 50. At the start of the second oscillation the displacement is approximately 17.05 centimeters.

(d) As t increases without bound, $e^{-0.8t/20} \to 0$, so the displacement of the bob approaches zero. As a result, the pendulum will eventually come to rest.

Now Work PROBLEM 21

4 Graph the Sum of Two Functions

Many physical and biological applications require the graph of the sum of two functions, such as

$$f(x) = x + \sin x \quad \text{or} \quad g(x) = \sin x + \cos(2x)$$

For example, if two tones are emitted, the sound produced is the sum of the waves produced by the two tones. See Problem 47 for an explanation of Touch-Tone phones.

To graph the sum of two (or more) functions, we can use the method of adding y-coordinates described next.

EXAMPLE 4 Graphing the Sum of Two Functions

Use the method of adding y-coordinates to graph $f(x) = x + \sin x$.

Solution First, we graph the component functions,

$$y = f_1(x) = x \qquad y = f_2(x) = \sin x$$

in the same coordinate system. See Figure 51(a). Now, select several values of x, say, $x = 0$, $x = \frac{\pi}{2}$, $x = \pi$, $x = \frac{3\pi}{2}$, and $x = 2\pi$, at which we compute $f(x) = f_1(x) + f_2(x)$. Table 1 shows the computation. We plot these points and connect them to get the graph, as shown in Figure 51(b).

Table 1

x	0	$\frac{\pi}{2}$	π	$\frac{3\pi}{2}$	2π
$y = f_1(x) = x$	0	$\frac{\pi}{2}$	π	$\frac{3\pi}{2}$	2π
$y = f_2(x) = \sin x$	0	1	0	−1	0
$f(x) = x + \sin x$	0	$\frac{\pi}{2} + 1 \approx 2.57$	π	$\frac{3\pi}{2} - 1 \approx 3.71$	2π
Point on graph of f	(0, 0)	$\left(\frac{\pi}{2}, 2.57\right)$	(π, π)	$\left(\frac{3\pi}{2}, 3.71\right)$	$(2\pi, 2\pi)$

Figure 51

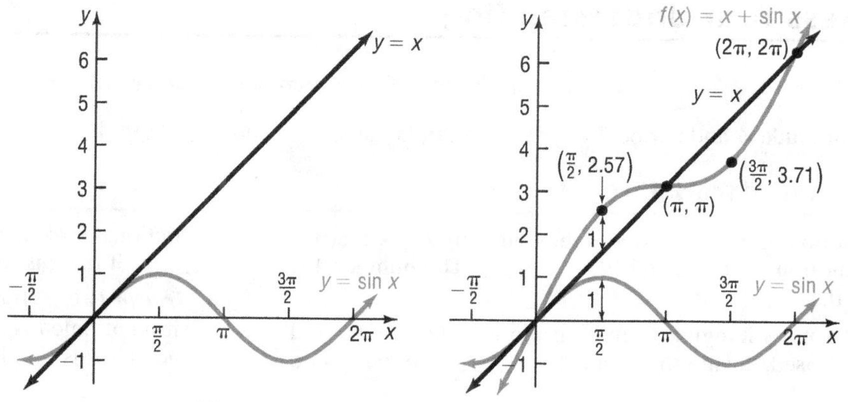

(a) (b)

In Figure 51(b), notice that the graph of $f(x) = x + \sin x$ intersects the line $y = x$ whenever $\sin x = 0$. Also, notice that the graph of f is not periodic.

Check: Graph $Y_1 = x$, $Y_2 = \sin x$, and $Y_3 = x + \sin x$ and compare the result with Figure 51(b). Use INTERSECT to verify that the graphs of Y_1 and Y_3 intersect when $\sin x = 0$.

The next example shows a periodic graph.

EXAMPLE 5 Graphing the Sum of Two Sinusoidal Functions

Use the method of adding y-coordinates to graph

$$f(x) = \sin x + \cos(2x)$$

Solution Table 2 shows the steps for computing several points on the graph of f. Figure 52 illustrates the graphs of the component functions, $y = f_1(x) = \sin x$ and $y = f_2(x) = \cos(2x)$, and the graph of $f(x) = \sin x + \cos(2x)$, which is shown in red.

Table 2

x	$-\frac{\pi}{2}$	0	$\frac{\pi}{2}$	π	$\frac{3\pi}{2}$	2π
$y = f_1(x) = \sin x$	−1	0	1	0	−1	0
$y = f_2(x) = \cos(2x)$	−1	1	−1	1	−1	1
$f(x) = \sin x + \cos(2x)$	−2	1	0	1	−2	1
Point on graph of f	$\left(-\frac{\pi}{2}, -2\right)$	(0, 1)	$\left(\frac{\pi}{2}, 0\right)$	$(\pi, 1)$	$\left(\frac{3\pi}{2}, -2\right)$	$(2\pi, 1)$

Figure 52

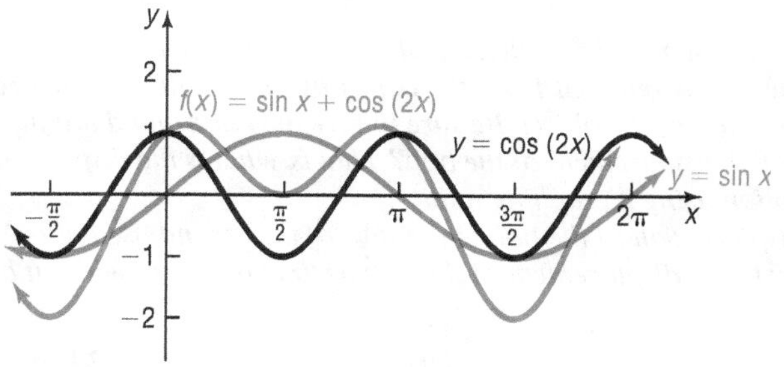

Notice that f is periodic, with period 2π.

Check: Graph $Y_1 = \sin x$, $Y_2 = \cos(2x)$, and $Y_3 = \sin x + \cos(2x)$ and compare the result with Figure 52.

Now Work PROBLEM 33

8.5 Assess Your Understanding

'Are You Prepared?' *Answer given at the end of these exercises. If you get a wrong answer, read the pages listed in red.*

1. The amplitude A and period T of $f(x) = 5\sin(4x)$ are _____ and _____. (pp. 400–401)

Concepts and Vocabulary

2. The motion of an object obeys the equation $d = 4\cos(6t)$. Such motion is described as _____ _____. The number 4 is called the _____.

3. When a mass hanging from a spring is pulled down and then released, the motion is called _____ _____ if there is no frictional force to retard the motion, and the motion is called _____ if there is friction.

4. ***True or False*** If the distance d of an object from its rest position at time t is given by a sinusoidal graph, the motion of the object is simple harmonic motion.

Skill Building

In Problems 5–8, an object attached to a coiled spring is pulled down a distance a from its rest position and then released. Assuming that the motion is simple harmonic with period T, develop a model that relates the displacement d of the object from its rest position after t seconds. Also assume that the positive direction of the motion is up.

5. $a = 5$; $T = 2$ seconds

6. $a = 10$; $T = 3$ seconds

7. $a = 6$; $T = \pi$ seconds

8. $a = 4$; $T = \frac{\pi}{2}$ seconds

9. Rework Problem 5 under the same conditions except that, at time $t = 0$, the object is at its resting position and moving down.

10. Rework Problem 6 under the same conditions except that, at time $t = 0$, the object is at its resting position and moving down.

11. Rework Problem 7 under the same conditions except that, at time $t = 0$, the object is at its resting position and moving down.

12. Rework Problem 8 under the same conditions except that, at time $t = 0$, the object is at its resting position and moving down.

In Problems 13–20, the displacement d (in meters) of an object at time t (in seconds) is given.
(a) Describe the motion of the object.
(b) What is the maximum displacement from its resting position?
(c) What is the time required for one oscillation?
(d) What is the frequency?

13. $d = 5\sin(3t)$

14. $d = 4\sin(2t)$

15. $d = 6\cos(\pi t)$

16. $d = 5\cos\left(\frac{\pi}{2}t\right)$

17. $d = -3\sin\left(\frac{1}{2}t\right)$

18. $d = -2\cos(2t)$

19. $d = 6 + 2\cos(2\pi t)$

20. $d = 4 + 3\sin(\pi t)$

In Problems 21–26, an object of mass m (in grams) attached to a coiled spring with damping factor b (in grams per second) is pulled down a distance a (in centimeters) from its rest position and then released. Assume that the positive direction of the motion is up and the period is T (in seconds) under simple harmonic motion.
(a) Develop a model that relates the distance d of the object from its rest position after t seconds.
(b) Graph the equation found in part (a) for 5 oscillations using a graphing utility.

21. $m = 25$, $a = 10$, $b = 0.7$, $T = 5$

22. $m = 20$, $a = 15$, $b = 0.75$, $T = 6$

23. $m = 30$, $a = 18$, $b = 0.6$, $T = 4$

24. $m = 15$, $a = 16$, $b = 0.65$, $T = 5$

25. $m = 10$, $a = 5$, $b = 0.8$, $T = 3$

26. $m = 10$, $a = 5$, $b = 0.7$, $T = 3$

In Problems 27–32, the distance d (in meters) of the bob of a pendulum of mass m (in kilograms) from its rest position at time t (in seconds) is given. The bob is released from the left of its rest position, which represents a negative direction.
(a) Describe the motion of the object. Be sure to give the mass and damping factor.
(b) What is the initial displacement of the bob? That is, what is the displacement at t = 0?
(c) Graph the motion using a graphing utility.
(d) What is the displacement of the bob at the start of the second oscillation?
(e) What happens to the displacement of the bob as time increases without bound?

27. $d = -20e^{-0.7t/40}\cos\left(\sqrt{\left(\frac{2\pi}{5}\right)^2 - \frac{0.49}{1600}}\,t\right)$

28. $d = -20e^{-0.8t/40}\cos\left(\sqrt{\left(\frac{2\pi}{5}\right)^2 - \frac{0.64}{1600}}\,t\right)$

29. $d = -30e^{-0.6t/80}\cos\left(\sqrt{\left(\frac{2\pi}{7}\right)^2 - \frac{0.36}{6400}}\,t\right)$

30. $d = -30e^{-0.5t/70}\cos\left(\sqrt{\left(\frac{\pi}{2}\right)^2 - \frac{0.25}{4900}}\,t\right)$

31. $d = -15e^{-0.9t/30}\cos\left(\sqrt{\left(\frac{\pi}{3}\right)^2 - \frac{0.81}{900}}\,t\right)$

32. $d = -10e^{-0.8t/50}\cos\left(\sqrt{\left(\frac{2\pi}{3}\right)^2 - \frac{0.64}{2500}}\,t\right)$

In Problems 33–40, use the method of adding y-coordinates to graph each function.

33. $f(x) = x + \cos x$ **34.** $f(x) = x + \cos(2x)$ **35.** $f(x) = x - \sin x$

36. $f(x) = x - \cos x$ **37.** $f(x) = \sin x + \cos x$ **38.** $f(x) = \sin(2x) + \cos x$

39. $g(x) = \sin x + \sin(2x)$ **40.** $g(x) = \cos(2x) + \cos x$

Applications and Extensions

41. Loudspeaker A loudspeaker diaphragm is oscillating in simple harmonic motion described by the equation $d = a\cos(\omega t)$ with a frequency of 520 hertz (cycles per second) and a maximum displacement of 0.80 millimeter. Find ω and then determine a model that describes the movement of the diaphragm.

42. Colossus Added to Six Flags St. Louis in 1986, the Colossus is a giant Ferris wheel. Its diameter is 165 feet, it rotates at a rate of about 1.6 revolutions per minute, and the bottom of the wheel is 15 feet above the ground. Determine a model that relates a rider's height above the ground at time t. Assume the passenger begins the ride at the bottom of the wheel.

Source: Six Flags Theme Parks, Inc.

43. Tuning Fork The end of a tuning fork moves in simple harmonic motion described by the equation $d = a\sin(\omega t)$. If a tuning fork for the note A above middle C on an even-tempered scale (A_4, the tone by which an orchestra tunes itself) has a frequency of 440 hertz (cycles per second), find ω. If the maximum displacement of the end of the tuning fork is 0.01 millimeter, determine a model that describes the movement of the tuning fork.

Source: David Lapp. *Physics of Music and Musical Instruments.* Medford, MA: Tufts University, 2003

44. Tuning Fork The end of a tuning fork moves in simple harmonic motion described by the equation $d = a\sin(\omega t)$. If a tuning fork for the note E above middle C on an even-tempered scale (E_4) has a frequency of approximately 329.63 hertz (cycles per second), find ω. If the maximum displacement of the end of the tuning fork is 0.025 millimeter, determine a model that describes the movement of the tuning fork.

Source: David Lapp. *Physics of Music and Musical Instruments.* Medford, MA: Tufts University, 2003

45. Charging a Capacitor If a charged capacitor is connected to a coil by closing a switch, energy is transferred to the coil and then back to the capacitor in an oscillatory motion. See the illustration. The voltage V (in volts) across the capacitor will gradually diminish to 0 with time t (in seconds).

(a) Graph the function relating V and t:

$$V(t) = e^{-t/3}\cos(\pi t), \qquad 0 \le t \le 3$$

(b) At what times t will the graph of V touch the graph of $y = e^{-t/3}$? When does the graph of V touch the graph of $y = -e^{-t/3}$?

(c) When will the voltage V be between -0.4 and 0.4 volt?

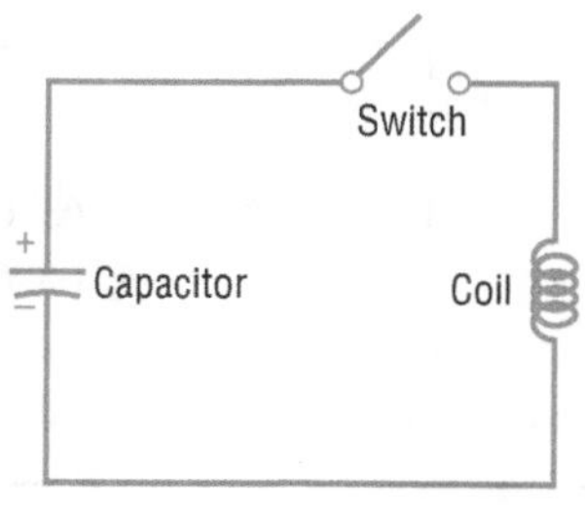

46. The Sawtooth Curve An oscilloscope often displays a *sawtooth curve*. This curve can be approximated by sinusoidal curves of varying periods and amplitudes.

(a) Use a graphing utility to graph the following function, which can be used to approximate the sawtooth curve.

$$f(x) = \frac{1}{2}\sin(2\pi x) + \frac{1}{4}\sin(4\pi x), \qquad 0 \le x \le 4$$

(b) A better approximation to the sawtooth curve is given by

$$f(x) = \frac{1}{2}\sin(2\pi x) + \frac{1}{4}\sin(4\pi x) + \frac{1}{8}\sin(8\pi x)$$

Use a graphing utility to graph this function for $0 \le x \le 4$ and compare the result to the graph obtained in part (a).

(c) A third and even better approximation to the sawtooth curve is given by

$$f(x) = \frac{1}{2}\sin(2\pi x) + \frac{1}{4}\sin(4\pi x) + \frac{1}{8}\sin(8\pi x) + \frac{1}{16}\sin(16\pi x)$$

Use a graphing utility to graph this function for $0 \le x \le 4$ and compare the result to the graphs obtained in parts (a) and (b).

(d) What do you think the next approximation to the sawtooth curve is?

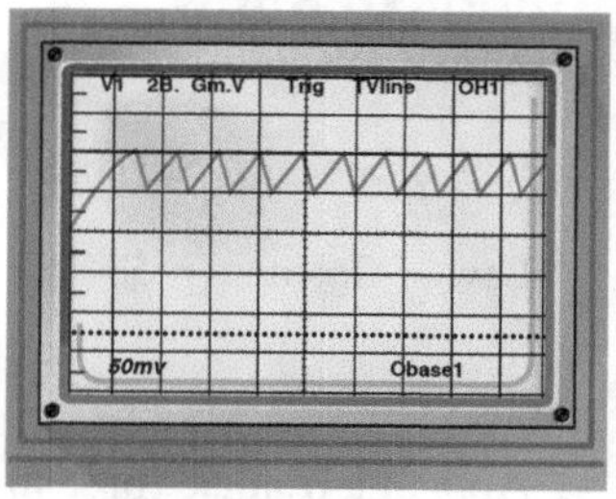

47. Touch-Tone Phones On a Touch-Tone phone, each button produces a unique sound. The sound produced is the sum of two tones, given by

$$y = \sin(2\pi lt) \quad \text{and} \quad y = \sin(2\pi ht)$$

where l and h are the low and high frequencies (cycles per second) shown in the illustration. For example, if you touch 7, the low frequency is $l = 852$ cycles per second and the high frequency is $h = 1209$ cycles per second. The sound emitted by touching 7 is

$$y = \sin[2\pi(852)t] + \sin[2\pi(1209)t]$$

Use a graphing utility to graph the sound emitted by touching 7.

Touch-Tone phone

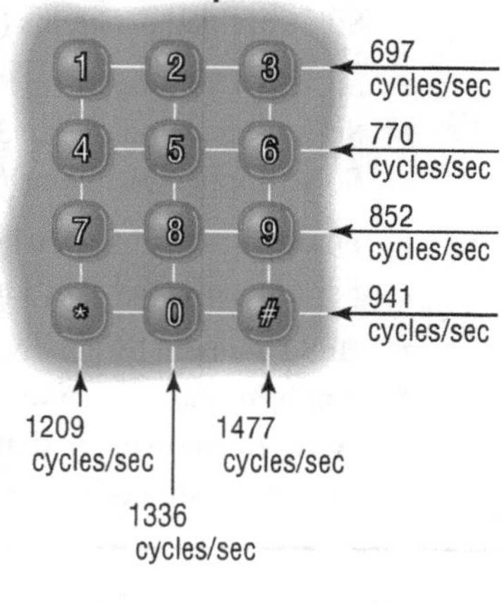

48. Use a graphing utility to graph the sound emitted by the * key on a Touch-Tone phone. See Problem 47.

49. CBL Experiment Pendulum motion is analyzed to estimate simple harmonic motion. A plot is generated with the position of the pendulum over time. The graph is used to find a sinusoidal curve of the form $y = A\cos[B(x - C)] + D$. Determine the amplitude, period, and frequency. (Activity 16, Real-World Math with the CBL System.)

50. CBL Experiment The sound from a tuning fork is collected over time. Determine the amplitude, frequency, and period of the graph. A model of the form $y = A\cos[B(x - C)]$ is fitted to the data. (Activity 23, Real-World Math with the CBL System.)

Discussion and Writing

51. Use a graphing utility to graph the function $f(x) = \frac{\sin x}{x}$, $x > 0$. Based on the graph, what do you conjecture about the value of $\frac{\sin x}{x}$ for x close to 0?

52. Use a graphing utility to graph $y = x\sin x$, $y = x^2\sin x$, and $y = x^3\sin x$ for $x > 0$. What patterns do you observe?

53. Use a graphing utility to graph $y = \frac{1}{x}\sin x$, $y = \frac{1}{x^2}\sin x$, and $y = \frac{1}{x^3}\sin x$ for $x > 0$. What patterns do you observe?

54. How would you explain to a friend what simple harmonic motion is? How would you explain damped motion?

'Are You Prepared?' Answer

1. $A = 5$; $T = \frac{\pi}{2}$

CHAPTER REVIEW

Things to Know

Formulas

Law of Sines (p. 523) $\qquad \frac{\sin A}{a} = \frac{\sin B}{b} = \frac{\sin C}{c}$

Law of Cosines (p. 534)

$$c^2 = a^2 + b^2 - 2ab\cos C$$
$$b^2 = a^2 + c^2 - 2ac\cos B$$
$$a^2 = b^2 + c^2 - 2bc\cos A$$

Area of a triangle (pp. 540–541)

$$K = \frac{1}{2}bh \quad K = \frac{1}{2}ab\sin C \quad K = \frac{1}{2}bc\sin A \quad K = \frac{1}{2}ac\sin B$$

$$K = \sqrt{s(s-a)(s-b)(s-c)} \quad \text{where} \quad s = \frac{1}{2}(a+b+c)$$

Objectives

Section		You should be able to . . .	Example(s)	Review Exercises
8.1	1	Find the value of trigonometric functions of acute angles using right triangles (p. 510)	1, 2	1–4, 46
	2	Use the complementary angle theorem (p. 512)	3	5–10
	3	Solve right triangles (p. 512)	4, 5	11–14, 46
	4	Solve applied problems (p. 513)	6–10	47–52, 60–62
8.2	1	Solve SAA or ASA triangles (p. 524)	1, 2	15, 16, 32
	2	Solve SSA triangles (p. 525)	3–5	17–20, 22, 27, 28, 31
	3	Solve applied problems (p. 527)	6, 7	53–55
8.3	1	Solve SAS triangles (p. 534)	1	21, 25, 26, 33, 34
	2	Solve SSS triangles (p. 535)	2	23, 24, 29, 30
	3	Solve applied problems (p. 536)	3	56, 57
8.4	1	Find the area of SAS triangles (p. 540)	1	35–38, 45, 58, 59
	2	Find the area of SSS triangles (p. 541)	2	39–42
8.5	1	Build a model for an object in simple harmonic motion (p. 546)	1	63, 64
	2	Analyze simple harmonic motion (p. 548)	2	65–68
	3	Analyze an object in damped motion (p. 549)	3	69–72
	4	Graph the sum of two functions (p. 550)	4, 5	73, 74

Review Exercises

In Problems 1–4, find the exact value of the six trigonometric functions of the angle θ in each figure.

1.

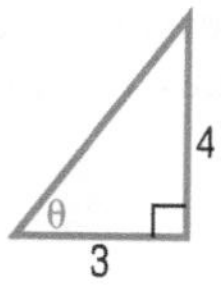

2.

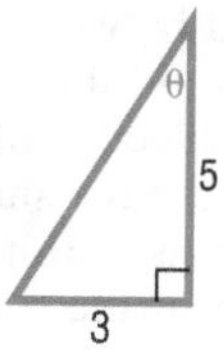

3.

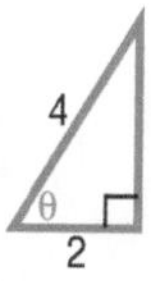

4.

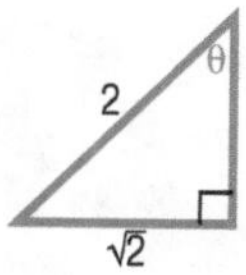

In Problems 5–10, find the exact value of each expression. Do not use a calculator.

5. $\cos 62° - \sin 28°$

6. $\tan 15° - \cot 75°$

7. $\dfrac{\sec 55°}{\csc 35°}$

8. $\dfrac{\tan 40°}{\cot 50°}$

9. $\cos^2 40° + \cos^2 50°$

10. $\tan^2 40° - \csc^2 50°$

In Problems 11–14, solve each triangle.

11.

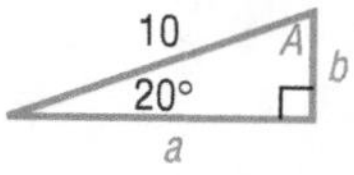

12.

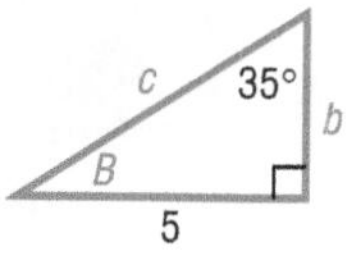

13.

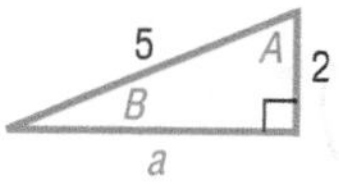

14.

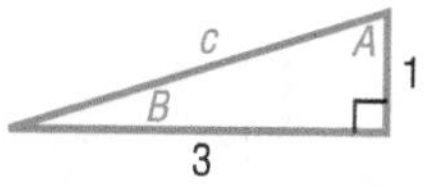

In Problems 15–34, find the remaining angle(s) and side(s) of each triangle, if it (they) exists. If no triangle exists, say "No triangle."

15. $A = 50°,\ B = 30°,\ a = 1$

16. $A = 10°,\ C = 40°,\ c = 2$

17. $A = 100°,\ a = 5,\ c = 2$

18. $a = 2,\ c = 5,\ A = 60°$

19. $a = 3,\ c = 1,\ C = 110°$

20. $a = 3,\ c = 1,\ C = 20°$

21. $a = 3,\ c = 1,\ B = 100°$

22. $a = 3,\ b = 5,\ B = 80°$

23. $a = 2,\ b = 3,\ c = 1$

24. $a = 10,\ b = 7,\ c = 8$

25. $a = 1,\ b = 3,\ C = 40°$

26. $a = 4,\ b = 1,\ C = 100°$

27. $a = 5,\ b = 3,\ A = 80°$

28. $a = 2,\ b = 3,\ A = 20°$

29. $a = 1,\ b = \dfrac{1}{2},\ c = \dfrac{4}{3}$

30. $a = 3,\ b = 2,\ c = 2$

31. $a = 3,\ A = 10°,\ b = 4$

32. $a = 4,\ A = 20°,\ B = 100°$

33. $c = 5,\ b = 4,\ A = 70°$

34. $a = 1,\ b = 2,\ C = 60°$

In Problems 35–44, find the area of each triangle.

35. $a = 2,\ b = 3,\ C = 40°$

36. $b = 5,\ c = 5,\ A = 20°$

37. $b = 4,\ c = 10,\ A = 70°$

38. $a = 2,\ b = 1,\ C = 100°$

39. $a = 4,\ b = 3,\ c = 5$

40. $a = 10,\ b = 7,\ c = 8$

41. $a = 4,\ b = 2,\ c = 5$

42. $a = 3,\ b = 2,\ c = 2$

43. $A = 50°,\ B = 30°,\ a = 1$

44. $A = 10°,\ C = 40°,\ c = 3$

45. Area of a Segment Find the area of the segment of a circle whose radius is 6 inches formed by a central angle of 50°.

46. Geometry The hypotenuse of a right triangle is 12 feet. If one leg is 8 feet, find the degree measure of each angle.

47. Finding the Width of a River Find the distance from A to C across the river illustrated in the figure.

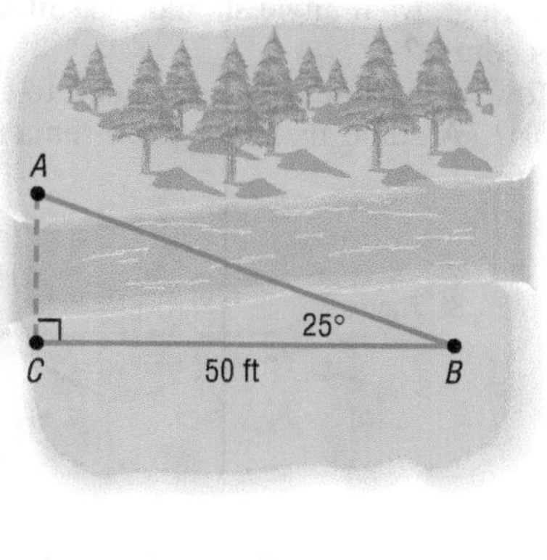

48. Finding the Height of a Building Find the height of the building shown in the figure.

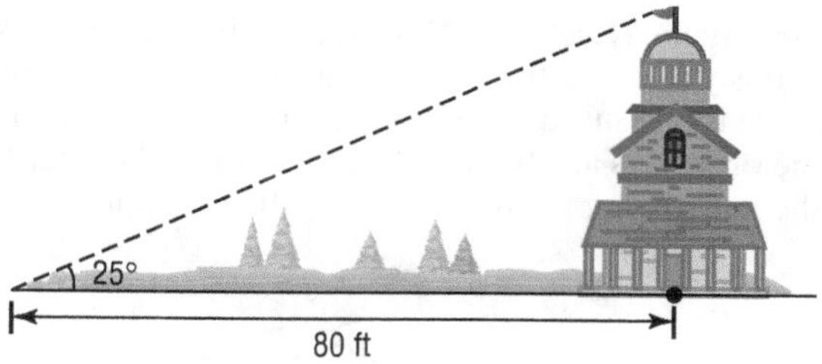

49. Finding the Distance to Shore The Sears Tower in Chicago is 1454 feet tall and is situated about 1 mile inland from the shore of Lake Michigan, as indicated in the figure. An observer in a pleasure boat on the lake directly in front of the Sears Tower looks at the top of the tower and measures the angle of elevation as 5°. How far offshore is the boat?

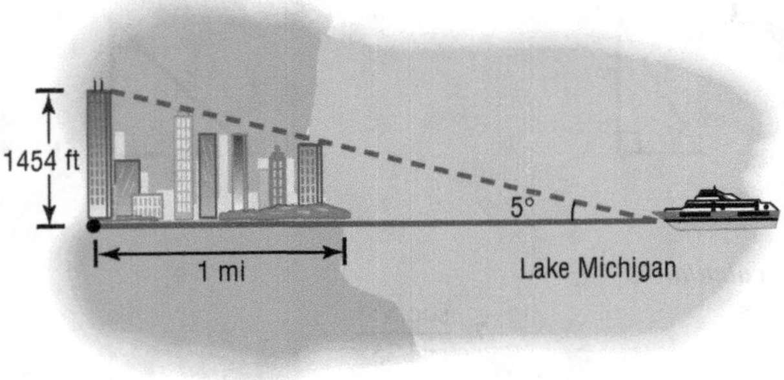

50. Measuring the Length of a Lake From a stationary hot-air balloon 500 feet above the ground, two sightings of a lake are made (see the figure). How long is the lake?

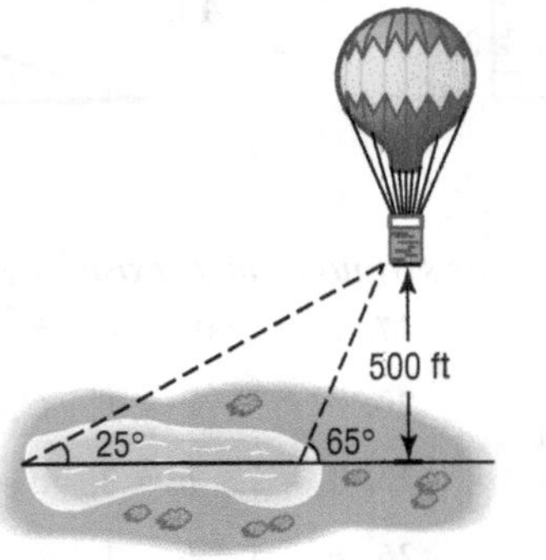

51. Finding the Speed of a Glider From a glider 200 feet above the ground, two sightings of a stationary object directly in front are taken 1 minute apart (see the figure). What is the speed of the glider?

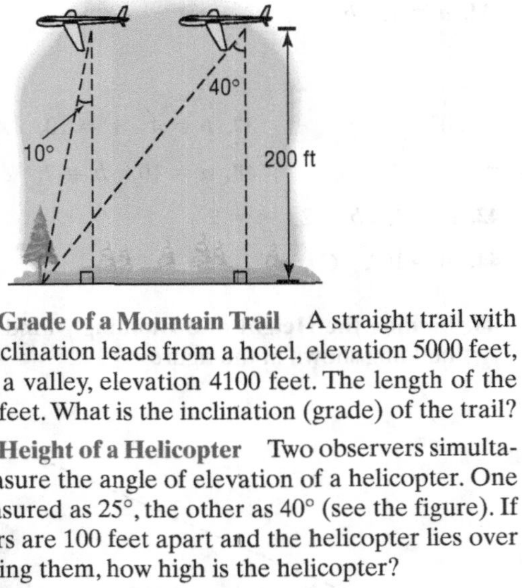

52. Finding the Grade of a Mountain Trail A straight trail with a uniform inclination leads from a hotel, elevation 5000 feet, to a lake in a valley, elevation 4100 feet. The length of the trail is 4100 feet. What is the inclination (grade) of the trail?

53. Finding the Height of a Helicopter Two observers simultaneously measure the angle of elevation of a helicopter. One angle is measured as 25°, the other as 40° (see the figure). If the observers are 100 feet apart and the helicopter lies over the line joining them, how high is the helicopter?

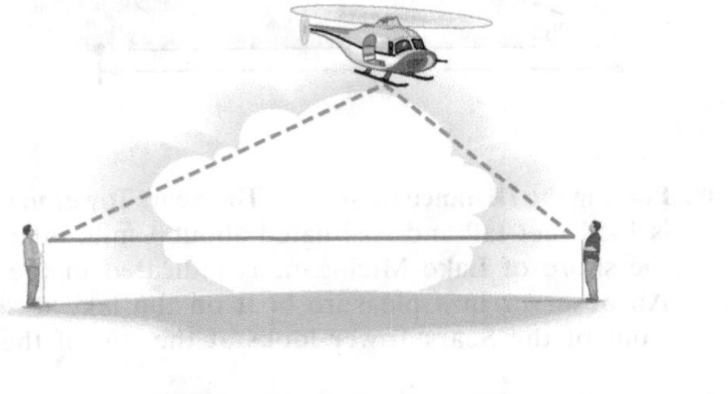

54. Determining Distances at Sea Rebecca, the navigator of a ship at sea, spots two lighthouses that she knows to be 2 miles apart along a straight shoreline. She determines that the angles formed between two line-of-sight observations of the lighthouses and the line from the ship directly to shore are 12° and 30°. See the illustration.

(a) How far is the ship from lighthouse L_1?
(b) How far is the ship from lighthouse L_2?
(c) How far is the ship from shore?

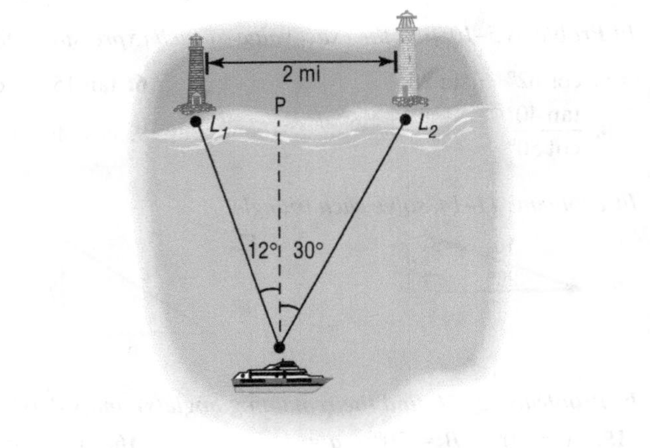

55. Constructing a Highway A highway whose primary directions are north–south is being constructed along the west coast of Florida. Near Naples, a bay obstructs the straight path of the road. Since the cost of a bridge is prohibitive, engineers decide to go around the bay. The illustration shows the path that they decide on and the measurements taken. What is the length of highway needed to go around the bay?

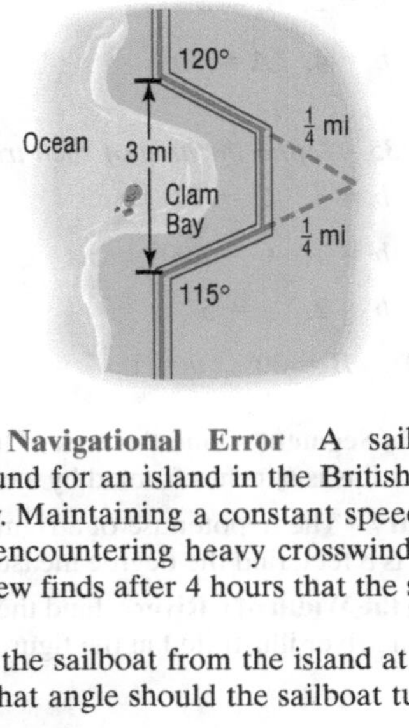

56. Correcting a Navigational Error A sailboat leaves St. Thomas bound for an island in the British West Indies, 200 miles away. Maintaining a constant speed of 18 miles per hour, but encountering heavy crosswinds and strong currents, the crew finds after 4 hours that the sailboat is off course by 15°.

(a) How far is the sailboat from the island at this time?
(b) Through what angle should the sailboat turn to correct its course?
(c) How much time has been added to the trip because of this? (Assume that the speed remains at 18 miles per hour.)

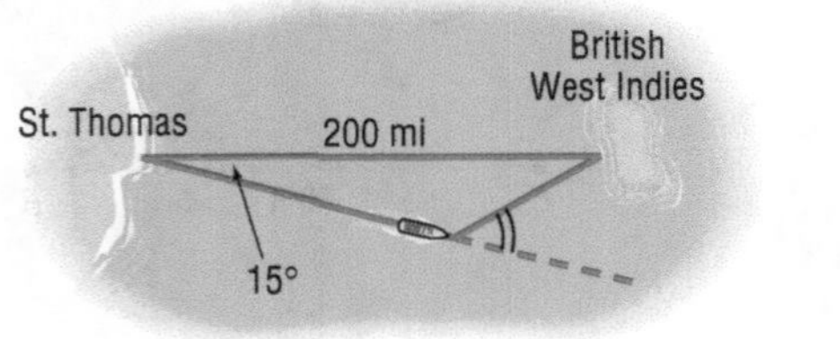

57. Surveying Two homes are located on opposite sides of a small hill. See the illustration. To measure the distance between them, a surveyor walks a distance of 50 feet from house P to point R, uses a transit to measure $\angle PRQ$, which is found to be 80°, and then walks to house Q, a distance of 60 feet. How far apart are the houses?

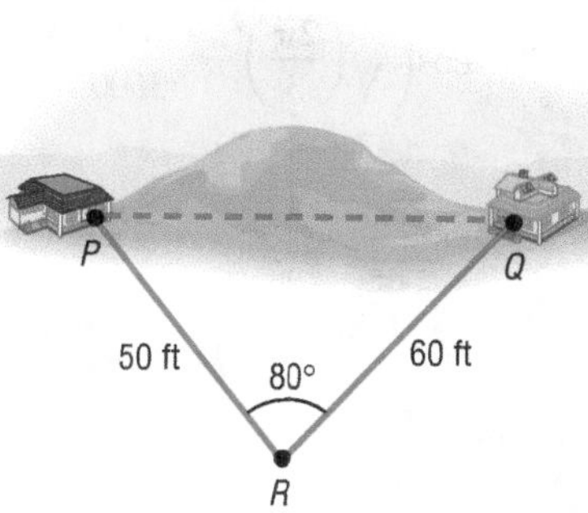

58. Approximating the Area of a Lake To approximate the area of a lake, Cindy walks around the perimeter of the lake, taking the measurements shown in the illustration. Using this technique, what is the approximate area of the lake?

[**Hint:** Use the Law of Cosines on the three triangles shown and then find the sum of their areas.]

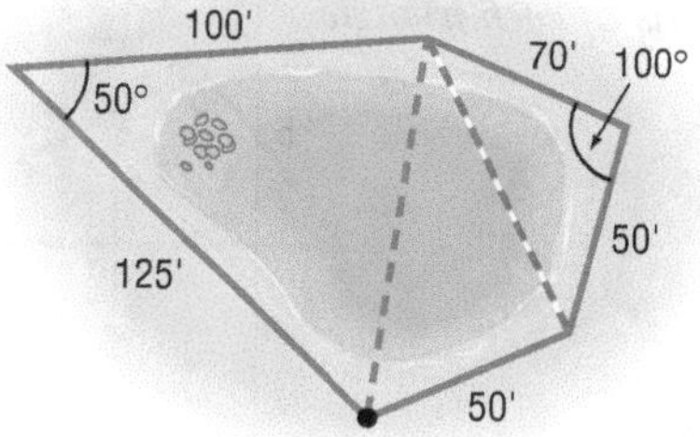

59. Calculating the Cost of Land The irregular parcel of land shown in the figure is being sold for \$100 per square foot. What is the cost of this parcel?

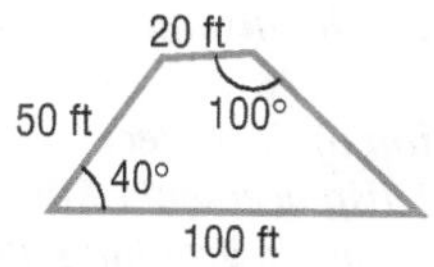

60. Finding the Bearing of a Ship The *Majesty* leaves the Port at Boston for Bermuda with a bearing of S80°E at an average speed of 10 knots. After 1 hour, the ship turns 90° toward the southwest. After 2 hours at an average speed of 20 knots, what is the bearing of the ship from Boston?

61. Drive Wheels of an Engine The drive wheel of an engine is 13 inches in diameter, and the pulley on the rotary pump is 5 inches in diameter. If the shafts of the drive wheel and the pulley are 2 feet apart, what length of belt is required to join them as shown in the figure?

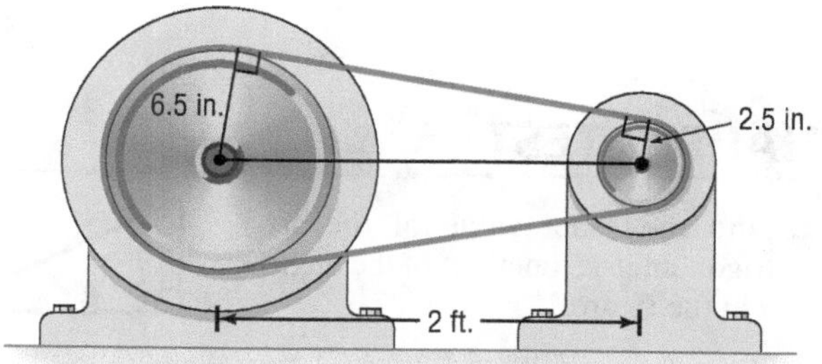

62. Rework Problem 61 if the belt is crossed, as shown in the figure.

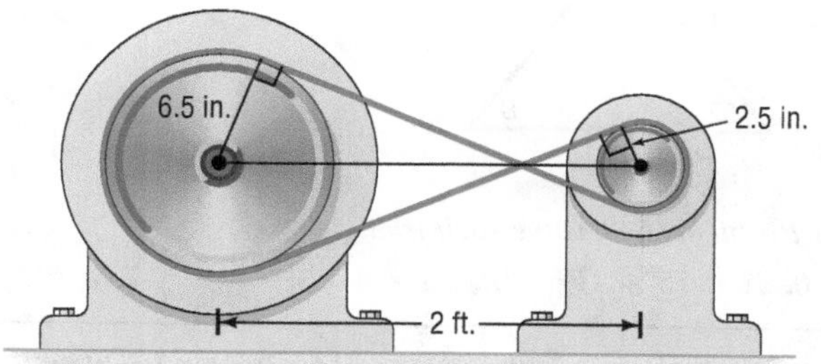

In Problems 63 and 64, an object attached to a coiled spring is pulled down a distance a from its rest position and then released. Assuming that the motion is simple harmonic with period T, develop a model that relates the displacement d of the object from its rest position after t seconds. Also assume that the positive direction of the motion is up.

63. $a = 3$; $T = 4$ seconds

64. $a = 5$; $T = 6$ seconds

In Problems 65–68, the distance d (in feet) that an object travels in time t (in seconds) is given.
(a) Describe the motion of the object.
(b) What is the maximum displacement from its rest position?
(c) What is the time required for one oscillation?
(d) What is the frequency?

65. $d = 6\sin(2t)$

66. $d = 2\cos(4t)$

67. $d = -2\cos(\pi t)$

68. $d = -3\sin\left[\frac{\pi}{2}t\right]$

In Problems 69 and 70, an object of mass m attached to a coiled spring with damping factor b is pulled down a distance a from its rest position and then released. Assume that the positive direction of the motion is up and the period is T under simple harmonic motion.
(a) Develop a model that relates the distance d of the object from its rest position after t seconds.
(b) Graph the equation found in part (a) for 5 oscillations.

69. $m = 40$ grams; $a = 15$ centimeters; $b = 0.75$ gram/second; $T = 5$ seconds

70. $m = 25$ grams; $a = 13$ centimeters; $b = 0.65$ gram/second; $T = 4$ seconds

In Problems 71 and 72, the distance d (in meters) of the bob of a pendulum of mass m (in kilograms) from its rest position at time t (in seconds) is given.
(a) Describe the motion of the object.
(b) What is the initial displacement of the bob? That is, what is the displacement at $t = 0$?
(c) Graph the motion using a graphing utility.
(d) What is the displacement of the bob at the start of the second oscillation?
(e) What happens to the displacement of the bob as time increases without bound?

71. $d = -15e^{-0.6t/40}\cos\left(\sqrt{\left(\frac{2\pi}{5}\right)^2 - \frac{0.36}{1600}}\,t\right)$

72. $d = -20e^{-0.5t/60}\cos\left(\sqrt{\left(\frac{2\pi}{3}\right)^2 - \frac{0.25}{3600}}\,t\right)$

In Problems 73 and 74, graph each function.

73. $y = 2\sin x + \cos(2x), \quad 0 \le x \le 2\pi$

74. $y = 2\cos(2x) + \sin\frac{x}{2}, \quad 0 \le x \le 2\pi$

CHAPTER TEST

1. Find the exact value of the six trigonometric functions of the angle θ in the figure.

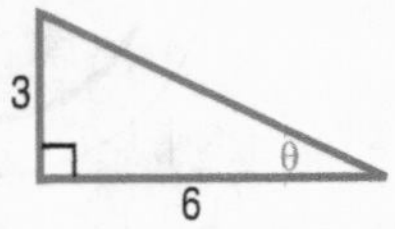

2. Find the exact value of $\sin 40° - \cos 50°$.

In Problems 3–5, use the given information to determine the three remaining parts of each triangle.

3.

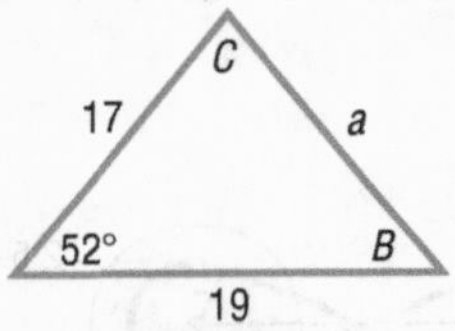

4.

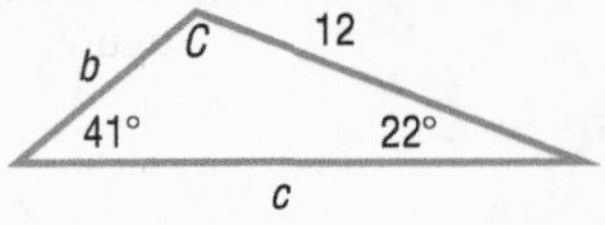

5.

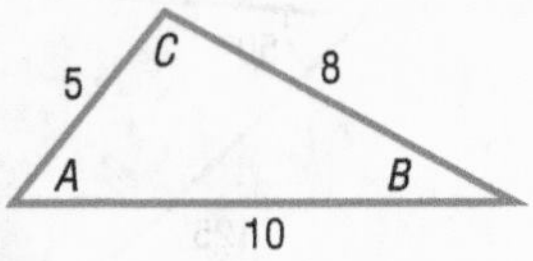

In Problems 6–8, solve each triangle.

6. $A = 55°, \quad C = 20°, \quad a = 4$

7. $a = 3, \quad b = 7, \quad A = 40°$

8. $a = 8, \quad b = 4, \quad C = 70°$

9. Find the area of the triangle described in Problem 8.

10. Find the area of the triangle described in Problem 5.

11. A 12-foot ladder leans against a building. The top of the ladder leans against the wall 10.5 feet from the ground. What is the angle formed by the ground and the ladder?

12. A hot-air balloon is flying at a height of 600 feet and is directly above the Marshall Space Flight Center in Huntsville, Alabama. The pilot of the balloon looks down at the airport that is known to be 5 miles from the Marshall Space Flight Center. What is the angle of depression from the balloon to the airport?

13. Find the area of the shaded region enclosed in a semicircle of diameter 8 centimeters. The length of the chord AB is 6 centimeters.

[Hint: Triangle ABC is a right triangle.]

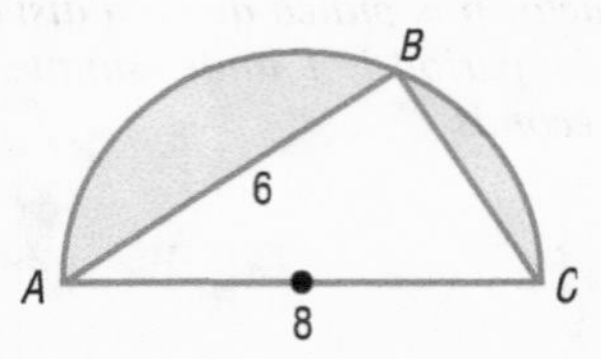

14. Find the area of the quadrilateral shown.

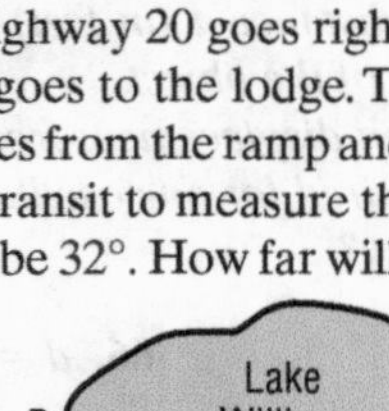

15. Madison wants to swim across Lake William from the fishing lodge (A) to the boat ramp (B), but she wants to know the distance first. Highway 20 goes right past the boat ramp and County Road 3 goes to the lodge. The two roads intersect at point (C), 4.2 miles from the ramp and 3.5 miles from the lodge. Madison uses a transit to measure the angle of intersection of the two roads to be 32°. How far will she need to swim?

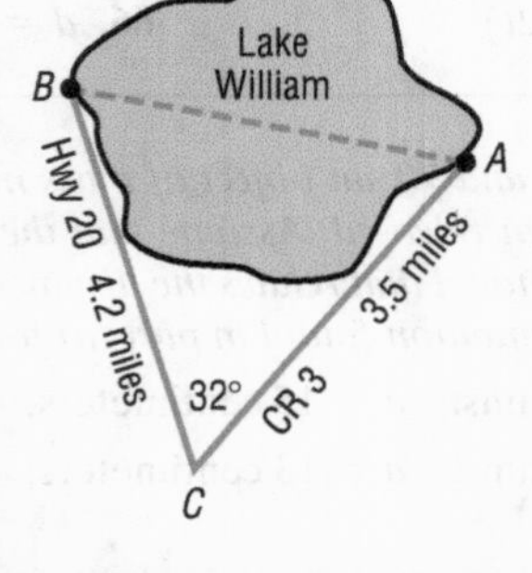

16. Given that $\triangle OAB$ is an isosceles triangle and the shaded sector is a semicircle, find the area of the entire region. Express your answer as a decimal rounded to two places.

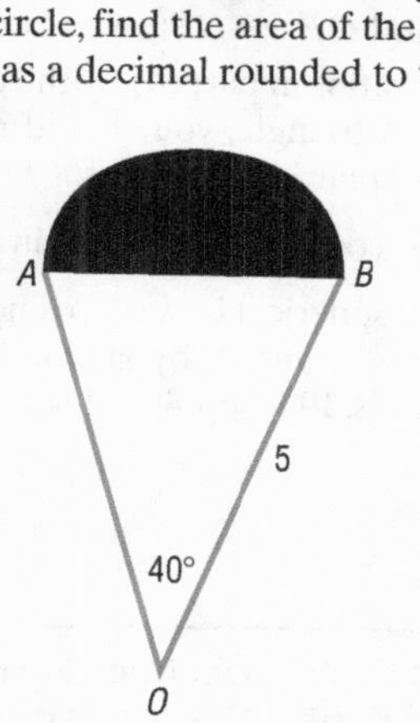

17. The area of the triangle shown below is $54\sqrt{6}$ square units; find the lengths of the sides.

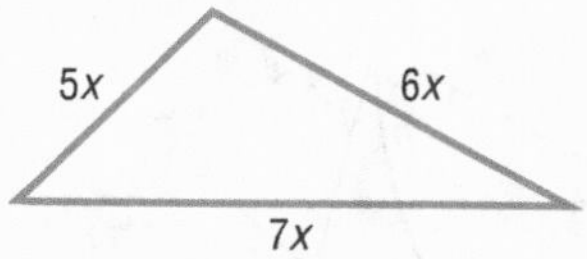

18. Logan is playing on her swing. One full swing (front to back to front) takes 6 seconds and at the peak of her swing she is at an angle of 42° with the vertical. If her swing is 5 feet long, and we ignore all resistive forces, develop a model that relates her horizontal displacement (from the rest position) after time t.

CUMULATIVE REVIEW

1. Find the real solutions, if any, of the equation $3x^2 + 1 = 4x$.

2. Find an equation for the circle with center at the point $(-5, 1)$ and radius 3. Graph this circle.

3. Determine the domain of the function

$$f(x) = \sqrt{x^2 - 3x - 4}$$

4. Graph the function $y = 3\sin(\pi x)$.

5. Graph the function $y = -2\cos(2x - \pi)$.

6. If $\tan\theta = -2$ and $\frac{3\pi}{2} < \theta < 2\pi$, find the exact value of:

(a) $\sin\theta$ (b) $\cos\theta$ (c) $\sin(2\theta)$

(d) $\cos(2\theta)$ (e) $\sin\left(\frac{1}{2}\theta\right)$ (f) $\cos\left(\frac{1}{2}\theta\right)$

7. Graph each of the following functions on the interval $[0, 4]$:

(a) $y = e^x$ (b) $y = \sin x$

(c) $y = e^x \sin x$ (d) $y = 2x + \sin x$

8. Sketch the graph of each of the following functions:

(a) $y = x$ (b) $y = x^2$ (c) $y = \sqrt{x}$

(d) $y = x^3$ (e) $y = e^x$ (f) $y = \ln x$

(g) $y = \sin x$ (h) $y = \cos x$ (i) $y = \tan x$

9. Solve the triangle:

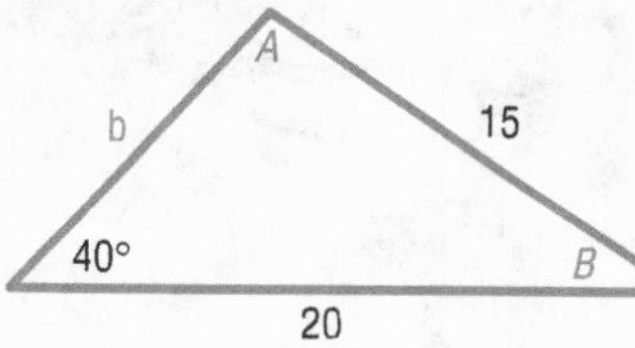

10. In the complex number system, solve the equation

$$3x^5 - 10x^4 + 21x^3 - 42x^2 + 36x - 8 = 0$$

11. Analyze the graph of the rational function

$$R(x) = \frac{2x^2 - 7x - 4}{x^2 + 2x - 15}$$

12. Solve $3^x = 12$. Round your answer to two decimal places.

13. Solve $\log_3(x + 8) + \log_3 x = 2$.

14. Suppose that $f(x) = 4x + 5$ and $g(x) = x^2 + 5x - 24$.

(a) Solve $f(x) = 0$. (e) Solve $g(x) \le 0$.

(b) Solve $f(x) = 13$. (f) Graph $y = f(x)$.

(c) Solve $f(x) = g(x)$. (g) Graph $y = g(x)$.

(d) Solve $f(x) > 0$.

CHAPTER PROJECTS

I. Spherical Trigonometry When the distance between two locations on the surface of Earth is small, we can compute the distance in statutory miles. Using this assumption, we can use the Law of Sines and the Law of Cosines to approximate distances and angles. However, if you look at a globe, you notice that Earth is a sphere, so, as the distance between two points on its surface increases, the linear distance is less accurate because of curvature. Under this circumstance, we need to take into account the curvature of Earth when using the Law of Sines and the Law of Cosines.

1. Draw a spherical triangle and label each vertex by A, B, and C. Then connect each vertex by a radius to the center O of the sphere. Now draw tangent lines to the sides a and b of the triangle that go through C. Extend the lines OA and OB to intersect the tangent lines at P and Q, respectively. See the figure. List the plane right triangles. Determine the measures of the central angles.
2. Apply the Law of Cosines to triangles OPQ and CPQ to find two expressions for the length of PQ.

3. Subtract the expressions in part (2) from each other. Solve for the term containing cos c.

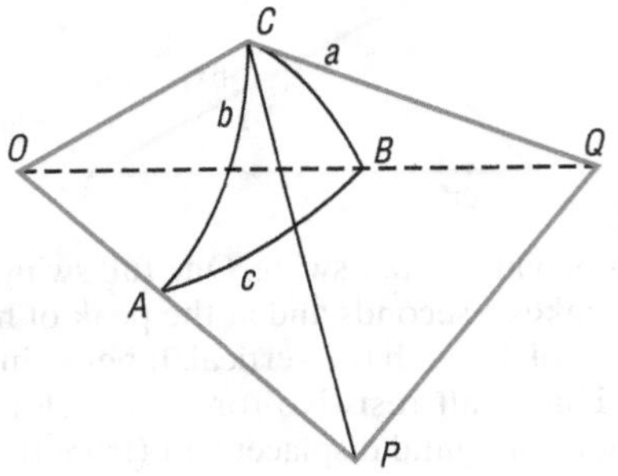

4. Use the Pythagorean Theorem to find another value for $OQ^2 - CQ^2$ and $OP^2 - CP^2$. Now solve for cos c.
5. Replacing the ratios in part (4) by the cosines of the sides of the spherical triangle, you should now have the Law of Cosines for spherical triangles:

$$\cos c = \cos a \cos b + \sin a \sin b \cos C$$

Source: For the spherical Law of Cosines; see *Mathematics from the Birth of Numbers* by Jan Gullberg. W. W. Norton & Co., Publishers, 1996, pp. 491–494.

II. The Lewis and Clark Expedition Lewis and Clark followed several rivers in their trek from what is now Great Falls, Montana, to the Pacific coast. First, they went down the Missouri and Jefferson rivers from Great Falls to Lemhi, Idaho. Because the two cities are on different longitudes and different latitudes, we must account for the curvature of Earth when computing the distance that they traveled. Assume that the radius of Earth is 3960 miles.

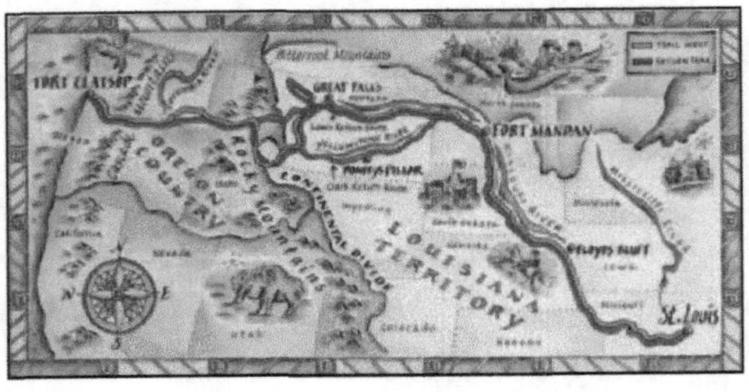

1. Great Falls is at approximately 47.5°N and 111.3°W. Lemhi is at approximately 45.5°N and 113.5°W. (We will assume that the rivers flow straight from Great Falls to Lemhi on the surface of Earth.) This line is called a geodesic line. Apply the Law of Cosines for a spherical triangle to find the angle between Great Falls and Lemhi. (The central angles are found by using the differences in the latitudes and longitudes of the towns. See the diagram.) Then find the length of the arc joining the two towns. (Recall $s = r\theta$.)

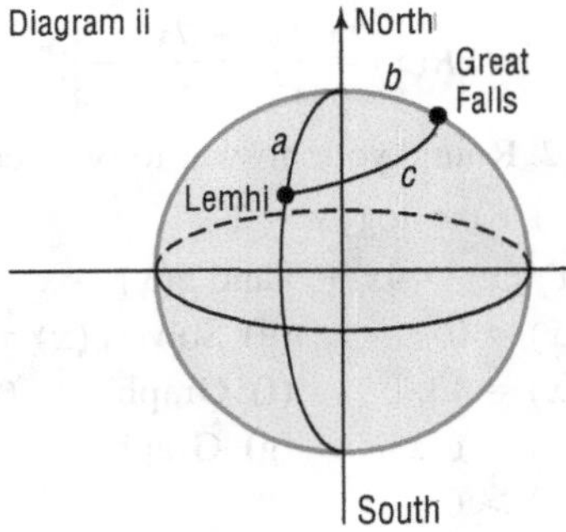

2. From Lemhi, they went up the Bitteroot River and the Snake River to what is now Lewiston and Clarkston on the border of Idaho and Washington. Although this is not really a side to a triangle, we will make a side that goes from Lemhi to Lewiston and Clarkston. If Lewiston and Clarkston are at about 46.5°N 117.0°W, find the distance from Lemhi using the Law of Cosines for a spherical triangle and the arc length.
3. How far did the explorers travel just to get that far?
4. Draw a plane triangle connecting the three towns. If the distance from Lewiston to Great Falls is 282 miles and the angle at Great Falls is 42° and the angle at Lewiston is 48.5°, find the distance from Great Falls to Lemhi and from Lemhi to Lewiston. How do these distances compare with the ones computed in parts (1) and (2)?

Source: For Lewis and Clark Expedition: *American Journey: The Quest for Liberty to 1877, Texas Edition*. Prentice Hall, 1992, p. 345.

Source: For map coordinates: *National Geographic Atlas of the World*, published by National Geographic Society, 1981, pp. 74–75.

The following projects are available at the Instructor's Resource Center (IRC):

III. Project at Motorola: *How Can You Build or Analyze a Vibration Profile?* Fourier functions are not only important to analyze vibrations, but they are also what a mathematician would call interesting. Complete the project to see why.

IV. Leaning Tower of Pisa Trigonometry is used to analyze the apparent height and tilt of the Leaning Tower of Pisa.

V. Locating Lost Treasure Clever treasure seekers who know the Law of Sines are able to efficiently find a buried treasure.

VI. Jacob's Field Angles of elevation and the Law of Sines are used to determine the height of the stadium wall and the distance from home plate to the top of the wall.

Polar Coordinates; Vectors

9

How Do Airplanes Fly?

Have you ever watched a big jetliner lumber into position on the runway for takeoff and wonder, "How does that thing ever get off the ground?" You know it's because of the wing that it stays up in the air, but how does it really work?

When air flows around a wing, it creates lift. The way it creates lift is based on the wing's movement through the air and the air pressure created around the wing. An airplane's wing, in varying degrees depending on the type and design of the airplane, is curved over the top of the wing and straighter underneath the wing. As air hits the wing, it is "split in two," with air moving both over and under the wing. Since the top of the wing has more curve than the bottom of the wing, the air moving over the top of the wing has farther to travel, and thus must move faster than the air moving underneath the wing. The air moving over the top of the wing now exerts less air pressure on the wing than the slower-moving air under the wing. Lift is created.

The difference in air pressure is the primary force creating lift on a wing, but one other force exerted on the wing also helps to produce lift. This is the force of deflection. Air moving along the underside of the wing is deflected downward. Remember the Newtonian principle: For every action, there is an equal and opposite reaction. The air that is deflected downward (action) helps to push the wing upward (reaction), producing more lift.

These two natural forces on the wing, pressure and deflection, produce lift. The faster the wing moves through the air, the greater the forces become, and the greater the lift.

Source: Thomas Schueneman. How do airplanes fly? http://meme.essortment.com/howdoairplane_rlmi.htm, accessed August 2006. © 2002 by Pagewise, Inc. Used with permission.

—See Chapter Project I—

A Look Back, A Look Ahead

This chapter is in two parts: Polar Coordinates, Sections 9.1–9.3, and Vectors, Sections 9.4–9.7. They are independent of each other and may be covered in any order.

Sections 9.1–9.3: In Chapter 1 we introduced rectangular coordinates x and y and discussed the graph of an equation in two variables involving x and y. In Sections 9.1 and 9.2, we introduce polar coordinates, an alternative to rectangular coordinates, and discuss graphing equations that involve polar coordinates. In Section 5.3, we discussed raising a real number to a real power. In Section 9.3 we extend this idea by raising a complex number to a real power. As it turns out, polar coordinates are useful for the discussion.

Sections 9.4–9.7: We have seen in many chapters that we are often required to solve an equation to obtain a solution to applied problems. In the last four sections of this chapter, we develop the notion of a vector and show how it can be used to model applied problems in physics and engineering.

Outline

9.1 Polar Coordinates

PREPARING FOR THIS SECTION *Before getting started, review the following:*

- Rectangular Coordinates (Section 1.1, pp. 2–3)
- Definitions of the Sine and Cosine Functions (Section 6.2, pp. 376–377)
- Inverse Tangent Function (Section 7.1, pp. 447–449)
- Completing the Square (Appendix A, Section A.6, p. A52)

Now Work the 'Are You Prepared?' problems on page 569.

OBJECTIVES
1 Plot Points Using Polar Coordinates (p. 562)
2 Convert from Polar Coordinates to Rectangular Coordinates (p. 564)
3 Convert from Rectangular Coordinates to Polar Coordinates (p. 566)
4 Transform Equations from Polar to Rectangular Form (p. 568)

So far, we have always used a system of rectangular coordinates to plot points in the plane. Now we are ready to describe another system, called *polar coordinates*. As we shall soon see, in many instances polar coordinates offer certain advantages over rectangular coordinates.

In a rectangular coordinate system, you will recall, a point in the plane is represented by an ordered pair of numbers (x, y), where x and y equal the signed distance of the point from the y-axis and x-axis, respectively. In a polar coordinate system, we select a point, called the **pole,** and then a ray with vertex at the pole, called the **polar axis.** See Figure 1. Comparing the rectangular and polar coordinate systems, we see that the origin in rectangular coordinates coincides with the pole in polar coordinates, and the positive x-axis in rectangular coordinates coincides with the polar axis in polar coordinates.

Figure 1

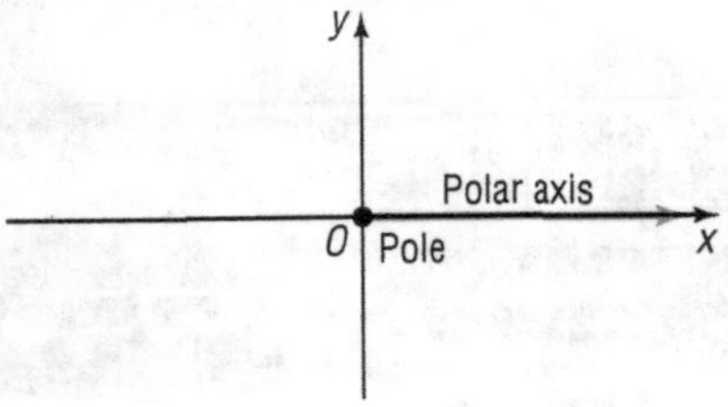

1 Plot Points Using Polar Coordinates

A point P in a polar coordinate system is represented by an ordered pair of numbers (r, θ). If $r > 0$, then r is the distance of the point from the pole; θ is an angle (in degrees or radians) formed by the polar axis and a ray from the pole through the point. We call the ordered pair (r, θ) the **polar coordinates** of the point. See Figure 2.

As an example, suppose that the polar coordinates of a point P are $\left(2, \frac{\pi}{4}\right)$. We locate P by first drawing an angle of $\frac{\pi}{4}$ radian, placing its vertex at the pole and its initial side along the polar axis. Then we go out a distance of 2 units along the terminal side of the angle to reach the point P. See Figure 3.

Figure 2

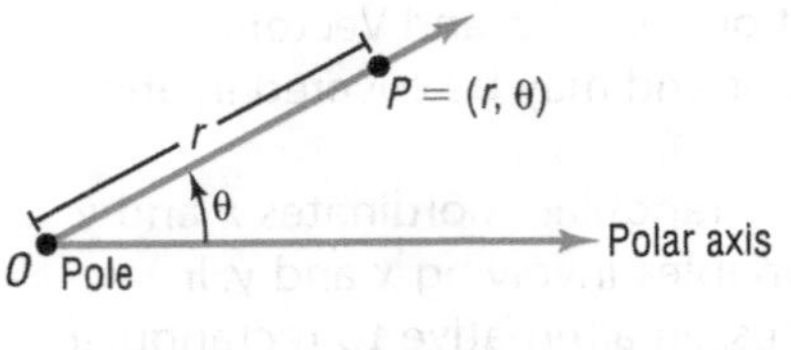

Figure 3

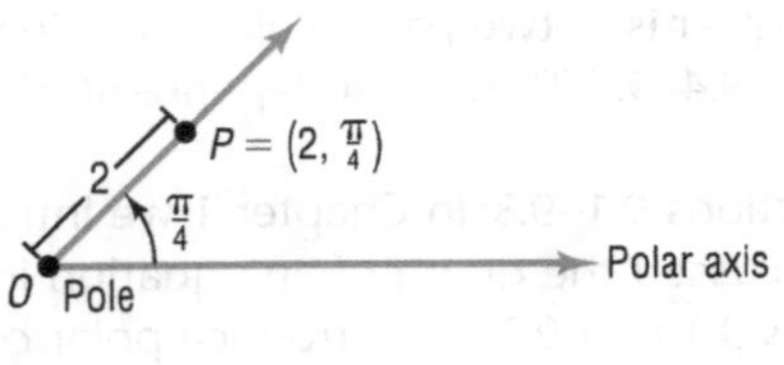

In using polar coordinates (r, θ), it is possible for r to be negative. When this happens, instead of the point being on the terminal side of θ, it is on the ray from the pole extending in the direction *opposite* the terminal side of θ at a distance $|r|$ units from the pole. See Figure 4 for an illustration.

For example, to plot the point $\left(-3, \frac{2\pi}{3}\right)$, we use the ray in the opposite direction of $\frac{2\pi}{3}$ and go out $|-3| = 3$ units along that ray. See Figure 5.

Figure 4

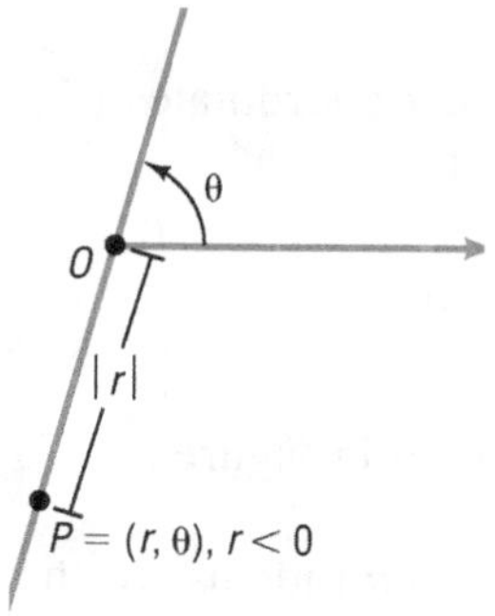

Figure 5

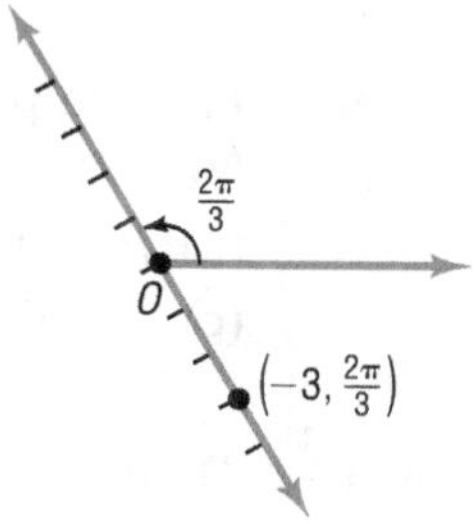

EXAMPLE 1

Plotting Points Using Polar Coordinates

Plot the points with the following polar coordinates:

(a) $\left(3, \dfrac{5\pi}{3}\right)$ (b) $\left(2, -\dfrac{\pi}{4}\right)$ (c) $(3, 0)$ (d) $\left(-2, \dfrac{\pi}{4}\right)$

Solution Figure 6 shows the points.

Figure 6

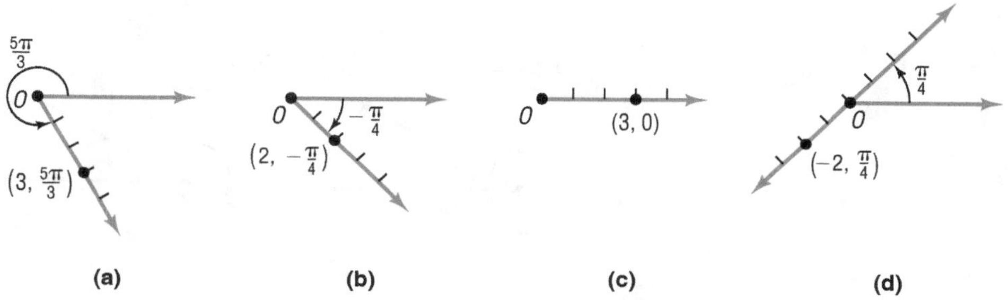

Now Work PROBLEMS 11, 19, AND 27

Recall that an angle measured counterclockwise is positive and an angle measured clockwise is negative. This convention has some interesting consequences relating to polar coordinates. Let's see what these consequences are.

EXAMPLE 2

Finding Several Polar Coordinates of a Single Point

Consider again the point P with polar coordinates $\left(2, \dfrac{\pi}{4}\right)$, as shown in Figure 7(a). Because $\dfrac{\pi}{4}$, $\dfrac{9\pi}{4}$, and $-\dfrac{7\pi}{4}$ all have the same terminal side, we also could have located this point P by using the polar coordinates $\left(2, \dfrac{9\pi}{4}\right)$ or $\left(2, -\dfrac{7\pi}{4}\right)$, as shown in Figures 7(b) and (c). The point $\left(2, \dfrac{\pi}{4}\right)$ can also be represented by the polar coordinates $\left(-2, \dfrac{5\pi}{4}\right)$. See Figure 7(d).

Figure 7

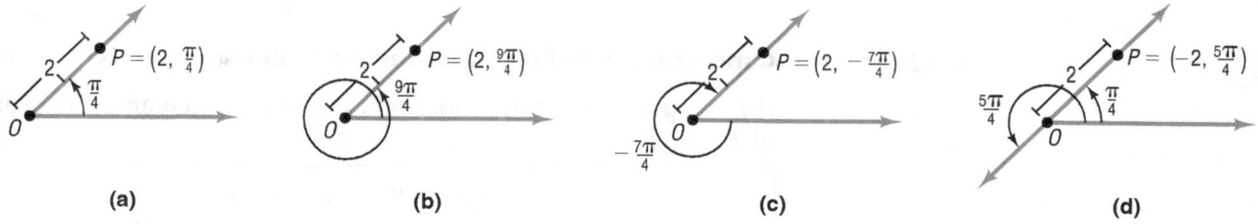

EXAMPLE 3 Finding Other Polar Coordinates of a Given Point

Plot the point P with polar coordinates $\left(3, \frac{\pi}{6}\right)$, and find other polar coordinates (r, θ) of this same point for which:

(a) $r > 0, \quad 2\pi \le \theta < 4\pi$ (b) $r < 0, \quad 0 \le \theta < 2\pi$

(c) $r > 0, \quad -2\pi \le \theta < 0$

Solution The point $\left(3, \frac{\pi}{6}\right)$ is plotted in Figure 8.

Figure 8

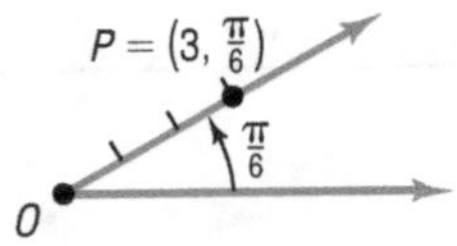

(a) We add 1 revolution (2π radians) to the angle $\frac{\pi}{6}$ to get $P = \left(3, \frac{\pi}{6} + 2\pi\right) = \left(3, \frac{13\pi}{6}\right)$. See Figure 9.

(b) We add $\frac{1}{2}$ revolution (π radians) to the angle $\frac{\pi}{6}$ and replace 3 by -3 to get $P = \left(-3, \frac{\pi}{6} + \pi\right) = \left(-3, \frac{7\pi}{6}\right)$. See Figure 10.

(c) We subtract 2π from the angle $\frac{\pi}{6}$ to get $P = \left(3, \frac{\pi}{6} - 2\pi\right) = \left(3, -\frac{11\pi}{6}\right)$. See Figure 11.

Figure 9

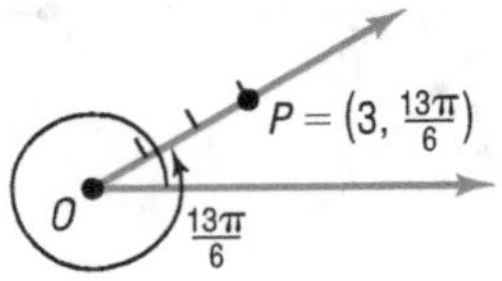

Figure 10

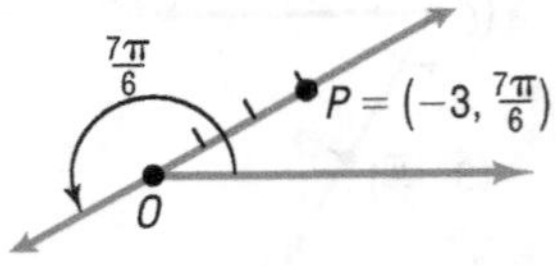

Figure 11

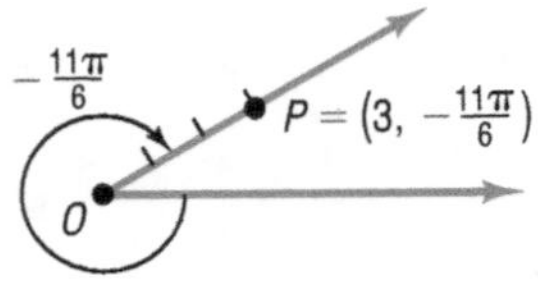

These examples show a major difference between rectangular coordinates and polar coordinates. In the former, each point has exactly one pair of rectangular coordinates; in the latter, a point can have infinitely many pairs of polar coordinates.

SUMMARY A point with polar coordinates (r, θ) can also be represented by either of the following:

$$(r, \theta + 2\pi k) \quad \text{or} \quad (-r, \theta + \pi + 2\pi k) \qquad k \text{ any integer}$$

The polar coordinates of the pole are $(0, \theta)$, where θ can be any angle.

Now Work PROBLEM 31

2 Convert from Polar Coordinates to Rectangular Coordinates

Sometimes we need to convert coordinates or equations in rectangular form to polar form, and vice versa. To do this, we recall that the origin in rectangular coordinates is the pole in polar coordinates and that the positive x-axis in rectangular coordinates is the polar axis in polar coordinates.

THEOREM **Conversion from Polar Coordinates to Rectangular Coordinates**

If P is a point with polar coordinates (r, θ), the rectangular coordinates (x, y) of P are given by

$$x = r\cos\theta \qquad y = r\sin\theta \tag{1}$$

Figure 12

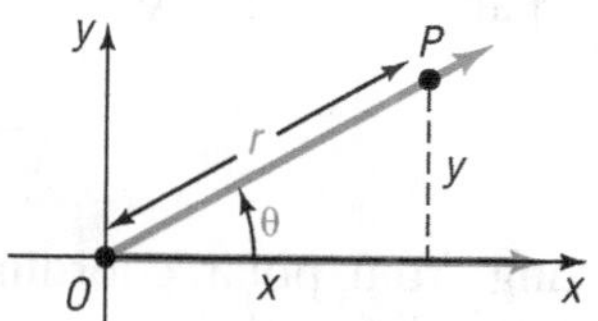

Proof Suppose that P has the polar coordinates (r, θ). We seek the rectangular coordinates (x, y) of P. Refer to Figure 12.

If $r = 0$, then, regardless of θ, the point P is the pole, for which the rectangular coordinates are $(0, 0)$. Formula (1) is valid for $r = 0$.

If $r > 0$, the point P is on the terminal side of θ, and $r = d(O, P) = \sqrt{x^2 + y^2}$. Since

$$\cos\theta = \frac{x}{r} \qquad \sin\theta = \frac{y}{r}$$

we have

$$x = r\cos\theta \qquad y = r\sin\theta$$

If $r < 0$, the point $P = (r, \theta)$ can be represented as $(-r, \pi + \theta)$, where $-r > 0$. Since

$$\cos(\pi + \theta) = -\cos\theta = \frac{x}{-r} \qquad \sin(\pi + \theta) = -\sin\theta = \frac{y}{-r}$$

we have

$$x = r\cos\theta \qquad y = r\sin\theta$$

■

EXAMPLE 4 Converting from Polar Coordinates to Rectangular Coordinates

Find the rectangular coordinates of the points with the following polar coordinates:

(a) $\left(6, \frac{\pi}{6}\right)$ (b) $\left(-4, -\frac{\pi}{4}\right)$

Solution We use formula (1): $x = r\cos\theta$ and $y = r\sin\theta$.

Figure 13

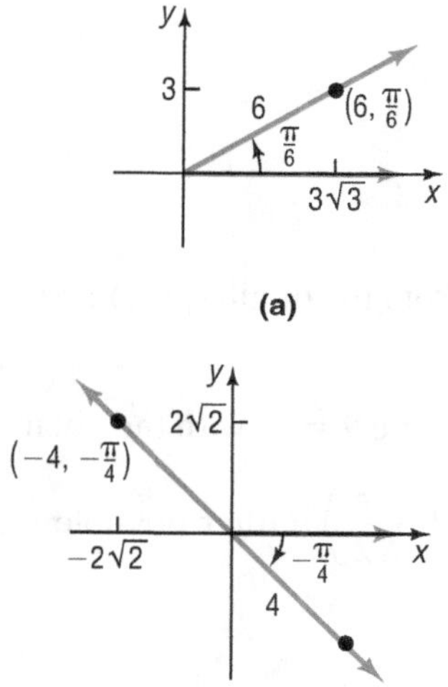

(a) (b)

(a) Figure 13(a) shows $\left(6, \frac{\pi}{6}\right)$ plotted. Notice that $\left(6, \frac{\pi}{6}\right)$ lies in quadrant I of the rectangular coordinate system. So we expect both the x-coordinate and the y-coordinate to be positive. With $r = 6$ and $\theta = \frac{\pi}{6}$, we have

$$x = r\cos\theta = 6\cos\frac{\pi}{6} = 6\cdot\frac{\sqrt{3}}{2} = 3\sqrt{3}$$

$$y = r\sin\theta = 6\sin\frac{\pi}{6} = 6\cdot\frac{1}{2} = 3$$

The rectangular coordinates of the point $\left(6, \frac{\pi}{6}\right)$ are $(3\sqrt{3}, 3)$, which lies in quadrant I, as expected.

(b) Figure 13(b) shows $\left(-4, -\frac{\pi}{4}\right)$ plotted. Notice that $\left(-4, -\frac{\pi}{4}\right)$ lies in quadrant II of the rectangular coordinate system. With $r = -4$ and $\theta = -\frac{\pi}{4}$, we have

$$x = r\cos\theta = -4\cos\left(-\frac{\pi}{4}\right) = -4\cdot\frac{\sqrt{2}}{2} = -2\sqrt{2}$$

$$y = r\sin\theta = -4\sin\left(-\frac{\pi}{4}\right) = -4\left(-\frac{\sqrt{2}}{2}\right) = 2\sqrt{2}$$

The rectangular coordinates of the point $\left(-4, -\frac{\pi}{4}\right)$ are $(-2\sqrt{2}, 2\sqrt{2})$, which lies in quadrant II, as expected.

Figure 14

Most calculators have the capability of converting from polar coordinates to rectangular coordinates. Consult your owner's manual for the proper key strokes. Since in most cases this procedure is tedious, you will find that using formula (1) is faster.

Figure 14 verifies the result obtained in Example 4(a) using a TI-84 Plus. Note that the calculator is in radian mode.

Now Work PROBLEMS 39 AND 51

3 Convert from Rectangular Coordinates to Polar Coordinates

Converting from rectangular coordinates (x, y) to polar coordinates (r, θ) is a little more complicated. Notice that we begin each example by plotting the given rectangular coordinates.

EXAMPLE 5 How to Convert from Rectangular Coordinates to Polar Coordinates with the Point on a Coordinate Axis

Find polar coordinates of a point whose rectangular coordinates are $(0, 3)$.

Step-by-Step Solution

STEP 1 Plot the point (x, y) and note the quadrant the point lies in or the coordinate axis the point lies on.

We plot the point $(0, 3)$ in a rectangular coordinate system. See Figure 15. The point lies on the positive y-axis

Figure 15

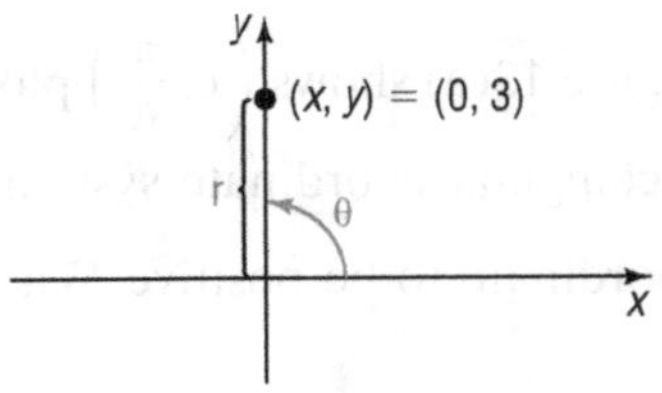

STEP 2 Determine the distance r from the origin to the point.

The point $(0, 3)$ lies on the y-axis a distance of 3 units from the origin (pole), so $r = 3$.

STEP 3 Determine θ.

A ray with vertex at the pole through $(0, 3)$ forms an angle $\theta = \frac{\pi}{2}$ with the polar axis.

Polar coordinates for this point can be given by $\left(3, \frac{\pi}{2}\right)$. Other possible representations include $\left(-3, -\frac{\pi}{2}\right)$ and $\left(3, \frac{5\pi}{2}\right)$.

Figure 16

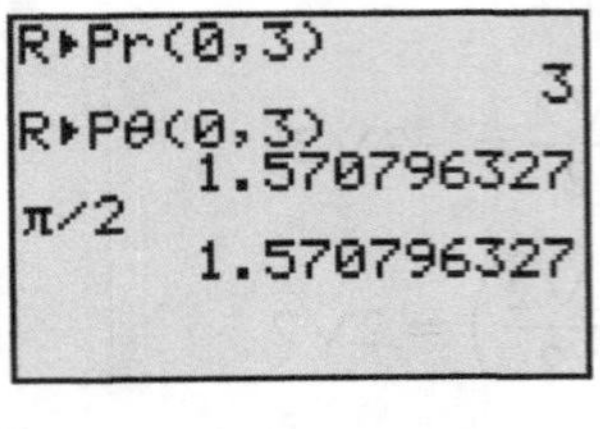

Most graphing calculators have the capability of converting from rectangular coordinates to polar coordinates. Consult your owner's manual for the proper keystrokes. Figure 16 verifies the results obtained in Example 5 using a TI-84 Plus. Note that the calculator is in radian mode.

Figure 17 shows polar coordinates of points that lie on either the x-axis or the y-axis. In each illustration, $a > 0$.

Figure 17

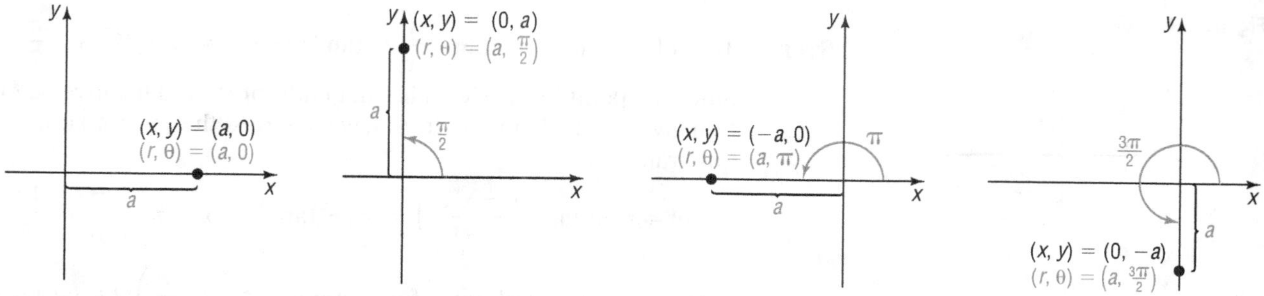

(a) $(x, y) = (a, 0)$, $a > 0$ **(b)** $(x, y) = (0, a)$, $a > 0$ **(c)** $(x, y) = (-a, 0)$, $a > 0$ **(d)** $(x, y) = (0, -a)$, $a > 0$

Now Work PROBLEM 55

EXAMPLE 6 How to Convert from Rectangular Coordinates to Polar Coordinates with the Point in a Quadrant

Find the polar coordinates of a point whose rectangular coordinates are $(2, -2)$.

Step-by-Step Solution

STEP 1 Plot the point (x, y) and note the quadrant the point lies in or the coordinate axis the point lies on.

We plot the point $(2, -2)$ in a rectangular coordinate system. See Figure 18. The point lies in quadrant IV.

Figure 18

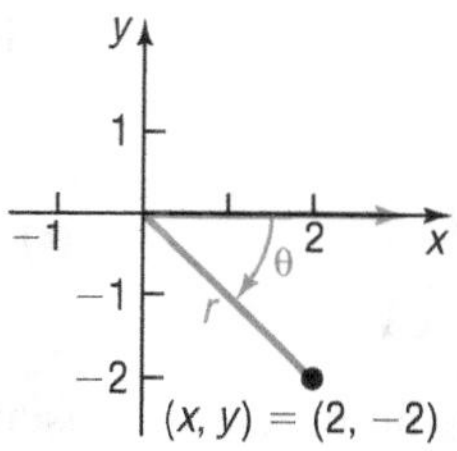

STEP 2 Determine the distance r from the origin to the point using $r = \sqrt{x^2 + y^2}$.

$$r = \sqrt{x^2 + y^2} = \sqrt{(2)^2 + (-2)^2} = \sqrt{8} = 2\sqrt{2}$$

STEP 3 Determine θ.

We find θ by recalling that $\tan\theta = \dfrac{y}{x}$, so $\theta = \tan^{-1}\dfrac{y}{x}$, $-\dfrac{\pi}{2} < \theta < \dfrac{\pi}{2}$. Since $(2, -2)$ lies in quadrant IV, we know that $-\dfrac{\pi}{2} < \theta < 0$. As a result,

$$\theta = \tan^{-1}\frac{y}{x} = \tan^{-1}\left(\frac{-2}{2}\right) = \tan^{-1}(-1) = -\frac{\pi}{4}$$

A set of polar coordinates for the point $(2,-2)$ is $\left(2\sqrt{2}, -\dfrac{\pi}{4}\right)$. Other possible representations include $\left(2\sqrt{2}, \dfrac{7\pi}{4}\right)$ and $\left(-2\sqrt{2}, \dfrac{3\pi}{4}\right)$.

EXAMPLE 7 Converting from Rectangular Coordinates to Polar Coordinates

Find polar coordinates of a point whose rectangular coordinates are $\left(-1, -\sqrt{3}\right)$.

Solution

STEP 1: See Figure 19. The point lies in quadrant III.

STEP 2: The distance r from the origin to the point $\left(-1, -\sqrt{3}\right)$ is

$$r = \sqrt{(-1)^2 + \left(-\sqrt{3}\right)^2} = \sqrt{4} = 2$$

Figure 19

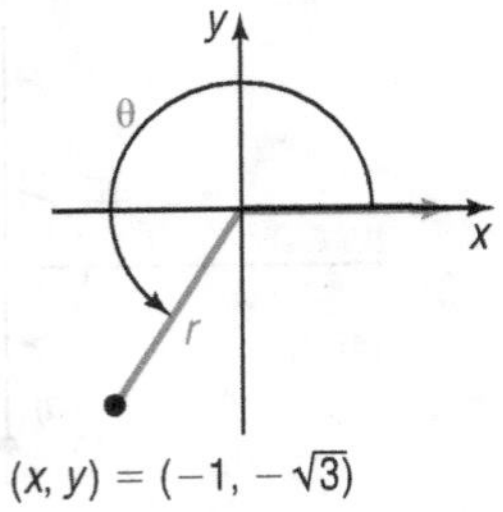

STEP 3: To find θ, we use $\theta = \tan^{-1}\frac{y}{x} = \tan^{-1}\frac{-\sqrt{3}}{-1} = \tan^{-1}\sqrt{3}, -\frac{\pi}{2} < \theta < \frac{\pi}{2}$. Since the point $\left(-1, -\sqrt{3}\right)$ lies in quadrant III and the inverse tangent function gives an angle in quadrant I, we add π to the result to obtain an angle in quadrant III.

$$\theta = \pi + \tan^{-1}\left(\frac{-\sqrt{3}}{-1}\right) = \pi + \tan^{-1}\sqrt{3} = \pi + \frac{\pi}{3} = \frac{4\pi}{3}$$

A set of polar coordinates for this point is $\left(2, \frac{4\pi}{3}\right)$. Other possible representations include $\left(-2, \frac{\pi}{3}\right)$ and $\left(2, -\frac{2\pi}{3}\right)$.

Figure 20 shows how to find polar coordinates of a point that lies in a quadrant when its rectangular coordinates (x, y) are given.

Figure 20

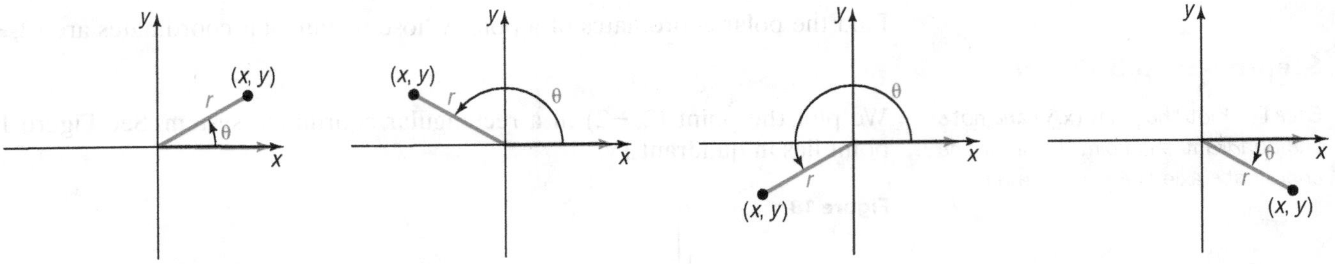

(a) $r = \sqrt{x^2 + y^2}$, $\theta = \tan^{-1}\frac{y}{x}$

(b) $r = \sqrt{x^2 + y^2}$, $\theta = \pi + \tan^{-1}\frac{y}{x}$

(c) $r = \sqrt{x^2 + y^2}$, $\theta = \pi + \tan^{-1}\frac{y}{x}$

(d) $r = \sqrt{x^2 + y^2}$, $\theta = \tan^{-1}\frac{y}{x}$

Based on the preceding discussion, we have the formulas

$$r^2 = x^2 + y^2 \qquad \tan\theta = \frac{y}{x} \quad \text{if } x \neq 0 \qquad \textbf{(2)}$$

To use formula (2) effectively, follow these steps:

Steps for Converting from Rectangular to Polar Coordinates

STEP 1: Always plot the point (x, y) first, as we did in Examples 5 and 6. Note the quadrant the point lies in or the coordinate axis the point lies on.

STEP 2: If $x = 0$ or $y = 0$, use your illustration to find r. See Figure 17. If $x \neq 0$ and $y \neq 0$, then $r = \sqrt{x^2 + y^2}$.

STEP 3: Find θ. If $x = 0$ or $y = 0$, use your illustration to find θ. See Figure 17. If $x \neq 0$ and $y \neq 0$, note the quadrant in which the point lies.

Quadrant I or IV: $\theta = \tan^{-1}\frac{y}{x}$

Quadrant II or III: $\theta = \pi + \tan^{-1}\frac{y}{x}$

See Figure 20.

Now Work PROBLEM 59

4 Transform Equations from Polar to Rectangular Form

Formulas (1) and (2) may also be used to transform equations from polar form to rectangular form, and vice versa. Two common techniques for transforming an equation from polar form to rectangular form are the following:

1. Multiplying both sides of the equation by r
2. Squaring both sides of the equation

EXAMPLE 8 **Transforming an Equation from Polar to Rectangular Form**

Transform the equation $r = 6\cos\theta$ from polar coordinates to rectangular coordinates, and identify the graph.

Solution If we multiply each side by r, it will be easier to apply formulas (1) and (2).

$$r = 6\cos\theta$$
$$r^2 = 6r\cos\theta \quad \text{Multiply each side by } r.$$
$$x^2 + y^2 = 6x \quad r^2 = x^2 + y^2;\ x = r\cos\theta$$

This is the equation of a circle, so we proceed to complete the square to obtain the standard form of the equation.

$$x^2 + y^2 = 6x$$
$$(x^2 - 6x) + y^2 = 0 \quad \text{General form}$$
$$(x^2 - 6x + 9) + y^2 = 9 \quad \text{Complete the square in } x.$$
$$(x - 3)^2 + y^2 = 9 \quad \text{Factor.}$$

This is the standard form of the equation of a circle with center $(3, 0)$ and radius 3.

Now Work PROBLEM 75

EXAMPLE 9 **Transforming an Equation from Rectangular to Polar Form**

Transform the equation $4xy = 9$ from rectangular coordinates to polar coordinates.

Solution We use formula (1): $x = r\cos\theta$ and $y = r\sin\theta$.

$$4xy = 9$$
$$4(r\cos\theta)(r\sin\theta) = 9 \quad x = r\cos\theta,\ y = r\sin\theta$$
$$4r^2\cos\theta\sin\theta = 9$$

This is the polar form of the equation. It can be simplified as shown next:

$$2r^2(2\sin\theta\cos\theta) = 9 \quad \text{Factor out } 2r^2.$$
$$2r^2\sin(2\theta) = 9 \quad \text{Double-angle Formula}$$

Now Work PROBLEM 69

9.1 Assess Your Understanding

'Are You Prepared?' *Answers are given at the end of these exercises. If you get a wrong answer, read the pages listed in red.*

1. Plot the point whose rectangular coordinates are $(3, -1)$. What quadrant does the point lie in? (pp. 2–3)
2. To complete the square of $x^2 + 6x$, add _____. (p. A52)
3. If $P = (a, b)$ is a point on the terminal side of the angle θ at a distance r from the origin, then $\sin\theta =$ _____. (pp. 376–377)
4. $\tan^{-1}(-1) =$ _____. (pp. 447–449)

Concepts and Vocabulary

5. In polar coordinates, the origin is called the _____ and the positive x-axis is referred to as the _____ _____.
6. Another representation in polar coordinates for the point $\left(2, \frac{\pi}{3}\right)$ is $\left(\_\_\_, \frac{4\pi}{3}\right)$.
7. The polar coordinates $\left(-2, \frac{\pi}{6}\right)$ are represented in rectangular coordinates by (_____, _____).
8. ***True or False*** The polar coordinates of a point are unique.
9. ***True or False*** The rectangular coordinates of a point are unique.
10. ***True or False*** In (r, θ), the number r can be negative.

Skill Building

In Problems 11–18, match each point in polar coordinates with either A, B, C, or D on the graph.

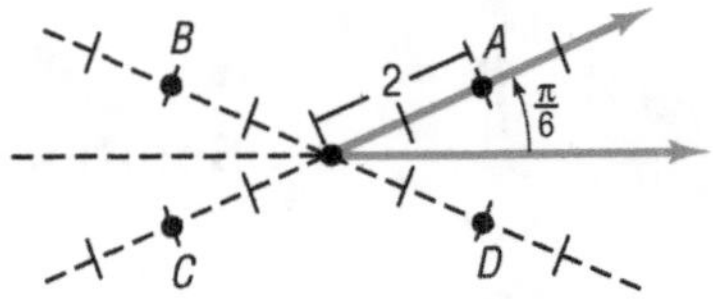

11. $\left(2, -\frac{11\pi}{6}\right)$ **12.** $\left(-2, -\frac{\pi}{6}\right)$ **13.** $\left(-2, \frac{\pi}{6}\right)$ **14.** $\left(2, \frac{7\pi}{6}\right)$

15. $\left(2, \frac{5\pi}{6}\right)$ **16.** $\left(-2, \frac{5\pi}{6}\right)$ **17.** $\left(-2, \frac{7\pi}{6}\right)$ **18.** $\left(2, \frac{11\pi}{6}\right)$

In Problems 19–30, plot each point given in polar coordinates.

19. $(3, 90°)$ **20.** $(4, 270°)$ **21.** $(-2, 0)$ **22.** $(-3, \pi)$

23. $\left(6, \frac{\pi}{6}\right)$ **24.** $\left(5, \frac{5\pi}{3}\right)$ **25.** $(-2, 135°)$ **26.** $(-3, 120°)$

27. $\left(-1, -\frac{\pi}{3}\right)$ **28.** $\left(-3, -\frac{3\pi}{4}\right)$ **29.** $(-2, -\pi)$ **30.** $\left(-3, -\frac{\pi}{2}\right)$

In Problems 31–38, plot each point given in polar coordinates, and find other polar coordinates (r, θ) of the point for which:

(a) $r > 0, \quad -2\pi \le \theta < 0$ (b) $r < 0, \quad 0 \le \theta < 2\pi$ (c) $r > 0, \quad 2\pi \le \theta < 4\pi$

31. $\left(5, \frac{2\pi}{3}\right)$ **32.** $\left(4, \frac{3\pi}{4}\right)$ **33.** $(-2, 3\pi)$ **34.** $(-3, 4\pi)$

35. $\left(1, \frac{\pi}{2}\right)$ **36.** $(2, \pi)$ **37.** $\left(-3, -\frac{\pi}{4}\right)$ **38.** $\left(-2, -\frac{2\pi}{3}\right)$

In Problems 39–54, the polar coordinates of a point are given. Find the rectangular coordinates of each point.

39. $\left(3, \frac{\pi}{2}\right)$ **40.** $\left(4, \frac{3\pi}{2}\right)$ **41.** $(-2, 0)$ **42.** $(-3, \pi)$

43. $(6, 150°)$ **44.** $(5, 300°)$ **45.** $\left(-2, \frac{3\pi}{4}\right)$ **46.** $\left(-2, \frac{2\pi}{3}\right)$

47. $\left(-1, -\frac{\pi}{3}\right)$ **48.** $\left(-3, -\frac{3\pi}{4}\right)$ **49.** $(-2, -180°)$ **50.** $(-3, -90°)$

51. $(7.5, 110°)$ **52.** $(-3.1, 182°)$ **53.** $(6.3, 3.8)$ **54.** $(8.1, 5.2)$

In Problems 55–66, the rectangular coordinates of a point are given. Find polar coordinates for each point.

55. $(3, 0)$ **56.** $(0, 2)$ **57.** $(-1, 0)$ **58.** $(0, -2)$

59. $(1, -1)$ **60.** $(-3, 3)$ **61.** $(\sqrt{3}, 1)$ **62.** $(-2, -2\sqrt{3})$

63. $(1.3, -2.1)$ **64.** $(-0.8, -2.1)$ **65.** $(8.3, 4.2)$ **66.** $(-2.3, 0.2)$

In Problems 67–74, the letters x and y represent rectangular coordinates. Write each equation using polar coordinates (r, θ).

67. $2x^2 + 2y^2 = 3$ **68.** $x^2 + y^2 = x$ **69.** $x^2 = 4y$ **70.** $y^2 = 2x$

71. $2xy = 1$ **72.** $4x^2y = 1$ **73.** $x = 4$ **74.** $y = -3$

In Problems 75–82, the letters r and θ represent polar coordinates. Write each equation using rectangular coordinates (x, y).

75. $r = \cos\theta$ **76.** $r = \sin\theta + 1$ **77.** $r^2 = \cos\theta$ **78.** $r = \sin\theta - \cos\theta$

79. $r = 2$ **80.** $r = 4$ **81.** $r = \dfrac{4}{1 - \cos\theta}$ **82.** $r = \dfrac{3}{3 - \cos\theta}$

Applications and Extensions

83. Chicago In Chicago, the road system is set up like a Cartesian plane, where streets are indicated by the number of blocks they are from Madison Street and State Street. For example, Wrigley Field in Chicago is located at 1060 West Addison, which is 10 blocks west of State Street and 36 blocks north of Madison Street. Treat the intersection of Madison Street and State Street as the origin of a coordinate system, with east being the positive x-axis.

(a) Write the location of Wrigley Field using rectangular coordinates.

(b) Write the location of Wrigley Field using polar coordinates. Use the east direction for the polar axis. Express θ in degrees.

(c) U.S. Cellular Field, home of the White Sox, is located at 35th and Princeton, which is 3 blocks west of State Street and 35 blocks south of Madison. Write the location of U.S. Cellular Field using rectangular coordinates.

(d) Write the location of U.S. Cellular Field using polar coordinates. Use the east direction for the polar axis. Express θ in degrees.

City of Chicago, Illinois

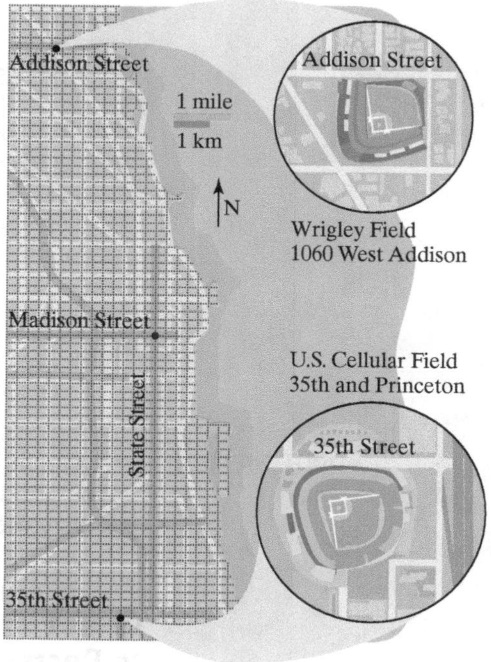

84. Show that the formula for the distance d between two points $P_1 = (r_1, \theta_1)$ and $P_2 = (r_2, \theta_2)$ is

$$d = \sqrt{r_1^2 + r_2^2 - 2r_1 r_2 \cos(\theta_2 - \theta_1)}$$

Discussion and Writing

85. In converting from polar coordinates to rectangular coordinates, what formulas will you use?

86. Explain how you proceed to convert from rectangular coordinates to polar coordinates.

87. Is the street system in your town based on a rectangular coordinate system, a polar coordinate system, or some other system? Explain.

'Are You Prepared?' Answers

1. 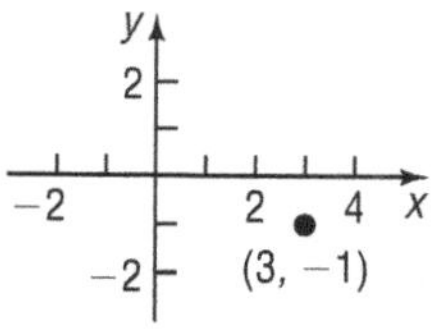

; quadrant IV **2.** 9 **3.** $\frac{b}{r}$ **4.** $-\frac{\pi}{4}$

9.2 Polar Equations and Graphs

PREPARING FOR THIS SECTION *Before getting started, review the following:*

- Symmetry (Section 1.2, pp. 19–21)
- Circles (Section 1.5, pp. 44–48)
- Even–Odd Properties of Trigonometric Functions (Section 6.3, pp. 391–392)
- Difference Formulas for Sine and Cosine (Section 7.4, pp. 466 and 469)
- Value of the Sine and Cosine Functions at Certain Angles (Section 6.2, pp. 368–375)

Now Work the 'Are You Prepared?' problems on page 586.

OBJECTIVES
1 Graph and Identify Polar Equations by Converting to Rectangular Equations (p. 572)
2 Graph Polar Equations Using a Graphing Utility (p. 573)
3 Test Polar Equations for Symmetry (p. 577)
4 Graph Polar Equations by Plotting Points (p. 578)

Just as a rectangular grid may be used to plot points given by rectangular coordinates, as in Figure 21(a), we can use a grid consisting of concentric circles (with centers at the pole) and rays (with vertices at the pole) to plot points given by polar coordinates, as shown in Figure 21(b). We shall use such **polar grids** to graph *polar equations*.

Figure 21

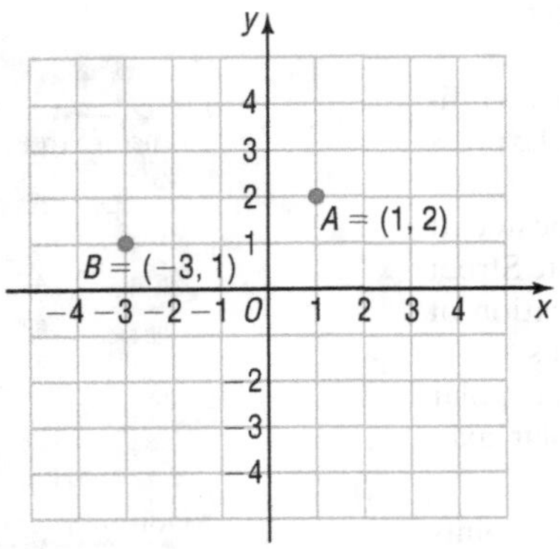

(a) Rectangular grid

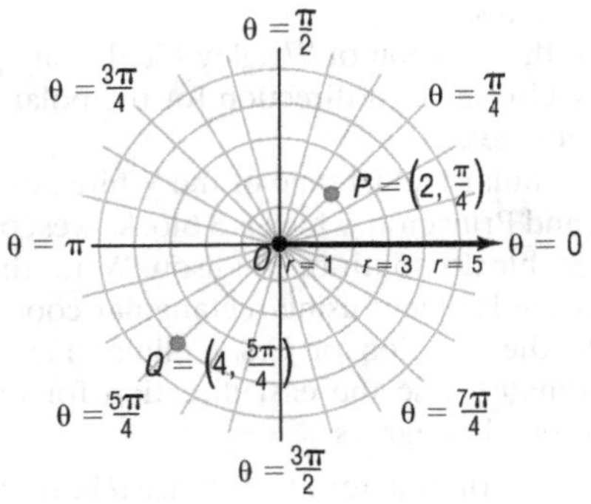

(b) Polar grid

DEFINITION An equation whose variables are polar coordinates is called a **polar equation.** The **graph of a polar equation** consists of all points whose polar coordinates satisfy the equation.

1 Graph and Identify Polar Equations by Converting to Rectangular Equations

One method that we can use to graph a polar equation is to convert the equation to rectangular coordinates. In the discussion that follows, (x, y) represent the rectangular coordinates of a point P, and (r, θ) represent polar coordinates of the point P.

EXAMPLE 1 Identifying and Graphing a Polar Equation (Circle)

Identify and graph the equation: $r = 3$

Solution We convert the polar equation to a rectangular equation.

$$r = 3$$

$$r^2 = 9 \quad \text{Square both sides.}$$

$$x^2 + y^2 = 9 \quad r^2 = x^2 + y^2$$

The graph of $r = 3$ is a circle, with center at the pole and radius 3. See Figure 22.

Figure 22
$r = 3$ or $x^2 + y^2 = 9$

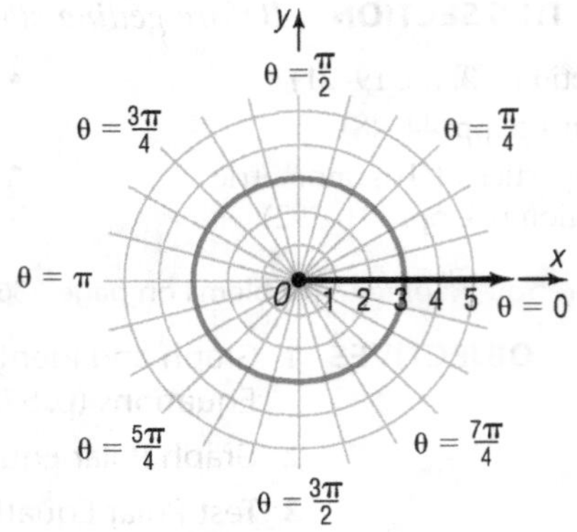

Now Work PROBLEM 13

EXAMPLE 2 Identifying and Graphing a Polar Equation (Line)

Identify and graph the equation: $\theta = \dfrac{\pi}{4}$

Solution We convert the polar equation to a rectangular equation.

$$\theta = \frac{\pi}{4}$$

$$\tan\theta = \tan\frac{\pi}{4} \quad \text{Take the tangent of both sides.}$$

$$\frac{y}{x} = 1 \quad \tan\theta = \frac{y}{x};\ \tan\frac{\pi}{4} = 1$$

$$y = x$$

The graph of $\theta = \frac{\pi}{4}$ is a line passing through the pole making an angle of $\frac{\pi}{4}$ with the polar axis. See Figure 23.

Figure 23
$\theta = \frac{\pi}{4}$ or $y = x$

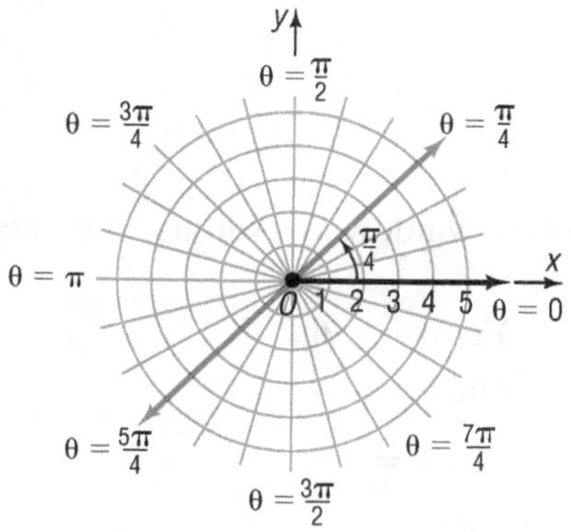

Now Work PROBLEM 15

EXAMPLE 3 Identifying and Graphing a Polar Equation (Horizontal Line)

Identify and graph the equation: $r\sin\theta = 2$

Solution Since $y = r\sin\theta$, we can write the equation as

$$y = 2$$

We conclude that the graph of $r\sin\theta = 2$ is a horizontal line 2 units above the pole. See Figure 24.

Figure 24
$r\sin\theta = 2$ or $y = 2$

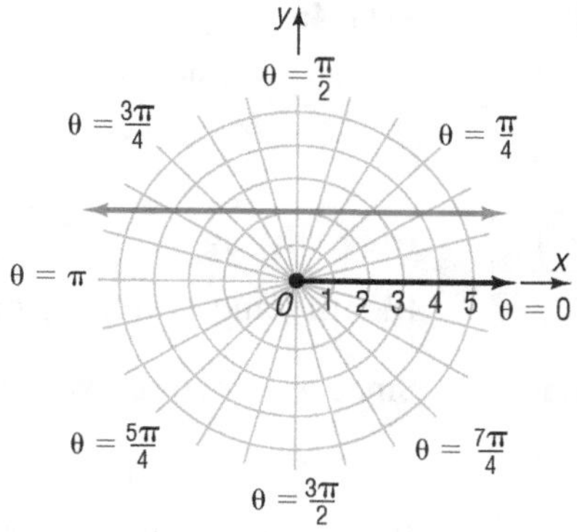

2 Graph Polar Equations Using a Graphing Utility

A second method we can use to graph a polar equation is to graph the equation using a graphing utility.

Most graphing utilities require the following steps to obtain the graph of an equation:

Graphing a Polar Equation Using a Graphing Utility

STEP 1: Solve the equation for r in terms of θ.

STEP 2: Select the viewing window in POLar mode. In addition to setting Xmin, Xmax, Xscl, and so forth, the viewing window in polar mode requires setting minimum and maximum values for θ and an increment setting for θ (θstep). Finally, a square screen and radian measure should be used.

STEP 3: Enter the expression involving θ that you found in Step 1. (Consult your manual for the correct way to enter the expression.)

STEP 4: Press graph.

EXAMPLE 4 **Graphing a Polar Equation Using a Graphing Utility**

Use a graphing utility to graph the polar equation $r \sin \theta = 2$.

Solution **STEP 1:** We solve the equation for r in terms of θ.

$$r \sin \theta = 2$$
$$r = \frac{2}{\sin \theta}$$

STEP 2: From the polar mode, select a square viewing window. We will use the one given next.

$$\theta\text{min} = 0 \qquad X\text{min} = -9 \qquad Y\text{min} = -6$$
$$\theta\text{max} = 2\pi \qquad X\text{max} = 9 \qquad Y\text{max} = 6$$
$$\theta\text{step} = \frac{\pi}{24} \qquad X\text{scl} = 1 \qquad Y\text{scl} = 1$$

θstep determines the number of points the graphing utility will plot. For example, if θstep is $\frac{\pi}{24}$, then the graphing utility will evaluate r at $\theta = 0\ (\theta\text{min}), \frac{\pi}{24}, \frac{2\pi}{24}, \frac{3\pi}{24}$, and so forth, up to $2\pi(\theta\text{max})$.

The smaller θstep is the more points the graphing utility will plot. The student is encouraged to experiment with different values for θmin, θmax, and θstep to see how the graph is affected.

STEP 3: Enter the expression $\frac{2}{\sin \theta}$ after the prompt $r =$.

STEP 4: Graph.

The graph is shown in Figure 25.

Figure 25

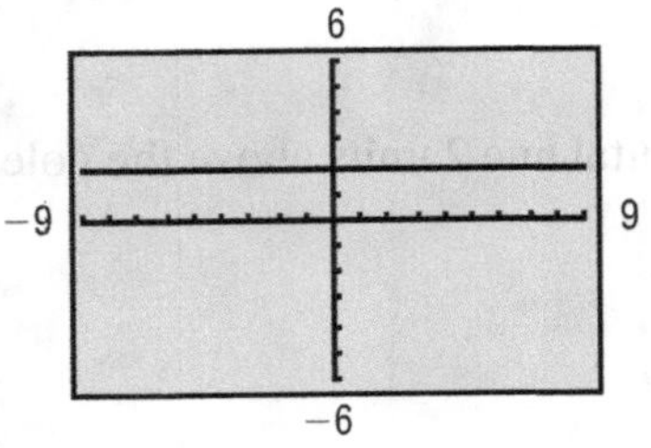

EXAMPLE 5 **Identifying and Graphing a Polar Equation (Vertical Line)**

Identify and graph the equation: $r \cos \theta = -3$

Solution Since $x = r \cos \theta$, we can write the equation as

$$x = -3$$

We conclude that the graph of $r \cos \theta = -3$ is a vertical line 3 units to the left of the pole. Figure 26(a) shows the graph drawn by hand. Figure 26(b) shows the graph using a graphing utility with $\theta\text{min} = 0$, $\theta\text{max} = 2\pi$, and $\theta\text{step} = \frac{\pi}{24}$.

Figure 26
$r \cos \theta = -3$ or $x = -3$

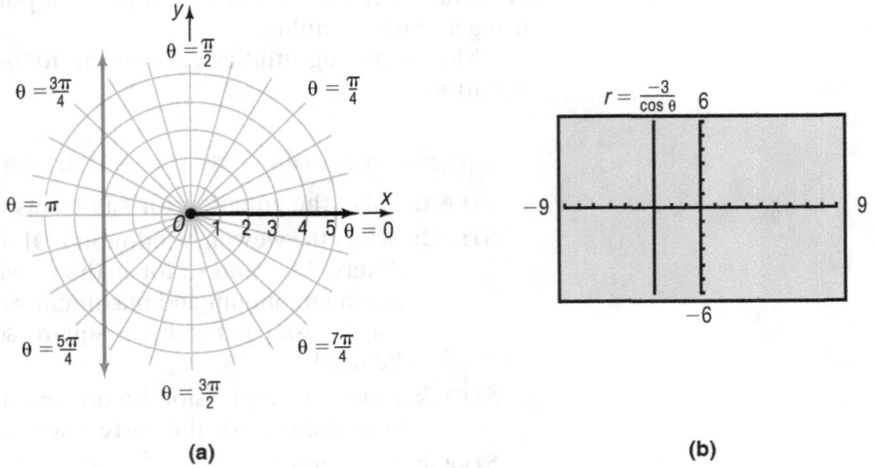

(a) (b)

Based on Examples 3, 4, and 5, we are led to the following results. (The proofs are left as exercises. See Problems 81 and 82.)

THEOREM

Let a be a nonzero real number. Then the graph of the equation

$$r \sin \theta = a$$

is a horizontal line a units above the pole if $a > 0$ and $|a|$ units below the pole if $a < 0$.

The graph of the equation

$$r \cos \theta = a$$

is a vertical line a units to the right of the pole if $a > 0$ and $|a|$ units to the left of the pole if $a < 0$.

Now Work PROBLEM 19

EXAMPLE 6 Identifying and Graphing a Polar Equation (Circle)

Identify and graph the equation: $r = 4 \sin \theta$

Solution To transform the equation to rectangular coordinates, we multiply each side by r.

$$r^2 = 4r \sin \theta$$

Now we use the facts that $r^2 = x^2 + y^2$ and $y = r \sin \theta$. Then

$$x^2 + y^2 = 4y$$
$$x^2 + (y^2 - 4y) = 0$$
$$x^2 + (y^2 - 4y + 4) = 4 \quad \text{Complete the square in } y.$$
$$x^2 + (y - 2)^2 = 4 \quad \text{Factor.}$$

This is the standard equation of a circle with center at $(0, 2)$ in rectangular coordinates and radius 2. Figure 27(a) shows the graph drawn by hand. Figure 27(b) shows the graph using a graphing utility with $\theta\text{min} = 0$, $\theta\text{max} = 2\pi$, and $\theta\text{step} = \frac{\pi}{24}$.

Figure 27
$r = 4 \sin \theta$ or $x^2 + (y - 2)^2 = 4$

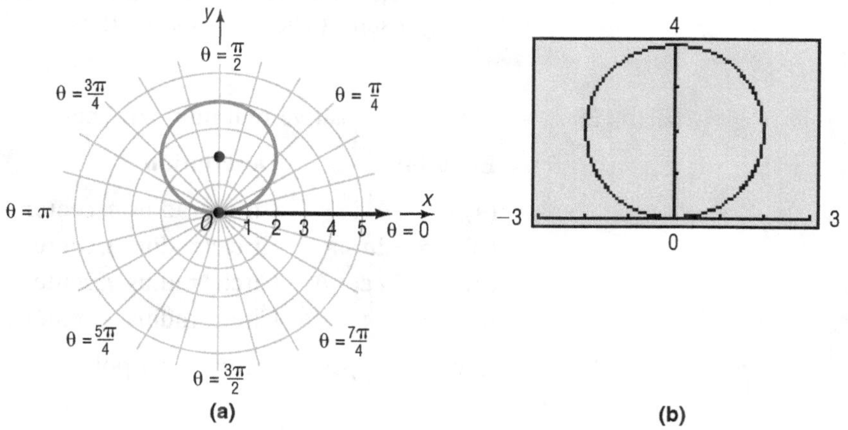

EXAMPLE 7 Identifying and Graphing a Polar Equation (Circle)

Identify and graph the equation: $r = -2\cos\theta$

Solution We proceed as in Example 6.

$$r^2 = -2r\cos\theta \qquad \text{Multiply both sides by } r.$$

$$x^2 + y^2 = -2x \qquad r^2 = x^2 + y^2;\ x = r\cos\theta$$

$$x^2 + 2x + y^2 = 0$$

$$(x^2 + 2x + 1) + y^2 = 1 \qquad \text{Complete the square in } x.$$

$$(x + 1)^2 + y^2 = 1 \qquad \text{Factor.}$$

This is the standard equation of a circle with center at $(-1, 0)$ in rectangular coordinates and radius 1. Figure 28(a) shows the graph drawn by hand. Figure 28(b) shows the graph using a graphing utility with $\theta\text{min} = 0$, $\theta\text{max} = 2\pi$, and $\theta\text{step} = \frac{\pi}{24}$.

Figure 28
$r = -2\cos\theta$ or $(x + 1)^2 + y^2 = 1$

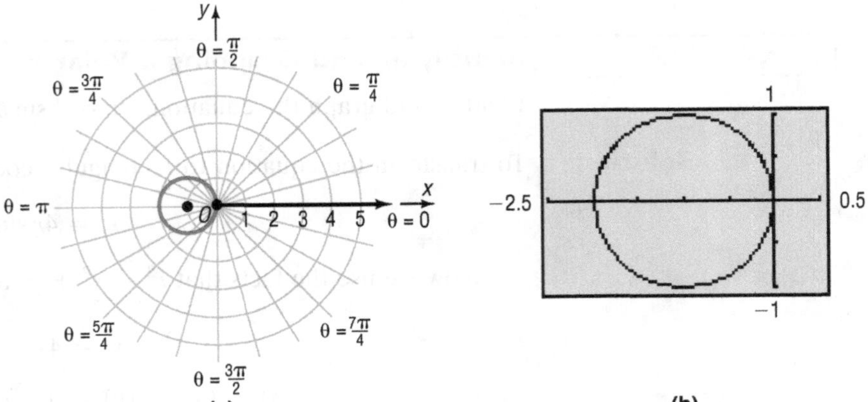

(a) (b)

Exploration

Using a square screen, graph $r_1 = \sin\theta$, $r_2 = 2\sin\theta$, and $r_3 = 3\sin\theta$. Do you see the pattern? Clear the screen and graph $r_1 = -\sin\theta$, $r_2 = -2\sin\theta$, and $r_3 = -3\sin\theta$. Do you see the pattern? Clear the screen and graph $r_1 = \cos\theta$, $r_2 = 2\cos\theta$, and $r_3 = 3\cos\theta$. Do you see the pattern? Clear the screen and graph $r_1 = -\cos\theta$, $r_2 = -2\cos\theta$, and $r_3 = -3\cos\theta$. Do you see the pattern?

Based on Examples 6 and 7 and the preceding Exploration, we are led to the following results. (The proofs are left as exercises. See Problems 83–86.)

THEOREM

Let a be a positive real number. Then

Equation	**Description**
(a) $r = 2a\sin\theta$	Circle: radius a; center at $(0, a)$ in rectangular coordinates
(b) $r = -2a\sin\theta$	Circle: radius a; center at $(0, -a)$ in rectangular coordinates
(c) $r = 2a\cos\theta$	Circle: radius a; center at $(a, 0)$ in rectangular coordinates
(d) $r = -2a\cos\theta$	Circle: radius a; center at $(-a, 0)$ in rectangular coordinates

Each circle passes through the pole.

Now Work PROBLEM 21

The method of converting a polar equation to an identifiable rectangular equation to obtain the graph is not always helpful, nor is it always necessary. Usually, we set up a table that lists several points on the graph. By checking for symmetry, it may be possible to reduce the number of points needed to draw the graph.

3 Test Polar Equations for Symmetry

In polar coordinates, the points (r, θ) and $(r, -\theta)$ are symmetric with respect to the polar axis (and to the x-axis). See Figure 29(a). The points (r, θ) and $(r, \pi - \theta)$ are symmetric with respect to the line $\theta = \dfrac{\pi}{2}$ (the y-axis). See Figure 29(b). The points (r, θ) and $(-r, \theta)$ are symmetric with respect to the pole (the origin). See Figure 29(c).

Figure 29

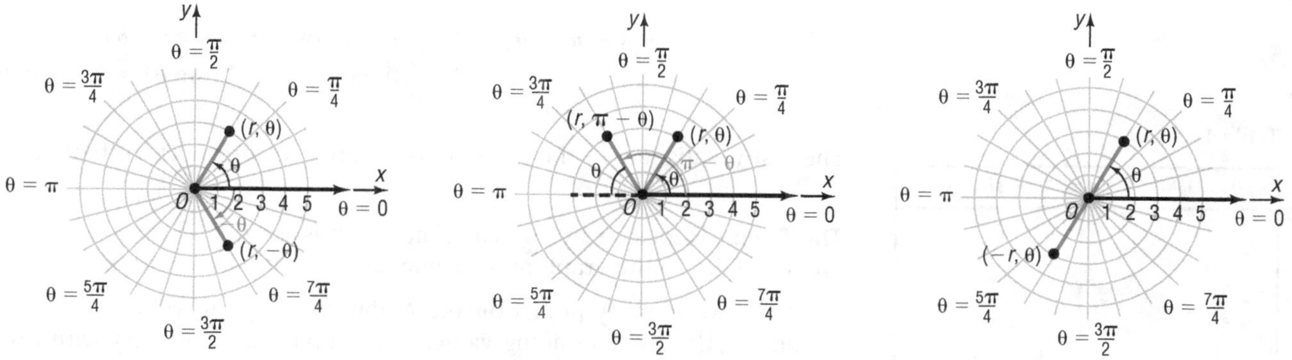

(a) Points symmetric with respect to the polar axis

(b) Points symmetric with respect to the line $\theta = \frac{\pi}{2}$

(c) Points symmetric with respect to the pole

The following tests are a consequence of these observations.

THEOREM

Tests for Symmetry

Symmetry with Respect to the Polar Axis (x-Axis)

In a polar equation, replace θ by $-\theta$. If an equivalent equation results, the graph is symmetric with respect to the polar axis.

Symmetry with Respect to the Line $\theta = \dfrac{\pi}{2}$ (y-Axis)

In a polar equation, replace θ by $\pi - \theta$. If an equivalent equation results, the graph is symmetric with respect to the line $\theta = \dfrac{\pi}{2}$.

Symmetry with Respect to the Pole (Origin)

In a polar equation, replace r by $-r$. If an equivalent equation results, the graph is symmetric with respect to the pole.

The three tests for symmetry given here are *sufficient* conditions for symmetry, but they are not *necessary* conditions. That is, an equation may fail these tests and still have a graph that is symmetric with respect to the polar axis, the line $\theta = \dfrac{\pi}{2}$, or the pole. For example, the graph of $r = \sin(2\theta)$ turns out to be symmetric with respect to the polar axis, the line $\theta = \dfrac{\pi}{2}$, and the pole, but all three tests given here fail. See also Problems 87–89.

4 Graph Polar Equations by Plotting Points

EXAMPLE 8 **Graphing a Polar Equation (Cardioid)**

Graph the equation: $r = 1 - \sin\theta$

Solution We check for symmetry first.

Polar Axis: Replace θ by $-\theta$. The result is

$$r = 1 - \sin(-\theta) = 1 + \sin\theta \quad \sin(-\theta) = -\sin\theta$$

The test fails, so the graph may or may not be symmetric with respect to the polar axis.

The Line $\theta = \frac{\pi}{2}$: Replace θ by $\pi - \theta$. The result is

$$r = 1 - \sin(\pi - \theta) = 1 - (\sin\pi\cos\theta - \cos\pi\sin\theta)$$
$$= 1 - [0 \cdot \cos\theta - (-1)\sin\theta] = 1 - \sin\theta$$

The test is satisfied, so the graph is symmetric with respect to the line $\theta = \frac{\pi}{2}$.

The Pole: Replace r by $-r$. Then the result is $-r = 1 - \sin\theta$, so $r = -1 + \sin\theta$. The test fails, so the graph may or may not be symmetric with respect to the pole.

Next, we identify points on the graph by assigning values to the angle θ and calculating the corresponding values of r. Due to the symmetry with respect to the line $\theta = \frac{\pi}{2}$, we only need to assign values to θ from $-\frac{\pi}{2}$ to $\frac{\pi}{2}$, as given in Table 1.

Now we plot the points (r, θ) from Table 1 and trace out the graph, beginning at the point $\left(2, -\frac{\pi}{2}\right)$ and ending at the point $\left(0, \frac{\pi}{2}\right)$. Then we reflect this portion of the graph about the line $\theta = \frac{\pi}{2}$ (the y-axis) to obtain the complete graph. Figure 30(a) shows the graph drawn by hand. Figure 30(b) shows the graph using a graphing utility with θmin = 0, θmax = 2π, and θstep = $\frac{\pi}{24}$.

Table 1

θ	$r = 1 - \sin\theta$
$-\frac{\pi}{2}$	$1 - (-1) = 2$
$-\frac{\pi}{3}$	$1 - \left(-\frac{\sqrt{3}}{2}\right) \approx 1.87$
$-\frac{\pi}{6}$	$1 - \left(-\frac{1}{2}\right) = \frac{3}{2}$
0	$1 - 0 = 1$
$\frac{\pi}{6}$	$1 - \frac{1}{2} = \frac{1}{2}$
$\frac{\pi}{3}$	$1 - \frac{\sqrt{3}}{2} \approx 0.13$
$\frac{\pi}{2}$	$1 - 1 = 0$

Figure 30

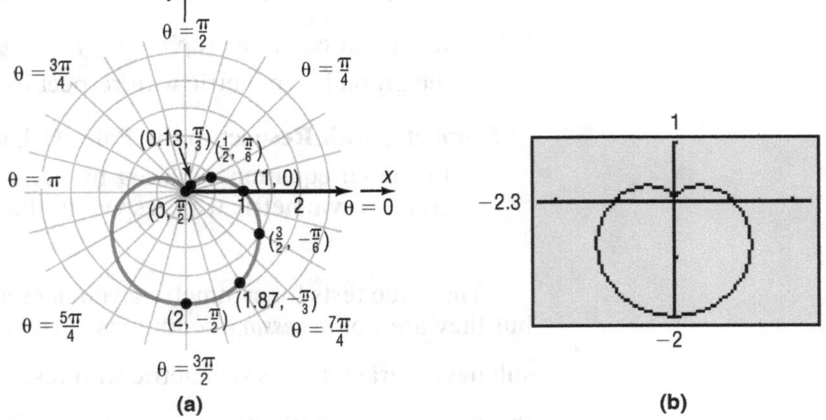

Exploration

Graph $r_1 = 1 + \sin\theta$. Clear the screen and graph $r_1 = 1 - \cos\theta$. Clear the screen and graph $r_1 = 1 + \cos\theta$. Do you see a pattern?

The curve in Figure 30 is an example of a *cardioid* (a heart-shaped curve).

DEFINITION

Cardioids are characterized by equations of the form

$$r = a(1 + \cos\theta) \qquad r = a(1 + \sin\theta)$$
$$r = a(1 - \cos\theta) \qquad r = a(1 - \sin\theta)$$

where $a > 0$. The graph of a cardioid passes through the pole.

Now Work PROBLEM 37

EXAMPLE 9 Graphing a Polar Equation (Limaçon without Inner Loop)

Graph the equation: $r = 3 + 2\cos\theta$

Solution We check for symmetry first.

Polar Axis: Replace θ by $-\theta$. The result is

$$r = 3 + 2\cos(-\theta) = 3 + 2\cos\theta \qquad \cos(-\theta) = \cos\theta$$

The test is satisfied, so the graph is symmetric with respect to the polar axis.

The Line $\theta = \frac{\pi}{2}$: Replace θ by $\pi - \theta$. The result is

$$r = 3 + 2\cos(\pi - \theta) = 3 + 2(\cos\pi\cos\theta + \sin\pi\sin\theta)$$
$$= 3 - 2\cos\theta$$

The test fails, so the graph may or may not be symmetric with respect to the line $\theta = \frac{\pi}{2}$.

The Pole: Replace r by $-r$. The test fails, so the graph may or may not be symmetric with respect to the pole.

Table 2

θ	$r = 3 + 2\cos\theta$
0	$3 + 2(1) = 5$
$\frac{\pi}{6}$	$3 + 2\left(\frac{\sqrt{3}}{2}\right) \approx 4.73$
$\frac{\pi}{3}$	$3 + 2\left(\frac{1}{2}\right) = 4$
$\frac{\pi}{2}$	$3 + 2(0) = 3$
$\frac{2\pi}{3}$	$3 + 2\left(-\frac{1}{2}\right) = 2$
$\frac{5\pi}{6}$	$3 + 2\left(-\frac{\sqrt{3}}{2}\right) \approx 1.27$
π	$3 + 2(-1) = 1$

Next, we identify points on the graph by assigning values to the angle θ and calculating the corresponding values of r. Due to the symmetry with respect to the polar axis, we only need to assign values to θ from 0 to π, as given in Table 2.

Now we plot the points (r, θ) from Table 2 and trace out the graph, beginning at the point $(5, 0)$ and ending at the point $(1, \pi)$. Then we reflect this portion of the graph about the polar axis (the x-axis) to obtain the complete graph. Figure 31(a) shows the graph drawn by hand. Figure 31(b) shows the graph using a graphing utility with $\theta\text{min} = 0$, $\theta\text{max} = 2\pi$, and $\theta\text{step} = \frac{\pi}{24}$.

Figure 31

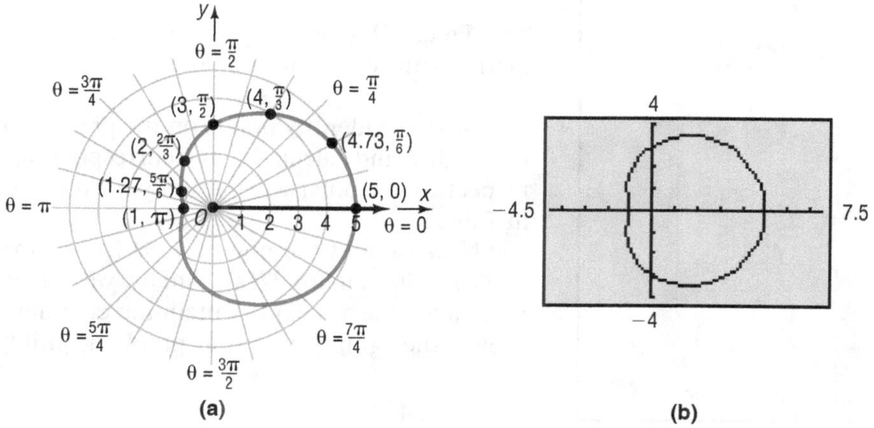

Exploration

Graph $r_1 = 3 - 2\cos\theta$. Clear the screen and graph $r_1 = 3 + 2\sin\theta$. Clear the screen and graph $r_1 = 3 - 2\sin\theta$. Do you see a pattern?

The curve in Figure 31 is an example of a *limaçon* (the French word for *snail*) *without an inner loop*.

DEFINITION

Limaçons without an inner loop are characterized by equations of the form

$$r = a + b\cos\theta \qquad r = a + b\sin\theta$$
$$r = a - b\cos\theta \qquad r = a - b\sin\theta$$

where $a > 0, b > 0$, and $a > b$. The graph of a limaçon without an inner loop does not pass through the pole.

Now Work PROBLEM 43

EXAMPLE 10 Graphing a Polar Equation (Limaçon with Inner Loop)

Graph the equation: $r = 1 + 2\cos\theta$

Solution First, we check for symmetry.

Polar Axis: Replace θ by $-\theta$. The result is

$$r = 1 + 2\cos(-\theta) = 1 + 2\cos\theta$$

The test is satisfied, so the graph is symmetric with respect to the polar axis.

The Line $\theta = \frac{\pi}{2}$: Replace θ by $\pi - \theta$. The result is

$$r = 1 + 2\cos(\pi - \theta) = 1 + 2(\cos\pi\cos\theta + \sin\pi\sin\theta)$$
$$= 1 - 2\cos\theta$$

The test fails, so the graph may or may not be symmetric with respect to the line $\theta = \frac{\pi}{2}$.

The Pole: Replace r by $-r$. The test fails, so the graph may or may not be symmetric with respect to the pole.

Next, we identify points on the graph of $r = 1 + 2\cos\theta$ by assigning values to the angle θ and calculating the corresponding values of r. Due to the symmetry with respect to the polar axis, we only need to assign values to θ from 0 to π, as given in Table 3.

Now we plot the points (r, θ) from Table 3, beginning at $(3, 0)$ and ending at $(-1, \pi)$. See Figure 32(a). Finally, we reflect this portion of the graph about the polar axis (the x-axis) to obtain the complete graph. See Figure 32(b). Figure 32(c) shows the graph using a graphing utility with $\theta\min = 0$, $\theta\max = 2\pi$, and $\theta\text{step} = \frac{\pi}{24}$.

Table 3

θ	$r = 1 + 2\cos\theta$
0	$1 + 2(1) = 3$
$\frac{\pi}{6}$	$1 + 2\left(\frac{\sqrt{3}}{2}\right) \approx 2.73$
$\frac{\pi}{3}$	$1 + 2\left(\frac{1}{2}\right) = 2$
$\frac{\pi}{2}$	$1 + 2(0) = 1$
$\frac{2\pi}{3}$	$1 + 2\left(-\frac{1}{2}\right) = 0$
$\frac{5\pi}{6}$	$1 + 2\left(-\frac{\sqrt{3}}{2}\right) \approx -0.73$
π	$1 + 2(-1) = -1$

Figure 32

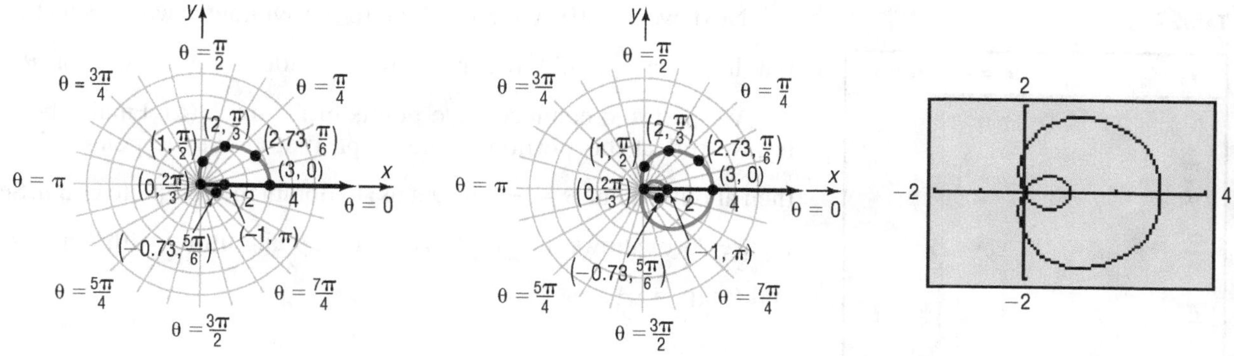

(a) (b) $r = 1 + 2\cos\theta$ (c)

Exploration

Graph $r_1 = 1 - 2\cos\theta$. Clear the screen and graph $r_1 = 1 + 2\sin\theta$. Clear the screen and graph $r_1 = 1 - 2\sin\theta$. Do you see a pattern?

The curve in Figure 32(b) or 32(c) is an example of a *limaçon with an inner loop*.

DEFINITION

Limaçons with an inner loop are characterized by equations of the form

$$r = a + b\cos\theta \qquad r = a + b\sin\theta$$
$$r = a - b\cos\theta \qquad r = a - b\sin\theta$$

where $a > 0, b > 0$, and $a < b$. The graph of a limaçon with an inner loop will pass through the pole twice.

Now Work PROBLEM 45

EXAMPLE 11 Graphing a Polar Equation (Rose)

Graph the equation: $r = 2\cos(2\theta)$

Solution We check for symmetry.

Polar Axis: If we replace θ by $-\theta$, the result is

$$r = 2\cos[2(-\theta)] = 2\cos(2\theta)$$

The test is satisfied, so the graph is symmetric with respect to the polar axis.

The Line $\theta = \frac{\pi}{2}$: If we replace θ by $\pi - \theta$, we obtain

$$r = 2\cos[2(\pi - \theta)] = 2\cos(2\pi - 2\theta) = 2\cos(2\theta)$$

The test is satisfied, so the graph is symmetric with respect to the line $\theta = \frac{\pi}{2}$.

The Pole: Since the graph is symmetric with respect to both the polar axis and the line $\theta = \frac{\pi}{2}$, it must be symmetric with respect to the pole.

Table 4

θ	$r = 2\cos(2\theta)$
0	$2(1) = 2$
$\frac{\pi}{6}$	$2\left(\frac{1}{2}\right) = 1$
$\frac{\pi}{4}$	$2(0) = 0$
$\frac{\pi}{3}$	$2\left(-\frac{1}{2}\right) = -1$
$\frac{\pi}{2}$	$2(-1) = -2$

Next, we construct Table 4. Due to the symmetry with respect to the polar axis, the line $\theta = \frac{\pi}{2}$, and the pole, we consider only values of θ from 0 to $\frac{\pi}{2}$.

We plot and connect these points in Figure 33(a). Finally, because of symmetry, we reflect this portion of the graph first about the polar axis (the x-axis) and then about the line $\theta = \frac{\pi}{2}$ (the y-axis) to obtain the complete graph. See Figure 33(b). Figure 33(c) shows the graph using a graphing utility with θmin $= 0$, θmax $= 2\pi$, and θstep $= \frac{\pi}{24}$.

Figure 33

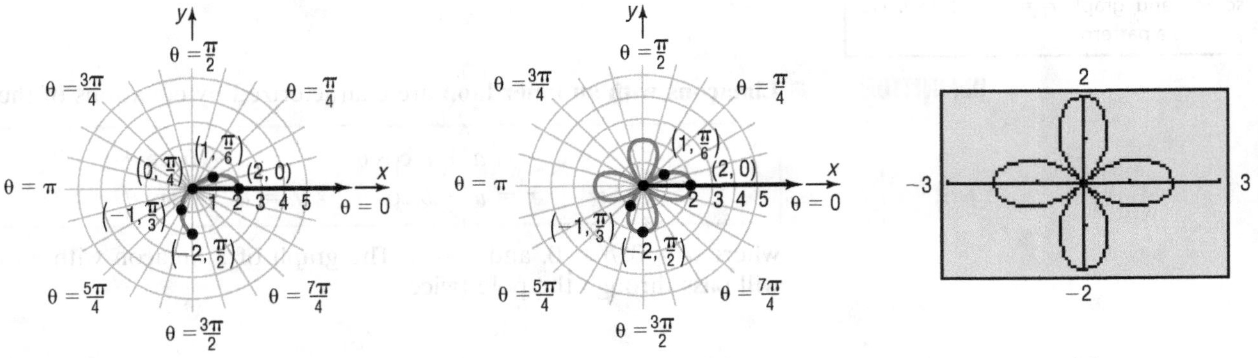

(a) (b) $r = 2\cos(2\theta)$ (c)

Exploration

Graph $r_1 = 2\cos(4\theta)$; clear the screen and graph $r_1 = 2\cos(6\theta)$. How many petals did each of these graphs have?

Clear the screen and graph, in order, each on a clear screen, $r_1 = 2\cos(3\theta)$, $r_1 = 2\cos(5\theta)$, and $r_1 = 2\cos(7\theta)$. What do you notice about the number of petals?

The curve in Figure 33(b) or 33(c) is called a *rose* with four petals.

DEFINITION

Rose curves are characterized by equations of the form

$$r = a\cos(n\theta), \qquad r = a\sin(n\theta), \qquad a \neq 0$$

and have graphs that are rose shaped. If $n \neq 0$ is even, the rose has $2n$ petals; if $n \neq \pm 1$ is odd, the rose has n petals.

Now Work PROBLEM 49

EXAMPLE 12 Graphing a Polar Equation (Lemniscate)

Graph the equation: $r^2 = 4\sin(2\theta)$

Table 5

θ	$r^2 = 4\sin(2\theta)$	r
0	$4(0) = 0$	0
$\frac{\pi}{6}$	$4\left(\frac{\sqrt{3}}{2}\right) = 2\sqrt{3}$	± 1.9
$\frac{\pi}{4}$	$4(1) = 4$	± 2
$\frac{\pi}{3}$	$4\left(\frac{\sqrt{3}}{2}\right) = 2\sqrt{3}$	± 1.9
$\frac{\pi}{2}$	$4(0) = 0$	0

Solution We leave it to you to verify that the graph is symmetric with respect to the pole. Because of the symmetry with respect to the pole, we only need to consider values of θ between $\theta = 0$ and $\theta = \pi$. Note that there are no points on the graph for $\frac{\pi}{2} < \theta < \pi$ (quadrant II), since $\sin(2\theta) < 0$ for such values. Table 5 lists points on the graph for values of $\theta = 0$ through $\theta = \frac{\pi}{2}$. The points from Table 5 where $r \geq 0$ are plotted in Figure 34(a). The remaining points on the graph may be obtained by using symmetry. Figure 34(b) shows the final graph drawn by hand. Figure 34(c) shows the graph using a graphing utility with $\theta\text{min} = 0$, $\theta\text{max} = 2\pi$, and $\theta\text{step} = \frac{\pi}{24}$.

Figure 34

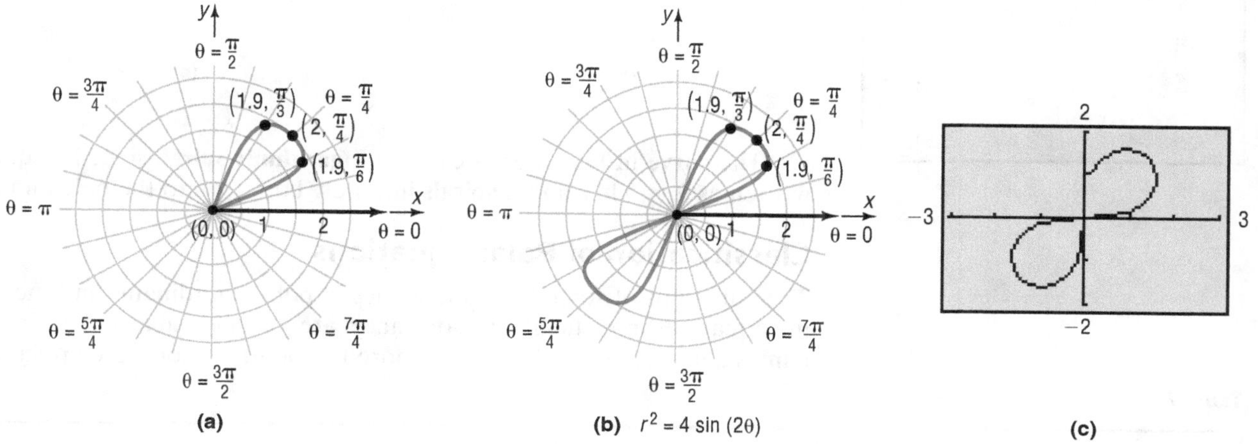

The curve in Figure 34(b) or 34(c) is an example of a *lemniscate* (from the Greek word *ribbon*).

DEFINITION

Lemniscates are characterized by equations of the form

$$r^2 = a^2\sin(2\theta) \qquad r^2 = a^2\cos(2\theta)$$

where $a \neq 0$, and have graphs that are propeller shaped.

Now Work PROBLEM 53

EXAMPLE 13 Graphing a Polar Equation (Spiral)

Graph the equation: $r = e^{\theta/5}$

Solution The tests for symmetry with respect to the pole, the polar axis, and the line $\theta = \frac{\pi}{2}$ fail. Furthermore, there is no number θ for which $r = 0$, so the graph does not pass through the pole. We observe that r is positive for all θ, r increases as θ increases, $r \to 0$ as $\theta \to -\infty$, and $r \to \infty$ as $\theta \to \infty$. With the help of a calculator, we obtain the values in Table 6. See Figure 35(a) for the graph drawn by hand. Figure 35(b)

Table 6

θ	$r = e^{\theta/5}$
$-\frac{3\pi}{2}$	0.39
$-\pi$	0.53
$-\frac{\pi}{2}$	0.73
$-\frac{\pi}{4}$	0.85
0	1
$\frac{\pi}{4}$	1.17
$\frac{\pi}{2}$	1.37
π	1.87
$\frac{3\pi}{2}$	2.57
2π	3.51

shows the graph using a graphing utility with $\theta\text{min} = -4\pi$, $\theta\text{max} = 3\pi$, and $\theta\text{step} = \frac{\pi}{24}$.

Figure 35
$r = e^{\theta/5}$

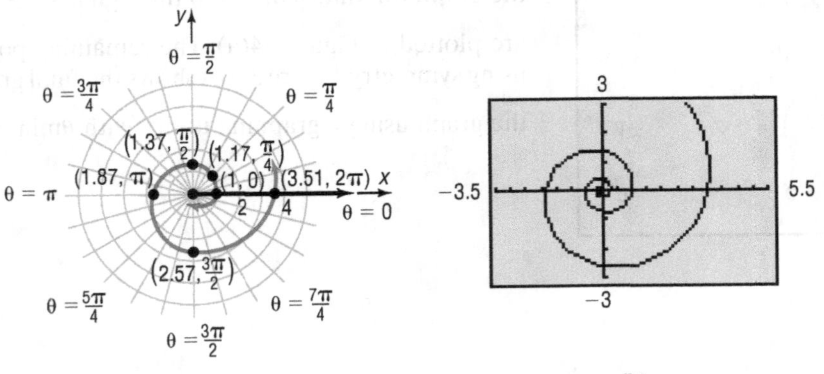

(a) (b)

The curve in Figure 35 is called a **logarithmic spiral,** since its equation may be written as $\theta = 5 \ln r$ and it spirals infinitely both toward the pole and away from it.

Classification of Polar Equations

The equations of some lines and circles in polar coordinates and their corresponding equations in rectangular coordinates are given in Table 7. Also included are the names and graphs of a few of the more frequently encountered polar equations.

Table 7

Lines			
Description	Line passing through the pole making an angle α with the polar axis	Vertical line	Horizontal line
Rectangular equation	$y = (\tan \alpha)x$	$x = a$	$y = b$
Polar equation	$\theta = \alpha$	$r \cos \theta = a$	$r \sin \theta = b$
Typical graph	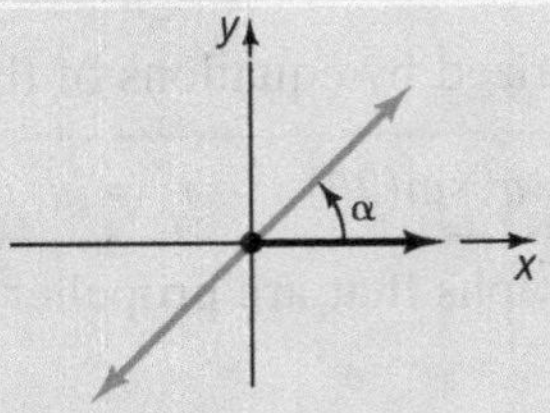	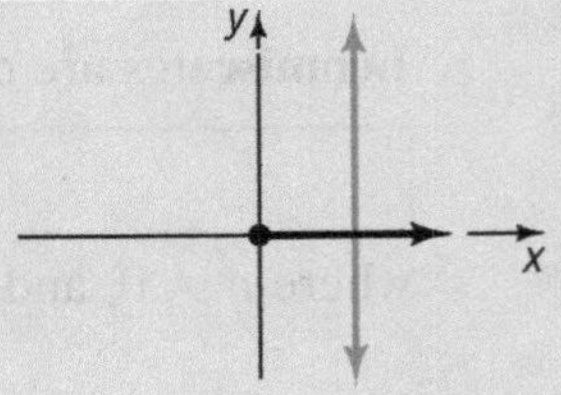	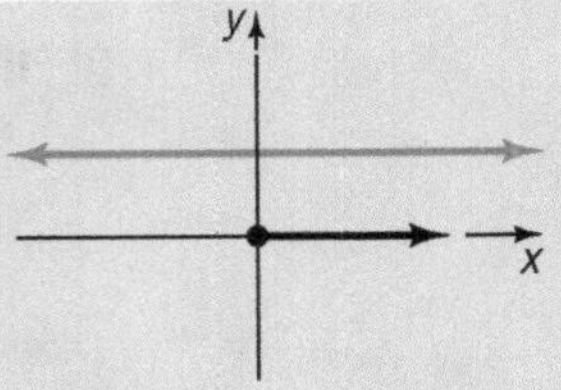

Circles			
Description	Center at the pole, radius a	Passing through the pole, tangent to the line $\theta = \frac{\pi}{2}$, center on the polar axis, radius a	Passing through the pole, tangent to the polar axis, center on the line $\theta = \frac{\pi}{2}$, radius a
Rectangular equation	$x^2 + y^2 = a^2, \quad a > 0$	$x^2 + y^2 = \pm 2ax, \quad a > 0$	$x^2 + y^2 = \pm 2ay, \quad a > 0$
Polar equation	$r = a, \quad a > 0$	$r = \pm 2a \cos \theta, \quad a > 0$	$r = \pm 2a \sin \theta, \quad a > 0$
Typical graph	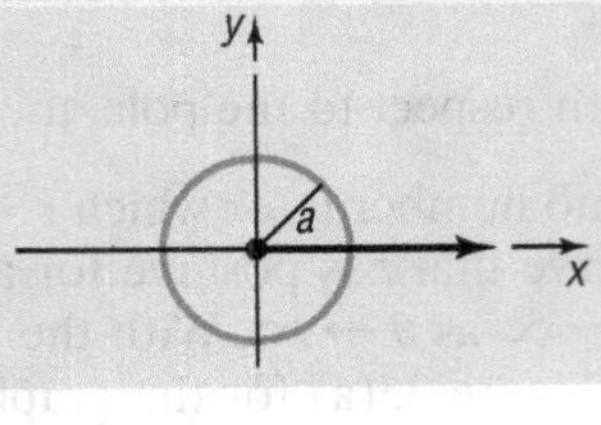	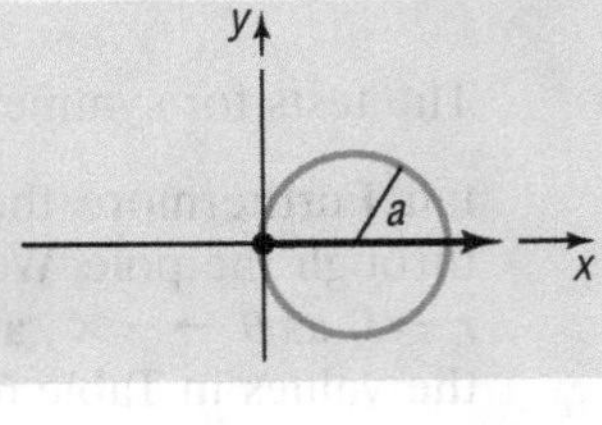	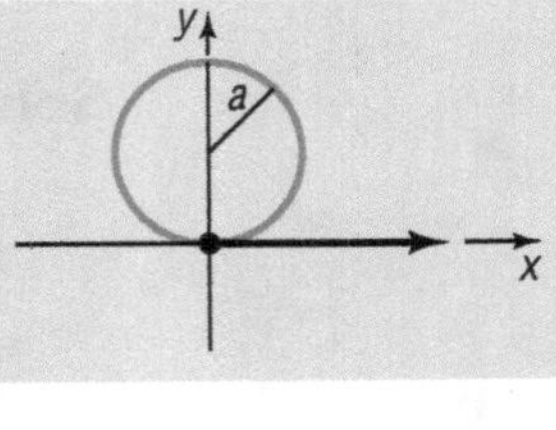

Other Equations

Name	Cardioid	Limaçon without inner loop	Limaçon with inner loop
Polar equations	$r = a \pm a\cos\theta,\quad a > 0$ $r = a \pm a\sin\theta,\quad a > 0$	$r = a \pm b\cos\theta,\quad 0 < b < a$ $r = a \pm b\sin\theta,\quad 0 < b < a$	$r = a \pm b\cos\theta,\quad 0 < a < b$ $r = a \pm b\sin\theta,\quad 0 < a < b$
Typical graph	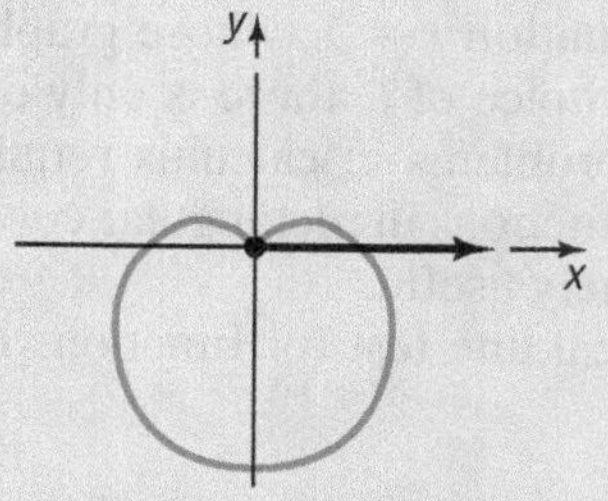	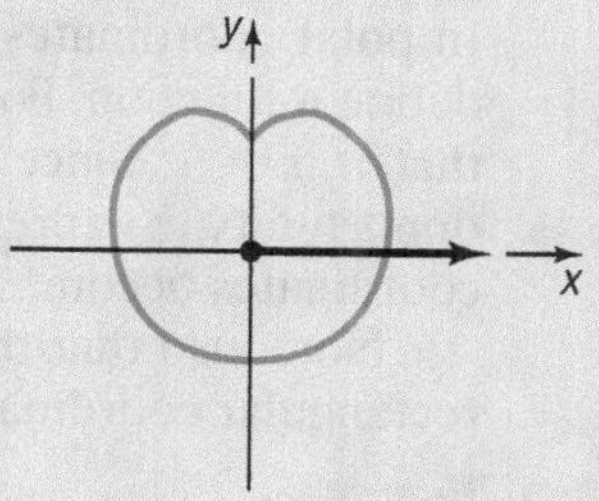	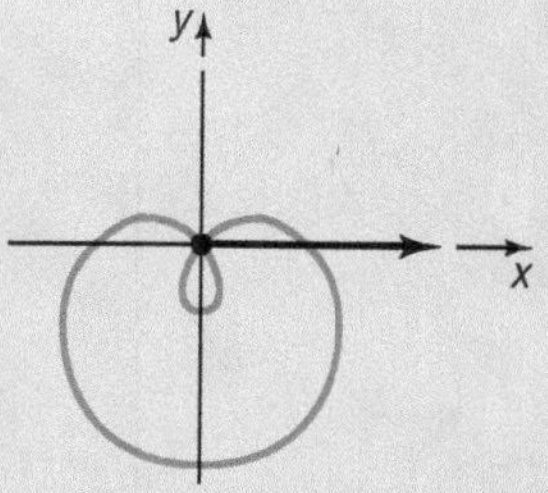
Name	Lemniscate	Rose with three petals	Rose with four petals
Polar equations	$r^2 = a^2\cos(2\theta),\quad a > 0$ $r^2 = a^2\sin(2\theta),\quad a > 0$	$r = a\sin(3\theta),\quad a > 0$ $r = a\cos(3\theta),\quad a > 0$	$r = a\sin(2\theta),\quad a > 0$ $r = a\cos(2\theta),\quad a > 0$
Typical graph	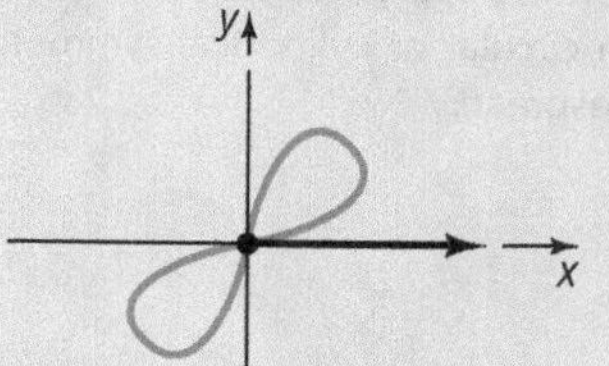	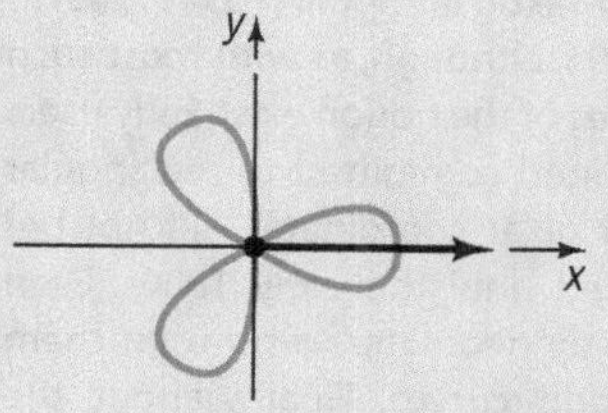	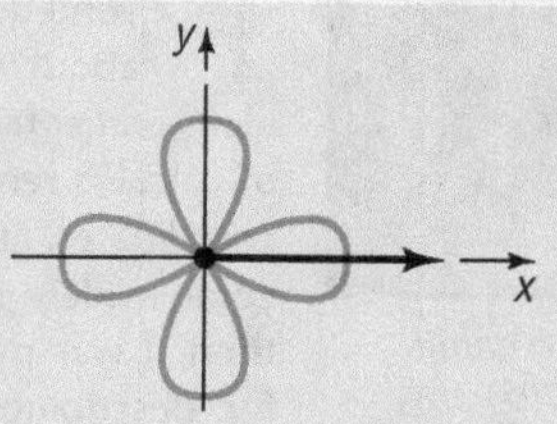

Sketching Quickly

If a polar equation involves only a sine (or cosine) function, you can quickly obtain a sketch of its graph by making use of Table 7, periodicity, and a short table.

EXAMPLE 14 **Sketching the Graph of a Polar Equation Quickly**

Graph the equation: $r = 2 + 2\sin\theta$

Solution We recognize the polar equation: Its graph is a cardioid. The period of $\sin\theta$ is 2π, so we form a table using $0 \le \theta \le 2\pi$, compute r, plot the points (r, θ), and sketch the graph of a cardioid as θ varies from 0 to 2π. See Table 8 and Figure 36.

Table 8

θ	$r = 2 + 2\sin\theta$
0	$2 + 2(0) = 2$
$\frac{\pi}{2}$	$2 + 2(1) = 4$
π	$2 + 2(0) = 2$
$\frac{3\pi}{2}$	$2 + 2(-1) = 0$
2π	$2 + 2(0) = 2$

Figure 36

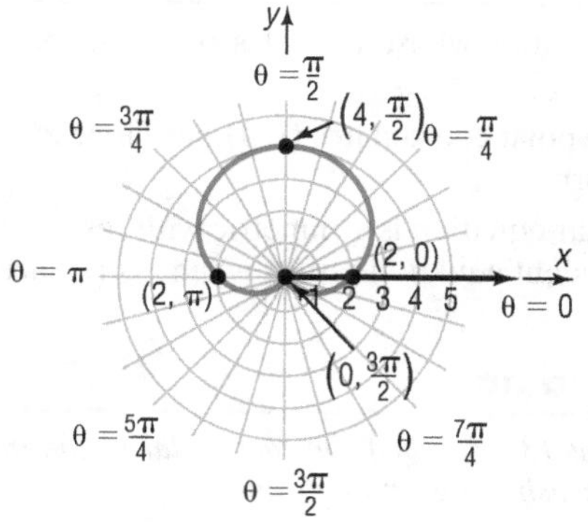

Now Work PROBLEM 37

Calculus Comment For those of you who are planning to study calculus, a comment about one important role of polar equations is in order.

In rectangular coordinates, the equation $x^2 + y^2 = 1$, whose graph is the unit circle, is not the graph of a function. In fact, it requires two functions to obtain the graph of the unit circle:

$$y_1 = \sqrt{1 - x^2} \quad \text{Upper semicircle} \qquad y_2 = -\sqrt{1 - x^2} \quad \text{Lower semicircle}$$

In polar coordinates, the equation $r = 1$, whose graph is also the unit circle, does define a function. For each choice of θ, there is only one corresponding value of r, that is, $r = 1$. Since many problems in calculus require the use of functions, the opportunity to express nonfunctions in rectangular coordinates as functions in polar coordinates becomes extremely useful.

Note also that the vertical-line test for functions is valid only for equations in rectangular coordinates.

Historical Feature

Jakob Bernoulli (1654–1705)

Polar coordinates seem to have been invented by Jakob Bernoulli (1654–1705) in about 1691, although, as with most such ideas, earlier traces of the notion exist. Early users of calculus remained committed to rectangular coordinates, and polar coordinates did not become widely used until the early 1800s. Even then, it was mostly geometers who used them for describing odd curves. Finally, about the mid-1800s, applied mathematicians realized the tremendous simplification that polar coordinates make possible in the description of objects with circular or cylindrical symmetry. From then on their use became widespread.

9.2 Assess Your Understanding

'Are You Prepared?' *Answers are given at the end of these exercises. If you get a wrong answer, read the pages listed in red.*

1. If the rectangular coordinates of a point are $(4, -6)$, the point symmetric to it with respect to the origin is ______. (pp. 19–20)
2. The difference formula for cosine is $\cos(A - B) =$ ______. (p. 466)
3. The standard equation of a circle with center at $(-2, 5)$ and radius 3 is ______. (pp. 44–45)
4. Is the sine function even, odd, or neither? (p. 391)
5. $\sin \frac{5\pi}{4} =$ ______. (pp. 374–375)
6. $\cos \frac{2\pi}{3} =$ ______. (pp. 374–375)

Concepts and Vocabulary

7. An equation whose variables are polar coordinates is called a(n) ______ ______.
8. Using polar coordinates (r, θ), the circle $x^2 + y^2 = 2x$ takes the form ______.
9. A polar equation is symmetric with respect to the pole if an equivalent equation results when r is replaced by ______.
10. ***True or False*** The tests for symmetry in polar coordinates are necessary, but not sufficient.
11. ***True or False*** The graph of a cardioid never passes through the pole.
12. ***True or False*** All polar equations have a symmetric feature.

Skill Building

In Problems 13–28, transform each polar equation to an equation in rectangular coordinates. Then identify and graph the equation. Verify your graph using a graphing utility.

13. $r = 4$	14. $r = 2$	15. $\theta = \frac{\pi}{3}$	16. $\theta = -\frac{\pi}{4}$
17. $r \sin\theta = 4$	18. $r \cos\theta = 4$	19. $r \cos\theta = -2$	20. $r \sin\theta = -2$
21. $r = 2\cos\theta$	22. $r = 2\sin\theta$	23. $r = -4\sin\theta$	24. $r = -4\cos\theta$
25. $r \sec\theta = 4$	26. $r \csc\theta = 8$	27. $r \csc\theta = -2$	28. $r \sec\theta = -4$

In Problems 29–36, match each of the graphs (A) through (H) to one of the following polar equations.

29. $r = 2$

30. $\theta = \dfrac{\pi}{4}$

31. $r = 2\cos\theta$

32. $r\cos\theta = 2$

33. $r = 1 + \cos\theta$

34. $r = 2\sin\theta$

35. $\theta = \dfrac{3\pi}{4}$

36. $r\sin\theta = 2$

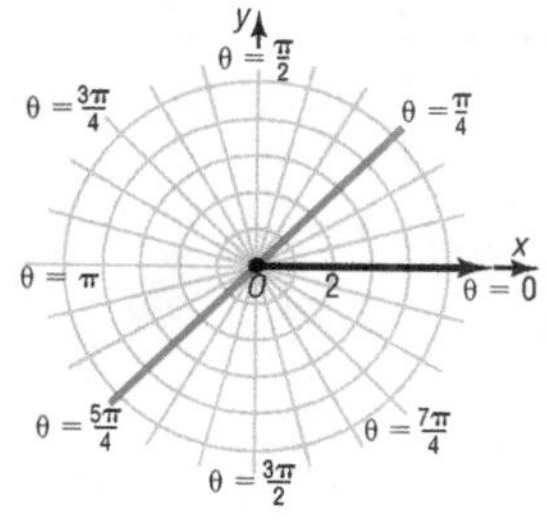

(A)

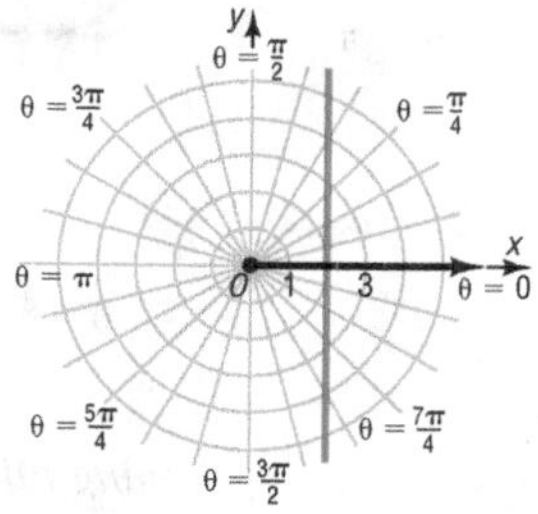

(B)

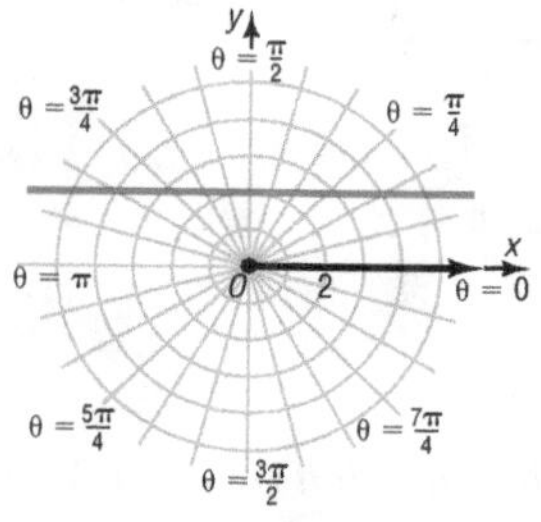

(C)

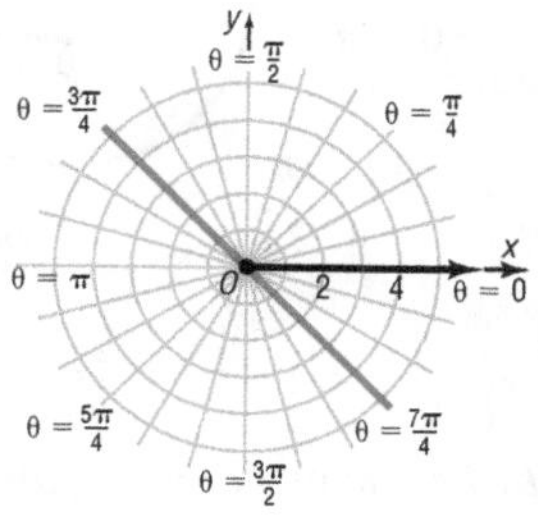

(D)

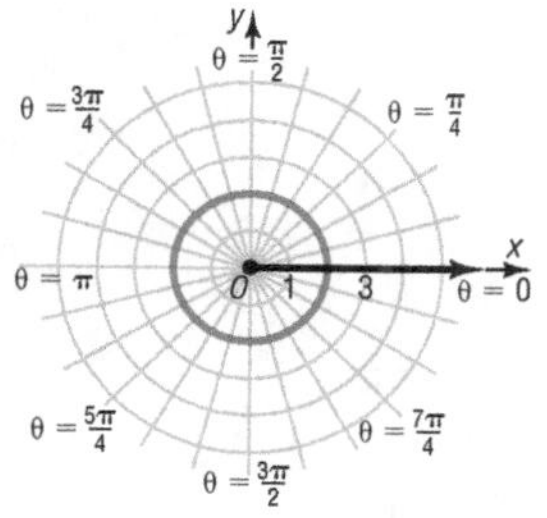

(E)

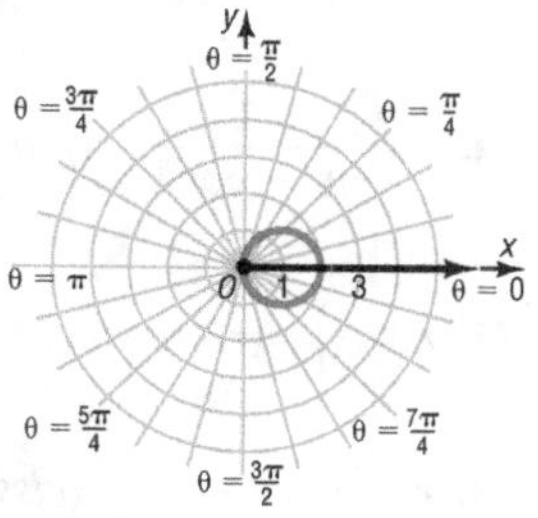

(F)

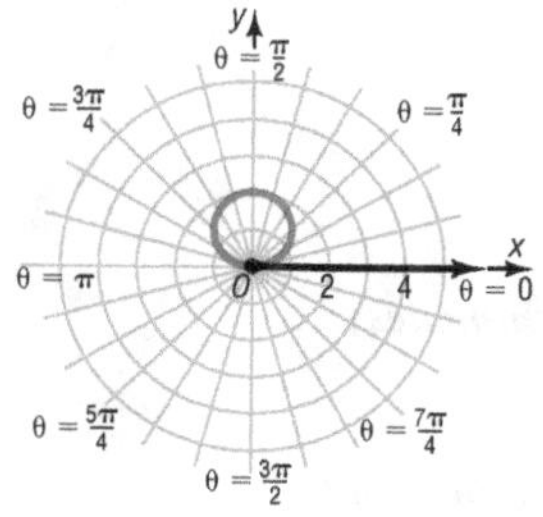

(G)

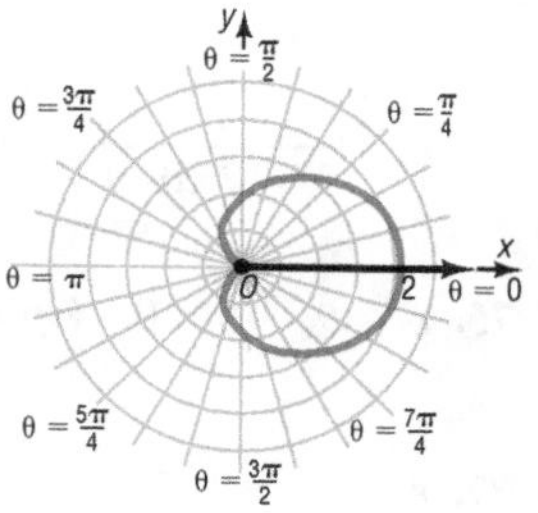

(H)

In Problems 37–60, identify and graph each polar equation. Verify your graph using a graphing utility.

37. $r = 2 + 2\cos\theta$

38. $r = 1 + \sin\theta$

39. $r = 3 - 3\sin\theta$

40. $r = 2 - 2\cos\theta$

41. $r = 2 + \sin\theta$

42. $r = 2 - \cos\theta$

43. $r = 4 - 2\cos\theta$

44. $r = 4 + 2\sin\theta$

45. $r = 1 + 2\sin\theta$

46. $r = 1 - 2\sin\theta$

47. $r = 2 - 3\cos\theta$

48. $r = 2 + 4\cos\theta$

49. $r = 3\cos(2\theta)$

50. $r = 2\sin(3\theta)$

51. $r = 4\sin(5\theta)$

52. $r = 3\cos(4\theta)$

53. $r^2 = 9\cos(2\theta)$

54. $r^2 = \sin(2\theta)$

55. $r = 2^\theta$

56. $r = 3^\theta$

57. $r = 1 - \cos\theta$

58. $r = 3 + \cos\theta$

59. $r = 1 - 3\cos\theta$

60. $r = 4\cos(3\theta)$

Mixed Practice

In Problems 61–66, graph each pair of polar equations on the same polar grid. Find the polar coordinates of the point(s) of intersection and label the point(s) on the graph.

61. $r = 8\cos\theta;\ r = 2\sec\theta$

62. $r = 8\sin\theta;\ r = 4\csc\theta$

63. $r = \sin\theta;\ r = 1 + \cos\theta$

64. $r = 3;\ r = 2 + 2\cos\theta$

65. $r = 1 + \sin\theta;\ r = 1 + \cos\theta$

66. $r = 1 + \cos\theta;\ r = 3\cos\theta$

Applications and Extensions

In Problems 67–70, the polar equation for each graph is either $r = a + b\cos\theta$ or $r = a + b\sin\theta$, $a > 0, b > 0$. Select the correct equation and find the values of a and b.

67.

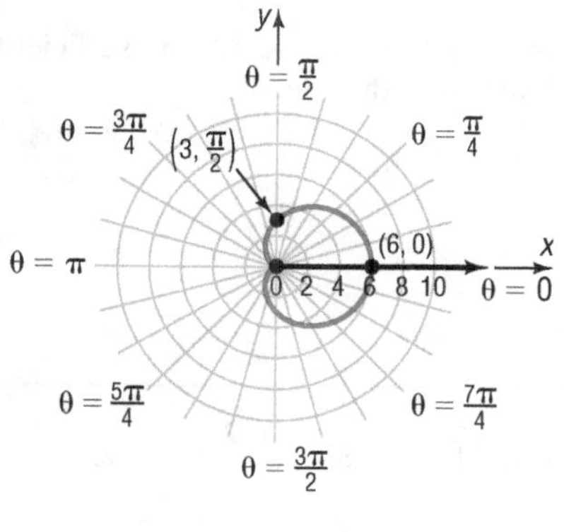

68.

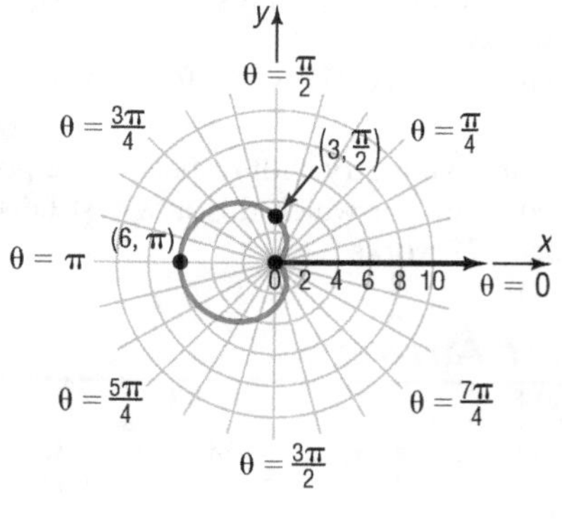

69.

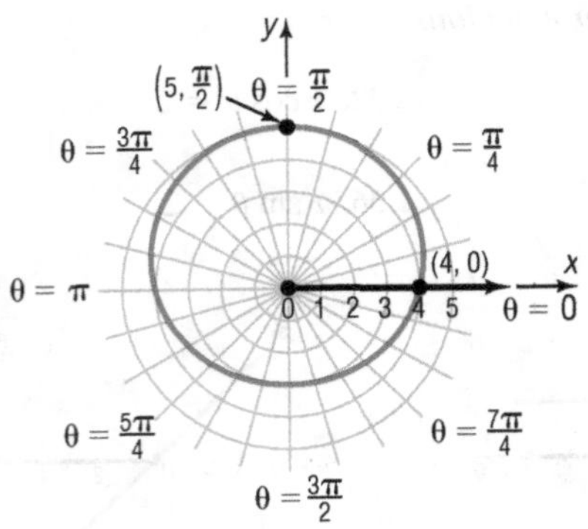

70.

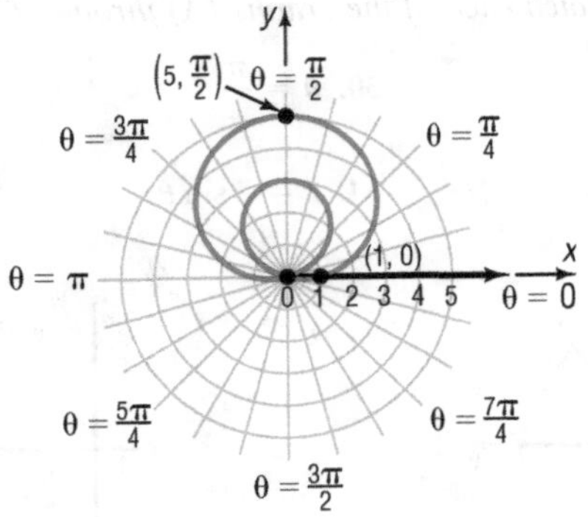

In Problems 71–80, graph each polar equation by hand. Verify your graph using a graphing utility.

71. $r = \dfrac{2}{1 - \cos\theta}$ *(parabola)*

72. $r = \dfrac{2}{1 - 2\cos\theta}$ *(hyperbola)*

73. $r = \dfrac{1}{3 - 2\cos\theta}$ *(ellipse)*

74. $r = \dfrac{1}{1 - \cos\theta}$ *(parabola)*

75. $r = \theta, \quad \theta \ge 0$ *(spiral of Archimedes)*

76. $r = \dfrac{3}{\theta}$ *(reciprocal spiral)*

77. $r = \csc\theta - 2, \quad 0 < \theta < \pi$ *(conchoid)*

78. $r = \sin\theta\tan\theta$ *(cissoid)*

79. $r = \tan\theta, \quad -\dfrac{\pi}{2} < \theta < \dfrac{\pi}{2}$ *(kappa curve)*

80. $r = \cos\dfrac{\theta}{2}$

81. Show that the graph of the equation $r\sin\theta = a$ is a horizontal line a units above the pole if $a > 0$ and $|a|$ units below the pole if $a < 0$.

82. Show that the graph of the equation $r\cos\theta = a$ is a vertical line a units to the right of the pole if $a > 0$ and $|a|$ units to the left of the pole if $a < 0$.

83. Show that the graph of the equation $r = 2a\sin\theta$, $a > 0$, is a circle of radius a with center at $(0, a)$ in rectangular coordinates.

84. Show that the graph of the equation $r = -2a\sin\theta$, $a > 0$, is a circle of radius a with center at $(0, -a)$ in rectangular coordinates.

85. Show that the graph of the equation $r = 2a\cos\theta$, $a > 0$, is a circle of radius a with center at $(a, 0)$ in rectangular coordinates.

86. Show that the graph of the equation $r = -2a\cos\theta$, $a > 0$, is a circle of radius a with center at $(-a, 0)$ in rectangular coordinates.

Discussion and Writing

87. Explain why the following test for symmetry is valid: Replace r by $-r$ and θ by $-\theta$ in a polar equation. If an equivalent equation results, the graph is symmetric with respect to the line $\theta = \dfrac{\pi}{2}$ (y-axis).
   (a) Show that the test on page 577 fails for $r^2 = \cos\theta$, yet this new test works.
   (b) Show that the test on page 577 works for $r^2 = \sin\theta$, yet this new test fails.

88. Develop a new test for symmetry with respect to the pole.
   (a) Find a polar equation for which this new test fails, yet the test on page 577 works.
   (b) Find a polar equation for which the test on page 577 fails, yet the new test works.

89. Write down two different tests for symmetry with respect to the polar axis. Find examples in which one test works and the other fails. Which test do you prefer to use? Justify your answer.

90. The tests for symmetry given on page 577 are sufficient, but not necessary. Explain what this means.

'Are You Prepared?' Answers

1. $(-4, 6)$ **2.** $\cos A\cos B + \sin A\sin B$ **3.** $(x + 2)^2 + (y - 5)^2 = 9$ **4.** Odd **5.** $-\dfrac{\sqrt{2}}{2}$ **6.** $-\dfrac{1}{2}$

9.3 The Complex Plane; De Moivre's Theorem

PREPARING FOR THIS SECTION *Before getting started, review the following:*

- Complex Numbers (Appendix A, Section A.7, pp. A60–A64)
- Value of the Sine and Cosine Functions at Certain Angles (Section 6.2, pp. 368–375)
- Sum and Difference Formulas for Sine and Cosine (Section 7.4, pp. 466 and 469)

Now Work the 'Are You Prepared?' problems on page 595.

OBJECTIVES
1. Plot Points in the Complex Plane (p. 589)
2. Convert a Complex Number from Rectangular Form to Polar Form (p. 590)
3. Find Products and Quotients of Complex Numbers in Polar Form (p. 591)
4. Use De Moivre's Theorem (p. 592)
5. Find Complex Roots (p. 593)

1 Plot Points in the Complex Plane

Complex numbers are discussed in Appendix A, Section A.7. In that discussion, we were not prepared to give a geometric interpretation of a complex number. Now we are ready. Although we could give several interpretations, the one that follows is the easiest to understand.

A complex number $z = x + yi$ can be interpreted geometrically as the point (x, y) in the xy-plane. Each point in the plane corresponds to a complex number and, conversely, each complex number corresponds to a point in the plane. We shall refer to the collection of such points as the **complex plane.** The x-axis will be referred to as the **real axis,** because any point that lies on the real axis is of the form $z = x + 0i = x$, a real number. The y-axis is called the **imaginary axis,** because any point that lies on it is of the form $z = 0 + yi = yi$, a pure imaginary number. See Figure 37.

Figure 37
Complex plane

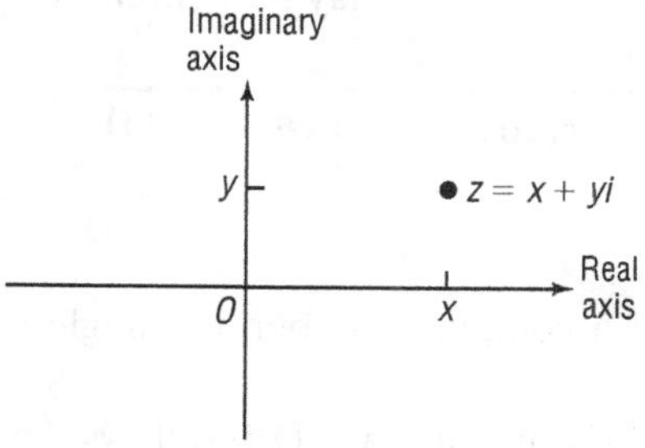

EXAMPLE 1 Plotting a Point in the Complex Plane

Plot the point corresponding to $z = \sqrt{3} - i$ in the complex plane.

Solution The point corresponding to $z = \sqrt{3} - i$ has the rectangular coordinates $(\sqrt{3}, -1)$. The point, located in quadrant IV, is plotted in Figure 38.

Figure 38

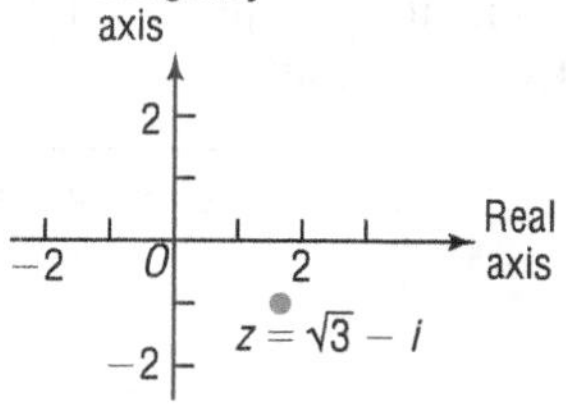

DEFINITION Let $z = x + yi$ be a complex number. The **magnitude** or **modulus** of z, denoted by $|z|$, is defined as the distance from the origin to the point (x, y). That is,

$$|z| = \sqrt{x^2 + y^2} \tag{1}$$

Figure 39

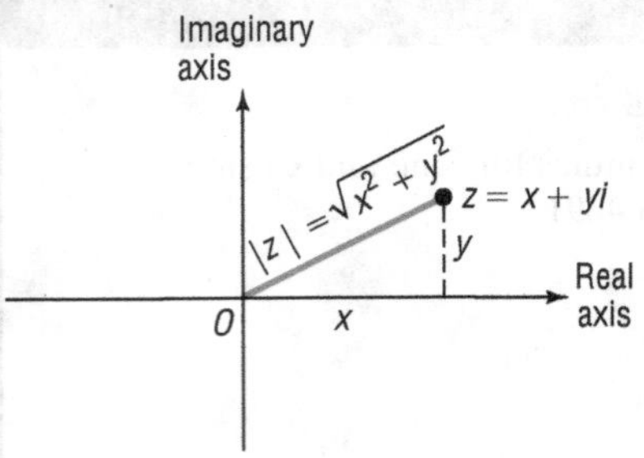

See Figure 39 for an illustration.

This definition for $|z|$ is consistent with the definition for the absolute value of a real number: If $z = x + yi$ is real, then $z = x + 0i$ and

$$|z| = \sqrt{x^2 + 0^2} = \sqrt{x^2} = |x|$$

For this reason, the magnitude of z is sometimes called the **absolute value of** z.

Recall that if $z = x + yi$ then its **conjugate,** denoted by $\bar{z}$, is $\bar{z} = x - yi$. Because $z\bar{z} = x^2 + y^2$, which is a nonnegative real number, it follows from equation (1) that the magnitude of z can be written as

$$|z| = \sqrt{z\bar{z}} \tag{2}$$

2 Convert a Complex Number from Rectangular Form to Polar Form

When a complex number is written in the standard form $z = x + yi$, we say that it is in **rectangular,** or **Cartesian, form,** because (x, y) are the rectangular coordinates of the corresponding point in the complex plane. Suppose that (r, θ) are the polar coordinates of this point. Then

$$x = r\cos\theta, \qquad y = r\sin\theta \tag{3}$$

DEFINITION If $r \geq 0$ and $0 \leq \theta < 2\pi$, the complex number $z = x + yi$ may be written in **polar form** as

$$z = x + yi = (r\cos\theta) + (r\sin\theta)i = r(\cos\theta + i\sin\theta) \tag{4}$$

Figure 40

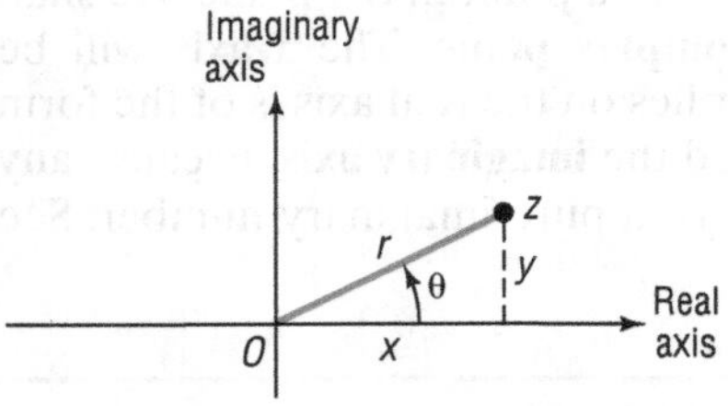

$z = x + yi = r(\cos\theta + i\sin\theta)$, $r \geq 0, 0 \leq \theta < 2\pi$

See Figure 40.

If $z = r(\cos\theta + i\sin\theta)$ is the polar form of a complex number, the angle θ, $0 \leq \theta < 2\pi$, is called the **argument of** z.

Also, because $r \geq 0$, we have $r = \sqrt{x^2 + y^2}$. From equation (1), it follows that the magnitude of $z = r(\cos\theta + i\sin\theta)$ is

$$|z| = r$$

EXAMPLE 2 **Writing a Complex Number in Polar Form**

Write an expression for $z = \sqrt{3} - i$ in polar form.

Solution The point, located in quadrant IV, is plotted in Figure 38. Because $x = \sqrt{3}$ and $y = -1$, it follows that

$$r = \sqrt{x^2 + y^2} = \sqrt{(\sqrt{3})^2 + (-1)^2} = \sqrt{4} = 2$$

So

$$\sin\theta = \frac{y}{r} = \frac{-1}{2}, \qquad \cos\theta = \frac{x}{r} = \frac{\sqrt{3}}{2}, \qquad 0 \leq \theta < 2\pi$$

Then $\theta = \frac{11\pi}{6}$ and $r = 2$, so the polar form of $z = \sqrt{3} - i$ is

$$z = r(\cos\theta + i\sin\theta) = 2\left(\cos\frac{11\pi}{6} + i\sin\frac{11\pi}{6}\right)$$

Now Work PROBLEM 11

EXAMPLE 3

Plotting a Point in the Complex Plane and Converting from Polar to Rectangular Form

Plot the point corresponding to $z = 2(\cos 30° + i \sin 30°)$ in the complex plane, and write an expression for z in rectangular form.

Solution To plot the complex number $z = 2(\cos 30° + i \sin 30°)$, we plot the point whose polar coordinates are $(r, \theta) = (2, 30°)$, as shown in Figure 41. In rectangular form,

Figure 41

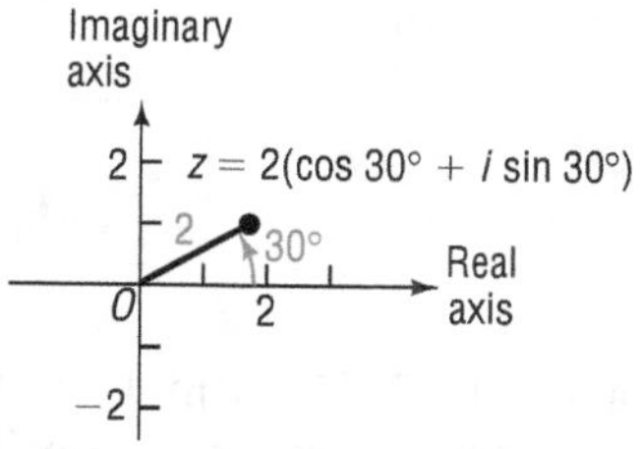

$$z = 2(\cos 30° + i \sin 30°) = 2\left(\frac{\sqrt{3}}{2} + \frac{1}{2}i\right) = \sqrt{3} + i$$

Now Work PROBLEM 23

3 Find Products and Quotients of Complex Numbers in Polar Form

The polar form of a complex number provides an alternative method for finding products and quotients of complex numbers.

THEOREM

Let $z_1 = r_1(\cos \theta_1 + i \sin \theta_1)$ and $z_2 = r_2(\cos \theta_2 + i \sin \theta_2)$ be two complex numbers. Then

$$z_1 z_2 = r_1 r_2[\cos(\theta_1 + \theta_2) + i \sin(\theta_1 + \theta_2)] \quad (5)$$

If $z_2 \neq 0$, then

$$\frac{z_1}{z_2} = \frac{r_1}{r_2}[\cos(\theta_1 - \theta_2) + i \sin(\theta_1 - \theta_2)] \quad (6)$$

In Words

The magnitude of a complex number z is r and its argument is θ, so when

$$z = r(\cos \theta + i \sin \theta)$$

the magnitude of the product (quotient) of two complex numbers equals the product (quotient) of their magnitudes; the argument of the product (quotient) of two complex numbers is determined by the sum (difference) of their arguments.

Proof We will prove formula (5). The proof of formula (6) is left as an exercise (see Problem 66).

$$\begin{aligned} z_1 z_2 &= [r_1(\cos \theta_1 + i \sin \theta_1)][r_2(\cos \theta_2 + i \sin \theta_2)] \\ &= r_1 r_2[(\cos \theta_1 + i \sin \theta_1)(\cos \theta_2 + i \sin \theta_2)] \\ &= r_1 r_2[(\cos \theta_1 \cos \theta_2 - \sin \theta_1 \sin \theta_2) + i(\sin \theta_1 \cos \theta_2 + \cos \theta_1 \sin \theta_2)] \\ &= r_1 r_2[\cos(\theta_1 + \theta_2) + i \sin(\theta_1 + \theta_2)] \end{aligned}$$

■

Let's look at an example of how this theorem can be used.

EXAMPLE 4

Finding Products and Quotients of Complex Numbers in Polar Form

If $z = 3(\cos 20° + i \sin 20°)$ and $w = 5(\cos 100° + i \sin 100°)$, find the following (leave your answers in polar form):

(a) zw (b) $\frac{z}{w}$

Solution

(a) $$\begin{aligned} zw &= [3(\cos 20° + i \sin 20°)][5(\cos 100° + i \sin 100°)] \\ &= (3 \cdot 5)[\cos(20° + 100°) + i \sin(20° + 100°)] \\ &= 15(\cos 120° + i \sin 120°) \end{aligned}$$

Apply equation (5).

(b) $$\frac{z}{w} = \frac{3(\cos 20° + i\sin 20°)}{5(\cos 100° + i\sin 100°)}$$

$$= \frac{3}{5}[\cos(20° - 100°) + i\sin(20° - 100°)]$$ Apply equation (6).

$$= \frac{3}{5}[\cos(-80°) + i\sin(-80°)]$$

$$= \frac{3}{5}(\cos 280° + i\sin 280°)$$ The argument must lie between 0° and 360°.

Now Work PROBLEM 33

4 Use De Moivre's Theorem

De Moivre's Theorem, stated by Abraham De Moivre (1667–1754) in 1730, but already known to many people by 1710, is important for the following reason: The fundamental processes of algebra are the four operations of addition, subtraction, multiplication, and division, together with powers and the extraction of roots. De Moivre's Theorem allows these latter fundamental algebraic operations to be applied to complex numbers.

De Moivre's Theorem, in its most basic form, is a formula for raising a complex number z to the power n, where $n \geq 1$ is a positive integer. Let's see if we can conjecture the form of the result.

Let $z = r(\cos\theta + i\sin\theta)$ be a complex number. Then, based on equation (5), we have

$n = 2$: $z^2 = r^2[\cos(2\theta) + i\sin(2\theta)]$ Equation (5)

$n = 3$: $z^3 = z^2 \cdot z$

$= \{r^2[\cos(2\theta) + i\sin(2\theta)]\}[r(\cos\theta + i\sin\theta)]$

$= r^3[\cos(3\theta) + i\sin(3\theta)]$ Equation (5)

$n = 4$: $z^4 = z^3 \cdot z$

$= \{r^3[\cos(3\theta) + i\sin(3\theta)]\}[r(\cos\theta + i\sin\theta)]$

$= r^4[\cos(4\theta) + i\sin(4\theta)]$ Equation (5)

Do you see the pattern?

THEOREM

De Moivre's Theorem

If $z = r(\cos\theta + i\sin\theta)$ is a complex number, then

$$z^n = r^n[\cos(n\theta) + i\sin(n\theta)] \quad (7)$$

where $n \geq 1$ is a positive integer.

The proof of De Moivre's Theorem requires mathematical induction (which is not discussed until Section 12.4), so it is omitted here.

Let's look at some examples.

EXAMPLE 5 **Using De Moivre's Theorem**

Write $[2(\cos 20° + i\sin 20°)]^3$ in the standard form $a + bi$.

Solution $[2(\cos 20° + i\sin 20°)]^3 = 2^3[\cos(3 \cdot 20°) + i\sin(3 \cdot 20°)]$ Apply De Moivre's Theorem.

$= 8(\cos 60° + i\sin 60°)$

$= 8\left(\frac{1}{2} + \frac{\sqrt{3}}{2}i\right) = 4 + 4\sqrt{3}i$

Now Work PROBLEM 41

EXAMPLE 6 Using De Moivre's Theorem

Write $(1 + i)^5$ in the standard form $a + bi$.

Algebraic Solution

To apply De Moivre's Theorem, we must first write the complex number in polar form. Since the magnitude of $1 + i$ is $\sqrt{1^2 + 1^2} = \sqrt{2}$, we begin by writing

$$1 + i = \sqrt{2}\left(\frac{1}{\sqrt{2}} + \frac{1}{\sqrt{2}}i\right) = \sqrt{2}\left(\cos\frac{\pi}{4} + i\sin\frac{\pi}{4}\right)$$

Now

$$\begin{aligned}(1 + i)^5 &= \left[\sqrt{2}\left(\cos\frac{\pi}{4} + i\sin\frac{\pi}{4}\right)\right]^5 \\ &= (\sqrt{2})^5\left[\cos\left(5\cdot\frac{\pi}{4}\right) + i\sin\left(5\cdot\frac{\pi}{4}\right)\right] \\ &= 4\sqrt{2}\left(\cos\frac{5\pi}{4} + i\sin\frac{5\pi}{4}\right) \\ &= 4\sqrt{2}\left[-\frac{1}{\sqrt{2}} + \left(-\frac{1}{\sqrt{2}}\right)i\right] = -4 - 4i\end{aligned}$$

Graphing Solution

Using a TI-84 Plus graphing calculator, we obtain the solution shown in Figure 42.

Figure 42

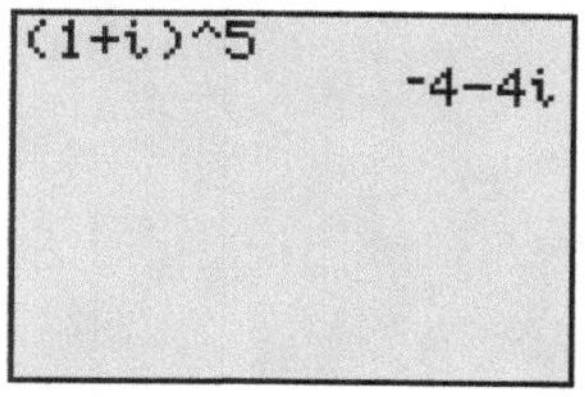

5 Find Complex Roots

Let w be a given complex number, and let $n \geq 2$ denote a positive integer. Any complex number z that satisfies the equation

$$z^n = w$$

is called a **complex nth root** of w. In keeping with previous usage, if $n = 2$, the solutions of the equation $z^2 = w$ are called **complex square roots** of w, and if $n = 3$, the solutions of the equation $z^3 = w$ are called **complex cube roots** of w.

THEOREM

Finding Complex Roots

Let $w = r(\cos\theta_0 + i\sin\theta_0)$ be a complex number, and let $n \geq 2$ be an integer. If $w \neq 0$, there are n distinct complex roots of w, given by the formula

$$z_k = \sqrt[n]{r}\left[\cos\left(\frac{\theta_0}{n} + \frac{2k\pi}{n}\right) + i\sin\left(\frac{\theta_0}{n} + \frac{2k\pi}{n}\right)\right] \qquad (8)$$

where $k = 0, 1, 2, \ldots, n - 1$.

Proof (Outline) We will not prove this result in its entirety. Instead, we shall show only that each z_k in equation (8) satisfies the equation $z_k^n = w$, proving that each z_k is a complex nth root of w.

$$\begin{aligned}z_k^n &= \left\{\sqrt[n]{r}\left[\cos\left(\frac{\theta_0}{n} + \frac{2k\pi}{n}\right) + i\sin\left(\frac{\theta_0}{n} + \frac{2k\pi}{n}\right)\right]\right\}^n \\ &= (\sqrt[n]{r})^n\left\{\cos\left[n\left(\frac{\theta_0}{n} + \frac{2k\pi}{n}\right)\right] + i\sin\left[n\left(\frac{\theta_0}{n} + \frac{2k\pi}{n}\right)\right]\right\} && \text{Apply De Moivre's Theorem.} \\ &= r[\cos(\theta_0 + 2k\pi) + i\sin(\theta_0 + 2k\pi)] && \text{Simplify.} \\ &= r(\cos\theta_0 + i\sin\theta_0) = w && \text{The Periodic Property}\end{aligned}$$

So each z_k, $k = 0, 1, \dots, n-1$, is a complex nth root of w. To complete the proof, we would need to show that each z_k, $k = 0, 1, \dots, n-1$, is, in fact, distinct and that there are no complex nth roots of w other than those given by equation (8). ■

EXAMPLE 7 Finding Complex Cube Roots

Find the complex cube roots of $-1 + \sqrt{3}i$. Leave your answers in polar form, with the argument in degrees.

Solution First, we express $-1 + \sqrt{3}i$ in polar form using degrees.

$$-1 + \sqrt{3}i = 2\left(-\frac{1}{2} + \frac{\sqrt{3}}{2}i\right) = 2(\cos 120° + i \sin 120°)$$

The three complex cube roots of $-1 + \sqrt{3}i = 2(\cos 120° + i \sin 120°)$ are

$$z_k = \sqrt[3]{2}\left[\cos\left(\frac{120°}{3} + \frac{360°k}{3}\right) + i \sin\left(\frac{120°}{3} + \frac{360°k}{3}\right)\right]$$
$$= \sqrt[3]{2}[\cos(40° + 120°k) + i \sin(40° + 120°k)] \qquad k = 0, 1, 2$$

So

$$z_0 = \sqrt[3]{2}[\cos(40° + 120° \cdot 0) + i \sin(40° + 120° \cdot 0)] = \sqrt[3]{2}(\cos 40° + i \sin 40°)$$
$$z_1 = \sqrt[3]{2}[\cos(40° + 120° \cdot 1) + i \sin(40° + 120° \cdot 1)] = \sqrt[3]{2}(\cos 160° + i \sin 160°)$$
$$z_2 = \sqrt[3]{2}[\cos(40° + 120° \cdot 2) + i \sin(40° + 120° \cdot 2)] = \sqrt[3]{2}(\cos 280° + i \sin 280°)$$

WARNING Most graphing utilities will only provide the answer z_0 to the calculation $(-1 + \sqrt{3}i) \wedge \left(\frac{1}{3}\right)$. The paragraph following Example 7 explains how to obtain z_1 and z_2 from z_0. ■

Notice that each of the three complex roots of $-1 + \sqrt{3}i$ has the same magnitude, $\sqrt[3]{2}$. This means that the points corresponding to each cube root lie the same distance from the origin; that is, the three points lie on a circle with center at the origin and radius $\sqrt[3]{2}$. Furthermore, the arguments of these cube roots are 40°, 160°, and 280°, the difference of consecutive pairs being $120° = \frac{360°}{3}$. This means that the three points are equally spaced on the circle, as shown in Figure 43. These results are not coincidental. In fact, you are asked to show that these results hold for complex nth roots in Problems 63 through 65.

Figure 43

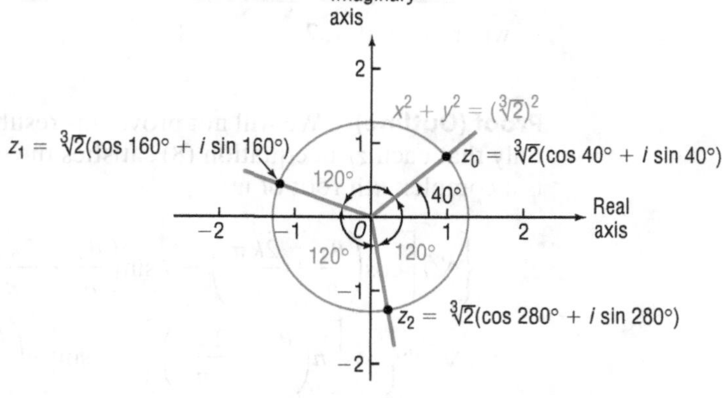

Now Work PROBLEM 53

Historical Feature

John Wallis

The Babylonians, Greeks, and Arabs considered square roots of negative quantities to be impossible and equations with complex solutions to be unsolvable. The first hint that there was some connection between real solutions of equations and complex numbers came when Girolamo Cardano (1501–1576) and Tartaglia (1499–1557) found *real* roots of cubic equations by taking cube roots of *complex* quantities. For centuries thereafter, mathematicians worked with complex numbers without much belief in their actual existence. In 1673, John Wallis appears to have been the first to suggest the graphical representation of complex numbers, a truly significant idea that was not pursued further until about 1800. Several people, including Karl Friedrich Gauss (1777–1855), then rediscovered the idea, and graphical representation helped to establish complex numbers as equal members of the number family. In practical applications, complex numbers have found their greatest uses in the study of alternating current, where they are a commonplace tool, and in the field of subatomic physics.

Historical Problems

1. The quadratic formula will work perfectly well if the coefficients are complex numbers. Solve the following. [**Hint:** The answers are "nice."]
   (a) $z^2 - (2 + 5i)z - 3 + 5i = 0$ **(b)** $z^2 - (1 + i)z - 2 - i = 0$

9.3 Assess Your Understanding

'Are You Prepared?' *Answers are given at the end of these exercises. If you get a wrong answer, read the pages listed in red.*

1. The conjugate of $-4 - 3i$ is ______. (p. A62)

2. The sum formula for the sine function is $\sin(A + B) =$ ______. (p. 469)

3. The sum formula for the cosine function is $\cos(A + B) =$ ______. (p. 466)

4. $\sin 120° =$ ______; $\cos 240° =$ ______. (pp. 374–375)

Concepts and Vocabulary

5. When a complex number z is written in the polar form $z = r(\cos\theta + i\sin\theta)$, the nonnegative number r is the ______ or ______ of z, and the angle θ, $0 \le \theta < 2\pi$, is the ______ of z.

6. ______ Theorem can be used to raise a complex number to a power.

7. Every nonzero complex number will have exactly ______ cube roots.

8. ***True or False*** De Moivre's Theorem is useful for raising a complex number to a positive integer power.

9. ***True or False*** Using De Moivre's Theorem, the square of a complex number will have two answers.

10. ***True or False*** The polar form of a complex number is unique.

Skill Building

In Problems 11–22, plot each complex number in the complex plane and write it in polar form. Express the argument in degrees.

11. $1 + i$
12. $-1 + i$
13. $\sqrt{3} - i$
14. $1 - \sqrt{3}i$
15. $-3i$
16. -2
17. $4 - 4i$
18. $9\sqrt{3} + 9i$
19. $3 - 4i$
20. $2 + \sqrt{3}i$
21. $-2 + 3i$
22. $\sqrt{5} - i$

In Problems 23–32, write each complex number in rectangular form.

23. $2(\cos 120° + i\sin 120°)$
24. $3(\cos 210° + i\sin 210°)$
25. $4\left(\cos\frac{7\pi}{4} + i\sin\frac{7\pi}{4}\right)$
26. $2\left(\cos\frac{5\pi}{6} + i\sin\frac{5\pi}{6}\right)$
27. $3\left(\cos\frac{3\pi}{2} + i\sin\frac{3\pi}{2}\right)$
28. $4\left(\cos\frac{\pi}{2} + i\sin\frac{\pi}{2}\right)$
29. $0.2(\cos 100° + i\sin 100°)$
30. $0.4(\cos 200° + i\sin 200°)$
31. $2\left(\cos\frac{\pi}{18} + i\sin\frac{\pi}{18}\right)$
32. $3\left(\cos\frac{\pi}{10} + i\sin\frac{\pi}{10}\right)$

In Problems 33–40, find zw and $\frac{z}{w}$. Leave your answers in polar form.

33. $z = 2(\cos 40° + i\sin 40°)$
    $w = 4(\cos 20° + i\sin 20°)$
34. $z = \cos 120° + i\sin 120°$
    $w = \cos 100° + i\sin 100°$
35. $z = 3(\cos 130° + i\sin 130°)$
    $w = 4(\cos 270° + i\sin 270°)$

36. $z = 2(\cos 80° + i \sin 80°)$
$w = 6(\cos 200° + i \sin 200°)$

37. $z = 2\left(\cos \frac{\pi}{8} + i \sin \frac{\pi}{8}\right)$
$w = 2\left(\cos \frac{\pi}{10} + i \sin \frac{\pi}{10}\right)$

38. $z = 4\left(\cos \frac{3\pi}{8} + i \sin \frac{3\pi}{8}\right)$
$w = 2\left(\cos \frac{9\pi}{16} + i \sin \frac{9\pi}{16}\right)$

39. $z = 2 + 2i$
$w = \sqrt{3} - i$

40. $z = 1 - i$
$w = 1 - \sqrt{3}i$

In Problems 41–52, write each expression in the standard form $a + bi$.

41. $[4(\cos 40° + i \sin 40°)]^3$

42. $[3(\cos 80° + i \sin 80°)]^3$

43. $\left[2\left(\cos \frac{\pi}{10} + i \sin \frac{\pi}{10}\right)\right]^5$

44. $\left[\sqrt{2}\left(\cos \frac{5\pi}{16} + i \sin \frac{5\pi}{16}\right)\right]^4$

45. $\left[\sqrt{3}(\cos 10° + i \sin 10°)\right]^6$

46. $\left[\frac{1}{2}(\cos 72° + i \sin 72°)\right]^5$

47. $\left[\sqrt{5}\left(\cos \frac{3\pi}{16} + i \sin \frac{3\pi}{16}\right)\right]^4$

48. $\left[\sqrt{3}\left(\cos \frac{5\pi}{18} + i \sin \frac{5\pi}{18}\right)\right]^6$

49. $(1 - i)^5$

50. $(\sqrt{3} - i)^6$

51. $(\sqrt{2} - i)^6$

52. $(1 - \sqrt{5}i)^8$

In Problems 53–60, find all the complex roots. Leave your answers in polar form with the argument in degrees.

53. The complex cube roots of $1 + i$

54. The complex fourth roots of $\sqrt{3} - i$

55. The complex fourth roots of $4 - 4\sqrt{3}i$

56. The complex cube roots of $-8 - 8i$

57. The complex fourth roots of $-16i$

58. The complex cube roots of -8

59. The complex fifth roots of i

60. The complex fifth roots of $-i$

Applications and Extensions

61. Find the four complex fourth roots of unity (1) and plot them.

62. Find the six complex sixth roots of unity (1) and plot them.

63. Show that each complex nth root of a nonzero complex number w has the same magnitude.

64. Use the result of Problem 63 to draw the conclusion that each complex nth root lies on a circle with center at the origin. What is the radius of this circle?

65. Refer to Problem 64. Show that the complex nth roots of a nonzero complex number w are equally spaced on the circle.

66. Prove formula (6).

67. Mandelbrot Sets

(a) Consider the expression $a_n = (a_{n-1})^2 + z$, where z is some complex number (called the **seed**) and $a_0 = z$. Compute $a_1 (= a_0^2 + z)$, $a_2 (= a_1^2 + z)$, $a_3 (= a_2^2 + z)$, a_4, a_5, and a_6 for the following seeds: $z_1 = 0.1 - 0.4i$, $z_2 = 0.5 + 0.8i$, $z_3 = -0.9 + 0.7i$, $z_4 = -1.1 + 0.1i$, $z_5 = 0 - 1.3i$, and $z_6 = 1 + 1i$.

(b) The dark portion of the graph represents the set of all values $z = x + yi$ that are in the Mandelbrot set. Determine which complex numbers in part (a) are in this set by plotting them on the graph. Do the complex numbers that are not in the Mandelbrot set have any common characteristics regarding the values of a_6 found in part (a)?

(c) Compute $|z| = \sqrt{x^2 + y^2}$ for each of the complex numbers in part (a). Now compute $|a_6|$ for each of the complex numbers in part (a). For which complex numbers is $|a_6| \le |z|$ and $|z| \le 2$? Conclude that the criterion for a complex number to be in the Mandelbrot set is that $|a_n| \le |z|$ and $|z| \le 2$.

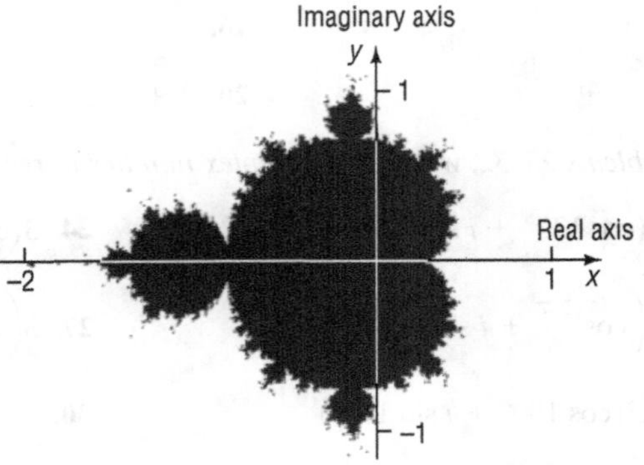

'Are You Prepared?' Answers

1. $-4 + 3i$ **2.** $\sin A \cos B + \cos A \sin B$ **3.** $\cos A \cos B - \sin A \sin B$ **4.** $\frac{\sqrt{3}}{2}; -\frac{1}{2}$

9.4 Vectors

OBJECTIVES
1. Graph Vectors (p. 599)
2. Find a Position Vector (p. 600)
3. Add and Subtract Vectors Algebraically (p. 601)
4. Find a Scalar Multiple and the Magnitude of a Vector (p. 602)
5. Find a Unit Vector (p. 602)
6. Find a Vector from Its Direction and Magnitude (p. 603)
7. Analyze Objects in Static Equilibrium (p. 604)

Figure 44

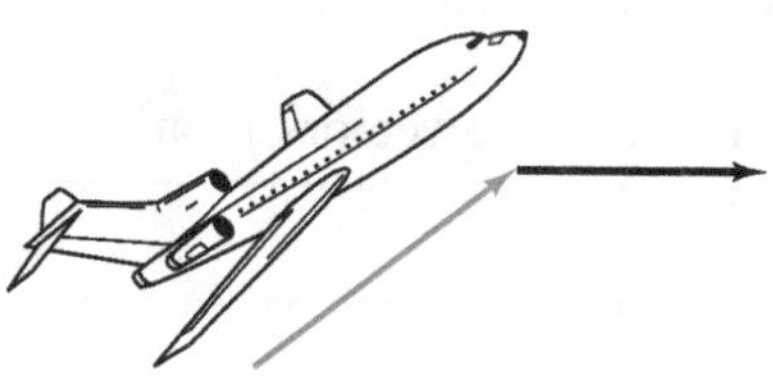

In simple terms, a **vector** (derived from the Latin *vehere,* meaning "to carry") is a quantity that has both magnitude and direction. It is customary to represent a vector by using an arrow. The length of the arrow represents the **magnitude** of the vector, and the arrowhead indicates the **direction** of the vector.

Many quantities in physics can be represented by vectors. For example, the velocity of an aircraft can be represented by an arrow that points in the direction of movement; the length of the arrow represents speed. If the aircraft speeds up, we lengthen the arrow; if the aircraft changes direction, we introduce an arrow in the new direction. See Figure 44. Based on this representation, it is not surprising that vectors and *directed line segments* are somehow related.

Geometric Vectors

If P and Q are two distinct points in the xy-plane, there is exactly one line containing both P and Q [Figure 45(a)]. The points on that part of the line that joins P to Q, including P and Q, form what is called the **line segment** $\overline{PQ}$ [Figure 45(b)]. If we order the points so that they proceed from P to Q, we have a **directed line segment** from P to Q, or a **geometric vector,** which we denote by $\overrightarrow{PQ}$. In a directed line segment $\overrightarrow{PQ}$, we call P the **initial point** and Q the **terminal point,** as indicated in Figure 45(c).

Figure 45

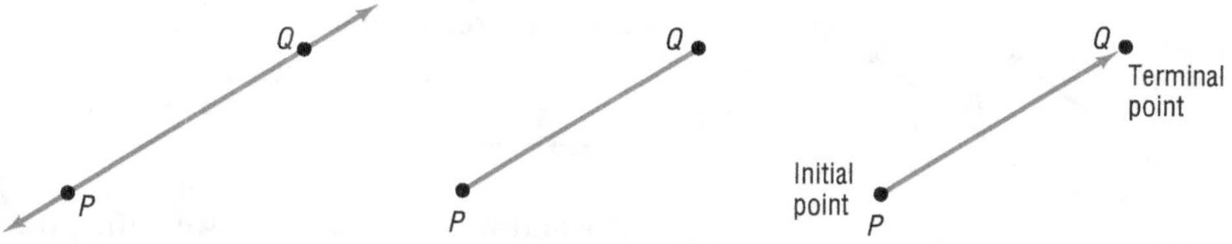

(a) Line containing P and Q **(b)** Line segment $\overline{PQ}$ **(c)** Directed line segment $\overrightarrow{PQ}$

The magnitude of the directed line segment $\overrightarrow{PQ}$ is the distance from the point P to the point Q; that is, it is the length of the line segment. The direction of $\overrightarrow{PQ}$ is from P to Q. If a vector $\mathbf{v}$* has the same magnitude and the same direction as the directed line segment $\overrightarrow{PQ}$, we write

$$\mathbf{v} = \overrightarrow{PQ}$$

Figure 46

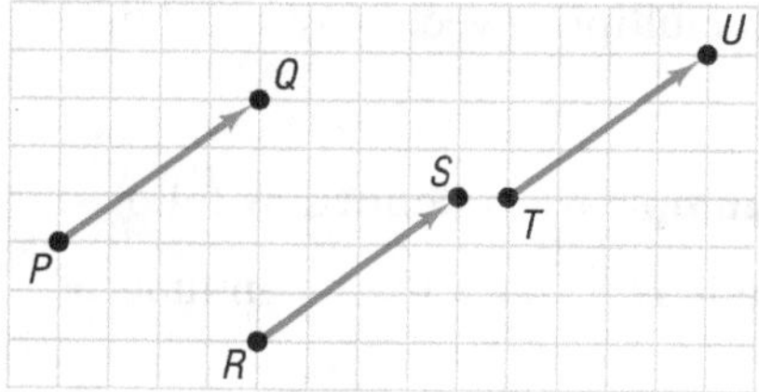

The vector $\mathbf{v}$ whose magnitude is 0 is called the **zero vector, 0.** The zero vector is assigned no direction.

Two vectors $\mathbf{v}$ and $\mathbf{w}$ are **equal,** written

$$\mathbf{v} = \mathbf{w}$$

if they have the same magnitude and the same direction.

For example, the three vectors shown in Figure 46 have the same magnitude and the same direction, so they are equal, even though they have different initial points

*Boldface letters will be used to denote vectors, to distinguish them from numbers. For handwritten work, an arrow is placed over the letter to signify a vector.

and different terminal points. As a result, we find it useful to think of a vector simply as an arrow, keeping in mind that two arrows (vectors) are equal if they have the same direction and the same magnitude (length).

Adding Vectors Geometrically

Figure 47

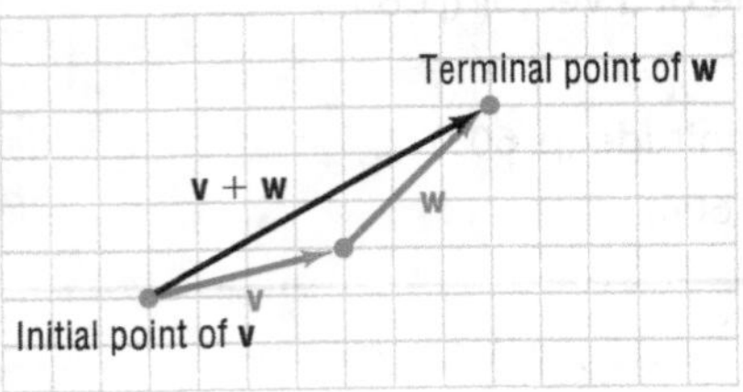

The **sum** **v** + **w** of two vectors is defined as follows: We position the vectors **v** and **w** so that the terminal point of **v** coincides with the initial point of **w**, as shown in Figure 47. The vector **v** + **w** is then the unique vector whose initial point coincides with the initial point of **v** and whose terminal point coincides with the terminal point of **w**.

Vector addition is **commutative.** That is, if **v** and **w** are any two vectors, then

$$\mathbf{v} + \mathbf{w} = \mathbf{w} + \mathbf{v}$$

Figure 48

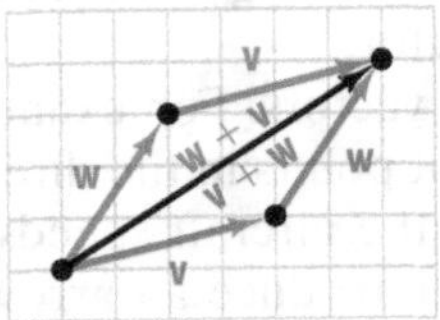

Figure 48 illustrates this fact. (Observe that the commutative property is another way of saying that opposite sides of a parallelogram are equal and parallel.)

Vector addition is also **associative.** That is, if **u**, **v**, and **w** are vectors, then

$$\mathbf{u} + (\mathbf{v} + \mathbf{w}) = (\mathbf{u} + \mathbf{v}) + \mathbf{w}$$

Figure 49 illustrates the associative property for vectors.

Figure 49
$(\mathbf{u} + \mathbf{v}) + \mathbf{w} = \mathbf{u} + (\mathbf{v} + \mathbf{w})$

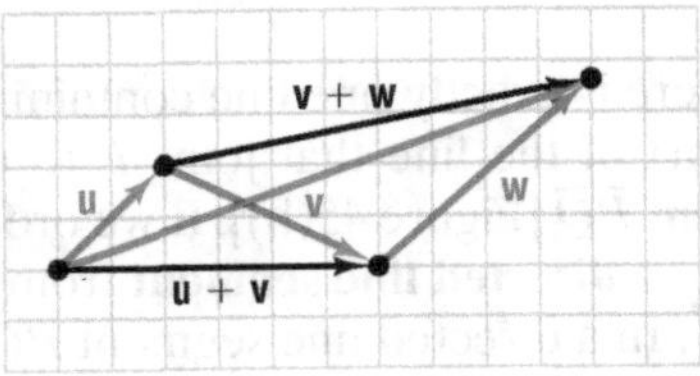

The zero vector **0** has the property that

$$\mathbf{v} + \mathbf{0} = \mathbf{0} + \mathbf{v} = \mathbf{v}$$

for any vector **v**.

If **v** is a vector, then −**v** is the vector having the same magnitude as **v**, but whose direction is opposite to **v**, as shown in Figure 50.

Figure 50

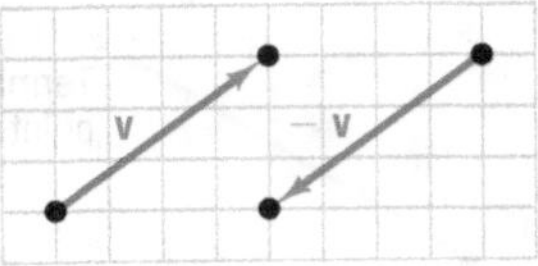

Furthermore,

$$\mathbf{v} + (-\mathbf{v}) = \mathbf{0}$$

If **v** and **w** are two vectors, we define the **difference** **v** − **w** as

$$\mathbf{v} - \mathbf{w} = \mathbf{v} + (-\mathbf{w})$$

Figure 51

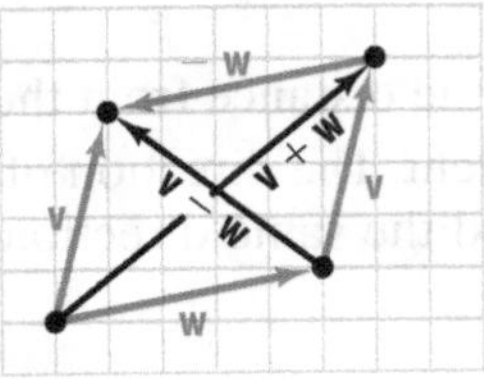

Figure 51 illustrates the relationships among **v**, **w**, **v** + **w**, and **v** − **w**.

Multiplying Vectors by Numbers Geometrically

When dealing with vectors, we refer to real numbers as **scalars.** Scalars are quantities that have only magnitude. Examples from physics of scalar quantities are temperature, speed, and time. We now define how to multiply a vector by a scalar.

DEFINITION

If α is a scalar and **v** is a vector, the **scalar multiple** $\alpha\mathbf{v}$ is defined as follows:

1. If $\alpha > 0$, $\alpha\mathbf{v}$ is the vector whose magnitude is α times the magnitude of **v** and whose direction is the same as **v**.
2. If $\alpha < 0$, $\alpha\mathbf{v}$ is the vector whose magnitude is $|\alpha|$ times the magnitude of **v** and whose direction is opposite that of **v**.
3. If $\alpha = 0$ or if $\mathbf{v} = \mathbf{0}$, then $\alpha\mathbf{v} = \mathbf{0}$.

Figure 52

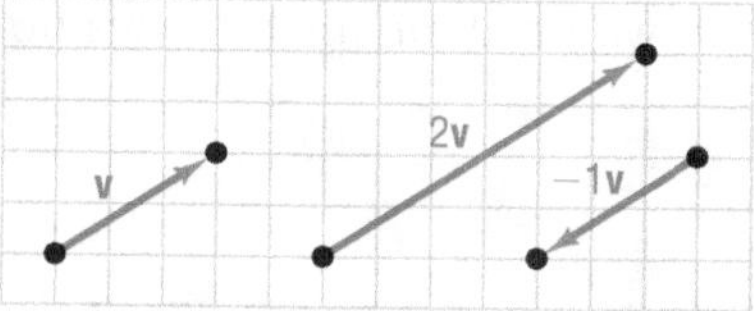

See Figure 52 for some illustrations.

For example, if **a** is the acceleration of an object of mass m due to a force **F** being exerted on it, then, by Newton's second law of motion, $\mathbf{F} = m\mathbf{a}$. Here, $m\mathbf{a}$ is the product of the scalar m and the vector **a**.

Scalar multiples have the following properties:

$$0\mathbf{v} = \mathbf{0} \qquad 1\mathbf{v} = \mathbf{v} \qquad -1\mathbf{v} = -\mathbf{v}$$
$$(\alpha + \beta)\mathbf{v} = \alpha\mathbf{v} + \beta\mathbf{v} \qquad \alpha(\mathbf{v} + \mathbf{w}) = \alpha\mathbf{v} + \alpha\mathbf{w}$$
$$\alpha(\beta\mathbf{v}) = (\alpha\beta)\mathbf{v}$$

1 Graph Vectors

EXAMPLE 1 **Graphing Vectors**

Use the vectors illustrated in Figure 53 to graph each of the following vectors:

(a) $\mathbf{v} - \mathbf{w}$ (b) $2\mathbf{v} + 3\mathbf{w}$ (c) $2\mathbf{v} - \mathbf{w} + \mathbf{u}$

Solution Figure 54 illustrates each graph.

Figure 53

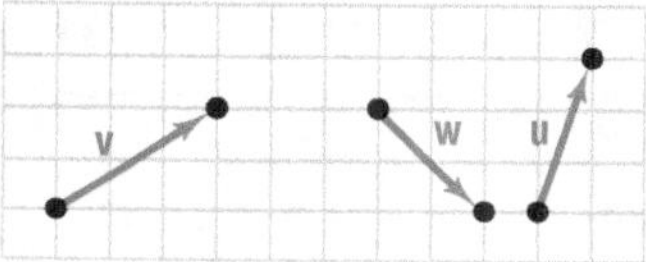

Figure 54

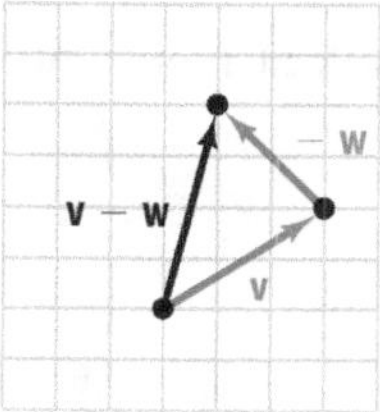

(a) v − w

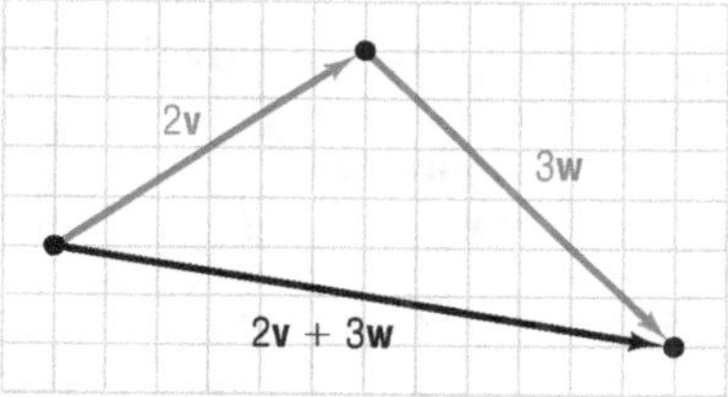

(b) 2v + 3w

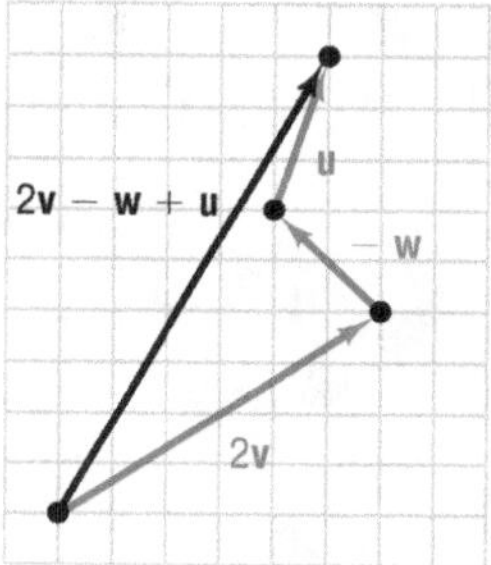

(c) 2v − w + u

Now Work PROBLEMS 7 AND 9

Magnitudes of Vectors

If **v** is a vector, we use the symbol $\|\mathbf{v}\|$ to represent the **magnitude** of **v**. Since $\|\mathbf{v}\|$ equals the length of a directed line segment, it follows that $\|\mathbf{v}\|$ has the following properties:

THEOREM **Properties of $\|\mathbf{v}\|$**

If **v** is a vector and if α is a scalar, then

(a) $\|\mathbf{v}\| \geq 0$ (b) $\|\mathbf{v}\| = 0$ if and only if $\mathbf{v} = \mathbf{0}$

(c) $\|-\mathbf{v}\| = \|\mathbf{v}\|$ (d) $\|\alpha\mathbf{v}\| = |\alpha|\|\mathbf{v}\|$

Property (a) is a consequence of the fact that distance is a nonnegative number. Property (b) follows, because the length of the directed line segment $\overrightarrow{PQ}$ is positive unless P and Q are the same point, in which case the length is 0. Property (c) follows because the length of the line segment $\overline{PQ}$ equals the length of the line segment $\overline{QP}$. Property (d) is a direct consequence of the definition of a scalar multiple.

DEFINITION A vector **u** for which $\|\mathbf{u}\| = 1$ is called a **unit vector.**

2 Find a Position Vector

To compute the magnitude and direction of a vector, we need an algebraic way of representing vectors.

DEFINITION

An **algebraic vector v** is represented as

$$\mathbf{v} = \langle a, b \rangle$$

where a and b are real numbers (scalars) called the **components** of the vector **v**.

Figure 55

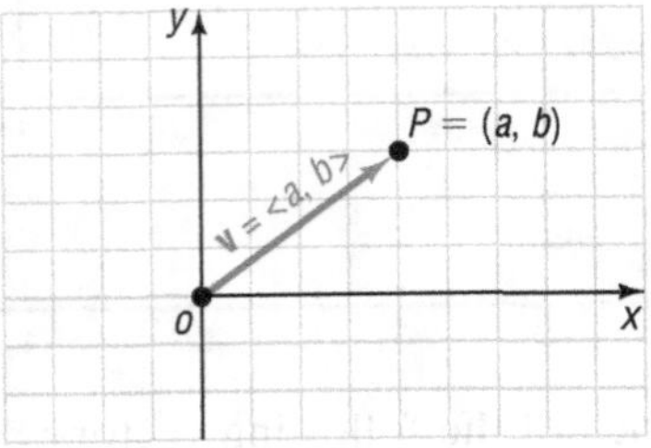

We use a rectangular coordinate system to represent algebraic vectors in the plane. If $\mathbf{v} = \langle a, b \rangle$ is an algebraic vector whose initial point is at the origin, then **v** is called a **position vector.** See Figure 55. Notice that the terminal point of the position vector $\mathbf{v} = \langle a, b \rangle$ is $P = (a, b)$.

The next result states that any vector whose initial point is not at the origin is equal to a unique position vector.

THEOREM

Suppose that **v** is a vector with initial point $P_1 = (x_1, y_1)$, not necessarily the origin, and terminal point $P_2 = (x_2, y_2)$. If $\mathbf{v} = \overrightarrow{P_1P_2}$, then **v** is equal to the position vector

$$\mathbf{v} = \langle x_2 - x_1, y_2 - y_1 \rangle \qquad (1)$$

To see why this is true, look at Figure 56.

Figure 56
$\mathbf{v} = \langle a, b \rangle = \langle x_2 - x_1, y_2 - y_1 \rangle$

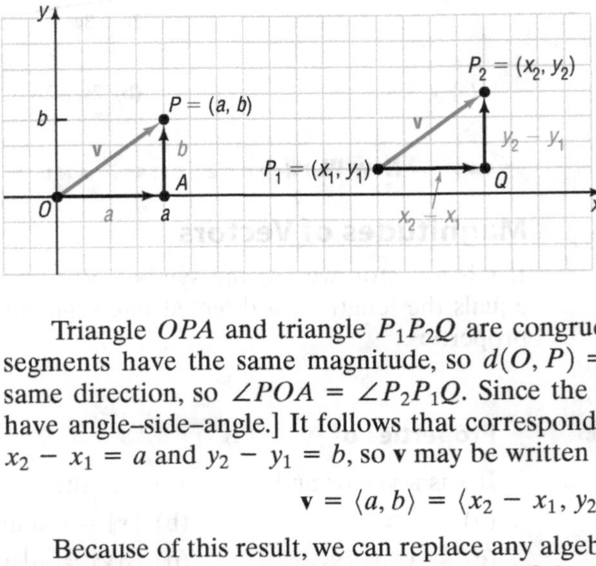

Triangle OPA and triangle P_1P_2Q are congruent. [Do you see why? The line segments have the same magnitude, so $d(O, P) = d(P_1, P_2)$; and they have the same direction, so $\angle POA = \angle P_2P_1Q$. Since the triangles are right triangles, we have angle–side–angle.] It follows that corresponding sides are equal. As a result, $x_2 - x_1 = a$ and $y_2 - y_1 = b$, so **v** may be written as

$$\mathbf{v} = \langle a, b \rangle = \langle x_2 - x_1, y_2 - y_1 \rangle$$

Because of this result, we can replace any algebraic vector by a unique position vector, and vice versa. This flexibility is one of the main reasons for the wide use of vectors.

EXAMPLE 2 Finding a Position Vector

Find the position vector of the vector $\mathbf{v} = \overrightarrow{P_1P_2}$ if $P_1 = (-1, 2)$ and $P_2 = (4, 6)$.

Solution By equation (1), the position vector equal to **v** is

$$\mathbf{v} = \langle 4 - (-1), 6 - 2 \rangle = \langle 5, 4 \rangle$$

See Figure 57.

Figure 57

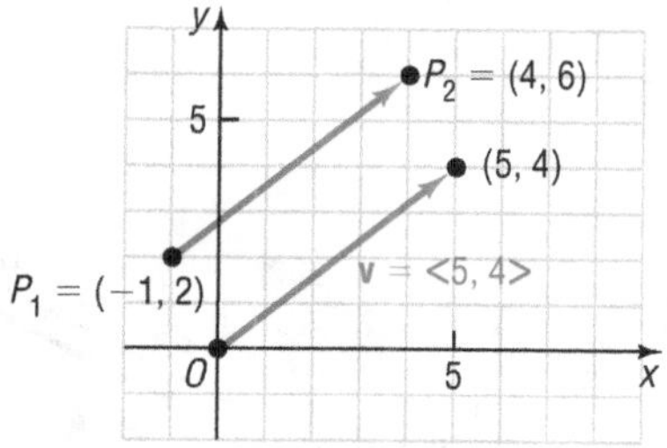

Two position vectors **v** and **w** are equal if and only if the terminal point of **v** is the same as the terminal point of **w**. This leads to the following result:

THEOREM

Equality of Vectors

Two vectors **v** and **w** are equal if and only if their corresponding components are equal. That is,

$$\text{If } \mathbf{v} = \langle a_1, b_1 \rangle \quad \text{and} \quad \mathbf{w} = \langle a_2, b_2 \rangle$$
$$\text{then} \quad \mathbf{v} = \mathbf{w} \quad \text{if and only if} \quad a_1 = a_2 \quad \text{and} \quad b_1 = b_2.$$

Figure 58

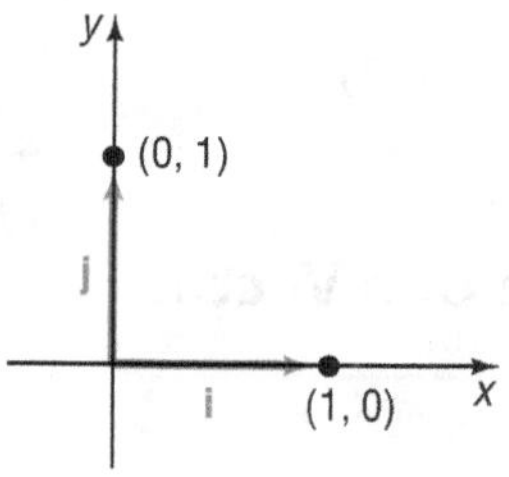

We now present an alternative representation of a vector in the plane that is common in the physical sciences. Let **i** denote the unit vector whose direction is along the positive x-axis; let **j** denote the unit vector whose direction is along the positive y-axis. Then $\mathbf{i} = \langle 1, 0 \rangle$ and $\mathbf{j} = \langle 0, 1 \rangle$, as shown in Figure 58. Any vector $\mathbf{v} = \langle a, b \rangle$ can be written using the unit vectors **i** and **j** as follows:

$$\mathbf{v} = \langle a, b \rangle = a\langle 1, 0 \rangle + b\langle 0, 1 \rangle = a\mathbf{i} + b\mathbf{j}$$

We call a and b the **horizontal** and **vertical components** of **v**, respectively. For example, if $\mathbf{v} = \langle 5, 4 \rangle = 5\mathbf{i} + 4\mathbf{j}$, then 5 is the horizontal component and 4 is the vertical component.

Now Work PROBLEM 27

3 Add and Subtract Vectors Algebraically

We define addition, subtraction, scalar multiple, and magnitude of algebraic vectors in terms of their components.

DEFINITION

Let $\mathbf{v} = a_1\mathbf{i} + b_1\mathbf{j} = \langle a_1, b_1 \rangle$ and $\mathbf{w} = a_2\mathbf{i} + b_2\mathbf{j} = \langle a_2, b_2 \rangle$ be two vectors, and let α be a scalar. Then

$$\mathbf{v} + \mathbf{w} = (a_1 + a_2)\mathbf{i} + (b_1 + b_2)\mathbf{j} = \langle a_1 + a_2, b_1 + b_2 \rangle \quad (2)$$
$$\mathbf{v} - \mathbf{w} = (a_1 - a_2)\mathbf{i} + (b_1 - b_2)\mathbf{j} = \langle a_1 - a_2, b_1 - b_2 \rangle \quad (3)$$
$$\alpha\mathbf{v} = (\alpha a_1)\mathbf{i} + (\alpha b_1)\mathbf{j} = \langle \alpha a_1, \alpha b_1 \rangle \quad (4)$$
$$\|\mathbf{v}\| = \sqrt{a_1^2 + b_1^2} \quad (5)$$

In Words
To add two vectors, add corresponding components. To subtract two vectors, subtract corresponding components.

These definitions are compatible with the geometric definitions given earlier in this section. See Figure 59 on the next page.

Figure 59

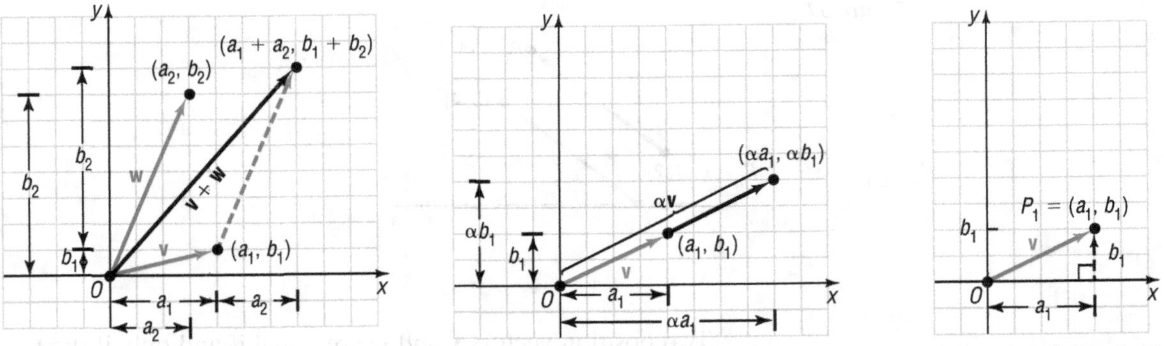

(a) Illustration of property (2) **(b)** Illustration of property (4), $\alpha > 0$ **(c)** Illustration of property (5): $\|\mathbf{v}\|$ = Distance from O to P_1; $\|\mathbf{v}\| = \sqrt{a_1^2 + b_1^2}$

EXAMPLE 3 **Adding and Subtracting Vectors**

If $\mathbf{v} = 2\mathbf{i} + 3\mathbf{j} = \langle 2, 3 \rangle$ and $\mathbf{w} = 3\mathbf{i} - 4\mathbf{j} = \langle 3, -4 \rangle$, find:

(a) $\mathbf{v} + \mathbf{w}$ (b) $\mathbf{v} - \mathbf{w}$

Solution (a) $\mathbf{v} + \mathbf{w} = (2\mathbf{i} + 3\mathbf{j}) + (3\mathbf{i} - 4\mathbf{j}) = (2 + 3)\mathbf{i} + (3 - 4)\mathbf{j} = 5\mathbf{i} - \mathbf{j}$

or

$$\mathbf{v} + \mathbf{w} = \langle 2, 3 \rangle + \langle 3, -4 \rangle = \langle 2 + 3, 3 + (-4) \rangle = \langle 5, -1 \rangle$$

(b) $\mathbf{v} - \mathbf{w} = (2\mathbf{i} + 3\mathbf{j}) - (3\mathbf{i} - 4\mathbf{j}) = (2 - 3)\mathbf{i} + [3 - (-4)]\mathbf{j} = -\mathbf{i} + 7\mathbf{j}$

or

$$\mathbf{v} - \mathbf{w} = \langle 2, 3 \rangle - \langle 3, -4 \rangle = \langle 2 - 3, 3 - (-4) \rangle = \langle -1, 7 \rangle$$

4 Find a Scalar Multiple and the Magnitude of a Vector

EXAMPLE 4 **Finding Scalar Multiples and Magnitudes of Vectors**

If $\mathbf{v} = 2\mathbf{i} + 3\mathbf{j} = \langle 2, 3 \rangle$ and $\mathbf{w} = 3\mathbf{i} - 4\mathbf{j} = \langle 3, -4 \rangle$, find:

(a) $3\mathbf{v}$ (b) $2\mathbf{v} - 3\mathbf{w}$ (c) $\|\mathbf{v}\|$

Solution (a) $3\mathbf{v} = 3(2\mathbf{i} + 3\mathbf{j}) = 6\mathbf{i} + 9\mathbf{j}$

or

$$3\mathbf{v} = 3\langle 2, 3 \rangle = \langle 6, 9 \rangle$$

(b)
$$2\mathbf{v} - 3\mathbf{w} = 2(2\mathbf{i} + 3\mathbf{j}) - 3(3\mathbf{i} - 4\mathbf{j}) = 4\mathbf{i} + 6\mathbf{j} - 9\mathbf{i} + 12\mathbf{j} = -5\mathbf{i} + 18\mathbf{j}$$

or

$$2\mathbf{v} - 3\mathbf{w} = 2\langle 2, 3 \rangle - 3\langle 3, -4 \rangle = \langle 4, 6 \rangle - \langle 9, -12 \rangle = \langle 4 - 9, 6 - (-12) \rangle = \langle -5, 18 \rangle$$

(c) $\|\mathbf{v}\| = \|2\mathbf{i} + 3\mathbf{j}\| = \sqrt{2^2 + 3^2} = \sqrt{13}$

Now Work PROBLEMS 33 AND 39

For the remainder of the section, we will express a vector $\mathbf{v}$ in the form $a\mathbf{i} + b\mathbf{j}$.

5 Find a Unit Vector

Recall that a unit vector $\mathbf{u}$ is a vector for which $\|\mathbf{u}\| = 1$. In many applications, it is useful to be able to find a unit vector $\mathbf{u}$ that has the same direction as a given vector $\mathbf{v}$.

THEOREM **Unit Vector in the Direction of v**

For any nonzero vector **v**, the vector

$$\mathbf{u} = \frac{\mathbf{v}}{\|\mathbf{v}\|}$$

is a unit vector that has the same direction as **v**.

Proof Let $\mathbf{v} = a\mathbf{i} + b\mathbf{j}$. Then $\|\mathbf{v}\| = \sqrt{a^2 + b^2}$ and

$$\mathbf{u} = \frac{\mathbf{v}}{\|\mathbf{v}\|} = \frac{a\mathbf{i} + b\mathbf{j}}{\sqrt{a^2 + b^2}} = \frac{a}{\sqrt{a^2 + b^2}}\mathbf{i} + \frac{b}{\sqrt{a^2 + b^2}}\mathbf{j}$$

The vector **u** is in the same direction as **v**, since $\|\mathbf{v}\| > 0$. Furthermore,

$$\|\mathbf{u}\| = \sqrt{\frac{a^2}{a^2 + b^2} + \frac{b^2}{a^2 + b^2}} = \sqrt{\frac{a^2 + b^2}{a^2 + b^2}} = 1$$

That is, **u** is a unit vector in the direction of **v**. ■

As a consequence of this theorem, if **u** is a unit vector in the same direction as a vector **v**, then **v** may be expressed as

$$\mathbf{v} = \|\mathbf{v}\|\mathbf{u} \tag{6}$$

This way of expressing a vector is useful in many applications.

EXAMPLE 5 **Finding a Unit Vector**

Find a unit vector in the same direction as $\mathbf{v} = 4\mathbf{i} - 3\mathbf{j}$.

Solution We find $\|\mathbf{v}\|$ first.

$$\|\mathbf{v}\| = \|4\mathbf{i} - 3\mathbf{j}\| = \sqrt{16 + 9} = 5$$

Now we multiply **v** by the scalar $\frac{1}{\|\mathbf{v}\|} = \frac{1}{5}$. A unit vector in the same direction as **v** is

$$\frac{\mathbf{v}}{\|\mathbf{v}\|} = \frac{4\mathbf{i} - 3\mathbf{j}}{5} = \frac{4}{5}\mathbf{i} - \frac{3}{5}\mathbf{j}$$

Check: This vector is, in fact, a unit vector because

$$\left(\frac{4}{5}\right)^2 + \left(-\frac{3}{5}\right)^2 = \frac{16}{25} + \frac{9}{25} = \frac{25}{25} = 1$$

Now Work PROBLEM 49

6 Find a Vector from Its Direction and Magnitude

If a vector represents the speed and direction of an object, it is called a **velocity vector.** If a vector represents the direction and amount of a force acting on an object, it is called a **force vector.** In many applications, a vector is described in terms of its magnitude and direction, rather than in terms of its components. For example, a ball thrown with an initial speed of 25 miles per hour at an angle 30° to the horizontal is a velocity vector.

Suppose that we are given the magnitude $\|\mathbf{v}\|$ of a nonzero vector **v** and the angle α, $0° \le \alpha < 360°$, between **v** and **i**. To express **v** in terms of $\|\mathbf{v}\|$ and α, we first find the unit vector **u** having the same direction as **v**.

$$\mathbf{u} = \frac{\mathbf{v}}{\|\mathbf{v}\|} \quad \text{or} \quad \mathbf{v} = \|\mathbf{v}\|\mathbf{u} \tag{7}$$

Figure 60

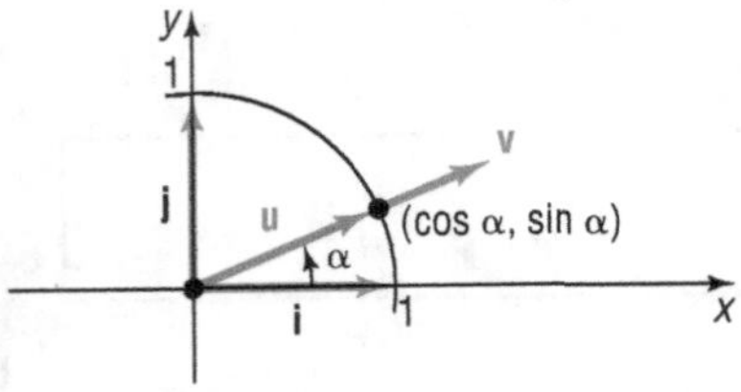

Look at Figure 60. The coordinates of the terminal point of **u** are $(\cos\alpha, \sin\alpha)$. Then $\mathbf{u} = \cos\alpha\mathbf{i} + \sin\alpha\mathbf{j}$ and, from (7),

$$\mathbf{v} = \|\mathbf{v}\|(\cos\alpha\,\mathbf{i} + \sin\alpha\,\mathbf{j}) \qquad \textbf{(8)}$$

where α is the angle between **v** and **i**.

EXAMPLE 6 Writing a Vector When Its Magnitude and Direction Are Given

A ball is thrown with an initial speed of 25 miles per hour in a direction that makes an angle of 30° with the positive x-axis. Express the velocity vector **v** in terms of **i** and **j**. What is the initial speed in the horizontal direction? What is the initial speed in the vertical direction?

Solution The magnitude of **v** is $\|\mathbf{v}\| = 25$ miles per hour, and the angle between the direction of **v** and **i**, the positive x-axis, is $\alpha = 30°$. By equation (8),

$$\mathbf{v} = \|\mathbf{v}\|(\cos\alpha\mathbf{i} + \sin\alpha\mathbf{j}) = 25(\cos 30°\mathbf{i} + \sin 30°\mathbf{j}) = 25\left(\frac{\sqrt{3}}{2}\mathbf{i} + \frac{1}{2}\mathbf{j}\right) = \frac{25\sqrt{3}}{2}\mathbf{i} + \frac{25}{2}\mathbf{j}$$

Figure 61

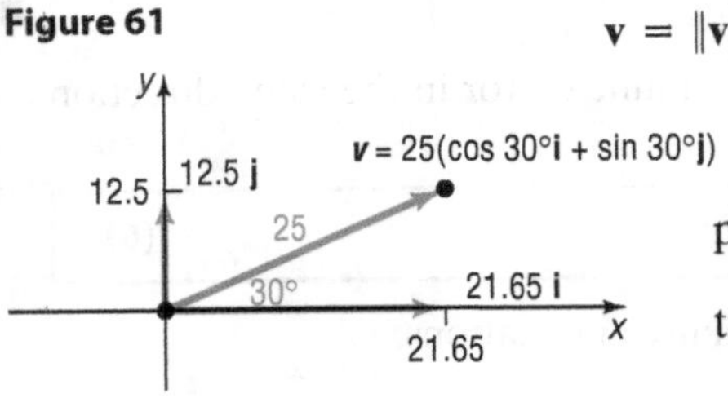

The initial speed of the ball in the horizontal direction is the horizontal component of **v**, $\frac{25\sqrt{3}}{2} \approx 21.65$ miles per hour. The initial speed in the vertical direction is the vertical component of **v**, $\frac{25}{2} = 12.5$ miles per hour. See Figure 61.

Now Work PROBLEM 63

7 Analyze Objects in Static Equilibrium

Figure 62

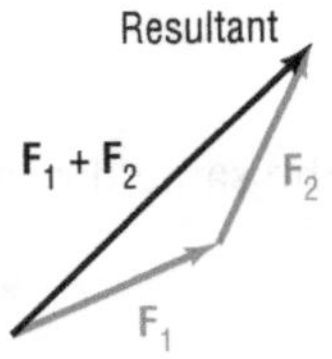

Because forces can be represented by vectors, two forces "combine" the way that vectors "add." If $\mathbf{F}_1$ and $\mathbf{F}_2$ are two forces simultaneously acting on an object, the vector sum $\mathbf{F}_1 + \mathbf{F}_2$ is the **resultant force.** The resultant force produces the same effect on the object as that obtained when the two forces $\mathbf{F}_1$ and $\mathbf{F}_2$ act on the object. See Figure 62. An application of this concept is *static equilibrium.* An object is said to be in **static equilibrium** if (1) the object is at rest and (2) the sum of all forces acting on the object is zero, that is, if the resultant force is 0.

EXAMPLE 7 An Object in Static Equilibrium

A box of supplies that weighs 1200 pounds is suspended by two cables attached to the ceiling, as shown in Figure 63. What are the tensions in the two cables?

Figure 63

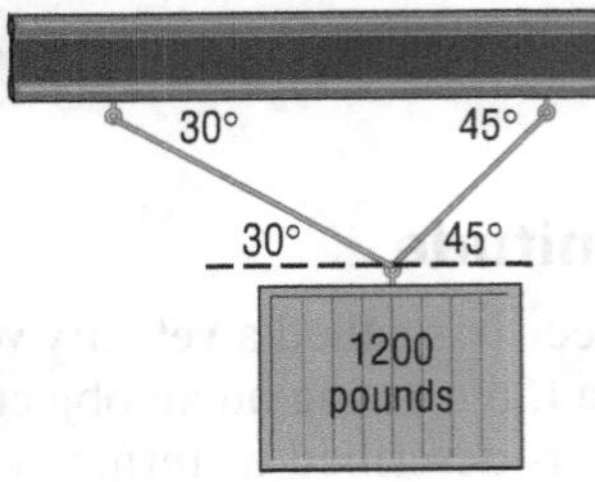

Solution We draw a force diagram using the vectors shown in Figure 64. The tensions in the cables are the magnitudes $\|\mathbf{F}_1\|$ and $\|\mathbf{F}_2\|$ of the force vectors $\mathbf{F}_1$ and $\mathbf{F}_2$. The magnitude of the force vector $\mathbf{F}_3$ equals 1200 pounds, the weight of the box. Now write each force vector in terms of the unit vectors **i** and **j**. For $\mathbf{F}_1$ and $\mathbf{F}_2$, we use equation (8). Remember that α is the angle between the vector and the positive x-axis.

Figure 64

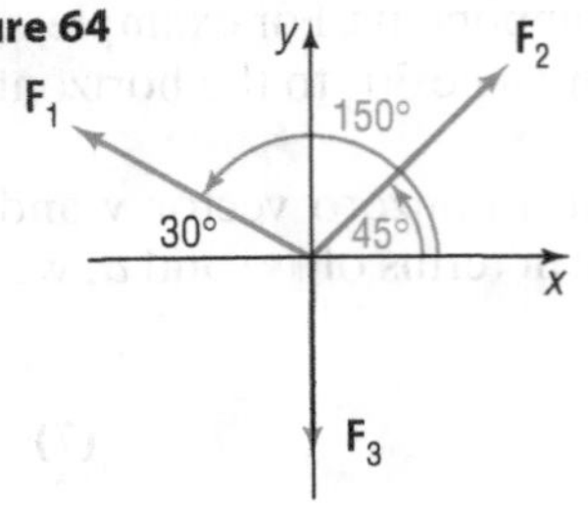

$$\mathbf{F}_1 = \|\mathbf{F}_1\|(\cos 150°\mathbf{i} + \sin 150°\mathbf{j}) = \|\mathbf{F}_1\|\left(-\frac{\sqrt{3}}{2}\mathbf{i} + \frac{1}{2}\mathbf{j}\right) = -\frac{\sqrt{3}}{2}\|\mathbf{F}_1\|\mathbf{i} + \frac{1}{2}\|\mathbf{F}_1\|\mathbf{j}$$

$$\mathbf{F}_2 = \|\mathbf{F}_2\|(\cos 45°\mathbf{i} + \sin 45°\mathbf{j}) = \|\mathbf{F}_2\|\left(\frac{\sqrt{2}}{2}\mathbf{i} + \frac{\sqrt{2}}{2}\mathbf{j}\right) = \frac{\sqrt{2}}{2}\|\mathbf{F}_2\|\mathbf{i} + \frac{\sqrt{2}}{2}\|\mathbf{F}_2\|\mathbf{j}$$

$$\mathbf{F}_3 = -1200\mathbf{j}$$

For static equilibrium, the sum of the force vectors must equal zero.

$$\mathbf{F}_1 + \mathbf{F}_2 + \mathbf{F}_3 = -\frac{\sqrt{3}}{2}\|\mathbf{F}_1\|\mathbf{i} + \frac{1}{2}\|\mathbf{F}_1\|\mathbf{j} + \frac{\sqrt{2}}{2}\|\mathbf{F}_2\|\mathbf{i} + \frac{\sqrt{2}}{2}\|\mathbf{F}_2\|\mathbf{j} - 1200\mathbf{j} = \mathbf{0}$$

The **i** component and **j** component will each equal zero. This results in the two equations

$$-\frac{\sqrt{3}}{2}\|\mathbf{F}_1\| + \frac{\sqrt{2}}{2}\|\mathbf{F}_2\| = 0 \qquad \textbf{(9)}$$

$$\frac{1}{2}\|\mathbf{F}_1\| + \frac{\sqrt{2}}{2}\|\mathbf{F}_2\| - 1200 = 0 \qquad \textbf{(10)}$$

We solve equation (9) for $\|\mathbf{F}_2\|$ and obtain

$$\|\mathbf{F}_2\| = \frac{\sqrt{3}}{\sqrt{2}}\|\mathbf{F}_1\| \qquad \textbf{(11)}$$

Substituting into equation (10) and solving for $\|\mathbf{F}_1\|$, we obtain

$$\frac{1}{2}\|\mathbf{F}_1\| + \frac{\sqrt{2}}{2}\left(\frac{\sqrt{3}}{\sqrt{2}}\|\mathbf{F}_1\|\right) - 1200 = 0$$

$$\frac{1}{2}\|\mathbf{F}_1\| + \frac{\sqrt{3}}{2}\|\mathbf{F}_1\| - 1200 = 0$$

$$\frac{1+\sqrt{3}}{2}\|\mathbf{F}_1\| = 1200$$

$$\|\mathbf{F}_1\| = \frac{2400}{1+\sqrt{3}} \approx 878.5 \text{ pounds}$$

Substituting this value into equation (11) yields $\|\mathbf{F}_2\|$.

$$\|\mathbf{F}_2\| = \frac{\sqrt{3}}{\sqrt{2}}\|\mathbf{F}_1\| = \frac{\sqrt{3}}{\sqrt{2}} \cdot \frac{2400}{1+\sqrt{3}} \approx 1075.9 \text{ pounds}$$

The left cable has tension of approximately 878.5 pounds and the right cable has tension of approximately 1075.9 pounds.

Now Work PROBLEM 67

Historical Feature

Josiah Gibbs (1839–1903)

The history of vectors is surprisingly complicated for such a natural concept. In the *xy*-plane, complex numbers do a good job of imitating vectors. About 1840, mathematicians became interested in finding a system that would do for three dimensions what the complex numbers do for two dimensions. Hermann Grassmann (1809–1877), in Germany, and William Rowan Hamilton (1805–1865), in Ireland, both attempted to find solutions.

Hamilton's system was the *quaternions,* which are best thought of as a real number plus a vector, and do for four dimensions what complex numbers do for two dimensions. In this system the order of multiplication matters; that is, $\mathbf{ab} \neq \mathbf{ba}$. Also, two products of vectors emerged, the scalar (or dot) product and the vector (or cross) product.

Grassmann's abstract style, although easily read today, was almost impenetrable during the previous century, and only a few of his ideas were appreciated. Among those few were the same scalar and vector products that Hamilton had found.

About 1880, the American physicist Josiah Willard Gibbs (1839–1903) worked out an algebra involving only the simplest concepts: the vectors and the two products. He then added some calculus, and the resulting system was simple, flexible, and well adapted to expressing a large number of physical laws. This system remains in use essentially unchanged. Hamilton's and Grassmann's more extensive systems each gave birth to much interesting mathematics, but little of this mathematics is seen at elementary levels.

9.4 Assess Your Understanding

Concepts and Vocabulary

1. A vector whose magnitude is 1 is called a(n) _____ vector.
2. The product of a vector by a number is called a(n) _____ multiple.
3. If $\mathbf{v} = a\mathbf{i} + b\mathbf{j}$, then a is called the _____ component of $\mathbf{v}$ and b is the _____ component of $\mathbf{v}$.
4. ***True or False*** Vectors are quantities that have magnitude and direction.
5. ***True or False*** Force is a physical example of a vector.
6. ***True or False*** Mass is a physical example of a vector.

Skill Building

In Problems 7–14, use the vectors in the figure at the right to graph each of the following vectors.

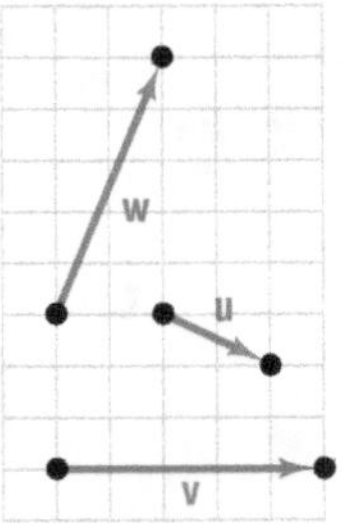

7. $\mathbf{v} + \mathbf{w}$
8. $\mathbf{u} + \mathbf{v}$
9. $3\mathbf{v}$
10. $4\mathbf{w}$
11. $\mathbf{v} - \mathbf{w}$
12. $\mathbf{u} - \mathbf{v}$
13. $3\mathbf{v} + \mathbf{u} - 2\mathbf{w}$
14. $2\mathbf{u} - 3\mathbf{v} + \mathbf{w}$

In Problems 15–22, use the figure at the right. Determine whether the given statement is true or false.

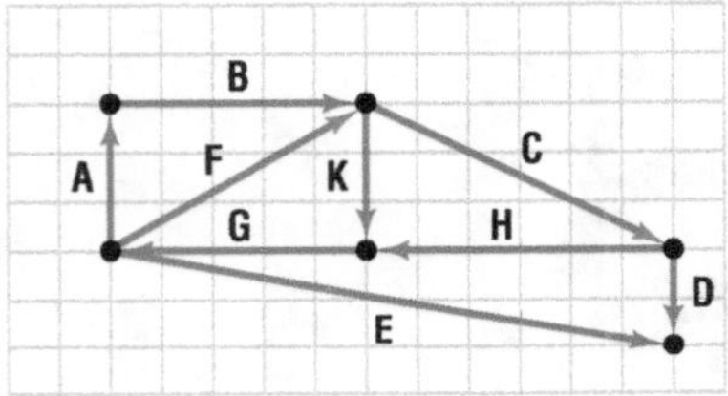

15. $\mathbf{A} + \mathbf{B} = \mathbf{F}$
16. $\mathbf{K} + \mathbf{G} = \mathbf{F}$
17. $\mathbf{C} = \mathbf{D} - \mathbf{E} + \mathbf{F}$
18. $\mathbf{G} + \mathbf{H} + \mathbf{E} = \mathbf{D}$
19. $\mathbf{E} + \mathbf{D} = \mathbf{G} + \mathbf{H}$
20. $\mathbf{H} - \mathbf{C} = \mathbf{G} - \mathbf{F}$
21. $\mathbf{A} + \mathbf{B} + \mathbf{K} + \mathbf{G} = \mathbf{0}$
22. $\mathbf{A} + \mathbf{B} + \mathbf{C} + \mathbf{H} + \mathbf{G} = \mathbf{0}$
23. If $\|\mathbf{v}\| = 4$, what is $\|3\mathbf{v}\|$?
24. If $\|\mathbf{v}\| = 2$, what is $\|-4\mathbf{v}\|$?

In Problems 25–32, the vector $\mathbf{v}$ has initial point P and terminal point Q. Write $\mathbf{v}$ in the form $a\mathbf{i} + b\mathbf{j}$; that is, find its position vector.

25. $P = (0, 0)$; $Q = (3, 4)$
26. $P = (0, 0)$; $Q = (-3, -5)$
27. $P = (3, 2)$; $Q = (5, 6)$
28. $P = (-3, 2)$; $Q = (6, 5)$
29. $P = (-2, -1)$; $Q = (6, -2)$
30. $P = (-1, 4)$; $Q = (6, 2)$
31. $P = (1, 0)$; $Q = (0, 1)$
32. $P = (1, 1)$; $Q = (2, 2)$

In Problems 33–38, find $\|\mathbf{v}\|$.

33. $\mathbf{v} = 3\mathbf{i} - 4\mathbf{j}$
34. $\mathbf{v} = -5\mathbf{i} + 12\mathbf{j}$
35. $\mathbf{v} = \mathbf{i} - \mathbf{j}$
36. $\mathbf{v} = -\mathbf{i} - \mathbf{j}$
37. $\mathbf{v} = -2\mathbf{i} + 3\mathbf{j}$
38. $\mathbf{v} = 6\mathbf{i} + 2\mathbf{j}$

In Problems 39–44, find each quantity if $\mathbf{v} = 3\mathbf{i} - 5\mathbf{j}$ and $\mathbf{w} = -2\mathbf{i} + 3\mathbf{j}$.

39. $2\mathbf{v} + 3\mathbf{w}$
40. $3\mathbf{v} - 2\mathbf{w}$
41. $\|\mathbf{v} - \mathbf{w}\|$
42. $\|\mathbf{v} + \mathbf{w}\|$
43. $\|\mathbf{v}\| - \|\mathbf{w}\|$
44. $\|\mathbf{v}\| + \|\mathbf{w}\|$

In Problems 45–50, find the unit vector in the same direction as $\mathbf{v}$.

45. $\mathbf{v} = 5\mathbf{i}$
46. $\mathbf{v} = -3\mathbf{j}$
47. $\mathbf{v} = 3\mathbf{i} - 4\mathbf{j}$
48. $\mathbf{v} = -5\mathbf{i} + 12\mathbf{j}$
49. $\mathbf{v} = \mathbf{i} - \mathbf{j}$
50. $\mathbf{v} = 2\mathbf{i} - \mathbf{j}$

51. Find a vector $\mathbf{v}$ whose magnitude is 4 and whose component in the $\mathbf{i}$ direction is twice the component in the $\mathbf{j}$ direction.
52. Find a vector $\mathbf{v}$ whose magnitude is 3 and whose component in the $\mathbf{i}$ direction is equal to the component in the $\mathbf{j}$ direction.
53. If $\mathbf{v} = 2\mathbf{i} - \mathbf{j}$ and $\mathbf{w} = x\mathbf{i} + 3\mathbf{j}$, find all numbers x for which $\|\mathbf{v} + \mathbf{w}\| = 5$.
54. If $P = (-3, 1)$ and $Q = (x, 4)$, find all numbers x such that the vector represented by $\overrightarrow{PQ}$ has length 5.

In Problems 55–60, write the vector $\mathbf{v}$ *in the form* $a\mathbf{i} + b\mathbf{j}$, *given its magnitude* $\|\mathbf{v}\|$ *and the angle* α *it makes with the positive x-axis.*

55. $\|\mathbf{v}\| = 5,\quad \alpha = 60°$
56. $\|\mathbf{v}\| = 8,\quad \alpha = 45°$
57. $\|\mathbf{v}\| = 14,\quad \alpha = 120°$
58. $\|\mathbf{v}\| = 3,\quad \alpha = 240°$
59. $\|\mathbf{v}\| = 25,\quad \alpha = 330°$
60. $\|\mathbf{v}\| = 15,\quad \alpha = 315°$

Applications and Extensions

61. Computer Graphics The field of computer graphics utilizes vectors to compute translations of points. For example, if the point $(-3, 2)$ is to be translated by $\mathbf{v} = \langle 5, 2\rangle$, then the new location will be $\mathbf{u}' = \mathbf{u} + \mathbf{v} = \langle -3, 2\rangle + \langle 5, 2\rangle = \langle 2, 4\rangle$. As illustrated in the figure, the point $(-3, 2)$ is translated to $(2, 4)$ by $\mathbf{v}$.

Source: *Phil Dadd. Vectors and Matrices: A Primer. www.gamedev.net/reference/articles/article1832.asp*

(a) Determine the new coordinates of $(3, -1)$ if it is translated by $\mathbf{v} = \langle -4, 5\rangle$

(b) Illustrate this translation graphically.

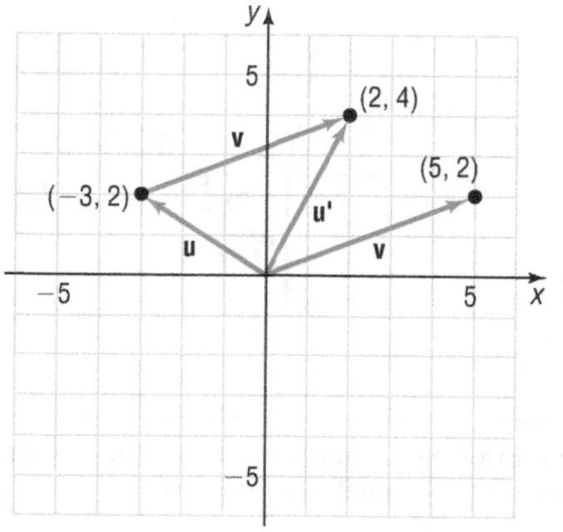

62. Computer Graphics Refer to Problem 61. The points $(-3, 0)$, $(-1, -2)$, $(3, 1)$ and $(1, 3)$ are the vertices of a parallelogram $ABCD$.

(a) Find the new vertices of a parallelogram $A'B'C'D'$ if it is translated by $\mathbf{v} = \langle 3, -2\rangle$.

(b) Find the new vertices of a parallelogram $A'B'C'D'$ if it is translated by $-\dfrac{1}{2}\mathbf{v}$.

63. Force Vectors A child pulls a wagon with a force of 40 pounds. The handle of the wagon makes an angle of 30° with the ground. Express the force vector $\mathbf{F}$ in terms of $\mathbf{i}$ and $\mathbf{j}$.

64. Force Vectors A man pushes a wheelbarrow up an incline of 20° with a force of 100 pounds. Express the force vector $\mathbf{F}$ in terms of $\mathbf{i}$ and $\mathbf{j}$.

65. Resultant Force Two forces of magnitude 40 newtons (N) and 60 N act on an object at angles of 30° and −45° with the positive x-axis, as shown in the figure. Find the direction and magnitude of the resultant force; that is, find $\mathbf{F}_1 + \mathbf{F}_2$.

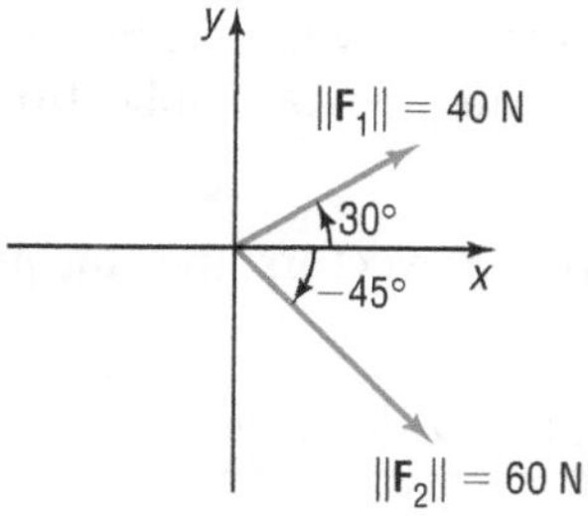

66. Resultant Force Two forces of magnitude 30 newtons (N) and 70 N act on an object at angles of 45° and 120° with the positive x-axis, as shown in the figure. Find the direction and magnitude of the resultant force; that is, find $\mathbf{F}_1 + \mathbf{F}_2$.

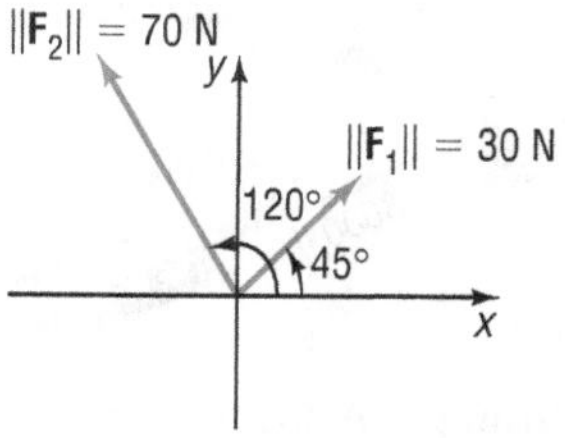

67. Static Equilibrium A weight of 1000 pounds is suspended from two cables as shown in the figure. What are the tensions in the two cables?

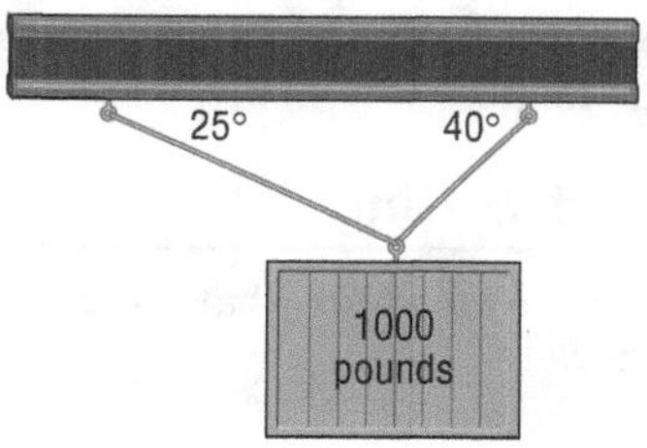

68. Static Equilibrium A weight of 800 pounds is suspended from two cables, as shown in the figure. What are the tensions in the two cables?

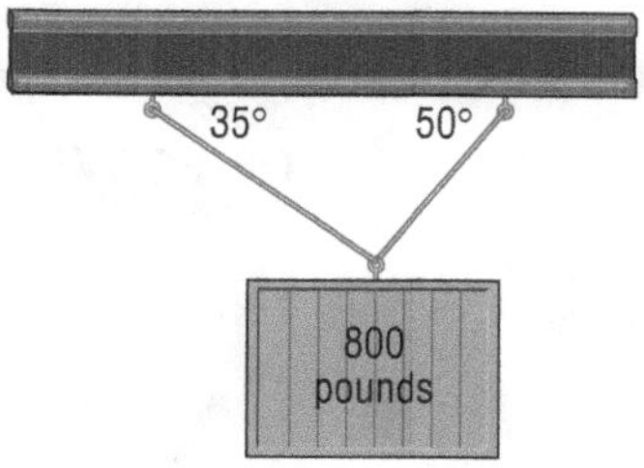

69. Static Equilibrium A tightrope walker located at a certain point deflects the rope as indicated in the figure. If the weight of the tightrope walker is 150 pounds, how much tension is in each part of the rope?

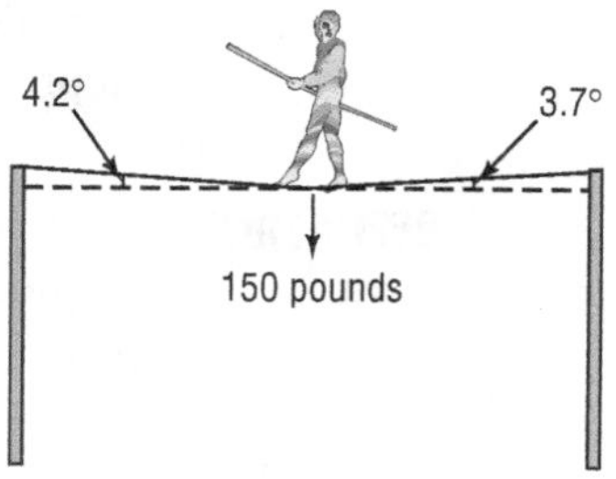

70. Static Equilibrium Repeat Problem 69 if the left angle is 3.8°, the right angle is 2.6°, and the weight of the tightrope walker is 135 pounds.

71. Truck Pull At a county fair truck pull, two pickup trucks are attached to the back end of a monster truck as illustrated in the figure. One of the pickups pulls with a force of 2000 pounds and the other pulls with a force of 3000 pounds with an angle of 45° between them. With how much force must the monster truck pull in order to remain unmoved? [**Hint:** Find the resultant force of the two trucks.]

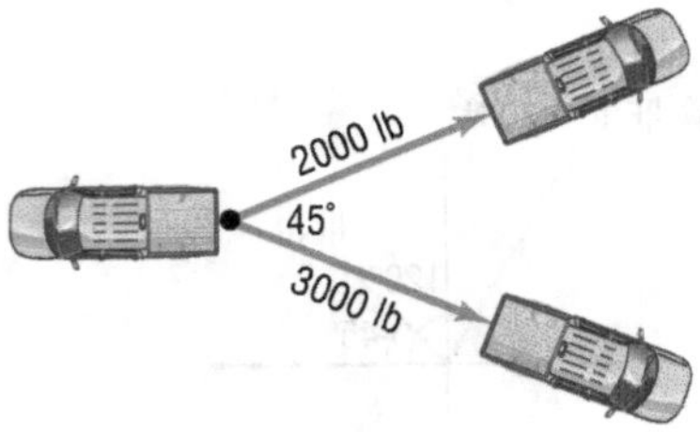

72. Removing a Stump A farmer wishes to remove a stump from a field by pulling it out with his tractor. Having removed many stumps before, he estimates that he will need 6 tons (12,000 pounds) of force to remove the stump. However, his tractor is only capable of pulling with a force of 7000 pounds, so he asks his neighbor to help. His neighbor's tractor can pull with a force of 5500 pounds. They attach the two tractors to the stump with a 40° angle between the forces as shown in the figure.

(a) Assuming the farmer's estimate of a needed 6-ton force is correct, will the farmer be successful in removing the stump? Explain.

(b) Had the farmer arranged the tractors with a 25° angle between the forces, would he have been successful in removing the stump? Explain.

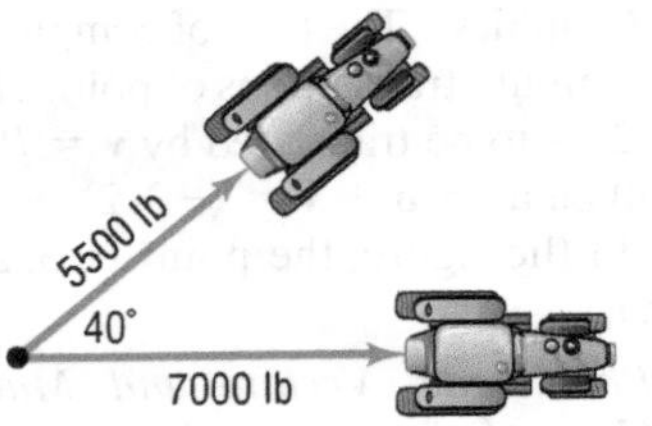

73. Static Equilibrium Show on the following graph the force needed for the object at P to be in static equilibrium.

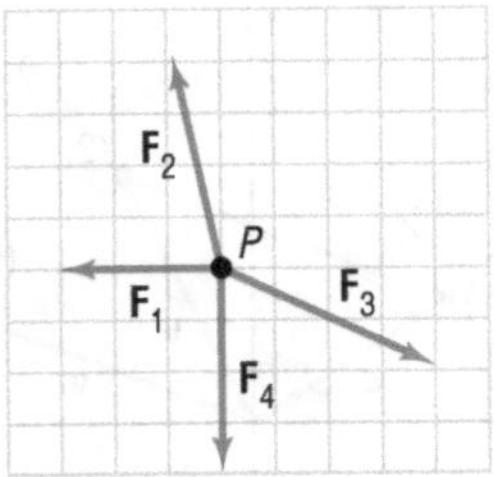

Discussion and Writing

74. Explain in your own words what a vector is. Give an example of a vector.

75. Write a brief paragraph comparing the algebra of complex numbers and the algebra of vectors.

9.5 The Dot Product

PREPARING FOR THIS SECTION *Before getting started, review the following:*

- Law of Cosines (Section 8.3, p. 534)

Now Work the 'Are You Prepared?' problem on page 614.

OBJECTIVES
1 Find the Dot Product of Two Vectors (p. 608)
2 Find the Angle between Two Vectors (p. 609)
3 Determine Whether Two Vectors Are Parallel (p. 611)
4 Determine Whether Two Vectors Are Orthogonal (p. 611)
5 Decompose a Vector into Two Orthogonal Vectors (p. 612)
6 Compute Work (p. 613)

1 Find the Dot Product of Two Vectors

The definition for a product of two vectors is somewhat unexpected. However, such a product has meaning in many geometric and physical applications.

DEFINITION If $\mathbf{v} = a_1\mathbf{i} + b_1\mathbf{j}$ and $\mathbf{w} = a_2\mathbf{i} + b_2\mathbf{j}$ are two vectors, the **dot product** $\mathbf{v} \cdot \mathbf{w}$ is defined as

$$\mathbf{v} \cdot \mathbf{w} = a_1a_2 + b_1b_2 \qquad (1)$$

EXAMPLE 1 **Finding Dot Products**

If $\mathbf{v} = 2\mathbf{i} - 3\mathbf{j}$ and $\mathbf{w} = 5\mathbf{i} + 3\mathbf{j}$, find:

(a) $\mathbf{v} \cdot \mathbf{w}$ (b) $\mathbf{w} \cdot \mathbf{v}$ (c) $\mathbf{v} \cdot \mathbf{v}$

(d) $\mathbf{w} \cdot \mathbf{w}$ (e) $\|\mathbf{v}\|$ (f) $\|\mathbf{w}\|$

Solution

(a) $\mathbf{v} \cdot \mathbf{w} = 2(5) + (-3)3 = 1$ (b) $\mathbf{w} \cdot \mathbf{v} = 5(2) + 3(-3) = 1$

(c) $\mathbf{v} \cdot \mathbf{v} = 2(2) + (-3)(-3) = 13$ (d) $\mathbf{w} \cdot \mathbf{w} = 5(5) + 3(3) = 34$

(e) $\|\mathbf{v}\| = \sqrt{2^2 + (-3)^2} = \sqrt{13}$ (f) $\|\mathbf{w}\| = \sqrt{5^2 + 3^2} = \sqrt{34}$

COMMENT A scalar multiple $\alpha\mathbf{v}$ is a vector. A dot product $\mathbf{u} \cdot \mathbf{v}$ is a scalar (real number).

Since the dot product $\mathbf{v} \cdot \mathbf{w}$ of two vectors $\mathbf{v}$ and $\mathbf{w}$ is a real number (scalar), we sometimes refer to it as the **scalar product.**

The results obtained in Example 1 suggest some general properties.

THEOREM

Properties of the Dot Product

If $\mathbf{u}$, $\mathbf{v}$, and $\mathbf{w}$ are vectors, then

Commutative Property

$$\mathbf{u} \cdot \mathbf{v} = \mathbf{v} \cdot \mathbf{u} \quad (2)$$

Distributive Property

$$\mathbf{u} \cdot (\mathbf{v} + \mathbf{w}) = \mathbf{u} \cdot \mathbf{v} + \mathbf{u} \cdot \mathbf{w} \quad (3)$$

$$\mathbf{v} \cdot \mathbf{v} = \|\mathbf{v}\|^2 \quad (4)$$

$$\mathbf{0} \cdot \mathbf{v} = 0 \quad (5)$$

Proof We will prove properties (2) and (4) here and leave properties (3) and (5) as exercises (see Problems 40 and 41).

To prove property (2), we let $\mathbf{u} = a_1\mathbf{i} + b_1\mathbf{j}$ and $\mathbf{v} = a_2\mathbf{i} + b_2\mathbf{j}$. Then

$$\mathbf{u} \cdot \mathbf{v} = a_1a_2 + b_1b_2 = a_2a_1 + b_2b_1 = \mathbf{v} \cdot \mathbf{u}$$

To prove property (4), we let $\mathbf{v} = a\mathbf{i} + b\mathbf{j}$. Then

$$\mathbf{v} \cdot \mathbf{v} = a^2 + b^2 = \|\mathbf{v}\|^2$$

2 Find the Angle between Two Vectors

One use of the dot product is to calculate the angle between two vectors. We proceed as follows.

Let $\mathbf{u}$ and $\mathbf{v}$ be two vectors with the same initial point A. Then the vectors $\mathbf{u}$, $\mathbf{v}$, and $\mathbf{u} - \mathbf{v}$ form a triangle. The angle θ at vertex A of the triangle is the angle between the vectors $\mathbf{u}$ and $\mathbf{v}$. See Figure 65. We wish to find a formula for calculating the angle θ.

Figure 65

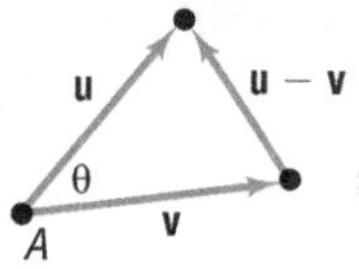

The sides of the triangle have lengths $\|\mathbf{v}\|$, $\|\mathbf{u}\|$, and $\|\mathbf{u} - \mathbf{v}\|$, and θ is the included angle between the sides of length $\|\mathbf{v}\|$ and $\|\mathbf{u}\|$. The Law of Cosines (Section 8.3) can be used to find the cosine of the included angle.

$$\|\mathbf{u} - \mathbf{v}\|^2 = \|\mathbf{u}\|^2 + \|\mathbf{v}\|^2 - 2\|\mathbf{u}\|\|\mathbf{v}\| \cos\theta$$

Now we use property (4) to rewrite this equation in terms of dot products.

$$(\mathbf{u} - \mathbf{v}) \cdot (\mathbf{u} - \mathbf{v}) = \mathbf{u} \cdot \mathbf{u} + \mathbf{v} \cdot \mathbf{v} - 2\|\mathbf{u}\|\|\mathbf{v}\| \cos\theta \quad (6)$$

Then we apply the distributive property (3) twice on the left side of (6) to obtain

$$\begin{aligned}(\mathbf{u}-\mathbf{v})\cdot(\mathbf{u}-\mathbf{v}) &= \mathbf{u}\cdot(\mathbf{u}-\mathbf{v}) - \mathbf{v}\cdot(\mathbf{u}-\mathbf{v})\\ &= \mathbf{u}\cdot\mathbf{u} - \mathbf{u}\cdot\mathbf{v} - \mathbf{v}\cdot\mathbf{u} + \mathbf{v}\cdot\mathbf{v}\\ &= \mathbf{u}\cdot\mathbf{u} + \mathbf{v}\cdot\mathbf{v} - 2\,\mathbf{u}\cdot\mathbf{v} \qquad (7)\end{aligned}$$

↑ Property (2)

Combining equations (6) and (7), we have

$$\mathbf{u}\cdot\mathbf{u} + \mathbf{v}\cdot\mathbf{v} - 2\,\mathbf{u}\cdot\mathbf{v} = \mathbf{u}\cdot\mathbf{u} + \mathbf{v}\cdot\mathbf{v} - 2\,\|\mathbf{u}\|\|\mathbf{v}\|\cos\theta$$
$$\mathbf{u}\cdot\mathbf{v} = \|\mathbf{u}\|\|\mathbf{v}\|\cos\theta$$

We have proved the following result:

THEOREM **Angle between Vectors**

If **u** and **v** are two nonzero vectors, the angle θ, $0 \le \theta \le \pi$, between **u** and **v** is determined by the formula

$$\cos\theta = \frac{\mathbf{u}\cdot\mathbf{v}}{\|\mathbf{u}\|\|\mathbf{v}\|} \qquad (8)$$

EXAMPLE 2 Finding the Angle θ between Two Vectors

Find the angle θ between $\mathbf{u} = 4\mathbf{i} - 3\mathbf{j}$ and $\mathbf{v} = 2\mathbf{i} + 5\mathbf{j}$.

Solution We compute the quantities $\mathbf{u}\cdot\mathbf{v}$, $\|\mathbf{u}\|$, and $\|\mathbf{v}\|$.

$$\mathbf{u}\cdot\mathbf{v} = 4(2) + (-3)(5) = -7$$
$$\|\mathbf{u}\| = \sqrt{4^2 + (-3)^2} = 5$$
$$\|\mathbf{v}\| = \sqrt{2^2 + 5^2} = \sqrt{29}$$

Figure 66

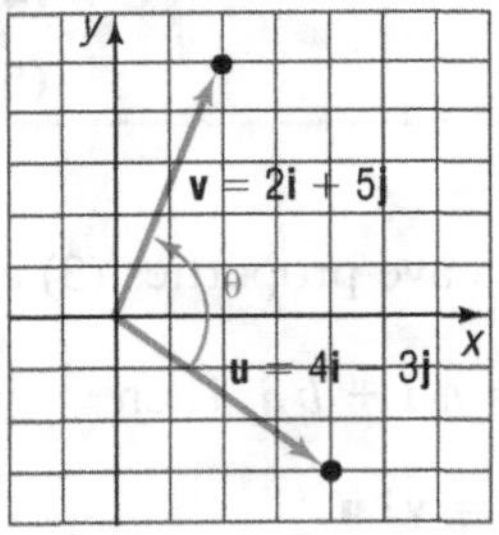

By formula (8), if θ is the angle between **u** and **v**, then

$$\cos\theta = \frac{\mathbf{u}\cdot\mathbf{v}}{\|\mathbf{u}\|\|\mathbf{v}\|} = \frac{-7}{5\sqrt{29}} \approx -0.26$$

We find that $\theta \approx 105°$. See Figure 66.

Now Work PROBLEMS 7(a) AND (b)

EXAMPLE 3 Finding the Actual Speed and Direction of an Aircraft

A Boeing 737 aircraft maintains a constant airspeed of 500 miles per hour in the direction due south. The velocity of the jet stream is 80 miles per hour in a northeasterly direction. Find the actual speed and direction of the aircraft relative to the ground.

Solution We set up a coordinate system in which north (N) is along the positive y-axis. See Figure 67. Let

$$\mathbf{v}_a = \text{velocity of aircraft relative to the air} = -500\mathbf{j}$$
$$\mathbf{v}_w = \text{velocity of jet stream}$$
$$\mathbf{v}_g = \text{velocity of aircraft relative to ground}$$

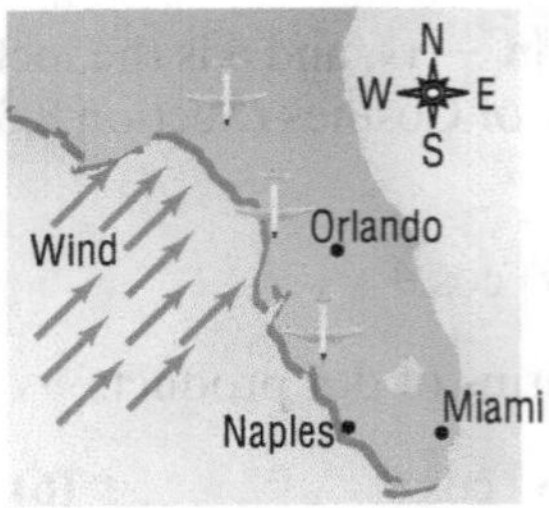

The velocity of the jet stream $\mathbf{v}_w$ has magnitude 80 and direction NE (northeast), so the angle between $\mathbf{v}_w$ and **i** is 45°. We express $\mathbf{v}_w$ in terms of **i** and **j** as

$$\mathbf{v}_w = 80(\cos 45°\mathbf{i} + \sin 45°\mathbf{j}) = 80\left(\frac{\sqrt{2}}{2}\mathbf{i} + \frac{\sqrt{2}}{2}\mathbf{j}\right) = 40\sqrt{2}(\mathbf{i} + \mathbf{j})$$

Figure 67

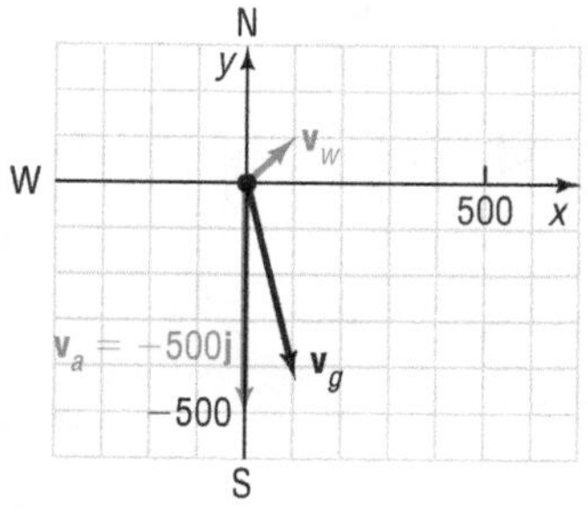

The velocity of the aircraft relative to the ground is

$$\mathbf{v}_g = \mathbf{v}_a + \mathbf{v}_w = -500\mathbf{j} + 40\sqrt{2}(\mathbf{i} + \mathbf{j}) = 40\sqrt{2}\mathbf{i} + \left(40\sqrt{2} - 500\right)\mathbf{j}$$

The actual speed of the aircraft is

$$\|\mathbf{v}_g\| = \sqrt{\left(40\sqrt{2}\right)^2 + \left(40\sqrt{2} - 500\right)^2} \approx 447 \text{ miles per hour}$$

The angle θ between $\mathbf{v}_g$ and the vector $\mathbf{v}_a = -500\mathbf{j}$ (the velocity of the aircraft relative to the air) is determined by the equation

$$\cos\theta = \frac{\mathbf{v}_g \cdot \mathbf{v}_a}{\|\mathbf{v}_g\|\|\mathbf{v}_a\|} \approx \frac{\left(40\sqrt{2} - 500\right)(-500)}{(447)(500)} \approx 0.9920$$

$$\theta \approx 7.3°$$

The direction of the aircraft relative to the ground is approximately S7.3°E (about 7.3° east of south).

Now Work PROBLEM 29

3 Determine Whether Two Vectors Are Parallel

Two vectors $\mathbf{v}$ and $\mathbf{w}$ are said to be **parallel** if there is a nonzero scalar α so that $\mathbf{v} = \alpha\mathbf{w}$. In this case, the angle θ between $\mathbf{v}$ and $\mathbf{w}$ is 0 or π.

EXAMPLE 4 **Determining Whether Vectors Are Parallel**

The vectors $\mathbf{v} = 3\mathbf{i} - \mathbf{j}$ and $\mathbf{w} = 6\mathbf{i} - 2\mathbf{j}$ are parallel, since $\mathbf{v} = \frac{1}{2}\mathbf{w}$. Furthermore, since

$$\cos\theta = \frac{\mathbf{v} \cdot \mathbf{w}}{\|\mathbf{v}\|\|\mathbf{w}\|} = \frac{18 + 2}{\sqrt{10}\sqrt{40}} = \frac{20}{\sqrt{400}} = 1$$

the angle θ between $\mathbf{v}$ and $\mathbf{w}$ is 0.

4 Determine Whether Two Vectors Are Orthogonal

If the angle θ between two nonzero vectors $\mathbf{v}$ and $\mathbf{w}$ is $\frac{\pi}{2}$, the vectors $\mathbf{v}$ and $\mathbf{w}$ are called **orthogonal.*** See Figure 68.

Figure 68
$\mathbf{v}$ is orthogonal to $\mathbf{w}$.

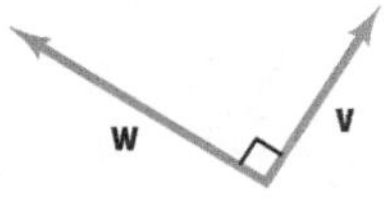

Since $\cos\frac{\pi}{2} = 0$, it follows from formula (8) that if $\mathbf{v}$ and $\mathbf{w}$ are orthogonal then $\mathbf{v} \cdot \mathbf{w} = 0$.

On the other hand, if $\mathbf{v} \cdot \mathbf{w} = 0$, then either $\mathbf{v} = \mathbf{0}$ or $\mathbf{w} = \mathbf{0}$ or $\cos\theta = 0$. In the latter case, $\theta = \frac{\pi}{2}$, and $\mathbf{v}$ and $\mathbf{w}$ are orthogonal. If $\mathbf{v}$ or $\mathbf{w}$ is the zero vector, then, since the zero vector has no specific direction, we adopt the convention that the zero vector is orthogonal to every vector.

THEOREM

Two vectors $\mathbf{v}$ and $\mathbf{w}$ are orthogonal if and only if

$$\mathbf{v} \cdot \mathbf{w} = 0$$

Orthogonal, perpendicular, and *normal* are all terms that mean "meet at a right angle." It is customary to refer to two vectors as being *orthogonal,* two lines as being *perpendicular,* and a line and a plane or a vector and a plane as being *normal.*

EXAMPLE 5 **Determining Whether Two Vectors Are Orthogonal**

Figure 69

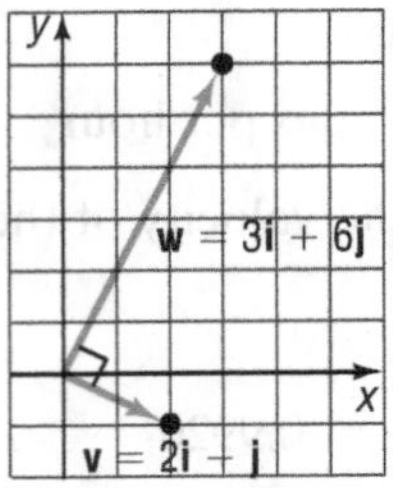

The vectors

$$\mathbf{v} = 2\mathbf{i} - \mathbf{j} \quad \text{and} \quad \mathbf{w} = 3\mathbf{i} + 6\mathbf{j}$$

are orthogonal, since

$$\mathbf{v} \cdot \mathbf{w} = 6 - 6 = 0$$

See Figure 69.

Now Work PROBLEM 7(c)

5 Decompose a Vector into Two Orthogonal Vectors

Figure 70

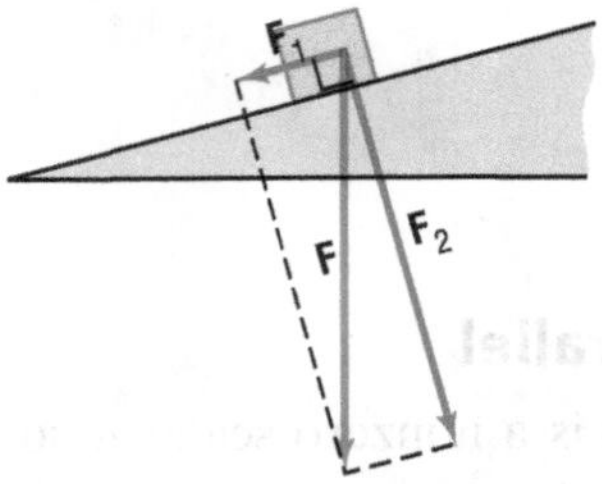

In many physical applications, it is necessary to find "how much" of a vector is applied in a given direction. Look at Figure 70. The force **F** due to gravity is pulling straight down (toward the center of Earth) on the block. To study the effect of gravity on the block, it is necessary to determine how much of **F** is actually pushing the block down the incline ($\mathbf{F}_1$) and how much is pressing the block against the incline ($\mathbf{F}_2$), at a right angle to the incline. Knowing the **decomposition** of **F** often will allow us to determine when friction (the force holding the block in place on the incline) is overcome and the block will slide down the incline.

Suppose that **v** and **w** are two nonzero vectors with the same initial point P. We seek to decompose **v** into two vectors: $\mathbf{v}_1$, which is parallel to **w**, and $\mathbf{v}_2$, which is orthogonal to **w**. See Figure 71(a) and (b). The vector $\mathbf{v}_1$ is called the **vector projection of v onto w.**

Figure 71

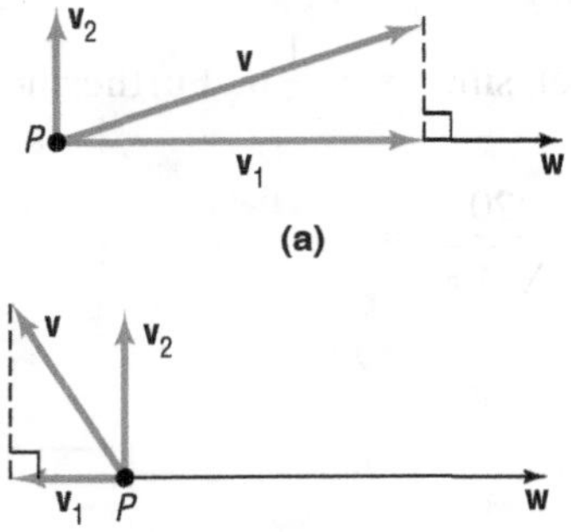

The vector $\mathbf{v}_1$ is obtained as follows: From the terminal point of **v**, drop a perpendicular to the line containing **w**. The vector $\mathbf{v}_1$ is the vector from P to the foot of this perpendicular. The vector $\mathbf{v}_2$ is given by $\mathbf{v}_2 = \mathbf{v} - \mathbf{v}_1$. Note that $\mathbf{v} = \mathbf{v}_1 + \mathbf{v}_2$, the vector $\mathbf{v}_1$ is parallel to **w**, and the vector $\mathbf{v}_2$ is orthogonal to **w**. This is the decomposition of **v** that we wanted.

Now we seek a formula for $\mathbf{v}_1$ that is based on a knowledge of the vectors **v** and **w**. Since $\mathbf{v} = \mathbf{v}_1 + \mathbf{v}_2$, we have

$$\mathbf{v} \cdot \mathbf{w} = (\mathbf{v}_1 + \mathbf{v}_2) \cdot \mathbf{w} = \mathbf{v}_1 \cdot \mathbf{w} + \mathbf{v}_2 \cdot \mathbf{w} \qquad (9)$$

Since $\mathbf{v}_2$ is orthogonal to **w**, we have $\mathbf{v}_2 \cdot \mathbf{w} = 0$. Since $\mathbf{v}_1$ is parallel to **w**, we have $\mathbf{v}_1 = \alpha\mathbf{w}$ for some scalar α. Equation (9) can be written as

$$\mathbf{v} \cdot \mathbf{w} = \alpha\mathbf{w} \cdot \mathbf{w} = \alpha\|\mathbf{w}\|^2 \qquad \mathbf{v}_1 = \alpha\mathbf{w};\ \mathbf{v}_2 \cdot \mathbf{w} = 0$$

$$\alpha = \frac{\mathbf{v} \cdot \mathbf{w}}{\|\mathbf{w}\|^2}$$

Then

$$\mathbf{v}_1 = \alpha\mathbf{w} = \frac{\mathbf{v} \cdot \mathbf{w}}{\|\mathbf{w}\|^2}\mathbf{w}$$

THEOREM If **v** and **w** are two nonzero vectors, the vector projection of **v** onto **w** is

$$\mathbf{v}_1 = \frac{\mathbf{v} \cdot \mathbf{w}}{\|\mathbf{w}\|^2}\mathbf{w} \qquad (10)$$

The decomposition of **v** into $\mathbf{v}_1$ and $\mathbf{v}_2$, where $\mathbf{v}_1$ is parallel to **w** and $\mathbf{v}_2$ is orthogonal to **w**, is

$$\mathbf{v}_1 = \frac{\mathbf{v} \cdot \mathbf{w}}{\|\mathbf{w}\|^2}\mathbf{w} \qquad \mathbf{v}_2 = \mathbf{v} - \mathbf{v}_1 \qquad (11)$$

EXAMPLE 6 Decomposing a Vector into Two Orthogonal Vectors

Find the vector projection of $\mathbf{v} = \mathbf{i} + 3\mathbf{j}$ onto $\mathbf{w} = \mathbf{i} + \mathbf{j}$. Decompose $\mathbf{v}$ into two vectors, $\mathbf{v}_1$ and $\mathbf{v}_2$, where $\mathbf{v}_1$ is parallel to $\mathbf{w}$ and $\mathbf{v}_2$ is orthogonal to $\mathbf{w}$.

Solution We use formulas (10) and (11).

Figure 72

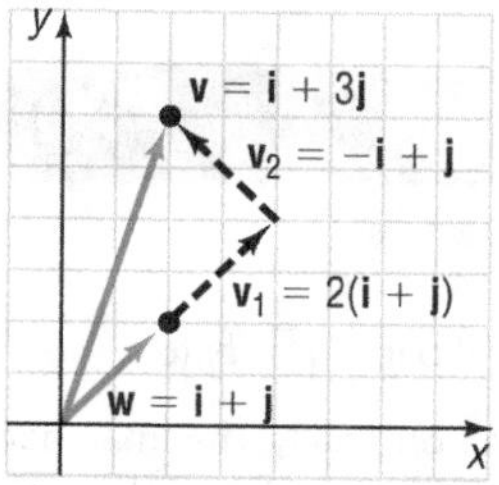

$$\mathbf{v}_1 = \frac{\mathbf{v}\cdot\mathbf{w}}{\|\mathbf{w}\|^2}\mathbf{w} = \frac{1+3}{(\sqrt{2})^2}\mathbf{w} = 2\mathbf{w} = 2(\mathbf{i}+\mathbf{j})$$

$$\mathbf{v}_2 = \mathbf{v} - \mathbf{v}_1 = (\mathbf{i} + 3\mathbf{j}) - 2(\mathbf{i}+\mathbf{j}) = -\mathbf{i} + \mathbf{j}$$

See Figure 72.

Now Work PROBLEM 19

6 Compute Work

In elementary physics, the **work** W done by a constant force $\mathbf{F}$ in moving an object from a point A to a point B is defined as

$$W = (\text{magnitude of force})(\text{distance}) = \|\mathbf{F}\|\|\overrightarrow{AB}\|$$

Figure 73

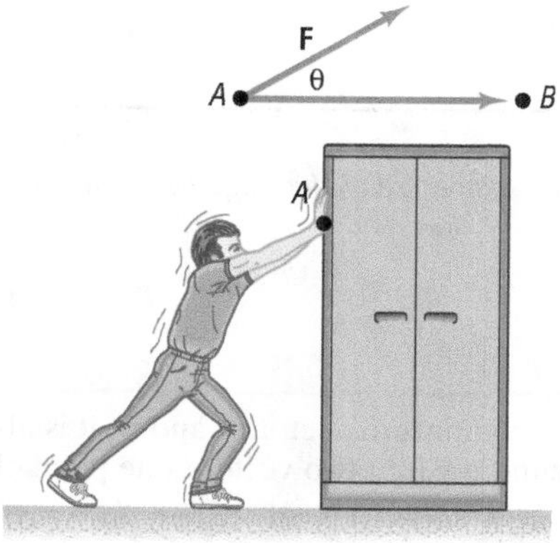

Work is commonly measured in foot-pounds or in newton-meters (joules).

In this definition, it is assumed that the force $\mathbf{F}$ is applied along the line of motion. If the constant force $\mathbf{F}$ is not along the line of motion, but, instead, is at an angle θ to the direction of the motion, as illustrated in Figure 73, the **work W done by F** in moving an object from A to B is defined as

$$W = \mathbf{F}\cdot\overrightarrow{AB} \tag{12}$$

This definition is compatible with the force times distance definition, since

$$W = (\text{amount of force in the direction of } \overrightarrow{AB})(\text{distance})$$

$$= \|\text{projection of } \mathbf{F} \text{ on } AB\|\|\overrightarrow{AB}\| = \frac{\mathbf{F}\cdot\overrightarrow{AB}}{\|\overrightarrow{AB}\|^2}\|\overrightarrow{AB}\|\|\overrightarrow{AB}\| = \mathbf{F}\cdot\overrightarrow{AB}$$

↑ Use formula (10).

EXAMPLE 7 Computing Work

Figure 74(a) shows a girl pulling a wagon with a force of 50 pounds. How much work is done in moving the wagon 100 feet if the handle makes an angle of 30° with the ground?

Figure 74

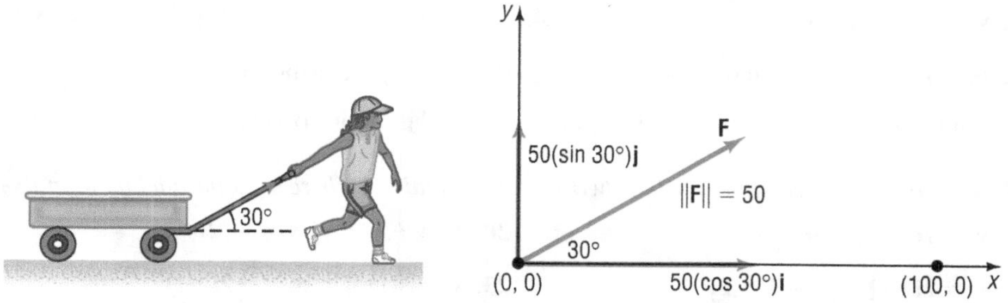

(a) (b)

Solution We position the vectors in a coordinate system in such a way that the wagon is moved from (0, 0) to (100, 0). The motion is from $A = (0, 0)$ to $B = (100, 0)$, so $\overrightarrow{AB} = 100\mathbf{i}$. The force vector $\mathbf{F}$, as shown in Figure 74(b), is

$$\mathbf{F} = 50(\cos 30°\mathbf{i} + \sin 30°\mathbf{j}) = 50\left(\frac{\sqrt{3}}{2}\mathbf{i} + \frac{1}{2}\mathbf{j}\right) = 25(\sqrt{3}\mathbf{i} + \mathbf{j})$$

By formula (12), the work done is

$$W = \mathbf{F} \cdot \overrightarrow{AB} = 25(\sqrt{3}\mathbf{i} + \mathbf{j}) \cdot 100\mathbf{i} = 2500\sqrt{3} \text{ foot-pounds}$$

Now Work PROBLEM 25

Historical Feature

We stated in an earlier Historical Feature that complex numbers were used as vectors in the plane before the general notion of a vector was clarified. Suppose that we make the correspondence

Vector ↔ Complex number

$$a\mathbf{i} + b\mathbf{j} \leftrightarrow a + bi$$
$$c\mathbf{i} + d\mathbf{j} \leftrightarrow c + di$$

Show that

$$(a\mathbf{i} + b\mathbf{j}) \cdot (c\mathbf{i} + d\mathbf{j}) = \text{real part } [(\overline{a + bi})(c + di)]$$

This is how the dot product was found originally. The imaginary part is also interesting. It is a determinant (see Section 11.3) and represents the area of the parallelogram whose edges are the vectors. This is close to some of Hermann Grassmann's ideas and is also connected with the scalar triple product of three-dimensional vectors.

9.5 Assess Your Understanding

'Are You Prepared?' *The answer is given at the end of these exercises. If you get the wrong answer, read the page listed in red.*

1. In a triangle with sides a, b, c and angles A, B, C, the Law of Cosines states that ______. (p. 534)

Concepts and Vocabulary

2. If $\mathbf{v} \cdot \mathbf{w} = 0$, then the two vectors $\mathbf{v}$ and $\mathbf{w}$ are ______.

3. If $\mathbf{v} = 3\mathbf{w}$, then the two vectors $\mathbf{v}$ and $\mathbf{w}$ are ______.

4. ***True or False*** If $\mathbf{v}$ and $\mathbf{w}$ are parallel vectors, then $\mathbf{v} \cdot \mathbf{w} = 0$.

5. ***True or False*** Given two nonzero vectors $\mathbf{v}$ and $\mathbf{w}$, it is always possible to decompose $\mathbf{v}$ into two vectors, one parallel to $\mathbf{w}$ and the other perpendicular to $\mathbf{w}$.

6. ***True or False*** Work is a physical example of a vector.

Skill Building

In Problems 7–16, (a) find the dot product $\mathbf{v} \cdot \mathbf{w}$; *(b) find the angle between* $\mathbf{v}$ *and* $\mathbf{w}$; *(c) state whether the vectors are parallel, orthogonal, or neither.*

7. $\mathbf{v} = \mathbf{i} - \mathbf{j}, \quad \mathbf{w} = \mathbf{i} + \mathbf{j}$

8. $\mathbf{v} = \mathbf{i} + \mathbf{j}, \quad \mathbf{w} = -\mathbf{i} + \mathbf{j}$

9. $\mathbf{v} = 2\mathbf{i} + \mathbf{j}, \quad \mathbf{w} = \mathbf{i} - 2\mathbf{j}$

10. $\mathbf{v} = 2\mathbf{i} + 2\mathbf{j}, \quad \mathbf{w} = \mathbf{i} + 2\mathbf{j}$

11. $\mathbf{v} = \sqrt{3}\mathbf{i} - \mathbf{j}, \quad \mathbf{w} = \mathbf{i} + \mathbf{j}$

12. $\mathbf{v} = \mathbf{i} + \sqrt{3}\mathbf{j}, \quad \mathbf{w} = \mathbf{i} - \mathbf{j}$

13. $\mathbf{v} = 3\mathbf{i} + 4\mathbf{j}, \quad \mathbf{w} = -6\mathbf{i} - 8\mathbf{j}$

14. $\mathbf{v} = 3\mathbf{i} - 4\mathbf{j}, \quad \mathbf{w} = 9\mathbf{i} - 12\mathbf{j}$

15. $\mathbf{v} = 4\mathbf{i}, \quad \mathbf{w} = \mathbf{j}$

16. $\mathbf{v} = \mathbf{i}, \quad \mathbf{w} = -3\mathbf{j}$

17. Find a so that the vectors $\mathbf{v} = \mathbf{i} - a\mathbf{j}$ and $\mathbf{w} = 2\mathbf{i} + 3\mathbf{j}$ are orthogonal.

18. Find b so that the vectors $\mathbf{v} = \mathbf{i} + \mathbf{j}$ and $\mathbf{w} = \mathbf{i} + b\mathbf{j}$ are orthogonal.

In Problems 19–24, decompose $\mathbf{v}$ *into two vectors* $\mathbf{v}_1$ *and* $\mathbf{v}_2$, *where* $\mathbf{v}_1$ *is parallel to* $\mathbf{w}$ *and* $\mathbf{v}_2$ *is orthogonal to* $\mathbf{w}$.

19. $\mathbf{v} = 2\mathbf{i} - 3\mathbf{j}, \quad \mathbf{w} = \mathbf{i} - \mathbf{j}$

20. $\mathbf{v} = -3\mathbf{i} + 2\mathbf{j}, \quad \mathbf{w} = 2\mathbf{i} + \mathbf{j}$

21. $\mathbf{v} = \mathbf{i} - \mathbf{j}, \quad \mathbf{w} = -\mathbf{i} - 2\mathbf{j}$

22. $\mathbf{v} = 2\mathbf{i} - \mathbf{j}, \quad \mathbf{w} = \mathbf{i} - 2\mathbf{j}$

23. $\mathbf{v} = 3\mathbf{i} + \mathbf{j}, \quad \mathbf{w} = -2\mathbf{i} - \mathbf{j}$

24. $\mathbf{v} = \mathbf{i} - 3\mathbf{j}, \quad \mathbf{w} = 4\mathbf{i} - \mathbf{j}$

Applications and Extensions

25. Computing Work Find the work done by a force of 3 pounds acting in the direction 60° to the horizontal in moving an object 6 feet from (0, 0) to (6, 0).

26. Computing Work A wagon is pulled horizontally by exerting a force of 20 pounds on the handle at an angle of 30° with the horizontal. How much work is done in moving the wagon 100 feet?

27. Solar Energy The amount of energy collected by a solar panel depends on the intensity of the sun's rays and the area of the panel. Let the vector **I** represent the intensity, in watts per square centimeter, having the direction of the sun's rays. Let the vector **A** represent the area, in square centimeters, whose direction is the orientation of a solar panel. See the figure. The total number of watts collected by the panel is given by $W = |\mathbf{I} \cdot \mathbf{A}|$.

Suppose $\mathbf{I} = \langle -0.02, -0.01 \rangle$ and $\mathbf{A} = \langle 300, 400 \rangle$.

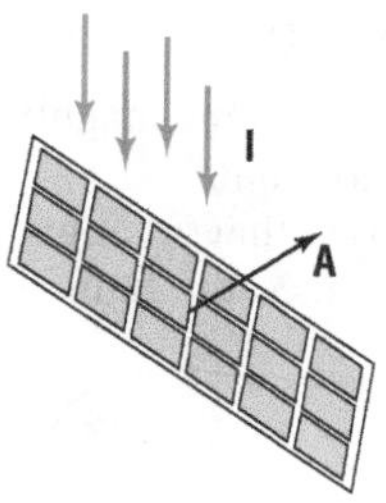

(a) Find $\|\mathbf{I}\|$ and $\|\mathbf{A}\|$ and interpret the meaning of each.
(b) Compute W and interpret its meaning.
(c) If the solar panel is to collect the maximum number of watts, what must be true about **I** and **A**?

28. Rainfall Measurement Let the vector **R** represent the amount of rainfall, in inches, whose direction is the inclination of the rain to a rain gauge. Let the vector **A** represent the area, in square inches, whose direction is the orientation of the opening of the rain gauge. See the figure. The volume of rain collected in the gauge, in cubic inches, is given by $V = |\mathbf{R} \cdot \mathbf{A}|$, even when the rain falls in a slanted direction or the gauge is not perfectly vertical.

Suppose $\mathbf{R} = \langle 0.75, -1.75 \rangle$ and $\mathbf{A} = \langle 0.3, 1 \rangle$.

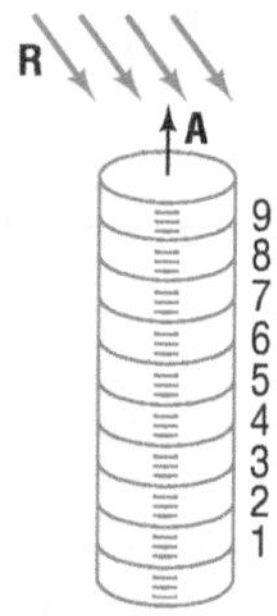

(a) Find $\|\mathbf{R}\|$ and $\|\mathbf{A}\|$ and interpret the meaning of each.
(b) Compute V and interpret its meaning
(c) If the gauge is to collect the maximum volume of rain, what must be true about **R** and **A**?

29. Finding the Actual Speed and Direction of an Aircraft A Boeing 747 jumbo jet maintains an airspeed of 550 miles per hour in a southwesterly direction. The velocity of the jet stream is a constant 80 miles per hour from the west. Find the actual speed and direction of the aircraft.

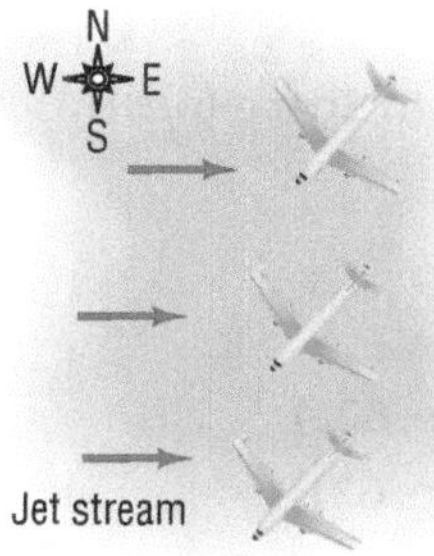

30. Finding the Correct Compass Heading The pilot of an aircraft wishes to head directly east, but is faced with a wind speed of 40 miles per hour from the northwest. If the pilot maintains an airspeed of 250 miles per hour, what compass heading should be maintained to head directly east? What is the actual speed of the aircraft?

31. Correct Direction for Crossing a River A river has a constant current of 3 kilometers per hour. At what angle to a boat dock should a motorboat, capable of maintaining a constant speed of 20 kilometers per hour, be headed in order to reach a point directly opposite the dock? If the river is $\frac{1}{2}$ kilometer wide, how long will it take to cross?

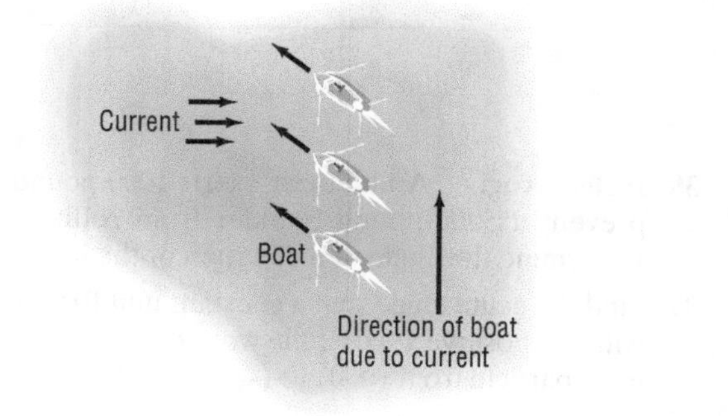

32. Crossing a River A small motorboat in still water maintains a speed of 20 miles per hour. In heading directly across a river (that is, perpendicular to the current) whose current is 3 miles per hour, find a vector representing the speed and direction of the motorboat. What is the true speed of the motorboat? What is its direction?

33. Braking Load A Toyota Sienna with a gross weight of 5300 pounds is parked on a street with a slope of 8°. See the figure. Find the force required to keep the Sienna from rolling down the hill. What is the force perpendicular to the hill?

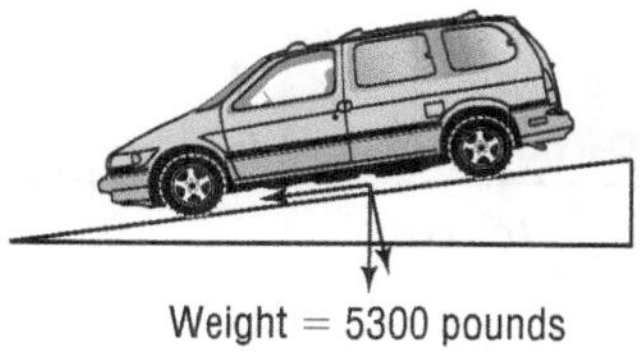

34. Braking Load A Pontiac Bonneville with a gross weight of 4500 pounds is parked on a street with a slope of 10°. Find the force required to keep the Bonneville from rolling down the hill. What is the force perpendicular to the hill?

35. Ground Speed and Direction of an Airplane An airplane has an airspeed of 500 kilometers per hour (km/hr) bearing N45°E. The wind velocity is 60 km/hr in the direction N30°W. Find the resultant vector representing the path of the plane relative to the ground. What is the ground speed of the plane? What is its direction?

36. Ground Speed and Direction of an Airplane An airplane has an airspeed of 600 km/hr bearing S30°E. The wind velocity is 40 km/hr in the direction S45°E. Find the resultant vector representing the path of the plane relative to the ground. What is the ground speed of the plane? What is its direction?

37. Ramp Angle Billy and Timmy are using a ramp to load furniture into a truck. While rolling a 250-pound piano up the ramp, they discover that the truck is too full of other furniture for the piano to fit. Timmy holds the piano in place on the ramp while Billy repositions other items to make room for it in the truck. If the angle of inclination of the ramp is 20°, how many pounds of force must Timmy exert to hold the piano in position?

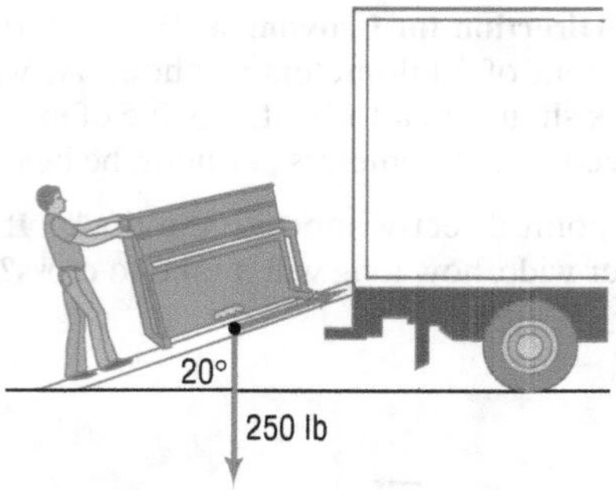

38. Incline Angle A bulldozer exerts 1000 pounds of force to prevent a 5000-pound boulder from rolling down a hill. Determine the angle of inclination of the hill.

39. Find the acute angle that a constant unit force vector makes with the positive x-axis if the work done by the force in moving a particle from $(0, 0)$ to $(4, 0)$ equals 2.

40. Prove the distributive property:

$$\mathbf{u} \cdot (\mathbf{v} + \mathbf{w}) = \mathbf{u} \cdot \mathbf{v} + \mathbf{u} \cdot \mathbf{w}$$

41. Prove property (5), $\mathbf{0} \cdot \mathbf{v} = 0$.

42. If $\mathbf{v}$ is a unit vector and the angle between $\mathbf{v}$ and $\mathbf{i}$ is α, show that $\mathbf{v} = \cos\alpha\mathbf{i} + \sin\alpha\mathbf{j}$.

43. Suppose that $\mathbf{v}$ and $\mathbf{w}$ are unit vectors. If the angle between $\mathbf{v}$ and $\mathbf{i}$ is α and that between $\mathbf{w}$ and $\mathbf{i}$ is β, use the idea of the dot product $\mathbf{v} \cdot \mathbf{w}$ to prove that

$$\cos(\alpha - \beta) = \cos\alpha\cos\beta + \sin\alpha\sin\beta$$

44. Show that the projection of $\mathbf{v}$ onto $\mathbf{i}$ is $(\mathbf{v} \cdot \mathbf{i})\mathbf{i}$. Then show that we can always write a vector $\mathbf{v}$ as

$$\mathbf{v} = (\mathbf{v} \cdot \mathbf{i})\mathbf{i} + (\mathbf{v} \cdot \mathbf{j})\mathbf{j}$$

45. (a) If $\mathbf{u}$ and $\mathbf{v}$ have the same magnitude, show that $\mathbf{u} + \mathbf{v}$ and $\mathbf{u} - \mathbf{v}$ are orthogonal.
(b) Use this to prove that an angle inscribed in a semicircle is a right angle (see the figure).

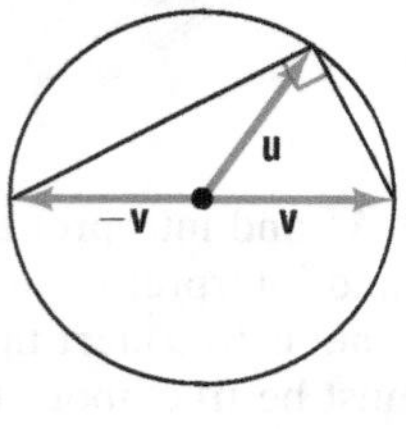

46. Let $\mathbf{v}$ and $\mathbf{w}$ denote two nonzero vectors. Show that the vector $\mathbf{v} - \alpha\mathbf{w}$ is orthogonal to $\mathbf{w}$ if $\alpha = \dfrac{\mathbf{v} \cdot \mathbf{w}}{\|\mathbf{w}\|^2}$.

47. Let $\mathbf{v}$ and $\mathbf{w}$ denote two nonzero vectors. Show that the vectors $\|\mathbf{w}\|\mathbf{v} + \|\mathbf{v}\|\mathbf{w}$ and $\|\mathbf{w}\|\mathbf{v} - \|\mathbf{v}\|\mathbf{w}$ are orthogonal.

48. In the definition of work given in this section, what is the work done if $\mathbf{F}$ is orthogonal to $\overrightarrow{AB}$?

49. Prove the **polarization identity,**

$$\|\mathbf{u} + \mathbf{v}\|^2 - \|\mathbf{u} - \mathbf{v}\|^2 = 4(\mathbf{u} \cdot \mathbf{v})$$

Discussion and Writing

50. Create an application different from any found in the text that requires a dot product.

'Are You Prepared?' Answer

1. $c^2 = a^2 + b^2 - 2ab\cos C$

9.6 Vectors in Space

PREPARING FOR THIS SECTION *Before getting started, review the following:*

- Distance Formula (Section 1.1, p. 5)

Now Work the 'Are You Prepared?' problem on page 624.

OBJECTIVES
1 Find the Distance between Two Points in Space (p. 618)
2 Find Position Vectors in Space (p. 618)
3 Perform Operations on Vectors (p. 619)
4 Find the Dot Product (p. 620)
5 Find the Angle between Two Vectors (p. 621)
6 Find the Direction Angles of a Vector (p. 621)

Figure 75

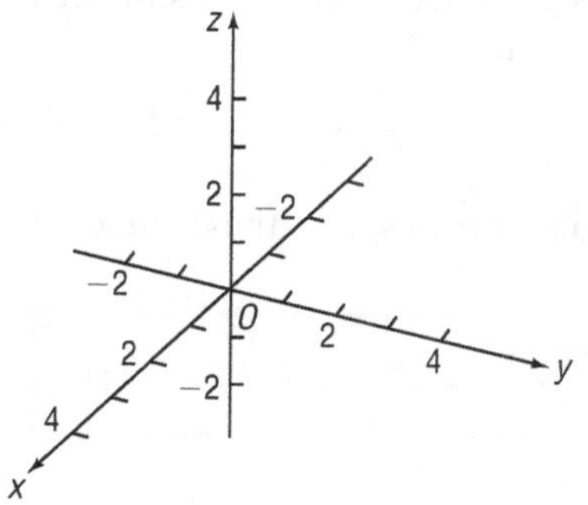

Rectangular Coordinates in Space

In the plane, each point is associated with an ordered pair of real numbers. In space, each point is associated with an ordered triple of real numbers. Through a fixed point, called the **origin** O, draw three mutually perpendicular lines, the x-axis, the y-axis, and the z-axis. On each of these axes, select an appropriate scale and the positive direction. See Figure 75.

The direction chosen for the positive z-axis in Figure 75 makes the system *right-handed*. This conforms to the *right-hand rule*, which states that, if the index finger of the right hand points in the direction of the positive x-axis and the middle finger points in the direction of the positive y-axis, then the thumb will point in the direction of the positive z-axis. See Figure 76.

We associate with each point P an ordered triple (x, y, z) of real numbers, the **coordinates of P.** For example, the point $(2, 3, 4)$ is located by starting at the origin and moving 2 units along the positive x-axis, 3 units in the direction of the positive y-axis, and 4 units in the direction of the positive z-axis. See Figure 77.

Figure 76

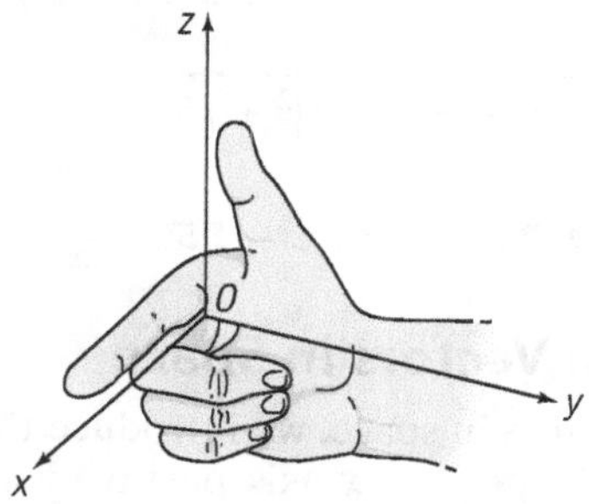

Figure 77

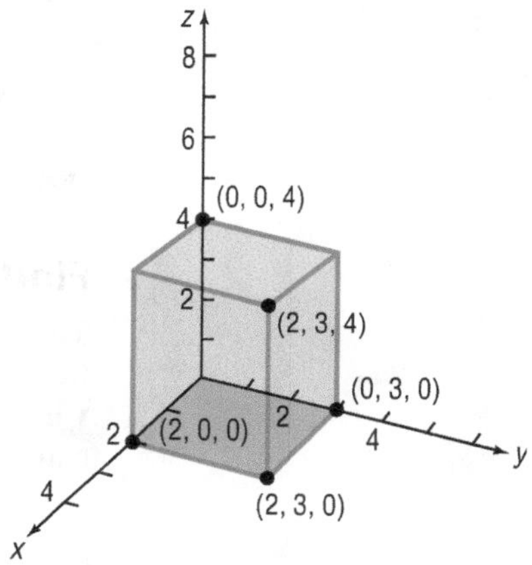

Figure 77 also shows the location of the points $(2, 0, 0)$, $(0, 3, 0)$, $(0, 0, 4)$, and $(2, 3, 0)$. Points of the form $(x, 0, 0)$ lie on the x-axis, while points of the form $(0, y, 0)$ and $(0, 0, z)$ lie on the y-axis and z-axis, respectively. Points of the form $(x, y, 0)$ lie in a plane, called the ***xy*-plane.** Its equation is $z = 0$. Similarly, points of the form $(x, 0, z)$ lie in the ***xz*-plane** (equation $y = 0$) and points of the form $(0, y, z)$ lie in the ***yz*-plane** (equation $x = 0$). See Figure 78(a). By extension of these ideas, all points obeying the equation $z = 3$ will lie in a plane parallel to and 3 units above the xy-plane. The equation $y = 4$ represents a plane parallel to the xz-plane and 4 units to the right of the plane $y = 0$. See Figure 78(b).

Figure 78

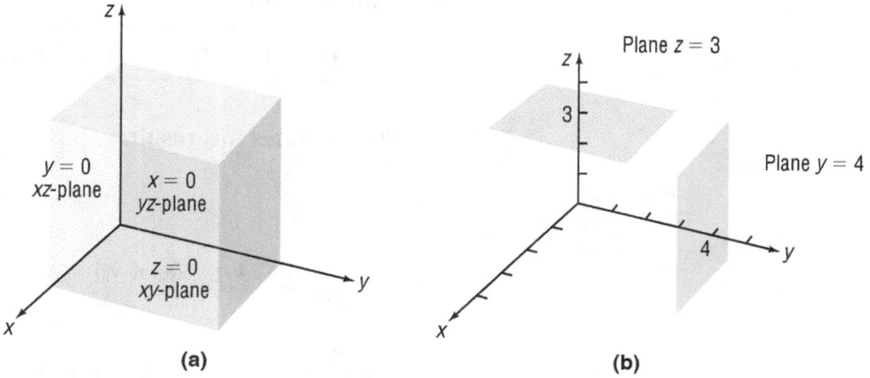

(a) (b)

Now Work PROBLEM 9

1 Find the Distance between Two Points in Space

The formula for the distance between two points in space is an extension of the Distance Formula for points in the plane given in Chapter 1.

THEOREM **Distance Formula in Space**

If $P_1 = (x_1, y_1, z_1)$ and $P_2 = (x_2, y_2, z_2)$ are two points in space, the distance d from P_1 to P_2 is

$$d = \sqrt{(x_2 - x_1)^2 + (y_2 - y_1)^2 + (z_2 - z_1)^2} \quad (1)$$

The proof, which we omit, utilizes a double application of the Pythagorean Theorem.

EXAMPLE 1 **Using the Distance Formula**

Find the distance from $P_1 = (-1, 3, 2)$ to $P_2 = (4, -2, 5)$.

Solution

$$d = \sqrt{[4 - (-1)]^2 + [-2 - 3]^2 + [5 - 2]^2} = \sqrt{25 + 25 + 9} = \sqrt{59}$$

Now Work PROBLEM 15

2 Find Position Vectors in Space

To represent vectors in space, we introduce the unit vectors **i**, **j**, and **k** whose directions are along the positive x-axis, positive y-axis, and positive z-axis, respectively. If **v** is a vector with initial point at the origin O and terminal point at $P = (a, b, c)$, we can represent **v** in terms of the vectors **i**, **j**, and **k** as

$$\mathbf{v} = a\mathbf{i} + b\mathbf{j} + c\mathbf{k}$$

Figure 79

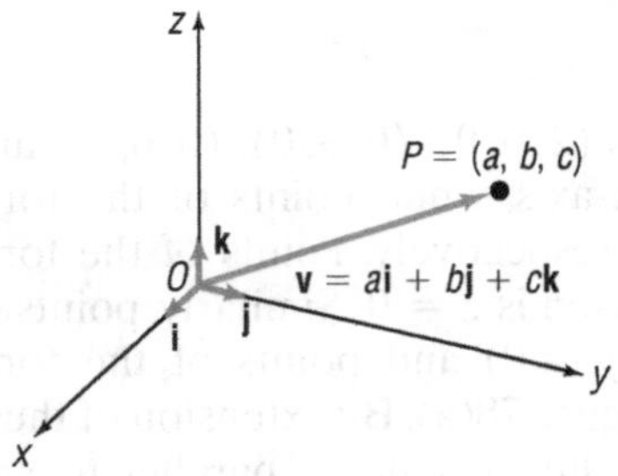

See Figure 79.

The scalars a, b, and c are called the **components** of the vector $\mathbf{v} = a\mathbf{i} + b\mathbf{j} + c\mathbf{k}$, with a being the component in the direction **i**, b the component in the direction **j**, and c the component in the direction **k**.

A vector whose initial point is at the origin is called a **position vector.** The next result states that any vector whose initial point is not at the origin is equal to a unique position vector.

THEOREM Suppose that **v** is a vector with initial point $P_1 = (x_1, y_1, z_1)$, not necessarily the origin, and terminal point $P_2 = (x_2, y_2, z_2)$. If $\mathbf{v} = \overrightarrow{P_1P_2}$, then **v** is equal to the position vector

$$\mathbf{v} = (x_2 - x_1)\mathbf{i} + (y_2 - y_1)\mathbf{j} + (z_2 - z_1)\mathbf{k} \quad (2)$$

Figure 80 illustrates this result.

Figure 80

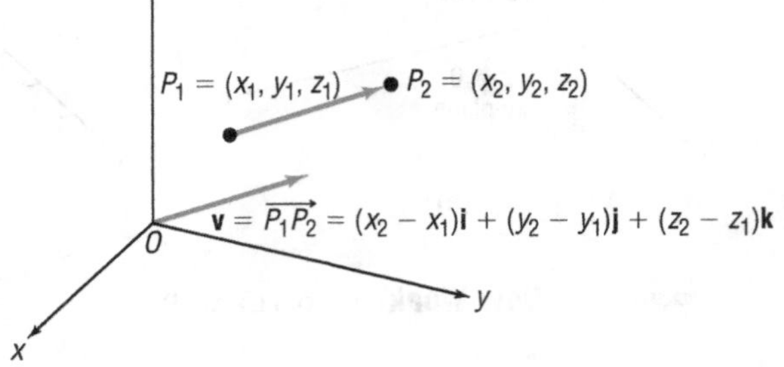

EXAMPLE 2 **Finding a Position Vector**

Find the position vector of the vector $\mathbf{v} = \overrightarrow{P_1P_2}$ if $P_1 = (-1, 2, 3)$ and $P_2 = (4, 6, 2)$.

Solution By equation (2), the position vector equal to $\mathbf{v}$ is

$$\mathbf{v} = [4 - (-1)]\mathbf{i} + (6 - 2)\mathbf{j} + (2 - 3)\mathbf{k} = 5\mathbf{i} + 4\mathbf{j} - \mathbf{k}$$

Now Work PROBLEM 29

3 Perform Operations on Vectors

We can define equality, addition, subtraction, scalar product, and magnitude in terms of the components of a vector.

DEFINITION

Let $\mathbf{v} = a_1\mathbf{i} + b_1\mathbf{j} + c_1\mathbf{k}$ and $\mathbf{w} = a_2\mathbf{i} + b_2\mathbf{j} + c_2\mathbf{k}$ be two vectors, and let α be a scalar. Then

$$\mathbf{v} = \mathbf{w} \quad \text{if and only if} \quad a_1 = a_2, b_1 = b_2, \text{and } c_1 = c_2$$
$$\mathbf{v} + \mathbf{w} = (a_1 + a_2)\mathbf{i} + (b_1 + b_2)\mathbf{j} + (c_1 + c_2)\mathbf{k}$$
$$\mathbf{v} - \mathbf{w} = (a_1 - a_2)\mathbf{i} + (b_1 - b_2)\mathbf{j} + (c_1 - c_2)\mathbf{k}$$
$$\alpha\mathbf{v} = (\alpha a_1)\mathbf{i} + (\alpha b_1)\mathbf{j} + (\alpha c_1)\mathbf{k}$$
$$\|\mathbf{v}\| = \sqrt{a_1^2 + b_1^2 + c_1^2}$$

These definitions are compatible with the geometric definitions given earlier in Section 9.4.

EXAMPLE 3 **Adding and Subtracting Vectors**

If $\mathbf{v} = 2\mathbf{i} + 3\mathbf{j} - 2\mathbf{k}$ and $\mathbf{w} = 3\mathbf{i} - 4\mathbf{j} + 5\mathbf{k}$, find:

(a) $\mathbf{v} + \mathbf{w}$ (b) $\mathbf{v} - \mathbf{w}$

Solution

(a)
$$\begin{aligned}\mathbf{v} + \mathbf{w} &= (2\mathbf{i} + 3\mathbf{j} - 2\mathbf{k}) + (3\mathbf{i} - 4\mathbf{j} + 5\mathbf{k})\\ &= (2 + 3)\mathbf{i} + (3 - 4)\mathbf{j} + (-2 + 5)\mathbf{k}\\ &= 5\mathbf{i} - \mathbf{j} + 3\mathbf{k}\end{aligned}$$

(b)
$$\begin{aligned}\mathbf{v} - \mathbf{w} &= (2\mathbf{i} + 3\mathbf{j} - 2\mathbf{k}) - (3\mathbf{i} - 4\mathbf{j} + 5\mathbf{k})\\ &= (2 - 3)\mathbf{i} + [3 - (-4)]\mathbf{j} + [-2 - 5]\mathbf{k}\\ &= -\mathbf{i} + 7\mathbf{j} - 7\mathbf{k}\end{aligned}$$

EXAMPLE 4 **Finding Scalar Products and Magnitudes**

If $\mathbf{v} = 2\mathbf{i} + 3\mathbf{j} - 2\mathbf{k}$ and $\mathbf{w} = 3\mathbf{i} - 4\mathbf{j} + 5\mathbf{k}$, find:

(a) $3\mathbf{v}$ (b) $2\mathbf{v} - 3\mathbf{w}$ (c) $\|\mathbf{v}\|$

Solution

(a) $3\mathbf{v} = 3(2\mathbf{i} + 3\mathbf{j} - 2\mathbf{k}) = 6\mathbf{i} + 9\mathbf{j} - 6\mathbf{k}$

(b)
$$\begin{aligned}2\mathbf{v} - 3\mathbf{w} &= 2(2\mathbf{i} + 3\mathbf{j} - 2\mathbf{k}) - 3(3\mathbf{i} - 4\mathbf{j} + 5\mathbf{k})\\ &= 4\mathbf{i} + 6\mathbf{j} - 4\mathbf{k} - 9\mathbf{i} + 12\mathbf{j} - 15\mathbf{k} = -5\mathbf{i} + 18\mathbf{j} - 19\mathbf{k}\end{aligned}$$

(c) $\|\mathbf{v}\| = \|2\mathbf{i} + 3\mathbf{j} - 2\mathbf{k}\| = \sqrt{2^2 + 3^2 + (-2)^2} = \sqrt{17}$

Now Work PROBLEMS 33 AND 39

Recall that a unit vector **u** is one for which $\|\mathbf{u}\| = 1$. In many applications, it is useful to be able to find a unit vector **u** that has the same direction as a given vector **v**.

THEOREM **Unit Vector in the Direction of v**

For any nonzero vector **v**, the vector

$$\mathbf{u} = \frac{\mathbf{v}}{\|\mathbf{v}\|}$$

is a unit vector that has the same direction as **v**.

As a consequence of this theorem, if **u** is a unit vector in the same direction as a vector **v**, then **v** may be expressed as

$$\mathbf{v} = \|\mathbf{v}\|\mathbf{u}$$

EXAMPLE 5 **Finding a Unit Vector**

Find the unit vector in the same direction as $\mathbf{v} = 2\mathbf{i} - 3\mathbf{j} - 6\mathbf{k}$.

Solution We find $\|\mathbf{v}\|$ first.

$$\|\mathbf{v}\| = \|2\mathbf{i} - 3\mathbf{j} - 6\mathbf{k}\| = \sqrt{4 + 9 + 36} = \sqrt{49} = 7$$

Now we multiply **v** by the scalar $\frac{1}{\|\mathbf{v}\|} = \frac{1}{7}$. The result is the unit vector

$$\mathbf{u} = \frac{\mathbf{v}}{\|\mathbf{v}\|} = \frac{2\mathbf{i} - 3\mathbf{j} - 6\mathbf{k}}{7} = \frac{2}{7}\mathbf{i} - \frac{3}{7}\mathbf{j} - \frac{6}{7}\mathbf{k}$$

Now Work PROBLEM 47

4 Find the Dot Product

The definition of *dot product* is an extension of the definition given for vectors in the plane.

DEFINITION If $\mathbf{v} = a_1\mathbf{i} + b_1\mathbf{j} + c_1\mathbf{k}$ and $\mathbf{w} = a_2\mathbf{i} + b_2\mathbf{j} + c_2\mathbf{k}$ are two vectors, the **dot product** $\mathbf{v} \cdot \mathbf{w}$ is defined as

$$\mathbf{v} \cdot \mathbf{w} = a_1a_2 + b_1b_2 + c_1c_2 \qquad (3)$$

EXAMPLE 6 **Finding Dot Products**

If $\mathbf{v} = 2\mathbf{i} - 3\mathbf{j} + 6\mathbf{k}$ and $\mathbf{w} = 5\mathbf{i} + 3\mathbf{j} - \mathbf{k}$, find:

(a) $\mathbf{v} \cdot \mathbf{w}$ (b) $\mathbf{w} \cdot \mathbf{v}$ (c) $\mathbf{v} \cdot \mathbf{v}$
(d) $\mathbf{w} \cdot \mathbf{w}$ (e) $\|\mathbf{v}\|$ (f) $\|\mathbf{w}\|$

Solution

(a) $\mathbf{v} \cdot \mathbf{w} = 2(5) + (-3)3 + 6(-1) = -5$

(b) $\mathbf{w} \cdot \mathbf{v} = 5(2) + 3(-3) + (-1)(6) = -5$

(c) $\mathbf{v} \cdot \mathbf{v} = 2(2) + (-3)(-3) + 6(6) = 49$

(d) $\mathbf{w} \cdot \mathbf{w} = 5(5) + 3(3) + (-1)(-1) = 35$

(e) $\|\mathbf{v}\| = \sqrt{2^2 + (-3)^2 + 6^2} = \sqrt{49} = 7$

(f) $\|\mathbf{w}\| = \sqrt{5^2 + 3^2 + (-1)^2} = \sqrt{35}$

The dot product in space has the same properties as the dot product in the plane.

THEOREM

Properties of the Dot Product

If **u**, **v**, and **w** are vectors, then

Commutative Property

$$\mathbf{u} \cdot \mathbf{v} = \mathbf{v} \cdot \mathbf{u}$$

Distributive Property

$$\mathbf{u} \cdot (\mathbf{v} + \mathbf{w}) = \mathbf{u} \cdot \mathbf{v} + \mathbf{u} \cdot \mathbf{w}$$

$$\mathbf{v} \cdot \mathbf{v} = \|\mathbf{v}\|^2$$
$$\mathbf{0} \cdot \mathbf{v} = 0$$

5 Find the Angle between Two Vectors

The angle θ between two vectors in space follows the same formula as for two vectors in the plane.

THEOREM

Angle between Vectors

If **u** and **v** are two nonzero vectors, the angle θ, $0 \leq \theta \leq \pi$, between **u** and **v** is determined by the formula

$$\cos \theta = \frac{\mathbf{u} \cdot \mathbf{v}}{\|\mathbf{u}\| \, \|\mathbf{v}\|} \qquad \textbf{(4)}$$

EXAMPLE 7 **Finding the Angle θ between Two Vectors**

Find the angle θ between $\mathbf{u} = 2\mathbf{i} - 3\mathbf{j} + 6\mathbf{k}$ and $\mathbf{v} = 2\mathbf{i} + 5\mathbf{j} - \mathbf{k}$.

Solution We compute the quantities $\mathbf{u} \cdot \mathbf{v}$, $\|\mathbf{u}\|$, and $\|\mathbf{v}\|$.

$$\mathbf{u} \cdot \mathbf{v} = 2(2) + (-3)(5) + 6(-1) = -17$$
$$\|\mathbf{u}\| = \sqrt{2^2 + (-3)^2 + 6^2} = \sqrt{49} = 7$$
$$\|\mathbf{v}\| = \sqrt{2^2 + 5^2 + (-1)^2} = \sqrt{30}$$

By formula (4), if θ is the angle between **u** and **v**, then

$$\cos \theta = \frac{\mathbf{u} \cdot \mathbf{v}}{\|\mathbf{u}\| \, \|\mathbf{v}\|} = \frac{-17}{7\sqrt{30}} \approx -0.443$$

We find that $\theta \approx 116.3°$.

Now Work PROBLEM 51

6 Find the Direction Angles of a Vector

A nonzero vector **v** in space can be described by specifying its magnitude and its three **direction angles** α, β, and γ. These direction angles are defined as

α = the angle between **v** and **i**, the positive x-axis, $0 \leq \alpha \leq \pi$

β = the angle between **v** and **j**, the positive y-axis, $0 \leq \beta \leq \pi$

γ = the angle between **v** and **k**, the positive z-axis, $0 \leq \gamma \leq \pi$

See Figure 81.

Figure 81

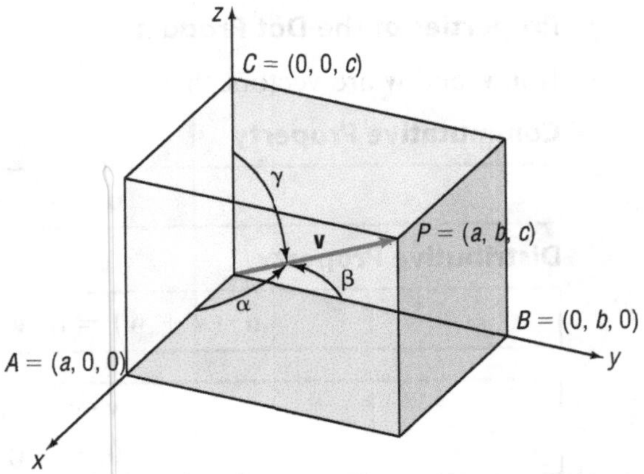

$0 \leq \alpha \leq \pi,\ 0 \leq \beta \leq \pi,\ 0 \leq \gamma \leq \pi$

Our first goal is to find expressions for α, β, and γ in terms of the components of a vector. Let $\mathbf{v} = a\mathbf{i} + b\mathbf{j} + c\mathbf{k}$ denote a nonzero vector. The angle α between $\mathbf{v}$ and $\mathbf{i}$, the positive x-axis, obeys

$$\cos\alpha = \frac{\mathbf{v}\cdot\mathbf{i}}{\|\mathbf{v}\|\,\|\mathbf{i}\|} = \frac{a}{\|\mathbf{v}\|}$$

Similarly,

$$\cos\beta = \frac{b}{\|\mathbf{v}\|} \qquad \cos\gamma = \frac{c}{\|\mathbf{v}\|}$$

Since $\|\mathbf{v}\| = \sqrt{a^2 + b^2 + c^2}$, we have the following result:

THEOREM **Direction Angles**

If $\mathbf{v} = a\mathbf{i} + b\mathbf{j} + c\mathbf{k}$ is a nonzero vector in space, the direction angles α, β, and γ obey

$$\cos\alpha = \frac{a}{\sqrt{a^2 + b^2 + c^2}} = \frac{a}{\|\mathbf{v}\|} \qquad \cos\beta = \frac{b}{\sqrt{a^2 + b^2 + c^2}} = \frac{b}{\|\mathbf{v}\|}$$

$$\cos\gamma = \frac{c}{\sqrt{a^2 + b^2 + c^2}} = \frac{c}{\|\mathbf{v}\|} \qquad \textbf{(5)}$$

The numbers $\cos\alpha$, $\cos\beta$, and $\cos\gamma$ are called the **direction cosines** of the vector $\mathbf{v}$.

EXAMPLE 8 Finding the Direction Angles of a Vector

Find the direction angles of $\mathbf{v} = -3\mathbf{i} + 2\mathbf{j} - 6\mathbf{k}$.

Solution

$$\|\mathbf{v}\| = \sqrt{(-3)^2 + 2^2 + (-6)^2} = \sqrt{49} = 7$$

Using the formulas in equation (5), we have

$$\cos\alpha = \frac{-3}{7} \qquad \cos\beta = \frac{2}{7} \qquad \cos\gamma = \frac{-6}{7}$$

$$\alpha \approx 115.4^\circ \qquad \beta \approx 73.4^\circ \qquad \gamma \approx 149.0^\circ$$

THEOREM **Property of the Direction Cosines**

If α, β, and γ are the direction angles of a nonzero vector $\mathbf{v}$ in space, then

$$\cos^2 \alpha + \cos^2 \beta + \cos^2 \gamma = 1 \qquad \textbf{(6)}$$

The proof is a direct consequence of the equations in (5).

Based on equation (6), when two direction cosines are known, the third is determined up to its sign. Knowing two direction cosines is not sufficient to uniquely determine the direction of a vector in space.

EXAMPLE 9 Finding the Direction Angle of a Vector

The vector $\mathbf{v}$ makes an angle of $\alpha = \frac{\pi}{3}$ with the positive x-axis, an angle of $\beta = \frac{\pi}{3}$ with the positive y-axis, and an acute angle γ with the positive z-axis. Find γ.

Solution By equation (6), we have

$$\cos^2\left(\frac{\pi}{3}\right) + \cos^2\left(\frac{\pi}{3}\right) + \cos^2 \gamma = 1 \qquad 0 < \gamma < \frac{\pi}{2}$$

$$\left(\frac{1}{2}\right)^2 + \left(\frac{1}{2}\right)^2 + \cos^2 \gamma = 1$$

$$\cos^2 \gamma = \frac{1}{2}$$

$$\cos \gamma = \frac{\sqrt{2}}{2} \quad \text{or} \quad \cos \gamma = -\frac{\sqrt{2}}{2}$$

$$\gamma = \frac{\pi}{4} \quad \text{or} \quad \gamma = \frac{3\pi}{4}$$

Since we are requiring that γ be acute, $\gamma = \frac{\pi}{4}$.

The direction cosines of a vector give information about only the direction of the vector; they provide no information about its magnitude. For example, *any* vector parallel to the xy-plane and making an angle of $\frac{\pi}{4}$ radian with the positive x-axis and y-axis has direction cosines

$$\cos \alpha = \frac{\sqrt{2}}{2} \qquad \cos \beta = \frac{\sqrt{2}}{2} \qquad \cos \gamma = 0$$

However, if the direction angles *and* the magnitude of a vector are known, the vector is uniquely determined.

EXAMPLE 10 Writing a Vector in Terms of Its Magnitude and Direction Cosines

Show that any nonzero vector $\mathbf{v}$ in space can be written in terms of its magnitude and direction cosines as

$$\mathbf{v} = \|\mathbf{v}\|[(\cos \alpha)\mathbf{i} + (\cos \beta)\mathbf{j} + (\cos \gamma)\mathbf{k}] \qquad \textbf{(7)}$$

Solution Let $\mathbf{v} = a\mathbf{i} + b\mathbf{j} + c\mathbf{k}$. From the equations in (5), we see that

$$a = \|\mathbf{v}\| \cos \alpha \qquad b = \|\mathbf{v}\| \cos \beta \qquad c = \|\mathbf{v}\| \cos \gamma$$

Substituting, we find that

$$\mathbf{v} = a\mathbf{i} + b\mathbf{j} + c\mathbf{k} = \|\mathbf{v}\|(\cos\alpha)\mathbf{i} + \|\mathbf{v}\|(\cos\beta)\mathbf{j} + \|\mathbf{v}\|(\cos\gamma)\mathbf{k}$$
$$= \|\mathbf{v}\|[(\cos\alpha)\mathbf{i} + (\cos\beta)\mathbf{j} + (\cos\gamma)\mathbf{k}]$$

Now Work PROBLEM 59

Example 10 shows that the direction cosines of a vector **v** are also the components of the unit vector in the direction of **v**.

9.6 Assess Your Understanding

'Are You Prepared?' *Answer is given at the end of these exercises. If you get the wrong answer, read the page listed in red.*

1. The distance d from $P_1 = (x_1, y_1)$ to $P_2 = (x_2, y_2)$ is $d =$ ________ (pp. 4–6)

Concepts and Vocabulary

2. In space, points of the form $(x, y, 0)$ lie in a plane called the ________.
3. If $\mathbf{v} = a\mathbf{i} + b\mathbf{j} + c\mathbf{k}$ is a vector in space, the scalars a, b, c are called the ________ of **v**.
4. The sum of the squares of the direction cosines of a vector in space add up to ________.
5. ***True or False*** In space, the dot product of two vectors is a positive number.
6. ***True or False*** A vector in space may be described by specifying its magnitude and its direction angles.

Skill Building

In Problems 7–14, describe the set of points (x, y, z) defined by the equation.

7. $y = 0$
8. $x = 0$
9. $z = 2$
10. $y = 3$
11. $x = -4$
12. $z = -3$
13. $x = 1$ and $y = 2$
14. $x = 3$ and $z = 1$

In Problems 15–20, find the distance from P_1 to P_2.

15. $P_1 = (0, 0, 0)$ and $P_2 = (4, 1, 2)$
16. $P_1 = (0, 0, 0)$ and $P_2 = (1, -2, 3)$
17. $P_1 = (-1, 2, -3)$ and $P_2 = (0, -2, 1)$
18. $P_1 = (-2, 2, 3)$ and $P_2 = (4, 0, -3)$
19. $P_1 = (4, -2, -2)$ and $P_2 = (3, 2, 1)$
20. $P_1 = (2, -3, -3)$ and $P_2 = (4, 1, -1)$

In Problems 21–26, opposite vertices of a rectangular box whose edges are parallel to the coordinate axes are given. List the coordinates of the other six vertices of the box.

21. $(0, 0, 0)$; $(2, 1, 3)$
22. $(0, 0, 0)$; $(4, 2, 2)$
23. $(1, 2, 3)$; $(3, 4, 5)$
24. $(5, 6, 1)$; $(3, 8, 2)$
25. $(-1, 0, 2)$; $(4, 2, 5)$
26. $(-2, -3, 0)$; $(-6, 7, 1)$

*In Problems 27–32, the vector **v** has initial point P and terminal point Q. Write **v** in the form $a\mathbf{i} + b\mathbf{j} + c\mathbf{k}$; that is, find its position vector.*

27. $P = (0, 0, 0)$; $Q = (3, 4, -1)$
28. $P = (0, 0, 0)$; $Q = (-3, -5, 4)$
29. $P = (3, 2, -1)$; $Q = (5, 6, 0)$
30. $P = (-3, 2, 0)$; $Q = (6, 5, -1)$
31. $P = (-2, -1, 4)$; $Q = (6, -2, 4)$
32. $P = (-1, 4, -2)$; $Q = (6, 2, 2)$

In Problems 33–38, find $\|\mathbf{v}\|$.

33. $\mathbf{v} = 3\mathbf{i} - 6\mathbf{j} - 2\mathbf{k}$
34. $\mathbf{v} = -6\mathbf{i} + 12\mathbf{j} + 4\mathbf{k}$
35. $\mathbf{v} = \mathbf{i} - \mathbf{j} + \mathbf{k}$
36. $\mathbf{v} = -\mathbf{i} - \mathbf{j} + \mathbf{k}$
37. $\mathbf{v} = -2\mathbf{i} + 3\mathbf{j} - 3\mathbf{k}$
38. $\mathbf{v} = 6\mathbf{i} + 2\mathbf{j} - 2\mathbf{k}$

In Problems 39–44, find each quantity if $\mathbf{v} = 3\mathbf{i} - 5\mathbf{j} + 2\mathbf{k}$ and $\mathbf{w} = -2\mathbf{i} + 3\mathbf{j} - 2\mathbf{k}$.

39. $2\mathbf{v} + 3\mathbf{w}$
40. $3\mathbf{v} - 2\mathbf{w}$
41. $\|\mathbf{v} - \mathbf{w}\|$
42. $\|\mathbf{v} + \mathbf{w}\|$
43. $\|\mathbf{v}\| - \|\mathbf{w}\|$
44. $\|\mathbf{v}\| + \|\mathbf{w}\|$

*In Problems 45–50, find the unit vector in the same direction as **v**.*

45. $\mathbf{v} = 5\mathbf{i}$
46. $\mathbf{v} = -3\mathbf{j}$
47. $\mathbf{v} = 3\mathbf{i} - 6\mathbf{j} - 2\mathbf{k}$
48. $\mathbf{v} = -6\mathbf{i} + 12\mathbf{j} + 4\mathbf{k}$
49. $\mathbf{v} = \mathbf{i} + \mathbf{j} + \mathbf{k}$
50. $\mathbf{v} = 2\mathbf{i} - \mathbf{j} + \mathbf{k}$

*In Problems 51–58, find the dot product $\mathbf{v} \cdot \mathbf{w}$ and the angle between **v** and **w**.*

51. $\mathbf{v} = \mathbf{i} - \mathbf{j}$, $\mathbf{w} = \mathbf{i} + \mathbf{j} + \mathbf{k}$
52. $\mathbf{v} = \mathbf{i} + \mathbf{j}$, $\mathbf{w} = -\mathbf{i} + \mathbf{j} - \mathbf{k}$
53. $\mathbf{v} = 2\mathbf{i} + \mathbf{j} - 3\mathbf{k}$, $\mathbf{w} = \mathbf{i} + 2\mathbf{j} + 2\mathbf{k}$
54. $\mathbf{v} = 2\mathbf{i} + 2\mathbf{j} - \mathbf{k}$, $\mathbf{w} = \mathbf{i} + 2\mathbf{j} + 3\mathbf{k}$

55. $\mathbf{v} = 3\mathbf{i} - \mathbf{j} + 2\mathbf{k}$, $\mathbf{w} = \mathbf{i} + \mathbf{j} - \mathbf{k}$

56. $\mathbf{v} = \mathbf{i} + 3\mathbf{j} + 2\mathbf{k}$, $\mathbf{w} = \mathbf{i} - \mathbf{j} + \mathbf{k}$

57. $\mathbf{v} = 3\mathbf{i} + 4\mathbf{j} + \mathbf{k}$, $\mathbf{w} = 6\mathbf{i} + 8\mathbf{j} + 2\mathbf{k}$

58. $\mathbf{v} = 3\mathbf{i} - 4\mathbf{j} + \mathbf{k}$, $\mathbf{w} = 6\mathbf{i} - 8\mathbf{j} + 2\mathbf{k}$

In Problems 59–66, find the direction angles of each vector. Write each vector in the form of equation (7).

59. $\mathbf{v} = 3\mathbf{i} - 6\mathbf{j} - 2\mathbf{k}$

60. $\mathbf{v} = -6\mathbf{i} + 12\mathbf{j} + 4\mathbf{k}$

61. $\mathbf{v} = \mathbf{i} + \mathbf{j} + \mathbf{k}$

62. $\mathbf{v} = \mathbf{i} - \mathbf{j} - \mathbf{k}$

63. $\mathbf{v} = \mathbf{i} + \mathbf{j}$

64. $\mathbf{v} = \mathbf{j} + \mathbf{k}$

65. $\mathbf{v} = 3\mathbf{i} - 5\mathbf{j} + 2\mathbf{k}$

66. $\mathbf{v} = 2\mathbf{i} + 3\mathbf{j} - 4\mathbf{k}$

Applications and Extensions

67. Robotic Arm Consider the double-jointed robotic arm shown in the figure. Let the lower arm be modeled by $\mathbf{a} = \langle 2, 3, 4 \rangle$, the middle arm be modeled by $\mathbf{b} = \langle 1, -1, 3 \rangle$, and the upper arm by $\mathbf{c} = \langle 4, -1, -2 \rangle$, where units are in feet.

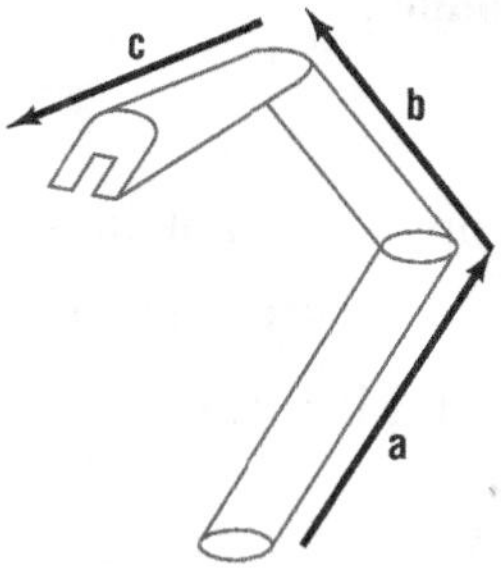

(a) Find a vector **d** that represents the position of the hand.
(b) Determine the distance of the hand from the origin.

68. The Sphere In space, the collection of all points that are the same distance from some fixed point is called a **sphere.** See the illustration. The constant distance is called the **radius,** and the fixed point is the **center** of the sphere. Show that the equation of a sphere with center at (x_0, y_0, z_0) and radius r is

$$(x - x_0)^2 + (y - y_0)^2 + (z - z_0)^2 = r^2$$

[**Hint:** Use the Distance Formula (1).]

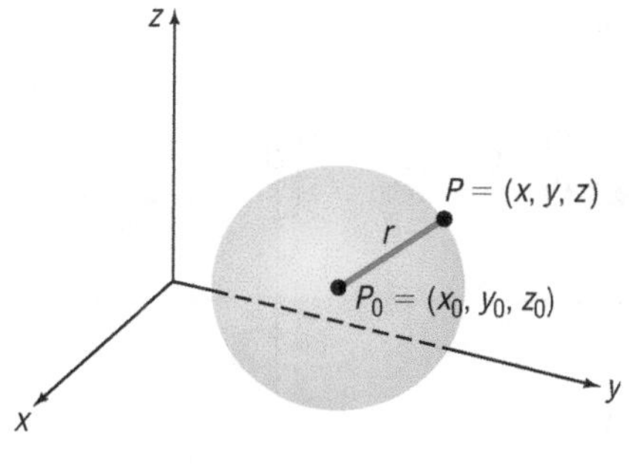

In Problems 69 and 70, find the equation of a sphere with radius r and center P_0.

69. $r = 1$; $P_0 = (3, 1, 1)$

70. $r = 2$; $P_0 = (1, 2, 2)$

In Problems 71–76, find the radius and center of each sphere. [**Hint:** *Complete the square in each variable.*]

71. $x^2 + y^2 + z^2 + 2x - 2y = 2$

72. $x^2 + y^2 + z^2 + 2x - 2z = -1$

73. $x^2 + y^2 + z^2 - 4x + 4y + 2z = 0$

74. $x^2 + y^2 + z^2 - 4x = 0$

75. $2x^2 + 2y^2 + 2z^2 - 8x + 4z = -1$

76. $3x^2 + 3y^2 + 3z^2 + 6x - 6y = 3$

The **work** *W done by a constant force* **F** *in moving an object from a point A in space to a point B in space is defined as* $W = \mathbf{F} \cdot \overrightarrow{AB}$. *Use this definition in Problems 77–79.*

77. Work Find the work done by a force of 3 newtons acting in the direction $2\mathbf{i} + \mathbf{j} + 2\mathbf{k}$ in moving an object 2 meters from $(0, 0, 0)$ to $(0, 2, 0)$.

78. Work Find the work done by a force of 1 newton acting in the direction $2\mathbf{i} + 2\mathbf{j} + \mathbf{k}$ in moving an object 3 meters from $(0, 0, 0)$ to $(1, 2, 2)$.

79. Work Find the work done in moving an object along a vector $\mathbf{u} = 3\mathbf{i} + 2\mathbf{j} - 5\mathbf{k}$ if the applied force is $\mathbf{F} = 2\mathbf{i} - \mathbf{j} - \mathbf{k}$. Use meters for distance and newtons for force.

'Are You Prepared?' Answer

1. $d = \sqrt{(x_2 - x_1)^2 + (y_2 - y_1)^2}$

9.7 The Cross Product

OBJECTIVES

1. Find the Cross Product of Two Vectors (p. 626)
2. Know Algebraic Properties of the Cross Product (p. 627)
3. Know Geometric Properties of the Cross Product (p. 628)
4. Find a Vector Orthogonal to Two Given Vectors (p. 628)
5. Find the Area of a Parallelogram (p. 629)

1 Find the Cross Product of Two Vectors

For vectors in space, and only for vectors in space, a second product of two vectors is defined, called the *cross product*. The cross product of two vectors in space is, in fact, also a vector that has applications in both geometry and physics.

DEFINITION

If $\mathbf{v} = a_1\mathbf{i} + b_1\mathbf{j} + c_1\mathbf{k}$ and $\mathbf{w} = a_2\mathbf{i} + b_2\mathbf{j} + c_2\mathbf{k}$ are two vectors in space, the **cross product** $\mathbf{v} \times \mathbf{w}$ is defined as the vector

$$\mathbf{v} \times \mathbf{w} = (b_1c_2 - b_2c_1)\mathbf{i} - (a_1c_2 - a_2c_1)\mathbf{j} + (a_1b_2 - a_2b_1)\mathbf{k} \qquad (1)$$

Notice that the cross product $\mathbf{v} \times \mathbf{w}$ of two vectors is a vector. Because of this, it is sometimes referred to as the **vector product.**

EXAMPLE 1 Finding Cross Products Using Equation (1)

If $\mathbf{v} = 2\mathbf{i} + 3\mathbf{j} + 5\mathbf{k}$ and $\mathbf{w} = \mathbf{i} + 2\mathbf{j} + 3\mathbf{k}$, an application of equation (1) gives

$$\begin{aligned}\mathbf{v} \times \mathbf{w} &= (3\cdot 3 - 2\cdot 5)\mathbf{i} - (2\cdot 3 - 1\cdot 5)\mathbf{j} + (2\cdot 2 - 1\cdot 3)\mathbf{k} \\ &= (9 - 10)\mathbf{i} - (6 - 5)\mathbf{j} + (4 - 3)\mathbf{k} \\ &= -\mathbf{i} - \mathbf{j} + \mathbf{k}\end{aligned}$$

Determinants* may be used as an aid in computing cross products. A **2 by 2 determinant,** symbolized by

$$\begin{vmatrix} a_1 & b_1 \\ a_2 & b_2 \end{vmatrix}$$

has the value $a_1b_2 - a_2b_1$; that is,

$$\begin{vmatrix} a_1 & b_1 \\ a_2 & b_2 \end{vmatrix} = a_1b_2 - a_2b_1$$

A **3 by 3 determinant** has the value

$$\begin{vmatrix} A & B & C \\ a_1 & b_1 & c_1 \\ a_2 & b_2 & c_2 \end{vmatrix} = \begin{vmatrix} b_1 & c_1 \\ b_2 & c_2 \end{vmatrix} A - \begin{vmatrix} a_1 & c_1 \\ a_2 & c_2 \end{vmatrix} B + \begin{vmatrix} a_1 & b_1 \\ a_2 & b_2 \end{vmatrix} C$$

EXAMPLE 2 Evaluating Determinants

(a) $$\begin{vmatrix} 2 & 3 \\ 1 & 2 \end{vmatrix} = 2\cdot 2 - 1\cdot 3 = 4 - 3 = 1$$

(b) $$\begin{aligned}\begin{vmatrix} A & B & C \\ 2 & 3 & 5 \\ 1 & 2 & 3 \end{vmatrix} &= \begin{vmatrix} 3 & 5 \\ 2 & 3 \end{vmatrix} A - \begin{vmatrix} 2 & 5 \\ 1 & 3 \end{vmatrix} B + \begin{vmatrix} 2 & 3 \\ 1 & 2 \end{vmatrix} C \\ &= (9 - 10)A - (6 - 5)B + (4 - 3)C \\ &= -A - B + C\end{aligned}$$

Now Work PROBLEM 7

The cross product of the vectors $\mathbf{v} = a_1\mathbf{i} + b_1\mathbf{j} + c_1\mathbf{k}$ and $\mathbf{w} = a_2\mathbf{i} + b_2\mathbf{j} + c_2\mathbf{k}$, that is,

$$\mathbf{v} \times \mathbf{w} = (b_1c_2 - b_2c_1)\mathbf{i} - (a_1c_2 - a_2c_1)\mathbf{j} + (a_1b_2 - a_2b_1)\mathbf{k}$$

*Determinants are discussed in detail in Section 11.3.

may be written symbolically using determinants as

$$\mathbf{v} \times \mathbf{w} = \begin{vmatrix} \mathbf{i} & \mathbf{j} & \mathbf{k} \\ a_1 & b_1 & c_1 \\ a_2 & b_2 & c_2 \end{vmatrix} = \begin{vmatrix} b_1 & c_1 \\ b_2 & c_2 \end{vmatrix}\mathbf{i} - \begin{vmatrix} a_1 & c_1 \\ a_2 & c_2 \end{vmatrix}\mathbf{j} + \begin{vmatrix} a_1 & b_1 \\ a_2 & b_2 \end{vmatrix}\mathbf{k}$$

EXAMPLE 3 **Using Determinants to Find Cross Products**

If $\mathbf{v} = 2\mathbf{i} + 3\mathbf{j} + 5\mathbf{k}$ and $\mathbf{w} = \mathbf{i} + 2\mathbf{j} + 3\mathbf{k}$, find:

(a) $\mathbf{v} \times \mathbf{w}$ (b) $\mathbf{w} \times \mathbf{v}$ (c) $\mathbf{v} \times \mathbf{v}$ (d) $\mathbf{w} \times \mathbf{w}$

Solution

(a) $$\mathbf{v} \times \mathbf{w} = \begin{vmatrix} \mathbf{i} & \mathbf{j} & \mathbf{k} \\ 2 & 3 & 5 \\ 1 & 2 & 3 \end{vmatrix} = \begin{vmatrix} 3 & 5 \\ 2 & 3 \end{vmatrix}\mathbf{i} - \begin{vmatrix} 2 & 5 \\ 1 & 3 \end{vmatrix}\mathbf{j} + \begin{vmatrix} 2 & 3 \\ 1 & 2 \end{vmatrix}\mathbf{k} = -\mathbf{i} - \mathbf{j} + \mathbf{k}$$

(b) $$\mathbf{w} \times \mathbf{v} = \begin{vmatrix} \mathbf{i} & \mathbf{j} & \mathbf{k} \\ 1 & 2 & 3 \\ 2 & 3 & 5 \end{vmatrix} = \begin{vmatrix} 2 & 3 \\ 3 & 5 \end{vmatrix}\mathbf{i} - \begin{vmatrix} 1 & 3 \\ 2 & 5 \end{vmatrix}\mathbf{j} + \begin{vmatrix} 1 & 2 \\ 2 & 3 \end{vmatrix}\mathbf{k} = \mathbf{i} + \mathbf{j} - \mathbf{k}$$

(c) $$\mathbf{v} \times \mathbf{v} = \begin{vmatrix} \mathbf{i} & \mathbf{j} & \mathbf{k} \\ 2 & 3 & 5 \\ 2 & 3 & 5 \end{vmatrix}$$

$$= \begin{vmatrix} 3 & 5 \\ 3 & 5 \end{vmatrix}\mathbf{i} - \begin{vmatrix} 2 & 5 \\ 2 & 5 \end{vmatrix}\mathbf{j} + \begin{vmatrix} 2 & 3 \\ 2 & 3 \end{vmatrix}\mathbf{k} = 0\mathbf{i} - 0\mathbf{j} + 0\mathbf{k} = \mathbf{0}$$

(d) $$\mathbf{w} \times \mathbf{w} = \begin{vmatrix} \mathbf{i} & \mathbf{j} & \mathbf{k} \\ 1 & 2 & 3 \\ 1 & 2 & 3 \end{vmatrix}$$

$$= \begin{vmatrix} 2 & 3 \\ 2 & 3 \end{vmatrix}\mathbf{i} - \begin{vmatrix} 1 & 3 \\ 1 & 3 \end{vmatrix}\mathbf{j} + \begin{vmatrix} 1 & 2 \\ 1 & 2 \end{vmatrix}\mathbf{k} = 0\mathbf{i} - 0\mathbf{j} + 0\mathbf{k} = \mathbf{0}$$

Now Work PROBLEM 15

2 Know Algebraic Properties of the Cross Product

Notice in Examples 3(a) and (b) that $\mathbf{v} \times \mathbf{w}$ and $\mathbf{w} \times \mathbf{v}$ are negatives of one another. From Examples 3(c) and (d), we might conjecture that the cross product of a vector with itself is the zero vector. These and other algebraic properties of the cross product are given next.

THEOREM **Algebraic Properties of the Cross Product**

If $\mathbf{u}$, $\mathbf{v}$, and $\mathbf{w}$ are vectors in space and if α is a scalar, then

$$\mathbf{u} \times \mathbf{u} = \mathbf{0} \quad (2)$$

$$\mathbf{u} \times \mathbf{v} = -(\mathbf{v} \times \mathbf{u}) \quad (3)$$

$$\alpha(\mathbf{u} \times \mathbf{v}) = (\alpha\mathbf{u}) \times \mathbf{v} = \mathbf{u} \times (\alpha\mathbf{v}) \quad (4)$$

$$\mathbf{u} \times (\mathbf{v} + \mathbf{w}) = (\mathbf{u} \times \mathbf{v}) + (\mathbf{u} \times \mathbf{w}) \quad (5)$$

Proof We will prove properties (2) and (4) here and leave properties (3) and (5) as exercises (see Problems 60 and 61).

To prove property (2), we let $\mathbf{u} = a_1\mathbf{i} + b_1\mathbf{j} + c_1\mathbf{k}$. Then

$$\mathbf{u} \times \mathbf{u} = \begin{vmatrix} \mathbf{i} & \mathbf{j} & \mathbf{k} \\ a_1 & b_1 & c_1 \\ a_1 & b_1 & c_1 \end{vmatrix} = \begin{vmatrix} b_1 & c_1 \\ b_1 & c_1 \end{vmatrix}\mathbf{i} - \begin{vmatrix} a_1 & c_1 \\ a_1 & c_1 \end{vmatrix}\mathbf{j} + \begin{vmatrix} a_1 & b_1 \\ a_1 & b_1 \end{vmatrix}\mathbf{k}$$

$$= 0\mathbf{i} - 0\mathbf{j} + 0\mathbf{k} = \mathbf{0}$$

To prove property (4), we let $\mathbf{u} = a_1\mathbf{i} + b_1\mathbf{j} + c_1\mathbf{k}$ and $\mathbf{v} = a_2\mathbf{i} + b_2\mathbf{j} + c_2\mathbf{k}$. Then

$$\alpha(\mathbf{u} \times \mathbf{v}) \underset{\substack{\uparrow \\ \text{Apply (1).}}}{=} \alpha[(b_1c_2 - b_2c_1)\mathbf{i} - (a_1c_2 - a_2c_1)\mathbf{j} + (a_1b_2 - a_2b_1)\mathbf{k}]$$

$$= \alpha(b_1c_2 - b_2c_1)\mathbf{i} - \alpha(a_1c_2 - a_2c_1)\mathbf{j} + \alpha(a_1b_2 - a_2b_1)\mathbf{k} \qquad \textbf{(6)}$$

Since $\alpha\mathbf{u} = \alpha a_1\mathbf{i} + \alpha b_1\mathbf{j} + \alpha c_1\mathbf{k}$, we have

$$(\alpha\mathbf{u}) \times \mathbf{v} = (\alpha b_1c_2 - b_2\alpha c_1)\mathbf{i} - (\alpha a_1c_2 - a_2\alpha c_1)\mathbf{j} + (\alpha a_1b_2 - a_2\alpha b_1)\mathbf{k}$$

$$= \alpha(b_1c_2 - b_2c_1)\mathbf{i} - \alpha(a_1c_2 - a_2c_1)\mathbf{j} + \alpha(a_1b_2 - a_2b_1)\mathbf{k} \qquad \textbf{(7)}$$

Based on equations (6) and (7), the first part of property (4) follows. The second part can be proved in like fashion. ■

Now Work PROBLEM 17

3 Know Geometric Properties of the Cross Product

The cross product has several interesting geometric properties.

THEOREM

Geometric Properties of the Cross Product

Let **u** and **v** be vectors in space.

$\mathbf{u} \times \mathbf{v}$ is orthogonal to both **u** and **v**. **(8)**

$\|\mathbf{u} \times \mathbf{v}\| = \|\mathbf{u}\|\,\|\mathbf{v}\| \sin\theta$, **(9)**
where θ is the angle between **u** and **v**.

$\|\mathbf{u} \times \mathbf{v}\|$ is the area of the parallelogram **(10)**
having $\mathbf{u} \neq \mathbf{0}$ and $\mathbf{v} \neq \mathbf{0}$ as adjacent sides.

$\mathbf{u} \times \mathbf{v} = \mathbf{0}$ if and only if **u** and **v** are parallel. **(11)**

Proof of Property (8) Let $\mathbf{u} = a_1\mathbf{i} + b_1\mathbf{j} + c_1\mathbf{k}$ and $\mathbf{v} = a_2\mathbf{i} + b_2\mathbf{j} + c_2\mathbf{k}$. Then

$$\mathbf{u} \times \mathbf{v} = (b_1c_2 - b_2c_1)\mathbf{i} - (a_1c_2 - a_2c_1)\mathbf{j} + (a_1b_2 - a_2b_1)\mathbf{k}$$

Now we compute the dot product $\mathbf{u} \cdot (\mathbf{u} \times \mathbf{v})$.

$$\mathbf{u} \cdot (\mathbf{u} \times \mathbf{v}) = (a_1\mathbf{i} + b_1\mathbf{j} + c_1\mathbf{k}) \cdot [(b_1c_2 - b_2c_1)\mathbf{i} - (a_1c_2 - a_2c_1)\mathbf{j} + (a_1b_2 - a_2b_1)\mathbf{k}]$$

$$= a_1(b_1c_2 - b_2c_1) - b_1(a_1c_2 - a_2c_1) + c_1(a_1b_2 - a_2b_1) = 0$$

Since two vectors are orthogonal if their dot product is zero, it follows that **u** and $\mathbf{u} \times \mathbf{v}$ are orthogonal. Similarly, $\mathbf{v} \cdot (\mathbf{u} \times \mathbf{v}) = 0$, so **v** and $\mathbf{u} \times \mathbf{v}$ are orthogonal. ■

Figure 82

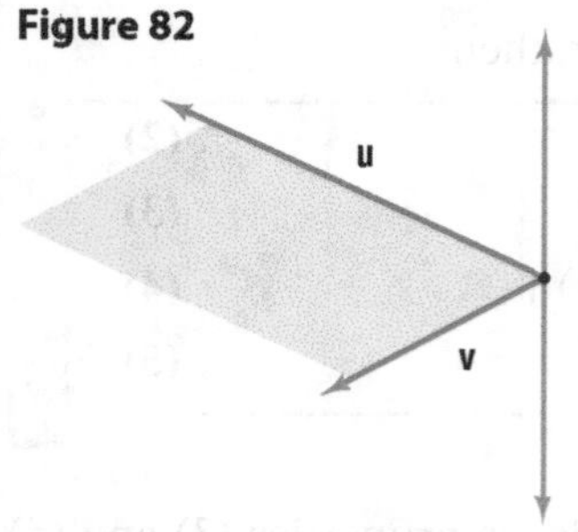

Figure 83

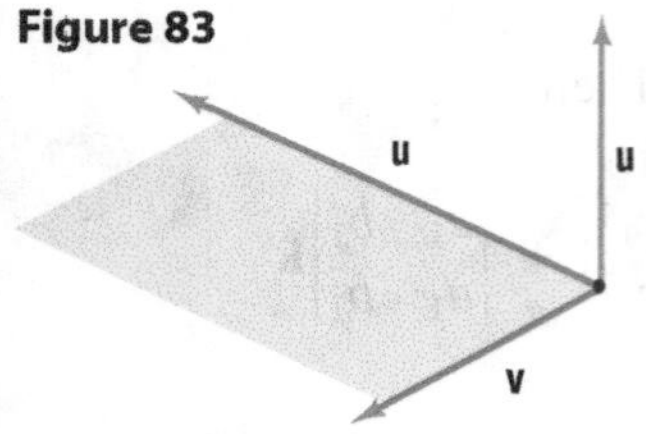

4 Find a Vector Orthogonal to Two Given Vectors

As long as the vectors **u** and **v** are not parallel, they will form a plane in space. See Figure 82. Based on property (8), the vector $\mathbf{u} \times \mathbf{v}$ is normal to this plane. As Figure 82 illustrates, there are essentially (without regard to magnitude) two vectors normal to the plane containing **u** and **v**. It can be shown that the vector $\mathbf{u} \times \mathbf{v}$ is the one determined by the thumb of the right hand when the other fingers of the right hand are cupped so that they point in a direction from **u** to **v**. See Figure 83.*

* This is a consequence of using a right-handed coordinate system.

EXAMPLE 4 Finding a Vector Orthogonal to Two Given Vectors

Find a vector that is orthogonal to $\mathbf{u} = 3\mathbf{i} - 2\mathbf{j} + \mathbf{k}$ and $\mathbf{v} = -\mathbf{i} + 3\mathbf{j} - \mathbf{k}$.

Solution Based on property (8), such a vector is $\mathbf{u} \times \mathbf{v}$.

$$\mathbf{u} \times \mathbf{v} = \begin{vmatrix} \mathbf{i} & \mathbf{j} & \mathbf{k} \\ 3 & -2 & 1 \\ -1 & 3 & -1 \end{vmatrix} = (2 - 3)\mathbf{i} - [-3 - (-1)]\mathbf{j} + (9 - 2)\mathbf{k} = -\mathbf{i} + 2\mathbf{j} + 7\mathbf{k}$$

The vector $-\mathbf{i} + 2\mathbf{j} + 7\mathbf{k}$ is orthogonal to both $\mathbf{u}$ and $\mathbf{v}$.

Check: Two vectors are orthogonal if their dot product is zero.

$$\mathbf{u} \cdot (-\mathbf{i} + 2\mathbf{j} + 7\mathbf{k}) = (3\mathbf{i} - 2\mathbf{j} + \mathbf{k}) \cdot (-\mathbf{i} + 2\mathbf{j} + 7\mathbf{k}) = -3 - 4 + 7 = 0$$
$$\mathbf{v} \cdot (-\mathbf{i} + 2\mathbf{j} + 7\mathbf{k}) = (-\mathbf{i} + 3\mathbf{j} - \mathbf{k}) \cdot (-\mathbf{i} + 2\mathbf{j} + 7\mathbf{k}) = 1 + 6 - 7 = 0$$

■

Now Work PROBLEM 41

The proof of property (9) is left as an exercise. See Problem 62.

Figure 84

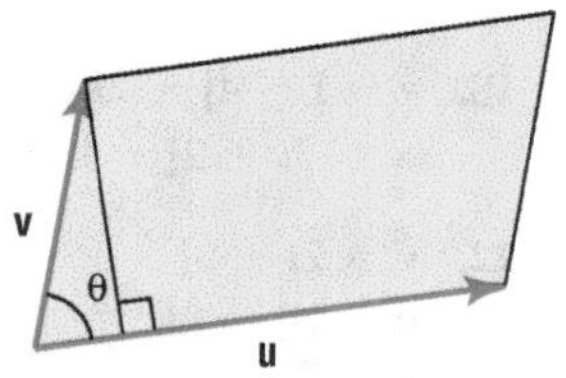

Proof of Property (10) Suppose that $\mathbf{u}$ and $\mathbf{v}$ are adjacent sides of a parallelogram. See Figure 84. Then the lengths of these sides are $\|\mathbf{u}\|$ and $\|\mathbf{v}\|$. If θ is the angle between $\mathbf{u}$ and $\mathbf{v}$, then the height of the parallelogram is $\|\mathbf{v}\| \sin\theta$ and its area is

$$\text{Area of parallelogram} = \text{Base} \times \text{Height} = \|\mathbf{u}\|[\|\mathbf{v}\| \sin\theta] \underset{\uparrow \text{ Property (9)}}{=} \|\mathbf{u} \times \mathbf{v}\|$$

■

5 Find the Area of a Parallelogram

EXAMPLE 5 Finding the Area of a Parallelogram

Find the area of the parallelogram whose vertices are $P_1 = (0, 0, 0)$, $P_2 = (3, -2, 1)$, $P_3 = (-1, 3, -1)$, and $P_4 = (2, 1, 0)$.

Solution Two adjacent sides of this parallelogram are

$$\mathbf{u} = \overrightarrow{P_1P_2} = 3\mathbf{i} - 2\mathbf{j} + \mathbf{k} \quad \text{and} \quad \mathbf{v} = \overrightarrow{P_1P_3} = -\mathbf{i} + 3\mathbf{j} - \mathbf{k}$$

WARNING Not all pairs of vertices give rise to a side. For example, $\overrightarrow{P_1P_4}$ is a diagonal of the parallelogram since $\overrightarrow{P_1P_3} + \overrightarrow{P_3P_4} = \overrightarrow{P_1P_4}$. Also, $\overrightarrow{P_1P_3}$ and $\overrightarrow{P_2P_4}$ are not adjacent sides; they are parallel sides. ■

Since $\mathbf{u} \times \mathbf{v} = -\mathbf{i} + 2\mathbf{j} + 7\mathbf{k}$ (Example 4), the area of the parallelogram is

$$\text{Area of parallelogram} = \|\mathbf{u} \times \mathbf{v}\| = \sqrt{1 + 4 + 49} = \sqrt{54} = 3\sqrt{6} \text{ square units}$$

■

Now Work PROBLEM 49

Proof of Property (11) The proof requires two parts. If $\mathbf{u}$ and $\mathbf{v}$ are parallel, then there is a scalar α such that $\mathbf{u} = \alpha\mathbf{v}$. Then

$$\mathbf{u} \times \mathbf{v} = (\alpha\mathbf{v}) \times \mathbf{v} \underset{\uparrow \text{ Property (4)}}{=} \alpha(\mathbf{v} \times \mathbf{v}) \underset{\uparrow \text{ Property (2)}}{=} \mathbf{0}$$

If $\mathbf{u} \times \mathbf{v} = \mathbf{0}$, then, by property (9), we have

$$\|\mathbf{u} \times \mathbf{v}\| = \|\mathbf{u}\| \, \|\mathbf{v}\| \sin\theta = 0$$

Since $\mathbf{u} \neq \mathbf{0}$ and $\mathbf{v} \neq \mathbf{0}$, we must have $\sin\theta = 0$, so $\theta = 0$ or $\theta = \pi$. In either case, since θ is the angle between $\mathbf{u}$ and $\mathbf{v}$, then $\mathbf{u}$ and $\mathbf{v}$ are parallel. ■

9.7 Assess Your Understanding

Concepts and Vocabulary

1. ***True or False*** If $\mathbf{u}$ and $\mathbf{v}$ are parallel vectors, then $\mathbf{u} \times \mathbf{v} = \mathbf{0}$.
2. ***True or False*** For any vector $\mathbf{v}$, $\mathbf{v} \times \mathbf{v} = \mathbf{0}$.
3. ***True or False*** If $\mathbf{u}$ and $\mathbf{v}$ are vectors, then $\mathbf{u} \times \mathbf{v} + \mathbf{v} \times \mathbf{u} = \mathbf{0}$.
4. ***True or False*** $\mathbf{u} \times \mathbf{v}$ is a vector that is parallel to both $\mathbf{u}$ and $\mathbf{v}$.
5. ***True or False*** $\|\mathbf{u} \times \mathbf{v}\| = \|\mathbf{u}\|\,\|\mathbf{v}\| \cos\theta$, where θ is the angle between $\mathbf{u}$ and $\mathbf{v}$.
6. ***True or False*** The area of the parallelogram having $\mathbf{u}$ and $\mathbf{v}$ as adjacent sides is the magnitude of the cross product of $\mathbf{u}$ and $\mathbf{v}$.

Skill Building

In Problems 7–14, find the value of each determinant.

7. $\begin{vmatrix} 3 & 4 \\ 1 & 2 \end{vmatrix}$

8. $\begin{vmatrix} -2 & 5 \\ 2 & -3 \end{vmatrix}$

9. $\begin{vmatrix} 6 & 5 \\ -2 & -1 \end{vmatrix}$

10. $\begin{vmatrix} -4 & 0 \\ 5 & 3 \end{vmatrix}$

11. $\begin{vmatrix} A & B & C \\ 2 & 1 & 4 \\ 1 & 3 & 1 \end{vmatrix}$

12. $\begin{vmatrix} A & B & C \\ 0 & 2 & 4 \\ 3 & 1 & 3 \end{vmatrix}$

13. $\begin{vmatrix} A & B & C \\ -1 & 3 & 5 \\ 5 & 0 & -2 \end{vmatrix}$

14. $\begin{vmatrix} A & B & C \\ 1 & -2 & -3 \\ 0 & 2 & -2 \end{vmatrix}$

In Problems 15–22, find (a) $\mathbf{v} \times \mathbf{w}$, *(b)* $\mathbf{w} \times \mathbf{v}$, *(c)* $\mathbf{w} \times \mathbf{w}$, *and (d)* $\mathbf{v} \times \mathbf{v}$.

15. $\mathbf{v} = 2\mathbf{i} - 3\mathbf{j} + \mathbf{k}$, $\mathbf{w} = 3\mathbf{i} - 2\mathbf{j} - \mathbf{k}$
16. $\mathbf{v} = -\mathbf{i} + 3\mathbf{j} + 2\mathbf{k}$, $\mathbf{w} = 3\mathbf{i} - 2\mathbf{j} - \mathbf{k}$
17. $\mathbf{v} = \mathbf{i} + \mathbf{j}$, $\mathbf{w} = 2\mathbf{i} + \mathbf{j} + \mathbf{k}$
18. $\mathbf{v} = \mathbf{i} - 4\mathbf{j} + 2\mathbf{k}$, $\mathbf{w} = 3\mathbf{i} + 2\mathbf{j} + \mathbf{k}$
19. $\mathbf{v} = 2\mathbf{i} - \mathbf{j} + 2\mathbf{k}$, $\mathbf{w} = \mathbf{j} - \mathbf{k}$
20. $\mathbf{v} = 3\mathbf{i} + \mathbf{j} + 3\mathbf{k}$, $\mathbf{w} = \mathbf{i} - \mathbf{k}$
21. $\mathbf{v} = \mathbf{i} - \mathbf{j} - \mathbf{k}$, $\mathbf{w} = 4\mathbf{i} - 3\mathbf{k}$
22. $\mathbf{v} = 2\mathbf{i} - 3\mathbf{j}$, $\mathbf{w} = 3\mathbf{j} - 2\mathbf{k}$

In Problems 23–44, use the given vectors $\mathbf{u}$, $\mathbf{v}$, *and* $\mathbf{w}$ *to find each expression.*

$$\mathbf{u} = 2\mathbf{i} - 3\mathbf{j} + \mathbf{k}, \quad \mathbf{v} = -3\mathbf{i} + 3\mathbf{j} + 2\mathbf{k}, \quad \mathbf{w} = \mathbf{i} + \mathbf{j} + 3\mathbf{k}$$

23. $\mathbf{u} \times \mathbf{v}$
24. $\mathbf{v} \times \mathbf{w}$
25. $\mathbf{v} \times \mathbf{u}$
26. $\mathbf{w} \times \mathbf{v}$
27. $\mathbf{v} \times \mathbf{v}$
28. $\mathbf{w} \times \mathbf{w}$
29. $(3\mathbf{u}) \times \mathbf{v}$
30. $\mathbf{v} \times (4\mathbf{w})$
31. $\mathbf{u} \times (2\mathbf{v})$
32. $(-3\mathbf{v}) \times \mathbf{w}$
33. $\mathbf{u} \cdot (\mathbf{u} \times \mathbf{v})$
34. $\mathbf{v} \cdot (\mathbf{v} \times \mathbf{w})$
35. $\mathbf{u} \cdot (\mathbf{v} \times \mathbf{w})$
36. $(\mathbf{u} \times \mathbf{v}) \cdot \mathbf{w}$
37. $\mathbf{v} \cdot (\mathbf{u} \times \mathbf{w})$
38. $(\mathbf{v} \times \mathbf{u}) \cdot \mathbf{w}$
39. $\mathbf{u} \times (\mathbf{v} \times \mathbf{v})$
40. $(\mathbf{w} \times \mathbf{w}) \times \mathbf{v}$
41. Find a vector orthogonal to both $\mathbf{u}$ and $\mathbf{v}$.
42. Find a vector orthogonal to both $\mathbf{u}$ and $\mathbf{w}$.
43. Find a vector orthogonal to both $\mathbf{u}$ and $\mathbf{i} + \mathbf{j}$.
44. Find a vector orthogonal to both $\mathbf{u}$ and $\mathbf{j} + \mathbf{k}$.

In Problems 45–48, find the area of the parallelogram with one corner at P_1 *and adjacent sides* $\overrightarrow{P_1P_2}$ *and* $\overrightarrow{P_1P_3}$.

45. $P_1 = (0, 0, 0)$, $P_2 = (1, 2, 3)$, $P_3 = (-2, 3, 0)$
46. $P_1 = (0, 0, 0)$, $P_2 = (2, 3, 1)$, $P_3 = (-2, 4, 1)$
47. $P_1 = (1, 2, 0)$, $P_2 = (-2, 3, 4)$, $P_3 = (0, -2, 3)$
48. $P_1 = (-2, 0, 2)$, $P_2 = (2, 1, -1)$, $P_3 = (2, -1, 2)$

In Problems 49–52, find the area of the parallelogram with vertices P_1, P_2, P_3, *and* P_4.

49. $P_1 = (1, 1, 2)$, $P_2 = (1, 2, 3)$, $P_3 = (-2, 3, 0)$, $P_4 = (-2, 4, 1)$
50. $P_1 = (2, 1, 1)$, $P_2 = (2, 3, 1)$, $P_3 = (-2, 4, 1)$, $P_4 = (-2, 6, 1)$
51. $P_1 = (1, 2, -1)$, $P_2 = (4, 2, -3)$, $P_3 = (6, -5, 2)$, $P_4 = (9, -5, 0)$
52. $P_1 = (-1, 1, 1)$, $P_2 = (-1, 2, 2)$, $P_3 = (-3, 4, -5)$, $P_4 = (-3, 5, -4)$

Applications and Extensions

53. Find a unit vector normal to the plane containing $\mathbf{v} = \mathbf{i} + 3\mathbf{j} - 2\mathbf{k}$ and $\mathbf{w} = -2\mathbf{i} + \mathbf{j} + 3\mathbf{k}$.
54. Find a unit vector normal to the plane containing $\mathbf{v} = 2\mathbf{i} + 3\mathbf{j} - \mathbf{k}$ and $\mathbf{w} = -2\mathbf{i} - 4\mathbf{j} - 3\mathbf{k}$.

55. Volume of a Parallelepiped A **parallelepiped** is a prism whose faces are all parallelograms. Let **A**, **B**, and **C** be the vectors that define the parallelepiped shown in the figure. The volume V of the parallelepiped is given by the formula $V = |(\mathbf{A} \times \mathbf{B}) \cdot \mathbf{C}|$.

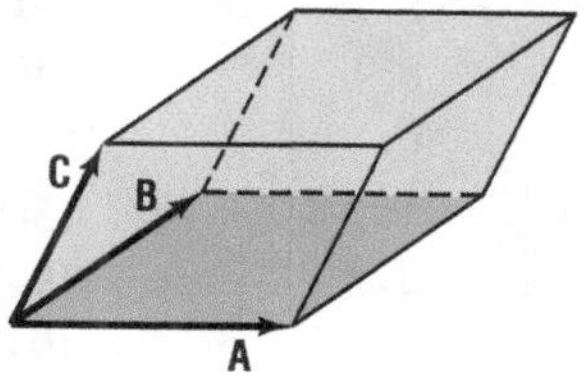

Find the volume of a parallelepiped if the defining vectors are $\mathbf{A} = 3\mathbf{i} - 2\mathbf{j} + 4\mathbf{k}$, $\mathbf{B} = 2\mathbf{i} + \mathbf{j} - 2\mathbf{k}$, and $\mathbf{C} = 3\mathbf{i} - 6\mathbf{j} - 2\mathbf{k}$.

56. Volume of a Parallelepiped Refer to Problems 55. Find the volume of a parallelepiped whose defining vectors are $\mathbf{A} = \langle 1, 0, 6\rangle$, $\mathbf{B} = \langle 2, 3, -8\rangle$, and $\mathbf{C} = \langle 8, -5, 6\rangle$.

57. Prove for vectors **u** and **v** that

$$\|\mathbf{u} \times \mathbf{v}\|^2 = \|\mathbf{u}\|^2\|\mathbf{v}\|^2 - (\mathbf{u} \cdot \mathbf{v})^2$$

[**Hint:** Proceed as in the proof of property (4), computing first the left side and then the right side.]

58. Show that if **u** and **v** are orthogonal then

$$\|\mathbf{u} \times \mathbf{v}\| = \|\mathbf{u}\|\,\|\mathbf{v}\|$$

59. Show that if **u** and **v** are orthogonal unit vectors then $\mathbf{u} \times \mathbf{v}$ is also a unit vector.

60. Prove property (3).

61. Prove property (5).

62. Prove property (9).

[**Hint:** Use the result of Problem 57 and the fact that if θ is the angle between **u** and **v** then $\mathbf{u} \cdot \mathbf{v} = \|\mathbf{u}\|\,\|\mathbf{v}\| \cos\theta$.]

Discussion and Writing

63. If $\mathbf{u} \cdot \mathbf{v} = \mathbf{0}$ and $\mathbf{u} \times \mathbf{v} = \mathbf{0}$, what, if anything, can you conclude about **u** and **v**?

CHAPTER REVIEW

Things to Know

Polar Coordinates (p. 562–568)

Relationship between polar coordinates (r, θ) and rectangular coordinates (x, y) (pp. 564 and 568)
$x = r\cos\theta,\; y = r\sin\theta$
$r^2 = x^2 + y^2,\; \tan\theta = \dfrac{y}{x},\quad x \neq 0$

Polar form of a complex number (p. 590)
If $z = x + yi$, then $z = r(\cos\theta + i\sin\theta)$,
where $r = |z| = \sqrt{x^2 + y^2}$, $\sin\theta = \dfrac{y}{r}$, $\cos\theta = \dfrac{x}{r}$, $0 \le \theta < 2\pi$.

De Moivre's Theorem (p. 592)
If $z = r(\cos\theta + i\sin\theta)$, then $z^n = r^n[\cos(n\theta) + i\sin(n\theta)]$, where $n \ge 1$ is a positive integer.

nth root of a complex number $w = r(\cos\theta_0 + i\sin\theta_0)$ (p. 593)
$$z_k = \sqrt[n]{r}\left[\cos\left(\frac{\theta_0}{n} + \frac{2k\pi}{n}\right) + i\sin\left(\frac{\theta_0}{n} + \frac{2k\pi}{n}\right)\right],\quad k = 0, \ldots, n-1,$$
where $n \ge 2$ is an integer.

Vector (pp. 597–604)
Quantity having magnitude and direction; equivalent to a directed line segment $\overrightarrow{PQ}$

Position vector (pp. 600 and 618)
Vector whose initial point is at the origin

Unit vector (pp. 603 and 620)
Vector whose magnitude is 1

Dot product (pp. 608 and 620)
If $\mathbf{v} = a_1\mathbf{i} + b_1\mathbf{j}$ and $\mathbf{w} = a_2\mathbf{i} + b_2\mathbf{j}$, then $\mathbf{v} \cdot \mathbf{w} = a_1a_2 + b_1b_2$.
If $\mathbf{v} = a_1\mathbf{i} + b_1\mathbf{j} + c_1\mathbf{k}$ and $\mathbf{w} = a_2\mathbf{i} + b_2\mathbf{j} + c_2\mathbf{k}_2$, then $\mathbf{v} \cdot \mathbf{w} = a_1a_2 + b_1b_2 + c_1c_2$.

Angle θ between two nonzero vectors **u** and **v** (pp. 610 and 621)
$\cos\theta = \dfrac{\mathbf{u} \cdot \mathbf{v}}{\|\mathbf{u}\|\,\|\mathbf{v}\|}$

Direction angles of a vector in space (p. 622–623)
If $\mathbf{v} = a\mathbf{i} + b\mathbf{j} + c\mathbf{k}$, then $\mathbf{v} = \|\mathbf{v}\|[(\cos\alpha)\mathbf{i} + (\cos\beta)\mathbf{j} + (\cos\gamma)\mathbf{k}]$,
where $\cos\alpha = \dfrac{a}{\|\mathbf{v}\|}$, $\cos\beta = \dfrac{b}{\|\mathbf{v}\|}$, $\cos\gamma = \dfrac{c}{\|\mathbf{v}\|}$.

Cross product (p. 626)
If $\mathbf{v} = a_1\mathbf{i} + b_1\mathbf{j} + c_1\mathbf{k}$ and $\mathbf{w} = a_2\mathbf{i} + b_2\mathbf{j} + c_2\mathbf{k}$,
then $\mathbf{v} \times \mathbf{w} = [b_1c_2 - b_2c_1]\mathbf{i} - [a_1c_2 - a_2c_1]\mathbf{j} + [a_1b_2 - a_2b_1]\mathbf{k}$.

Area of a parallelogram (pp. 628 and 629)
$\|\mathbf{u} \times \mathbf{v}\| = \|\mathbf{u}\|\,\|\mathbf{v}\|\sin\theta$, where θ is the angle between **u** and **v**.

Objectives

Section		You should be able to . . .	Example(s)	Review Exercises
9.1	1	Plot points using polar coordinates (p. 562)	1–3	1–6
	2	Convert from polar coordinates to rectangular coordinates (p. 564)	4	1–6
	3	Convert from rectangular coordinates to polar coordinates (p. 566)	5–7	7–12
	4	Transform equations from polar to rectangular form (p. 568)	8, 9	13(a)–18(a)
9.2	1	Graph and identify polar equations by converting to rectangular equations (p. 572)	1–7	13(b)–18(b)
	2	Graph polar equations using a graphing utility (p. 573)	4–7	19–24
	3	Test polar equations for symmetry (p. 577)	8–11	19–24
	4	Graph polar equations by plotting points (p. 578)	8–13	19–24
9.3	1	Plot points in the complex plane (p. 589)	1	25–28
	2	Convert a complex number from rectangular form to polar form (p. 590)	2, 3	29–34
	3	Find products and quotients of complex numbers in polar form (p. 591)	4	35–40
	4	Use De Moivre's Theorem (p. 592)	5, 6	41–48
	5	Find complex roots (p. 593)	7	49–50
9.4	1	Graph vectors (p. 599)	1	51–54
	2	Find a position vector (p. 600)	2	55–58
	3	Add and subtract vectors algebraically (p. 601)	3	59, 60
	4	Find a scalar multiple and the magnitude of a vector (p. 602)	4	55–58, 61–66
	5	Find a unit vector (p. 602)	5	67, 68
	6	Find a vector from its direction and magnitude (p. 603)	6	69, 70
	7	Analyze objects in static equilibrium (p. 604)	7	111
9.5	1	Find the dot product of two vectors (p. 608)	1	85–88
	2	Find the angle between two vectors (p. 609)	2, 3	85–88, 109, 110, 112
	3	Determine whether two vectors are parallel (p. 611)	4	93–98
	4	Determine whether two vectors are orthogonal (p. 611)	5	93–98
	5	Decompose a vector into two orthogonal vectors (p. 612)	6	99–102
	6	Compute work (p. 613)	7	113
9.6	1	Find the distance between two points in space (p. 618)	1	71, 72
	2	Find position vectors in space (p. 618)	2	73, 74
	3	Perform operations on vectors (p. 619)	3–5	75–80
	4	Find the dot product (p. 620)	6	89–92
	5	Find the angle between two vectors (p. 621)	7	89–92
	6	Find the direction angles of a vector (p. 621)	8–10	103, 104
9.7	1	Find the cross product of two vectors (p. 626)	1–3	81, 82
	2	Know algebraic properties of the cross product (p. 627)	pp. 627–628	107, 108
	3	Know geometric properties of the cross product (p. 628)	p. 628	105, 106
	4	Find a vector orthogonal to two given vectors (p. 628)	4	84
	5	Find the area of a parallelogram (p. 629)	5	105, 106

Review Exercises

In Problems 1–6, plot each point given in polar coordinates, and find its rectangular coordinates.

1. $\left(3, \frac{\pi}{6}\right)$ **2.** $\left(4, \frac{2\pi}{3}\right)$ **3.** $\left(-2, \frac{4\pi}{3}\right)$ **4.** $\left(-1, \frac{5\pi}{4}\right)$ **5.** $\left(-3, -\frac{\pi}{2}\right)$ **6.** $\left(-4, -\frac{\pi}{4}\right)$

In Problems 7–12, the rectangular coordinates of a point are given. Find two pairs of polar coordinates (r, θ) for each point, one with $r > 0$ and the other with $r < 0$. Express θ in radians.

7. $(-3, 3)$ **8.** $(1, -1)$ **9.** $(0, -2)$ **10.** $(2, 0)$ **11.** $(3, 4)$ **12.** $(-5, 12)$

In Problems 13–18, the variables r and θ represent polar coordinates. (a) Write each polar equation as an equation in rectangular coordinates (x, y). (b) Identify the equation and graph it.

13. $r = 2\sin\theta$
14. $3r = \sin\theta$
15. $r = 5$
16. $\theta = \frac{\pi}{4}$
17. $r\cos\theta + 3r\sin\theta = 6$
18. $r^2 + 4r\sin\theta - 8r\cos\theta = 5$

In Problems 19–24, by hand sketch the graph of each polar equation. Be sure to test for symmetry. Verify your graph using a graphing utility.

19. $r = 4\cos\theta$
20. $r = 3\sin\theta$
21. $r = 3 - 3\sin\theta$
22. $r = 2 + \cos\theta$
23. $r = 4 - \cos\theta$
24. $r = 1 - 2\sin\theta$

In Problems 25–28, write each complex number in polar form. Express each argument in degrees.

25. $-1 - i$
26. $-\sqrt{3} + i$
27. $4 - 3i$
28. $3 - 2i$

In Problems 29–34, write each complex number in the standard form a + bi and plot each in the complex plane.

29. $2(\cos 150° + i\sin 150°)$
30. $3(\cos 60° + i\sin 60°)$
31. $3\left(\cos\frac{2\pi}{3} + i\sin\frac{2\pi}{3}\right)$
32. $4\left(\cos\frac{3\pi}{4} + i\sin\frac{3\pi}{4}\right)$
33. $0.1(\cos 350° + i\sin 350°)$
34. $0.5(\cos 160° + i\sin 160°)$

In Problems 35–40, find zw and $\frac{z}{w}$. Leave your answers in polar form.

35. $z = \cos 80° + i\sin 80°$
$w = \cos 50° + i\sin 50°$

36. $z = \cos 205° + i\sin 205°$
$w = \cos 85° + i\sin 85°$

37. $z = 3\left(\cos\frac{9\pi}{5} + i\sin\frac{9\pi}{5}\right)$
$w = 2\left(\cos\frac{\pi}{5} + i\sin\frac{\pi}{5}\right)$

38. $z = 2\left(\cos\frac{5\pi}{3} + i\sin\frac{5\pi}{3}\right)$
$w = 3\left(\cos\frac{\pi}{3} + i\sin\frac{\pi}{3}\right)$

39. $z = 5(\cos 10° + i\sin 10°)$
$w = \cos 355° + i\sin 355°$

40. $z = 4(\cos 50° + i\sin 50°)$
$w = \cos 340° + i\sin 340°$

In Problems 41–48, write each expression in the standard form a + bi.

41. $[3(\cos 20° + i\sin 20°)]^3$
42. $[2(\cos 50° + i\sin 50°)]^3$
43. $\left[\sqrt{2}\left(\cos\frac{5\pi}{8} + i\sin\frac{5\pi}{8}\right)\right]^4$
44. $\left[2\left(\cos\frac{5\pi}{16} + i\sin\frac{5\pi}{16}\right)\right]^4$
45. $(1 - \sqrt{3}i)^6$
46. $(2 - 2i)^8$
47. $(3 + 4i)^4$
48. $(1 - 2i)^4$
49. Find all the complex cube roots of 27.
50. Find all the complex fourth roots of -16.

In Problems 51–54, use the figure to graph each of the following:

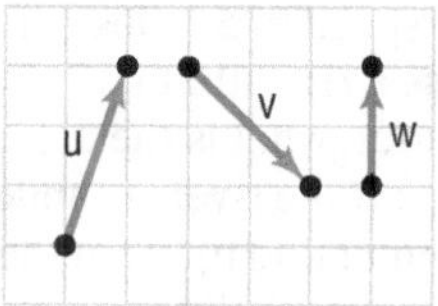

51. $\mathbf{u} + \mathbf{v}$
52. $\mathbf{v} + \mathbf{w}$
53. $2\mathbf{u} + 3\mathbf{v}$
54. $5\mathbf{v} - 2\mathbf{w}$

*In Problems 55–58, the vector **v** is represented by the directed line segment $\overrightarrow{PQ}$. Write **v** in the form a**i** + b**j** and find $\|\mathbf{v}\|$.*

55. $P = (1, -2);\ Q = (3, -6)$
56. $P = (-3, 1);\ Q = (4, -2)$
57. $P = (0, -2);\ Q = (-1, 1)$
58. $P = (3, -4);\ Q = (-2, 0)$

In Problems 59–68, use the vectors $\mathbf{v} = -2\mathbf{i} + \mathbf{j}$ and $\mathbf{w} = 4\mathbf{i} - 3\mathbf{j}$ to find:

59. $\mathbf{v} + \mathbf{w}$
60. $\mathbf{v} - \mathbf{w}$
61. $4\mathbf{v} - 3\mathbf{w}$
62. $-\mathbf{v} + 2\mathbf{w}$
63. $\|\mathbf{v}\|$
64. $\|\mathbf{v} + \mathbf{w}\|$
65. $\|\mathbf{v}\| + \|\mathbf{w}\|$
66. $\|2\mathbf{v}\| - 3\|\mathbf{w}\|$
67. Find a unit vector in the same direction as **v**.
68. Find a unit vector in the opposite direction of **w**.

69. Find the vector **v** in the *xy*-plane with magnitude 3 if the angle between **v** and **i** is 60°.

70. Find the vector **v** in the *xy*-plane with magnitude 5 if the angle between **v** and **i** is 150°.

71. Find the distance from $P_1 = (1, 3, -2)$ to $P_2 = (4, -2, 1)$.

72. Find the distance from $P_1 = (0, -4, 3)$ to $P_2 = (6, -5, -1)$.

73. A vector **v** has initial point $P = (1, 3, -2)$ and terminal point $Q = (4, -2, 1)$. Write **v** in the form $\mathbf{v} = a\mathbf{i} + b\mathbf{j} + c\mathbf{k}$.

74. A vector **v** has initial point $P = (0, -4, 3)$ and terminal point $Q = (6, -5, -1)$. Write **v** in the form $\mathbf{v} = a\mathbf{i} + b\mathbf{j} + c\mathbf{k}$.

In Problems 75–84, use the vectors $\mathbf{v} = 3\mathbf{i} + \mathbf{j} - 2\mathbf{k}$ *and* $\mathbf{w} = -3\mathbf{i} + 2\mathbf{j} - \mathbf{k}$ *to find each expression.*

75. $4\mathbf{v} - 3\mathbf{w}$

76. $-\mathbf{v} + 2\mathbf{w}$

77. $\|\mathbf{v} - \mathbf{w}\|$

78. $\|\mathbf{v} + \mathbf{w}\|$

79. $\|\mathbf{v}\| - \|\mathbf{w}\|$

80. $\|\mathbf{v}\| + \|\mathbf{w}\|$

81. $\mathbf{v} \times \mathbf{w}$

82. $\mathbf{v} \cdot (\mathbf{v} \times \mathbf{w})$

83. Find a unit vector in the same direction as **v** and then in the opposite direction of **v**.

84. Find a unit vector orthogonal to both **v** and **w**.

In Problems 85–92, find the dot product $\mathbf{v} \cdot \mathbf{w}$ *and the angle between* **v** *and* **w**.

85. $\mathbf{v} = -2\mathbf{i} + \mathbf{j}, \quad \mathbf{w} = 4\mathbf{i} - 3\mathbf{j}$

86. $\mathbf{v} = 3\mathbf{i} - \mathbf{j}, \quad \mathbf{w} = \mathbf{i} + \mathbf{j}$

87. $\mathbf{v} = \mathbf{i} - 3\mathbf{j}, \quad \mathbf{w} = -\mathbf{i} + \mathbf{j}$

88. $\mathbf{v} = \mathbf{i} + 4\mathbf{j}, \quad \mathbf{w} = 3\mathbf{i} - 2\mathbf{j}$

89. $\mathbf{v} = \mathbf{i} + \mathbf{j} + \mathbf{k}, \quad \mathbf{w} = \mathbf{i} - \mathbf{j} + \mathbf{k}$

90. $\mathbf{v} = \mathbf{i} - \mathbf{j} + \mathbf{k}, \quad \mathbf{w} = 2\mathbf{i} + \mathbf{j} + \mathbf{k}$

91. $\mathbf{v} = 4\mathbf{i} - \mathbf{j} + 2\mathbf{k}, \quad \mathbf{w} = \mathbf{i} - 2\mathbf{j} - 3\mathbf{k}$

92. $\mathbf{v} = -\mathbf{i} - 2\mathbf{j} + 3\mathbf{k}, \quad \mathbf{w} = 5\mathbf{i} + \mathbf{j} + \mathbf{k}$

In Problems 93–98, determine whether **v** *and* **w** *are parallel, orthogonal, or neither.*

93. $\mathbf{v} = 2\mathbf{i} + 3\mathbf{j}; \quad \mathbf{w} = -4\mathbf{i} - 6\mathbf{j}$

94. $\mathbf{v} = -2\mathbf{i} - \mathbf{j}; \quad \mathbf{w} = 2\mathbf{i} + \mathbf{j}$

95. $\mathbf{v} = 3\mathbf{i} - 4\mathbf{j}; \quad \mathbf{w} = -3\mathbf{i} + 4\mathbf{j}$

96. $\mathbf{v} = -2\mathbf{i} + 2\mathbf{j}; \quad \mathbf{w} = -3\mathbf{i} + 2\mathbf{j}$

97. $\mathbf{v} = 3\mathbf{i} - 2\mathbf{j}; \quad \mathbf{w} = 4\mathbf{i} + 6\mathbf{j}$

98. $\mathbf{v} = -4\mathbf{i} + 2\mathbf{j}; \quad \mathbf{w} = 2\mathbf{i} + 4\mathbf{j}$

In Problems 99–102, decompose **v** *into two vectors, one parallel to* **w** *and the other orthogonal to* **w**.

99. $\mathbf{v} = 2\mathbf{i} + \mathbf{j}; \quad \mathbf{w} = -4\mathbf{i} + 3\mathbf{j}$

100. $\mathbf{v} = -3\mathbf{i} + 2\mathbf{j}; \quad \mathbf{w} = -2\mathbf{i} + \mathbf{j}$

101. $\mathbf{v} = 2\mathbf{i} + 3\mathbf{j}; \quad \mathbf{w} = 3\mathbf{i} + \mathbf{j}$

102. $\mathbf{v} = -\mathbf{i} + 2\mathbf{j}; \quad \mathbf{w} = 3\mathbf{i} - \mathbf{j}$

---

103. Find the direction angles of the vector $\mathbf{v} = 3\mathbf{i} - 4\mathbf{j} + 2\mathbf{k}$.

104. Find the direction angles of the vector $\mathbf{v} = \mathbf{i} - \mathbf{j} + 2\mathbf{k}$.

105. Find the area of the parallelogram with vertices $P_1 = (1, 1, 1)$, $P_2 = (2, 3, 4)$, $P_3 = (6, 5, 2)$, and $P_4 = (7, 7, 5)$.

106. Find the area of the parallelogram with vertices $P_1 = (2, -1, 1)$, $P_2 = (5, 1, 4)$, $P_3 = (0, 1, 1)$, and $P_4 = (3, 3, 4)$.

107. If $\mathbf{u} \times \mathbf{v} = 2\mathbf{i} - 3\mathbf{j} + \mathbf{k}$, what is $\mathbf{v} \times \mathbf{u}$?

108. Suppose that $\mathbf{u} = 3\mathbf{v}$. What is $\mathbf{u} \times \mathbf{v}$?

109. Actual Speed and Direction of a Swimmer A swimmer can maintain a constant speed of 5 miles per hour. If the swimmer heads directly across a river that has a current moving at the rate of 2 miles per hour, what is the actual speed of the swimmer? (See the figure.) If the river is 1 mile wide, how far downstream will the swimmer end up from the point directly across the river from the starting point?

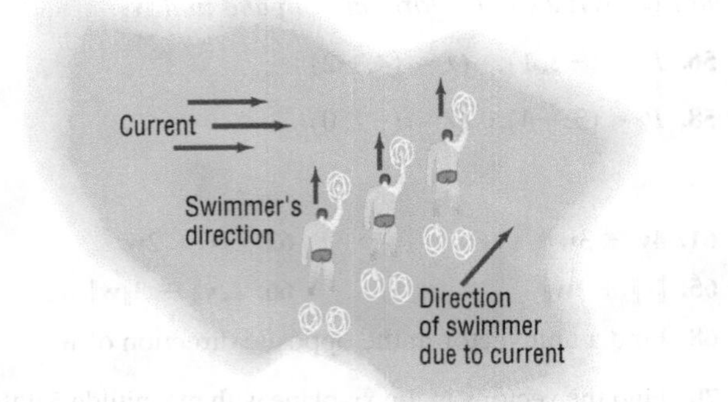

110. Actual Speed and Direction of an Airplane An airplane has an airspeed of 500 kilometers per hour in a northerly direction. The wind velocity is 60 kilometers per hour in a southeasterly direction. Find the actual speed and direction of the plane relative to the ground.

111. Static Equilibrium A weight of 2000 pounds is suspended from two cables, as shown in the figure. What are the tensions in each cable?

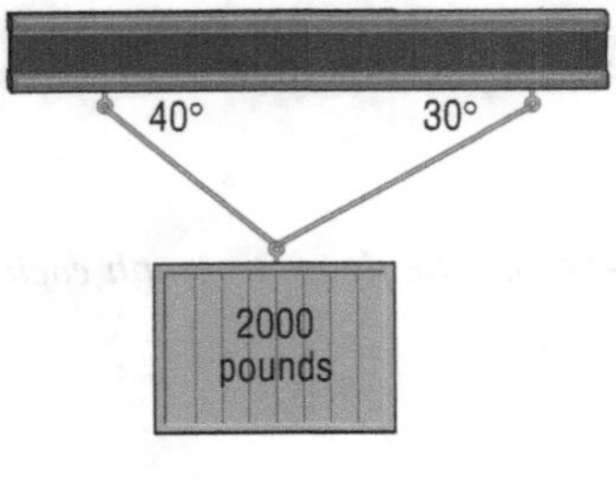

112. Actual Speed and Distance of a Motorboat A small motorboat is moving at a true speed of 11 miles per hour in a southerly direction. The current is known to be from the northeast at 3 miles per hour. What is the speed of the motorboat relative to the water? In what direction does the compass indicate that the boat is headed?

113. Computing Work Find the work done by a force of 5 pounds acting in the direction 60° to the horizontal in moving an object 20 feet from (0, 0) to (20, 0).

CHAPTER TEST

In Problems 1–3, plot each point given in polar coordinates.

1. $\left(2, \frac{3\pi}{4}\right)$
2. $\left(3, -\frac{\pi}{6}\right)$
3. $\left(-4, \frac{\pi}{3}\right)$

4. Convert $(2, 2\sqrt{3})$ from rectangular coordinates to polar coordinates (r, θ), where $r > 0$ and $0 \le \theta < 2\pi$.

In Problems 5–7, convert the polar equation to a rectangular equation. Graph the equation.

5. $r = 7$
6. $\tan\theta = 3$
7. $r\sin^2\theta + 8\sin\theta = r$

In Problems 8 and 9, test the polar equation for symmetry with respect to the pole, the polar axis, and the line $\theta = \frac{\pi}{2}$.

8. $r^2\cos\theta = 5$
9. $r = 5\sin\theta\cos^2\theta$

In Problems 10–12, perform the given operation, where $z = 2(\cos 85° + i\sin 85°)$ *and* $w = 3(\cos 22° + i\sin 22°)$. *Write your answer in polar form.*

10. $z \cdot w$
11. $\frac{w}{z}$
12. w^5

13. Find all the cube roots of $-8 + 8\sqrt{3}i$. Write all answers in the form $a + bi$ and then plot them in rectangular coordinates.

In Problems 14–18, $P_1 = (3\sqrt{2}, 7\sqrt{2})$ *and* $P_2 = (8\sqrt{2}, 2\sqrt{2})$.

14. Find the position vector **v** equal to $\overrightarrow{P_1P_2}$.

15. Find $\|\mathbf{v}\|$.

16. Find the unit vector in the direction of **v**.

17. Find the angle between **v** and **i**.

18. Decompose **v** into its vertical and horizontal components.

In Problems 19–22, $\mathbf{v}_1 = \langle 4, 6\rangle$, $\mathbf{v}_2 = \langle -3, -6\rangle$, $\mathbf{v}_3 = \langle -8, 4\rangle$, and $\mathbf{v}_4 = \langle 10, 15\rangle$.

19. Find the vector $\mathbf{v}_1 + 2\mathbf{v}_2 - \mathbf{v}_3$.

20. Which two vectors are parallel?

21. Which two vectors are orthogonal?

22. Find the angle between vectors $\mathbf{v}_1$ and $\mathbf{v}_2$.

In Problems 23–25, use the vectors $\mathbf{u} = 2\mathbf{i} - 3\mathbf{j} + \mathbf{k}$ and $\mathbf{v} = -\mathbf{i} + 3\mathbf{j} + 2\mathbf{k}$.

23. Find $\mathbf{u} \times \mathbf{v}$.

24. Find the direction angles for **u**.

25. Find the area of the parallelogram that has **u** and **v** as adjacent sides.

26. A 1200-pound chandelier is to be suspended over a large ballroom; the chandelier will be hung on a cable whose ends will be attached to the ceiling, 16 feet apart. The chandelier will be free hanging so that the ends of the cable will make equal angles with the ceiling. If the top of the chandelier is to be 16 feet from the ceiling, what is the minimum tension the cable must be able to endure?

CUMULATIVE REVIEW

1. Find the real solutions, if any, of the equation $e^{x^2-9} = 1$.

2. Find an equation for the line containing the origin that makes an angle of 30° with the positive x-axis.

3. Find an equation for the circle with center at the point $(0, 1)$ and radius 3. Graph this circle.

4. What is the domain of the function $f(x) = \ln(1 - 2x)$?

5. Test the equation $x^2 + y^3 = 2x^4$ for symmetry with respect to the x-axis, the y-axis, and the origin.

6. Graph the function $y = |\ln x|$.

7. Graph the function $y = |\sin x|$.

8. Graph the function $y = \sin|x|$.

9. Find the exact value of $\sin^{-1}\left(-\frac{1}{2}\right)$.

10. Graph the equations $x = 3$ and $y = 4$ on the same set of rectangular coordinates.

11. Graph the equations $r = 2$ and $\theta = \frac{\pi}{3}$ on the same set of polar coordinates.

12. What is the amplitude and period of $y = -4\cos(\pi x)$?

CHAPTER PROJECTS

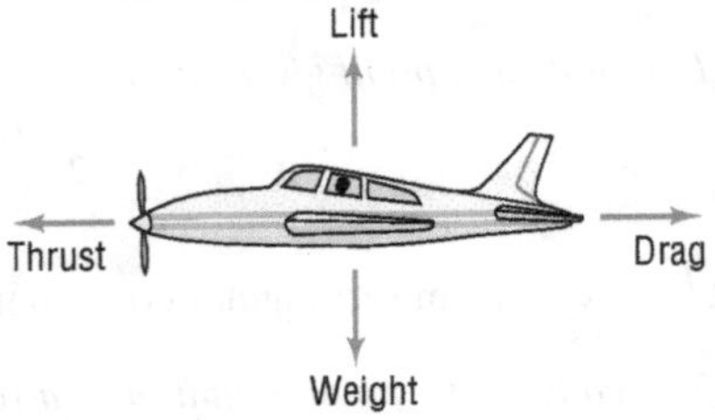

Source: www.aeromuseum.org/eduHowtoFly.html

I. Modeling Aircraft Motion Four aerodynamic forces act on an airplane in flight: lift, weight, thrust, and drag. While an aircraft is in flight, these four forces continuously battle each other. Weight opposes lift and drag opposes thrust. See the figure. In balanced flight at constant speed, both the lift and weight are equal and the thrust and drag are equal.

1. What will happen to the aircraft if the lift is held constant while the weight is decreased (say from burning off fuel)?
2. What will happen to the aircraft if the lift is decreased while the weight is held constant?
3. What will happen to the aircraft if the thrust is increased while the drag is held constant?
4. What will happen to the aircraft if the drag is increased while the thrust is held constant?

In 1903 the Wright brothers made the first controlled powered flight. The weight of their plane was approximately 700 pounds (lb). Newton's Second Law of motion states that force = mass × acceleration ($F = ma$). If the mass is measured in kilograms (kg) and acceleration in meters per second squared (m/sec^2), then the force will be measured in newtons (N). [**Note:** $1\text{ N} = 1\text{kg}\cdot\text{m/sec}^2$.]

5. If 1 kg = 2.205 lb, convert the weight of the Wright brother's plane to kilograms.
6. If acceleration due to gravity is $a = 9.80$ m/sec^2, determine the force due to weight on the Wright brother's plane.
7. What must be true about the lift force of the Wright brother's plane in order for it to get off the ground?
8. The weight of a fully loaded Cessna 170B is 2200 lb. What lift force is required to get this plane off the ground?
9. The maximum gross weight of a Boeing 747 is 255,000 lb. What lift force is required to get this jet off the ground?

The following projects are available at the Instructor's Resource Center (IRC):

II. Project at Motorola ***Signal Fades Due to Interference*** Complex trigonometric functions are used to assure that a cellphone has optimal reception as the user travels up and down an elevator.

III. Compound Interest The effect of continuously compounded interest is analyzed using polar coordinates.

IV. Complex Equations Analysis of complex equations illustrates the connections between complex and real equations. At times, using complex equations is more efficient for proving mathematical theorems.

Analytic Geometry

10

Pluto's Unusual Orbit

Pluto is about 39 times as far from the Sun as Earth is. Its average distance from the Sun is about 3,647,240,000 miles (5,869,660,000 kilometers). Pluto travels around the Sun in an elliptical (oval-shaped) orbit. At some point in its orbit, it comes closer to the Sun than Neptune, the outermost planet. It stays inside Neptune's orbit for about 20 Earth-years. This event occurs every 248 Earth-years, which is about the same number of Earth-years it takes Pluto to travel once around the Sun. Pluto entered Neptune's orbit on January 23, 1979, and remained there until February 11, 1999.

Source: Adapted from: Gulbis, Amanda A. S. "Pluto." World Book Online Reference Center © 2007. By permission of the publisher. http://www.worldbookonline.com.

—See Chapter Project I—

A Look Back

In Chapter 1, we introduced rectangular coordinates and showed how geometry problems can be solved algebraically. We defined a circle geometrically and then used the distance formula and rectangular coordinates to obtain an equation for a circle.

A Look Ahead

In this chapter we give geometric definitions for the conics and use the distance formula and rectangular coordinates to obtain their equations. We will learn that a circle is a conic.

Historically, Apollonius (200 BC) was among the first to study *conics* and discover some of their interesting properties. Today, conics are still studied because of their many uses. *Paraboloids of revolution* (parabolas rotated about their axes of symmetry) are used as signal collectors (the satellite dishes used with radar and dish TV, for example), as solar energy collectors, and as reflectors (telescopes, light projection, and so on). The planets circle the Sun in approximately *elliptical* orbits. Elliptical surfaces can be used to reflect signals such as light and sound from one place to another. A third conic, the *hyperbola,* can be used to determine the location of lightning strikes.

The Greeks used the methods of Euclidean geometry to study conics. However, we shall use the more powerful methods of analytic geometry, bringing to bear both algebra and geometry, for our study of conics.

This chapter concludes with a section on equations of conics in polar coordinates and a section on plane curves and parametric equations.

Outline

10.1 Conics

OBJECTIVE 1 Know the Names of the Conics (p. 638)

1 Know the Names of the Conics

The word *conic* derives from the word *cone*, which is a geometric figure that can be constructed in the following way: Let a and g be two distinct lines that intersect at a point V. Keep the line a fixed. Now rotate the line g about a while maintaining the same angle between a and g. The collection of points swept out (generated) by the line g is called a **(right circular) cone.** See Figure 1. The fixed line a is called the **axis** of the cone; the point V is its **vertex;** the lines that pass through V and make the same angle with a as g are **generators** of the cone. Each generator is a line that lies entirely on the cone. The cone consists of two parts, called **nappes,** that intersect at the vertex.

Figure 1

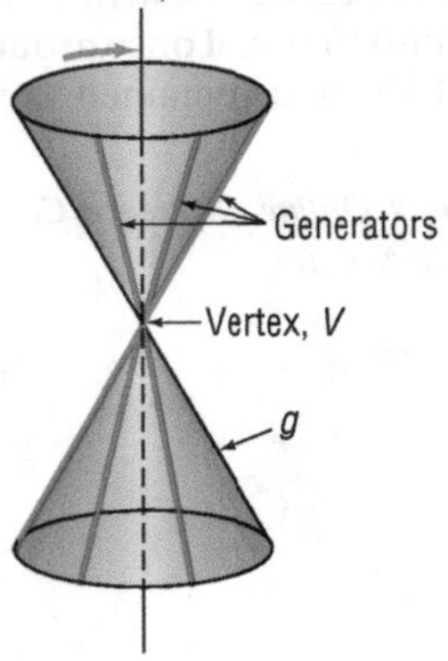

Conics, an abbreviation for **conic sections,** are curves that result from the intersection of a right circular cone and a plane. The conics we shall study arise when the plane does not contain the vertex, as shown in Figure 2. These conics are **circles** when the plane is perpendicular to the axis of the cone and intersects each generator; **ellipses** when the plane is tilted slightly so that it intersects each generator, but intersects only one nappe of the cone; **parabolas** when the plane is tilted farther so that it is parallel to one (and only one) generator and intersects only one nappe of the cone; and **hyperbolas** when the plane intersects both nappes.

If the plane does contain the vertex, the intersection of the plane and the cone is a point, a line, or a pair of intersecting lines. These are usually called **degenerate conics.**

Figure 2

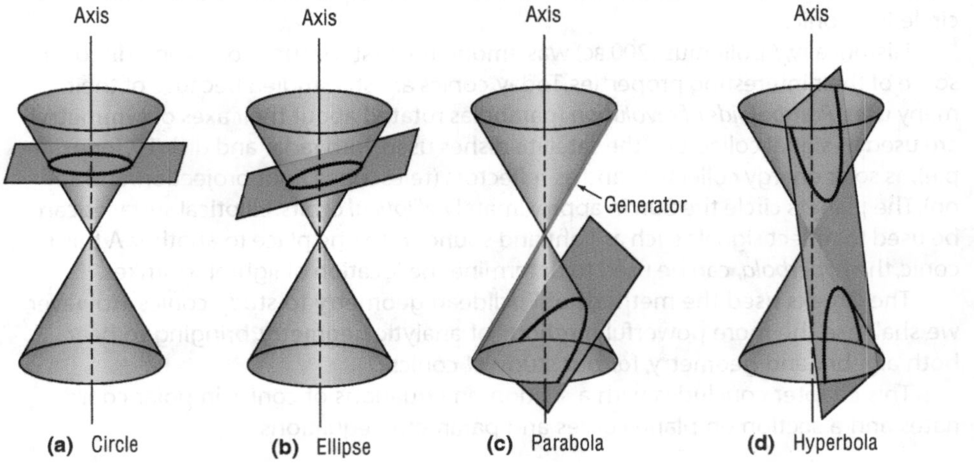

10.2 The Parabola

PREPARING FOR THIS SECTION *Before getting started, review the following:*

- Distance Formula (Section 1.1, p. 5)
- Symmetry (Section 1.2, pp. 19–21)
- Square Root Method (Appendix A, Section A.6, p. A51)
- Completing the Square (Appendix A, Section A.6, pp. A52–A53)
- Graphing Techniques: Transformations (Section 2.5, pp. 100–108)

Now Work the 'Are You Prepared?' problems on page 646.

OBJECTIVES 1 Analyze Parabolas with Vertex at the Origin (p. 639)
2 Analyze Parabolas with Vertex at (*h*, *k*) (p. 643)
3 Solve Applied Problems Involving Parabolas (p. 644)

We stated earlier (Section 3.3) that the graph of a quadratic function is a parabola. In this section, we begin with a geometric definition of a parabola and use it to obtain an equation.

DEFINITION

A **parabola** is the collection of all points P in the plane that are the same distance from a fixed point F as they are from a fixed line D. The point F is called the **focus** of the parabola, and the line D is its **directrix.** As a result, a parabola is the set of points P for which

$$d(F, P) = d(P, D) \qquad \textbf{(1)}$$

Figure 3

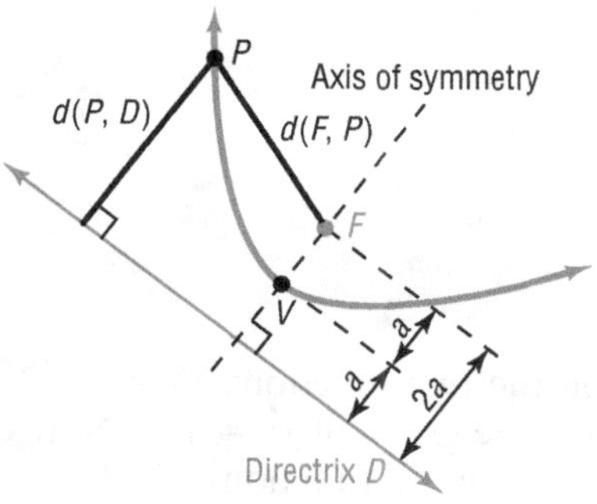

Figure 3 shows a parabola (in blue). The line through the focus F and perpendicular to the directrix D is called the **axis of symmetry** of the parabola. The point of intersection of the parabola with its axis of symmetry is called the **vertex** V.

Because the vertex V lies on the parabola, it must satisfy equation (1): $d(F, V) = d(V, D)$. The vertex is midway between the focus and the directrix. We shall let a equal the distance $d(F, V)$ from F to V. Now we are ready to derive an equation for a parabola. To do this, we use a rectangular system of coordinates positioned so that the vertex V, focus F, and directrix D of the parabola are conveniently located.

1 Analyze Parabolas with Vertex at the Origin

If we choose to locate the vertex V at the origin $(0, 0)$, we can conveniently position the focus F on either the x-axis or the y-axis. First, we consider the case where the focus F is on the positive x-axis, as shown in Figure 4. Because the distance from F to V is a, the coordinates of F will be $(a, 0)$ with $a > 0$. Similarly, because the distance from V to the directrix D is also a and, because D must be perpendicular to the x-axis (since the x-axis is the axis of symmetry), the equation of the directrix D must be $x = -a$.

Figure 4

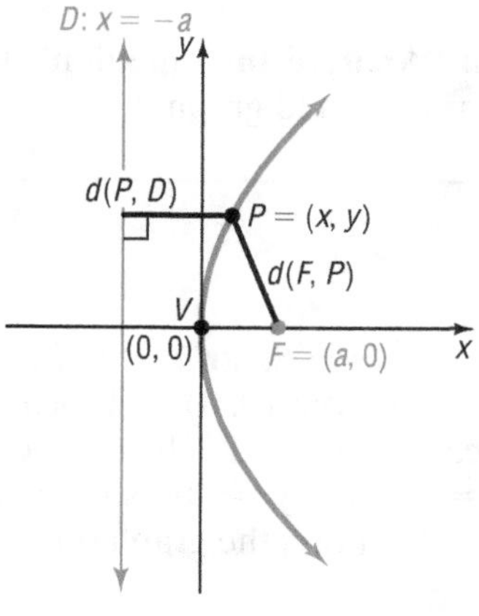

Now, if $P = (x, y)$ is any point on the parabola, P must obey equation (1):

$$d(F, P) = d(P, D)$$

So we have

$$\sqrt{(x - a)^2 + (y - 0)^2} = |x + a| \qquad \text{Use the Distance Formula.}$$
$$(x - a)^2 + y^2 = (x + a)^2 \qquad \text{Square both sides.}$$
$$x^2 - 2ax + a^2 + y^2 = x^2 + 2ax + a^2 \qquad \text{Remove parentheses.}$$
$$y^2 = 4ax \qquad \text{Simplify.}$$

THEOREM **Equation of a Parabola: Vertex at (0, 0), Focus at (a, 0), $a > 0$**

The equation of a parabola with vertex at (0, 0), focus at $(a, 0)$, and directrix $x = -a, a > 0$, is

$$y^2 = 4ax \quad (2)$$

EXAMPLE 1 **Finding the Equation of a Parabola and Graphing It**

Find an equation of the parabola with vertex at (0, 0) and focus at (3, 0). Graph the equation.

Solution The distance from the vertex (0, 0) to the focus (3, 0) is $a = 3$. Based on equation (2), the equation of this parabola is

$$y^2 = 4ax$$

$$y^2 = 12x \qquad a = 3$$

Figure 5

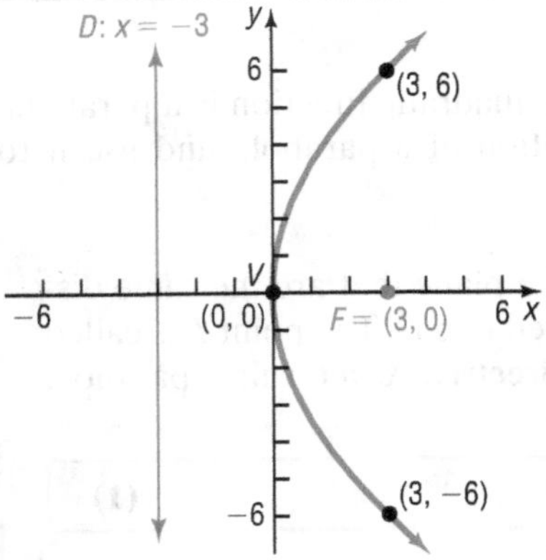

To graph this parabola, it is helpful to plot the points on the graph directly above or below the focus. To locate these two points, we let $x = 3$. Then

$$y^2 = 12x = 12(3) = 36$$

$$y = \pm 6 \qquad \text{Solve for } y.$$

The points on the parabola directly above or below the focus are (3, 6) and (3, −6). These points help in graphing the parabola because they determine the "opening." See Figure 5.

In general, the points on a parabola $y^2 = 4ax$ that lie above and below the focus $(a, 0)$ are each at a distance $2a$ from the focus. This follows from the fact that if $x = a$ then $y^2 = 4ax = 4a^2$, so $y = \pm 2a$. The line segment joining these two points is called the **latus rectum;** its length is $4a$.

Now Work PROBLEM 19

EXAMPLE 2 **Graphing a Parabola Using a Graphing Utility**

Graph the parabola $y^2 = 12x$.

Solution To graph the parabola $y^2 = 12x$, we need to graph the two functions $Y_1 = \sqrt{12x}$ and $Y_2 = -\sqrt{12x}$ on a square screen. Figure 6 shows the graph of $y^2 = 12x$. Notice that the graph fails the vertical line test, so $y^2 = 12x$ is not a function.

Figure 6

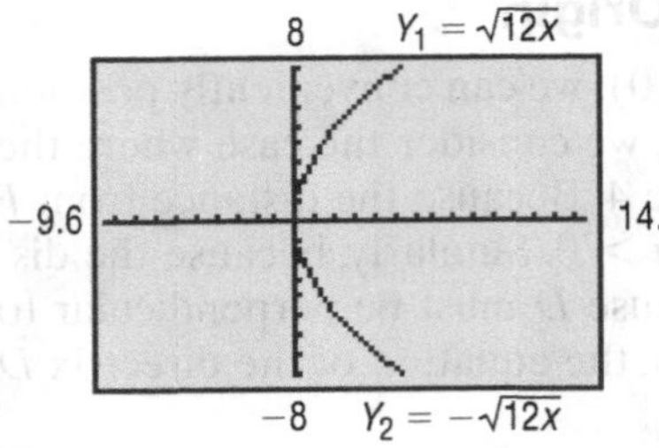

By reversing the steps we used to obtain equation (2), it follows that the graph of an equation of the form of equation (2), $y^2 = 4ax$, is a parabola; its vertex is at (0, 0), its focus is at $(a, 0)$, its directrix is the line $x = -a$, and its axis of symmetry is the x-axis.

For the remainder of this section, the direction **"Analyze the equation"** will mean to find the vertex, focus, and directrix of the parabola and graph it.

EXAMPLE 3 **Analyzing the Equation of a Parabola**

Analyze the equation: $y^2 = 8x$

Solution The equation $y^2 = 8x$ is of the form $y^2 = 4ax$, where $4a = 8$, so $a = 2$. Consequently, the graph of the equation is a parabola with vertex at (0, 0) and focus on the positive x-axis at (2, 0). The directrix is the vertical line $x = -2$. The two points defining the latus rectum are obtained by letting $x = 2$. Then $y^2 = 16$, so $y = \pm 4$. See Figure 7(a) for the graph drawn by hand. Figure 7(b) shows the graph obtained using a graphing utility.

Figure 7

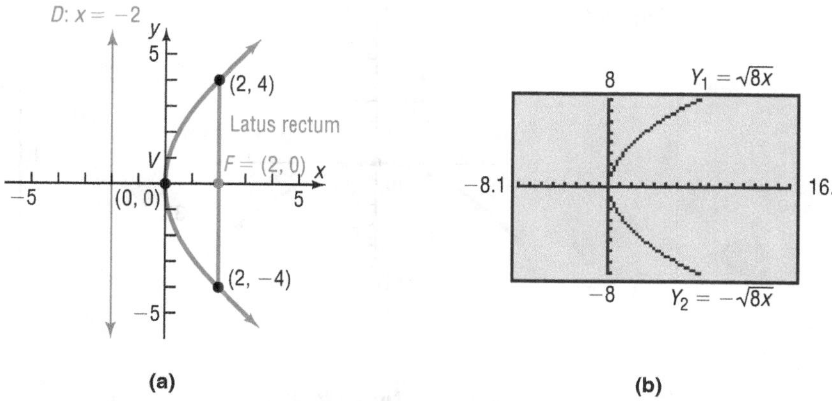

Recall that we arrived at equation (2) after placing the focus on the positive x-axis. If the focus is placed on the negative x-axis, positive y-axis, or negative y-axis, a different form of the equation for the parabola results. The four forms of the equation of a parabola with vertex at (0, 0) and focus on a coordinate axis a distance a from (0, 0) are given in Table 1, and their graphs are given in Figure 8. Notice that each graph is symmetric with respect to its axis of symmetry.

Table 1

EQUATIONS OF A PARABOLA VERTEX AT (0,0); FOCUS ON AN AXIS; $a > 0$

Vertex	Focus	Directrix	Equation	Description
(0, 0)	$(a, 0)$	$x = -a$	$y^2 = 4ax$	Parabola, axis of symmetry is the x-axis, opens right
(0, 0)	$(-a, 0)$	$x = a$	$y^2 = -4ax$	Parabola, axis of symmetry is the x-axis, opens left
(0, 0)	$(0, a)$	$y = -a$	$x^2 = 4ay$	Parabola, axis of symmetry is the y-axis, opens up
(0, 0)	$(0, -a)$	$y = a$	$x^2 = -4ay$	Parabola, axis of symmetry is the y-axis, opens down

Figure 8

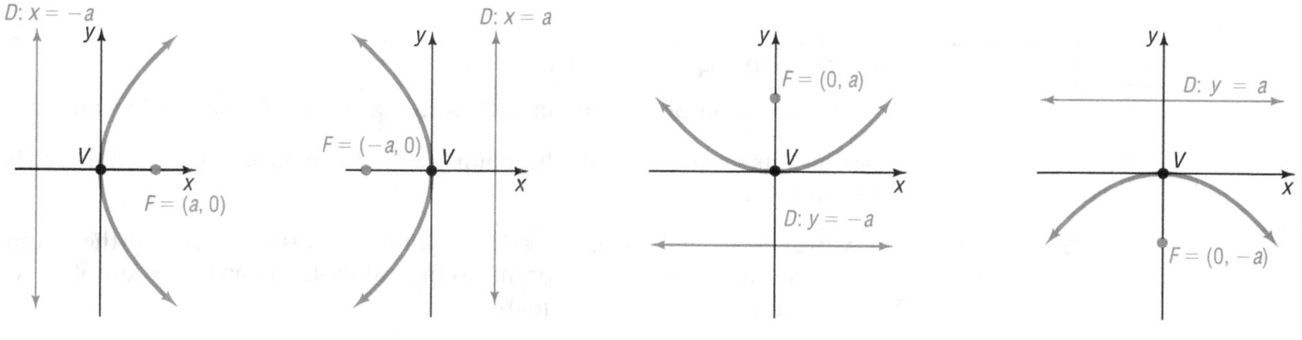

(a) $y^2 = 4ax$ **(b)** $y^2 = -4ax$ **(c)** $x^2 = 4ay$ **(d)** $x^2 = -4ay$

EXAMPLE 4 Analyzing the Equation of a Parabola

Analyze the equation: $x^2 = -12y$

Solution The equation $x^2 = -12y$ is of the form $x^2 = -4ay$, with $a = 3$. Consequently, the graph of the equation is a parabola with vertex at $(0, 0)$, focus at $(0, -3)$ and directrix the line $y = 3$. The parabola opens down, and its axis of symmetry is the y-axis. To obtain the points defining the latus rectum, let $y = -3$. Then $x^2 = 36$, so $x = \pm 6$. See Figure 9(a) for the graph drawn by hand. Figure 9(b) shows the graph using a graphing utility.

Figure 9

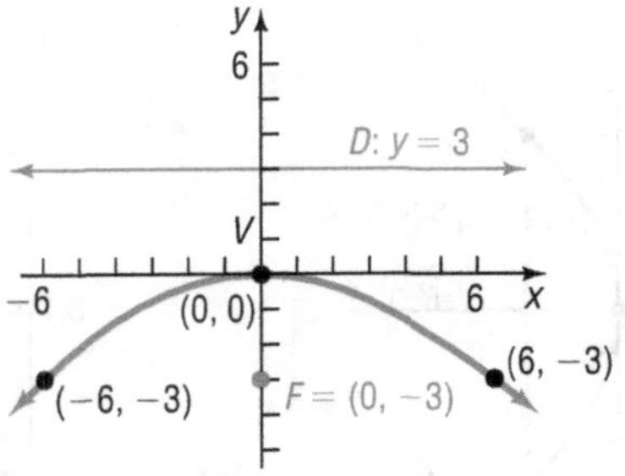

(a)

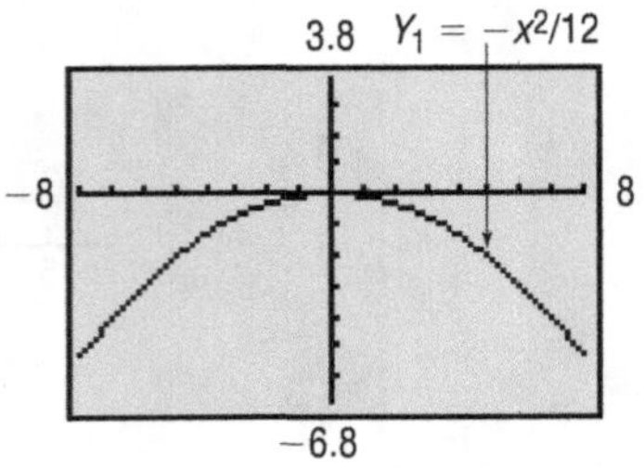

(b)

Now Work PROBLEM 39

EXAMPLE 5

Finding the Equation of a Parabola

Find the equation of the parabola with focus at $(0, 4)$ and directrix the line $y = -4$. Graph the equation.

Solution A parabola whose focus is at $(0, 4)$ and whose directrix is the horizontal line $y = -4$ will have its vertex at $(0, 0)$. (Do you see why? The vertex is midway between the focus and the directrix.) Since the focus is on the positive y-axis at $(0, 4)$, the equation of this parabola is of the form $x^2 = 4ay$, with $a = 4$; that is,

$$x^2 = \underset{\substack{\uparrow \\ a = 4}}{4ay} = 4(4)y = 16y$$

Figure 10

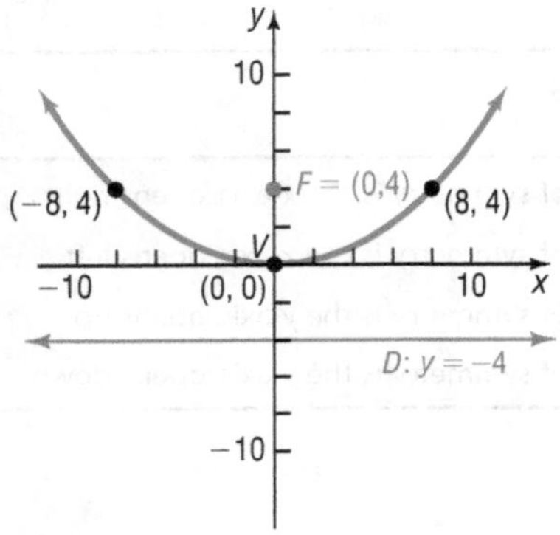

Letting $y = 4$, we find $x^2 = 64$, so $x = \pm 8$. The points $(8, 4)$ and $(-8, 4)$ determine the latus rectum. Figure 10 shows the graph of $x^2 = 16y$.

✓Check: Verify the graph drawn in Figure 10 by graphing $Y_1 = \dfrac{x^2}{16}$ using a graphing utility.

EXAMPLE 6

Finding the Equation of a Parabola

Find the equation of a parabola with vertex at $(0, 0)$ if its axis of symmetry is the x-axis and its graph contains the point $\left(-\frac{1}{2}, 2\right)$. Find its focus and directrix, and graph the equation.

Solution The vertex is at the origin, the axis of symmetry is the x-axis, and the graph contains a point in the second quadrant, so the parabola opens to the left. We see from Table 1 that the form of the equation is

$$y^2 = -4ax$$

Because the point $\left(-\frac{1}{2}, 2\right)$ is on the parabola, the coordinates $x = -\frac{1}{2}$, $y = 2$ must satisfy the equation $y^2 = -4ax$. Substituting $x = -\frac{1}{2}$ and $y = 2$ into the equation, we find that

$$2^2 = -4a\left(-\frac{1}{2}\right) \qquad y^2 = -4ax;\ x = -\frac{1}{2},\ y = 2$$

$$a = 2$$

The equation of the parabola is

$$y^2 = -4(2)x = -8x$$

Figure 11

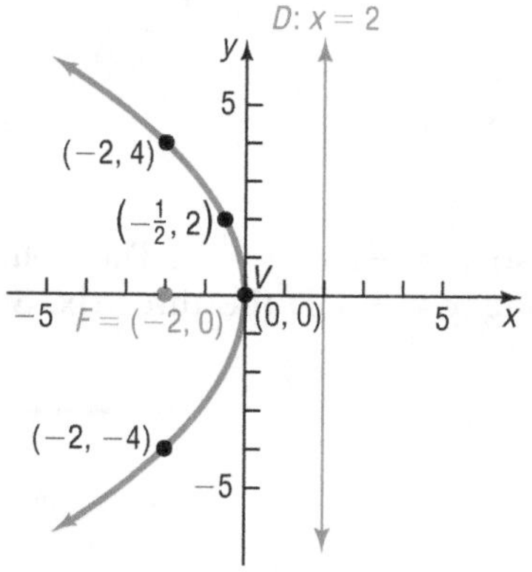

The focus is at $(-2, 0)$ and the directrix is the line $x = 2$. Letting $x = -2$, we find $y^2 = 16$, so $y = \pm 4$. The points $(-2, 4)$ and $(-2, -4)$ define the latus rectum. See Figure 11.

Now Work PROBLEM 27

2 Analyze Parabolas with Vertex at (h, k)

If a parabola with vertex at the origin and axis of symmetry along a coordinate axis is shifted horizontally h units and then vertically k units, the result is a parabola with vertex at (h, k) and axis of symmetry parallel to a coordinate axis. The equations of such parabolas have the same forms as those in Table 1, but with x replaced by $x - h$ (the horizontal shift) and y replaced by $y - k$ (the vertical shift). Table 2 gives the forms of the equations of such parabolas. Figures 12(a)–(d) illustrate the graphs for $h > 0, k > 0$.

Table 2

PARABOLAS WITH VERTEX AT (h, k); AXIS OF SYMMETRY PARALLEL TO A COORDINATE AXIS; $a > 0$

Vertex	Focus	Directrix	Equation	Description
(h, k)	$(h + a, k)$	$x = h - a$	$(y - k)^2 = 4a(x - h)$	Parabola, axis of symmetry parallel to x-axis, opens right
(h, k)	$(h - a, k)$	$x = h + a$	$(y - k)^2 = -4a(x - h)$	Parabola, axis of symmetry parallel to x-axis, opens left
(h, k)	$(h, k + a)$	$y = k - a$	$(x - h)^2 = 4a(y - k)$	Parabola, axis of symmetry parallel to y-axis, opens up
(h, k)	$(h, k - a)$	$y = k + a$	$(x - h)^2 = -4a(y - k)$	Parabola, axis of symmetry parallel to y-axis, opens down

Figure 12

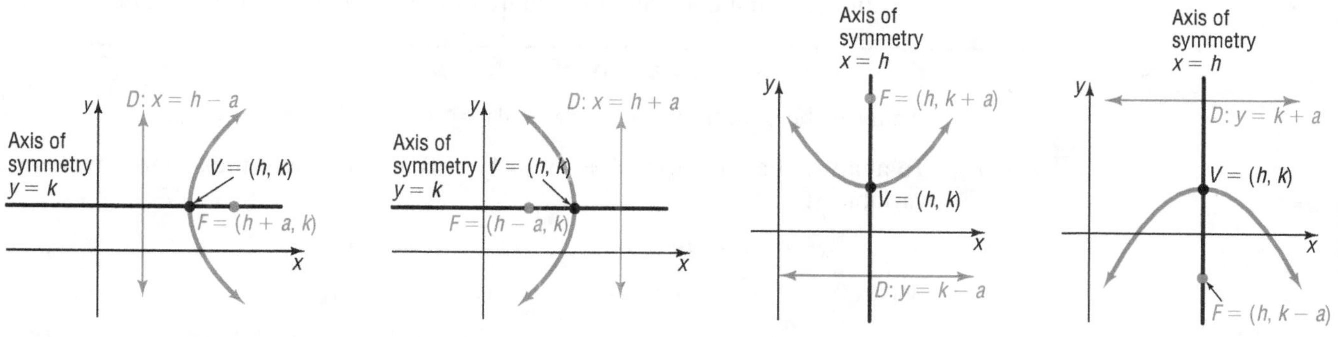

(a) $(y - k)^2 = 4a(x - h)$ **(b)** $(y - k)^2 = -4a(x - h)$ **(c)** $(x - h)^2 = 4a(y - k)$ **(d)** $(x - h)^2 = -4a(y - k)$

EXAMPLE 7 **Finding the Equation of a Parabola, Vertex Not at Origin**

Find an equation of the parabola with vertex at $(-2, 3)$ and focus at $(0, 3)$. Graph the equation.

Solution The vertex $(-2, 3)$ and focus $(0, 3)$ both lie on the horizontal line $y = 3$ (the axis of symmetry). The distance a from the vertex $(-2, 3)$ to the focus $(0, 3)$ is $a = 2$. Also, because the focus lies to the right of the vertex, we know that the parabola opens to the right. Consequently, the form of the equation is

$$(y - k)^2 = 4a(x - h)$$

where $(h, k) = (-2, 3)$ and $a = 2$. Therefore, the equation is

$$(y - 3)^2 = 4 \cdot 2[x - (-2)]$$
$$(y - 3)^2 = 8(x + 2)$$

If $x = 0$, then $(y - 3)^2 = 16$. Then $y - 3 = \pm 4$, so $y = -1$ or $y = 7$. The points $(0, -1)$ and $(0, 7)$ define the latus rectum; the line $x = -4$ is the directrix. See Figure 13.

Figure 13

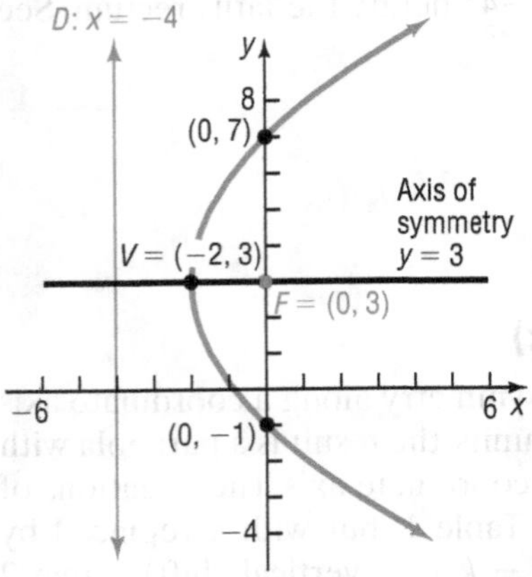

Now Work PROBLEM 29

EXAMPLE 8 **Using a Graphing Utility to Graph a Parabola, Vertex Not at Origin**

Using a graphing utility, graph the equation $(y - 3)^2 = 8(x + 2)$.

Solution First, we must solve the equation for y.

$$(y - 3)^2 = 8(x + 2)$$
$$y - 3 = \pm\sqrt{8(x + 2)} \quad \text{Use the Square Root Method.}$$
$$y = 3 \pm \sqrt{8(x + 2)} \quad \text{Add 3 to both sides.}$$

Figure 14

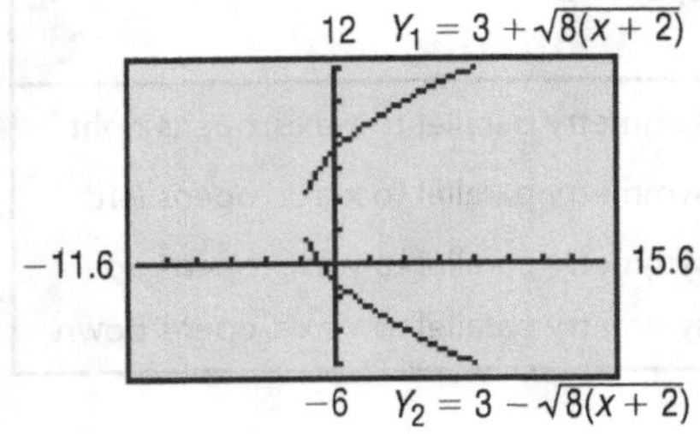

Figure 14 shows the graphs of the equations $Y_1 = 3 + \sqrt{8(x + 2)}$ and $Y_2 = 3 - \sqrt{8(x + 2)}$.

Polynomial equations define parabolas whenever they involve two variables that are quadratic in one variable and linear in the other. To analyze this type of equation, we first complete the square of the variable that is quadratic.

EXAMPLE 9 **Analyzing the Equation of a Parabola**

Analyze the equation: $x^2 + 4x - 4y = 0$

Solution To analyze the equation $x^2 + 4x - 4y = 0$, we complete the square involving the variable x.

$$x^2 + 4x - 4y = 0$$
$$x^2 + 4x = 4y \quad \text{Isolate the terms involving } x \text{ on the left side.}$$
$$x^2 + 4x + 4 = 4y + 4 \quad \text{Complete the square on the left side.}$$
$$(x + 2)^2 = 4(y + 1) \quad \text{Factor.}$$

Figure 15

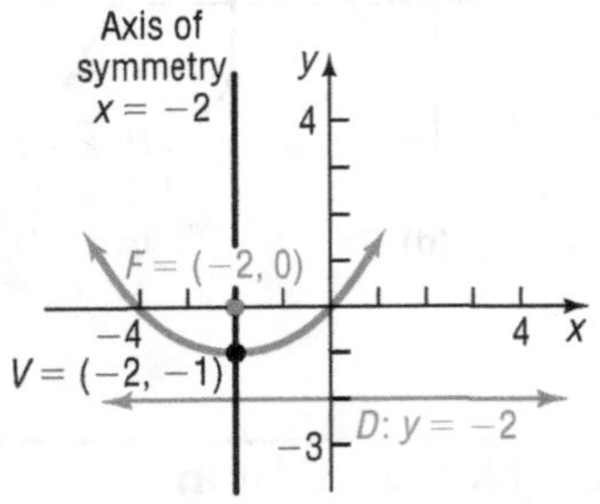

This equation is of the form $(x - h)^2 = 4a(y - k)$, with $h = -2, k = -1$, and $a = 1$. The graph is a parabola with vertex at $(h, k) = (-2, -1)$ that opens up. The focus is $a = 1$ unit above the vertex at $(-2, 0)$, and the directrix is the line $y = -2$. See Figure 15.

Now Work PROBLEM 47

3 Solve Applied Problems Involving Parabolas

Parabolas find their way into many applications. For example, as we discussed in Section 3.4, suspension bridges have cables in the shape of a parabola. Another property of parabolas that is used in applications is their reflecting property.

Suppose that a mirror is shaped like a **paraboloid of revolution,** a surface formed by rotating a parabola about its axis of symmetry. If a light (or any other emitting source) is placed at the focus of the parabola, all the rays emanating from the light will reflect off the mirror in lines parallel to the axis of symmetry. This principle is used in the design of searchlights, flashlights, certain automobile headlights, and other such devices. See Figure 16.

Conversely, suppose that rays of light (or other signals) emanate from a distant source so that they are essentially parallel. When these rays strike the surface of a parabolic mirror whose axis of symmetry is parallel to these rays, they are reflected to a single point at the focus. This principle is used in the design of some solar energy devices, satellite dishes, and the mirrors used in some types of telescopes. See Figure 17.

Figure 16
Searchlight

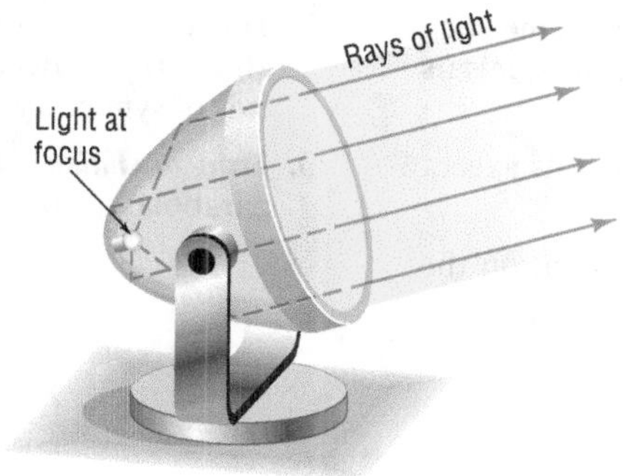

Figure 17
Telescope

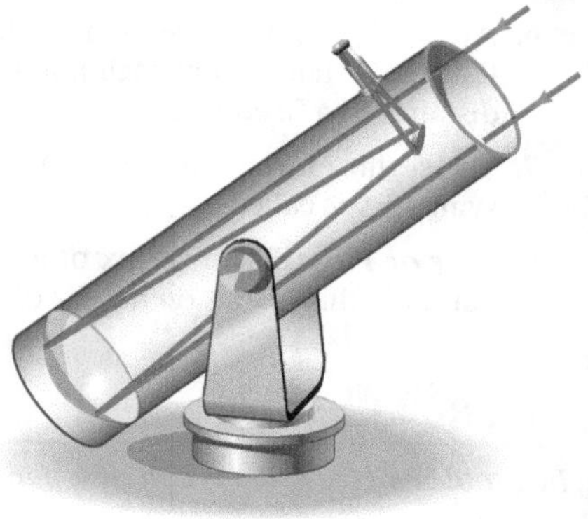

EXAMPLE 10 Satellite Dish

A satellite dish is shaped like a paraboloid of revolution. The signals that emanate from a satellite strike the surface of the dish and are reflected to a single point, where the receiver is located. If the dish is 8 feet across at its opening and 3 feet deep at its center, at what position should the receiver be placed? That is, where is the focus?

Solution Figure 18(a) shows the satellite dish. We draw the parabola used to form the dish on a rectangular coordinate system so that the vertex of the parabola is at the origin and its focus is on the positive y-axis. See Figure 18(b).

Figure 18

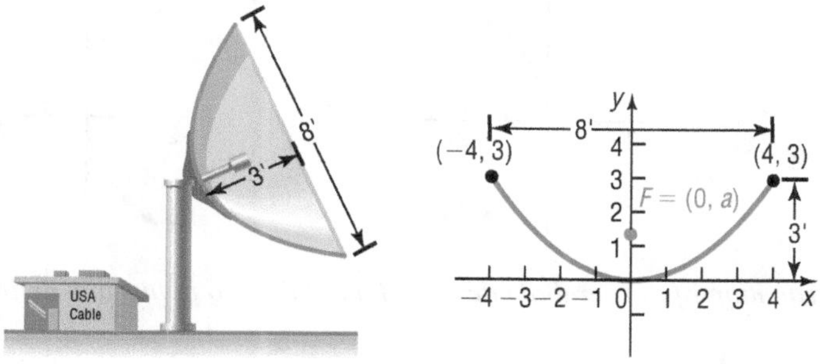

(a) (b)

The form of the equation of the parabola is

$$x^2 = 4ay$$

and its focus is at $(0, a)$. Since $(4, 3)$ is a point on the graph, we have

$$4^2 = 4a(3) \quad x = 4, y = 3$$

$$a = \frac{4}{3} \quad \text{Solve for } a.$$

The receiver should be located $1\frac{1}{3}$ feet from the base of the dish, along its axis of symmetry.

Now Work PROBLEM 63

10.2 Assess Your Understanding

'Are You Prepared?' *Answers are given at the end of these exercises. If you get a wrong answer, read the pages listed in red.*

1. The formula for the distance d from $P_1 = (x_1, y_1)$ to $P_2 = (x_2, y_2)$ is $d =$ ______. (p. 5)
2. To complete the square of $x^2 - 4x$, add ______. (p. A52)
3. Use the Square Root Method to find the real solutions of $(x + 4)^2 = 9$. (p. A51)
4. The point that is symmetric with respect to the x-axis to the point $(-2, 5)$ is ______. (pp. 19–20)
5. To graph $y = (x - 3)^2 + 1$, shift the graph of $y = x^2$ to the right ______ units and then ______ 1 unit. (pp. 100–102)

Concepts and Vocabulary

6. A(n) ______ is the collection of all points in the plane such that the distance from each point to a fixed point equals its distance to a fixed line.
7. The surface formed by rotating a parabola about its axis of symmetry is called a ______ ______ ______.
8. ***True or False*** The vertex of a parabola is a point on the parabola that also is on its axis of symmetry.
9. ***True or False*** If a light is placed at the focus of a parabola, all the rays reflected off the parabola will be parallel to the axis of symmetry.
10. ***True or False*** The graph of a quadratic function is a parabola.

Skill Building

In Problems 11–18, the graph of a parabola is given. Match each graph to its equation.

(A) $y^2 = 4x$
(B) $x^2 = 4y$
(C) $y^2 = -4x$
(D) $x^2 = -4y$
(E) $(y - 1)^2 = 4(x - 1)$
(F) $(x + 1)^2 = 4(y + 1)$
(G) $(y - 1)^2 = -4(x - 1)$
(H) $(x + 1)^2 = -4(y + 1)$

11.
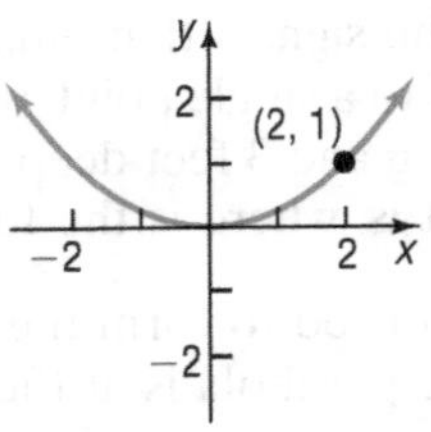

12.
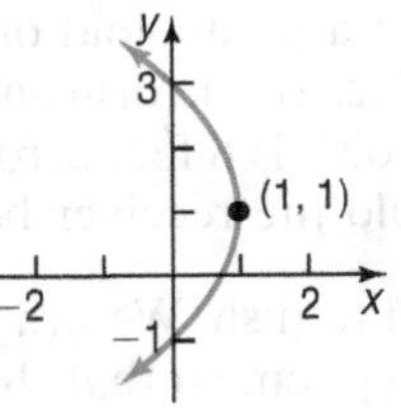

13.
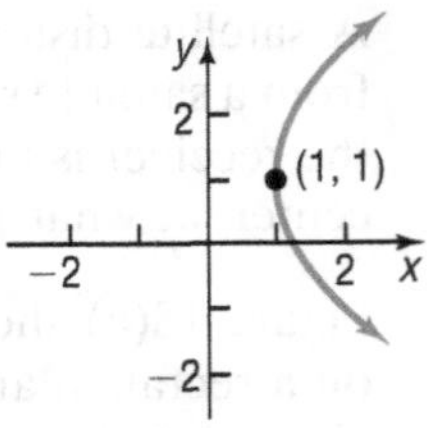

14.
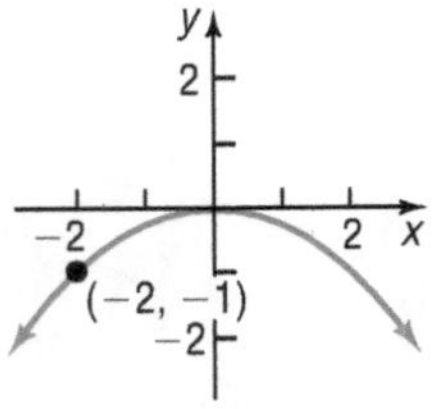

15.
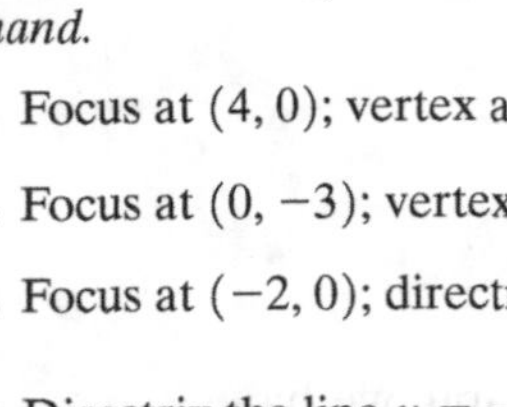

16.
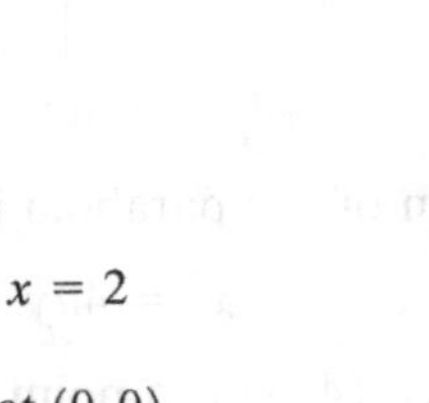

17.
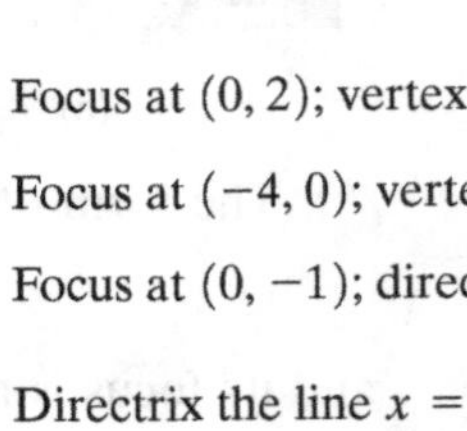

18.
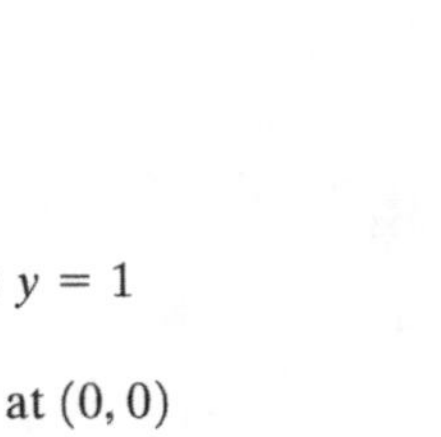

In Problems 19–36, find the equation of the parabola described. Find the two points that define the latus rectum, and graph the equation by hand.

19. Focus at $(4, 0)$; vertex at $(0, 0)$
20. Focus at $(0, 2)$; vertex at $(0, 0)$
21. Focus at $(0, -3)$; vertex at $(0, 0)$
22. Focus at $(-4, 0)$; vertex at $(0, 0)$
23. Focus at $(-2, 0)$; directrix the line $x = 2$
24. Focus at $(0, -1)$; directrix the line $y = 1$
25. Directrix the line $y = -\frac{1}{2}$; vertex at $(0, 0)$
26. Directrix the line $x = -\frac{1}{2}$; vertex at $(0, 0)$
27. Vertex at $(0, 0)$; axis of symmetry the y-axis; containing the point $(2, 3)$
28. Vertex at $(0, 0)$; axis of symmetry the x-axis; containing the point $(2, 3)$
29. Vertex at $(2, -3)$; focus at $(2, -5)$
30. Vertex at $(4, -2)$; focus at $(6, -2)$
31. Vertex at $(-1, -2)$; focus at $(0, -2)$
32. Vertex at $(3, 0)$; focus at $(3, -2)$
33. Focus at $(-3, 4)$; directrix the line $y = 2$
34. Focus at $(2, 4)$; directrix the line $x = -4$
35. Focus at $(-3, -2)$; directrix the line $x = 1$
36. Focus at $(-4, 4)$; directrix the line $y = -2$

In Problems 37–54, find the vertex, focus, and directrix of each parabola. Graph the equation by hand. Verify your graph using a graphing utility.

37. $x^2 = 4y$ **38.** $y^2 = 8x$ **39.** $y^2 = -16x$ **40.** $x^2 = -4y$

41. $(y - 2)^2 = 8(x + 1)$ **42.** $(x + 4)^2 = 16(y + 2)$ **43.** $(x - 3)^2 = -(y + 1)$ **44.** $(y + 1)^2 = -4(x - 2)$

45. $(y + 3)^2 = 8(x - 2)$ **46.** $(x - 2)^2 = 4(y - 3)$ **47.** $y^2 - 4y + 4x + 4 = 0$ **48.** $x^2 + 6x - 4y + 1 = 0$

49. $x^2 + 8x = 4y - 8$ **50.** $y^2 - 2y = 8x - 1$ **51.** $y^2 + 2y - x = 0$ **52.** $x^2 - 4x = 2y$

53. $x^2 - 4x = y + 4$ **54.** $y^2 + 12y = -x + 1$

In Problems 55–62, write an equation for each parabola.

55.

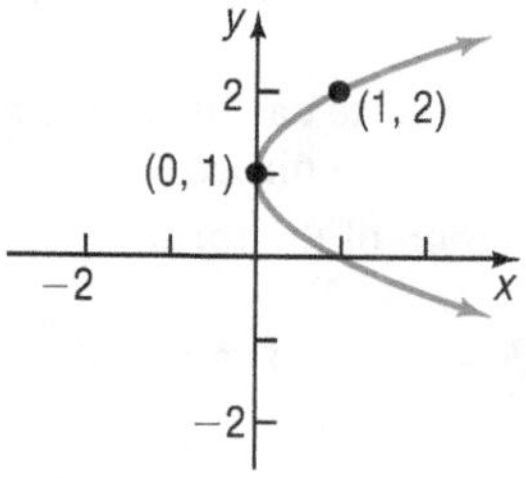

56.

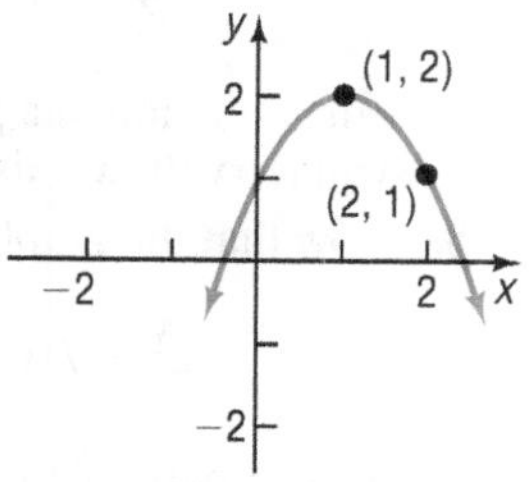

57.

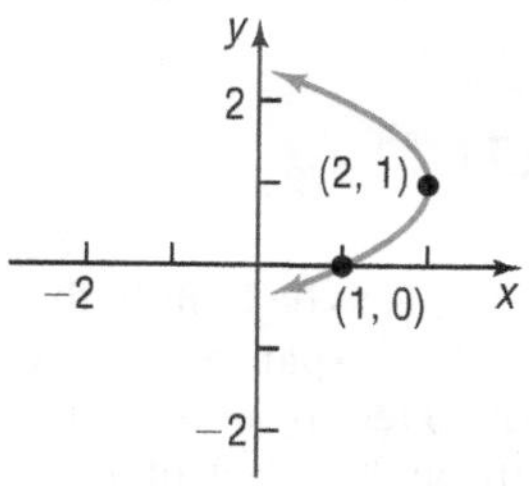

58.

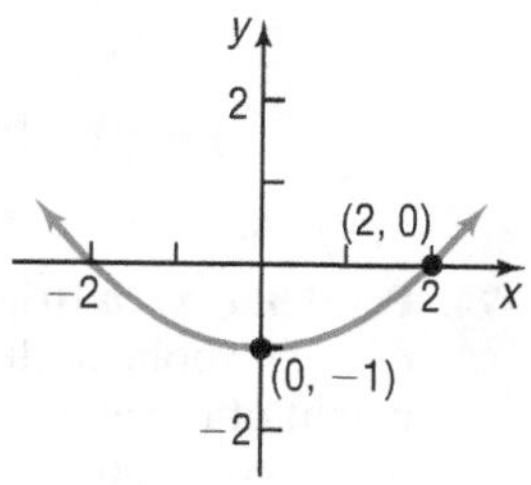

59.

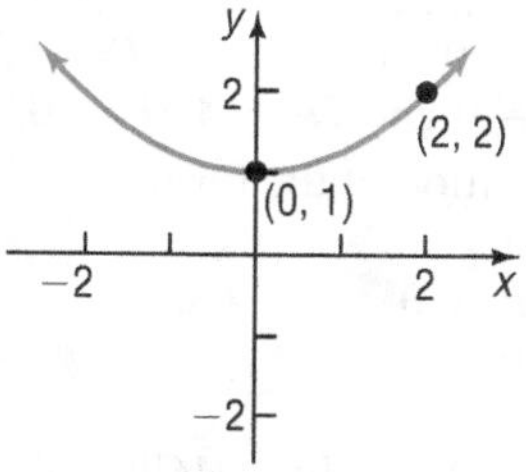

60.

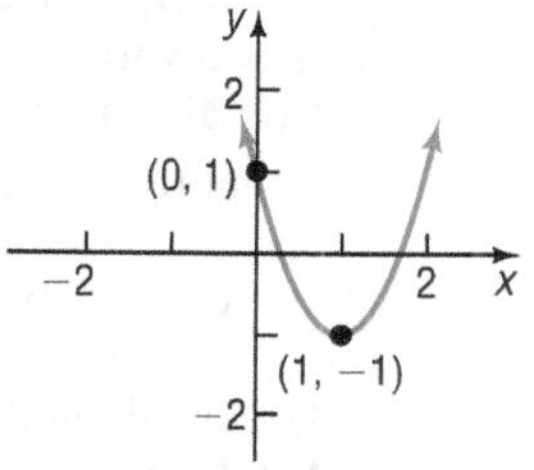

61.

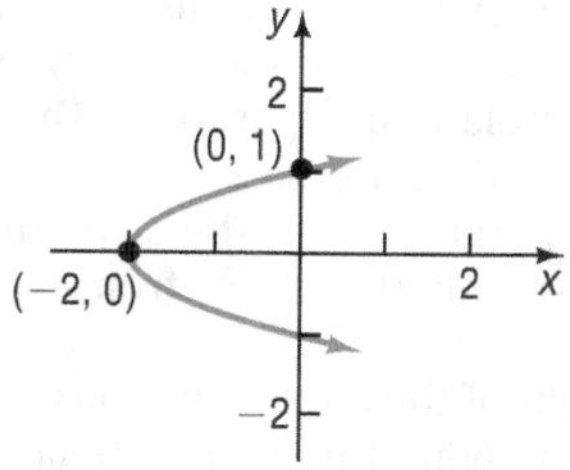

62.

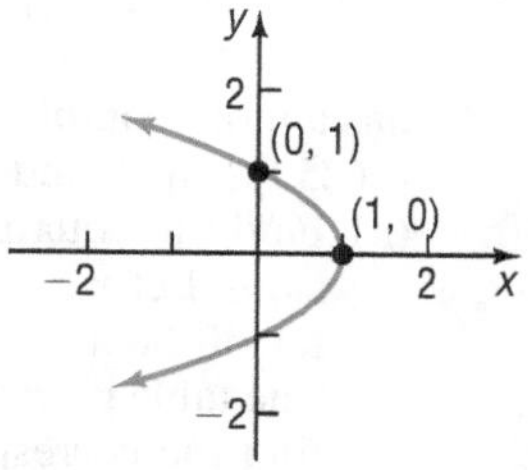

Applications and Extensions

63. Satellite Dish A satellite dish is shaped like a paraboloid of revolution. The signals that emanate from a satellite strike the surface of the dish and are reflected to a single point, where the receiver is located. If the dish is 10 feet across at its opening and 4 feet deep at its center, at what position should the receiver be placed?

64. Constructing a TV Dish A cable TV receiving dish is in the shape of a paraboloid of revolution. Find the location of the receiver, which is placed at the focus, if the dish is 6 feet across at its opening and 2 feet deep.

65. Constructing a Flashlight The reflector of a flashlight is in the shape of a paraboloid of revolution. Its diameter is 4 inches and its depth is 1 inch. How far from the vertex should the light bulb be placed so that the rays will be reflected parallel to the axis?

66. Constructing a Headlight A sealed-beam headlight is in the shape of a paraboloid of revolution. The bulb, which is placed at the focus, is 1 inch from the vertex. If the depth is to be 2 inches, what is the diameter of the headlight at its opening?

67. Suspension Bridge The cables of a suspension bridge are in the shape of a parabola, as shown in the figure. The towers supporting the cable are 600 feet apart and 80 feet high. If the cables touch the road surface midway between the towers, what is the height of the cable from the road at a point 150 feet from the center of the bridge?

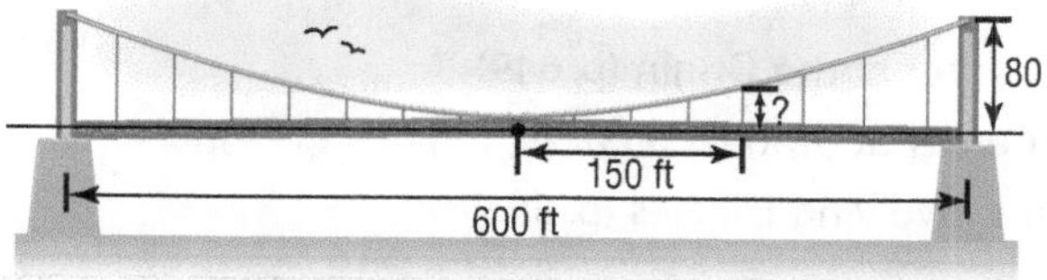

68. Suspension Bridge The cables of a suspension bridge are in the shape of a parabola. The towers supporting the cable are 400 feet apart and 100 feet high. If the cables are at a height of 10 feet midway between the towers, what is the height of the cable at a point 50 feet from the center of the bridge?

69. Searchlight A searchlight is shaped like a paraboloid of revolution. If the light source is located 2 feet from the base along the axis of symmetry and the opening is 5 feet across, how deep should the searchlight be?

70. Searchlight A searchlight is shaped like a paraboloid of revolution. If the light source is located 2 feet from the base along the axis of symmetry and the depth of the searchlight is 4 feet, what should the width of the opening be?

71. Solar Heat A mirror is shaped like a paraboloid of revolution and will be used to concentrate the rays of the sun at its focus, creating a heat source. See the figure. If the mirror is 20 feet across at its opening and is 6 feet deep, where will the heat source be concentrated?

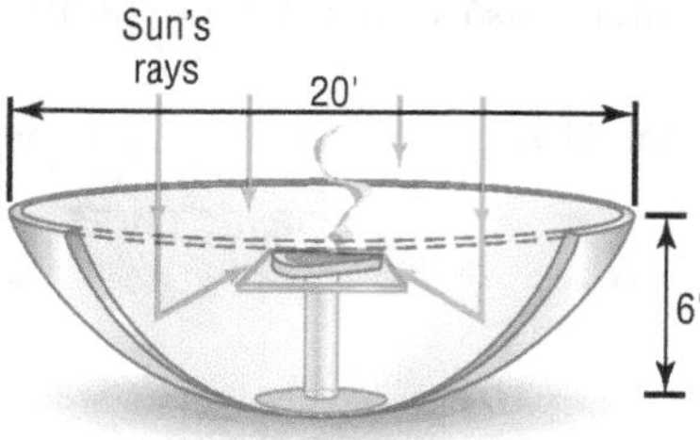

72. Reflecting Telescope A reflecting telescope contains a mirror shaped like a paraboloid of revolution. If the mirror is 4 inches across at its opening and is 3 inches deep, where will the collected light be concentrated?

73. Parabolic Arch Bridge A bridge is built in the shape of a parabolic arch. The bridge has a span of 120 feet and a maximum height of 25 feet. See the illustration. Choose a suitable rectangular coordinate system and find the height of the arch at distances of 10, 30, and 50 feet from the center.

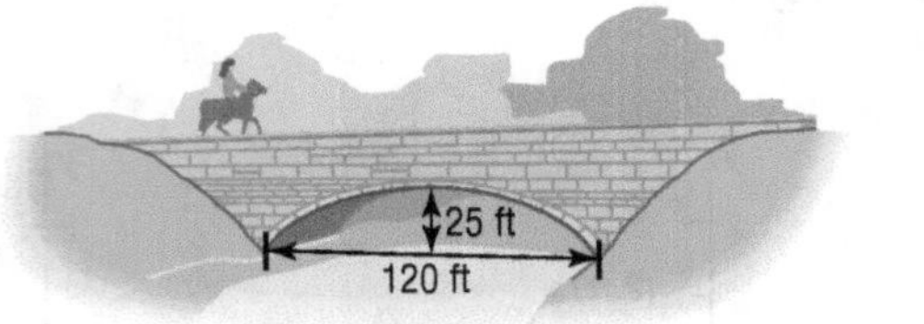

74. Parabolic Arch Bridge A bridge is to be built in the shape of a parabolic arch and is to have a span of 100 feet. The height of the arch a distance of 40 feet from the center is to be 10 feet. Find the height of the arch at its center.

75. Gateway Arch The Gateway Arch in St. Louis is often mistaken to be parabolic is shape. In fact, it is a *catenary,* which has a more complicated formula than a parabola. The Arch is 625 feet high and 598 feet wide at its base.

(a) Find the equation of a parabola with the same dimensions. Let x equal the horizontal distance from the center of the arc.

(b) The table gives the height of the Arch at various widths; find the corresponding heights for the parabola found in part (a).

Width (ft)	Height (ft)
567	100
478	312.5
308	525

(c) Do the data support the notion that the Arch is in the shape of a parabola?

Source: Wikipedia, the free encyclopedia

76. Show that an equation of the form

$$Ax^2 + Ey = 0 \qquad A \neq 0, E \neq 0$$

is the equation of a parabola with vertex at (0, 0) and axis of symmetry the y-axis. Find its focus and directrix.

77. Show that an equation of the form

$$Cy^2 + Dx = 0 \qquad C \neq 0, D \neq 0$$

is the equation of a parabola with vertex at (0, 0) and axis of symmetry the x-axis. Find its focus and directrix.

78. Show that the graph of an equation of the form

$$Ax^2 + Dx + Ey + F = 0 \qquad A \neq 0$$

(a) Is a parabola if $E \neq 0$.
(b) Is a vertical line if $E = 0$ and $D^2 - 4AF = 0$.
(c) Is two vertical lines if $E = 0$ and $D^2 - 4AF > 0$.
(d) Contains no points if $E = 0$ and $D^2 - 4AF < 0$.

79. Show that the graph of an equation of the form

$$Cy^2 + Dx + Ey + F = 0 \qquad C \neq 0$$

(a) Is a parabola if $D \neq 0$.
(b) Is a horizontal line if $D = 0$ and $E^2 - 4CF = 0$.
(c) Is two horizontal lines if $D = 0$ and $E^2 - 4CF > 0$.
(d) Contains no points if $D = 0$ and $E^2 - 4CF < 0$.

'Are You Prepared?' Answers

1. $d = \sqrt{(x_2 - x_1)^2 + (y_2 - y_1)^2}$ **2.** 4 **3.** $x + 4 = \pm 3$; $\{-7, -1\}$ **4.** $(-2, -5)$ **5.** 3; up

10.3 The Ellipse

PREPARING FOR THIS SECTION *Before getting started, review the following:*

- Distance Formula (Section 1.1, p. 5)
- Completing the Square (Appendix A, Section A.6, pp. A52–A53)
- Intercepts (Section 1.2, pp. 18–19)
- Symmetry (Section 1.2, pp. 19–21)
- Circles (Section 1.5, pp. 44–48)
- Graphing Techniques: Transformations (Section 2.5, pp. 100–108)

Now Work the 'Are You Prepared?' problems on page 657.

OBJECTIVES
1 Analyze Ellipses with Center at the Origin (p. 649)
2 Analyze Ellipses with Center at (h, k) (p. 653)
3 Solve Applied Problems Involving Ellipses (p. 656)

DEFINITION An **ellipse** is the set of all points P in the plane the sum of whose distances from two fixed points, called the **foci,** is a constant.

The definition contains within it a physical means for drawing an ellipse. Find a piece of string (the length of this string is the constant referred to in the definition). Then take two thumbtacks (the foci) and stick them into a piece of cardboard so that the distance between them is less than the length of the string. Now attach the ends of the string to the thumbtacks and, using the point of a pencil, pull the string taut. See Figure 19. Keeping the string taut, rotate the pencil around the two thumbtacks. The pencil traces out an ellipse, as shown in Figure 19.

Figure 19

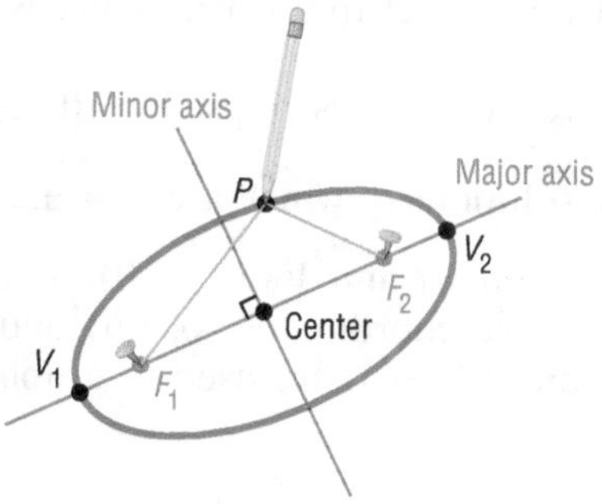

In Figure 19, the foci are labeled F_1 and F_2. The line containing the foci is called the **major axis.** The midpoint of the line segment joining the foci is the **center** of the ellipse. The line through the center and perpendicular to the major axis is the **minor axis.**

The two points of intersection of the ellipse and the major axis are the **vertices,** V_1 and V_2, of the ellipse. The distance from one vertex to the other is the **length of the major axis.** The ellipse is symmetric with respect to its major axis, with respect to its minor axis, and with respect to its center.

Figure 20

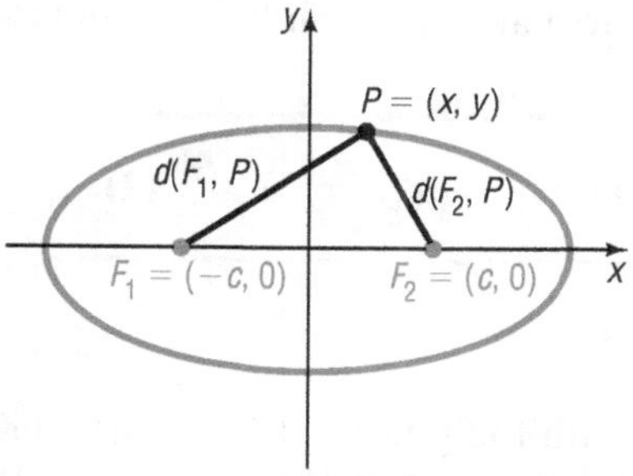

1 Analyze Ellipses with Center at the Origin

With these ideas in mind, we are now ready to find the equation of an ellipse in a rectangular coordinate system. First, we place the center of the ellipse at the origin. Second, we position the ellipse so that its major axis coincides with a coordinate axis. Suppose that the major axis coincides with the x-axis, as shown in Figure 20. If c is the distance from the center to a focus, one focus will be at $F_1 = (-c, 0)$ and the other at $F_2 = (c, 0)$. As we shall see, it is convenient to let $2a$ denote the constant distance referred to in the definition. Then, if $P = (x, y)$ is any point on the ellipse, we have

$$d(F_1, P) + d(F_2, P) = 2a$$ Sum of the distances from P to the foci equals a constant, $2a$.

$$\sqrt{(x + c)^2 + (y - 0)^2} + \sqrt{(x - c)^2 + (y - 0)^2} = 2a$$ Use the Distance Formula.

$$\sqrt{(x + c)^2 + y^2} = 2a - \sqrt{(x - c)^2 + y^2}$$ Isolate one radical.

$$(x + c)^2 + y^2 = 4a^2 - 4a\sqrt{(x - c)^2 + y^2} + (x - c)^2 + y^2$$ Square both sides.

$$x^2 + 2cx + c^2 + y^2 = 4a^2 - 4a\sqrt{(x - c)^2 + y^2} + x^2 - 2cx + c^2 + y^2$$ Remove parentheses.

$$4cx - 4a^2 = -4a\sqrt{(x - c)^2 + y^2}$$ Simplify; isolate the radical.

$$cx - a^2 = -a\sqrt{(x - c)^2 + y^2}$$ Divide each side by 4.

$$(cx - a^2)^2 = a^2[(x - c)^2 + y^2]$$ Square both sides again.

$$c^2x^2 - 2a^2cx + a^4 = a^2(x^2 - 2cx + c^2 + y^2)$$ Remove parentheses.

$$(c^2 - a^2)x^2 - a^2y^2 = a^2c^2 - a^4$$ Rearrange the terms.

$$(a^2 - c^2)x^2 + a^2y^2 = a^2(a^2 - c^2) \quad (1)$$ Multiply each side by -1; factor a^2 on the right side.

To obtain points on the ellipse off the x-axis, it must be that $a > c$. To see why, look again at Figure 20. Then

$$d(F_1, P) + d(F_2, P) > d(F_1, F_2)$$ The sum of the lengths of two sides of a triangle is greater than the length of the third side.

$$2a > 2c$$ $d(F_1, P) + d(F_2, P) = 2a$, $d(F_1, F_2) = 2c$

$$a > c$$

Since $a > c$, we also have $a^2 > c^2$, so $a^2 - c^2 > 0$. Let $b^2 = a^2 - c^2$, $b > 0$. Then $a > b$ and equation (1) can be written as

$$b^2x^2 + a^2y^2 = a^2b^2$$

$$\frac{x^2}{a^2} + \frac{y^2}{b^2} = 1 \qquad \text{Divide each side by } a^2b^2.$$

As you can verify, this equation is symmetric with respect to the x-axis, y-axis, and origin.

Because the major axis is the x-axis, we find the vertices of this ellipse by letting $y = 0$. The vertices satisfy the equation $\frac{x^2}{a^2} = 1$, the solutions of which are $x = \pm a$. Consequently, the vertices of this ellipse are $V_1 = (-a, 0)$ and $V_2 = (a, 0)$. The y-intercepts of the ellipse, found by letting $x = 0$, have coordinates $(0, -b)$ and $(0, b)$. These four intercepts, $(a, 0)$, $(-a, 0)$, $(0, b)$, and $(0, -b)$, are used to graph the ellipse.

THEOREM **Equation of an Ellipse: Center at (0, 0); Major Axis along the x-Axis**

An equation of the ellipse with center at $(0, 0)$, foci at $(-c, 0)$ and $(c, 0)$, and vertices at $(-a, 0)$ and $(a, 0)$ is

$$\frac{x^2}{a^2} + \frac{y^2}{b^2} = 1 \quad \text{where } a > b > 0 \text{ and } b^2 = a^2 - c^2 \qquad (2)$$

The major axis is the x-axis. See Figure 21.

Figure 21

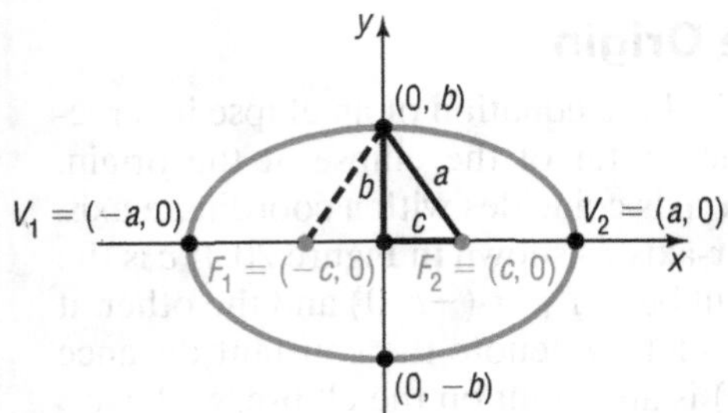

Notice in Figure 21 the right triangle formed with the points $(0, 0)$, $(c, 0)$, and $(0, b)$. Because $b^2 = a^2 - c^2$ (or $b^2 + c^2 = a^2$), the distance from the focus at $(c, 0)$ to the point $(0, b)$ is a.

This can be seen another way. Look at the two right triangles in Figure 21. They are congruent. Do you see why? Because the sum of the distances from the foci to a point on the ellipse is $2a$, it follows that the distance from $(c, 0)$ to $(0, b)$ is a.

EXAMPLE 1 **Finding an Equation of an Ellipse**

Find an equation of the ellipse with center at the origin, one focus at $(3, 0)$, and a vertex at $(-4, 0)$. Graph the equation.

Figure 22 $\frac{x^2}{16} + \frac{y^2}{7} = 1$

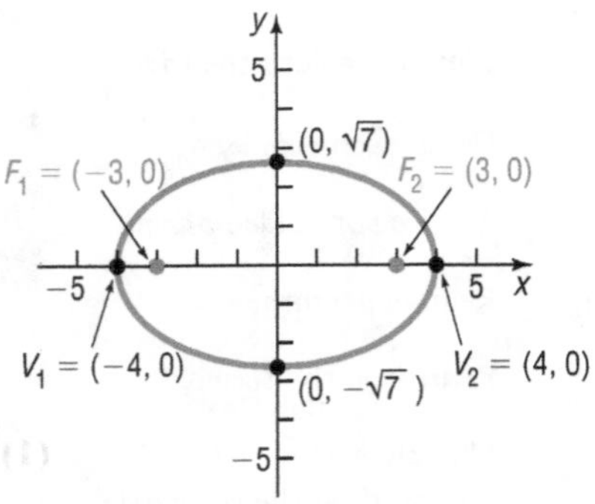

Solution The ellipse has its center at the origin and, since the given focus and vertex lie on the x-axis, the major axis is the x-axis. The distance from the center, $(0, 0)$, to one of the foci, $(3, 0)$, is $c = 3$. The distance from the center, $(0, 0)$, to one of the vertices, $(-4, 0)$, is $a = 4$. Because the center is the origin, the other focus is $(-3, 0)$ and the other vertex is $(4, 0)$. With $a = 4$ and $c = 3$, from equation (2), it follows that

$$b^2 = a^2 - c^2 = 16 - 9 = 7$$

so an equation of the ellipse is

$$\frac{x^2}{16} + \frac{y^2}{7} = 1$$

The y-intercepts are $(0, \pm b) = (0, \pm\sqrt{7})$. Figure 22 shows the graph.

Notice in Figure 22 how we used the intercepts of the equation to graph the ellipse. Following this practice will make it easier for you to obtain an accurate graph of an ellipse when graphing by hand. The intercepts also tell you how to set the initial viewing window when using a graphing utility.

Now Work PROBLEM 27

EXAMPLE 2 Graphing an Ellipse Using a Graphing Utility

Use a graphing utility to graph the ellipse $\frac{x^2}{16} + \frac{y^2}{7} = 1$.

Solution First, we must solve $\frac{x^2}{16} + \frac{y^2}{7} = 1$ for y.

$$\frac{y^2}{7} = 1 - \frac{x^2}{16} \quad \text{Subtract } \frac{x^2}{16} \text{ from each side.}$$

$$y^2 = 7\left(1 - \frac{x^2}{16}\right) \quad \text{Multiply both sides by 7.}$$

$$y = \pm\sqrt{7\left(1 - \frac{x^2}{16}\right)} \quad \text{Apply the Square Root Method.}$$

Figure 23

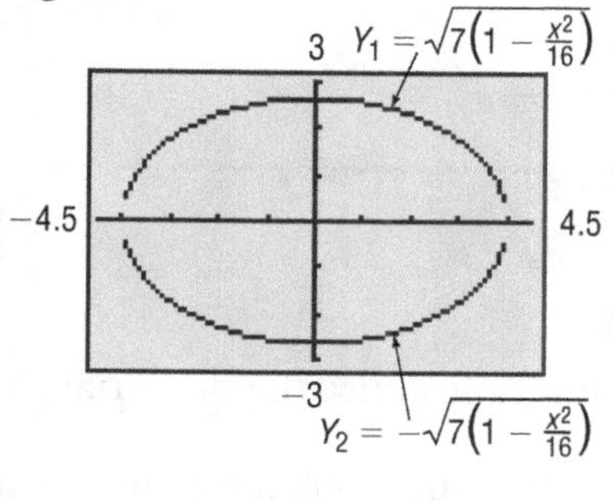

Figure 23* shows the graphs of $Y_1 = \sqrt{7\left(1 - \frac{x^2}{16}\right)}$ and $Y_2 = -\sqrt{7\left(1 - \frac{x^2}{16}\right)}$.

Notice in Figure 23 that we used a square screen. As with circles and parabolas, this is done to avoid a distorted view of the graph.

An equation of the form of equation (2), with $a > b$, is the equation of an ellipse with center at the origin, foci on the x-axis at $(-c, 0)$ and $(c, 0)$, where $c^2 = a^2 - b^2$, and major axis along the x-axis.

For the remainder of this section, the direction **"Analyze the equation"** will mean to find the center, major axis, foci, and vertices of the ellipse and graph it.

EXAMPLE 3 Analyzing the Equation of an Ellipse

Analyze the equation: $\frac{x^2}{25} + \frac{y^2}{9} = 1$

Solution The given equation is of the form of equation (2), with $a^2 = 25$ and $b^2 = 9$. The equation is that of an ellipse with center $(0, 0)$ and major axis along the x-axis. The vertices are at $(\pm a, 0) = (\pm 5, 0)$. Because $b^2 = a^2 - c^2$, we find that

$$c^2 = a^2 - b^2 = 25 - 9 = 16$$

The foci are at $(\pm c, 0) = (\pm 4, 0)$. The y-intercepts are $(0, \pm b) = (0, \pm 3)$. Figure 24(a) shows the graph drawn by hand. Figure 24(b) shows the graph obtained using a graphing utility.

Figure 24

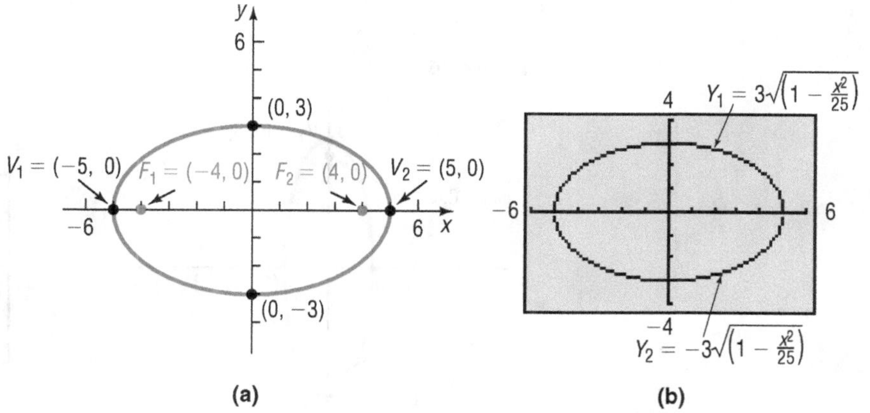

Now Work PROBLEM 17

*The initial viewing window selected was $X\text{min} = -4$, $X\text{max} = 4$, $Y\text{min} = -3$, $Y\text{max} = 3$. Then we used the ZOOM-SQUARE option to obtain the window shown.

If the major axis of an ellipse with center at $(0, 0)$ lies on the y-axis, then the foci are at $(0, -c)$ and $(0, c)$. Using the same steps as before, the definition of an ellipse leads to the following result:

THEOREM

Equation of an Ellipse; Center at (0, 0); Major Axis along the y-Axis

An equation of the ellipse with center at $(0, 0)$, foci at $(0, -c)$ and $(0, c)$, and vertices at $(0, -a)$ and $(0, a)$ is

$$\frac{x^2}{b^2} + \frac{y^2}{a^2} = 1 \qquad \text{where } a > b > 0 \text{ and } b^2 = a^2 - c^2 \tag{3}$$

The major axis is the y-axis.

Figure 25

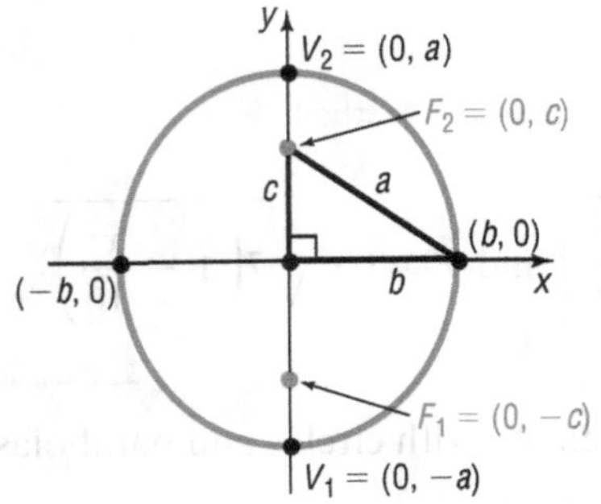

Figure 25 illustrates the graph of such an ellipse. Again, notice the right triangle with the points at $(0, 0)$, $(b, 0)$, and $(0, c)$.

Look closely at equations (2) and (3). Although they may look alike, there is a difference! In equation (2), the larger number, a^2, is in the denominator of the x^2-term, so the major axis of the ellipse is along the x-axis. In equation (3), the larger number, a^2, is in the denominator of the y^2-term, so the major axis is along the y-axis.

EXAMPLE 4 **Analyzing the Equation of an Ellipse**

Analyze the equation: $9x^2 + y^2 = 9$

Solution To put the equation in proper form, we divide each side by 9.

$$x^2 + \frac{y^2}{9} = 1$$

The larger number, 9, is in the denominator of the y^2 term so, based on equation (3), this is the equation of an ellipse with center at the origin and major axis along the y-axis. Also, we conclude that $a^2 = 9$, $b^2 = 1$, and $c^2 = a^2 - b^2 = 9 - 1 = 8$. The vertices are at $(0, \pm a) = (0, \pm 3)$, and the foci are at $(0, \pm c) = (0, \pm 2\sqrt{2})$. The x-intercepts are at $(\pm b, 0) = (\pm 1, 0)$. Figure 26(a) shows the graph drawn by hand. Figure 26(b) shows the graph obtained using a graphing utility.

Figure 26

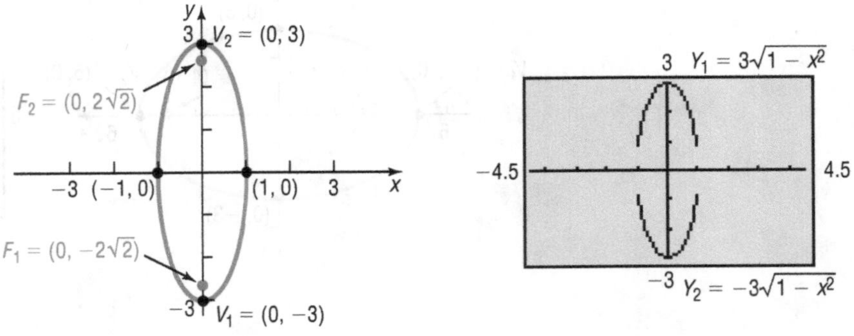

(a) (b)

Now Work PROBLEM 21

EXAMPLE 5 **Finding an Equation of an Ellipse**

Find an equation of the ellipse having one focus at $(0, 2)$ and vertices at $(0, -3)$ and $(0, 3)$. Graph the equation by hand.

Solution Because the vertices are at $(0, -3)$ and $(0, 3)$, the center of this ellipse is at their midpoint, the origin. The vertices and foci lie on the y-axis, so the major axis lies on the y-axis. The distance from the center, $(0, 0)$, to one of the foci, $(0, 2)$, is $c = 2$. The distance from the center, $(0, 0)$, to one of the vertices, $(0, 3)$, is $a = 3$. So $b^2 = a^2 - c^2 = 9 - 4 = 5$. The form of the equation of this ellipse is given by equation (3).

$$\frac{x^2}{b^2} + \frac{y^2}{a^2} = 1$$

$$\frac{x^2}{5} + \frac{y^2}{9} = 1$$

Figure 27

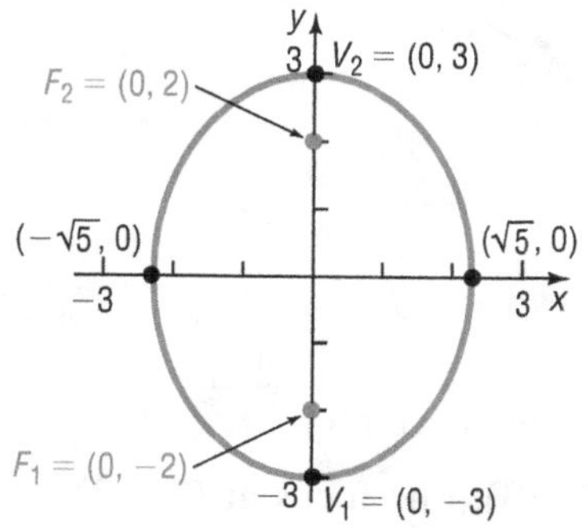

Figure 27 shows the graph.

Now Work PROBLEM 29

The circle may be considered a special kind of ellipse. To see why, let $a = b$ in equation (2) or (3). Then

$$\frac{x^2}{a^2} + \frac{y^2}{a^2} = 1$$

$$x^2 + y^2 = a^2$$

This is the equation of a circle with center at the origin and radius a. The value of c is

$$c^2 = a^2 - b^2 = 0$$

We conclude that the closer the two foci of an ellipse are to the center the more the ellipse will look like a circle.

2 Analyze Ellipses with Center at (h, k)

If an ellipse with center at the origin and major axis coinciding with a coordinate axis is shifted horizontally h units and then vertically k units, the result is an ellipse with center at (h, k) and major axis parallel to a coordinate axis. The equations of such ellipses have the same forms as those given in equations (2) and (3), except that x is replaced by $x - h$ (the horizontal shift) and y is replaced by $y - k$ (the vertical shift). Table 3 gives the forms of the equations of such ellipses and Figure 28 on the next page shows their graphs.

Table 3

ELLIPSES WITH CENTER AT (h, k) AND MAJOR AXIS PARALLEL TO A COORDINATE AXIS

Center	Major Axis	Foci	Vertices	Equation
(h, k)	Parallel to x-axis	$(h + c, k)$	$(h + a, k)$	$\frac{(x-h)^2}{a^2} + \frac{(y-k)^2}{b^2} = 1,$
		$(h - c, k)$	$(h - a, k)$	$a > b$ and $b^2 = a^2 - c^2$
(h, k)	Parallel to y-axis	$(h, k + c)$	$(h, k + a)$	$\frac{(x-h)^2}{b^2} + \frac{(y-k)^2}{a^2} = 1,$
		$(h, k - c)$	$(h, k - a)$	$a > b$ and $b^2 = a^2 - c^2$

Figure 28

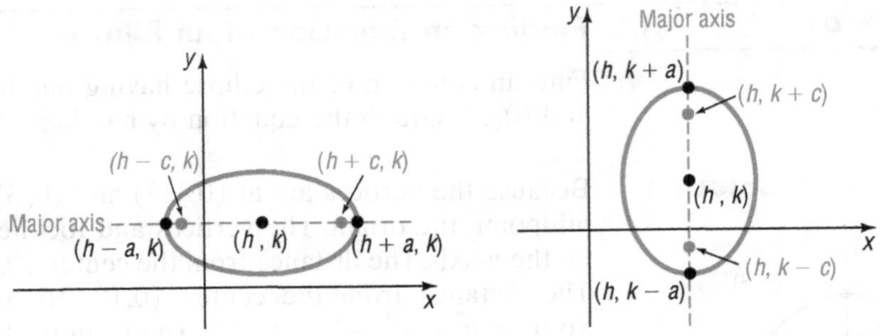

(a) $\dfrac{(x-h)^2}{a^2}+\dfrac{(y-k)^2}{b^2}=1$ **(b)** $\dfrac{(x-h)^2}{b^2}+\dfrac{(y-k)^2}{a^2}=1$

EXAMPLE 6 Finding an Equation of an Ellipse, Center Not at the Origin

Find an equation for the ellipse with center at $(2, -3)$, one focus at $(3, -3)$, and one vertex at $(5, -3)$. Graph the equation by hand.

Solution The center is at $(h, k) = (2, -3)$, so $h = 2$ and $k = -3$. Since the center, focus, and vertex all lie on the line $y = -3$, the major axis is parallel to the x-axis. The distance from the center $(2, -3)$ to a focus $(3, -3)$ is $c = 1$; the distance from the center $(2, -3)$ to a vertex $(5, -3)$ is $a = 3$. Then $b^2 = a^2 - c^2 = 9 - 1 = 8$. The form of the equation is

$$\frac{(x-h)^2}{a^2}+\frac{(y-k)^2}{b^2}=1 \qquad \text{where } h = 2, k = -3, a = 3, b = 2\sqrt{2}$$

$$\frac{(x-2)^2}{9}+\frac{(y+3)^2}{8}=1$$

To graph the equation, we use the center $(h, k) = (2, -3)$ to locate the vertices. The major axis is parallel to the x-axis, so the vertices are $a = 3$ units left and right of the center $(2, -3)$. Therefore, the vertices are

$$V_1 = (2-3, -3) = (-1, -3) \quad \text{and} \quad V_2 = (2+3, -3) = (5, -3)$$

Since $c = 1$ and the major axis is parallel to the x-axis, the foci are 1 unit left and right of the center. Therefore, the foci are

$$F_1 = (2-1, -3) = (1, -3) \quad \text{and} \quad F_2 = (2+1, -3) = (3, -3)$$

Finally, we use the value of $b = 2\sqrt{2}$ to find the two points above and below the center.

$$\left(2, -3 - 2\sqrt{2}\right) \quad \text{and} \quad \left(2, -3 + 2\sqrt{2}\right)$$

Figure 29 shows the graph.

Figure 29

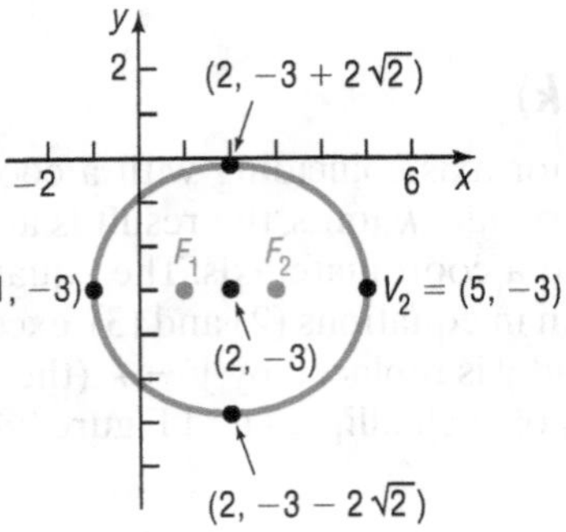

Now Work PROBLEM 55

EXAMPLE 7 Using a Graphing Utility to Graph an Ellipse, Center Not at the Origin

Using a graphing utility, graph the ellipse: $\dfrac{(x-2)^2}{9}+\dfrac{(y+3)^2}{8}=1$

Solution First, we must solve the equation $\frac{(x-2)^2}{9} + \frac{(y+3)^2}{8} = 1$ for y.

$$\frac{(y+3)^2}{8} = 1 - \frac{(x-2)^2}{9} \qquad \text{Subtract } \frac{(x-2)^2}{9} \text{ from each side.}$$

$$(y+3)^2 = 8\left[1 - \frac{(x-2)^2}{9}\right] \qquad \text{Multiply each side by 8.}$$

$$y + 3 = \pm\sqrt{8\left[1 - \frac{(x-2)^2}{9}\right]} \qquad \text{Apply the Square Root Method.}$$

$$y = -3 \pm \sqrt{8\left[1 - \frac{(x-2)^2}{9}\right]} \qquad \text{Subtract 3 from each side.}$$

Figure 30

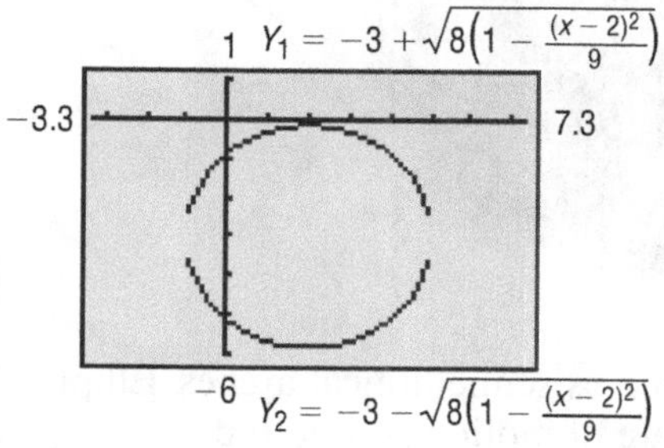

Figure 30 shows the graphs of $Y_1 = -3 + \sqrt{8\left[1 - \frac{(x-2)^2}{9}\right]}$ and $Y_2 = -3 - \sqrt{8\left[1 - \frac{(x-2)^2}{9}\right]}$.

EXAMPLE 8 Analyzing the Equation of an Ellipse

Analyze the equation: $4x^2 + y^2 - 8x + 4y + 4 = 0$

Solution We proceed to complete the squares in x and in y.

$$4x^2 + y^2 - 8x + 4y + 4 = 0$$

$$4x^2 - 8x + y^2 + 4y = -4 \qquad \text{Group like variables; place the constant on the right side.}$$

$$4(x^2 - 2x) + (y^2 + 4y) = -4 \qquad \text{Factor out 4 from the first two terms.}$$

$$4(x^2 - 2x + 1) + (y^2 + 4y + 4) = -4 + 4 + 4 \qquad \text{Complete each square.}$$

$$4(x-1)^2 + (y+2)^2 = 4 \qquad \text{Factor.}$$

$$(x-1)^2 + \frac{(y+2)^2}{4} = 1 \qquad \text{Divide each side by 4.}$$

This is the equation of an ellipse with center at $(1, -2)$ and major axis parallel to the y-axis. Since $a^2 = 4$ and $b^2 = 1$, we have $c^2 = a^2 - b^2 = 4 - 1 = 3$. The vertices are at $(h, k \pm a) = (1, -2 \pm 2)$ or $(1, 0)$ and $(1, -4)$. The foci are at $(h, k \pm c) = (1, -2 \pm \sqrt{3})$ or $(1, -2 - \sqrt{3})$ and $(1, -2 + \sqrt{3})$. Figure 31(a) shows the graph drawn by hand. Figure 31(b) shows the graph obtained using a graphing utility.

Figure 31

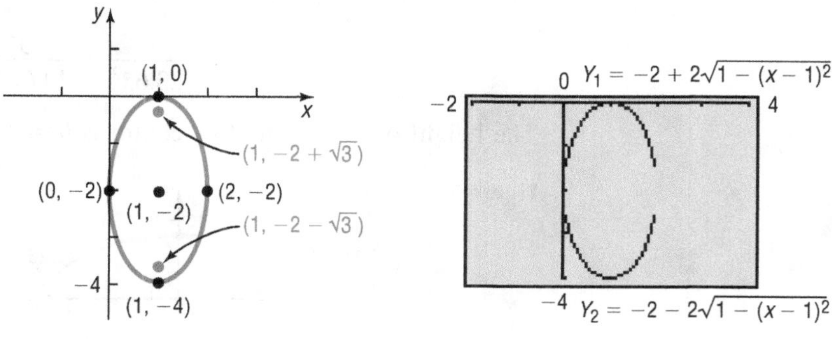

Now Work PROBLEM 47

3 Solve Applied Problems Involving Ellipses

Ellipses are found in many applications in science and engineering. For example, the orbits of the planets around the Sun are elliptical, with the Sun's position at a focus. See Figure 32.

Figure 32

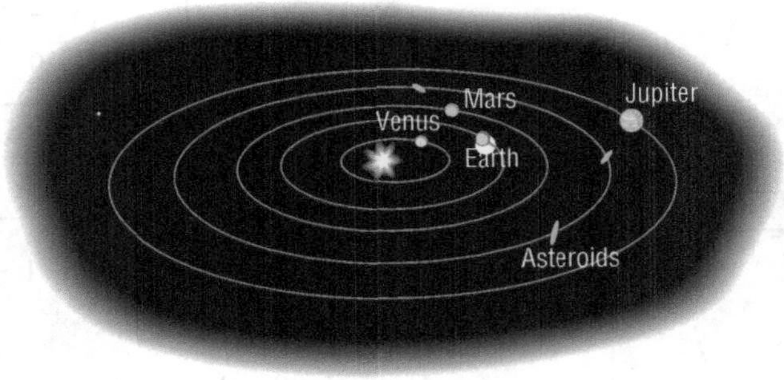

Stone and concrete bridges are often shaped as semielliptical arches. Elliptical gears are used in machinery when a variable rate of motion is required.

Ellipses also have an interesting reflection property. If a source of light (or sound) is placed at one focus, the waves transmitted by the source will reflect off the ellipse and concentrate at the other focus. This is the principle behind *whispering galleries,* which are rooms designed with elliptical ceilings. A person standing at one focus of the ellipse can whisper and be heard by a person standing at the other focus, because all the sound waves that reach the ceiling are reflected to the other person.

EXAMPLE 9 A Whispering Gallery

The whispering gallery in the Museum of Science and Industry in Chicago is 47.3 feet long. The distance from the center of the room to the foci is 20.3 feet. Find an equation that describes the shape of the room. How high is the room at its center?

Source: Chicago Museum of Science and Industry Web site; www.msichicago.org

Solution We set up a rectangular coordinate system so that the center of the ellipse is at the origin and the major axis is along the x-axis. The equation of the ellipse is

$$\frac{x^2}{a^2} + \frac{y^2}{b^2} = 1$$

Since the length of the room is 47.3 feet, the distance from the center of the room to each vertex (the end of the room) will be $\frac{47.3}{2} = 23.65$ feet; so $a = 23.65$ feet. The distance from the center of the room to each focus is $c = 20.3$ feet. See Figure 33.

Since $b^2 = a^2 - c^2$, we find $b^2 = 23.65^2 - 20.3^2 = 147.2325$. An equation that describes the shape of the room is given by

$$\frac{x^2}{23.65^2} + \frac{y^2}{147.2325} = 1$$

The height of the room at its center is $b = \sqrt{147.2325} \approx 12.1$ feet.

Figure 33

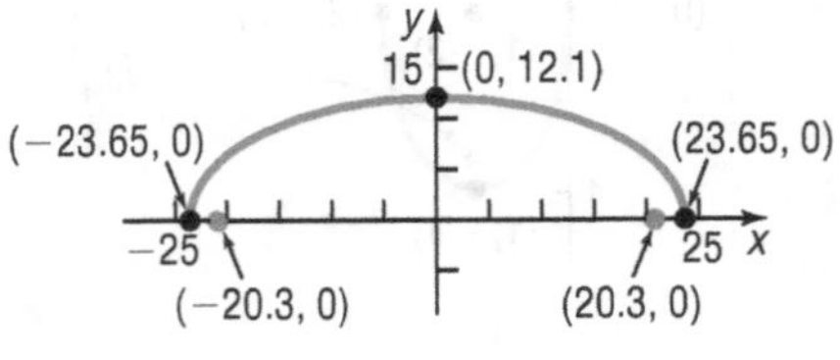

Now Work PROBLEM 71

10.3 Assess Your Understanding

'Are You Prepared?' *Answers are given at the end of these exercises. If you get a wrong answer, read the pages listed in red.*

1. The distance d from $P_1 = (2, -5)$ to $P_2 = (4, -2)$ is $d =$ _____. (pp. 4–6)
2. To complete the square of $x^2 - 3x$, add _____. (p. A52)
3. Find the intercepts of the equation $y^2 = 16 - 4x^2$. (pp. 18–19)
4. The point that is symmetric with respect to the y-axis to the point $(-2, 5)$ is _____. (pp. 19–20)
5. To graph $y = (x + 1)^2 - 4$, shift the graph of $y = x^2$ to the (left/right) _____ unit(s) and then (up/down) _____ unit(s). (pp. 100–102)
6. The standard equation of a circle with center at $(2, -3)$ and radius 1 is _____. (pp. 44–45)

Concepts and Vocabulary

7. A(n) _____ is the collection of all points in the plane the sum of whose distances from two fixed points is a constant.
8. For an ellipse, the foci lie on a line called the _____ axis.
9. For the ellipse $\frac{x^2}{4} + \frac{y^2}{25} = 1$, the vertices are the points _____ and _____.
10. ***True or False*** The foci, vertices, and center of an ellipse lie on a line called the axis of symmetry.
11. ***True or False*** If the center of an ellipse is at the origin and the foci lie on the y-axis, the ellipse is symmetric with respect to the x-axis, the y-axis, and the origin.
12. ***True or False*** A circle is a certain type of ellipse.

Skill Building

In Problems 13–16, the graph of an ellipse is given. Match each graph to its equation.

(A) $\frac{x^2}{4} + y^2 = 1$ (B) $x^2 + \frac{y^2}{4} = 1$ (C) $\frac{x^2}{16} + \frac{y^2}{4} = 1$ (D) $\frac{x^2}{4} + \frac{y^2}{16} = 1$

13.
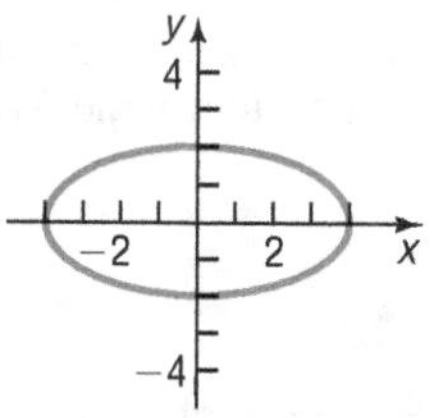

14.
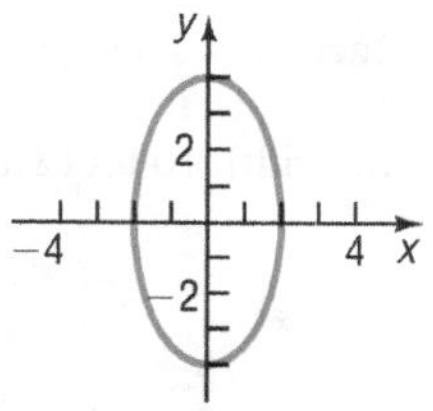

15.
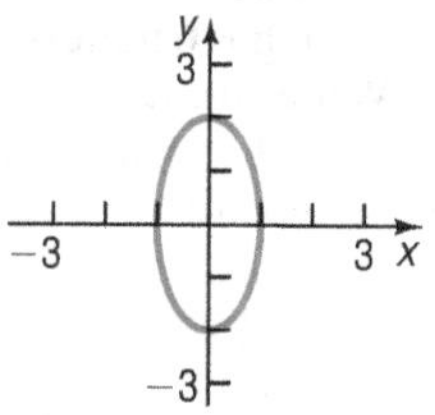

16.
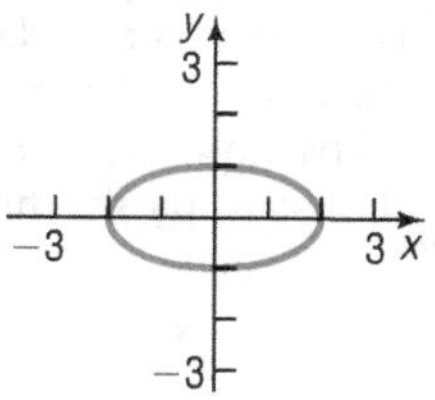

In Problems 17–26, find the vertices and foci of each ellipse. Graph each equation by hand. Verify your graph using a graphing utility.

17. $\frac{x^2}{25} + \frac{y^2}{4} = 1$
18. $\frac{x^2}{9} + \frac{y^2}{4} = 1$
19. $\frac{x^2}{9} + \frac{y^2}{25} = 1$
20. $x^2 + \frac{y^2}{16} = 1$
21. $4x^2 + y^2 = 16$
22. $x^2 + 9y^2 = 18$
23. $4y^2 + x^2 = 8$
24. $4y^2 + 9x^2 = 36$
25. $x^2 + y^2 = 16$
26. $x^2 + y^2 = 4$

In Problems 27–38, find an equation for each ellipse. Graph the equation by hand.

27. Center at $(0, 0)$; focus at $(3, 0)$; vertex at $(5, 0)$
28. Center at $(0, 0)$; focus at $(-1, 0)$; vertex at $(3, 0)$
29. Center at $(0, 0)$; focus at $(0, -4)$; vertex at $(0, 5)$
30. Center at $(0, 0)$; focus at $(0, 1)$; vertex at $(0, -2)$
31. Foci at $(\pm 2, 0)$; length of the major axis is 6
32. Foci at $(0, \pm 2)$; length of the major axis is 8
33. Focus at $(-4, 0)$; vertices at $(\pm 5, 0)$
34. Focus at $(0, -4)$; vertices at $(0, \pm 8)$
35. Foci at $(0, \pm 3)$; x-intercepts are ± 2
36. Vertices at $(\pm 4, 0)$; y-intercepts are ± 1
37. Center at $(0, 0)$; vertex at $(0, 4)$; $b = 1$
38. Vertices at $(\pm 5, 0)$; $c = 2$

In Problems 39–42, write an equation for each ellipse.

39.
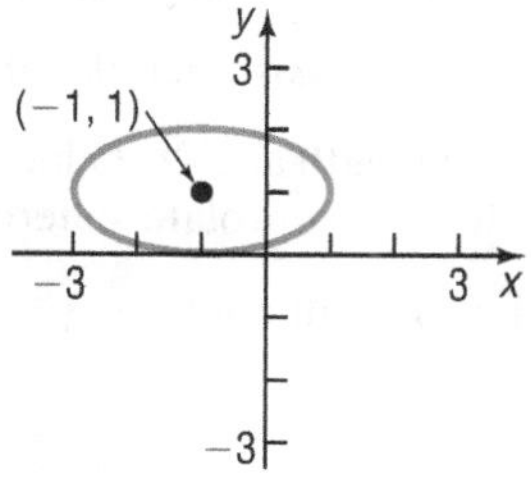

40.
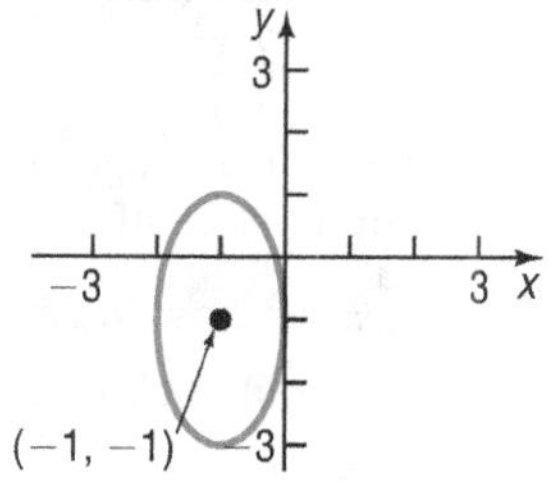

41.
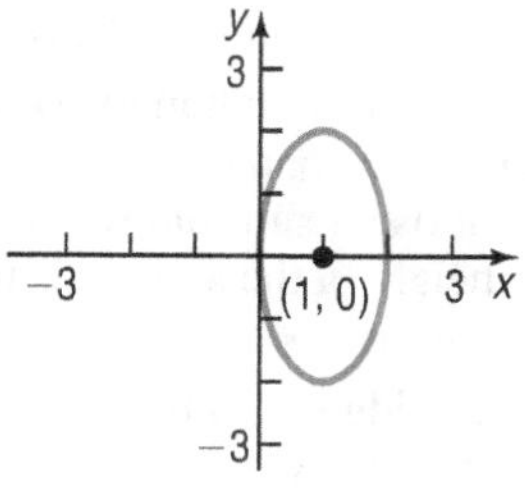

42.
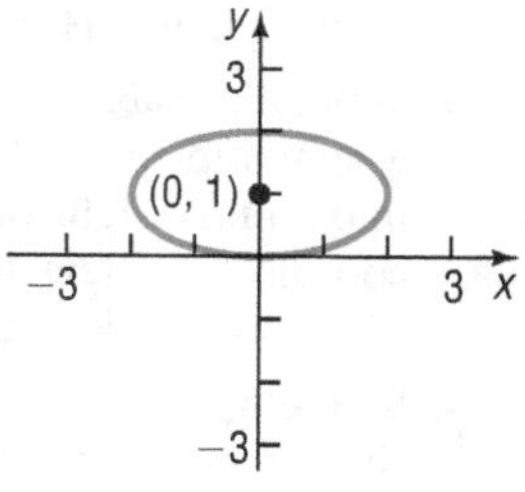

In Problems 43–54, analyze each equation; that is, find the center, foci, and vertices of each ellipse. Graph each equation by hand. Verify your graph using a graphing utility.

43. $\frac{(x-3)^2}{4} + \frac{(y+1)^2}{9} = 1$

44. $\frac{(x+4)^2}{9} + \frac{(y+2)^2}{4} = 1$

45. $(x+5)^2 + 4(y-4)^2 = 16$

46. $9(x-3)^2 + (y+2)^2 = 18$

47. $x^2 + 4x + 4y^2 - 8y + 4 = 0$

48. $x^2 + 3y^2 - 12y + 9 = 0$

49. $2x^2 + 3y^2 - 8x + 6y + 5 = 0$

50. $4x^2 + 3y^2 + 8x - 6y = 5$

51. $9x^2 + 4y^2 - 18x + 16y - 11 = 0$

52. $x^2 + 9y^2 + 6x - 18y + 9 = 0$

53. $4x^2 + y^2 + 4y = 0$

54. $9x^2 + y^2 - 18x = 0$

In Problems 55–64, find an equation for each ellipse. Graph the equation by hand.

55. Center at $(2, -2)$; vertex at $(7, -2)$; focus at $(4, -2)$

56. Center at $(-3, 1)$; vertex at $(-3, 3)$; focus at $(-3, 0)$

57. Vertices at $(4, 3)$ and $(4, 9)$; focus at $(4, 8)$

58. Foci at $(1, 2)$ and $(-3, 2)$; vertex at $(-4, 2)$

59. Foci at $(5, 1)$ and $(-1, 1)$; length of the major axis is 8

60. Vertices at $(2, 5)$ and $(2, -1)$; $c = 2$

61. Center at $(1, 2)$; focus at $(4, 2)$; contains the point $(1, 3)$

62. Center at $(1, 2)$; focus at $(1, 4)$; contains the point $(2, 2)$

63. Center at $(1, 2)$; vertex at $(4, 2)$; contains the point $(1, 3)$

64. Center at $(1, 2)$; vertex at $(1, 4)$; contains the point $(2, 2)$

In Problems 65–68, graph each function. Be sure to label all the intercepts.
[**Hint:** *Notice that each function is half an ellipse.*]

65. $f(x) = \sqrt{16 - 4x^2}$

66. $f(x) = \sqrt{9 - 9x^2}$

67. $f(x) = -\sqrt{64 - 16x^2}$

68. $f(x) = -\sqrt{4 - 4x^2}$

Applications and Extensions

69. Semielliptical Arch Bridge An arch in the shape of the upper half of an ellipse is used to support a bridge that is to span a river 20 meters wide. The center of the arch is 6 meters above the center of the river. See the figure. Write an equation for the ellipse in which the x-axis coincides with the water level and the y-axis passes through the center of the arch.

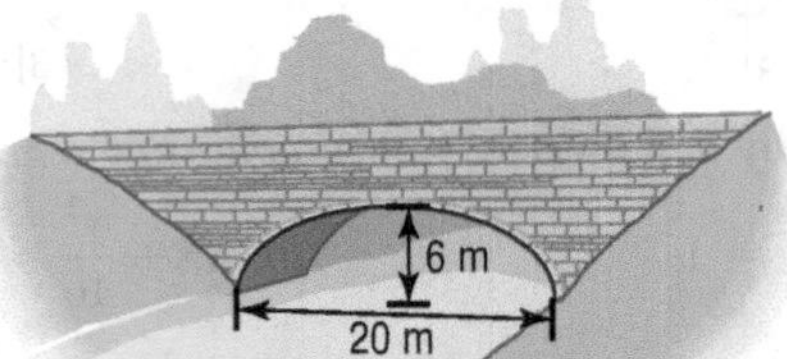

70. Semielliptical Arch Bridge The arch of a bridge is a semiellipse with a horizontal major axis. The span is 30 feet, and the top of the arch is 10 feet above the major axis. The roadway is horizontal and is 2 feet above the top of the arch. Find the vertical distance from the roadway to the arch at 5-foot intervals along the roadway.

71. Whispering Gallery A hall 100 feet in length is to be designed as a whispering gallery. If the foci are located 25 feet from the center, how high will the ceiling be at the center?

72. Whispering Gallery Jim, standing at one focus of a whispering gallery, is 6 feet from the nearest wall. His friend is standing at the other focus, 100 feet away. What is the length of this whispering gallery? How high is its elliptical ceiling at the center?

73. Semielliptical Arch Bridge A bridge is built in the shape of a semielliptical arch. The bridge has a span of 120 feet and a maximum height of 25 feet. Choose a suitable rectangular coordinate system and find the height of the arch at distances of 10, 30, and 50 feet from the center.

74. Semielliptical Arch Bridge A bridge is to be built in the shape of a semielliptical arch and is to have a span of 100 feet. The height of the arch, at a distance of 40 feet from the center, is to be 10 feet. Find the height of the arch at its center.

75. Racetrack Design Consult the figure. A racetrack is in the shape of an ellipse, 100 feet long and 50 feet wide. What is the width 10 feet from a vertex?

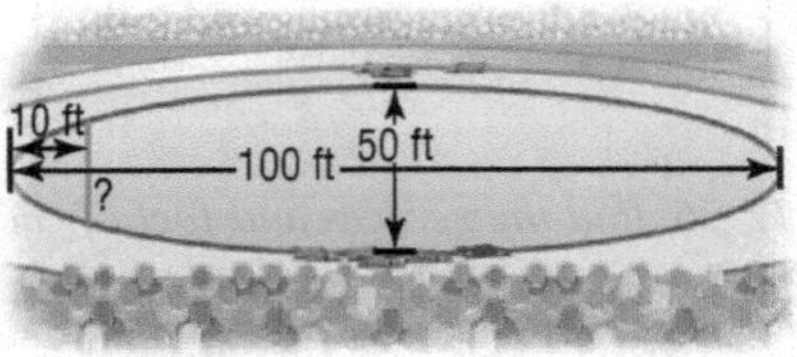

76. Semielliptical Arch Bridge An arch for a bridge over a highway is in the form of half an ellipse. The top of the arch is 20 feet above the ground level (the major axis). The highway has four lanes, each 12 feet wide; a center safety strip 8 feet wide; and two side strips, each 4 feet wide. What should the span of the bridge be (the length of its major axis) if the height 28 feet from the center is to be 13 feet?

77. Installing a Vent Pipe A homeowner is putting in a fireplace that has a 4-inch-radius vent pipe. He needs to cut an elliptical hole in his roof to accommodate the pipe. If the pitch of his roof is $\frac{5}{4}$ (a rise of 5, run of 4), what are the dimensions of the hole?

Source: www.pen.k12.va.us

78. Volume of a Football A football is in the shape of a **prolate spheroid,** which is simply a solid obtained by rotating an ellipse $\left(\frac{x^2}{a^2} + \frac{y^2}{b^2} = 1\right)$ about its major axis. An inflated NFL football averages 11.125 inches in length and 28.25 inches in center circumference. If the volume of a prolate spheroid is $\frac{4}{3}\pi ab^2$, how much air does the football contain? (Neglect material thickness.)

Source: www.answerbag.com

In Problems 79–82, use the fact that the orbit of a planet about the Sun is an ellipse, with the Sun at one focus. The ***aphelion*** *of a planet is its greatest distance from the Sun, and the* ***perihelion*** *is its shortest distance. The* ***mean distance*** *of a planet from the Sun is the length of the semimajor axis of the elliptical orbit. See the illustration.*

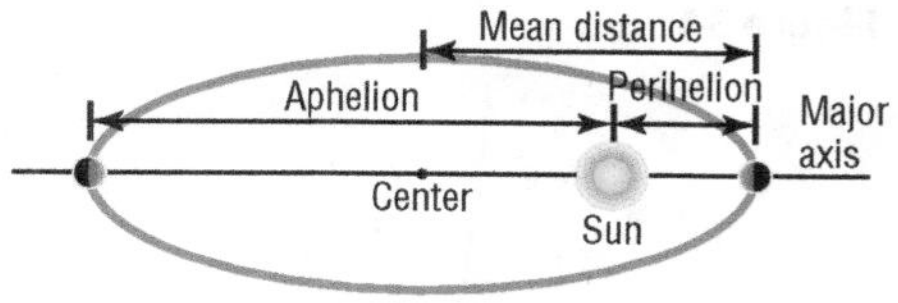

79. **Earth** The mean distance of Earth from the Sun is 93 million miles. If the aphelion of Earth is 94.5 million miles, what is the perihelion? Write an equation for the orbit of Earth around the Sun.

80. **Mars** The mean distance of Mars from the Sun is 142 million miles. If the perihelion of Mars is 128.5 million miles, what is the aphelion? Write an equation for the orbit of Mars about the Sun.

81. **Jupiter** The aphelion of Jupiter is 507 million miles. If the distance from the center of its elliptical orbit to the Sun is 23.2 million miles, what is the perihelion? What is the mean distance? Write an equation for the orbit of Jupiter around the Sun.

82. **Pluto** The perihelion of Pluto is 4551 million miles, and the distance from the center of its elliptical orbit to the Sun is 897.5 million miles. Find the aphelion of Pluto. What is the mean distance of Pluto from the Sun? Write an equation for the orbit of Pluto about the Sun.

83. Show that an equation of the form

$$Ax^2 + Cy^2 + F = 0 \qquad A \neq 0, C \neq 0, F \neq 0$$

where A and C are of the same sign and F is of opposite sign,
(a) Is the equation of an ellipse with center at $(0, 0)$ if $A \neq C$.
(b) Is the equation of a circle with center $(0, 0)$ if $A = C$.

84. Show that the graph of an equation of the form

$$Ax^2 + Cy^2 + Dx + Ey + F = 0 \qquad A \neq 0, C \neq 0$$

where A and C are of the same sign,
(a) Is an ellipse if $\frac{D^2}{4A} + \frac{E^2}{4C} - F$ is the same sign as A.
(b) Is a point if $\frac{D^2}{4A} + \frac{E^2}{4C} - F = 0$.
(c) Contains no points if $\frac{D^2}{4A} + \frac{E^2}{4C} - F$ is of opposite sign to A.

Discussion and Writing

85. The **eccentricity** e of an ellipse is defined as the number $\frac{c}{a}$, where a and c are the numbers given in equation (2). Because $a > c$, it follows that $e < 1$. Write a brief paragraph about the general shape of each of the following ellipses. Be sure to justify your conclusions.
(a) Eccentricity close to 0 (b) Eccentricity $= 0.5$ (c) Eccentricity close to 1

'Are You Prepared?' Answers

1. $\sqrt{13}$ **2.** $\frac{9}{4}$ **3.** $(-2, 0), (2, 0), (0, -4), (0, 4)$ **4.** $(2, 5)$ **5.** left; 1; down: 4 **6.** $(x - 2)^2 + (y + 3)^2 = 1$

10.4 The Hyperbola

PREPARING FOR THIS SECTION *Before getting started, review the following:*

- Distance Formula (Section 1.1, p. 5)
- Completing the Square (Appendix A, Section A.6, pp. A52–A53)
- Intercepts (Section 1.2, pp. 18–19)
- Symmetry (Section 1.2, pp. 19–21)
- Asymptotes (Section 4.2, pp. 194–199)
- Graphing Techniques: Transformations (Section 2.5, pp. 100–108)
- Square Root Method (Appendix A, Section A.6, p. A51)

Now Work the 'Are You Prepared?' problems on page 670.

OBJECTIVES
1. Analyze Hyperbolas with Center at the Origin (p. 660)
2. Find the Asymptotes of a Hyperbola (p. 665)
3. Analyze Hyperbolas with Center at (h, k) (p. 666)
4. Solve Applied Problems Involving Hyperbolas (p. 668)

DEFINITION A **hyperbola** is the set of all points P in the plane, the difference of whose distances from two fixed points, called the **foci,** is a constant.

Figure 34

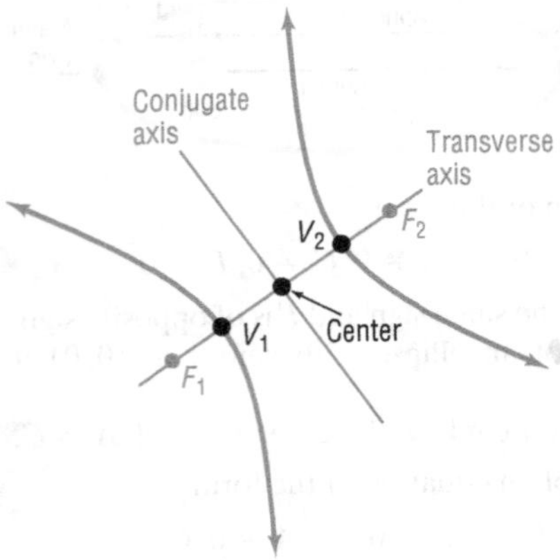

Figure 34 illustrates a hyperbola with foci F_1 and F_2. The line containing the foci is called the **transverse axis.** The midpoint of the line segment joining the foci is the **center** of the hyperbola. The line through the center and perpendicular to the transverse axis is the **conjugate axis.** The hyperbola consists of two separate curves, called **branches,** that are symmetric with respect to the transverse axis, conjugate axis, and center. The two points of intersection of the hyperbola and the transverse axis are the **vertices,** V_1 and V_2, of the hyperbola.

1 Analyze Hyperbolas with Center at the Origin

With these ideas in mind, we are now ready to find the equation of a hyperbola in the rectangular coordinate system. First, we place the center at the origin. Next, we position the hyperbola so that its transverse axis coincides with a coordinate axis. Suppose that the transverse axis coincides with the x-axis, as shown in Figure 35.

Figure 35
$d(F_1, P) - d(F_2, P) = \pm 2a$

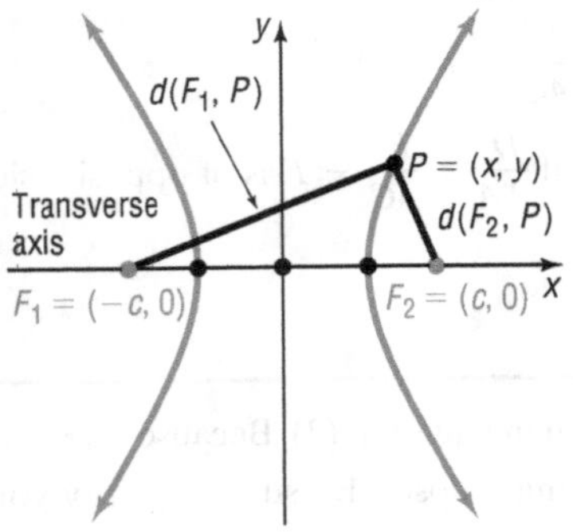

If c is the distance from the center to a focus, one focus will be at $F_1 = (-c, 0)$ and the other at $F_2 = (c, 0)$. Now we let the constant difference of the distances from any point $P = (x, y)$ on the hyperbola to the foci F_1 and F_2 be denoted by $\pm 2a$. (If P is on the right branch, the + sign is used; if P is on the left branch, the − sign is used.) The coordinates of P must satisfy the equation

$$d(F_1, P) - d(F_2, P) = \pm 2a$$ Difference of the distances from P to the foci equals $\pm 2a$.

$$\sqrt{(x + c)^2 + y^2} - \sqrt{(x - c)^2 + y^2} = \pm 2a$$ Use the Distance Formula.

$$\sqrt{(x + c)^2 + y^2} = \pm 2a + \sqrt{(x - c)^2 + y^2}$$ Isolate one radical.

$$(x + c)^2 + y^2 = 4a^2 \pm 4a\sqrt{(x - c)^2 + y^2} + (x - c)^2 + y^2$$ Square both sides.

Next we remove the parentheses by expanding the binomials.

$$x^2 + 2cx + c^2 + y^2 = 4a^2 \pm 4a\sqrt{(x - c)^2 + y^2} + x^2 - 2cx + c^2 + y^2$$

$$4cx - 4a^2 = \pm 4a\sqrt{(x - c)^2 + y^2}$$ Simplify; isolate the radical.

$$cx - a^2 = \pm a\sqrt{(x - c)^2 + y^2}$$ Divide each side by 4.

$$(cx - a^2)^2 = a^2[(x - c)^2 + y^2]$$ Square both sides.

$$c^2x^2 - 2ca^2x + a^4 = a^2(x^2 - 2cx + c^2 + y^2)$$ Simplify.

$$c^2x^2 + a^4 = a^2x^2 + a^2c^2 + a^2y^2$$ Distribute and simplify.

$$(c^2 - a^2)x^2 - a^2y^2 = a^2c^2 - a^4$$ Rearrange terms.

$$(c^2 - a^2)x^2 - a^2y^2 = a^2(c^2 - a^2) \quad (1)$$ Factor a^2 on the right side.

To obtain points on the hyperbola off the x-axis, it must be that $a < c$. To see why, look again at Figure 35.

$$d(F_1, P) < d(F_2, P) + d(F_1, F_2)$$ Use triangle F_1PF_2.

$$d(F_1, P) - d(F_2, P) < d(F_1, F_2)$$

$$2a < 2c$$ P is on the right branch, so $d(F_1, P) - d(F_2, P) = 2a$; $d(F_1, F_2) = 2c$.

$$a < c$$

Since $a < c$, we also have $a^2 < c^2$, so $c^2 - a^2 > 0$. Let $b^2 = c^2 - a^2, b > 0$. Then equation (1) can be written as

$$b^2x^2 - a^2y^2 = a^2b^2$$

$$\frac{x^2}{a^2} - \frac{y^2}{b^2} = 1 \qquad \text{Divide each side by } a^2b^2.$$

To find the vertices of the hyperbola defined by this equation, let $y = 0$. The vertices satisfy the equation $\frac{x^2}{a^2} = 1$, the solutions of which are $x = \pm a$. Consequently, the vertices of the hyperbola are $V_1 = (-a, 0)$ and $V_2 = (a, 0)$. Notice that the distance from the center $(0, 0)$ to either vertex is a.

THEOREM

Equation of a Hyperbola: Center at (0, 0); Transverse Axis along the *x*-Axis

An equation of the hyperbola with center at $(0, 0)$, foci at $(-c, 0)$ and $(c, 0)$, and vertices at $(-a, 0)$ and $(a, 0)$ is

$$\frac{x^2}{a^2} - \frac{y^2}{b^2} = 1 \quad \text{where } b^2 = c^2 - a^2 \qquad (2)$$

The transverse axis is the x-axis.

Figure 36

$\frac{x^2}{a^2} - \frac{y^2}{b^2} = 1, \quad b^2 = c^2 - a^2$

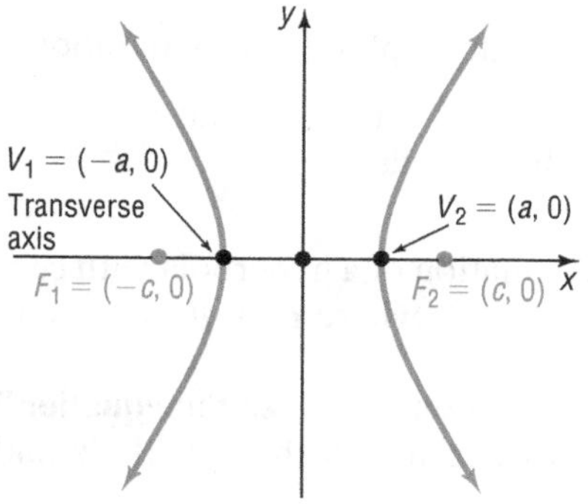

See Figure 36. As you can verify, the hyperbola defined by equation (2) is symmetric with respect to the x-axis, y-axis, and origin. To find the y-intercepts, if any, let $x = 0$ in equation (2). This results in the equation $\frac{y^2}{b^2} = -1$, which has no real solution. We conclude that the hyperbola defined by equation (2) has no y-intercepts. In fact, since $\frac{x^2}{a^2} - 1 = \frac{y^2}{b^2} \geq 0$, it follows that $\frac{x^2}{a^2} \geq 1$. There are no points on the graph for $-a < x < a$.

EXAMPLE 1 **Finding and Graphing an Equation of a Hyperbola**

Find an equation of the hyperbola with center at the origin, one focus at $(3, 0)$, and one vertex at $(-2, 0)$. Graph the equation.

Solution The hyperbola has its center at the origin. Because the focus and vertex lie on the x-axis, the transverse axis coincides with the x-axis. One focus is at $(c, 0) = (3, 0)$, so $c = 3$. One vertex is at $(-a, 0) = (-2, 0)$, so $a = 2$. From equation (2), it follows that $b^2 = c^2 - a^2 = 9 - 4 = 5$, so an equation of the hyperbola is

$$\frac{x^2}{4} - \frac{y^2}{5} = 1$$

To graph a hyperbola, it is helpful to locate and plot other points on the graph. For example, to find the points above and below the foci, we let $x = \pm 3$. Then

$$\frac{x^2}{4} - \frac{y^2}{5} = 1$$

$$\frac{(\pm 3)^2}{4} - \frac{y^2}{5} = 1 \qquad x = \pm 3$$

$$\frac{9}{4} - \frac{y^2}{5} = 1$$

Figure 37

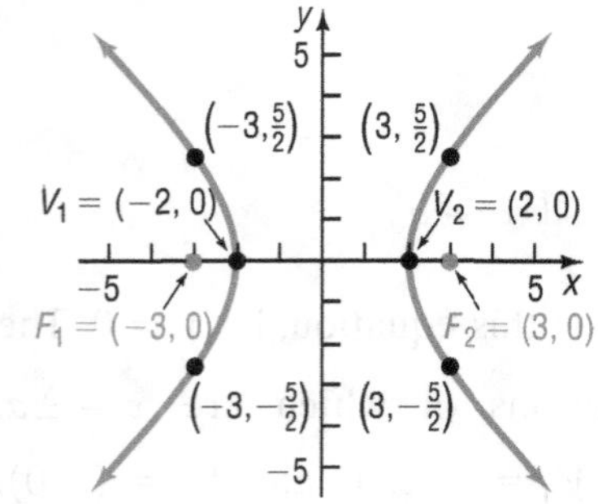

$$\frac{y^2}{5} = \frac{5}{4}$$
$$y^2 = \frac{25}{4}$$
$$y = \pm\frac{5}{2}$$

The points above and below the foci are $\left(\pm 3, \frac{5}{2}\right)$ and $\left(\pm 3, -\frac{5}{2}\right)$. These points determine the "opening" of the hyperbola. See Figure 37.

Now Work PROBLEM 17

EXAMPLE 2 Using a Graphing Utility to Graph a Hyperbola

Using a graphing utility, graph the hyperbola: $\frac{x^2}{4} - \frac{y^2}{5} = 1$

Solution To graph the hyperbola $\frac{x^2}{4} - \frac{y^2}{5} = 1$, we need to graph the two functions $Y_1 = \sqrt{5}\sqrt{\frac{x^2}{4} - 1}$ and $Y_2 = -\sqrt{5}\sqrt{\frac{x^2}{4} - 1}$. As with graphing circles, parabolas, and ellipses on a graphing utility, we use a square screen setting so that the graph is not distorted. Figure 38 shows the graph of the hyperbola.

Figure 38

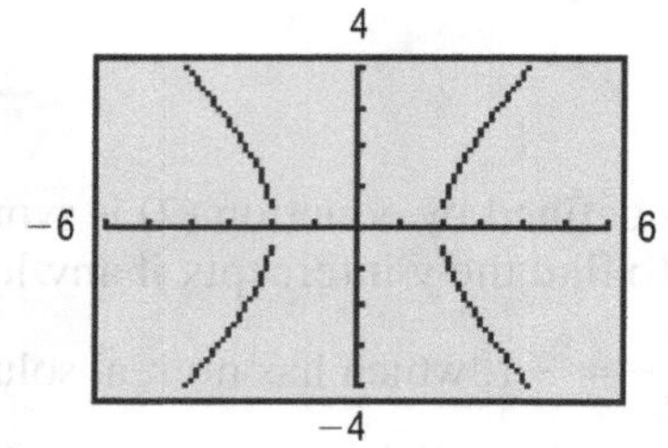

An equation of the form of equation (2) is the equation of a hyperbola with center at the origin, foci on the x-axis at $(-c, 0)$ and $(c, 0)$, where $c^2 = a^2 + b^2$, and transverse axis along the x-axis.

For the next two examples of this section, the direction **"Analyze the equation"** will mean to find the center, transverse axis, vertices, and foci of the hyperbola and graph it.

EXAMPLE 3 Analyzing the Equation of a Hyperbola

Analyze the equation: $\frac{x^2}{16} - \frac{y^2}{4} = 1$

Solution The given equation is of the form of equation (2), with $a^2 = 16$ and $b^2 = 4$. The graph of the equation is a hyperbola with center at $(0, 0)$ and transverse axis along the x-axis. Also, we know that $c^2 = a^2 + b^2 = 16 + 4 = 20$. The vertices are at $(\pm a, 0) = (\pm 4, 0)$, and the foci are at $(\pm c, 0) = (\pm 2\sqrt{5}, 0)$.

To locate the points on the graph above and below the foci, we let $x = \pm 2\sqrt{5}$. Then

$$\frac{x^2}{16} - \frac{y^2}{4} = 1$$
$$\frac{(\pm 2\sqrt{5})^2}{16} - \frac{y^2}{4} = 1 \quad x = \pm 2\sqrt{5}$$
$$\frac{20}{16} - \frac{y^2}{4} = 1$$
$$\frac{5}{4} - \frac{y^2}{4} = 1$$
$$\frac{y^2}{4} = \frac{1}{4}$$
$$y = \pm 1$$

The points above and below the foci are $(\pm 2\sqrt{5}, 1)$ and $(\pm 2\sqrt{5}, -1)$. See Figure 39(a) for the graph drawn by hand. Figure 39(b) shows the graph obtained using a graphing utility, where $Y_1 = \sqrt{4\left(\dfrac{x^2}{16} - 1\right)}$ and $Y_2 = -\sqrt{4\left(\dfrac{x^2}{16} - 1\right)}$.

Figure 39

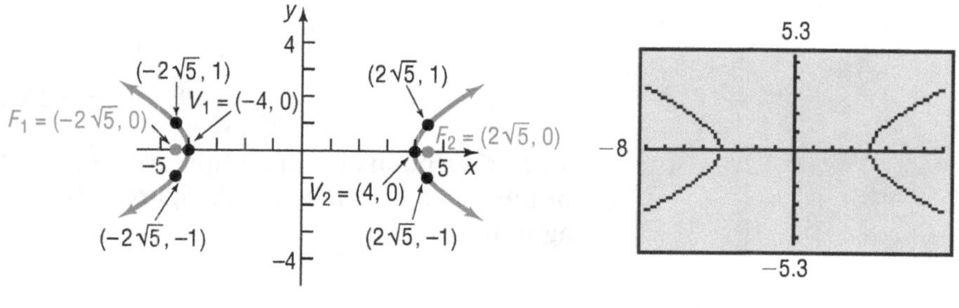

(a) (b)

The next result gives the form of the equation of a hyperbola with center at the origin and transverse axis along the y-axis.

THEOREM

Equation of a Hyperbola; Center at (0, 0); Transverse Axis along the *y*-Axis

An equation of the hyperbola with center at $(0, 0)$, foci at $(0, -c)$ and $(0, c)$, and vertices at $(0, -a)$ and $(0, a)$ is

$$\frac{y^2}{a^2} - \frac{x^2}{b^2} = 1 \qquad \text{where } b^2 = c^2 - a^2 \tag{3}$$

The transverse axis is the y-axis.

Figure 40

$\dfrac{y^2}{a^2} - \dfrac{x^2}{b^2} = 1, b^2 = c^2 - a^2$

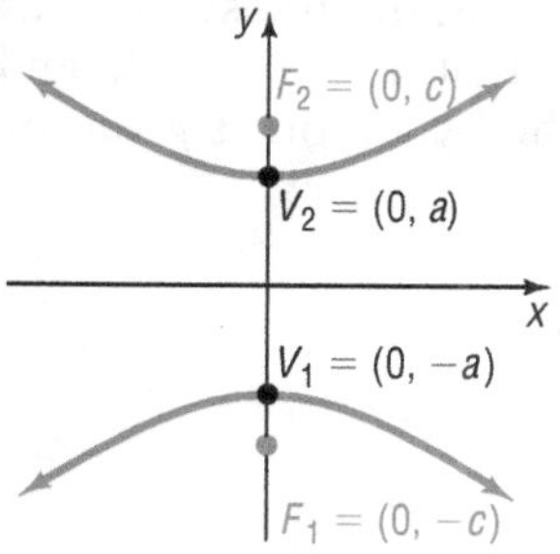

Figure 40 shows the graph of a typical hyperbola defined by equation (3).

An equation of the form of equation (2), $\dfrac{x^2}{a^2} - \dfrac{y^2}{b^2} = 1$, is the equation of a hyperbola with center at the origin, foci on the x-axis at $(-c, 0)$ and $(c, 0)$, where $c^2 = a^2 + b^2$, and transverse axis along the x-axis.

An equation of the form of equation (3), $\dfrac{y^2}{a^2} - \dfrac{x^2}{b^2} = 1$, is the equation of a hyperbola with center at the origin, foci on the y-axis at $(0, -c)$ and $(0, c)$, where $c^2 = a^2 + b^2$, and transverse axis along the y-axis.

Notice the difference in the forms of equations (2) and (3). When the y^2-term is subtracted from the x^2-term, the transverse axis is along the x-axis. When the x^2-term is subtracted from the y^2-term, the transverse axis is along the y-axis.

EXAMPLE 4 Analyzing the Equation of a Hyperbola

Analyze the equation: $y^2 - 4x^2 = 4$

Solution To put the equation in proper form, we divide each side by 4:

$$\frac{y^2}{4} - x^2 = 1$$

Since the x^2-term is subtracted from the y^2-term, the equation is that of a hyperbola with center at the origin and transverse axis along the y-axis. Also, comparing the above equation to equation (3), we find $a^2 = 4$, $b^2 = 1$, and $c^2 = a^2 + b^2 = 5$. The vertices are at $(0, \pm a) = (0, \pm 2)$, and the foci are at $(0, \pm c) = (0, \pm\sqrt{5})$.

To locate other points on the graph, we let $x = \pm 2$. Then

$$
\begin{aligned}
y^2 - 4x^2 &= 4 \\
y^2 - 4(\pm 2)^2 &= 4 \qquad x = \pm 2 \\
y^2 - 16 &= 4 \\
y^2 &= 20 \\
y &= \pm 2\sqrt{5}
\end{aligned}
$$

Four other points on the graph are $(\pm 2, 2\sqrt{5})$ and $(\pm 2, -2\sqrt{5})$. See Figure 41(a) for the graph drawn by hand. Figure 41(b) shows the graph obtained using a graphing utility.

Figure 41

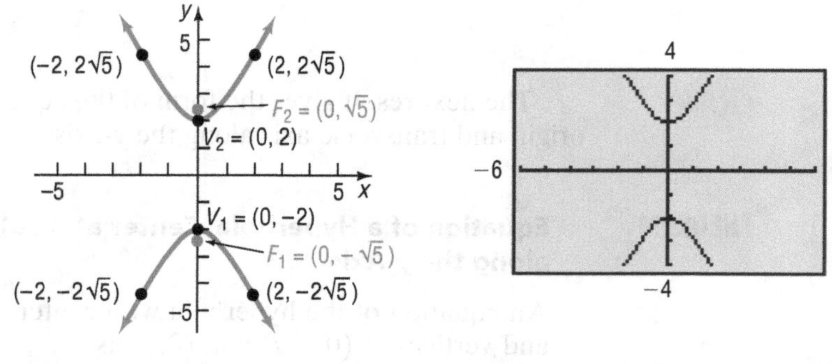

(a) **(b)**

EXAMPLE 5 Finding an Equation of a Hyperbola

Find an equation of the hyperbola having one vertex at $(0, 2)$ and foci at $(0, -3)$ and $(0, 3)$. Graph the equation.

Solution Since the foci are at $(0, -3)$ and $(0, 3)$, the center of the hyperbola, which is at their midpoint, is the origin. Because the foci lie on the y-axis, the transverse axis is along the y-axis. The given information also reveals that $c = 3$, $a = 2$, and $b^2 = c^2 - a^2 = 9 - 4 = 5$. The form of the equation of the hyperbola is given by equation (3):

$$\frac{y^2}{a^2} - \frac{x^2}{b^2} = 1$$

$$\frac{y^2}{4} - \frac{x^2}{5} = 1$$

Let $y = \pm 3$ to obtain points on the graph on either side of the foci. See Figure 42.

Figure 42

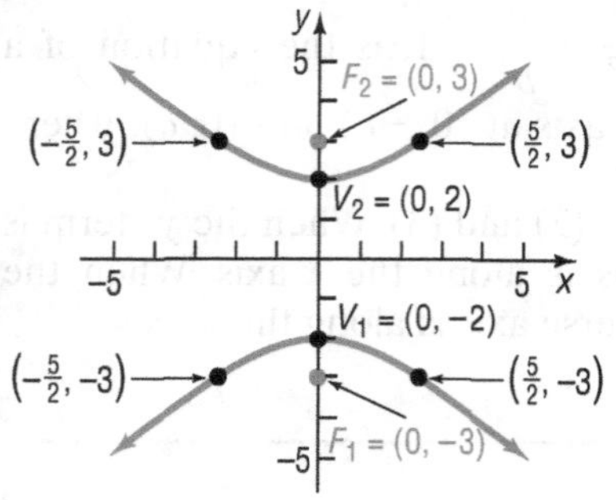

Now Work PROBLEM 19

Look at the equations of the hyperbolas in Examples 3 and 5. For the hyperbola in Example 3, $a^2 = 16$ and $b^2 = 4$, so $a > b$; for the hyperbola in Example 5, $a^2 = 4$ and $b^2 = 5$, so $a < b$. We conclude that, for hyperbolas, there are no requirements involving the relative sizes of a and b. Contrast this situation to the case of an ellipse, in which the relative sizes of a and b dictate which axis is the major axis. Hyperbolas have another feature to distinguish them from ellipses and parabolas: Hyperbolas have asymptotes.

2 Find the Asymptotes of a Hyperbola

Recall from Section 4.2 that a horizontal or oblique asymptote of a graph is a line with the property that the distance from the line to points on the graph approaches 0 as $x \to -\infty$ or as $x \to \infty$. The asymptotes provide information about the end behavior of the graph of a hyperbola.

THEOREM

Asymptotes of a Hyperbola

The hyperbola $\frac{x^2}{a^2} - \frac{y^2}{b^2} = 1$ has the two oblique asymptotes

$$y = \frac{b}{a}x \quad \text{and} \quad y = -\frac{b}{a}x \tag{4}$$

Proof We begin by solving for y in the equation of the hyperbola.

$$\frac{x^2}{a^2} - \frac{y^2}{b^2} = 1$$

$$\frac{y^2}{b^2} = \frac{x^2}{a^2} - 1$$

$$y^2 = b^2\left(\frac{x^2}{a^2} - 1\right)$$

Since $x \neq 0$, we can rearrange the right side in the form

$$y^2 = \frac{b^2x^2}{a^2}\left(1 - \frac{a^2}{x^2}\right)$$

$$y = \pm\frac{bx}{a}\sqrt{1 - \frac{a^2}{x^2}}$$

Now, as $x \to -\infty$ or as $x \to \infty$, the term $\frac{a^2}{x^2}$ approaches 0, so the expression under the radical approaches 1. So, as $x \to -\infty$ or as $x \to \infty$, the value of y approaches $\pm\frac{bx}{a}$; that is, the graph of the hyperbola approaches the lines

$$y = -\frac{b}{a}x \quad \text{and} \quad y = \frac{b}{a}x$$

These lines are oblique asymptotes of the hyperbola. ■

The asymptotes of a hyperbola are not part of the hyperbola, but they do serve as a guide for graphing a hyperbola. For example, suppose that we want to graph the equation

$$\frac{x^2}{a^2} - \frac{y^2}{b^2} = 1$$

We begin by plotting the vertices $(-a, 0)$ and $(a, 0)$. Then we plot the points $(0, -b)$ and $(0, b)$ and use these four points to construct a rectangle, as shown in Figure 43. The diagonals of this rectangle have slopes $\frac{b}{a}$ and $-\frac{b}{a}$, and their extensions are the asymptotes $y = \frac{b}{a}x$ and $y = -\frac{b}{a}x$ of the hyperbola. If we graph the asymptotes, we can use them to establish the "opening" of the hyperbola and avoid plotting other points.

Figure 43 $\frac{x^2}{a^2} - \frac{y^2}{b^2} = 1$

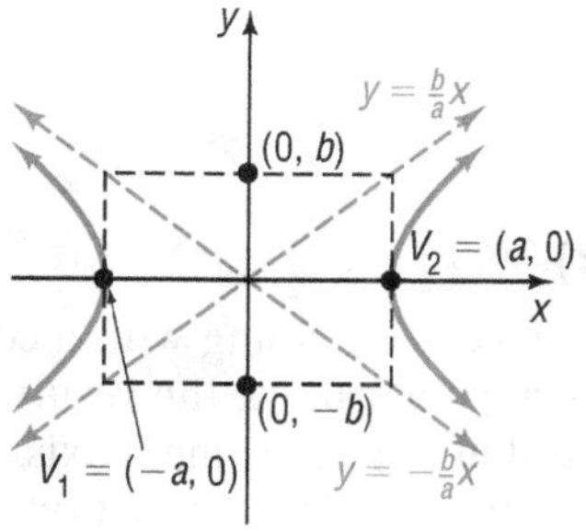

THEOREM **Asymptotes of a Hyperbola**

The hyperbola $\frac{y^2}{a^2} - \frac{x^2}{b^2} = 1$ has the two oblique asymptotes:

$$y = \frac{a}{b}x \quad \text{and} \quad y = -\frac{a}{b}x \tag{5}$$

You are asked to prove this result in Problem 82.

For the remainder of this section, the direction **"Analyze the equation"** will mean to find the center, transverse axis, vertices, foci, and asymptotes of the hyperbola and graph it.

EXAMPLE 6 Analyzing the Equation of a Hyperbola

Analyze the equation: $9x^2 - 4y^2 = 36$

Solution Divide each side of the equation by 36 to put the equation in proper form.

$$\frac{x^2}{4} - \frac{y^2}{9} = 1$$

We now proceed to analyze the equation. The center of the hyperbola is the origin. Since the x^2-term is first in the equation, we know that the transverse axis is along the x-axis and the vertices and foci will lie on the x-axis. Using equation (2), we find $a^2 = 4, b^2 = 9$, and $c^2 = a^2 + b^2 = 13$. The vertices are $a = 2$ units left and right of the center at $(\pm a, 0) = (\pm 2, 0)$, the foci are $c = \sqrt{13}$ units left and right of the center at $(\pm c, 0) = (\pm\sqrt{13}, 0)$, and the asymptotes have the equations

$$y = \frac{b}{a}x = \frac{3}{2}x \quad \text{and} \quad y = -\frac{b}{a}x = -\frac{3}{2}x$$

To graph the hyperbola by hand, form the rectangle containing the points $(\pm a, 0)$ and $(0, \pm b)$, that is, $(-2, 0), (2, 0), (0, -3)$, and $(0, 3)$. The extensions of the diagonals of this rectangle are the asymptotes. See Figure 44(a) for the graph drawn by hand. Figure 44(b) shows the graph obtained using a graphing utility.

Figure 44

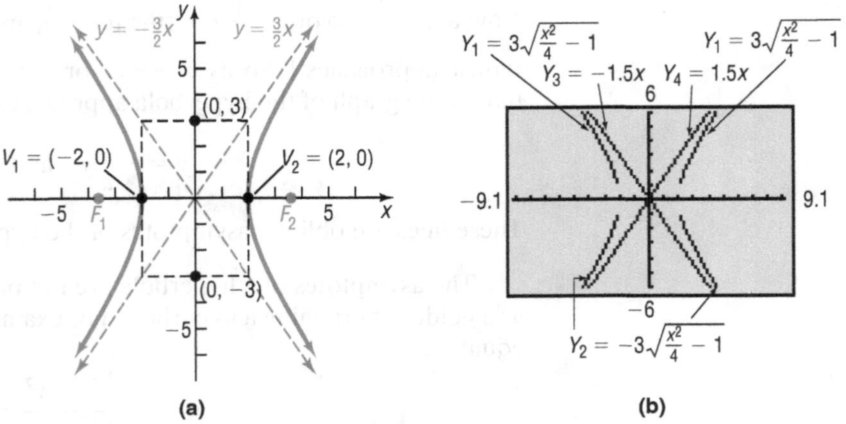

Seeing the Concept

Refer to Figure 44(b). Create a TABLE using Y_1 and Y_4 with $x = 10, 100, 1000$, and 10,000. Compare the values of Y_1 and Y_4. Repeat for Y_1 and Y_3, Y_2 and Y_3, and Y_2 and Y_4.

Now Work PROBLEM 29

3 Analyze Hyperbolas with Center at (h, k)

If a hyperbola with center at the origin and transverse axis coinciding with a coordinate axis is shifted horizontally h units and then vertically k units, the result is a hyperbola with center at (h, k) and transverse axis parallel to a coordinate axis. The equations of such hyperbolas have the same forms as those given in equations (2) and (3), except that x is replaced by $x - h$ (the horizontal shift) and y is replaced by $y - k$ (the vertical shift). Table 4 gives the forms of the equations of such hyperbolas. See Figure 45 for typical graphs.

Table 4

HYPERBOLAS WITH CENTER AT (h, k) AND TRANSVERSE AXIS PARALLEL TO A COORDINATE AXIS

Center	Transverse Axis	Foci	Vertices	Equation	Asymptotes
(h, k)	Parallel to the x-axis	$(h \pm c, k)$	$(h \pm a, k)$	$\frac{(x-h)^2}{a^2} - \frac{(y-k)^2}{b^2} = 1, \quad b^2 = c^2 - a^2$	$y - k = \pm\frac{b}{a}(x - h)$
(h, k)	Parallel to the y-axis	$(h, k \pm c)$	$(h, k \pm a)$	$\frac{(y-k)^2}{a^2} - \frac{(x-h)^2}{b^2} = 1, \quad b^2 = c^2 - a^2$	$y - k = \pm\frac{a}{b}(x - h)$

Figure 45

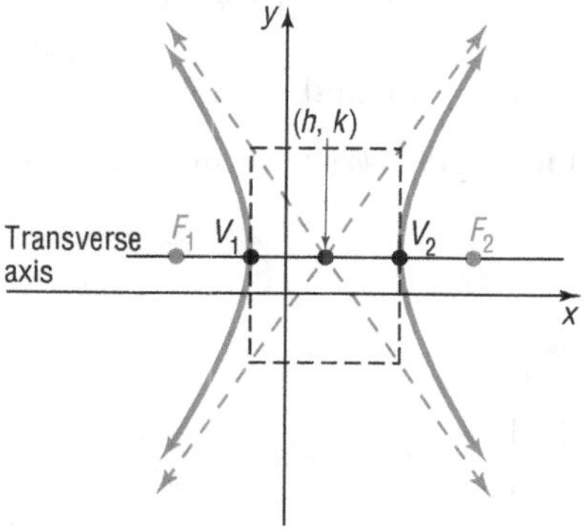

(a) $\frac{(x-h)^2}{a^2} - \frac{(y-k)^2}{b^2} = 1$

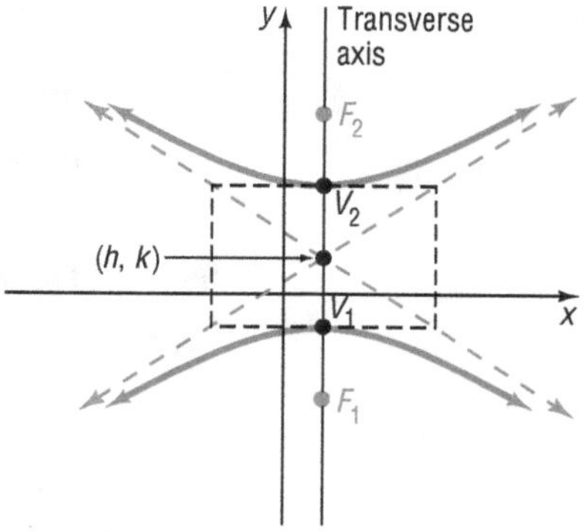

(b) $\frac{(y-k)^2}{a^2} - \frac{(x-h)^2}{b^2} = 1$

EXAMPLE 7 Finding an Equation of a Hyperbola, Center Not at the Origin

Find an equation for the hyperbola with center at $(1, -2)$, one focus at $(4, -2)$, and one vertex at $(3, -2)$. Graph the equation by hand.

Solution The center is at $(h, k) = (1, -2)$, so $h = 1$ and $k = -2$. Since the center, focus, and vertex all lie on the line $y = -2$, the transverse axis is parallel to the x-axis. The distance from the center $(1, -2)$ to the focus $(4, -2)$ is $c = 3$; the distance from the center $(1, -2)$ to the vertex $(3, -2)$ is $a = 2$. Thus, $b^2 = c^2 - a^2 = 9 - 4 = 5$. The equation is

$$\frac{(x-h)^2}{a^2} - \frac{(y-k)^2}{b^2} = 1$$

$$\frac{(x-1)^2}{4} - \frac{(y+2)^2}{5} = 1$$

See Figure 46.

Figure 46

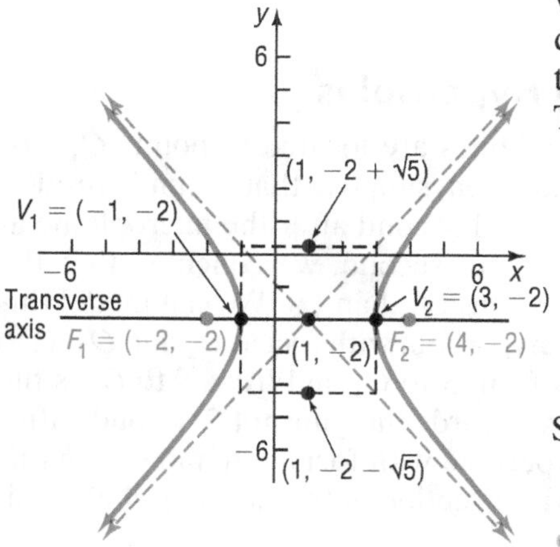

Now Work PROBLEM 39

EXAMPLE 8 Analyzing the Equation of a Hyperbola

Analyze the equation: $-x^2 + 4y^2 - 2x - 16y + 11 = 0$

Solution We complete the squares in x and in y.

$$-x^2 + 4y^2 - 2x - 16y + 11 = 0$$

$$-(x^2 + 2x) + 4(y^2 - 4y) = -11 \quad \text{Group terms.}$$

$$-(x^2 + 2x + 1) + 4(y^2 - 4y + 4) = -11 - 1 + 16 \quad \text{Complete each square.}$$

$$-(x + 1)^2 + 4(y - 2)^2 = 4$$

$$(y - 2)^2 - \frac{(x + 1)^2}{4} = 1 \quad \text{Divide each side by 4.}$$

This is the equation of a hyperbola with center at $(-1, 2)$ and transverse axis parallel to the y-axis. Also, $a^2 = 1$ and $b^2 = 4$, so $c^2 = a^2 + b^2 = 5$. Since the transverse axis is parallel to the y-axis, the vertices and foci are located a and c units above and below the center, respectively. The vertices are at $(h, k \pm a) = (-1, 2 \pm 1)$, or $(-1, 1)$ and $(-1, 3)$. The foci are at $(h, k \pm c) = \left(-1, 2 \pm \sqrt{5}\right)$. The asymptotes are $y - 2 = \frac{1}{2}(x + 1)$ and $y - 2 = -\frac{1}{2}(x + 1)$. Figure 47(a) shows the graph drawn by hand. Figure 47(b) shows the graph obtained using a graphing utility.

Figure 47

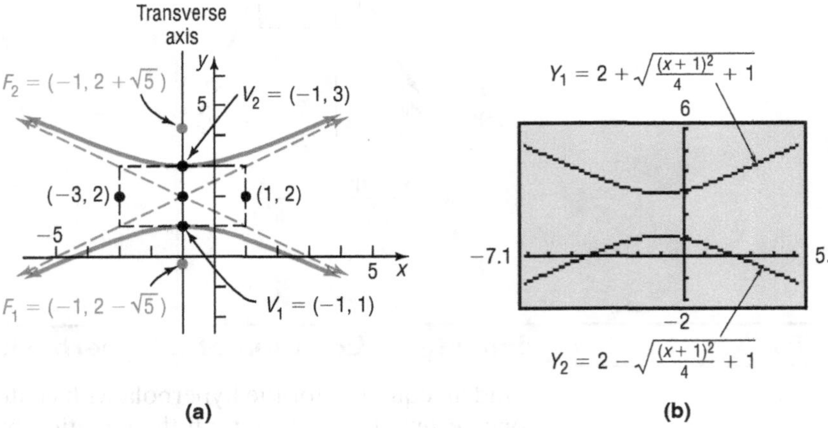

(a) (b)

Now Work PROBLEM 53

4 Solve Applied Problems Involving Hyperbolas

Look at Figure 48. Suppose that three microphones are located at points O_1, O_2, and O_3 (the foci of the two hyperbolas). In addition, suppose that a gun is fired at S and the microphone at O_1 records the gun shot 1 second after the microphone at O_2. Because sound travels at about 1100 feet per second, we conclude that the microphone at O_1 is 1100 feet farther from the gunshot than O_2. We can model this situation by saying that S lies on a branch of a hyperbola with foci at O_1 and O_2. (Do you see why? The difference of the distances from S to O_1 and from S to O_2 is the constant 1100.) If the third microphone at O_3 records the gunshot 2 seconds after O_1, then S will lie on a branch of a second hyperbola with foci at O_1 and O_3. In this case, the constant difference will be 2200. The intersection of the two hyperbolas will identify the location of S.

Figure 48

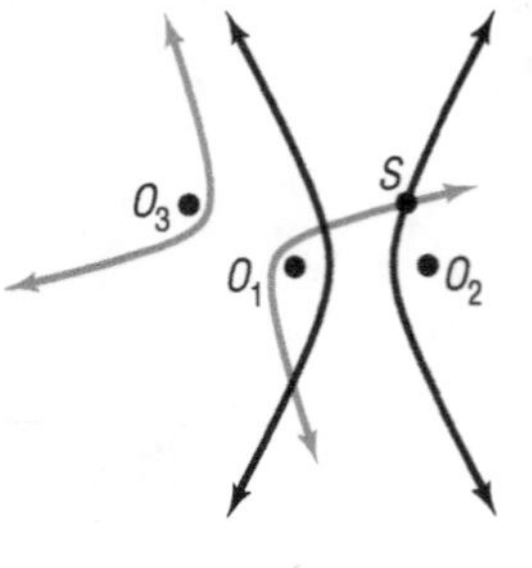

EXAMPLE 9 Lightning Strikes

Suppose that two people standing 1 mile apart both see a flash of lightning. After a period of time, the person standing at point A hears the thunder. One second later, the person standing at point B hears the thunder. If the person at B is due west of the person at A and the lightning strike is known to occur due north of the person standing at point A, where did the lightning strike?

Solution See Figure 49 in which the ordered pair (x, y) represents the location of the lightning strike. We know that sound travels at 1100 feet per second, so the person at point A is 1100 feet closer to the lightning strike than the person at point B. Since the difference of the distance from (x, y) to A and the distance from (x, y) to B is the constant 1100, the point (x, y) lies on a hyperbola whose foci are at A and B.

Figure 49

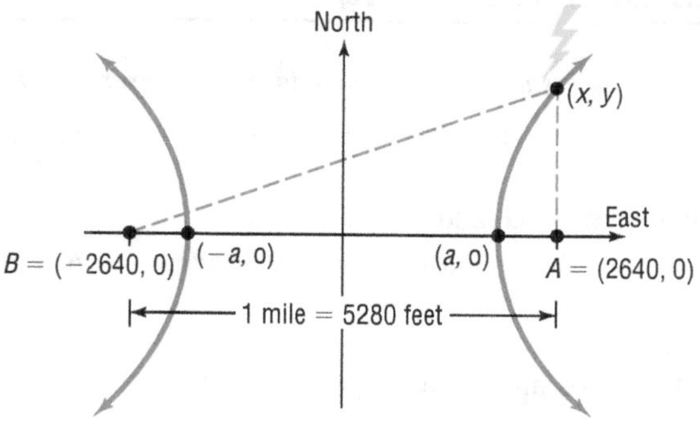

An equation of the hyperbola is

$$\frac{x^2}{a^2} - \frac{y^2}{b^2} = 1$$

where $2a = 1100$, so $a = 550$.

Because the distance between the two people is 1 mile (5280 feet) and each person is at a focus of the hyperbola, we have

$$2c = 5280$$
$$c = \frac{5280}{2} = 2640$$

Since $b^2 = c^2 - a^2 = 2640^2 - 550^2 = 6{,}667{,}100$, the equation of the hyperbola that describes the location of the lightning strike is

$$\frac{x^2}{550^2} - \frac{y^2}{6{,}667{,}100} = 1$$

Refer again to Figure 49. Since the lightning strikes due north of the individual at the point $A = (2640, 0)$, we let $x = 2640$ and solve the resulting equation.

$$\frac{2640^2}{550^2} - \frac{y^2}{6{,}667{,}100} = 1$$

$$-\frac{y^2}{6{,}667{,}100} = -22.04 \qquad \text{Subtract } \frac{2640^2}{550^2} \text{ from both sides.}$$

$$y^2 = 146{,}942{,}884 \qquad \text{Multiply both sides by } -6{,}667{,}100.$$

$$y = 12{,}122 \qquad y > 0 \text{ since the lightning strike occured in quadrant I.}$$

Check: The difference between the distance from (2640, 12,122) to the person at the point $B = (-2640, 0)$ and the distance from (2640, 12,122) to the person at the point $A = (2640, 0)$ should be 1100. Using the distance formula, we find the difference in the distances is

$$\sqrt{[2640 - (-2640)]^2 + (12{,}122 - 0)^2} - \sqrt{(2640 - 2640)^2 + (12{,}122 - 0)^2} = 1100$$

as required.

The lightning strike is 12,122 feet north of the person standing at point A. ■

Now Work PROBLEM 73

10.4 Assess Your Understanding

'Are You Prepared?' *Answers are given at the end of these exercises. If you get a wrong answer, read the pages listed in red.*

1. The distance d from $P_1 = (3, -4)$ to $P_2 = (-2, 1)$ is $d =$ _____. (pp. 4–6)
2. To complete the square of $x^2 + 5x$, add _____. (p. A52)
3. Find the intercepts of the equation $y^2 = 9 + 4x^2$. (pp. 18–19)
4. ***True or False*** The equation $y^2 = 9 + x^2$ is symmetric with respect to the x-axis, the y-axis, and the origin. (pp. 19–21)
5. To graph $y = (x - 5)^3 - 4$, shift the graph of $y = x^3$ to the (left/right) _____ unit(s) and then (up/down) _____ unit(s). (pp. 100–102)
6. Find the vertical asymptotes, if any, and the horizontal or oblique asymptotes, if any, of $y = \dfrac{x^2 - 9}{x^2 - 4}$. (pp. 194–199)

Concepts and Vocabulary

7. A(n) _____ is the collection of points in the plane the difference of whose distances from two fixed points is a constant.
8. For a hyperbola, the foci lie on a line called the _____ _____.
9. The asymptotes of the hyperbola $\dfrac{x^2}{4} - \dfrac{y^2}{9} = 1$ are _____ and _____.
10. ***True or False*** The foci of a hyperbola lie on a line called the axis of symmetry.
11. ***True or False*** Hyperbolas always have asymptotes.
12. ***True or False*** A hyperbola will never intersect its transverse axis.

Skill Building

In Problems 13–16, the graph of a hyperbola is given. Match each graph to its equation.

(A) $\dfrac{x^2}{4} - y^2 = 1$ (B) $x^2 - \dfrac{y^2}{4} = 1$ (C) $\dfrac{y^2}{4} - x^2 = 1$ (D) $y^2 - \dfrac{x^2}{4} = 1$

13.
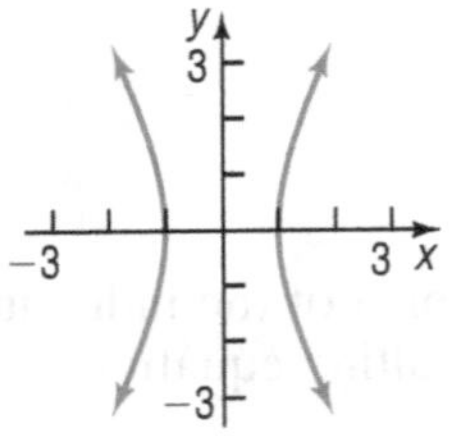

14.
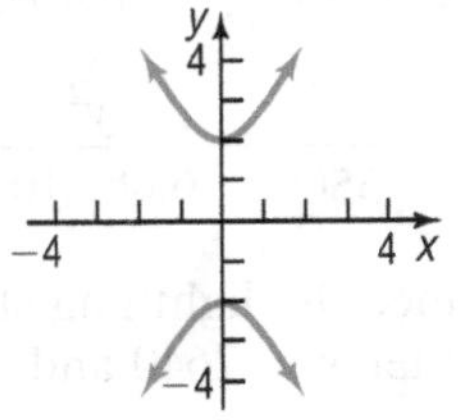

15.
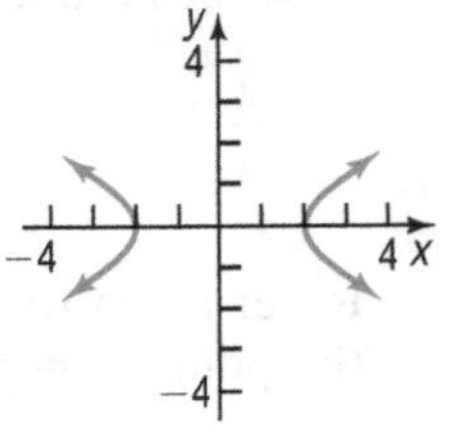

16.
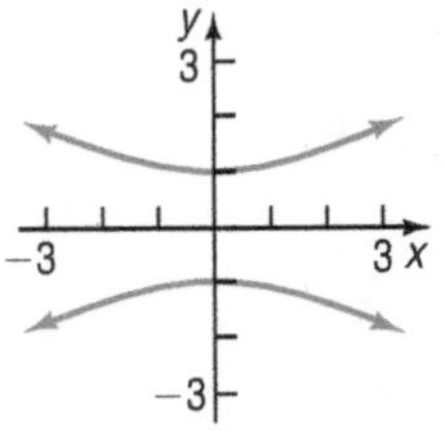

In Problems 17–26, find an equation for the hyperbola described. Graph the equation by hand.

17. Center at (0, 0); focus at (3, 0); vertex at (1, 0)
18. Center at (0, 0); focus at (0, 5); vertex at (0, 3)
19. Center at (0, 0); focus at (0, −6); vertex at (0, 4)
20. Center at (0, 0); focus at (−3, 0); vertex at (2, 0)
21. Foci at (−5, 0) and (5, 0); vertex at (3, 0)
22. Focus at (0, 6); vertices at (0, −2) and (0, 2)
23. Vertices at (0, −6) and (0, 6); asymptote the line $y = 2x$
24. Vertices at (−4, 0) and (4, 0); asymptote the line $y = 2x$
25. Foci at (−4, 0) and (4, 0); asymptote the line $y = -x$
26. Foci at (0, −2) and (0, 2); asymptote the line $y = -x$

In Problems 27–34, find the center, transverse axis, vertices, foci, and asymptotes. Graph each equation by hand. Verify your graph using a graphing utility.

27. $\frac{x^2}{25} - \frac{y^2}{9} = 1$ **28.** $\frac{y^2}{16} - \frac{x^2}{4} = 1$ **29.** $4x^2 - y^2 = 16$ **30.** $4y^2 - x^2 = 16$

31. $y^2 - 9x^2 = 9$ **32.** $x^2 - y^2 = 4$ **33.** $y^2 - x^2 = 25$ **34.** $2x^2 - y^2 = 4$

In Problems 35–38, write an equation for each hyperbola.

35.

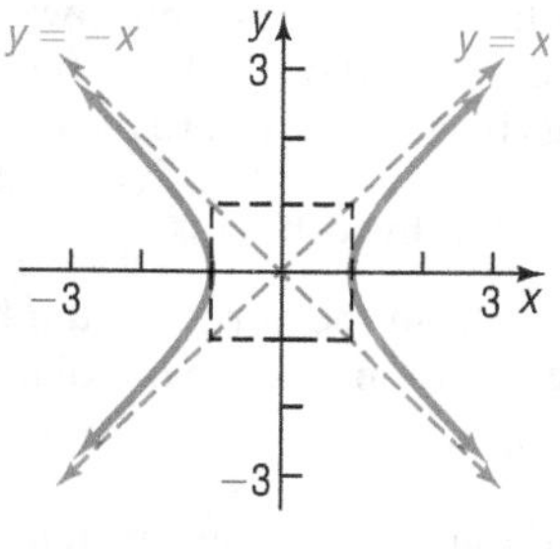

36.

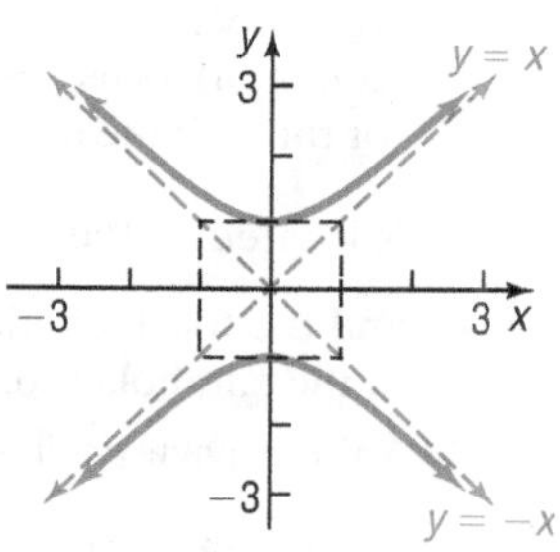

37.

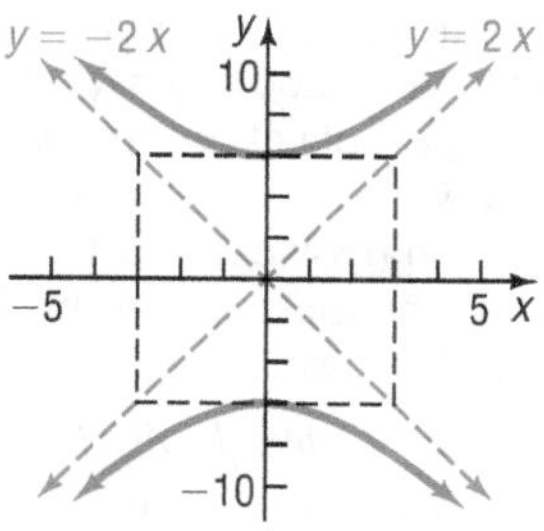

38.

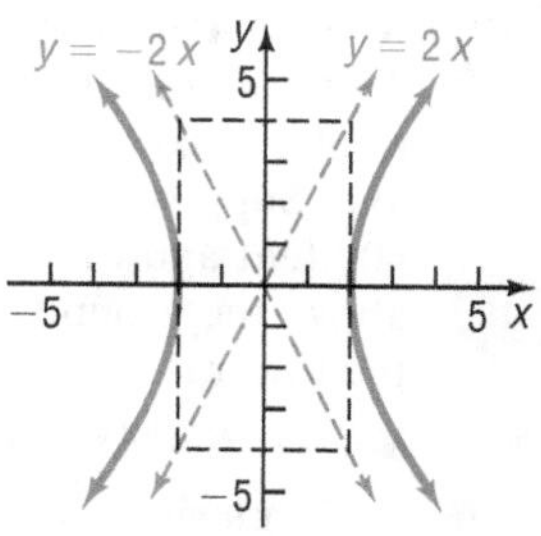

In Problems 39–46, find an equation for the hyperbola described. Graph each equation by hand.

39. Center at $(4, -1)$; focus at $(7, -1)$; vertex at $(6, -1)$

40. Center at $(-3, 1)$; focus at $(-3, 6)$; vertex at $(-3, 4)$

41. Center at $(-3, -4)$; focus at $(-3, -8)$; vertex at $(-3, -2)$

42. Center at $(1, 4)$; focus at $(-2, 4)$; vertex at $(0, 4)$

43. Foci at $(3, 7)$ and $(7, 7)$; vertex at $(6, 7)$

44. Focus at $(-4, 0)$ vertices at $(-4, 4)$ and $(-4, 2)$

45. Vertices at $(-1, -1)$ and $(3, -1)$; asymptote the line $y + 1 = \frac{3}{2}(x - 1)$

46. Vertices at $(1, -3)$ and $(1, 1)$; asymptote the line $y + 1 = \frac{3}{2}(x - 1)$

In Problems 47–60, find the center, transverse axis, vertices, foci, and asymptotes. Graph each equation by hand. Verify your graph using a graphing utility.

47. $\frac{(x-2)^2}{4} - \frac{(y+3)^2}{9} = 1$ **48.** $\frac{(y+3)^2}{4} - \frac{(x-2)^2}{9} = 1$ **49.** $(y-2)^2 - 4(x+2)^2 = 4$

50. $(x+4)^2 - 9(y-3)^2 = 9$ **51.** $(x+1)^2 - (y+2)^2 = 4$ **52.** $(y-3)^2 - (x+2)^2 = 4$

53. $x^2 - y^2 - 2x - 2y - 1 = 0$ **54.** $y^2 - x^2 - 4y + 4x - 1 = 0$ **55.** $y^2 - 4x^2 - 4y - 8x - 4 = 0$

56. $2x^2 - y^2 + 4x + 4y - 4 = 0$ **57.** $4x^2 - y^2 - 24x - 4y + 16 = 0$ **58.** $2y^2 - x^2 + 2x + 8y + 3 = 0$

59. $y^2 - 4x^2 - 16x - 2y - 19 = 0$ **60.** $x^2 - 3y^2 + 8x - 6y + 4 = 0$

In Problems 61–64, graph each function. Be sure to label any intercepts.
[**Hint:** *Notice that each function is half a hyperbola.*]

61. $f(x) = \sqrt{16 + 4x^2}$ **62.** $f(x) = -\sqrt{9 + 9x^2}$ **63.** $f(x) = -\sqrt{-25 + x^2}$ **64.** $f(x) = \sqrt{-1 + x^2}$

Mixed Practice

In Problems 65–72, analyze each conic section.

65. $\frac{(x-3)^2}{4} - \frac{y^2}{25} = 1$ **66.** $\frac{(y+2)^2}{16} - \frac{(x-2)^2}{4} = 1$ **67.** $x^2 = 16(y - 3)$

68. $y^2 = -12(x + 1)$ **69.** $25x^2 + 9y^2 - 250x + 400 = 0$ **70.** $x^2 + 36y^2 - 2x + 288y + 541 = 0$

71. $x^2 - 6x - 8y - 31 = 0$ **72.** $9x^2 - y^2 - 18x - 8y - 88 = 0$

Applications and Extensions

73. Fireworks Display Suppose that two people standing 2 miles apart both see the burst from a fireworks display. After a period of time, the first person standing at point *A* hears the burst. One second later, the second person standing at point *B* hears the burst. If the person at point *B* is due west of the person at point *A* and if the display is known to occur due north of the person at point *A*, where did the fireworks display occur?

74. **Lightning Strikes** Suppose that two people standing 1 mile apart both see a flash of lightning. After a period of time, the first person standing at point A hears the thunder. Two seconds later, the second person standing at point B hears the thunder. If the person at point B is due west of the person at point A and if the lightning strike is known to occur due north of the person standing at point A, where did the lightning strike?

75. **Nuclear Power Plant** Some nuclear power plants utilize "natural draft" cooling towers in the shape of a **hyperboloid,** a solid obtained by rotating a hyperbola about its conjugate axis. Suppose such a cooling tower has a base diameter of 400 feet and the diameter at its narrowest point, 360 feet above the ground, is 200 feet. If the diameter at the top of the tower is 300 feet, how tall is the tower?

Source: Bay Area Air Quality Management District

76. **An Explosion** Two recording devices are set 2400 feet apart, with the device at point A to the west of the device at point B. At a point between the devices, 300 feet from point B, a small amount of explosive is detonated. The recording devices record the time until the sound reaches each. How far directly north of point B should a second explosion be done so that the measured time difference recorded by the devices is the same as that for the first detonation?

77. **Rutherford's Experiment** In May 1911, Ernest Rutherford published a paper in *Philosophical Magazine*. In this article, he described the motion of alpha particles as they are shot at a piece of gold foil 0.00004 cm thick. Before conducting this experiment, Rutherford expected that the alpha particles would shoot through the foil just as a bullet would shoot through snow. Instead, a small fraction of the alpha particles bounced off the foil. This led to the conclusion that the nucleus of an atom is dense, while the remainder of the atom is sparse. Only the density of the nucleus could cause the alpha particles to deviate from their path. The figure shows a diagram from Rutherford's paper that indicates that the deflected alpha particles follow the path of one branch of a hyperbola.

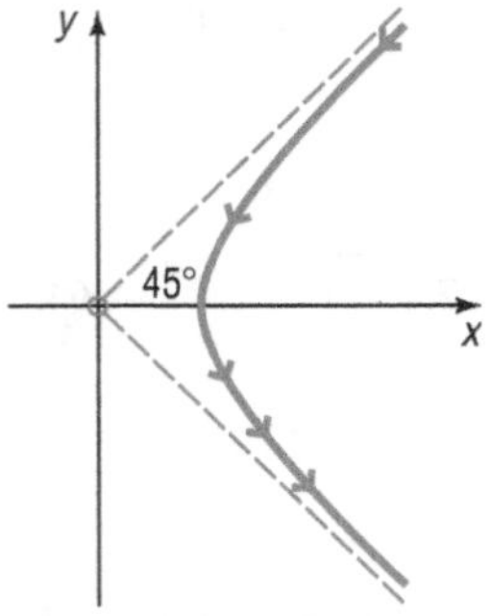

(a) Find an equation of the asymptotes under this scenario.
(b) If the vertex of the path of the alpha particles is 10 cm from the center of the hyperbola, find a model that describes the path of the particle.

78. **Hyperbolic Mirrors** Hyperbolas have interesting reflective properties that make them useful for lenses and mirrors. For example, if a ray of light strikes a convex hyperbolic mirror on a line that would (theoretically) pass through its rear focus, it is reflected through the front focus. This property, and that of the parabola, were used to develop the *Cassegrain* telescope in 1672. The focus of the parabolic mirror and the rear focus of the hyperbolic mirror are the same point. The rays are collected by the parabolic mirror, reflected toward the (common) focus, and thus are reflected by the hyperbolic mirror through the opening to its front focus, where the eyepiece is located. If the equation of the hyperbola is $\frac{y^2}{9} - \frac{x^2}{16} = 1$ and the focal length (distance from the vertex to the focus) of the parabola is 6, find the equation of the parabola.

Source: www.enchantedlearning.com

79. The **eccentricity** e of a hyperbola is defined as the number $\frac{c}{a}$, where a and c are the numbers given in equation (2). Because $c > a$, it follows that $e > 1$. Describe the general shape of a hyperbola whose eccentricity is close to 1. What is the shape if e is very large?

80. A hyperbola for which $a = b$ is called an **equilateral hyperbola.** Find the eccentricity e of an equilateral hyperbola.

[**Note:** The eccentricity of a hyperbola is defined in Problem 79.]

81. Two hyperbolas that have the same set of asymptotes are called **conjugate.** Show that the hyperbolas

$$\frac{x^2}{4} - y^2 = 1 \quad \text{and} \quad y^2 - \frac{x^2}{4} = 1$$

are conjugate. Graph each hyperbola on the same set of coordinate axes.

82. Prove that the hyperbola

$$\frac{y^2}{a^2} - \frac{x^2}{b^2} = 1$$

has the two oblique asymptotes

$$y = \frac{a}{b}x \quad \text{and} \quad y = -\frac{a}{b}x$$

83. Show that the graph of an equation of the form

$$Ax^2 + Cy^2 + F = 0 \qquad A \neq 0, C \neq 0, F \neq 0$$

where A and C are of opposite sign, is a hyperbola with center at $(0, 0)$.

84. Show that the graph of an equation of the form

$$Ax^2 + Cy^2 + Dx + Ey + F = 0 \qquad A \neq 0, C \neq 0$$

where A and C are of opposite sign,

(a) is a hyperbola if $\frac{D^2}{4A} + \frac{E^2}{4C} - F \neq 0$

(b) is two intersecting lines if $\frac{D^2}{4A} + \frac{E^2}{4C} - F = 0$

'Are You Prepared?' Answers

1. $5\sqrt{2}$ **2.** $\frac{25}{4}$ **3.** $(0, -3), (0, 3)$ **4.** True **5.** right; 5; down; 4 **6.** Vertical: $x = -2$, $x = 2$; horizontal: $y = 1$

10.5 Rotation of Axes; General Form of a Conic

PREPARING FOR THIS SECTION *Before getting started, review the following:*

- Sum Formulas for Sine and Cosine (Section 7.4, pp. 466 and 469)
- Double-angle Formulas for Sine and Cosine (Section 7.5, p. 476)
- Half-angle Formulas for Sine and Cosine (Section 7.5, p. 480)

Now Work the 'Are You Prepared?' problems on page 679.

OBJECTIVES
1. Identify a Conic (p. 673)
2. Use a Rotation of Axes to Transform Equations (p. 674)
3. Analyze an Equation Using a Rotation of Axes (p. 676)
4. Identify Conics without a Rotation of Axes (p. 678)

In this section, we show that the graph of a general second-degree polynomial containing two variables x and y, that is, an equation of the form

$$Ax^2 + Bxy + Cy^2 + Dx + Ey + F = 0 \tag{1}$$

where A, B, and C are not simultaneously 0, is a conic. We shall not concern ourselves here with the degenerate cases of equation (1), such as $x^2 + y^2 = 0$, whose graph is a single point $(0, 0)$; or $x^2 + 3y^2 + 3 = 0$, whose graph contains no points; or $x^2 - 4y^2 = 0$, whose graph is two lines, $x - 2y = 0$ and $x + 2y = 0$.

We begin with the case where $B = 0$. In this case, the term containing xy is not present, so equation (1) has the form

$$Ax^2 + Cy^2 + Dx + Ey + F = 0$$

where either $A \neq 0$ or $C \neq 0$.

1 Identify a Conic

We have already discussed the procedure for identifying the graph of this kind of equation; we complete the squares of the quadratic expressions in x or y, or both. Once this has been done, the conic can be identified by comparing it to one of the forms studied in Sections 10.2 through 10.4.

In fact, though, we can identify the conic directly from the equation without completing the squares.

THEOREM **Identifying Conics without Completing the Squares**

Excluding degenerate cases, the equation

$$Ax^2 + Cy^2 + Dx + Ey + F = 0 \tag{2}$$

where A and C cannot both equal zero:

(a) Defines a parabola if $AC = 0$.
(b) Defines an ellipse (or a circle) if $AC > 0$.
(c) Defines a hyperbola if $AC < 0$.

Proof

(a) If $AC = 0$, then either $A = 0$ or $C = 0$, but not both, so the form of equation (2) is either

$$Ax^2 + Dx + Ey + F = 0, \qquad A \neq 0$$

or

$$Cy^2 + Dx + Ey + F = 0, \qquad C \neq 0$$

Using the results of Problems 78 and 79 in Exercise 10.2, it follows that, except for the degenerate cases, the equation is a parabola.

(b) If $AC > 0$, then A and C are of the same sign. Using the results of Problem 84 in Exercise 10.3, except for the degenerate cases, the equation is an ellipse if $A \neq C$ or a circle if $A = C$.

(c) If $AC < 0$, then A and C are of opposite sign. Using the results of Problem 84 in Exercise 10.4, except for the degenerate cases, the equation is a hyperbola. ■

We will not be concerned with the degenerate cases of equation (2). However, in practice, you should be alert to the possibility of degeneracy.

EXAMPLE 1 **Identifying a Conic without Completing the Squares**

Identify each equation without completing the squares.

(a) $3x^2 + 6y^2 + 6x - 12y = 0$ (b) $2x^2 - 3y^2 + 6y + 4 = 0$

(c) $y^2 - 2x + 4 = 0$

Solution (a) We compare the given equation to equation (2) and conclude that $A = 3$ and $C = 6$. Since $AC = 18 > 0$, the equation is an ellipse.

(b) Here $A = 2$ and $C = -3$, so $AC = -6 < 0$. The equation is a hyperbola.

(c) Here $A = 0$ and $C = 1$, so $AC = 0$. The equation is a parabola.

Now Work PROBLEM 11

Although we can now identify the type of conic represented by any equation of the form of equation (2) without completing the squares, we will still need to complete the squares if we desire additional information about the conic, such as its graph.

Now we turn our attention to equations of the form of equation (1), where $B \neq 0$. To discuss this case, we first need to investigate a new procedure: *rotation of axes*.

2 Use a Rotation of Axes to Transform Equations

In a **rotation of axes,** the origin remains fixed while the x-axis and y-axis are rotated through an angle θ to a new position; the new positions of the x-axis and the y-axis are denoted by x' and y', respectively, as shown in Figure 50(a).

Now look at Figure 50(b). There the point P has the coordinates (x, y) relative to the xy-plane, while the same point P has coordinates (x', y') relative to the $x'y'$-plane. We seek relationships that will enable us to express x and y in terms of x', y', and θ.

Figure 50

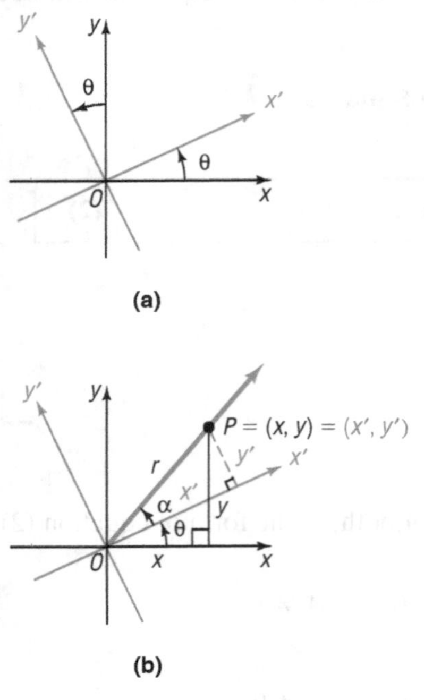

As Figure 50(b) shows, r denotes the distance from the origin O to the point P, and α denotes the angle between the positive x'-axis and the ray from O through P. Then, using the definitions of sine and cosine, we have

$$x' = r\cos\alpha \qquad y' = r\sin\alpha \tag{3}$$

$$x = r\cos(\theta + \alpha) \qquad y = r\sin(\theta + \alpha) \tag{4}$$

Now

$$\begin{aligned} x &= r\cos(\theta + \alpha) \\ &= r(\cos\theta\cos\alpha - \sin\theta\sin\alpha) && \text{Apply the Sum Formula for cosine.} \\ &= (r\cos\alpha)(\cos\theta) - (r\sin\alpha)(\sin\theta) \\ &= x'\cos\theta - y'\sin\theta && \text{By equation (3)} \end{aligned}$$

Similarly,

$$\begin{aligned} y &= r\sin(\theta + \alpha) \\ &= r(\sin\theta\cos\alpha + \cos\theta\sin\alpha) && \text{Apply the Sum Formula for sine.} \\ &= x'\sin\theta + y'\cos\theta && \text{By equation (3)} \end{aligned}$$

THEOREM **Rotation Formulas**

If the x- and y-axes are rotated through an angle θ, the coordinates (x, y) of a point P relative to the xy-plane and the coordinates (x', y') of the same point relative to the new x'- and y'-axes are related by the formulas

$$x = x'\cos\theta - y'\sin\theta \qquad y = x'\sin\theta + y'\cos\theta \tag{5}$$

EXAMPLE 2 Rotating Axes

Express the equation $xy = 1$ in terms of new $x'y'$-coordinates by rotating the axes through a $45°$ angle. Discuss the new equation.

Solution Let $\theta = 45°$ in equation (5). Then

$$x = x'\cos 45° - y'\sin 45° = x'\frac{\sqrt{2}}{2} - y'\frac{\sqrt{2}}{2} = \frac{\sqrt{2}}{2}(x' - y')$$

$$y = x'\sin 45° + y'\cos 45° = x'\frac{\sqrt{2}}{2} + y'\frac{\sqrt{2}}{2} = \frac{\sqrt{2}}{2}(x' + y')$$

Figure 51

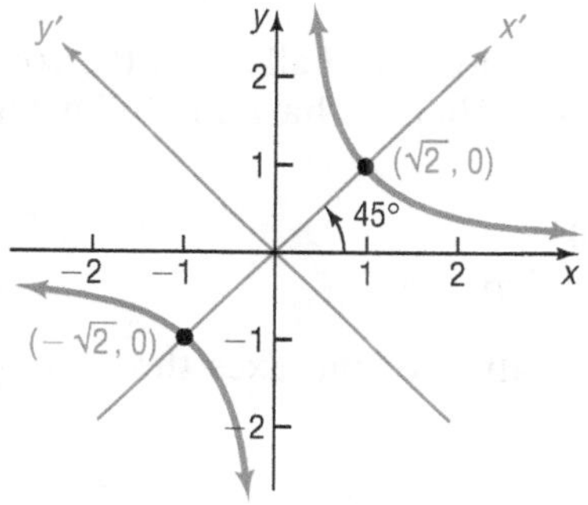

Substituting these expressions for x and y in $xy = 1$ gives

$$\left[\frac{\sqrt{2}}{2}(x' - y')\right]\left[\frac{\sqrt{2}}{2}(x' + y')\right] = 1$$

$$\frac{1}{2}(x'^2 - y'^2) = 1$$

$$\frac{x'^2}{2} - \frac{y'^2}{2} = 1$$

This is the equation of a hyperbola with center at $(0, 0)$ and transverse axis along the x'-axis. The vertices are at $(\pm\sqrt{2}, 0)$ on the x'-axis; the asymptotes are $y' = x'$ and $y' = -x'$ (which correspond to the original x- and y-axes). See Figure 51 for the graph.

As Example 2 illustrates, a rotation of axes through an appropriate angle can transform a second-degree equation in x and y containing an xy-term into one in x' and y' in which no $x'y'$-term appears. In fact, we will show that a rotation of axes through an appropriate angle will transform any equation of the form of equation (1) into an equation in x' and y' without an $x'y'$-term.

To find the formula for choosing an appropriate angle θ through which to rotate the axes, we begin with equation (1),

$$Ax^2 + Bxy + Cy^2 + Dx + Ey + F = 0 \qquad B \neq 0$$

Next we rotate through an angle θ using rotation formulas (5).

$$\begin{aligned} A(x'\cos\theta - y'\sin\theta)^2 &+ B(x'\cos\theta - y'\sin\theta)(x'\sin\theta + y'\cos\theta) \\ &+ C(x'\sin\theta + y'\cos\theta)^2 + D(x'\cos\theta - y'\sin\theta) \\ &+ E(x'\sin\theta + y'\cos\theta) + F = 0 \end{aligned}$$

By expanding and collecting like terms, we obtain

$$\begin{aligned} (A\cos^2\theta + B\sin\theta\cos\theta + C\sin^2\theta)x'^2 &+ [B(\cos^2\theta - \sin^2\theta) + 2(C - A)(\sin\theta\cos\theta)]x'y' \\ &+ (A\sin^2\theta - B\sin\theta\cos\theta + C\cos^2\theta)y'^2 \\ &+ (D\cos\theta + E\sin\theta)x' \\ &+ (-D\sin\theta + E\cos\theta)y' + F = 0 \end{aligned} \tag{6}$$

In equation (6), the coefficient of $x'y'$ is

$$B(\cos^2\theta - \sin^2\theta) + 2(C - A)(\sin\theta\cos\theta)$$

Since we want to eliminate the $x'y'$-term, we select an angle θ so that this coefficient is 0.

$$B(\cos^2\theta - \sin^2\theta) + 2(C - A)(\sin\theta\cos\theta) = 0$$

$$B\cos(2\theta) + (C - A)\sin(2\theta) = 0 \quad \text{Double-angle Formulas}$$

$$B\cos(2\theta) = (A - C)\sin(2\theta)$$

$$\cot(2\theta) = \frac{A - C}{B} \qquad B \neq 0$$

THEOREM

To transform the equation

$$Ax^2 + Bxy + Cy^2 + Dx + Ey + F = 0 \qquad B \neq 0$$

into an equation in x' and y' without an $x'y'$-term, rotate the axes through an angle θ that satisfies the equation

$$\cot(2\theta) = \frac{A - C}{B} \qquad \textbf{(7)}$$

Equation (7) has an infinite number of solutions for θ. We shall adopt the convention of choosing the acute angle θ that satisfies (7). Then we have the following two possibilities:

If $\cot(2\theta) \geq 0$, then $0° < 2\theta \leq 90°$, so $0° < \theta \leq 45°$.
If $\cot(2\theta) < 0$, then $90° < 2\theta < 180°$, so $45° < \theta < 90°$.

Each of these results in a counterclockwise rotation of the axes through an acute angle θ.*

WARNING Be careful if you use a calculator to solve equation (7).

1. If $\cot(2\theta) = 0$, then $2\theta = 90°$ and $\theta = 45°$.
2. If $\cot(2\theta) \neq 0$, first find $\cos(2\theta)$. Then use the inverse cosine function key(s) to obtain 2θ, $0° < 2\theta < 180°$. Finally, divide by 2 to obtain the correct acute angle θ. ■

3 Analyze an Equation Using a Rotation of Axes

For the remainder of this section, the direction **"Analyze the equation"** will mean to transform the given equation so that it contains no xy-term and to graph the equation.

EXAMPLE 3 Analyzing an Equation Using a Rotation of Axes

Analyze the equation: $x^2 + \sqrt{3}xy + 2y^2 - 10 = 0$

Solution Since an xy-term is present, we must rotate the axes. Using $A = 1$, $B = \sqrt{3}$, and $C = 2$ in equation (7), the appropriate acute angle θ through which to rotate the axes satisfies the equation

$$\cot(2\theta) = \frac{A - C}{B} = \frac{-1}{\sqrt{3}} = -\frac{\sqrt{3}}{3} \qquad 0° < 2\theta < 180°$$

* Any rotation through an angle θ that satisfies $\cot(2\theta) = \frac{A - C}{B}$ will eliminate the $x'y'$-term. However, the final form of the transformed equation may be different (but equivalent), depending on the angle chosen.

Since $\cot(2\theta) = -\frac{\sqrt{3}}{3}$, we find $2\theta = 120°$, so $\theta = 60°$. Using $\theta = 60°$ in rotation formulas (5), we find

$$x = x'\cos 60° - y'\sin 60° = \frac{1}{2}x' - \frac{\sqrt{3}}{2}y' = \frac{1}{2}\left(x' - \sqrt{3}y'\right)$$

$$y = x'\sin 60° + y'\cos 60° = \frac{\sqrt{3}}{2}x' + \frac{1}{2}y' = \frac{1}{2}\left(\sqrt{3}x' + y'\right)$$

Substituting these values into the original equation and simplifying, we have

$$x^2 + \sqrt{3}xy + 2y^2 - 10 = 0$$

$$\frac{1}{4}\left(x' - \sqrt{3}y'\right)^2 + \sqrt{3}\left[\frac{1}{2}\left(x' - \sqrt{3}y'\right)\right]\left[\frac{1}{2}\left(\sqrt{3}x' + y'\right)\right] + 2\left[\frac{1}{4}\left(\sqrt{3}x' + y'\right)^2\right] = 10$$

Multiply both sides by 4 and expand to obtain

$$x'^2 - 2\sqrt{3}x'y' + 3y'^2 + \sqrt{3}\left(\sqrt{3}x'^2 - 2x'y' - \sqrt{3}y'^2\right) + 2\left(3x'^2 + 2\sqrt{3}x'y' + y'^2\right) = 40$$

$$10x'^2 + 2y'^2 = 40$$

$$\frac{x'^2}{4} + \frac{y'^2}{20} = 1$$

Figure 52

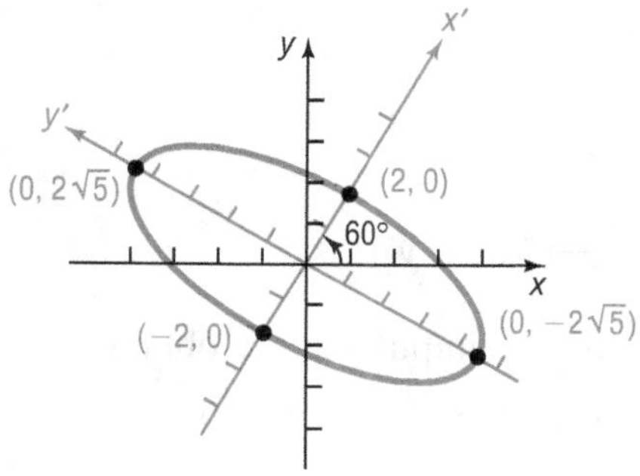

This is the equation of an ellipse with center at $(0, 0)$ and major axis along the y'-axis. The vertices are at $(0, \pm 2\sqrt{5})$ on the y'-axis. See Figure 52 for the graph.

To graph the equation $x^2 + \sqrt{3}xy + 2y^2 - 10 = 0$ using a graphing utility, we need to solve the equation for y. Rearranging the terms, we observe that the equation is quadratic in the variable y: $2y^2 + \sqrt{3}xy + (x^2 - 10) = 0$. We can solve the equation for y using the quadratic formula with $a = 2$, $b = \sqrt{3}x$, and $c = x^2 - 10$.

Figure 53

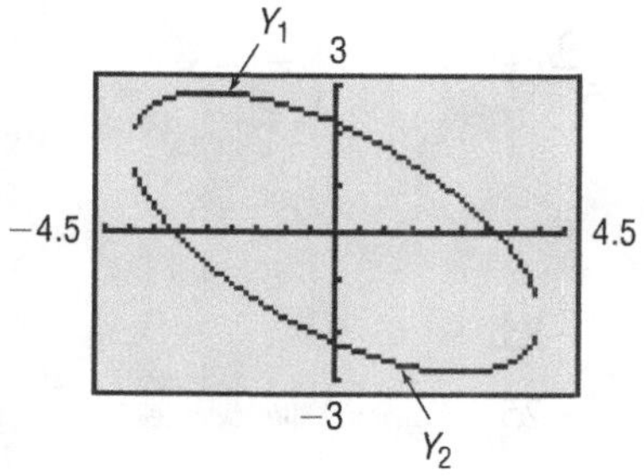

$$Y_1 = \frac{-\sqrt{3}x + \sqrt{\left(\sqrt{3}x\right)^2 - 4(2)(x^2 - 10)}}{2(2)} = \frac{-\sqrt{3}x + \sqrt{-5x^2 + 80}}{4}$$

and

$$Y_2 = \frac{-\sqrt{3}x - \sqrt{\left(\sqrt{3}x\right)^2 - 4(2)(x^2 - 10)}}{2(2)} = \frac{-\sqrt{3}x - \sqrt{-5x^2 + 80}}{4}$$

Figure 53 shows the graph of Y_1 and Y_2.

Now Work PROBLEM 31

In Example 3, the acute angle θ through which to rotate the axes was easy to find because of the numbers that we used in the given equation. In general, the equation $\cot(2\theta) = \frac{A - C}{B}$ will not have such a "nice" solution. As the next example shows, we can still find the appropriate rotation formulas without using a calculator approximation by applying Half-angle Formulas.

EXAMPLE 4 Analyzing an Equation Using a Rotation of Axes

Analyze the equation: $4x^2 - 4xy + y^2 + 5\sqrt{5}x + 5 = 0$

Solution Letting $A = 4$, $B = -4$, and $C = 1$ in equation (7), the appropriate angle θ through which to rotate the axes satisfies

$$\cot(2\theta) = \frac{A - C}{B} = \frac{3}{-4} = -\frac{3}{4}$$

To use rotation formulas (5), we need to know the values of $\sin\theta$ and $\cos\theta$. Since we seek an acute angle θ, we know that $\sin\theta > 0$ and $\cos\theta > 0$. We use the Half-angle Formulas in the form

$$\sin\theta = \sqrt{\frac{1-\cos(2\theta)}{2}} \qquad \cos\theta = \sqrt{\frac{1+\cos(2\theta)}{2}}$$

Now we need to find the value of $\cos(2\theta)$. Since $\cot(2\theta) = -\frac{3}{4}$, then $90° < 2\theta < 180°$ (Do you know why?), so $\cos(2\theta) = -\frac{3}{5}$. Then

$$\sin\theta = \sqrt{\frac{1-\cos(2\theta)}{2}} = \sqrt{\frac{1-\left(-\frac{3}{5}\right)}{2}} = \sqrt{\frac{4}{5}} = \frac{2}{\sqrt{5}} = \frac{2\sqrt{5}}{5}$$

$$\cos\theta = \sqrt{\frac{1+\cos(2\theta)}{2}} = \sqrt{\frac{1+\left(-\frac{3}{5}\right)}{2}} = \sqrt{\frac{1}{5}} = \frac{1}{\sqrt{5}} = \frac{\sqrt{5}}{5}$$

With these values, the rotation formulas (5) are

$$x = \frac{\sqrt{5}}{5}x' - \frac{2\sqrt{5}}{5}y' = \frac{\sqrt{5}}{5}(x' - 2y')$$

$$y = \frac{2\sqrt{5}}{5}x' + \frac{\sqrt{5}}{5}y' = \frac{\sqrt{5}}{5}(2x' + y')$$

Substituting these values in the original equation and simplifying, we obtain

$$4x^2 - 4xy + y^2 + 5\sqrt{5}x + 5 = 0$$

$$4\left[\frac{\sqrt{5}}{5}(x' - 2y')\right]^2 - 4\left[\frac{\sqrt{5}}{5}(x' - 2y')\right]\left[\frac{\sqrt{5}}{5}(2x' + y')\right] + \left[\frac{\sqrt{5}}{5}(2x' + y')\right]^2 + 5\sqrt{5}\left[\frac{\sqrt{5}}{5}(x' - 2y')\right] = -5$$

Multiply both sides by 5 and expand to obtain

$$4(x'^2 - 4x'y' + 4y'^2) - 4(2x'^2 - 3x'y' - 2y'^2) + 4x'^2 + 4x'y' + y'^2 + 25(x' - 2y') = -25$$

$$25y'^2 - 50y' + 25x' = -25 \quad \text{Combine like terms.}$$

$$y'^2 - 2y' + x' = -1 \quad \text{Divide by 25.}$$

$$y'^2 - 2y' + 1 = -x' \quad \text{Complete the square in } y'.$$

$$(y' - 1)^2 = -x'$$

Figure 54

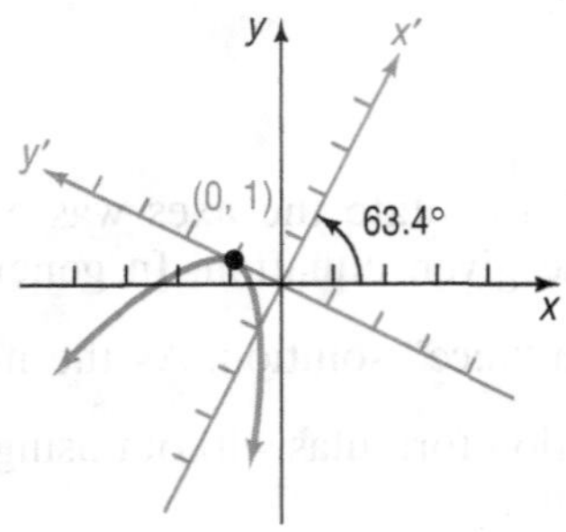

This is the equation of a parabola with vertex at $(0, 1)$ in the $x'y'$-plane. The axis of symmetry is parallel to the x'-axis. Using a calculator to solve $\sin\theta = \frac{2\sqrt{5}}{5}$, we find that $\theta \approx 63.4°$. See Figure 54 for the graph.

Now Work PROBLEM 37

4 Identify Conics without a Rotation of Axes

Suppose that we are required only to identify (rather than analyze) an equation of the form

$$Ax^2 + Bxy + Cy^2 + Dx + Ey + F = 0 \qquad B \neq 0 \qquad \textbf{(8)}$$

If we apply the rotation formulas (5) to this equation, we obtain an equation of the form

$$A'x'^2 + B'x'y' + C'y'^2 + D'x' + E'y' + F' = 0 \qquad \textbf{(9)}$$

where A', B', C', D', E', and F' can be expressed in terms of A, B, C, D, E, F and the angle θ of rotation (see Problem 53). It can be shown that the value of $B^2 - 4AC$ in equation (8) and the value of $B'^2 - 4A'C'$ in equation (9) are equal no matter what angle θ of rotation is chosen (see Problem 55). In particular, if the angle θ of rotation satisfies equation (7), then $B' = 0$ in equation (9), and $B^2 - 4AC = -4A'C'$. Since equation (9) then has the form of equation (2),

$$A'x'^2 + C'y'^2 + D'x' + E'y' + F' = 0$$

we can identify it without completing the squares, as we did in the beginning of this section. In fact, now we can identify the conic described by any equation of the form of equation (8) without a rotation of axes.

THEOREM

Identifying Conics without a Rotation of Axes

Except for degenerate cases, the equation

$$Ax^2 + Bxy + Cy^2 + Dx + Ey + F = 0$$

(a) Defines a parabola if $B^2 - 4AC = 0$.
(b) Defines an ellipse (or a circle) if $B^2 - 4AC < 0$.
(c) Defines a hyperbola if $B^2 - 4AC > 0$.

You are asked to prove this theorem in Problem 56.

EXAMPLE 5 **Identifying a Conic without a Rotation of Axes**

Identify the equation: $8x^2 - 12xy + 17y^2 - 4\sqrt{5}x - 2\sqrt{5}y - 15 = 0$

Solution Here $A = 8$, $B = -12$, and $C = 17$, so $B^2 - 4AC = -400$. Since $B^2 - 4AC < 0$, the equation defines an ellipse.

Now Work PROBLEM 43

10.5 Assess Your Understanding

'Are You Prepared?' *Answers are given at the end of these exercises. If you get a wrong answer, read the pages listed in red.*

1. The sum formula for the sine function is $\sin(A + B) =$ _____. (p. 469)
2. The Double-angle Formula for the sine function is $\sin(2\theta) =$ _____. (p. 476)
3. If θ is acute, the Half-angle Formula for the sine function is $\sin\frac{\theta}{2} =$ _____. (p. 480)
4. If θ is acute, the Half-angle Formula for the cosine function is $\cos\frac{\theta}{2} =$ _____. (p. 480)

Concepts and Vocabulary

5. To transform the equation

$$Ax^2 + Bxy + Cy^2 + Dx + Ey + F = 0, \qquad B \neq 0$$

into one in x' and y' without an $x'y'$-term, rotate the axes through an acute angle θ that satisfies the equation _____.

6. Identify the conic: $x^2 - 2y^2 - x - y - 18 = 0$ _____.
7. Identify the conic: $x^2 + 2xy + 3y^2 - 2x + 4y + 10 = 0$ _____.
8. ***True or False*** The equation $ax^2 + 6y^2 - 12y = 0$ defines an ellipse if $a > 0$.
9. ***True or False*** The equation $3x^2 + bxy + 12y^2 = 10$ defines a parabola if $b = -12$.
10. ***True or False*** To eliminate the xy-term from the equation $x^2 - 2xy + y^2 - 2x + 3y + 5 = 0$, rotate the axes through an angle θ, where $\cot\theta = B^2 - 4AC$.

Skill Building

In Problems 11–20, identify each equation without completing the squares.

11. $x^2 + 4x + y + 3 = 0$
12. $2y^2 - 3y + 3x = 0$
13. $6x^2 + 3y^2 - 12x + 6y = 0$
14. $2x^2 + y^2 - 8x + 4y + 2 = 0$
15. $3x^2 - 2y^2 + 6x + 4 = 0$
16. $4x^2 - 3y^2 - 8x + 6y + 1 = 0$
17. $2y^2 - x^2 - y + x = 0$
18. $y^2 - 8x^2 - 2x - y = 0$
19. $x^2 + y^2 - 8x + 4y = 0$
20. $2x^2 + 2y^2 - 8x + 8y = 0$

In Problems 21–30, determine the appropriate rotation formulas to use so that the new equation contains no xy-term.

21. $x^2 + 4xy + y^2 - 3 = 0$
22. $x^2 - 4xy + y^2 - 3 = 0$
23. $5x^2 + 6xy + 5y^2 - 8 = 0$
24. $3x^2 - 10xy + 3y^2 - 32 = 0$
25. $13x^2 - 6\sqrt{3}xy + 7y^2 - 16 = 0$
26. $11x^2 + 10\sqrt{3}xy + y^2 - 4 = 0$
27. $4x^2 - 4xy + y^2 - 8\sqrt{5}x - 16\sqrt{5}y = 0$
28. $x^2 + 4xy + 4y^2 + 5\sqrt{5}y + 5 = 0$
29. $25x^2 - 36xy + 40y^2 - 12\sqrt{13}x - 8\sqrt{13}y = 0$
30. $34x^2 - 24xy + 41y^2 - 25 = 0$

In Problems 31–42, rotate the axes so that the new equation contains no xy-term. Analyze and graph the new equation. Refer to Problems 21–30 for Problems 31–40. Verify your graph using a graphing utility.

31. $x^2 + 4xy + y^2 - 3 = 0$
32. $x^2 - 4xy + y^2 - 3 = 0$
33. $5x^2 + 6xy + 5y^2 - 8 = 0$
34. $3x^2 - 10xy + 3y^2 - 32 = 0$
35. $13x^2 - 6\sqrt{3}xy + 7y^2 - 16 = 0$
36. $11x^2 + 10\sqrt{3}xy + y^2 - 4 = 0$
37. $4x^2 - 4xy + y^2 - 8\sqrt{5}x - 16\sqrt{5}y = 0$
38. $x^2 + 4xy + 4y^2 + 5\sqrt{5}y + 5 = 0$
39. $25x^2 - 36xy + 40y^2 - 12\sqrt{13}x - 8\sqrt{13}y = 0$
40. $34x^2 - 24xy + 41y^2 - 25 = 0$
41. $16x^2 + 24xy + 9y^2 - 130x + 90y = 0$
42. $16x^2 + 24xy + 9y^2 - 60x + 80y = 0$

In Problems 43–52, identify each equation without applying a rotation of axes.

43. $x^2 + 3xy - 2y^2 + 3x + 2y + 5 = 0$
44. $2x^2 - 3xy + 4y^2 + 2x + 3y - 5 = 0$
45. $x^2 - 7xy + 3y^2 - y - 10 = 0$
46. $2x^2 - 3xy + 2y^2 - 4x - 2 = 0$
47. $9x^2 + 12xy + 4y^2 - x - y = 0$
48. $10x^2 + 12xy + 4y^2 - x - y + 10 = 0$
49. $10x^2 - 12xy + 4y^2 - x - y - 10 = 0$
50. $4x^2 + 12xy + 9y^2 - x - y = 0$
51. $3x^2 - 2xy + y^2 + 4x + 2y - 1 = 0$
52. $3x^2 + 2xy + y^2 + 4x - 2y + 10 = 0$

Applications and Extensions

In Problems 53–56, apply the rotation formulas (5) to

$$Ax^2 + Bxy + Cy^2 + Dx + Ey + F = 0$$

to obtain the equation

$$A'x'^2 + B'x'y' + C'y'^2 + D'x' + E'y' + F' = 0$$

53. Express A', B', C', D', E', and F' in terms of A, B, C, D, E, F, and the angle θ of rotation.

    [**Hint:** Refer to equation (6).]

54. Show that $A + C = A' + C'$, and thus show that $A + C$ is **invariant;** that is, its value does not change under a rotation of axes.

55. Refer to Problem 54. Show that $B^2 - 4AC$ is invariant.

56. Prove that, except for degenerate cases, the equation

$$Ax^2 + Bxy + Cy^2 + Dx + Ey + F = 0$$

    (a) Defines a parabola if $B^2 - 4AC = 0$.
    (b) Defines an ellipse (or a circle) if $B^2 - 4AC < 0$.
    (c) Defines a hyperbola if $B^2 - 4AC > 0$.

57. Use rotation formulas (5) to show that distance is invariant under a rotation of axes. That is, show that the distance from $P_1 = (x_1, y_1)$ to $P_2 = (x_2, y_2)$ in the xy-plane equals the distance from $P_1 = (x_1', y_1')$ to $P_2 = (x_2', y_2')$ in the $x'y'$-plane.

58. Show that the graph of the equation $x^{1/2} + y^{1/2} = a^{1/2}$ is part of the graph of a parabola.

Discussion and Writing

59. Formulate a strategy for discussing and graphing an equation of the form

$$Ax^2 + Cy^2 + Dx + Ey + F = 0$$

60. How does your strategy change if the equation is of the following form?

$$Ax^2 + Bxy + Cy^2 + Dx + Ey + F = 0$$

'Are You Prepared?' Answers

1. $\sin A \cos B + \cos A \sin B$ **2.** $2 \sin \theta \cos \theta$ **3.** $\sqrt{\dfrac{1 - \cos \theta}{2}}$ **4.** $\sqrt{\dfrac{1 + \cos \theta}{2}}$

10.6 Polar Equations of Conics

PREPARING FOR THIS SECTION *Before getting started, review the following:*

- Polar Coordinates (Section 9.1, pp. 562–569)

Now Work the 'Are You Prepared?' problems on page 685.

OBJECTIVES 1 Analyze and Graph Polar Equations of Conics (p. 681)
2 Convert the Polar Equation of a Conic to a Rectangular Equation (p. 685)

1 Analyze and Graph Polar Equations of Conics

In Sections 10.2 through 10.4, we gave separate definitions for the parabola, ellipse, and hyperbola based on geometric properties and the distance formula. In this section, we present an alternative definition that simultaneously defines all these conics. As we shall see, this approach is well suited to polar coordinate representation. (Refer to Section 9.1.)

DEFINITION

Let D denote a fixed line called the **directrix;** let F denote a fixed point called the **focus,** which is not on D; and let e be a fixed positive number called the **eccentricity.** A **conic** is the set of points P in the plane such that the ratio of the distance from F to P to the distance from D to P equals e. That is, a conic is the collection of points P for which

$$\frac{d(F, P)}{d(D, P)} = e \qquad (1)$$

If $e = 1$, the conic is a **parabola.**
If $e < 1$, the conic is an **ellipse.**
If $e > 1$, the conic is a **hyperbola.**

Observe that if $e = 1$ the definition of a parabola in equation (1) is exactly the same as the definition used earlier in Section 10.2.

In the case of an ellipse, the **major axis** is a line through the focus perpendicular to the directrix. In the case of a hyperbola, the **transverse axis** is a line through the focus perpendicular to the directrix. For both an ellipse and a hyperbola, the eccentricity e satisfies

$$e = \frac{c}{a} \qquad (2)$$

where c is the distance from the center to the focus and a is the distance from the center to a vertex.

Just as we did earlier using rectangular coordinates, we derive equations for the conics in polar coordinates by choosing a convenient position for the focus F and the directrix D. The focus F is positioned at the pole, and the directrix D is either parallel or perpendicular to the polar axis.

Suppose that we start with the directrix D perpendicular to the polar axis at a distance p units to the left of the pole (the focus F). See Figure 55.

Figure 55

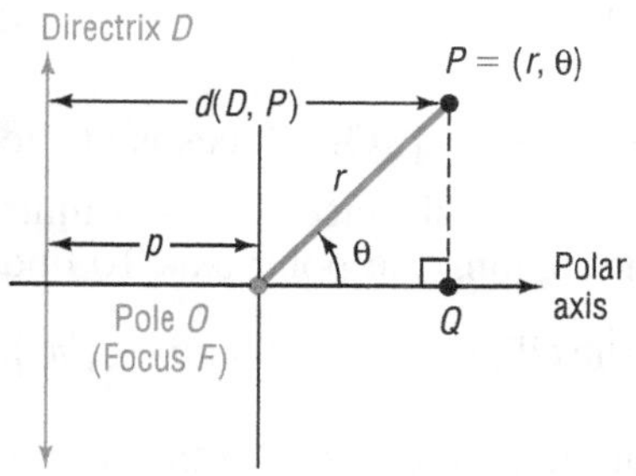

If $P = (r, \theta)$ is any point on the conic, then, by equation (1),

$$\frac{d(F, P)}{d(D, P)} = e \quad \text{or} \quad d(F, P) = e \cdot d(D, P) \tag{3}$$

Now we use the point Q obtained by dropping the perpendicular from P to the polar axis to calculate $d(D, P)$.

$$d(D, P) = p + d(O, Q) = p + r\cos\theta$$

Using this expression and the fact that $d(F, P) = d(O, P) = r$ in equation (3), we get

$$\begin{aligned} d(F, P) &= e \cdot d(D, P) \\ r &= e(p + r\cos\theta) \\ r &= ep + er\cos\theta \\ r - er\cos\theta &= ep \\ r(1 - e\cos\theta) &= ep \\ r &= \frac{ep}{1 - e\cos\theta} \end{aligned}$$

THEOREM **Polar Equation of a Conic; Focus at the Pole; Directrix Perpendicular to the Polar Axis a Distance p to the Left of the Pole**

The polar equation of a conic with focus at the pole and directrix perpendicular to the polar axis at a distance p to the left of the pole is

$$r = \frac{ep}{1 - e\cos\theta} \tag{4}$$

where e is the eccentricity of the conic.

EXAMPLE 1 **Analyzing and Graphing the Polar Equation of a Conic**

Analyze and graph the equation: $r = \dfrac{4}{2 - \cos\theta}$

Solution The given equation is not quite in the form of equation (4), since the first term in the denominator is 2 instead of 1. We divide the numerator and denominator by 2 to obtain

$$r = \frac{2}{1 - \frac{1}{2}\cos\theta} \qquad r = \frac{ep}{1 - e\cos\theta}$$

This equation is in the form of equation (4), with

$$e = \frac{1}{2} \quad \text{and} \quad ep = 2$$

Then

$$\frac{1}{2}p = 2, \quad \text{so} \quad p = 4$$

We conclude that the conic is an ellipse, since $e = \frac{1}{2} < 1$. One focus is at the pole, and the directrix is perpendicular to the polar axis, a distance of $p = 4$ units to the left of the pole. It follows that the major axis is along the polar axis. To find the vertices, we let $\theta = 0$ and $\theta = \pi$. The vertices of the ellipse are $(4, 0)$ and $\left(\frac{4}{3}, \pi\right)$. The midpoint of the vertices, $\left(\frac{4}{3}, 0\right)$ in polar coordinates, is the center of the ellipse.

Figure 56

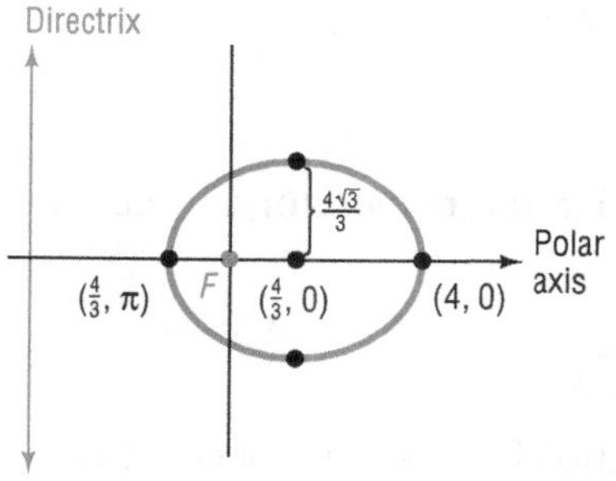

(a)

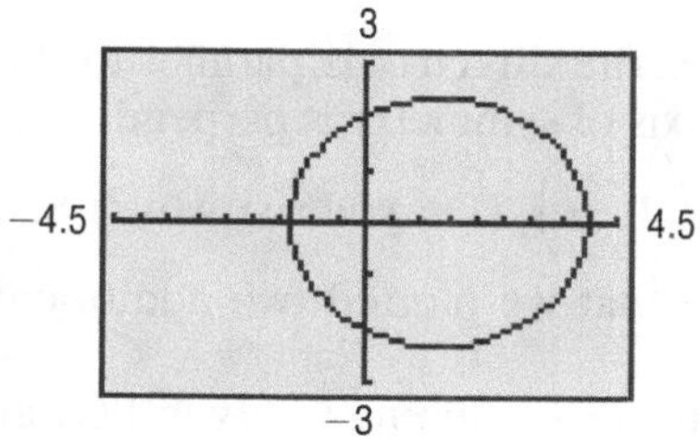

(b)

[Do you see why? The vertices $(4, 0)$ and $\left(\frac{4}{3}, \pi\right)$ in polar coordinates are $(4, 0)$ and $\left(-\frac{4}{3}, 0\right)$ in rectangular coordinates. The midpoint in rectangular coordinates is $\left(\frac{4}{3}, 0\right)$, which is also $\left(\frac{4}{3}, 0\right)$ in polar coordinates.] Then a = distance from the center to a vertex $= \frac{8}{3}$. Using $a = \frac{8}{3}$ and $e = \frac{1}{2}$ in equation (2), $e = \frac{c}{a}$, we find $c = ae = \frac{4}{3}$. Finally, using $a = \frac{8}{3}$ and $c = \frac{4}{3}$ in $b^2 = a^2 - c^2$, we have

$$b^2 = a^2 - c^2 = \frac{64}{9} - \frac{16}{9} = \frac{48}{9}$$

$$b = \frac{4\sqrt{3}}{3}$$

Figure 56(a) shows the graph drawn by hand.

Figure 56(b) shows the graph of the equation obtained using a graphing utility in POLar mode with $\theta\text{min} = 0$, $\theta\text{max} = 2\pi$, and $\theta\text{step} = \frac{\pi}{24}$.

Exploration

Graph $r_1 = \frac{4}{2 + \cos\theta}$ and compare the result with Figure 56. What do you conclude? Clear the screen and graph $r_1 = \frac{4}{2 - \sin\theta}$ and then $r_1 = \frac{4}{2 + \sin\theta}$. Compare each of these graphs with Figure 56. What do you conclude?

Now Work PROBLEM 11

Equation (4) was obtained under the assumption that the directrix was perpendicular to the polar axis at a distance p units to the left of the pole. A similar derivation (see Problem 43), in which the directrix is perpendicular to the polar axis at a distance p units to the right of the pole, results in the equation

$$r = \frac{ep}{1 + e\cos\theta}$$

In Problems 44 and 45, you are asked to derive the polar equations of conics with focus at the pole and directrix parallel to the polar axis. Table 5 summarizes the polar equations of conics.

Table 5

POLAR EQUATIONS OF CONICS (FOCUS AT THE POLE, ECCENTRICITY e)

Equation	Description
(a) $r = \frac{ep}{1 - e\cos\theta}$	Directrix is perpendicular to the polar axis at a distance p units to the left of the pole.
(b) $r = \frac{ep}{1 + e\cos\theta}$	Directrix is perpendicular to the polar axis at a distance p units to the right of the pole.
(c) $r = \frac{ep}{1 + e\sin\theta}$	Directrix is parallel to the polar axis at a distance p units above the pole.
(d) $r = \frac{ep}{1 - e\sin\theta}$	Directrix is parallel to the polar axis at a distance p units below the pole.

Eccentricity

If $e = 1$, the conic is a parabola; the axis of symmetry is perpendicular to the directrix.

If $e < 1$, the conic is an ellipse; the major axis is perpendicular to the directrix.

If $e > 1$, the conic is a hyperbola; the transverse axis is perpendicular to the directrix.

EXAMPLE 2 Analyzing and Graphing the Polar Equation of a Conic

Analyze and graph the equation: $r = \dfrac{6}{3 + 3\sin\theta}$

Solution To place the equation in proper form, we divide the numerator and denominator by 3 to get

$$r = \frac{2}{1 + \sin\theta}$$

Referring to Table 5, we conclude that this equation is in the form of equation (c) with

$$e = 1 \quad \text{and} \quad ep = 2$$

$$p = 2 \qquad e = 1$$

Figure 57

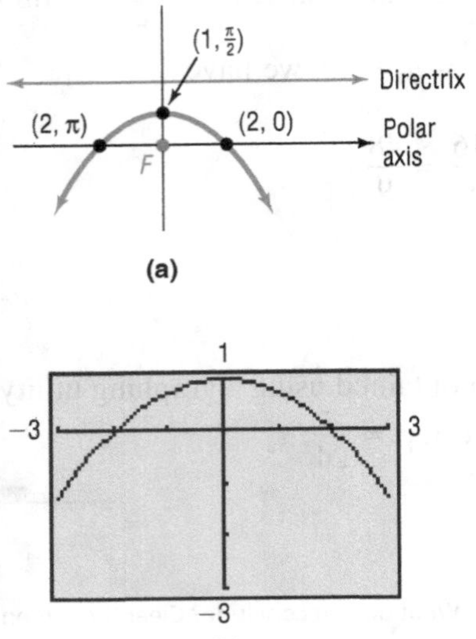

(a)

(b)

The conic is a parabola with focus at the pole. The directrix is parallel to the polar axis at a distance 2 units above the pole; the axis of symmetry is perpendicular to the polar axis. The vertex of the parabola is at $\left(1, \dfrac{\pi}{2}\right)$. (Do you see why?) See Figure 57(a) for the graph drawn by hand. Notice that we plotted two additional points, $(2, 0)$ and $(2, \pi)$, to assist in graphing.

Figure 57(b) shows the graph of the equation using a graphing utility in POLar mode with $\theta\text{min} = 0$, $\theta\text{max} = 2\pi$, and $\theta\text{step} = \dfrac{\pi}{24}$.

Now Work PROBLEM 13

EXAMPLE 3 Analyzing and Graphing the Polar Equation of a Conic

Analyze and graph the equation: $r = \dfrac{3}{1 + 3\cos\theta}$

Solution This equation is in the form of equation (b) in Table 5. We conclude that

$$e = 3 \quad \text{and} \quad ep = 3$$

$$p = 1 \qquad e = 3$$

This is the equation of a hyperbola with a focus at the pole. The directrix is perpendicular to the polar axis, 1 unit to the right of the pole. The transverse axis is along the polar axis. To find the vertices, we let $\theta = 0$ and $\theta = \pi$. The vertices are $\left(\dfrac{3}{4}, 0\right)$ and $\left(-\dfrac{3}{2}, \pi\right)$. The center, which is at the midpoint of $\left(\dfrac{3}{4}, 0\right)$ and $\left(-\dfrac{3}{2}, \pi\right)$, is $\left(\dfrac{9}{8}, 0\right)$. Then c = distance from the center to a focus $= \dfrac{9}{8}$. Since $e = 3$, it follows from equation (2), $e = \dfrac{c}{a}$, that $a = \dfrac{3}{8}$. Finally, using $a = \dfrac{3}{8}$ and $c = \dfrac{9}{8}$ in $b^2 = c^2 - a^2$, we find

$$b^2 = c^2 - a^2 = \frac{81}{64} - \frac{9}{64} = \frac{72}{64} = \frac{9}{8}$$

$$b = \frac{3}{2\sqrt{2}} = \frac{3\sqrt{2}}{4}$$

Figure 58(a) shows the graph drawn by hand. Notice that we plotted two additional points, $\left(3, \dfrac{\pi}{2}\right)$ and $\left(3, \dfrac{3\pi}{2}\right)$, on the left branch and used symmetry to obtain the right branch. The asymptotes of this hyperbola were found in the usual way by constructing the rectangle shown.

Figures 58(b) and (c) show the graph of the equation using a graphing utility in POLar mode with $\theta\text{min} = 0$, $\theta\text{max} = 2\pi$, and $\theta\text{step} = \frac{\pi}{24}$, using both dot mode and connected mode. Notice the extraneous asymptotes in connected mode.

Figure 58

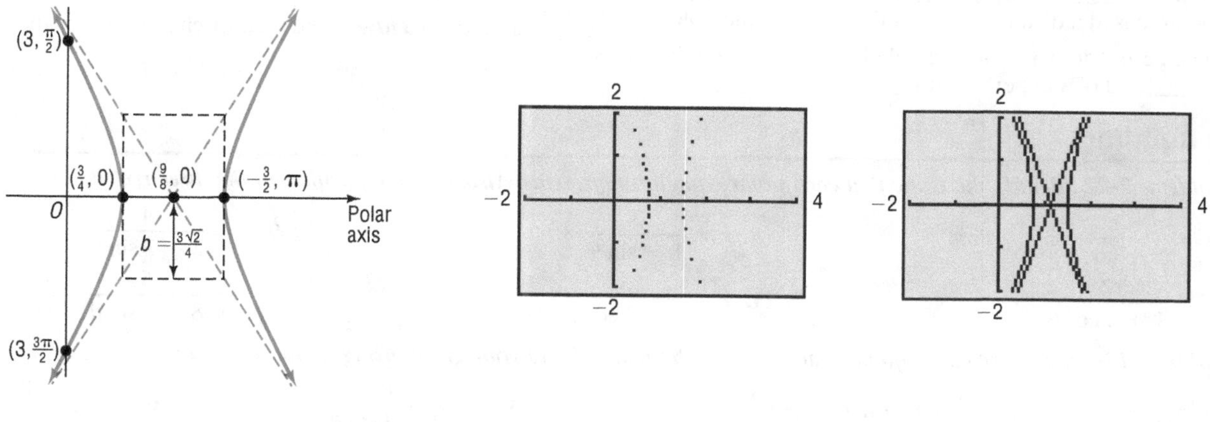

(a) (b) Dot Mode (c) Connected Mode

Now Work PROBLEM 17

2 Convert the Polar Equation of a Conic to a Rectangular Equation

EXAMPLE 4 **Converting a Polar Equation to a Rectangular Equation**

Convert the polar equation

$$r = \frac{1}{3 - 3\cos\theta}$$

to a rectangular equation.

Solution The strategy here is first to rearrange the equation and square each side before using the transformation equations.

$$r = \frac{1}{3 - 3\cos\theta}$$

$$3r - 3r\cos\theta = 1$$

$$3r = 1 + 3r\cos\theta \quad \text{Rearrange the equation.}$$

$$9r^2 = (1 + 3r\cos\theta)^2 \quad \text{Square each side.}$$

$$9(x^2 + y^2) = (1 + 3x)^2 \quad x^2 + y^2 = r^2;\ x = r\cos\theta$$

$$9x^2 + 9y^2 = 9x^2 + 6x + 1$$

$$9y^2 = 6x + 1$$

This is the equation of a parabola in rectangular coordinates.

Now Work PROBLEM 25

10.6 Assess Your Understanding

'Are You Prepared?' *Answers are given at the end of these exercises. If you get a wrong answer, read the pages listed in red.*

1. If (x, y) are the rectangular coordinates of a point P and (r, θ) are its polar coordinates, then $x =$ _____ and $y =$ _____. (p. 564)

2. Transform the equation $r = 6\cos\theta$ from polar coordinates to rectangular coordinates. (pp. 568–569)

Concepts and Vocabulary

3. The polar equation $r = \dfrac{8}{4 - 2\sin\theta}$ is a conic whose eccentricity is _____. It is a(n) _____ whose directrix is _____ to the polar axis at a distance _____ units _____ of the pole.

4. The eccentricity e of a parabola is _____, of an ellipse it is _____, and of a hyperbola it is _____.

5. ***True or False*** If (r, θ) are polar coordinates, the equation $r = \dfrac{2}{2 + 3\sin\theta}$ defines a hyperbola.

6. ***True or False*** The eccentricity of any parabola is 1.

Skill Building

In Problems 7–12, identify the conic that each polar equation represents. Also, give the position of the directrix.

7. $r = \dfrac{1}{1 + \cos\theta}$
8. $r = \dfrac{3}{1 - \sin\theta}$
9. $r = \dfrac{4}{2 - 3\sin\theta}$
10. $r = \dfrac{2}{1 + 2\cos\theta}$
11. $r = \dfrac{3}{4 - 2\cos\theta}$
12. $r = \dfrac{6}{8 + 2\sin\theta}$

In Problems 13–24, analyze each equation and graph it by hand. Verify your graph using a graphing utility.

13. $r = \dfrac{1}{1 + \cos\theta}$
14. $r = \dfrac{3}{1 - \sin\theta}$
15. $r = \dfrac{8}{4 + 3\sin\theta}$
16. $r = \dfrac{10}{5 + 4\cos\theta}$
17. $r = \dfrac{9}{3 - 6\cos\theta}$
18. $r = \dfrac{12}{4 + 8\sin\theta}$
19. $r = \dfrac{8}{2 - \sin\theta}$
20. $r = \dfrac{8}{2 + 4\cos\theta}$
21. $r(3 - 2\sin\theta) = 6$
22. $r(2 - \cos\theta) = 2$
23. $r = \dfrac{6\sec\theta}{2\sec\theta - 1}$
24. $r = \dfrac{3\csc\theta}{\csc\theta - 1}$

In Problems 25–36, convert each polar equation to a rectangular equation.

25. $r = \dfrac{1}{1 + \cos\theta}$
26. $r = \dfrac{3}{1 - \sin\theta}$
27. $r = \dfrac{8}{4 + 3\sin\theta}$
28. $r = \dfrac{10}{5 + 4\cos\theta}$
29. $r = \dfrac{9}{3 - 6\cos\theta}$
30. $r = \dfrac{12}{4 + 8\sin\theta}$
31. $r = \dfrac{8}{2 - \sin\theta}$
32. $r = \dfrac{8}{2 + 4\cos\theta}$
33. $r(3 - 2\sin\theta) = 6$
34. $r(2 - \cos\theta) = 2$
35. $r = \dfrac{6\sec\theta}{2\sec\theta - 1}$
36. $r = \dfrac{3\csc\theta}{\csc\theta - 1}$

In Problems 37–42, find a polar equation for each conic. For each, a focus is at the pole.

37. $e = 1$; directrix is parallel to the polar axis 1 unit above the pole.
38. $e = 1$; directrix is parallel to the polar axis 2 units below the pole.
39. $e = \dfrac{4}{5}$; directrix is perpendicular to the polar axis 3 units to the left of the pole.
40. $e = \dfrac{2}{3}$; directrix is parallel to the polar axis 3 units above the pole.
41. $e = 6$; directrix is parallel to the polar axis 2 units below the pole.
42. $e = 5$; directrix is perpendicular to the polar axis 5 units to the right of the pole.

Applications and Extensions

43. Derive equation (b) in Table 5:
$$r = \frac{ep}{1 + e\cos\theta}$$

44. Derive equation (c) in Table 5:
$$r = \frac{ep}{1 + e\sin\theta}$$

45. Derive equation (d) in Table 5:
$$r = \frac{ep}{1 - e\sin\theta}$$

46. **Orbit of Mercury** The planet Mercury travels around the Sun in an elliptical orbit given approximately by
$$r = \frac{(3.442)10^7}{1 - 0.206\cos\theta}$$
where r is measured in miles and the Sun is at the pole. Find the distance from Mercury to the Sun at *aphelion* (greatest distance from the Sun) and at *perihelion* (shortest distance from the Sun). See the figure. Use the aphelion and perihelion to graph the orbit of Mercury using a graphing utility.

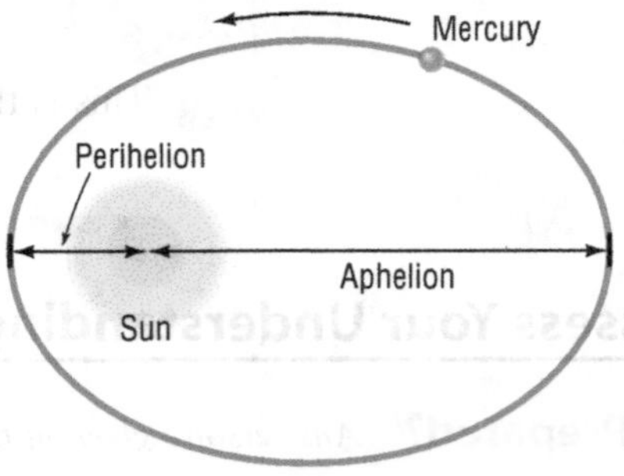

'Are You Prepared?' Answers

1. $r\cos\theta$; $r\sin\theta$
2. $x^2 + y^2 = 6x$ or $(x - 3)^2 + y^2 = 9$

10.7 Plane Curves and Parametric Equations

PREPARING FOR THIS SECTION *Before getting started, review the following:*

- Amplitude and Period of Sinusoidal Graphs (Section 6.4, pp. 400–401)

Now Work the 'Are You Prepared?' problem on page 697.

OBJECTIVES
1. Graph Parametric Equations by Hand (p. 687)
2. Graph Parametric Equations Using a Graphing Utility (p. 688)
3. Find a Rectangular Equation for a Curve Defined Parametrically (p. 689)
4. Use Time as a Parameter in Parametric Equations (p. 691)
5. Find Parametric Equations for Curves Defined by Rectangular Equations (p. 694)

Equations of the form $y = f(x)$, where f is a function, have graphs that are intersected no more than once by any vertical line. The graphs of many of the conics and certain other, more complicated, graphs do not have this characteristic. Yet each graph, like the graph of a function, is a collection of points (x, y) in the xy-plane; that is, each is a *plane curve*. In this section, we discuss another way of representing such graphs.

Let $x = f(t)$ and $y = g(t)$, where f and g are two functions whose common domain is some interval I. The collection of points defined by

$$(x, y) = (f(t), g(t))$$

is called a **plane curve.** The equations

$$x = f(t) \qquad y = g(t)$$

where t is in I, are called **parametric equations** of the curve. The variable t is called a **parameter.**

1 Graph Parametric Equations by Hand

Parametric equations are particularly useful in describing movement along a curve. Suppose that a curve is defined by the parametric equations

$$x = f(t), \qquad y = g(t), \qquad a \le t \le b$$

where f and g are each defined over the interval $a \le t \le b$. For a given value of t, we can find the value of $x = f(t)$ and $y = g(t)$, obtaining a point (x, y) on the curve. In fact, as t varies over the interval from $t = a$ to $t = b$, successive values of t give rise to a directed movement along the curve; that is, the curve is traced out in a certain direction by the corresponding succession of points (x, y). See Figure 59. The arrows show the direction, or **orientation,** along the curve as t varies from a to b.

Figure 59

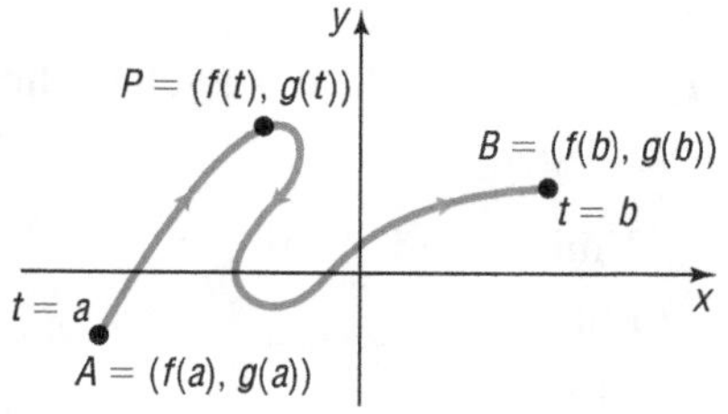

EXAMPLE 1 Graphing a Curve Defined by Parametric Equations

Graph the curve defined by the parametric equations

$$x = 3t^2, \qquad y = 2t, \qquad -2 \le t \le 2$$

Solution For each number t, $-2 \le t \le 2$, there corresponds a number x and a number y. For example, when $t = -2$, then $x = 3(-2)^2 = 12$ and $y = 2(-2) = -4$. When $t = 0$, then $x = 0$ and $y = 0$. We can set up a table listing various choices of the parameter t and the corresponding values for x and y, as shown in Table 6. Plotting these points and connecting them with a smooth curve leads to Figure 60. The arrows in Figure 60 are used to indicate the orientation.

Table 6

t	x	y	(x, y)
−2	12	−4	(12, −4)
−1	3	−2	(3, −2)
0	0	0	(0, 0)
1	3	2	(3, 2)
2	12	4	(12, 4)

Figure 60

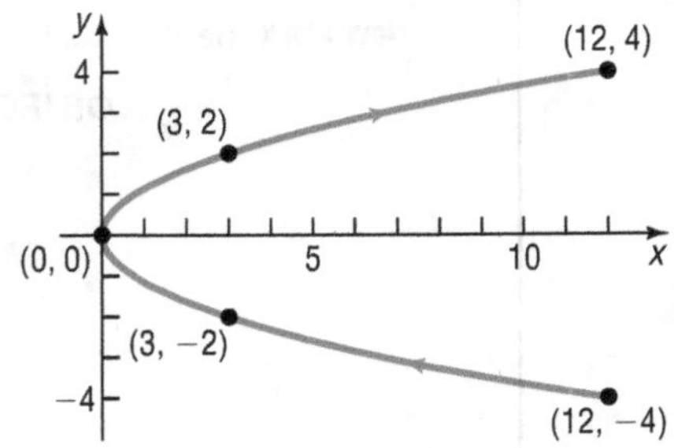

2 Graph Parametric Equations Using a Graphing Utility

Most graphing utilities have the capability of graphing parametric equations. The following steps are usually required to obtain the graph of parametric equations. Check your owner's manual to see how yours works.

Graphing Parametric Equations Using a Graphing Utility

STEP 1: Set the mode to PARametric, Enter $x(t)$ and $y(t)$.

STEP 2: Select the viewing window. In addition to setting Xmin, Xmax, Xscl, and so on, the viewing window in parametric mode requires setting minimum and maximum values for the parameter t and an increment setting for t(Tstep).

STEP 3: Graph.

EXAMPLE 2 Graphing a Curve Defined by Parametric Equations Using a Graphing Utility

Graph the curve defined by the parametric equations

$$x = 3t^2, \quad y = 2t, \quad -2 \le t \le 2 \qquad (1)$$

Solution **STEP 1:** Enter the equations $x(t) = 3t^2$, $y(t) = 2t$ with the graphing utility in PARametric mode.

STEP 2: Select the viewing window. The interval I is $-2 \le t \le 2$, so we select the following square viewing window:

$T\text{min} = -2$	$X\text{min} = 0$	$Y\text{min} = -5$
$T\text{max} = 2$	$X\text{max} = 15$	$Y\text{max} = 5$
$T\text{step} = 0.1$	$X\text{scl} = 1$	$Y\text{scl} = 1$

We choose Tmin $= -2$ and Tmax $= 2$ because $-2 \le t \le 2$. Finally, the choice for Tstep will determine the number of points the graphing utility will plot. For example, with Tstep at 0.1, the graphing utility will evaluate x and y at $t = -2, -1.9, -1.8$, and so on. The smaller the Tstep, the more points the graphing utility will plot. The reader is encouraged to experiment with different values of Tstep to see how the graph is affected.

STEP 3: Graph. Notice the direction the graph is drawn in. This direction shows the orientation of the curve. See Figure 61.

Figure 61

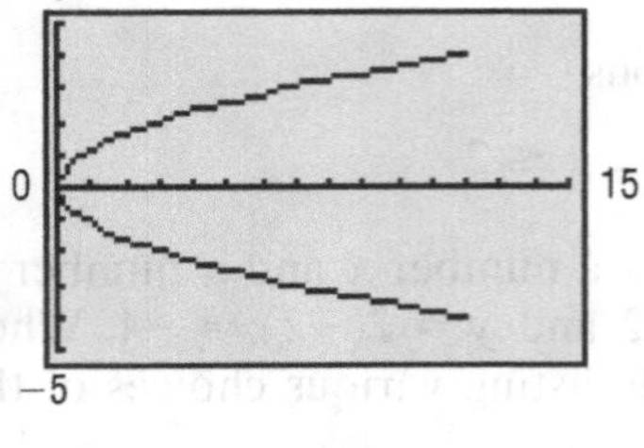

Exploration

Graph the following parametric equations using a graphing utility with $Xmin = 0, Xmax = 15$, $Ymin = -5, Ymax = 5$, and $Tstep = 0.1$:

1. $x = \dfrac{3t^2}{4}, y = t, -4 \le t \le 4$
2. $x = 3t^2 + 12t + 12, y = 2t + 4, -4 \le t \le 0$
3. $x = 3t^{\frac{2}{3}}, y = 2\sqrt[3]{t}, -8 \le t \le 8$

Compare these graphs to the graph in Figure 61. Conclude that parametric equations defining a curve are not unique; that is, different parametric equations can represent the same graph.

3 Find a Rectangular Equation for a Curve Defined Parametrically

The curve given in Examples 1 and 2 should be familiar. To identify it accurately, we find the corresponding rectangular equation by eliminating the parameter t from the parametric equations given in Example 1:

$$x = 3t^2, \qquad y = 2t, \qquad -2 \le t \le 2$$

Noting that we can easily solve for t in $y = 2t$, obtaining $t = \dfrac{y}{2}$, we substitute this expression in the other equation.

$$x = 3t^2 = 3\left(\frac{y}{2}\right)^2 = \frac{3y^2}{4}$$

$$\uparrow \quad t = \frac{y}{2}$$

This equation, $x = \dfrac{3y^2}{4}$, is the equation of a parabola with vertex at $(0, 0)$ and axis of symmetry along the x-axis.

Exploration

In FUNCtion mode, graph $x = \dfrac{3y^2}{4}\left(Y_1 = \sqrt{\dfrac{4x}{3}} \text{ and } Y_2 = -\sqrt{\dfrac{4x}{3}}\right)$ with $Xmin = 0, Xmax = 15$, $Ymin = -5, Ymax = 5$. Compare this graph with Figure 61. Why do the graphs differ?

Note that the parameterized curve defined by equation (1) and shown in Figure 60 (or 61) is only a part of the parabola $x = \dfrac{3y^2}{4}$. The graph of the rectangular equation obtained by eliminating the parameter will, in general, contain more points than the original parameterized curve. Care must therefore be taken when a parameterized curve is sketched by hand after eliminating the parameter. Even so, the process of eliminating the parameter t of a parameterized curve to identify it accurately is sometimes a better approach than plotting points. However, the elimination process sometimes requires a little ingenuity.

EXAMPLE 3 **Finding the Rectangular Equation of a Curve Defined Parametrically**

Find the rectangular equation of the curve whose parametric equations are

$$x = a\cos t, \qquad y = a\sin t, \qquad -\infty < t < \infty$$

where $a > 0$ is a constant. By hand, graph this curve, indicating its orientation.

Solution The presence of sines and cosines in the parametric equations suggests that we use a Pythagorean Identity. In fact, since

$$\cos t = \frac{x}{a} \qquad \sin t = \frac{y}{a}$$

we find that

$$\cos^2 t + \sin^2 t = 1$$
$$\left(\frac{x}{a}\right)^2 + \left(\frac{y}{a}\right)^2 = 1$$
$$x^2 + y^2 = a^2$$

Figure 62

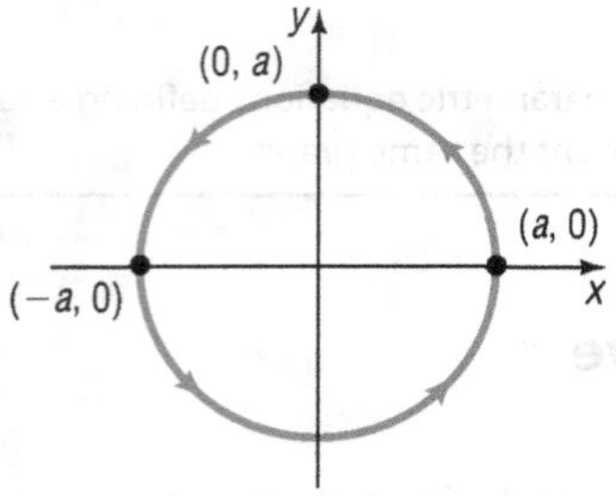

The curve is a circle with center at $(0, 0)$ and radius a. As the parameter t increases, say from $t = 0$ [the point $(a, 0)$] to $t = \frac{\pi}{2}$ [the point $(0, a)$] to $t = \pi$ [the point $(-a, 0)$], we see that the corresponding points are traced in a counterclockwise direction around the circle. The orientation is as indicated in Figure 62.

Now Work PROBLEMS 7 AND 19

Let's analyze the curve in Example 3 further. The domain of each parametric equation is $-\infty < t < \infty$. Thus, the graph in Figure 62 is actually being repeated each time that t increases by 2π.

If we wanted the curve to consist of exactly 1 revolution in the counterclockwise direction, we could write

$$x = a\cos t, \qquad y = a\sin t, \qquad 0 \le t \le 2\pi$$

This curve starts at $t = 0$ [the point $(a, 0)$] and, proceeding counterclockwise around the circle, ends at $t = 2\pi$ [also the point $(a, 0)$].

If we wanted the curve to consist of exactly three revolutions in the counterclockwise direction, we could write

$$x = a\cos t, \qquad y = a\sin t, \qquad -2\pi \le t \le 4\pi$$

or

$$x = a\cos t, \qquad y = a\sin t, \qquad 0 \le t \le 6\pi$$

or

$$x = a\cos t, \qquad y = a\sin t, \qquad 2\pi \le t \le 8\pi$$

EXAMPLE 4 Describing Parametric Equations

Find rectangular equations for the following curves defined by parametric equations. Graph each curve.

(a) $x = a\cos t, \quad y = a\sin t, \quad 0 \le t \le \pi, \quad a > 0$

(b) $x = -a\sin t, \quad y = -a\cos t, \quad 0 \le t \le \pi, \quad a > 0$

Solution (a) We eliminate the parameter t using a Pythagorean Identity.

$$\cos^2 t + \sin^2 t = 1$$
$$\left(\frac{x}{a}\right)^2 + \left(\frac{y}{a}\right)^2 = 1$$
$$x^2 + y^2 = a^2$$

The curve defined by these parametric equations is a circle, with radius a and center at $(0, 0)$. The circle begins at the point $(a, 0)$, $t = 0$; passes through the point $(0, a)$, $t = \frac{\pi}{2}$; and ends at the point $(-a, 0)$, $t = \pi$.

Figure 63

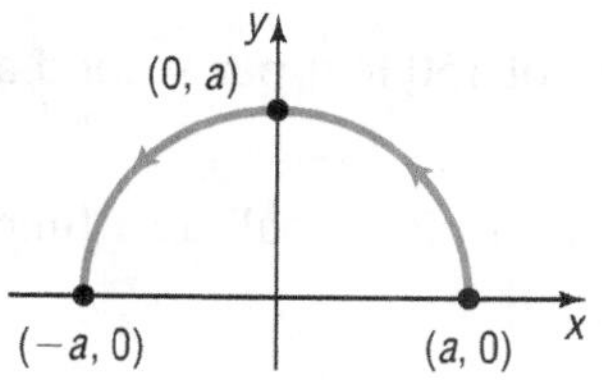

The parametric equations define an upper semicircle of radius a with a counterclockwise orientation. See Figure 63. The rectangular equation is

$$y = \sqrt{a^2 - x^2} \qquad -a \le x \le a$$

(b) We eliminate the parameter t using a Pythagorean Identity.

$$\sin^2 t + \cos^2 t = 1$$

$$\left(\frac{x}{-a}\right)^2 + \left(\frac{y}{-a}\right)^2 = 1$$

$$x^2 + y^2 = a^2$$

Figure 64

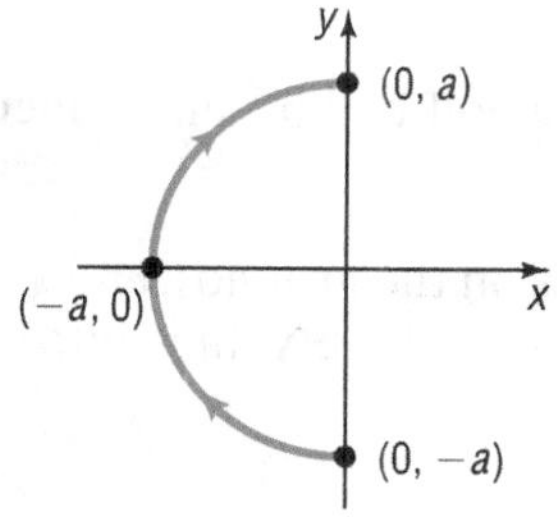

The curve defined by these parametric equations is a circle, with radius a and center at $(0, 0)$. The circle begins at the point $(0, -a)$, $t = 0$; passes through the point $(-a, 0)$, $t = \frac{\pi}{2}$; and ends at the point $(0, a)$, $t = \pi$. The parametric equations define a left semicircle of radius a with a clockwise orientation. See Figure 64. The rectangular equation is

$$x = -\sqrt{a^2 - y^2} \qquad -a \le y \le a$$

Seeing the Concept

Graph $x = \cos t, y = \sin t$ for $0 \le t \le 2\pi$. Compare to Figure 62. Graph $x = \cos t, y = \sin t$ for $0 \le t \le \pi$. Compare to Figure 63. Graph $x = -\sin t, y = -\cos t$ for $0 \le t \le \pi$. Compare to Figure 64.

Example 4 illustrates the versatility of parametric equations for replacing complicated rectangular equations, while providing additional information about orientation. These characteristics make parametric equations very useful in applications, such as projectile motion.

4 Use Time as a Parameter in Parametric Equations

If we think of the parameter t as time, then the parametric equations $x = f(t)$ and $y = g(t)$ of a curve C specify how the x- and y-coordinates of a moving point vary with time.

For example, we can use parametric equations to model the motion of an object, sometimes referred to as **curvilinear motion.** Using parametric equations, we can specify not only where the object travels, that is, its location (x, y), but also when it gets there, that is, the time t.

When an object is propelled upward at an inclination θ to the horizontal with initial speed v_0, the resulting motion is called **projectile motion.** See Figure 65(a).

In calculus it is shown that the parametric equations of the path of a projectile fired at an inclination θ to the horizontal, with an initial speed v_0, from a height h above the horizontal are

$$x = (v_0 \cos \theta)t \qquad y = -\frac{1}{2}gt^2 + (v_0 \sin \theta)t + h \qquad \textbf{(2)}$$

where t is the time and g is the constant acceleration due to gravity (approximately 32 ft/sec/sec or 9.8 m/sec/sec). See Figure 65(b).

Figure 65

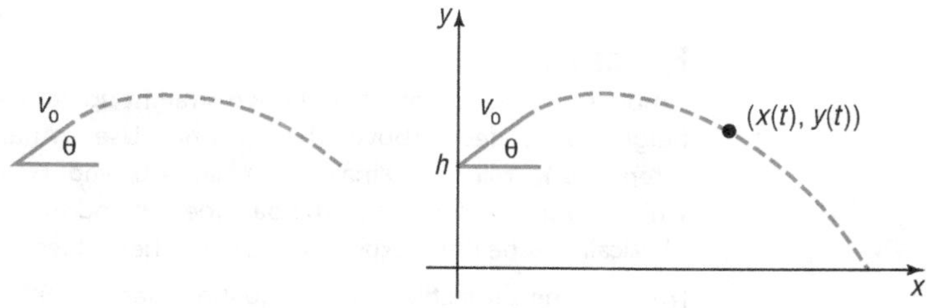

(a) (b)

EXAMPLE 5 Projectile Motion

Figure 66

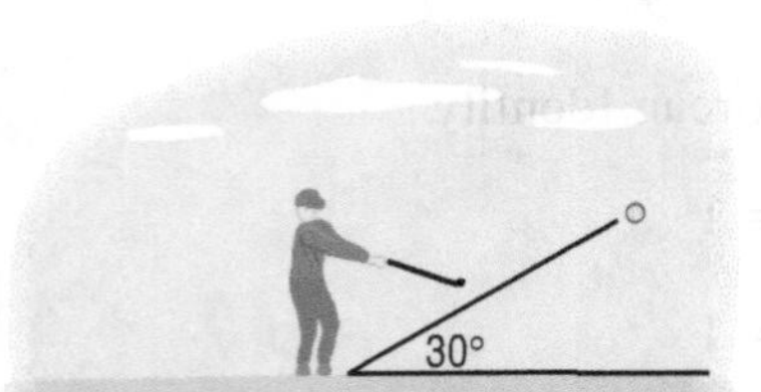

Suppose that Jim hit a golf ball with an initial velocity of 150 feet per second at an angle of 30° to the horizontal. See Figure 66.

(a) Find parametric equations that describe the position of the ball as a function of time.

(b) How long is the golf ball in the air?

(c) When is the ball at its maximum height? Determine the maximum height of the ball.

(d) Determine the distance that the ball traveled.

(e) Using a graphing utility, simulate the motion of the golf ball by simultaneously graphing the equations found in part (a).

Solution (a) We have $v_0 = 150$ ft/sec, $\theta = 30°$, $h = 0$ (the ball is on the ground), and $g = 32$ (since the units are in feet and seconds). Substituting these values into equations (2), we find that

$$x = (v_0 \cos\theta)t = (150 \cos 30°)t = 75\sqrt{3}t$$

$$y = -\frac{1}{2}gt^2 + (v_0 \sin\theta)t + h = -\frac{1}{2}(32)t^2 + (150 \sin 30°)t + 0$$

$$= -16t^2 + 75t$$

(b) To determine the length of time that the ball is in the air, we solve the equation $y = 0$.

$$-16t^2 + 75t = 0$$

$$t(-16t + 75) = 0$$

$$t = 0 \text{ sec} \quad \text{or} \quad t = \frac{75}{16} = 4.6875 \text{ sec}$$

The ball will strike the ground after 4.6875 seconds.

(c) Notice that the height y of the ball is a quadratic function of t, so the maximum height of the ball can be found by determining the vertex of $y = -16t^2 + 75t$. The value of t at the vertex is

$$t = \frac{-b}{2a} = \frac{-75}{-32} = 2.34375 \text{ sec}$$

The ball is at its maximum height after 2.34375 seconds. The maximum height of the ball is found by evaluating the function y at $t = 2.34375$ seconds.

$$\text{Maximum height} = -16(2.34375)^2 + (75)2.34375 \approx 87.89 \text{ feet}$$

(d) Since the ball is in the air for 4.6875 seconds, the horizontal distance that the ball travels is

$$x = (75\sqrt{3})4.6875 \approx 608.92 \text{ feet}$$

(e) We enter the equations from part (a) into a graphing utility with $T\text{min} = 0$, $T\text{max} = 4.7$, and $T\text{step} = 0.1$. We use ZOOM-SQUARE to avoid any distortion to the angle of elevation. See Figure 67.

Figure 67

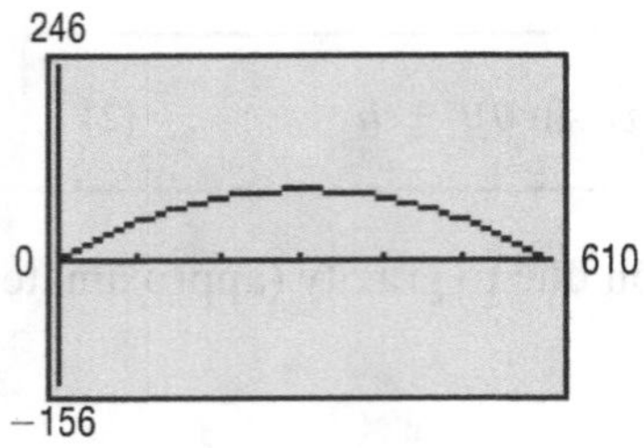

Exploration

Simulate the motion of a ball thrown straight up with an initial speed of 100 feet per second from a height of 5 feet above the ground. Use PARametric mode with $T\text{min} = 0$, $T\text{max} = 6.5$, $T\text{step} = 0.1$, $X\text{min} = 0$, $X\text{max} = 5$, $Y\text{min} = 0$, and $Y\text{max} = 180$. What happens to the speed with which the graph is drawn as the ball goes up and then comes back down? How do you interpret this physically? Repeat the experiment using other values for $T\text{step}$. How does this affect the experiment?

[**Hint:** In the projectile motion equations, let $\theta = 90°$, $v_0 = 100$, $h = 5$, and $g = 32$. We use $x = 3$ instead of $x = 0$ to see the vertical motion better.]

Result See Figure 68. In Figure 68(a) the ball is going up. In Figure 68(b) the ball is near its highest point. Finally, in Figure 68(c) the ball is coming back down.

Figure 68

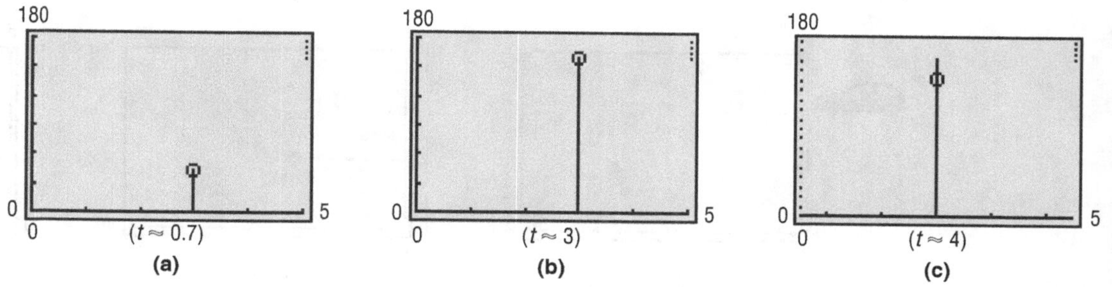

Notice that, as the ball goes up, its speed decreases, until at the highest point it is zero. Then the speed increases as the ball comes back down.

Now Work PROBLEM 49

A graphing utility can be used to simulate other kinds of motion as well. Let's work again Example 5 from Appendix A, Section A.8.

EXAMPLE 6 Simulating Motion

Tanya, who is a long distance runner, runs at an average speed of 8 miles per hour. Two hours after Tanya leaves your house, you leave in your Honda and follow the same route. If your average speed is 40 miles per hour, how long will it be before you catch up to Tanya? See Figure 69. Use a simulation of the two motions to verify the answer.

Figure 69

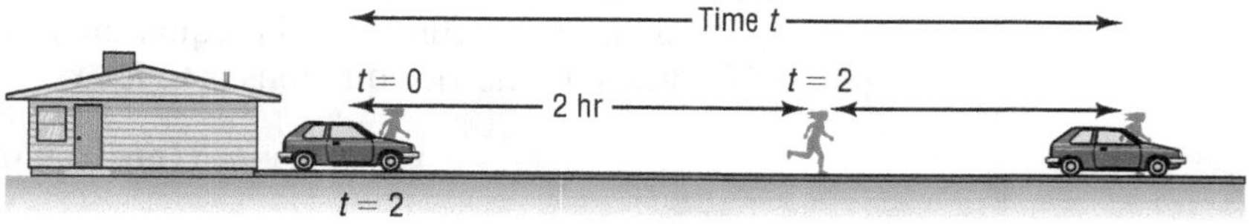

Solution We begin with two sets of parametric equations: one to describe Tanya's motion, the other to describe the motion of the Honda. We choose time $t = 0$ to be when Tanya leaves the house. If we choose $y_1 = 2$ as Tanya's path, then we can use $y_2 = 4$ as the parallel path of the Honda. The horizontal distances traversed in time t (Distance = Rate × Time) are

$$\text{Tanya: } x_1 = 8t \qquad \text{Honda: } x_2 = 40(t - 2)$$

The Honda catches up to Tanya when $x_1 = x_2$.

$$\begin{aligned} 8t &= 40(t - 2) \\ 8t &= 40t - 80 \\ -32t &= -80 \\ t &= \frac{-80}{-32} = 2.5 \end{aligned}$$

The Honda catches up to Tanya 2.5 hours after Tanya leaves the house.

In PARametric mode with Tstep = 0.01, we simultaneously graph

$$\begin{aligned} &\text{Tanya: } x_1 = 8t \qquad &&\text{Honda: } x_2 = 40(t - 2) \\ &\phantom{\text{Tanya: }} y_1 = 2 &&\phantom{\text{Honda: }} y_2 = 4 \end{aligned}$$

for $0 \le t \le 3$.

Figure 70 shows the relative position of Tanya and the Honda for $t = 0, t = 2, t = 2.25, t = 2.5$, and $t = 2.75$.

Figure 70

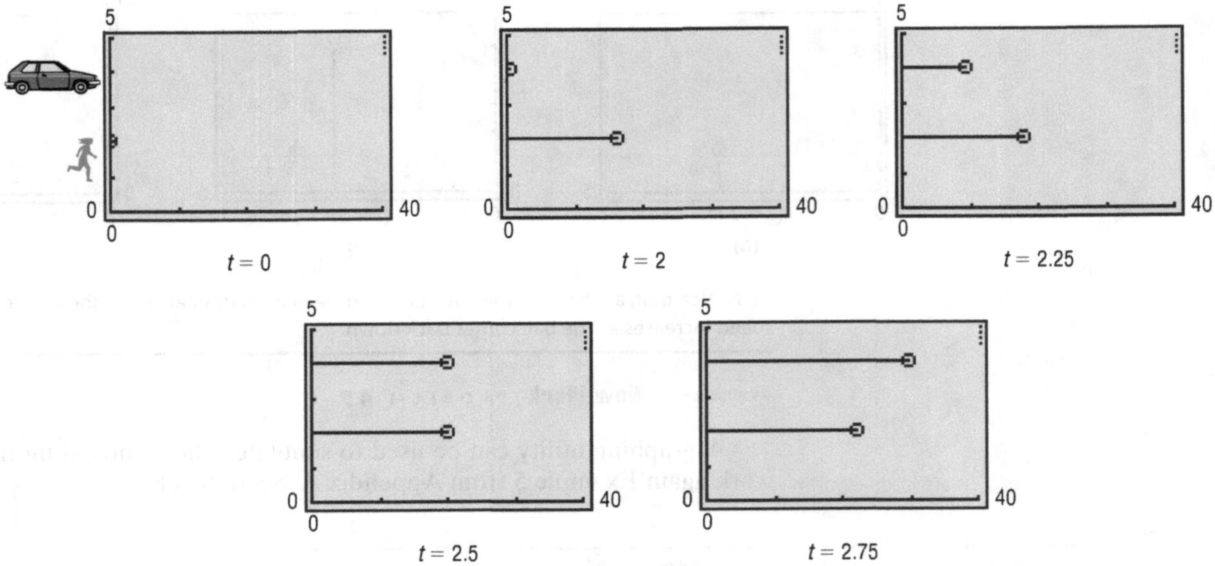

5 Find Parametric Equations for Curves Defined by Rectangular Equations

We now take up the question of how to find parametric equations of a given curve.

If a curve is defined by the equation $y = f(x)$, where f is a function, one way of finding parametric equations is to let $x = t$. Then $y = f(t)$ and

$$x = t, \quad y = f(t), \qquad t \text{ in the domain of } f$$

are parametric equations of the curve.

EXAMPLE 7 **Finding Parametric Equations for a Curve Defined by a Rectangular Equation**

Find two different parametric equations for the equation $y = x^2 - 4$.

Solution For the first parametric equation, let $x = t$. Then the parametric equations are

$$x = t, \quad y = t^2 - 4, \qquad -\infty < t < \infty$$

A second parametric equation is found by letting $x = t^3$. Then the parametric equations become

$$x = t^3, \quad y = t^6 - 4, \qquad -\infty < t < \infty$$

Care must be taken when using the second approach in Example 7, since the substitution for x must be a function that allows x to take on all the values stipulated by the domain of f. For example, letting $x = t^2$ so that $y = t^4 - 4$ does not result in equivalent parametric equations for $y = x^2 - 4$, since only points for which $x \geq 0$ are obtained; yet the domain of $y = x^2 - 4$ is $\{x \mid x \text{ is any real number}\}$.

Now Work PROBLEM 33

EXAMPLE 8 Finding Parametric Equations for an Object in Motion

Find parametric equations for the ellipse

$$x^2 + \frac{y^2}{9} = 1$$

where the parameter t is time (in seconds) and

(a) The motion around the ellipse is clockwise, begins at the point $(0, 3)$, and requires 1 second for a complete revolution.

(b) The motion around the ellipse is counterclockwise, begins at the point $(1, 0)$, and requires 2 seconds for a complete revolution.

Solution

Figure 71

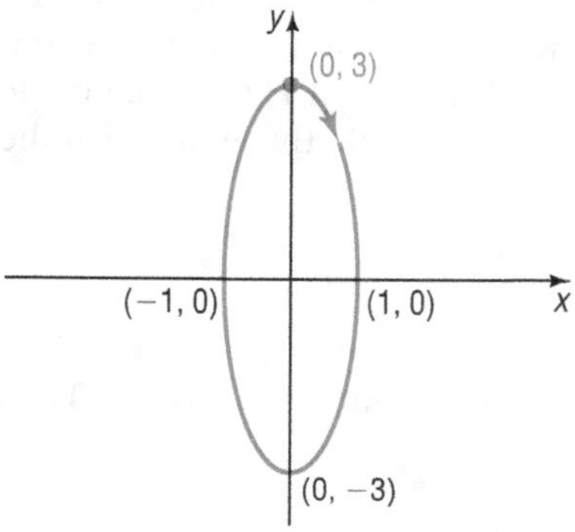

(a) See Figure 71. Since the motion begins at the point $(0, 3)$, we want $x = 0$ and $y = 3$ when $t = 0$. Furthermore, since the given equation is an ellipse, we begin by letting

$$x = \sin(\omega t) \qquad \frac{y}{3} = \cos(\omega t)$$

for some constant ω. These parametric equations satisfy the equation of the ellipse. Furthermore, with this choice, when $t = 0$, we have $x = 0$ and $y = 3$.

For the motion to be clockwise, the motion will have to begin with the value of x increasing and y decreasing as t increases. This requires that $\omega > 0$. [Do you know why? If $\omega > 0$, then $x = \sin(\omega t)$ is increasing when $t > 0$ is near zero and $y = 3\cos(\omega t)$ is decreasing when $t > 0$ is near zero.] See the red part of the graph in Figure 71.

Finally, since 1 revolution requires 1 second, the period $\frac{2\pi}{\omega} = 1$, so $\omega = 2\pi$. Parametric equations that satisfy the conditions stipulated are

$$x = \sin(2\pi t), \qquad y = 3\cos(2\pi t), \qquad 0 \le t \le 1 \tag{3}$$

Figure 72

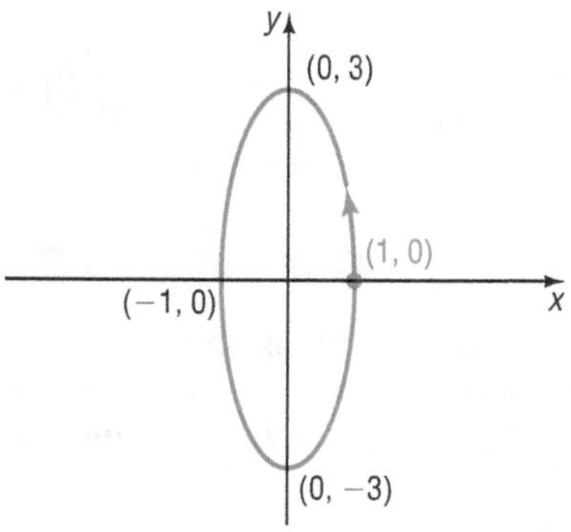

(b) See Figure 72. Since the motion begins at the point $(1, 0)$, we want $x = 1$ and $y = 0$ when $t = 0$. The given equation is an ellipse, so we begin by letting

$$x = \cos(\omega t) \qquad \frac{y}{3} = \sin(\omega t)$$

for some constant ω. These parametric equations satisfy the equation of the ellipse. Furthermore, with this choice, when $t = 0$, we have $x = 1$ and $y = 0$.

For the motion to be counterclockwise, the motion will have to begin with the value of x decreasing and y increasing as t increases. This requires that $\omega > 0$. [Do you know why?] Finally, since 1 revolution requires 2 seconds, the period is $\frac{2\pi}{\omega} = 2$, so $\omega = \pi$. The parametric equations that satisfy the conditions stipulated are

$$x = \cos(\pi t), \qquad y = 3\sin(\pi t), \qquad 0 \le t \le 2 \tag{4}$$

Either equation (3) or (4) can serve as a parametric equation for the ellipse $x^2 + \frac{y^2}{9} = 1$ given in Example 8. The direction of the motion, the beginning point, and the time for 1 revolution serve to help us arrive at a particular parametric representation.

Now Work PROBLEM 39

The Cycloid

Suppose that a circle of radius a rolls along a horizontal line without slipping. As the circle rolls along the line, a point P on the circle will trace out a curve called a **cycloid** (see Figure 73). We now seek parametric equations* for a cycloid.

Figure 73

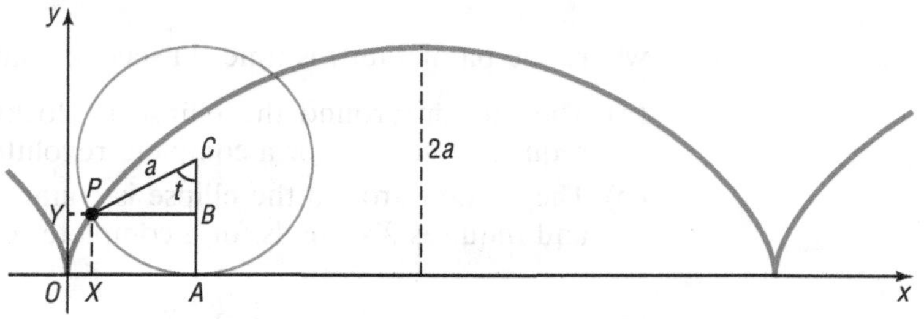

We begin with a circle of radius a and take the fixed line on which the circle rolls as the x-axis. Let the origin be one of the points at which the point P comes in contact with the x-axis. Figure 73 illustrates the position of this point P after the circle has rolled somewhat. The angle t (in radians) measures the angle through which the circle has rolled.

Since we require no slippage, it follows that

$$\text{Arc } AP = d(O, A)$$

The length of the arc AP is given by $s = r\theta$, where $r = a$ and $\theta = t$ radians. Then

$$at = d(O, A) \quad s = r\theta, \text{ where } r = a \text{ and } \theta = t$$

The x-coordinate of the point P is

$$d(O, X) = d(O, A) - d(X, A) = at - a \sin t = a(t - \sin t)$$

The y-coordinate of the point P is equal to

$$d(O, Y) = d(A, C) - d(B, C) = a - a \cos t = a(1 - \cos t)$$

The parametric equations of the cycloid are

$$x = a(t - \sin t) \qquad y = a(1 - \cos t) \tag{5}$$

Exploration

Graph $x = t - \sin t, y = 1 - \cos t$, $0 \le t \le 3\pi$, using your graphing utility with Tstep $= \frac{\pi}{36}$ and a square screen. Compare your results with Figure 73.

Applications to Mechanics

If a is negative in equation (5), we obtain an inverted cycloid, as shown in Figure 74(a). The inverted cycloid occurs as a result of some remarkable applications in the field of mechanics. We shall mention two of them: the *brachistochrone* and the *tautochrone*.†

Figure 74

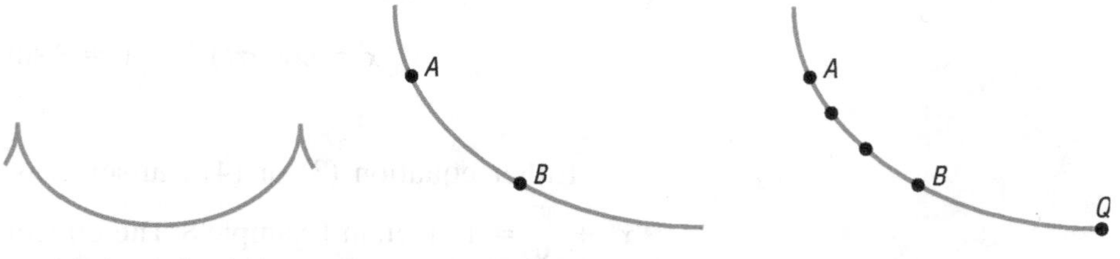

(a) Inverted cycloid (b) Curve of quickest descent (c) All reach Q at the same time

*Any attempt to derive the rectangular equation of a cycloid would soon demonstrate how complicated the task is.

†In Greek, *brachistochrone* means "the shortest time" and *tautochrone* means "equal time."

The **brachistochrone** is the curve of quickest descent. If a particle is constrained to follow some path from one point A to a lower point B (not on the same vertical line) and is acted on only by gravity, the time needed to make the descent is least if the path is an inverted cycloid. See Figure 74(b). This remarkable discovery, which is attributed to many famous mathematicians (including Johann Bernoulli and Blaise Pascal), was a significant step in creating the branch of mathematics known as the *calculus of variations*.

To define the **tautochrone,** let Q be the lowest point on an inverted cycloid. If several particles placed at various positions on an inverted cycloid simultaneously begin to slide down the cycloid, they will reach the point Q at the same time, as indicated in Figure 74(c). The tautochrone property of the cycloid was used by Christiaan Huygens (1629–1695), the Dutch mathematician, physicist, and astronomer, to construct a pendulum clock with a bob that swings along a cycloid (see Figure 75). In Huygen's clock, the bob was made to swing along a cycloid by suspending the bob on a thin wire constrained by two plates shaped like cycloids. In a clock of this design, the period of the pendulum is independent of its amplitude.

Figure 75

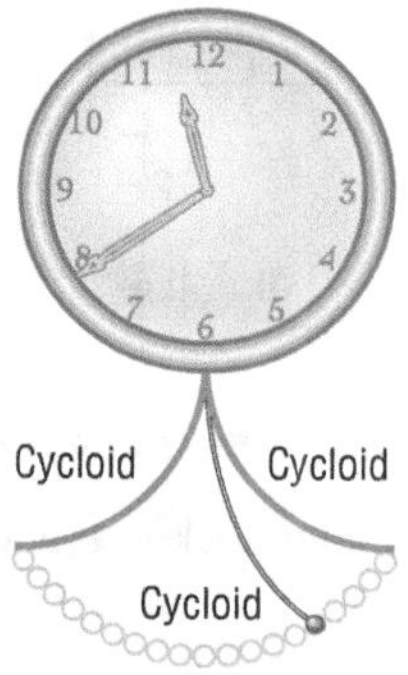

10.7 Assess Your Understanding

'Are You Prepared?' *Answers are given at the end of this exercise. If you get a wrong answer, read the page listed in red.*

1. The function $f(x) = 3\sin(4x)$ has amplitude _____ and period _____. (p. 401)

Concepts and Vocabulary

2. Let $x = f(t)$ and $y = g(t)$, where f and g are two functions whose common domain is some interval I. The collection of points defined by $(x, y) = (f(t), g(t))$ is called a(n) _____ _____. The variable t is called a(n) _____.

3. The parametric equations $x = 2\sin t$, $y = 3\cos t$ define a(n) _____.

4. If a circle rolls along a horizontal line without slippage, a point P on the circle will trace out a curve called a(n) _____.

5. ***True or False*** Parametric equations defining a curve are unique.

6. ***True or False*** Curves defined using parametric equations have an orientation.

Skill Building

In Problems 7–26, graph the curve whose parametric equations are given and show its orientation. Find the rectangular equation of each curve. Verify your graph using a graphing utility.

7. $x = 3t + 2, \quad y = t + 1; \quad 0 \le t \le 4$

8. $x = t - 3, \quad y = 2t + 4; \quad 0 \le t \le 2$

9. $x = t + 2, \quad y = \sqrt{t}; \quad t \ge 0$

10. $x = \sqrt{2t}, \quad y = 4t; \quad t \ge 0$

11. $x = t^2 + 4, \quad y = t^2 - 4; \quad -\infty < t < \infty$

12. $x = \sqrt{t} + 4, \quad y = \sqrt{t} - 4; \quad t \ge 0$

13. $x = 3t^2, \quad y = t + 1; \quad -\infty < t < \infty$

14. $x = 2t - 4, \quad y = 4t^2; \quad -\infty < t < \infty$

15. $x = 2e^t, \quad y = 1 + e^t; \quad t \ge 0$

16. $x = e^t, \quad y = e^{-t}; \quad t \ge 0$

17. $x = \sqrt{t}, \quad y = t^{3/2}; \quad t \ge 0$

18. $x = t^{3/2} + 1, \quad y = \sqrt{t}; \quad t \ge 0$

19. $x = 2\cos t, \quad y = 3\sin t; \quad 0 \le t \le 2\pi$

20. $x = 2\cos t, \quad y = 3\sin t; \quad 0 \le t \le \pi$

21. $x = 2\cos t, \quad y = 3\sin t; \quad -\pi \le t \le 0$

22. $x = 2\cos t, \quad y = \sin t; \quad 0 \le t \le \frac{\pi}{2}$

23. $x = \sec t, \quad y = \tan t; \quad 0 \le t \le \frac{\pi}{4}$

24. $x = \csc t, \quad y = \cot t; \quad \frac{\pi}{4} \le t \le \frac{\pi}{2}$

25. $x = \sin^2 t, \quad y = \cos^2 t; \quad 0 \le t \le 2\pi$

26. $x = t^2, \quad y = \ln t; \quad t > 0$

In Problems 27–34, find two different parametric equations for each rectangular equation.

27. $y = 4x - 1$

28. $y = -8x + 3$

29. $y = x^2 + 1$

30. $y = -2x^2 + 1$

31. $y = x^3$

32. $y = x^4 + 1$

33. $x = y^{3/2}$

34. $x = \sqrt{y}$

In Problems 35–38, find parametric equations that define the curve shown.

35.

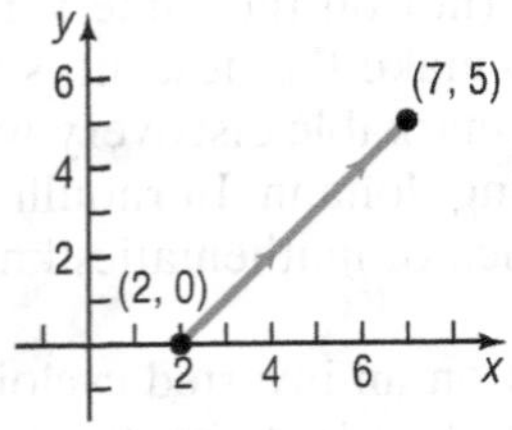

36.

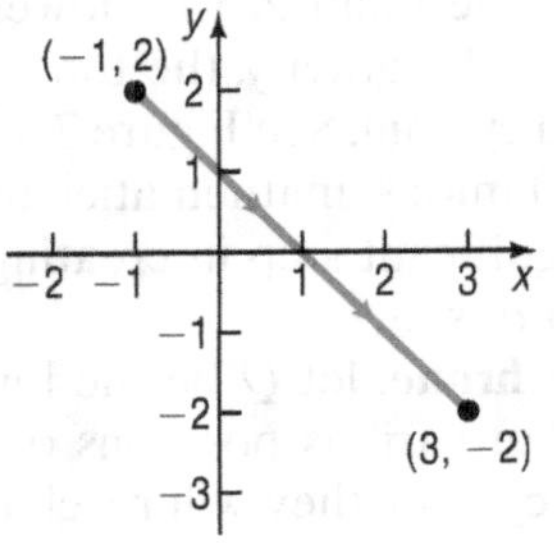

37.

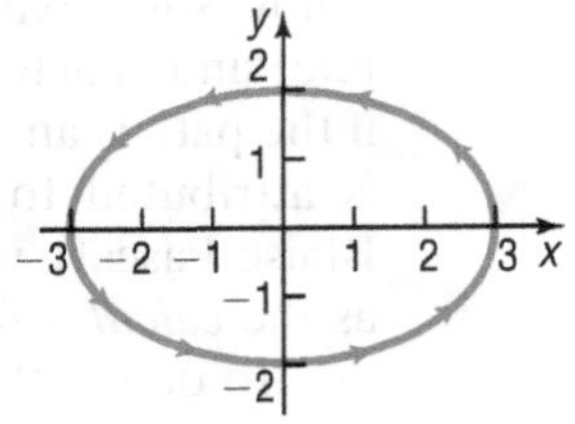

38.

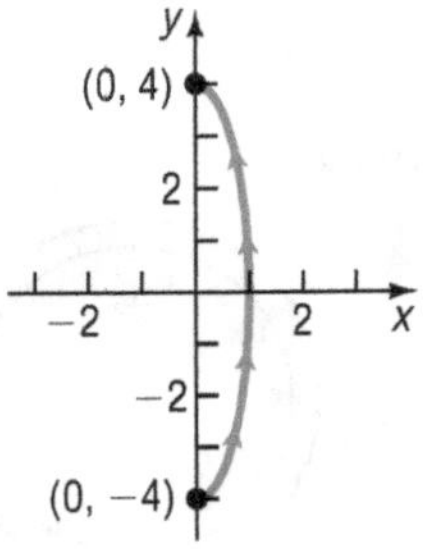

In Problems 39–42, find parametric equations for an object that moves along the ellipse $\frac{x^2}{4} + \frac{y^2}{9} = 1$ *with the motion described.*

39. The motion begins at $(2, 0)$, is clockwise, and requires 2 seconds for a complete revolution.

40. The motion begins at $(0, 3)$, is counterclockwise, and requires 1 second for a complete revolution.

41. The motion begins at $(0, 3)$, is clockwise, and requires 1 second for a complete revolution.

42. The motion begins at $(2, 0)$, is counterclockwise, and requires 3 seconds for a complete revolution.

In Problems 43 and 44, the parametric equations of four curves are given. Graph each of them, indicating the orientation.

43. C_1: $x = t, \quad y = t^2; \quad -4 \le t \le 4$
C_2: $x = \cos t, \quad y = 1 - \sin^2 t; \quad 0 \le t \le \pi$
C_3: $x = e^t, \quad y = e^{2t}; \quad 0 \le t \le \ln 4$
C_4: $x = \sqrt{t}, \quad y = t; \quad 0 \le t \le 16$

44. C_1: $x = t, \quad y = \sqrt{1 - t^2}; \quad -1 \le t \le 1$
C_2: $x = \sin t, \quad y = \cos t; \quad 0 \le t \le 2\pi$
C_3: $x = \cos t, \quad y = \sin t; \quad 0 \le t \le 2\pi$
C_4: $x = \sqrt{1 - t^2}, \quad y = t; \quad -1 \le t \le 1$

In Problems 45–48, use a graphing utility to graph the curve defined by the given parametric equations.

45. $x = t \sin t, \quad y = t \cos t, \quad t > 0$

46. $x = \sin t + \cos t, \quad y = \sin t - \cos t$

47. $x = 4 \sin t - 2 \sin(2t)$
$y = 4 \cos t - 2 \cos(2t)$

48. $x = 4 \sin t + 2 \sin(2t)$
$y = 4 \cos t + 2 \cos(2t)$

Applications and Extensions

49. Projectile Motion Bob throws a ball straight up with an initial speed of 50 feet per second from a height of 6 feet.
(a) Find parametric equations that model the motion of the ball as a function of time.
(b) How long is the ball in the air?
(c) When is the ball at its maximum height? Determine the maximum height of the ball.
(d) Simulate the motion of the ball by graphing the equations found in part (a).

50. Projectile Motion Alice throws a ball straight up with an initial speed of 40 feet per second from a height of 5 feet.
(a) Find parametric equations that model the motion of the ball as a function of time.
(b) How long is the ball in the air?
(c) When is the ball at its maximum height? Determine the maximum height of the ball.
(d) Simulate the motion of the ball by graphing the equations found in part (a).

51. Catching a Train Bill's train leaves at 8:06 AM and accelerates at the rate of 2 meters per second per second. Bill, who can run 5 meters per second, arrives at the train station 5 seconds after the train has left and runs for the train.
(a) Find parametric equations that model the motions of the train and Bill as a function of time.

[**Hint:** The position s at time t of an object having acceleration a is $s = \frac{1}{2}at^2$.]

(b) Determine algebraically whether Bill will catch the train. If so, when?
(c) Simulate the motion of the train and Bill by simultaneously graphing the equations found in part (a).

52. Catching a Bus Jodi's bus leaves at 5:30 PM and accelerates at the rate of 3 meters per second per second. Jodi, who can run 5 meters per second, arrives at the bus station 2 seconds after the bus has left and runs for the bus.
(a) Find parametric equations that model the motions of the bus and Jodi as a function of time.

[**Hint:** The position s at time t of an object having acceleration a is $s = \frac{1}{2}at^2$.]

(b) Determine algebraically whether Jodi will catch the bus. If so, when?
(c) Simulate the motion of the bus and Jodi by simultaneously graphing the equations found in part (a).

53. Projectile Motion Ichiro throws a baseball with an initial speed of 145 feet per second at an angle of 20° to the horizontal. The ball leaves Ichiro's hand at a height of 5 feet.
(a) Find parametric equations that model the position of the ball as a function of time.
(b) How long is the ball in the air?
(c) Determine the horizontal distance that the ball traveled.
(d) When is the ball at its maximum height? Determine the maximum height of the ball.
(e) Using a graphing utility, simultaneously graph the equations found in part (a).

54. Projectile Motion Barry Bonds hit a baseball with an initial speed of 125 feet per second at an angle of 40° to the horizontal. The ball was hit at a height of 3 feet off the ground.
(a) Find parametric equations that model the position of the ball as a function of time.
(b) How long is the ball in the air?
(c) Determine the horizontal distance that the ball traveled.
(d) When is the ball at its maximum height? Determine the maximum height of the ball.
(e) Using a graphing utility, simultaneously graph the equations found in part (a).

55. Projectile Motion Suppose that Adam hits a golf ball off a cliff 300 meters high with an initial speed of 40 meters per second at an angle of 45° to the horizontal.
(a) Find parametric equations that model the position of the ball as a function of time.
(b) How long is the ball in the air?
(c) Determine the horizontal distance that the ball traveled.
(d) When is the ball at its maximum height? Determine the maximum height of the ball.
(e) Using a graphing utility, simultaneously graph the equations found in part (a).

56. Projectile Motion Suppose that Karla hits a golf ball off a cliff 300 meters high with an initial speed of 40 meters per second at an angle of 45° to the horizontal on the Moon (gravity on the Moon is one-sixth of that on Earth).
(a) Find parametric equations that model the position of the ball as a function of time.
(b) How long is the ball in the air?
(c) Determine the horizontal distance that the ball traveled.
(d) When is the ball at its maximum height? Determine the maximum height of the ball.
(e) Using a graphing utility, simultaneously graph the equations found in part (a).

57. Uniform Motion A Toyota Camry (traveling east at 40 mph) and a Chevy Impala (traveling north at 30 mph) are heading toward the same intersection. The Camry is 5 miles from the intersection when the Impala is 4 miles from the intersection. See the figure.

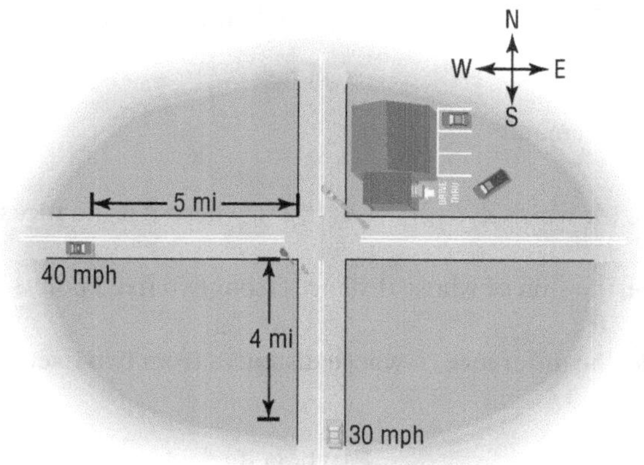

(a) Find parametric equations that model the motion of the Camry and Impala.
(b) Find a formula for the distance between the cars as a function of time.
(c) Graph the function in part (b) using a graphing utility.
(d) What is the minimum distance between the cars? When are the cars closest?
(e) Simulate the motion of the cars by simultaneously graphing the equations found in part (a).

58. Uniform Motion A Cessna (heading south at 120 mph) and a Boeing 747 (heading west at 600 mph) are flying toward the same point at the same altitude. The Cessna is 100 miles from the point where the flight patterns intersect, and the 747 is 550 miles from this intersection point. See the figure.

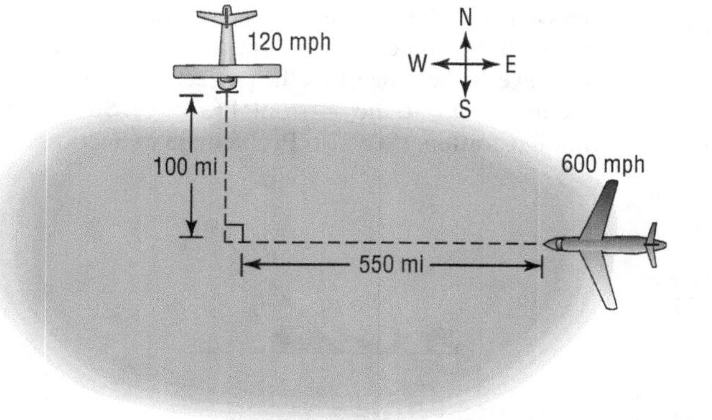

(a) Find parametric equations that model the motion of the Cessna and the 747.
(b) Find a formula for the distance between the planes as a function of time.
(c) Graph the function in part (b) using a graphing utility.
(d) What is the minimum distance between the planes? When are the planes closest?
(e) Simulate the motion of the planes by simultaneously graphing the equations found in part (a).

59. The Green Monster The left field wall at Fenway Park is 310 feet from home plate; the wall itself (affectionately named the Green Monster) is 37 feet high. A batted ball must clear the wall to be a home run. Suppose a ball leaves the bat 3 feet off the ground, at an angle of 45°. Use $g = 32$ feet per second^2 as the acceleration due to gravity and ignore any air resistance.
(a) Find parametric equations that model the position of the ball as a function of time.
(b) What is the maximum height of the ball if it leaves the bat with a speed of 90 miles per hour? Give your answer in feet.
(c) How far is the ball from home plate at its maximum height? Give your answer in feet.
(d) If the ball is hit straight down the left field wall, will it clear the Green Monster? If it does, by how much does it clear the wall?

Source: The Boston Red Sox

60. Projectile Motion The position of a projectile fired with an initial velocity v_0 feet per second and at an angle θ to the horizontal at the end of t seconds is given by the parametric equations

$$x = (v_0 \cos \theta)t \qquad y = (v_0 \sin \theta)t - 16t^2$$

See the illustration.

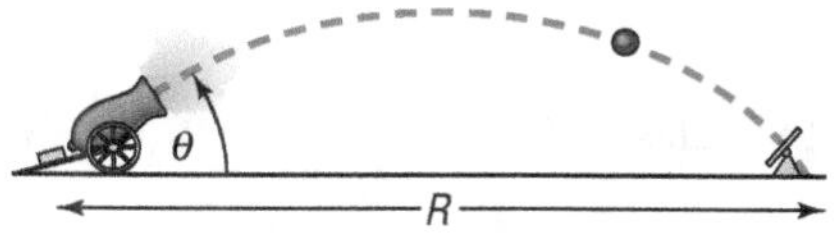

(a) Obtain the rectangular equation of the trajectory and identify the curve.

(b) Show that the projectile hits the ground ($y = 0$) when $t = \frac{1}{16} v_0 \sin \theta$.

(c) How far has the projectile traveled (horizontally) when it strikes the ground? In other words, find the range R.

(d) Find the time t when $x = y$. Then find the horizontal distance x and the vertical distance y traveled by the projectile in this time. Then compute $\sqrt{x^2 + y^2}$. This is the distance R, the range, that the projectile travels up a plane inclined at 45° to the horizontal ($x = y$). See the following illustration. (See also Problem 83 in Section 7.5.)

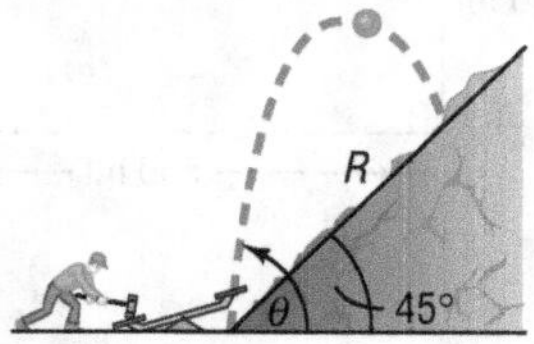

61. Show that the parametric equations for a line passing through the points (x_1, y_1) and (x_2, y_2) are

$$x = (x_2 - x_1)t + x_1$$
$$y = (y_2 - y_1)t + y_1, \quad -\infty < t < \infty$$

What is the orientation of this line?

62. Hypocycloid The hypocycloid is a curve defined by the parametric equations

$$x(t) = \cos^3 t, \quad y(t) = \sin^3 t, \quad 0 \le t \le 2\pi$$

(a) Graph the hypocycloid using a graphing utility.
(b) Find rectangular equations of the hypocycloid.

Discussion and Writing

63. In Problem 62, we graphed the hypocycloid. Now graph the rectangular equations of the hypocycloid. Did you obtain a complete graph? If not, experiment until you do.

64. Look up the curves called *hypocycloid* and *epicycloid*. Write a report on what you find. Be sure to draw comparisons with the cycloid.

'Are You Prepared?' Answers

1. 3; $\frac{\pi}{2}$

CHAPTER REVIEW

Things to Know

Equations

Parabola (pp. 639–644) — See Tables 1 and 2 (pp. 641 and 643).

Ellipse (pp. 648–655) — See Table 3 (p. 653).

Hyperbola (pp. 659–668) — See Table 4 (p. 667).

General equation of a conic (p. 679) — $Ax^2 + Bxy + Cy^2 + Dx + Ey + F = 0$
- Parabola if $B^2 - 4AC = 0$
- Ellipse (or circle) if $B^2 - 4AC < 0$
- Hyperbola if $B^2 - 4AC > 0$

Polar equations of a conic with focus at the pole (pp. 681–685) — See Table 5 (p. 683).

Parametric equations of a curve (p. 687) — $x = f(t)$, $y = g(t)$, t is the parameter

Definitions

Parabola (p. 639) — Set of points P in the plane for which $d(F, P) = d(P, D)$, where F is the focus and D is the directrix

Ellipse (p. 649) — Set of points P in the plane, the sum of whose distances from two fixed points (the foci) is a constant

Hyperbola (p. 659) — Set of points P in the plane, the difference of whose distances from two fixed points (the foci) is a constant

Conic in polar coordinates (p. 681) — $\frac{d(F, P)}{d(P, D)} = e$
- Parabola if $e = 1$
- Ellipse if $e < 1$
- Hyperbola if $e > 1$

Formulas

Rotation formulas (p. 675)

$$x = x' \cos \theta - y' \sin \theta$$
$$y = x' \sin \theta + y' \cos \theta$$

Angle θ of rotation that eliminates the $x'y'$-term (p. 676)

$$\cot(2\theta) = \frac{A - C}{B}, \quad 0° < \theta < 90°$$

Objectives

Section		You should be able to . . .	Example(s)	Review Exercises
10.1	1	Know the names of the conics (p. 638)		1–32
10.2	1	Analyze parabolas with vertex at the origin (p. 639)	1–6	1, 2, 21, 24
	2	Analyze parabolas with vertex at (h, k) (p. 643)	7–9	7, 11, 12, 17, 18, 27, 30
	3	Solve applied problems involving parabolas (p. 644)	10	77, 78
10.3	1	Analyze ellipses with center at the origin (p. 649)	1–5	5, 6, 10, 22, 25
	2	Analyze ellipses with center at (h, k) (p. 653)	6–8	14–16, 19, 28, 31
	3	Solve applied problems involving ellipses (p. 656)	9	79, 80
10.4	1	Analyze hyperbolas with center at the origin (p. 660)	1–5	3, 4, 8, 9, 23, 26
	2	Find the asymptotes of a hyperbola (p. 665)	6	3, 4, 8, 9
	3	Analyze hyperbolas with center at (h, k) (p. 666)	7, 8	13, 20, 29, 32–36
	4	Solve applied problems involving hyperbolas (p. 668)	9	81
10.5	1	Identify a conic (p. 673)	1	37–40
	2	Use a rotation of axes to transform equations (p. 674)	2	47–52
	3	Analyze an equation using a rotation of axes (p. 676)	3, 4	47–52
	4	Identify conics without a rotation of axes (p. 678)	5	41–46
10.6	1	Analyze and graph polar equations of conics (p. 681)	1–3	53–58
	2	Convert the polar equation of a conic to a rectangular equation (p. 685)	4	59–62
10.7	1	Graph parametric equations by hand (p. 687)	1	63–68
	2	Graph parametric equations using a graphing utility (p. 688)	2	63–68
	3	Find a rectangular equation for a curve defined parametrically (p. 689)	3, 4	63–68
	4	Use time as a parameter in parametric equations (p. 691)	5, 6	82, 83
	5	Find parametric equations for curves defined by rectangular equations (p. 694)	7, 8	69–72

Review Exercises

In Problems 1–20, identify each equation. If it is a parabola, give its vertex, focus, and directrix; if it is an ellipse, give its center, vertices, and foci; if it is a hyperbola, give its center, vertices, foci, and asymptotes.

1. $y^2 = -16x$

2. $16x^2 = y$

3. $\dfrac{x^2}{25} - y^2 = 1$

4. $\dfrac{y^2}{25} - x^2 = 1$

5. $\dfrac{y^2}{25} + \dfrac{x^2}{16} = 1$

6. $\dfrac{x^2}{9} + \dfrac{y^2}{16} = 1$

7. $x^2 + 4y = 4$

8. $3y^2 - x^2 = 9$

9. $4x^2 - y^2 = 8$

10. $9x^2 + 4y^2 = 36$

11. $x^2 - 4x = 2y$

12. $2y^2 - 4y = x - 2$

13. $y^2 - 4y - 4x^2 + 8x = 4$

14. $4x^2 + y^2 + 8x - 4y + 4 = 0$

15. $4x^2 + 9y^2 - 16x - 18y = 11$

16. $4x^2 + 9y^2 - 16x + 18y = 11$

17. $4x^2 - 16x + 16y + 32 = 0$

18. $4y^2 + 3x - 16y + 19 = 0$

19. $9x^2 + 4y^2 - 18x + 8y = 23$

20. $x^2 - y^2 - 2x - 2y = 1$

In Problems 21–36, find an equation of the conic described. Graph the equation by hand.

21. Parabola; focus at $(-2, 0)$; directrix the line $x = 2$

22. Ellipse; center at $(0, 0)$; focus at $(0, 3)$; vertex at $(0, 5)$

23. Hyperbola; center at $(0,0)$; focus at $(0,4)$; vertex at $(0, -2)$

24. Parabola; vertex at $(0, 0)$; directrix the line $y = -3$

25. Ellipse; foci at $(-3, 0)$ and $(3, 0)$; vertex at $(4, 0)$

26. Hyperbola; vertices at $(-2, 0)$ and $(2, 0)$; focus at $(4, 0)$

27. Parabola; vertex at $(2, -3)$; focus at $(2, -4)$

28. Ellipse; center at $(-1, 2)$; focus at $(0, 2)$; vertex at $(2, 2)$

29. Hyperbola; center at $(-2, -3)$; focus at $(-4, -3)$; vertex at $(-3, -3)$

30. Parabola; focus at $(3, 6)$; directrix the line $y = 8$

31. Ellipse; foci at $(-4, 2)$ and $(-4, 8)$; vertex at $(-4, 10)$

32. Hyperbola; vertices at $(-3, 3)$ and $(5, 3)$; focus at $(7, 3)$

33. Center at $(-1, 2)$; $a = 3$; $c = 4$; transverse axis parallel to the x-axis

34. Center at $(4, -2)$; $a = 1$; $c = 4$; transverse axis parallel to the y-axis

35. Vertices at $(0, 1)$ and $(6, 1)$; asymptote the line $3y + 2x = 9$

36. Vertices at $(4, 0)$ and $(4, 4)$; asymptote the line $y + 2x = 10$

In Problems 37–46, identify each conic without completing the squares and without applying a rotation of axes.

37. $y^2 + 4x + 3y - 8 = 0$

38. $2x^2 - y + 8x = 0$

39. $x^2 + 2y^2 + 4x - 8y + 2 = 0$

40. $x^2 - 8y^2 - x - 2y = 0$

41. $9x^2 - 12xy + 4y^2 + 8x + 12y = 0$

42. $4x^2 + 4xy + y^2 - 8\sqrt{5}x + 16\sqrt{5}y = 0$

43. $4x^2 + 10xy + 4y^2 - 9 = 0$

44. $4x^2 - 10xy + 4y^2 - 9 = 0$

45. $x^2 - 2xy + 3y^2 + 2x + 4y - 1 = 0$

46. $4x^2 + 12xy - 10y^2 + x + y - 10 = 0$

In Problems 47–52, rotate the axes so that the new equation contains no xy-term. Analyze and graph the new equation.

47. $2x^2 + 5xy + 2y^2 - \frac{9}{2} = 0$

48. $2x^2 - 5xy + 2y^2 - \frac{9}{2} = 0$

49. $6x^2 + 4xy + 9y^2 - 20 = 0$

50. $x^2 + 4xy + 4y^2 + 16\sqrt{5}x - 8\sqrt{5}y = 0$

51. $4x^2 - 12xy + 9y^2 + 12x + 8y = 0$

52. $9x^2 - 24xy + 16y^2 + 80x + 60y = 0$

In Problems 53–58, identify the conic that each polar equation represents and graph it by hand. Verify your graph using a graphing utility.

53. $r = \frac{4}{1 - \cos\theta}$

54. $r = \frac{6}{1 + \sin\theta}$

55. $r = \frac{6}{2 - \sin\theta}$

56. $r = \frac{2}{3 + 2\cos\theta}$

57. $r = \frac{8}{4 + 8\cos\theta}$

58. $r = \frac{10}{5 + 20\sin\theta}$

In Problems 59–62, convert each polar equation to a rectangular equation.

59. $r = \frac{4}{1 - \cos\theta}$

60. $r = \frac{6}{2 - \sin\theta}$

61. $r = \frac{8}{4 + 8\cos\theta}$

62. $r = \frac{2}{3 + 2\cos\theta}$

In Problems 63–68, by hand, graph the curve whose parametric equations are given and show its orientation. Find the rectangular equation of each curve. Verify your graph using a graphing utility.

63. $x = 4t - 2, \quad y = 1 - t; \quad -\infty < t < \infty$

64. $x = 2t^2 + 6, \quad y = 5 - t; \quad -\infty < t < \infty$

65. $x = 3\sin t, \quad y = 4\cos t + 2; \quad 0 \le t \le 2\pi$

66. $x = \ln t, \quad y = t^3; \quad t > 0$

67. $x = \sec^2 t, \quad y = \tan^2 t; \quad 0 \le t \le \frac{\pi}{4}$

68. $x = t^{\frac{3}{2}}, \quad y = 2t + 4; \quad t \ge 0$

In Problems 69 and 70, find two different parametric equations for each rectangular equation.

69. $y = -2x + 4$

70. $y = 2x^2 - 8$

In Problems 71 and 72, find parametric equations for an object that moves along the ellipse $\frac{x^2}{16} + \frac{y^2}{9} = 1$ *with the motion described.*

71. The motion begins at $(4, 0)$, is counterclockwise, and requires 4 seconds for a complete revolution.

72. The motion begins at $(0, 3)$, is clockwise, and requires 5 seconds for a complete revolution.

---

73. Find an equation of the hyperbola whose foci are the vertices of the ellipse $4x^2 + 9y^2 = 36$ and whose vertices are the foci of this ellipse.

74. Find an equation of the ellipse whose foci are the vertices of the hyperbola $x^2 - 4y^2 = 16$ and whose vertices are the foci of this hyperbola.

75. Describe the collection of points in a plane so that the distance from each point to the point $(3, 0)$ is three-fourths of its distance from the line $x = \frac{16}{3}$.

76. Describe the collection of points in a plane so that the distance from each point to the point $(5, 0)$ is five-fourths of its distance from the line $x = \frac{16}{5}$.

77. Searchlight A searchlight is shaped like a paraboloid of revolution. If a light source is located 1 foot from the vertex along the axis of symmetry and the opening is 2 feet across, how deep should the mirror be in order to reflect the light rays parallel to the axis of symmetry?

78. Parabolic Arch Bridge A bridge is built in the shape of a parabolic arch. The bridge has a span of 60 feet and a maximum height of 20 feet. Find the height of the arch at distances of 5, 10, and 20 feet from the center.

79. Semielliptical Arch Bridge A bridge is built in the shape of a semielliptical arch. The bridge has a span of 60 feet and a maximum height of 20 feet. Find the height of the arch at distances of 5, 10, and 20 feet from the center.

80. Whispering Gallery The figure shows the specifications for an elliptical ceiling in a hall designed to be a whispering gallery. Where are the foci located in the hall?

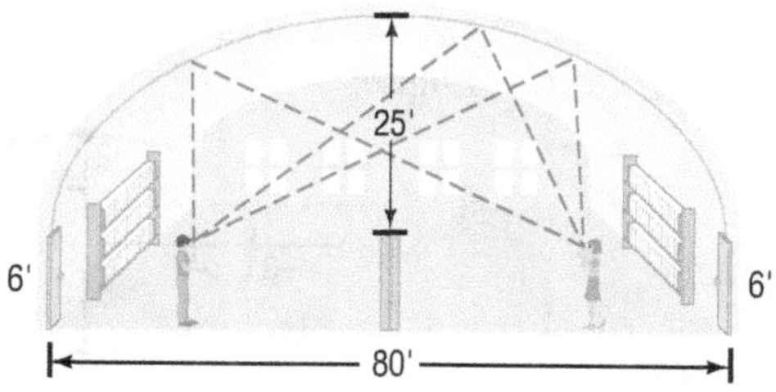

81. Calibrating Instruments In a test of their recording devices, a team of seismologists positioned two of the devices 2000 feet apart, with the device at point A to the west of the device at point B. At a point between the devices and 200 feet from point B, a small amount of explosive was detonated and a note made of the time at which the sound reached each device. A second explosion is to be carried out at a point directly north of point B. How far north should the site of the second explosion be chosen so that the measured time difference recorded by the devices for the second detonation is the same as that recorded for the first detonation?

82. Uniform Motion Mary's train leaves at 7:15 AM and accelerates at the rate of 3 meters per second per second. Mary, who can run 6 meters per second, arrives at the train station 2 seconds after the train has left.

(a) Find parametric equations that model the motion of the train and Mary as a function of time.

[**Hint:** The position s at time t of an object having acceleration a is $s = \frac{1}{2}at^2$.]

(b) Determine algebraically whether Mary will catch the train. If so, when?

(c) Simulate the motions of the train and Mary by simultaneously graphing the equations found in part (a).

83. Projectile Motion Drew Brees throws a football with an initial speed of 80 feet per second at an angle of 35° to the horizontal. The ball leaves Brees's hand at a height of 6 feet.

(a) Find parametric equations that model the position of the ball as a function of time.

(b) How long is the ball in the air?

(c) When is the ball at its maximum height? Determine the maximum height of the ball.

(d) Determine the horizontal distance that the ball travels.

(e) Using a graphing utility, simultaneously graph the equations found in part (a).

84. Formulate a strategy for discussing and graphing an equation of the form

$$Ax^2 + Bxy + Cy^2 + Dx + Ey + F = 0$$

CHAPTER TEST

In Problems 1–3, identify each equation. If it is a parabola, give its vertex, focus, and directrix; if an ellipse, give its center, vertices, and foci; if a hyperbola, give its center, vertices, foci, and asymptotes.

1. $\dfrac{(x+1)^2}{4} - \dfrac{y^2}{9} = 1$ **2.** $8y = (x-1)^2 - 4$ **3.** $2x^2 + 3y^2 + 4x - 6y = 13$

In Problems 4–6, find an equation of the conic described; graph the equation by hand.

4. Parabola: focus $(-1, 4.5)$, vertex $(-1, 3)$ **5.** Ellipse: center $(0, 0)$, vertex $(0, -4)$, focus $(0, 3)$

6. Hyperbola: center $(2, 2)$, vertex $(2, 4)$, contains the point $\left(2 + \sqrt{10}, 5\right)$

In Problems 7–9, identify each conic without completing the square or rotating axes.

7. $2x^2 + 5xy + 3y^2 + 3x - 7 = 0$ **8.** $3x^2 - xy + 2y^2 + 3y + 1 = 0$ **9.** $x^2 - 6xy + 9y^2 + 2x - 3y - 2 = 0$

10. Given the equation $41x^2 - 24xy + 34y^2 - 25 = 0$, rotate the axes so that there is no xy-term. Analyze and graph the new equation.

11. Identify the conic represented by the polar equation $r = \dfrac{3}{1 - 2\cos\theta}$. Find the rectangular equation.

12. Graph the curve whose parametric equations are given and show its orientation. Find the rectangular equation for the curve.

$$x = 3t - 2, \quad y = 1 - \sqrt{t}, \quad 0 \le t \le 9$$

13. A parabolic reflector (paraboloid of revolution) is used by TV crews at football games to pick up the referee's announcements, quarterback signals, and so on. A microphone is placed at the focus of the parabola. If a certain reflector is 4 feet wide and 1.5 feet deep, where should the microphone be placed?

CUMULATIVE REVIEW

1. For $f(x) = -3x^2 + 5x - 2$, find

$$\frac{f(x+h) - f(x)}{h} \qquad h \neq 0$$

2. In the complex number system, solve the equation

$$9x^4 + 33x^3 - 71x^2 - 57x - 10 = 0$$

3. For what numbers x is $6 - x \ge x^2$?

4. (a) Find the domain and range of $y = 3^x + 2$.

(b) Find the inverse of $y = 3^x + 2$ and state its domain and range.

5. $f(x) = \log_4(x - 2)$

(a) Solve $f(x) = 2$.

(b) Solve $f(x) \le 2$.

6. Find an equation for each of the following graphs:

(a) Line:

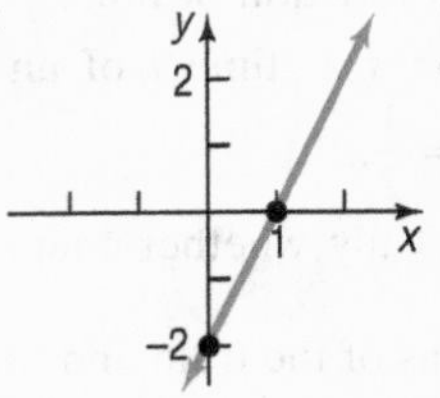

(b) Circle:

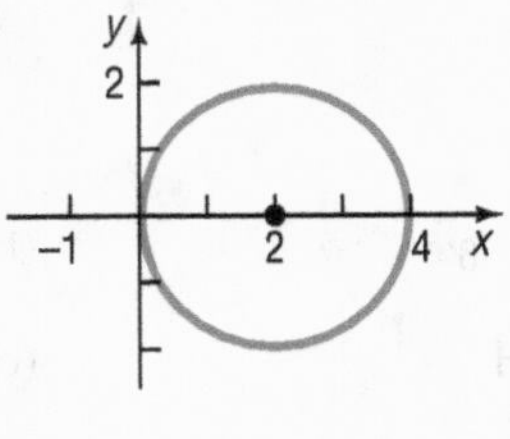

(c) Ellipse:

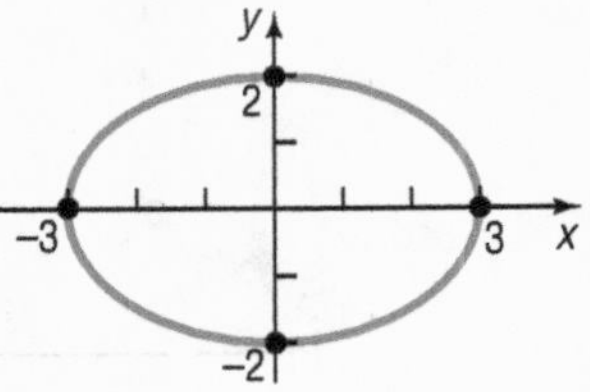

(d) Parabola:

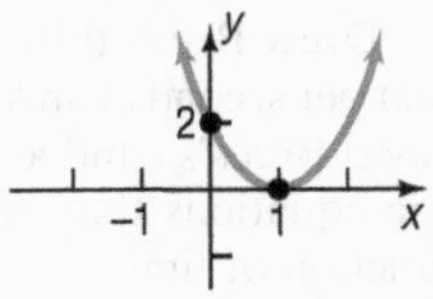

(e) Hyperbola:

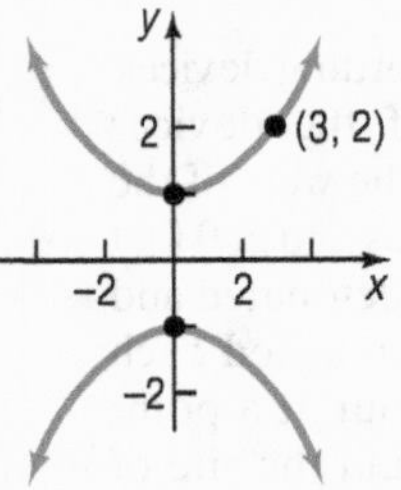

(f) Exponential:

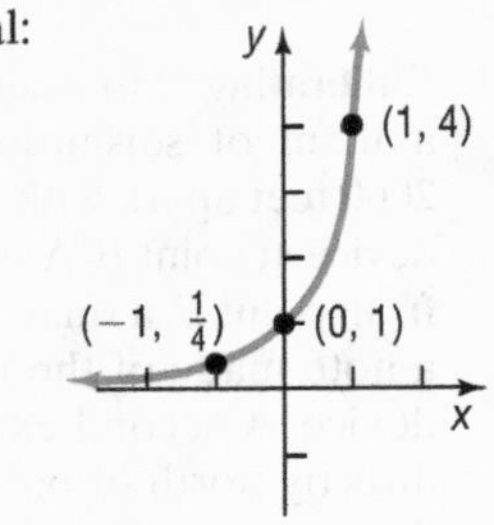

7. Find all the solutions of the equation $\sin(2\theta) = 0.5$.

8. Find a polar equation for the line containing the origin that makes an angle of 30° with the positive x-axis.

9. Find a polar equation for the circle with center at the point $(0, 4)$ and radius 4. Graph this circle.

10. What is the domain of the function $f(x) = \dfrac{3}{\sin x + \cos x}$?

11. Solve the equation $\cot(2\theta) = 1$, where $0° < \theta < 90°$.

12. Find the rectangular equation of the curve

$$x = 5 \tan t,\ y = 5 \sec^2 t,\ -\frac{\pi}{2} < t < \frac{\pi}{2}$$

CHAPTER PROJECTS

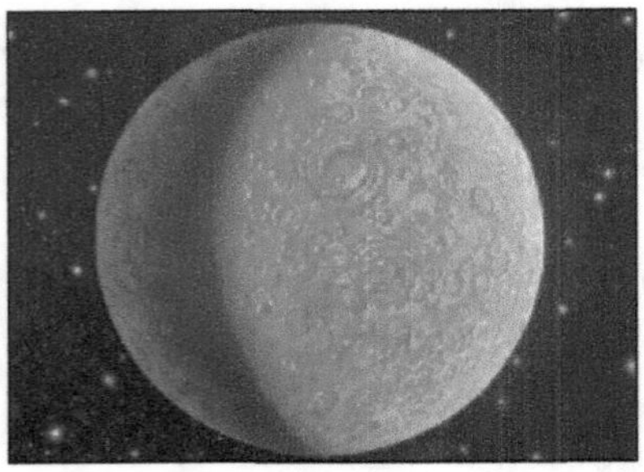

I. The Orbits of Neptune and Pluto The orbit of a planet about the Sun is an ellipse, with the Sun at one focus. The **aphelion** of a planet is its greatest distance from the Sun and the **perihelion** is its shortest distance. The **mean distance** of a planet from the Sun is the length of the semimajor axis of the elliptical orbit. See the illustration.

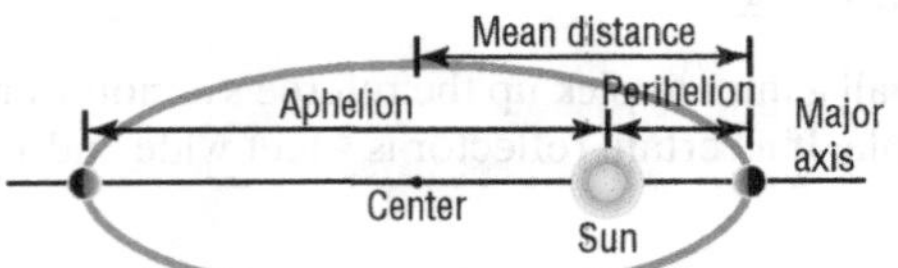

1. The aphelion of Neptune is 4532.2×10^6 kilometers (km) and its perihelion is 4458.0×10^6 km. Find a model for the orbit of Neptune around the Sun.
2. The aphelion of Pluto* is 7381.2×10^6 km and its perihelion is 4445.8×10^6 km. Find a model for the orbit of Pluto around the Sun.
3. Graph the orbits of Pluto and Neptune on a graphing utility. Knowing that the orbits of the planets intersect, what is wrong with the graphs you obtained?
4. The graphs of the orbits drawn in part 3 have the same center, but their foci lie in different locations. To see an accurate representation, the location of the Sun (a focus) needs to be the same for both graphs. This can be accomplished by shifting Pluto's orbit to the left. The shift amount is equal to Pluto's distance from the center (in the graph in part 3) to the Sun minus Neptune's distance from the center to the Sun. Find the new model representing the orbit of Pluto.
5. Graph the equation for the orbit of Pluto found in part 4 along with the equation of the orbit of Neptune. Do you see that Pluto's orbit is sometimes inside Neptune's?
6. Find the point(s) of intersection of the two orbits.
7. Do you think two planets will ever collide?

The following projects can be found on the Instructor's Resource Center (IRC):

II. Project at Motorola ***Distorted Deployable Space Reflector Antennas*** An engineer designs an antenna that will deploy in space to collect sunlight.

III. Constructing a Bridge over the East River The size of ships using a river and fluctuations in water height due to tides or flooding must be considered when designing a bridge that will cross a major waterway.

IV. Systems of Parametric Equations Choosing an approach to use when solving a system of equations depends on the form of the system and on the domains of the equations.

*Pluto's status was reduced to a dwarf planet in September 2006.

Answers

CHAPTER 1 Graphs

1.1 Assess Your Understanding *(page 14)*

5. abscissa; ordinate **6.** quadrants **7.** midpoint **8.** F **9.** F **10.** T

11. (a) Quadrant II **(b)** Positive x-axis **(c)** Quadrant III **(d)** Quadrant I **(e)** Negative y-axis **(f)** Quadrant IV

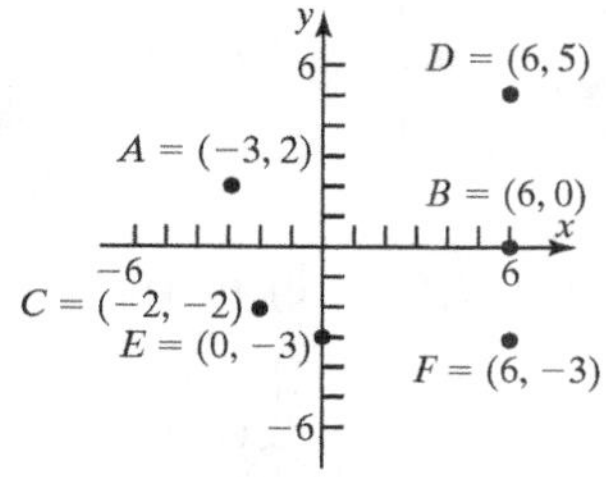

13. The points will be on a vertical line that is 2 units to the right of the y-axis.

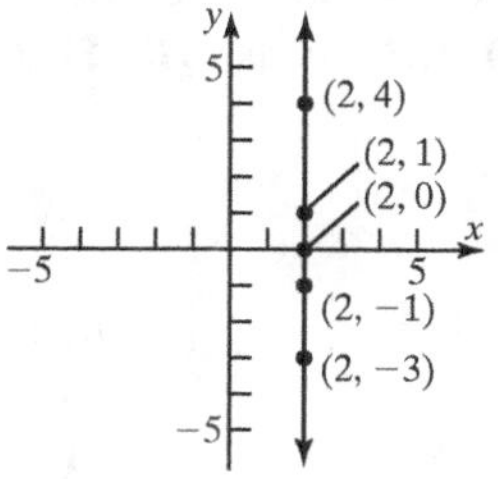

15. $(-1, 4)$; Quadrant II
17. $(3, 1)$; Quadrant I
19. $X\text{min} = -11$, $X\text{max} = 5$, $X\text{scl} = 1$, $Y\text{min} = -3$, $Y\text{max} = 6$, $Y\text{scl} = 1$
21. $X\text{min} = -30$, $X\text{max} = 50$, $X\text{scl} = 10$, $Y\text{min} = -90$, $Y\text{max} = 50$, $Y\text{scl} = 10$
23. $X\text{min} = -10$, $X\text{max} = 110$, $X\text{scl} = 10$, $Y\text{min} = -10$, $Y\text{max} = 160$, $Y\text{scl} = 10$
25. $X\text{min} = -6$, $X\text{max} = 6$, $X\text{scl} = 2$, $Y\text{min} = -4$, $Y\text{max} = 4$, $Y\text{scl} = 2$
27. $X\text{min} = -6$, $X\text{max} = 6$, $X\text{scl} = 2$, $Y\text{min} = -1$, $Y\text{max} = 3$, $Y\text{scl} = 1$
29. $X\text{min} = 3$, $X\text{max} = 9$, $X\text{scl} = 1$, $Y\text{min} = 2$, $Y\text{max} = 10$, $Y\text{scl} = 2$

31. $\sqrt{5}$ **33.** $\sqrt{10}$ **35.** $2\sqrt{17}$ **37.** 20 **39.** $\sqrt{53}$ **41.** $\sqrt{5.49} \approx 2.34$ **43.** $\sqrt{a^2 + b^2}$ **45.** $4\sqrt{10}$ **47.** $2\sqrt{65}$

49. $d(A, B) = \sqrt{13}$
$d(B, C) = \sqrt{13}$
$d(A, C) = \sqrt{26}$
$(\sqrt{13})^2 + (\sqrt{13})^2 = (\sqrt{26})^2$
Area $= \dfrac{13}{2}$ square units

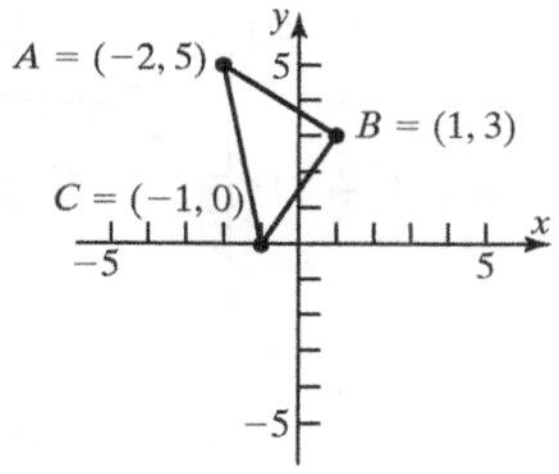

51. $d(A, B) = \sqrt{130}$
$d(B, C) = \sqrt{26}$
$d(A, C) = 2\sqrt{26}$
$(\sqrt{26})^2 + (2\sqrt{26})^2 = (\sqrt{130})^2$
Area $= 26$ square units

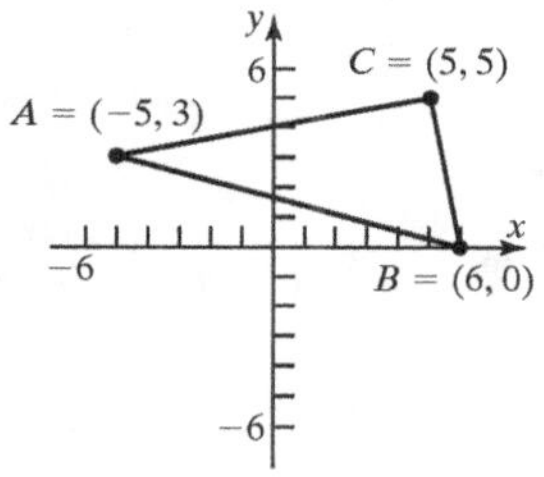

53. $d(A, B) = 4$
$d(A, C) = 5$
$d(B, C) = \sqrt{41}$
$4^2 + 5^2 = (\sqrt{41})^2$
Area $= 10$ square units

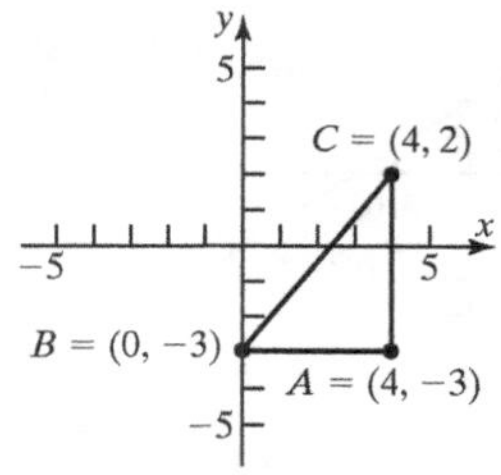

55. $(4, 0)$ **57.** $(3, 3)$ **59.** $(5, -1)$ **61.** $(0.55, 1.2)$ **63.** $\left(\dfrac{a}{2}, \dfrac{b}{2}\right)$ **65.** $(0, 0)$ is on the graph. **67.** $(0, 3)$ is on the graph.

69. $(0, 2)$ and $(\sqrt{2}, \sqrt{2})$ are on the graph. **71.** $(-1, 0)$, $(1, 0)$ **73.** $\left(-\dfrac{\pi}{2}, 0\right)$, $(0, 1)$, $\left(\dfrac{\pi}{2}, 0\right)$ **75.** $(0, 2)$, $(1, 0)$, $(0, -2)$

77. $(-4, 0)$, $(-1, 0)$, $(0, -3)$, $(4, 0)$

79.

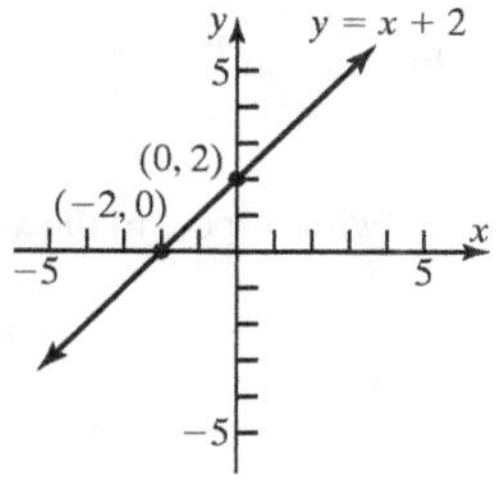

81.

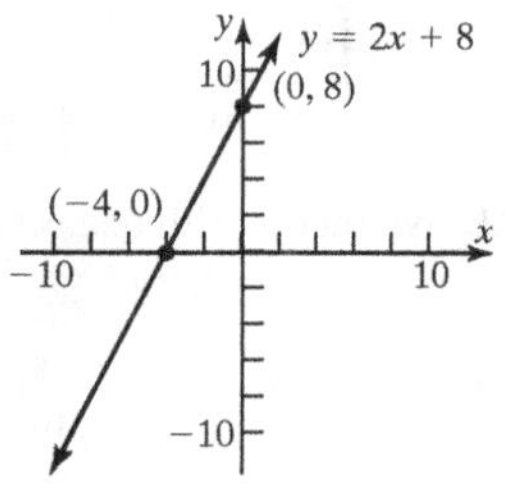

83.

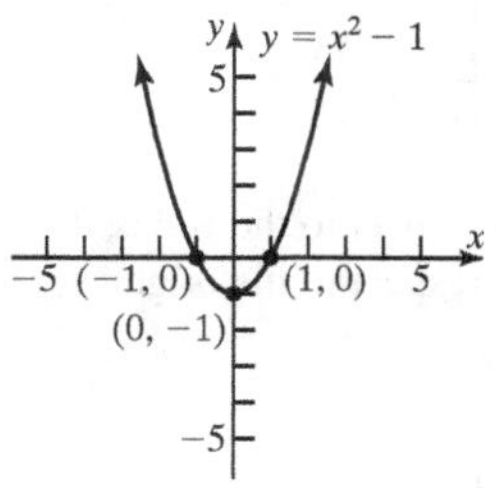

85.

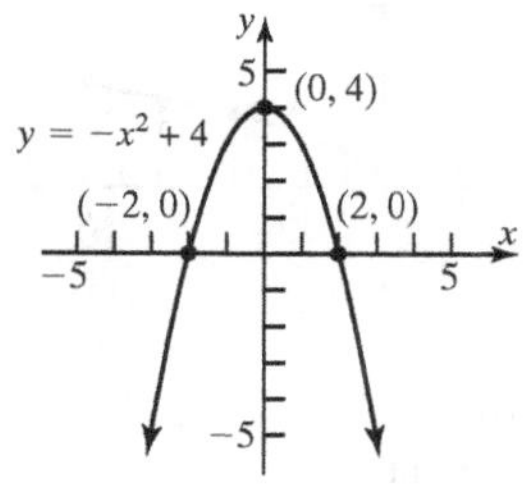

87.

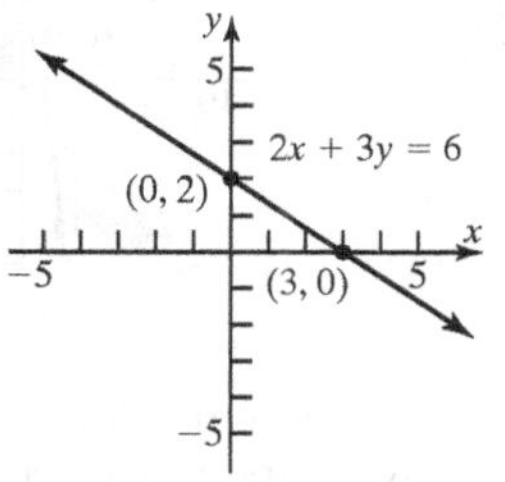

89.

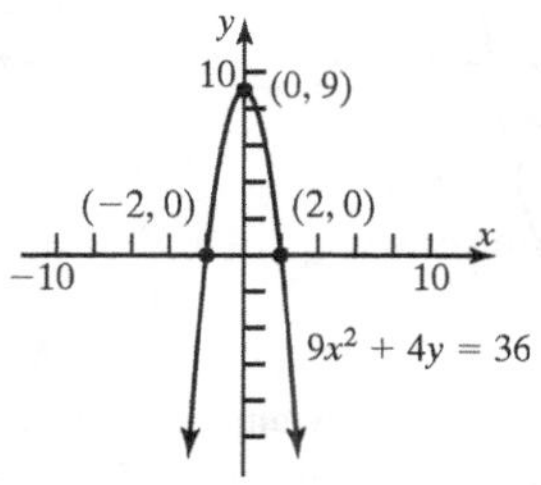

91. x-intercept: 6.5
y-intercept: −13

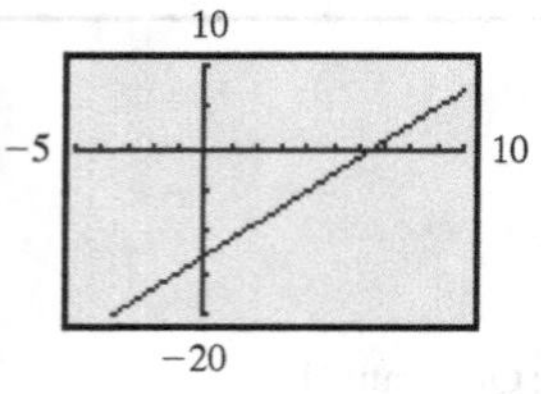

93. x-intercepts: −2.74, 2.74
y-intercept: −15

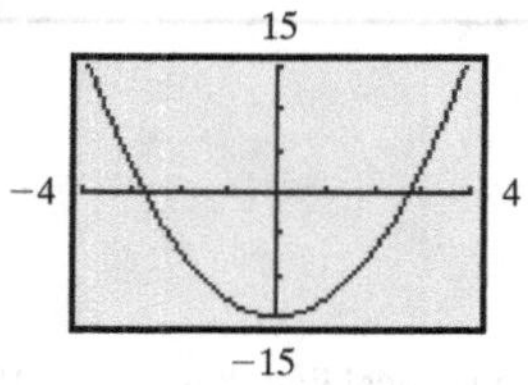

95. x-intercept: 14.33
y-intercept: −21.5

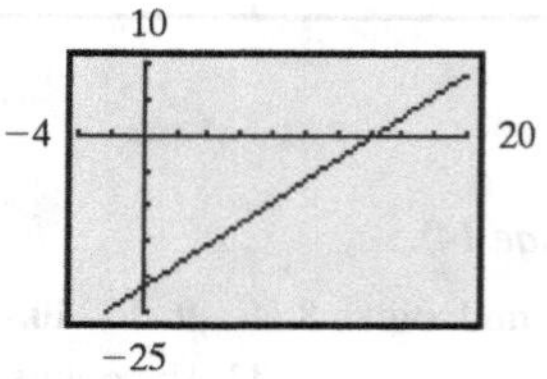

97. x-intercepts: −2.72, 2.72
y-intercept: 12.33

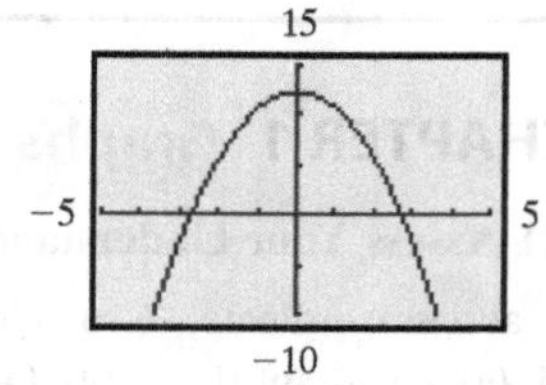

99. $\sqrt{17}$; $2\sqrt{5}$; $\sqrt{29}$ **101.** $d(P_1, P_2) = 6$; $d(P_2, P_3) = 4$; $d(P_1, P_3) = 2\sqrt{13}$; right triangle **103.** $d(P_1, P_2) = 2\sqrt{17}$; $d(P_2, P_3) = \sqrt{34}$; $d(P_1, P_3) = \sqrt{34}$; isosceles right triangle **105.** $90\sqrt{2} \approx 127.28$ ft **107. (a)** (90, 0), (90, 90), (0, 90) **(b)** $5\sqrt{2161} \approx 232.43$ ft **(c)** $30\sqrt{149} \approx 366.20$ ft **109.** $d = 50t$ **111. (a)** (2.65, 1.6) **(b)** ≈1.285 units **113.** $17,630.50 **115.** $B = (5, -2)$

1.2 Assess Your Understanding *(page 23)*

3. $y = 0$ **4.** y-axis **5.** 4 **6.** $(-3, 4)$ **7.** T **8.** F

9. $(-2, 0)$, $(0, 2)$

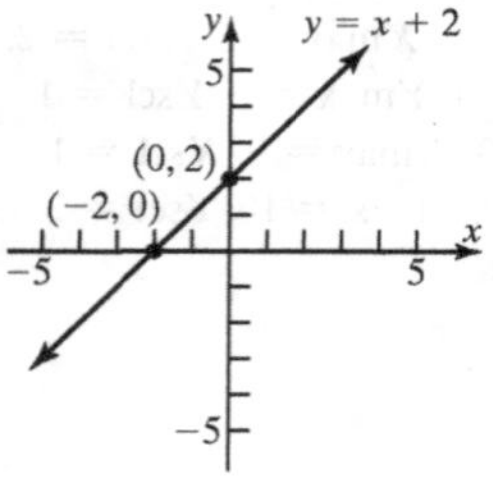

11. $(-4, 0)$, $(0, 8)$

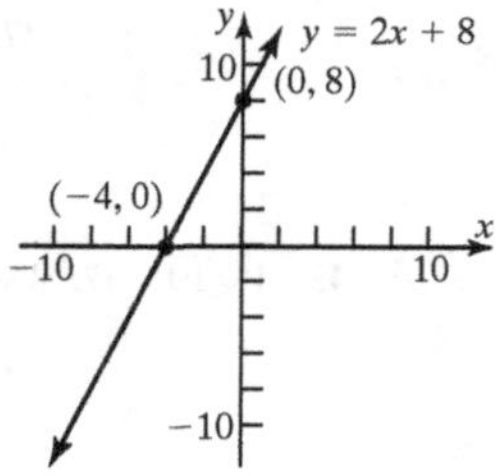

13. $(-1, 0)$, $(1, 0)$, $(0, -1)$

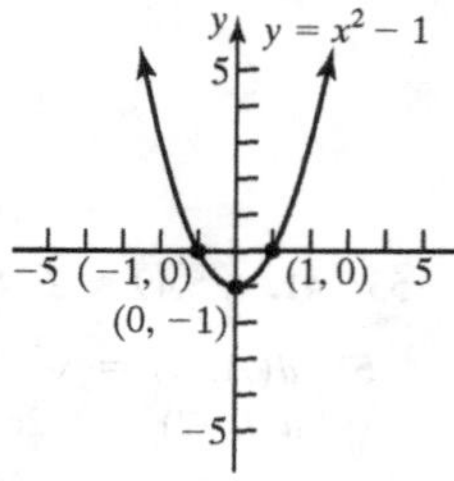

15. $(-2, 0)$, $(2, 0)$, $(0, 4)$

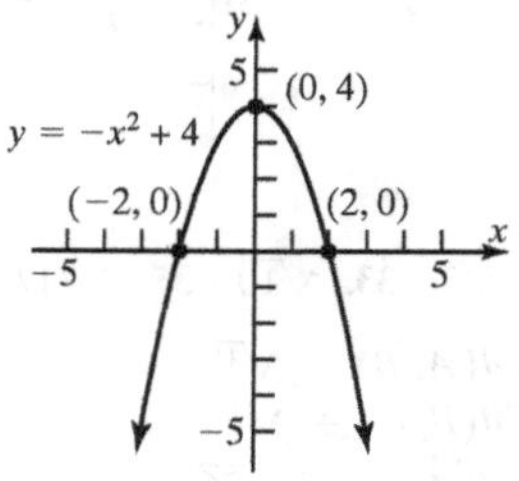

17. $(3, 0)$, $(0, 2)$

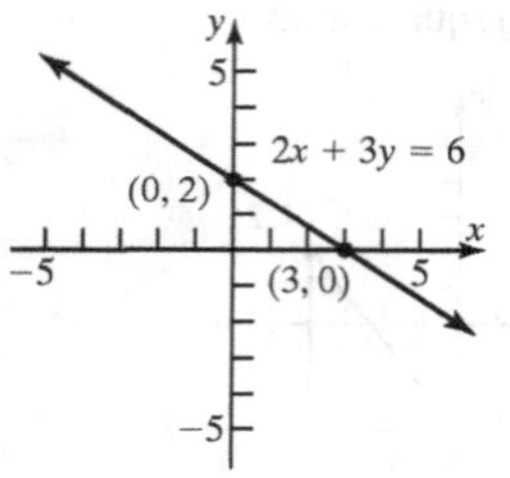

19. $(-2, 0)$, $(2, 0)$, $(0, 9)$

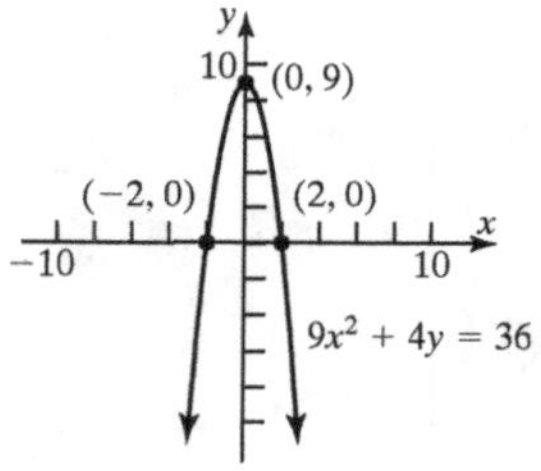

21.

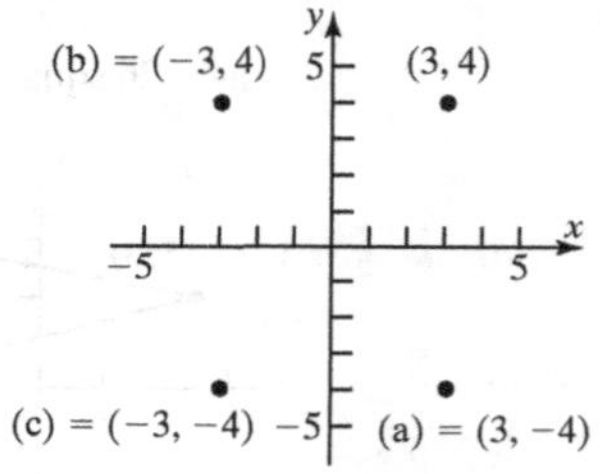

23.

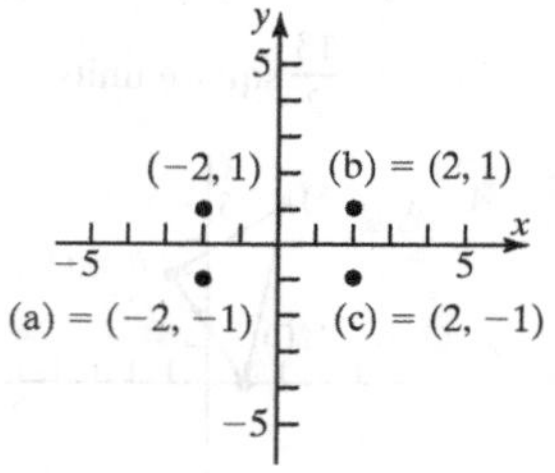

25.

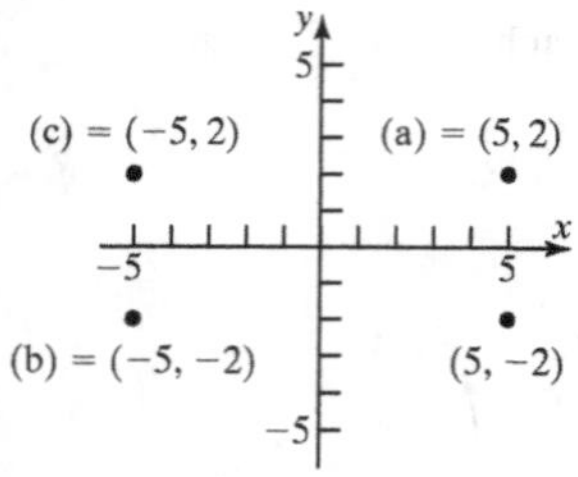

27.

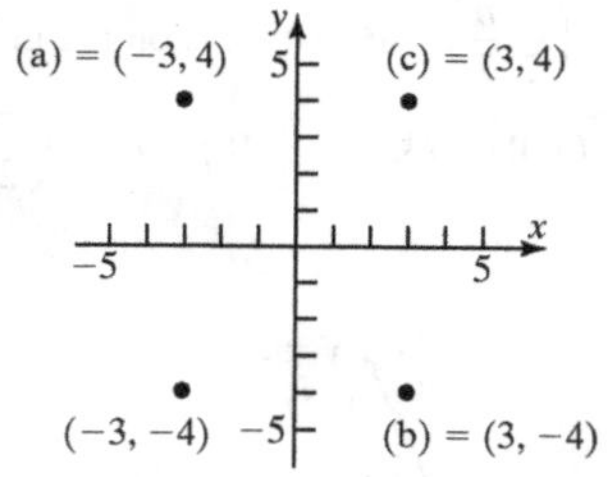

29.

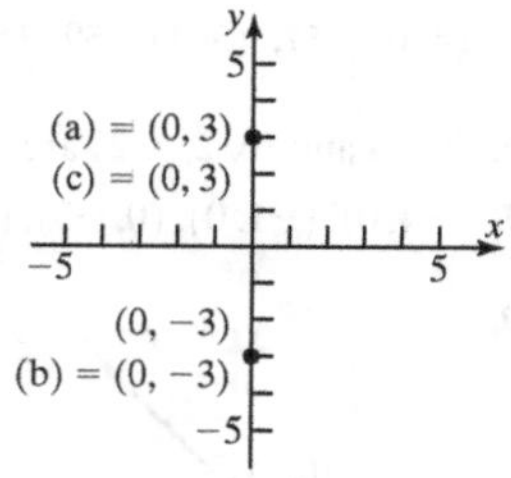

31. Symmetric with respect to the x-axis, the y-axis, and the origin **33.** Symmetric with respect to the y-axis **35.** Symmetric with respect to the x-axis **37.** Symmetric with respect to the origin

39.

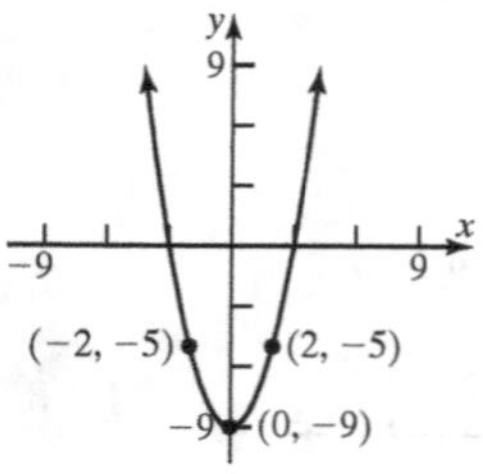

41.

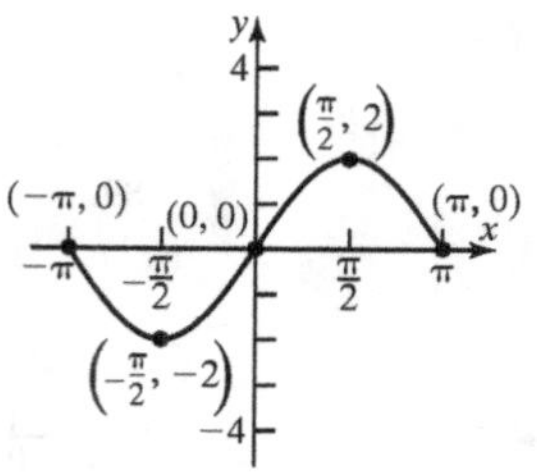

43.

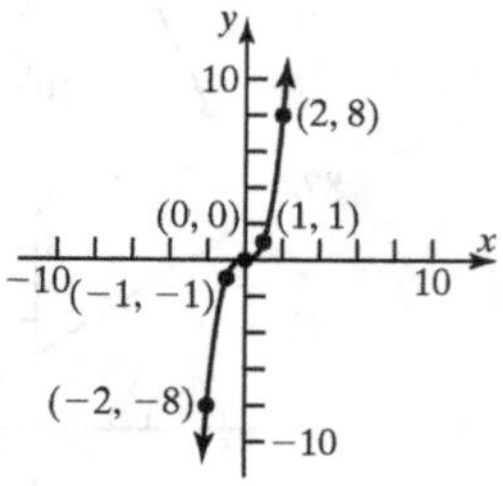

45.

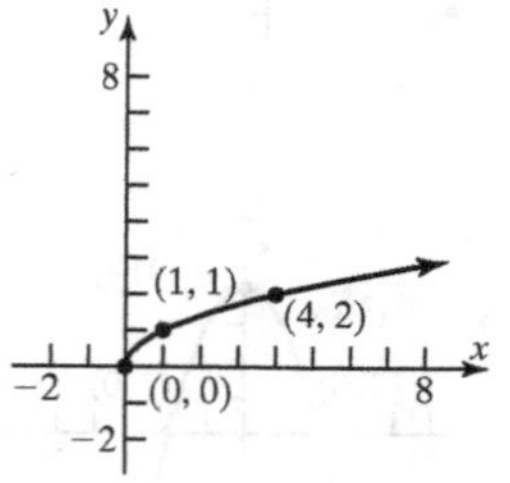

47. $(-4, 0)$, $(0, -2)$, $(0, 2)$; symmetric with respect to the x-axis **49.** $(0, 0)$; symmetric with respect to the origin **51.** $(0, -9)$, $(3, 0)$, $(-3, 0)$; symmetric with respect to the y-axis **53.** $(-2, 0)$, $(2, 0)$, $(0, -3)$, $(0, 3)$; symmetric with respect to the x-axis, y-axis, and origin

55. $(0, -9), (3, 0), (-3, 0), (-1, 0)$; no symmetry **57.** $(0, -4), (4, 0), (-4, 0)$; symmetric with respect to the y-axis
59. $(0, 0)$; symmetric with respect to the origin **61.** $(0, 0)$; symmetric with respect to the origin

63. **(a)** $(0, -5), (-\sqrt{5}, 0), (\sqrt{5}, 0)$
(b) symmetric with respect to the y-axis
(c)

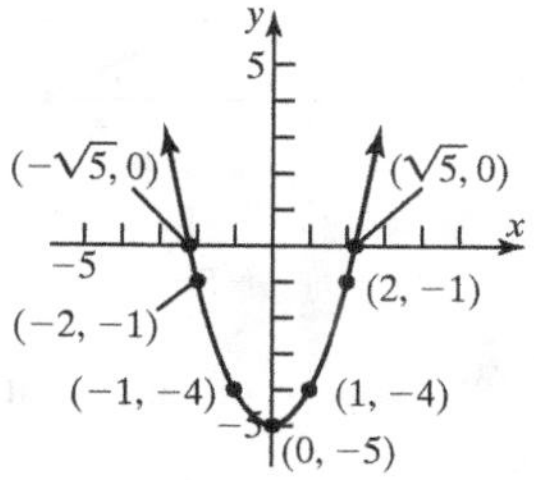

65. **(a)** $(-9, 0), (0, -3), (0, 3)$
(b) symmetric with respect to the x-axis
(c)

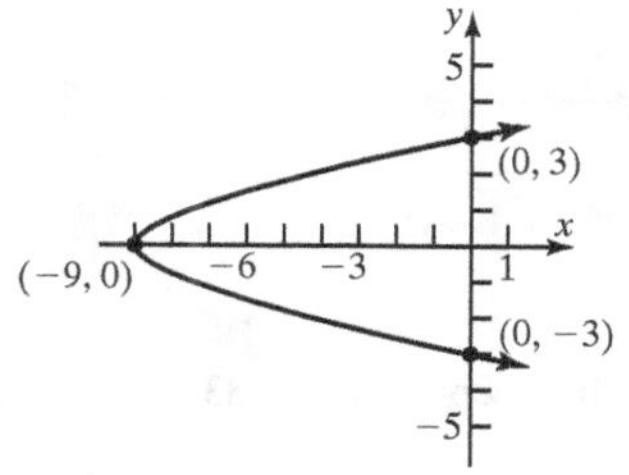

67. **(a)** $(0, 3), (0, -3), (-3, 0), (3, 0)$
(b) symmetric with respect to the x-axis, y-axis, and origin
(c)

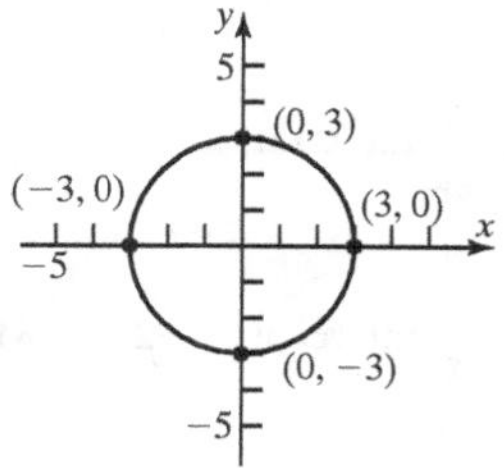

69. **(a)** $(0, 0), (-2, 0), (2, 0)$
(b) symmetric with respect to the origin
(c)

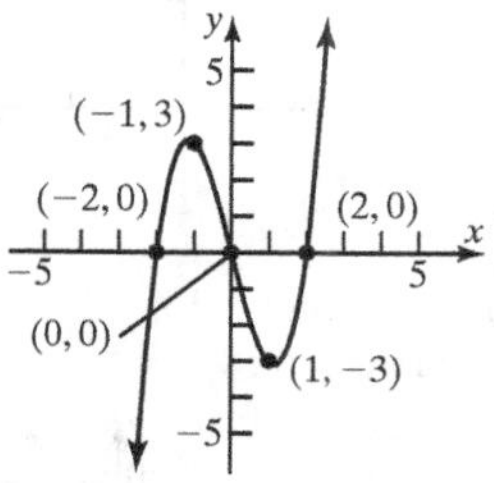

71. $(-1, -2)$
73. 4
75. **(a)** $(0, 0), (2, 0), (0, 1), (0, -1)$
(b) x-axis symmetry

1.3 Assess Your Understanding *(page 28)*

3. ZERO **4.** F **5.** $\{-2.21, 0.54, 1.68\}$ **7.** $\{-1.55, 1.15\}$ **9.** $\{-1.12, 0.36\}$ **11.** $\{-2.69, -0.49, 1.51\}$ **13.** $\{-2.86, -1.34, 0.20, 1.00\}$
15. No real solutions **17.** $\{-18\}$ **19.** $\{-4\}$ **21.** $\left\{\frac{46}{5}\right\}$ **23.** $\{3\}$ **25.** $\{2\}$ **27.** $\{-4, 7\}$ **29.** $\left\{-\frac{2}{3}, 2\right\}$ **31.** $\{-2, -1, 2\}$ **33.** $\{15\}$ **35.** $\left\{-4, -\frac{1}{8}\right\}$

1.4 Assess Your Understanding *(page 40)*

1. undefined; 0 **2.** 3; 2 **3.** $y = b$; y-intercept **4.** T **5.** F **6.** T **7.** $m_1 = m_2$; y-intercepts; $m_1 m_2 = -1$ **8.** 2 **9.** $-\frac{1}{2}$ **10.** F

11. **(a)** Slope $= \frac{1}{2}$
(b) If x increases by 2 units, y will increase by 1 unit.

13. **(a)** Slope $= -\frac{1}{3}$
(b) If x increases by 3 units, y will decrease by 1 unit.

15. Slope $= -\frac{3}{2}$

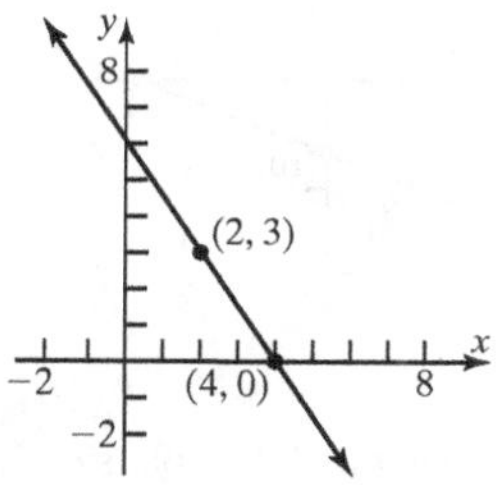

17. Slope $= -\frac{1}{2}$

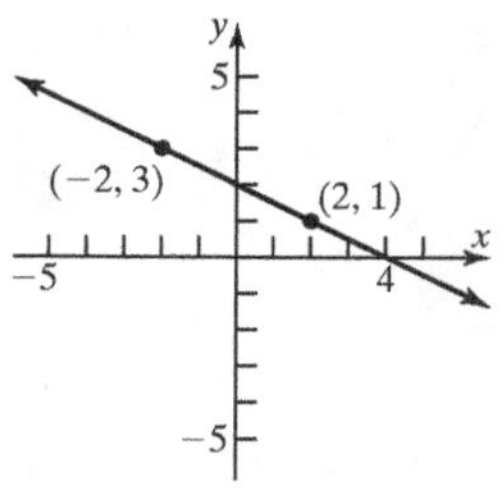

19. Slope $= 0$

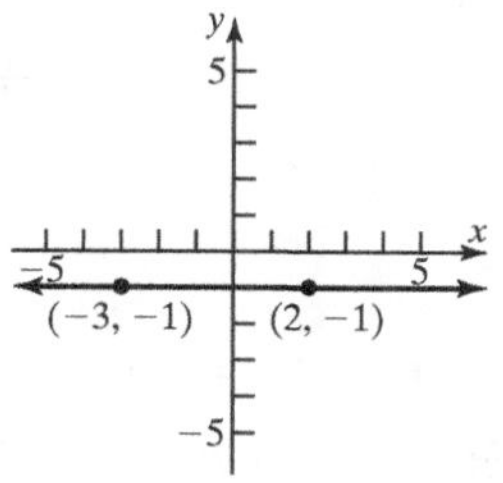

21. Slope undefined

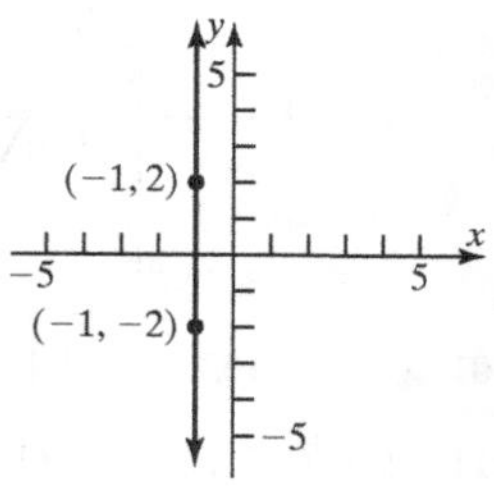

23.

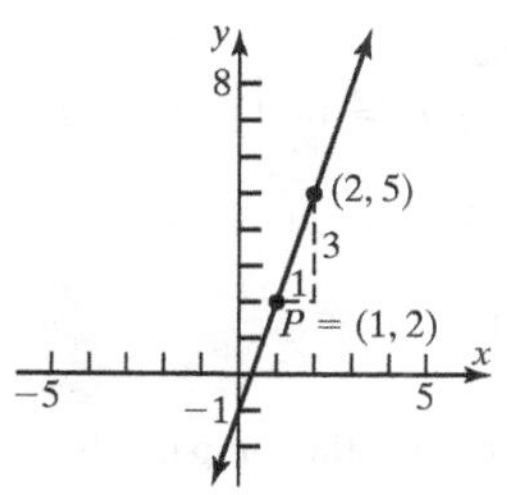

25.

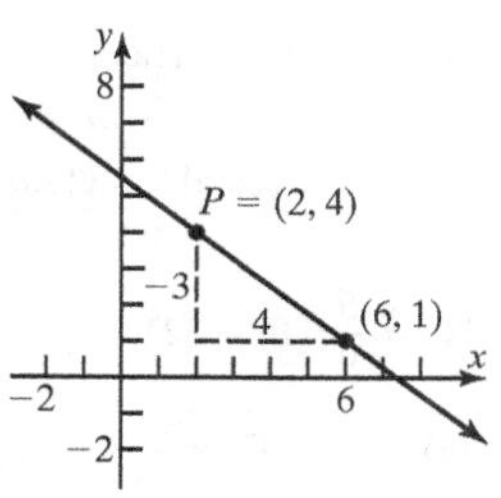

27.

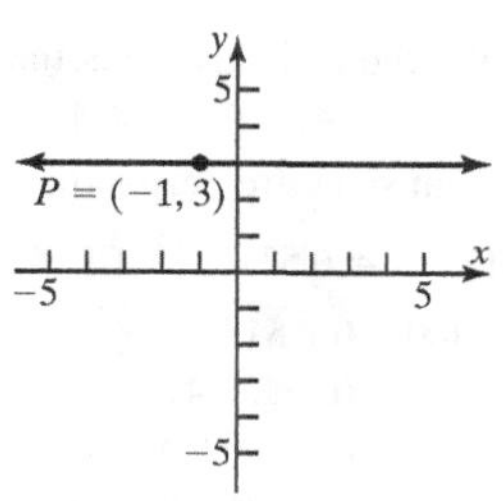

29.

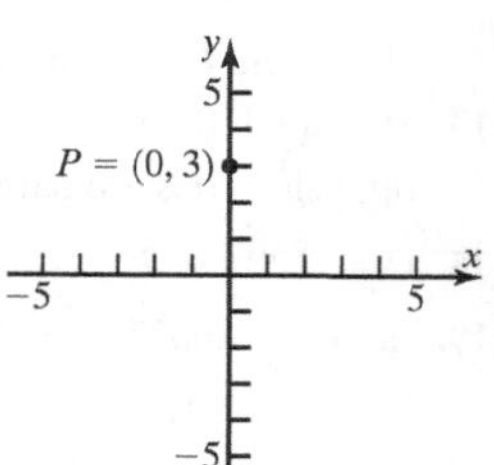

31. $(2, 6); (3, 10); (4, 14)$ **33.** $(4, -7); (6, -10); (8, -13)$ **35.** $(-1, -5); (0, -7); (1, -9)$ **37.** $x - 2y = 0$ or $y = \frac{1}{2}x$ **39.** $x + y = 2$ or $y = -x + 2$
41. $2x - y = 3$ or $y = 2x - 3$ **43.** $x + 2y = 5$ or $y = -\frac{1}{2}x + \frac{5}{2}$ **45.** $3x - y = -9$ or $y = 3x + 9$ **47.** $2x + 3y = -1$ or $y = -\frac{2}{3}x - \frac{1}{3}$
49. $x - 2y = -5$ or $y = \frac{1}{2}x + \frac{5}{2}$ **51.** $3x + y = 3$ or $y = -3x + 3$ **53.** $x - 2y = 2$ or $y = \frac{1}{2}x - 1$ **55.** $x = 2$; no slope–intercept form
57. $y = 2$ **59.** $2x - y = -4$ or $y = 2x + 4$ **61.** $2x - y = 0$ or $y = 2x$ **63.** $x = 4$; no slope–intercept form **65.** $2x + y = 0$ or $y = -2x$
67. $x - 2y = -3$ or $y = \frac{1}{2}x + \frac{3}{2}$ **69.** $y = 4$

71. Slope = 2; y-intercept = 3

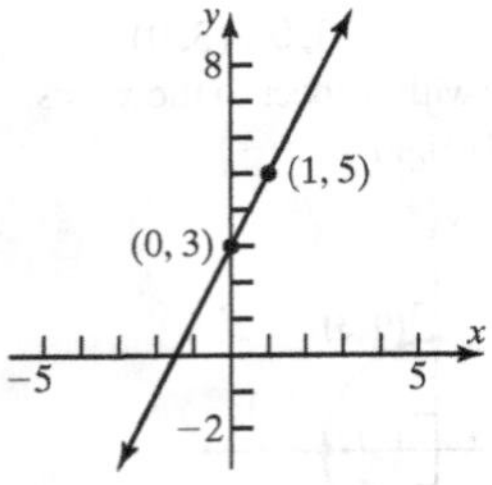

73. Slope = 2; y-intercept = − 2

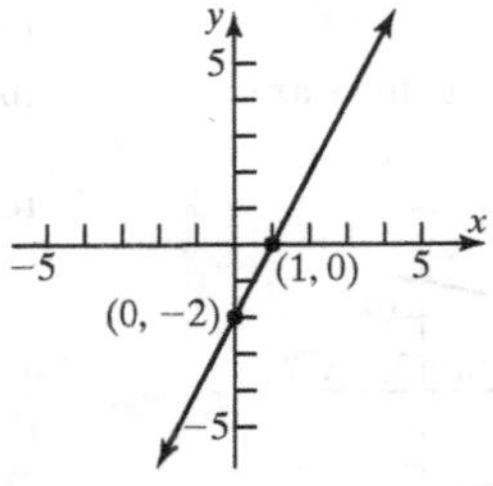

75. Slope $= \frac{1}{2}$; y-intercept = 2

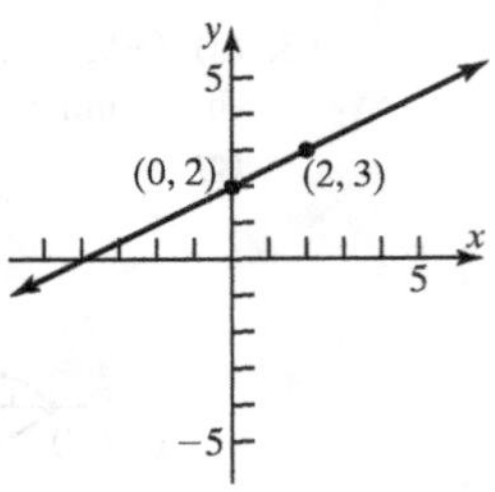

77. Slope $= -\frac{1}{2}$; y-intercept = 2

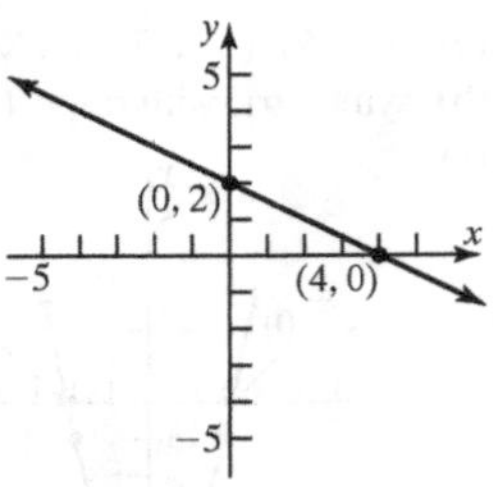

79. Slope $= \frac{2}{3}$; y-intercept = −2

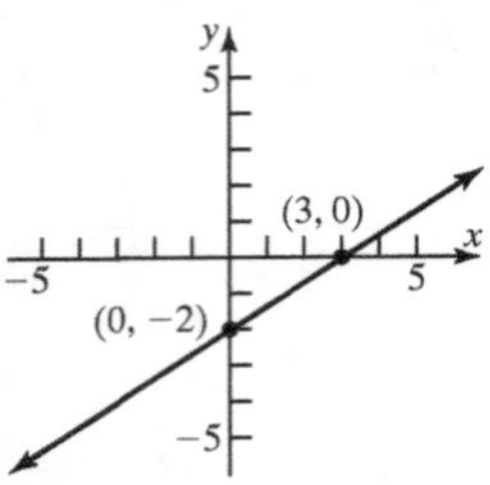

81. Slope = −1; y-intercept = 1

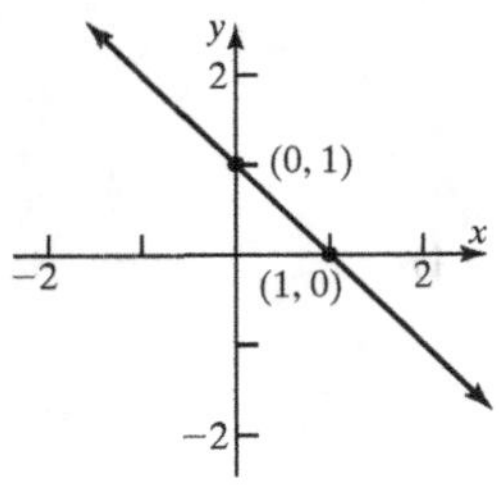

83. Slope undefined; no y-intercept

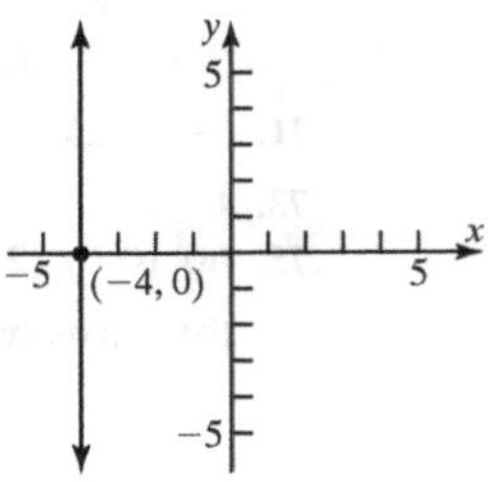

85. Slope = 0; y-intercept = 5

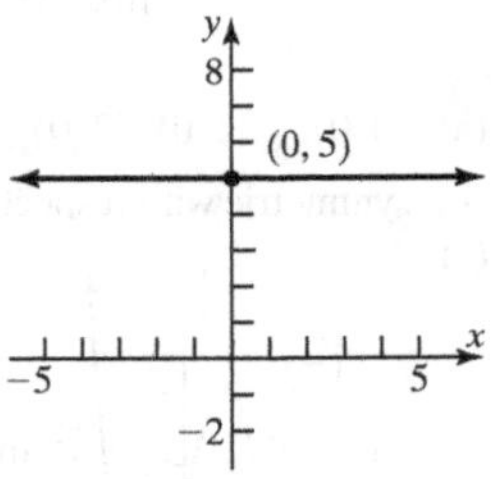

87. Slope = 1; y-intercept = 0

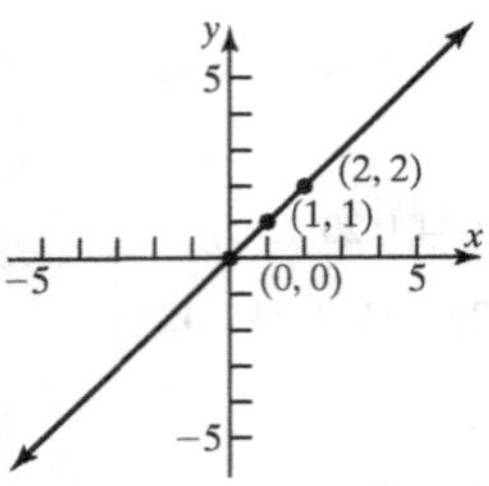

89. Slope $= \frac{3}{2}$; y-intercept = 0

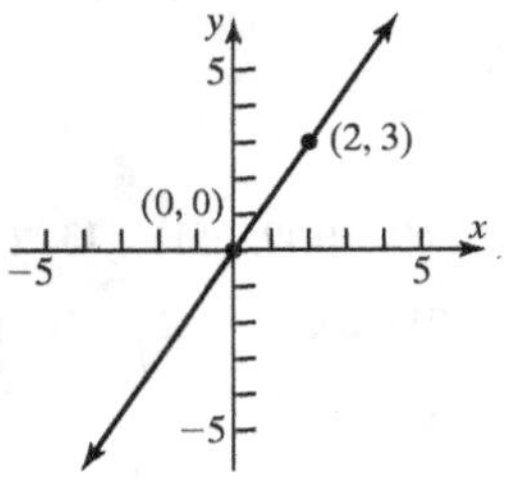

91. (a) x-intercept: 3; y-intercept: 2

(b)

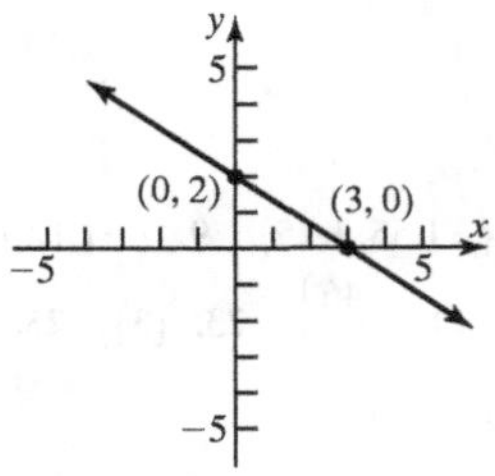

93. (a) x-intercept: −10; y-intercept: 8

(b)

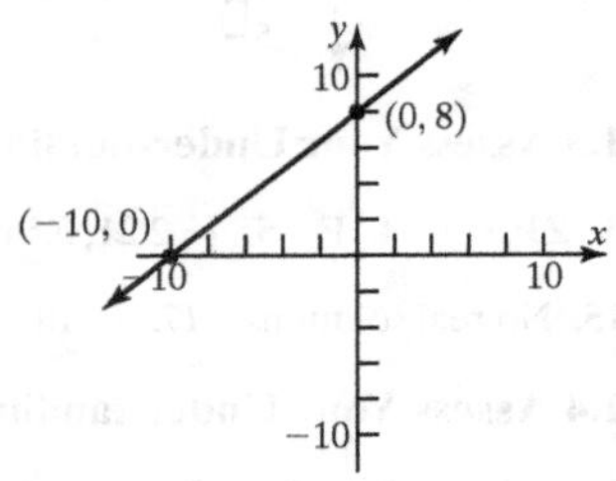

95. (a) x-intercept: 3; y-intercept: $\frac{21}{2}$

(b)

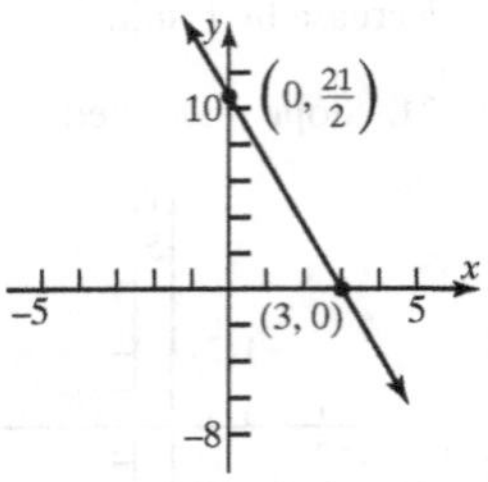

97. (a) x-intercept: 2; y-intercept: 3

(b)

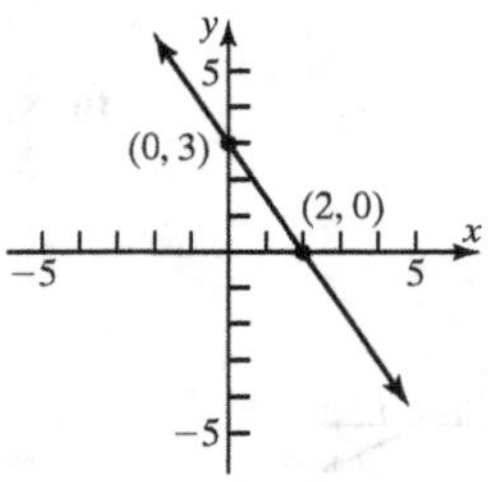

99. (a) x-intercept: 5; y-intercept: −2

(b)

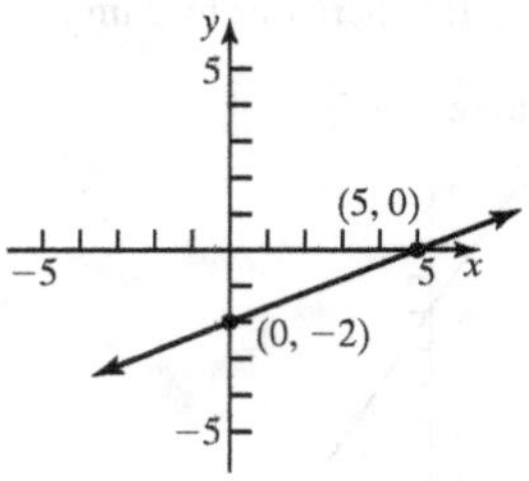

101. $y = 0$ **103.** Parallel **105.** Neither **107.** (b) **109.** (d)

111. $P_1 = (-2, 5)$, $P_2 = (1, 3)$, $m_1 = -\frac{2}{3}$; $P_2 = (1, 3)$, $P_3 = (-1, 0)$, $m_2 = \frac{3}{2}$; because $m_1 m_2 = -1$, the lines are perpendicular and the points $(-2, 5)$, $(1, 3)$, and $(-1, 0)$ are the vertices of a right triangle; thus, the points P_1, P_2, and P_3 are the vertices of a right triangle.

113. $P_1 = (-1, 0)$, $P_2 = (2, 3)$, $m = 1$; $P_3 = (1, -2)$, $P_4 = (4, 1)$, $m = 1$; $P_1 = (-1, 0)$, $P_3 = (1, -2)$, $m = -1$; $P_2 = (2, 3)$, $P_4 = (4, 1)$, $m = -1$; opposite sides are parallel, and adjacent sides are perpendicular; the points are the vertices of a rectangle.

115. $C = 0.20x + 29$; \$51.00; \$75.00 **117.** $C = 0.53x + 1{,}070{,}000$

119. (a) $C = 0.08275x + 7.58$, $0 \le x \le 400$

(b)

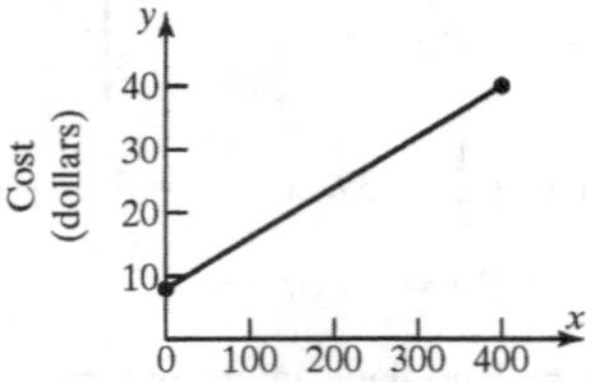

(c) \$15.86
(d) \$32.41
(e) Each additional kW-hr used adds \$0.08275 to the bill.

121. $°C = \frac{5}{9}(°F - 32)$; approximately 21.1°C

123. (a) $y = -\frac{2}{25}x + 30$ **(b)** x-intercept: 375; the ramp meets the floor 375 in. (31.25 ft) from the base of the platform.
(c) The ramp does not meet design requirements. It has a run of 31.25 ft long.
(d) The only slope possible for the ramp to comply with the requirement is for it to drop 1 in. for every 12-in. run.

125. (a) $A = \frac{1}{5}x + 20{,}000$ **(b)** \$80,000 **(c)** Each additional box sold requires an additional \$0.20 in advertising.

127. All have the same slope, 2; the lines are parallel.

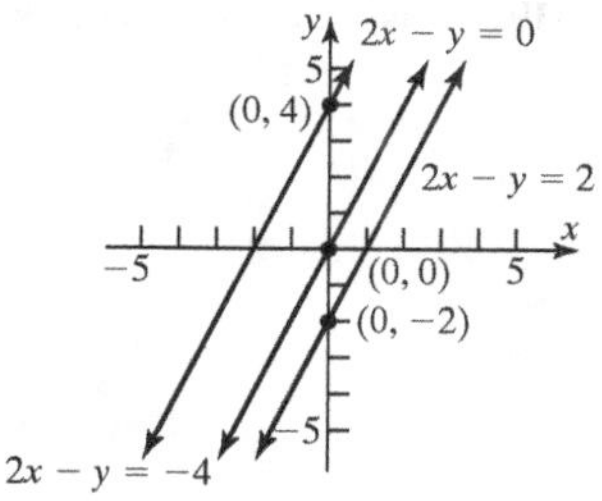

129. (b), (c), (e), (g)
131. (c)
137. No; no
139. They are the same line.
141. Yes, if the y-intercept is 0.

1.5 Assess Your Understanding *(page 49)*

3. F **4.** radius **5.** T **6.** F **7.** Center (2, 1); radius = 2; $(x-2)^2+(y-1)^2=4$ **9.** Center $\left(\frac{5}{2}, 2\right)$; radius = $\frac{3}{2}$; $\left(x-\frac{5}{2}\right)^2+(y-2)^2=\frac{9}{4}$

11. $x^2+y^2=4$; $x^2+y^2-4=0$

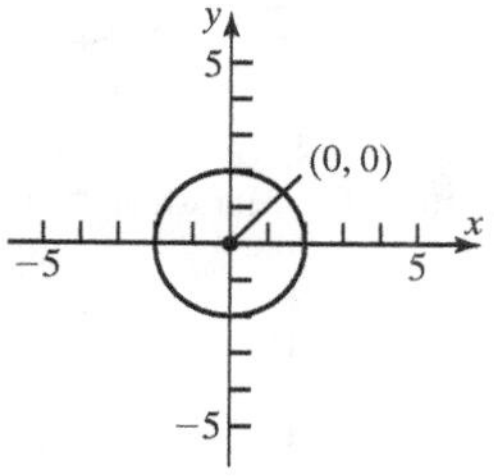

13. $x^2+(y-2)^2=4$; $x^2+y^2-4y=0$

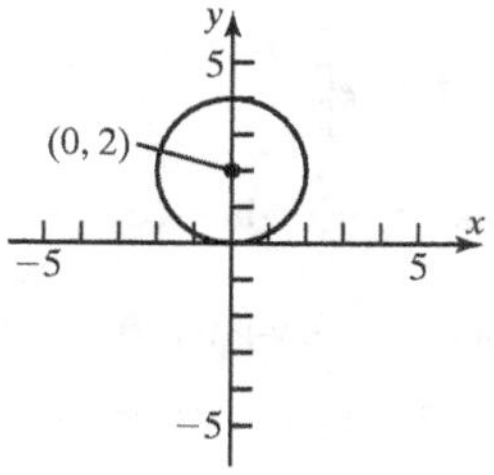

15. $(x-4)^2+(y+3)^2=25$; $x^2+y^2-8x+6y=0$

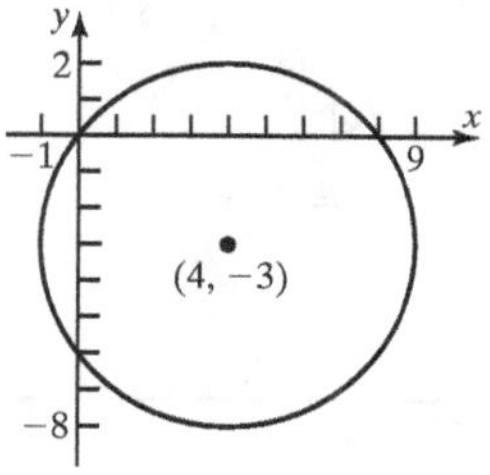

17. $(x+2)^2+(y-1)^2=16$; $x^2+y^2+4x-2y-11=0$

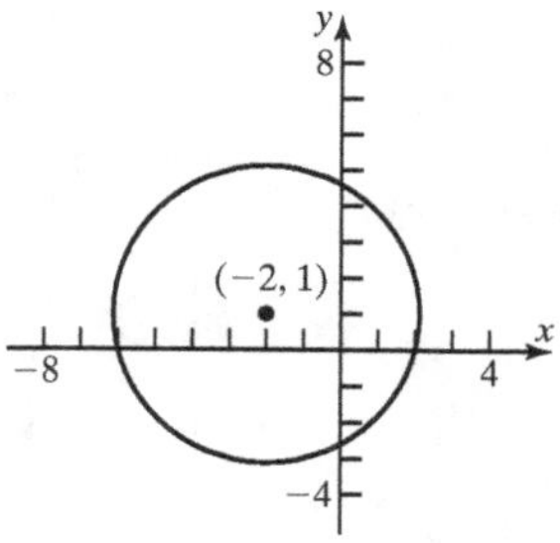

19. $\left(x-\frac{1}{2}\right)^2+y^2=\frac{1}{4}$; $x^2+y^2-x=0$

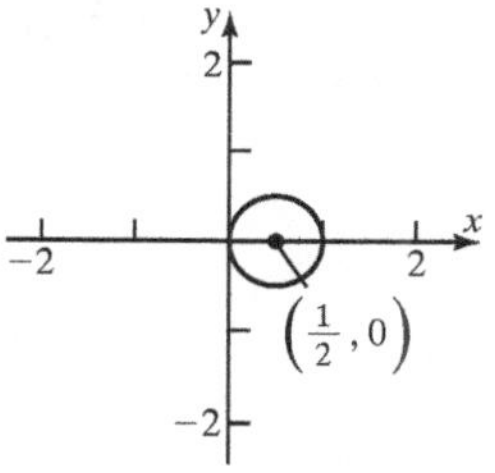

21. **(a)** $(h, k)=(0, 0)$; $r=2$ **(b)**

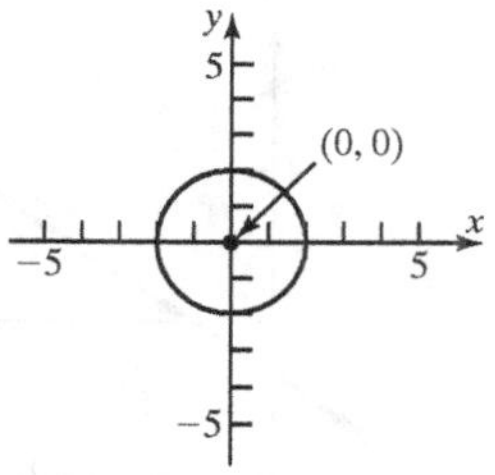

(c) $(\pm 2, 0)$; $(0, \pm 2)$

23. **(a)** $(h, k)=(3, 0)$; $r=2$ **(b)**

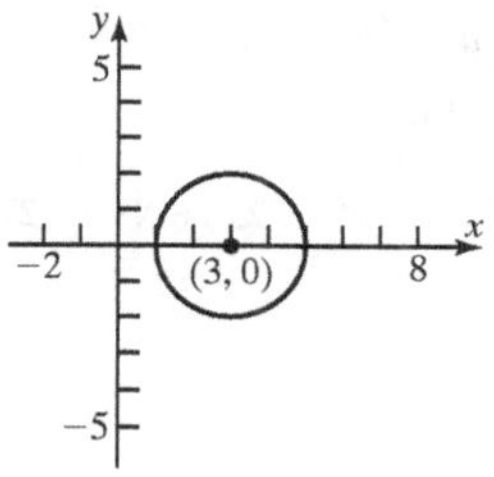

(c) (1, 0); (5, 0)

25. **(a)** $(h, k)=(1, 2)$; $r=3$ **(b)**

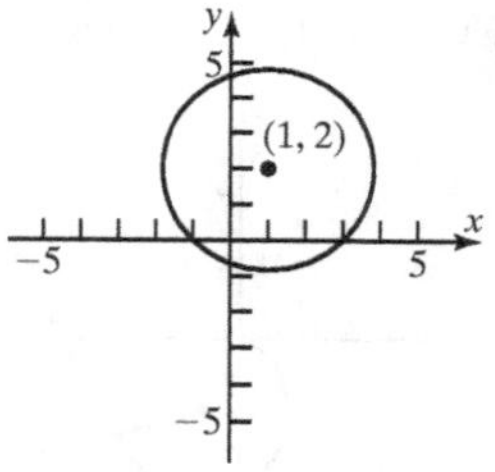

(c) $\left(1\pm\sqrt{5}, 0\right)$; $\left(0, 2\pm 2\sqrt{2}\right)$

27. **(a)** $(h, k)=(-2, 2)$; $r=3$ **(b)**

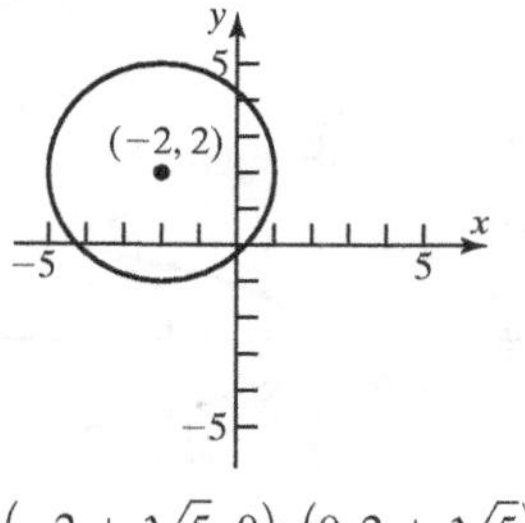

(c) $\left(-2\pm\sqrt{5}, 0\right)$; $\left(0, 2\pm\sqrt{5}\right)$

29. **(a)** $(h, k)=\left(\frac{1}{2}, -1\right)$; $r=\frac{1}{2}$ **(b)**

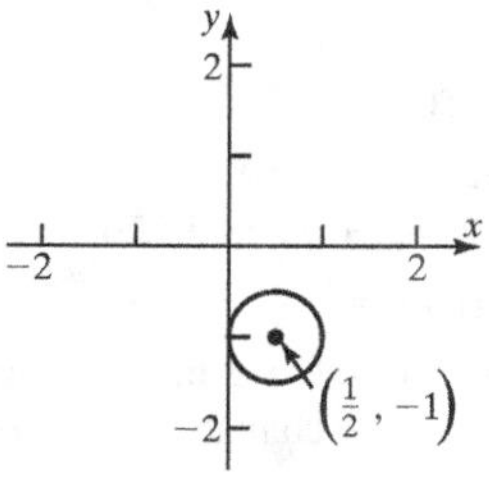

(c) $(0, -1)$

31. **(a)** $(h, k)=(3, -2)$; $r=5$ **(b)**

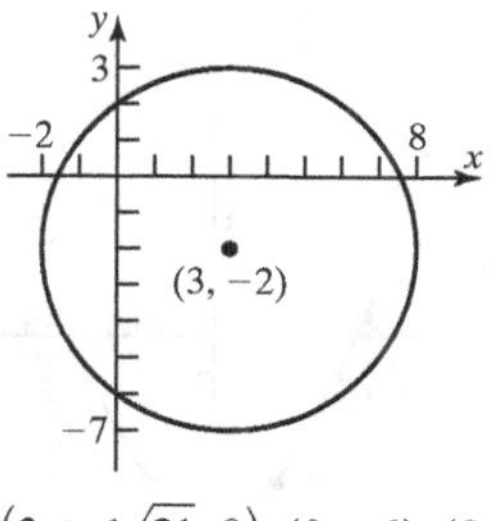

(c) $\left(3\pm\sqrt{21}, 0\right)$; $(0, -6)$, $(0, 2)$

33. **(a)** $(h, k)=(-2, 0)$; $r=2$ **(b)**

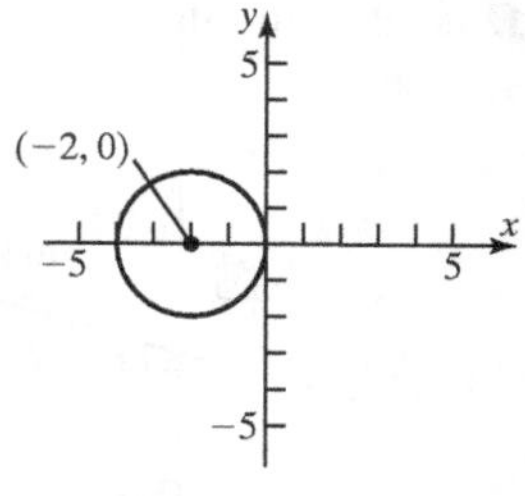

(c) $(0, 0)$, $(-4, 0)$

35. $x^2+y^2=13$ **37.** $(x-2)^2+(y-3)^2=9$ **39.** $(x+1)^2+(y-3)^2=5$ **41.** $(x+1)^2+(y-3)^2=1$ **43.** (c) **45.** (b) **47.** 18 units^2 **49.** $x^2+(y-139)^2=15{,}625$ **51.** $x^2+y^2+2x+4y-4168.16=0$ **53.** $\sqrt{2}x+4y=9\sqrt{2}$ **55.** (1, 0) **57.** $y=2$ **59.** (b), (c), (e), (g)

Review Exercises *(page 52)*

1. **(a)** $2\sqrt{5}$ **(b)** (2, 1) **(c)** $\frac{1}{2}$ **(d)** For each run of 2, there is a rise of 1. **3.** **(a)** 5 **(b)** $\left(-\frac{1}{2}, 1\right)$ **(c)** $-\frac{4}{3}$ **(d)** For each run of 3, there is a rise of −4. **5.** **(a)** 12 **(b)** (4, 2) **(c)** Undefined **(d)** No change in x **7.** $(-4, 0)$, $(0, 2)$, $(0, 0)$, $(0, -2)$, $(2, 0)$

9.

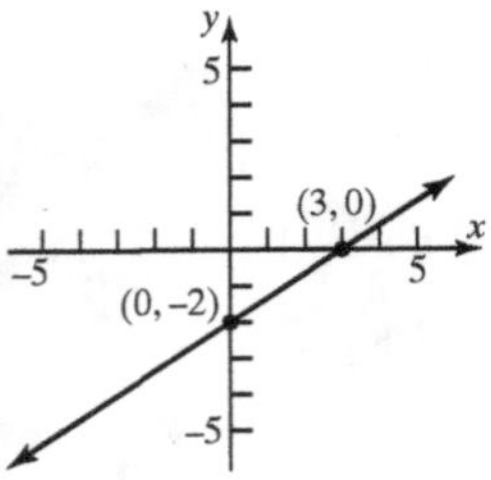

11.

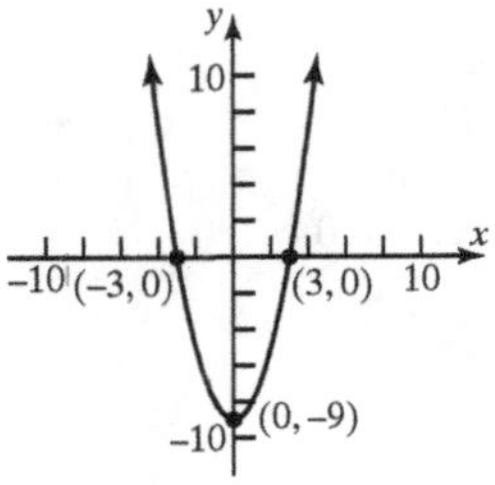

13.

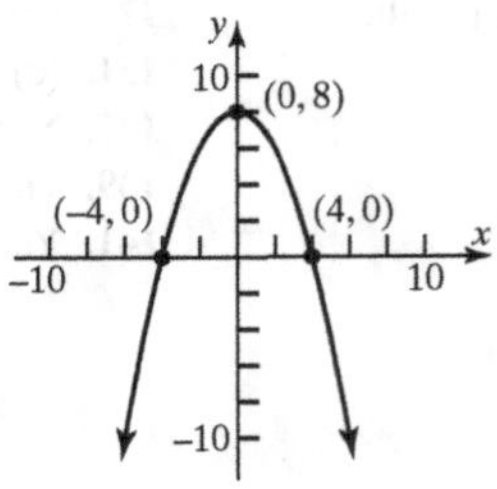

15. x-axis **17.** x-axis, y-axis, origin **19.** y-axis **21.** no symmetry

23.

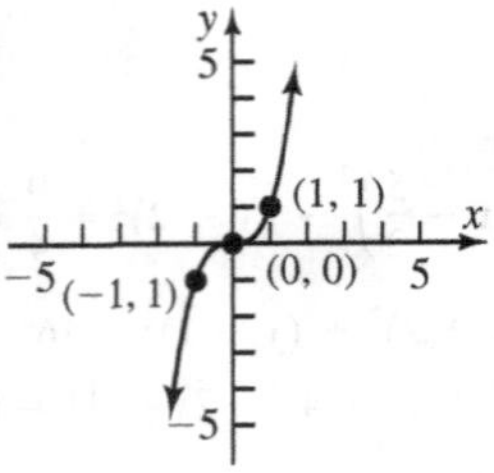

25. $\{-2.49, 0.66, 1.83\}$ **27.** $\{-1.14, 1.64\}$

29. $2x + y = 5$ or $y = -2x + 5$

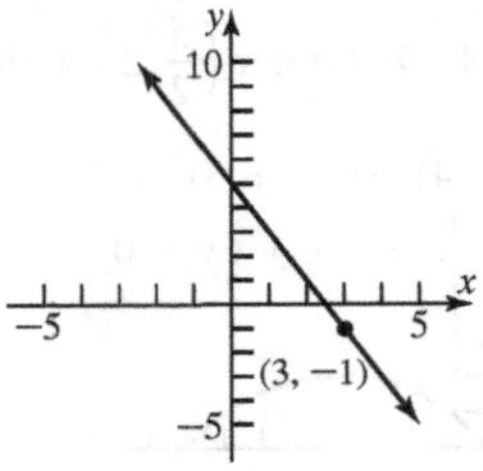

31. $x = -3$; no slope–intercept form

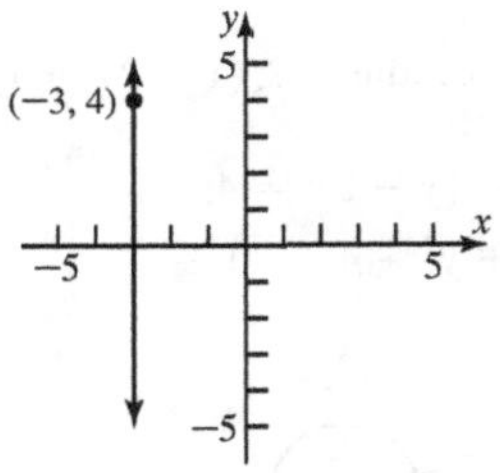

33. $x + 5y = -10$ or $y = -\frac{1}{5}x - 2$

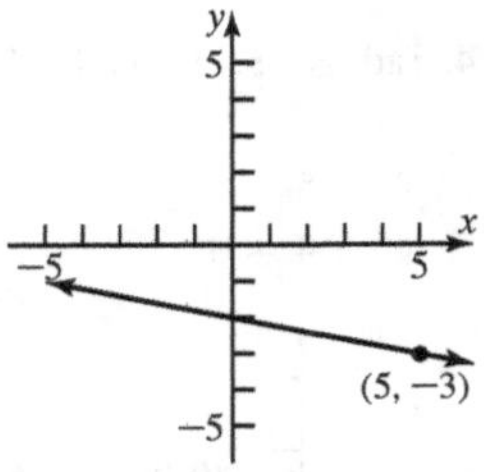

35. $2x - 3y = -19$ or $y = \frac{2}{3}x + \frac{19}{3}$

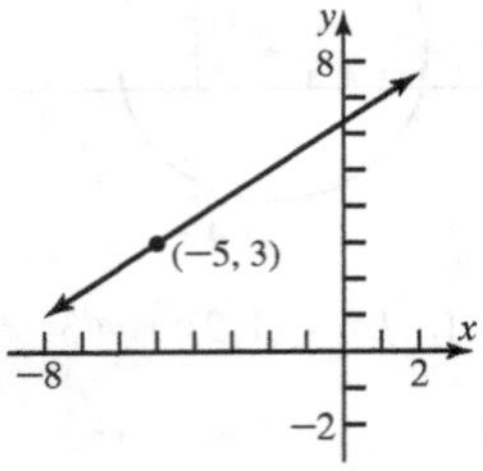

37. $x - y = 7$ or $y = x - 7$

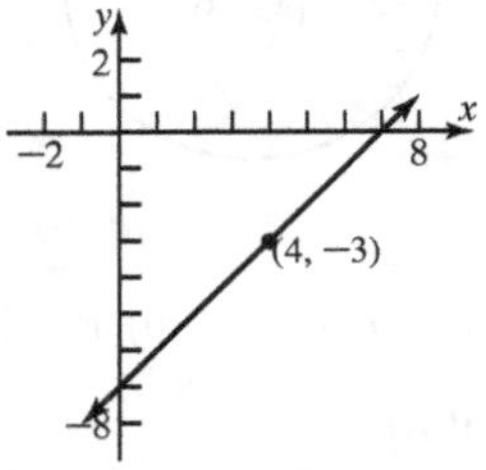

39. Slope $= -\frac{2}{3}$, y-intercept $= 6$

41. Slope $= -\frac{1}{5}$, y-intercept $= 4$

43. $(x + 2)^2 + (y - 3)^2 = 16$

45. $(x + 1)^2 + (y + 2)^2 = 1$

47. Center $(1, -2)$; radius $= 3$

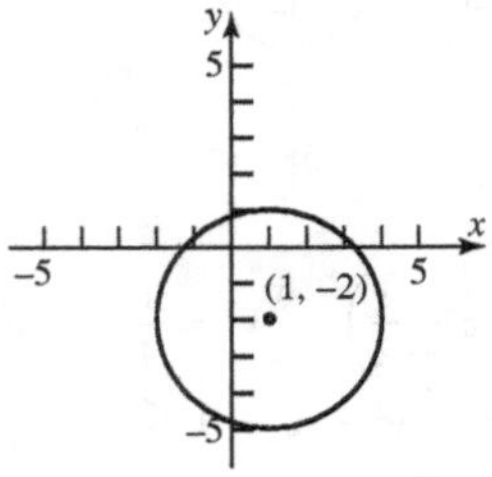

$(0, -2 \pm 2\sqrt{2}), (1 \pm \sqrt{5}, 0)$

49. Center $(1, -2)$; radius $= \sqrt{5}$

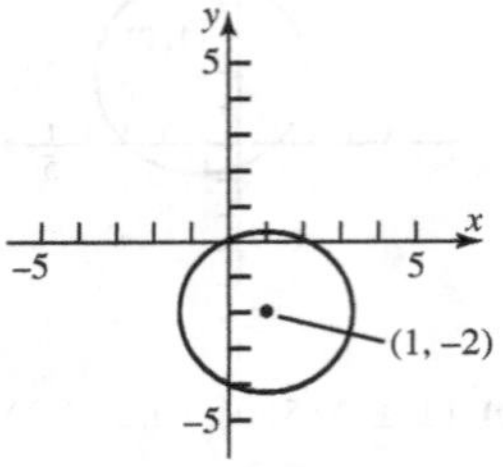

$(0, 0), (0, -4), (2, 0)$

51. $d(A, B) = \sqrt{13}$; $d(B, C) = \sqrt{13}$

53. $m_{AB} = -1$; $m_{BC} = -1$

55. Center $(1, -2)$; radius $= 4\sqrt{2}$; $x^2 + y^2 - 2x + 4y - 27 = 0$

57.

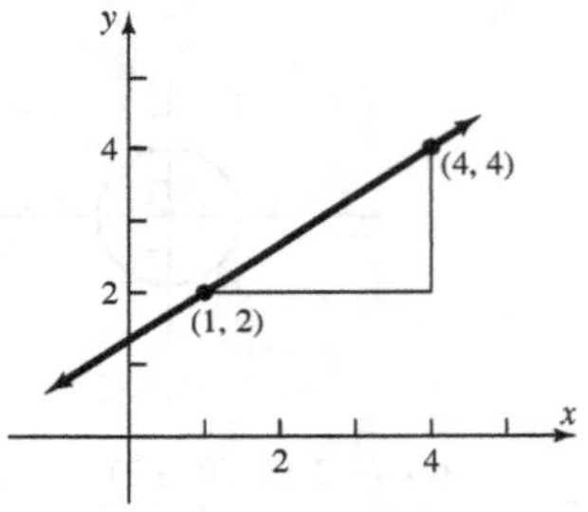

Chapter Test *(page 54)*

1. (a) $d = 10$ **(b)** $m = (1, 1)$

2.

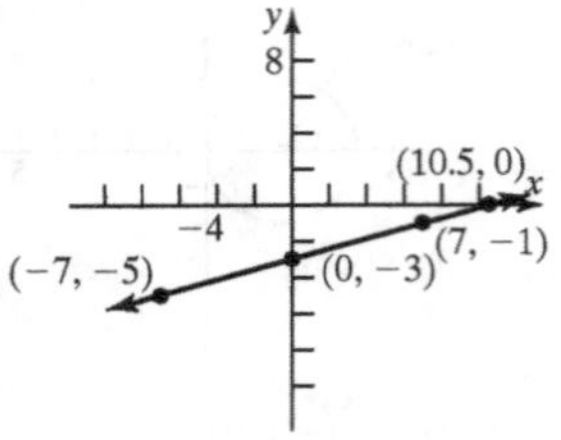

3.

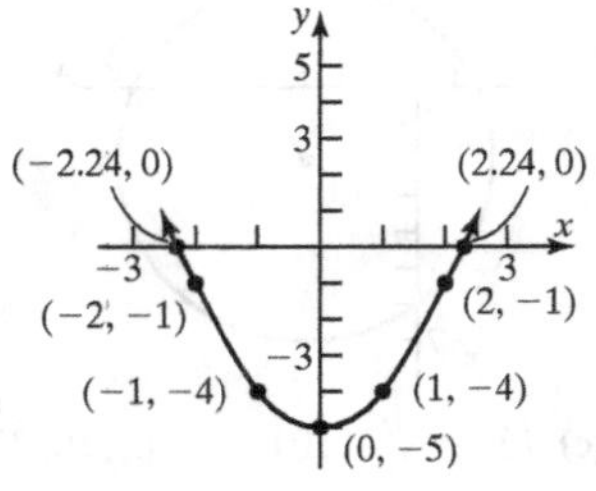

4. −1, 0.5, and 1

5. −2.50 and 2.50

6. −2.46, −0.24, and 1.70

7. (a) $m = -\frac{2}{3}$

(b) For every 3-unit change in x, y will change by −2 units.

8.

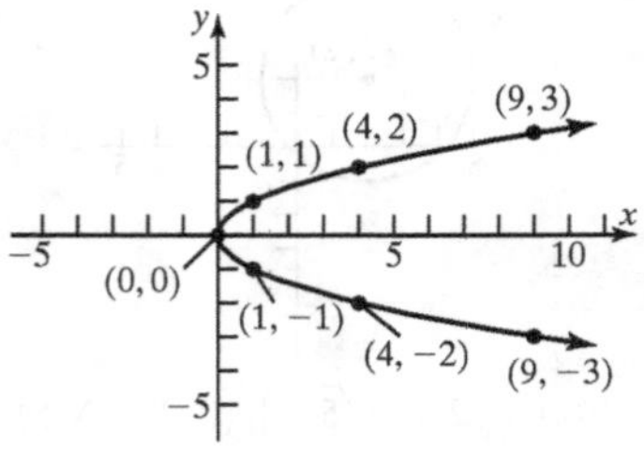

9. Intercepts: (−3, 0), (3, 0), (0, 9); symmetric with respect to the y-axis

10. $y = -2x + 2$

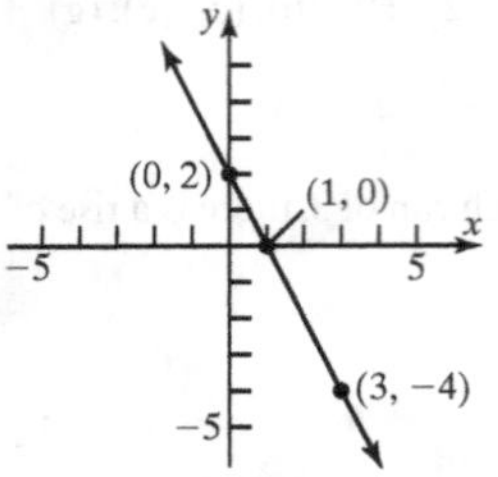

11. $x^2 + y^2 - 8x + 6y = 0$

12. Center: (−2, 1); radius: 3

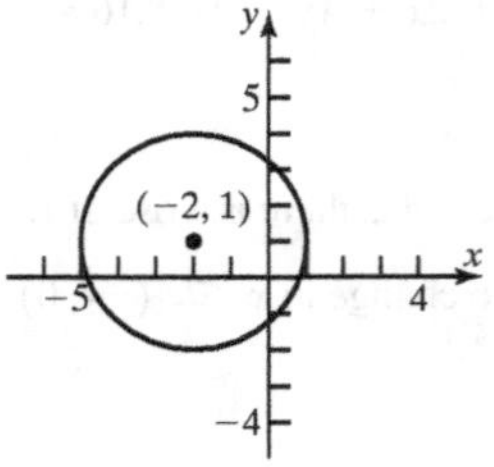

13. Parallel line: $y = -\frac{2}{3}x - \frac{1}{3}$; perpendicular line: $y = \frac{3}{2}x + 3$

CHAPTER 2 Functions and Their Graphs

2.1 Assess Your Understanding *(page 67)*

5. independent; dependent **6.** range **7.** $[0, 5]$ **8.** image **9.** $(g - f)(x)$ **10.** F **11.** T **13.** F
15. Function; Domain: {Elvis, Colleen, Kaleigh, Marissa}, Range: {January 8, March 15, September 17} **17.** Not a function **19.** Not a function
21. Function; Domain: $\{1, 2, 3, 4\}$; Range: $\{3\}$ **23.** Not a function **25.** Function; Domain: $\{-2, -1, 0, 1\}$, Range: $\{0, 1, 4\}$ **27.** Function
29. Function **31.** Not a function **33.** Not a function **35.** Function **37.** Not a function **39. (a)** -4 **(b)** 1 **(c)** -3 **(d)** $3x^2 - 2x - 4$
(e) $-3x^2 - 2x + 4$ **(f)** $3x^2 + 8x + 1$ **(g)** $12x^2 + 4x - 4$ **(h)** $3x^2 + 6xh + 3h^2 + 2x + 2h - 4$ **41. (a)** 0 **(b)** $\frac{1}{2}$ **(c)** $-\frac{1}{2}$ **(d)** $\frac{-x}{x^2+1}$
(e) $\frac{-x}{x^2+1}$ **(f)** $\frac{x+1}{x^2+2x+2}$ **(g)** $\frac{2x}{4x^2+1}$ **(h)** $\frac{x+h}{x^2+2xh+h^2+1}$ **43. (a)** 4 **(b)** 5 **(c)** 5 **(d)** $|x| + 4$ **(e)** $-|x| - 4$ **(f)** $|x+1| + 4$
(g) $2|x| + 4$ **(h)** $|x+h| + 4$ **45. (a)** $-\frac{1}{5}$ **(b)** $-\frac{3}{2}$ **(c)** $\frac{1}{8}$ **(d)** $\frac{2x-1}{3x+5}$ **(e)** $\frac{-2x-1}{3x-5}$ **(f)** $\frac{2x+3}{3x-2}$ **(g)** $\frac{4x+1}{6x-5}$ **(h)** $\frac{2x+2h+1}{3x+3h-5}$
47. All real numbers **49.** All real numbers **51.** $\{x|x \neq -4, x \neq 4\}$ **53.** $\{x|x \neq 0\}$ **55.** $\{x|x \geq 4\}$ **57.** $\{x|x > 9\}$ **59.** $\{x|x > 1\}$
61. (a) $(f+g)(x) = 5x + 1$; All real numbers **(b)** $(f-g)(x) = x + 7$; All real numbers **(c)** $(f \cdot g)(x) = 6x^2 - x - 12$; All real numbers
(d) $\left(\frac{f}{g}\right)(x) = \frac{3x+4}{2x-3}$; $\left\{x \middle| x \neq \frac{3}{2}\right\}$ **(e)** 16 **(f)** 11 **(g)** 10 **(h)** -7 **63. (a)** $(f+g)(x) = 2x^2 + x - 1$; All real numbers
(b) $(f-g)(x) = -2x^2 + x - 1$; All real numbers **(c)** $(f \cdot g)(x) = 2x^3 - 2x^2$; All real numbers **(d)** $\left(\frac{f}{g}\right)(x) = \frac{x-1}{2x^2}$; $\{x|x \neq 0\}$ **(e)** 20
(f) -29 **(g)** 8 **(h)** 0 **65. (a)** $(f+g)(x) = \sqrt{x} + 3x - 5$; $\{x|x \geq 0\}$ **(b)** $(f-g)(x) = \sqrt{x} - 3x + 5$; $\{x|x \geq 0\}$
(c) $(f \cdot g)(x) = 3x\sqrt{x} - 5\sqrt{x}$; $\{x|x \geq 0\}$ **(d)** $\left(\frac{f}{g}\right)(x) = \frac{\sqrt{x}}{3x-5}$ $\left\{x \middle| x \geq 0, x \neq \frac{5}{3}\right\}$ **(e)** $\sqrt{3} + 4$ **(f)** -5 **(g)** $\sqrt{2}$ **(h)** $-\frac{1}{2}$
67. (a) $(f+g)(x) = 1 + \frac{2}{x}$; $\{x|x \neq 0\}$ **(b)** $(f-g)(x) = 1$; $\{x|x \neq 0\}$ **(c)** $(f \cdot g)(x) = \frac{1}{x} + \frac{1}{x^2}$; $\{x|x \neq 0\}$
(d) $\left(\frac{f}{g}\right)(x) = x + 1$; $\{x|x \neq 0\}$ **(e)** $\frac{5}{3}$ **(f)** 1 **(g)** $\frac{3}{4}$ **(h)** 2 **69. (a)** $(f+g)(x) = \frac{6x+3}{3x-2}$; $\left\{x \middle| x \neq \frac{2}{3}\right\}$
(b) $(f-g)(x) = \frac{-2x+3}{3x-2}$; $\left\{x \middle| x \neq \frac{2}{3}\right\}$ **(c)** $(f \cdot g)(x) = \frac{8x^2+12x}{(3x-2)^2}$; $\left\{x \middle| x \neq \frac{2}{3}\right\}$ **(d)** $\left(\frac{f}{g}\right)(x) = \frac{2x+3}{4x}$; $\left\{x \middle| x \neq 0; x \neq \frac{2}{3}\right\}$ **(e)** 3
(f) $-\frac{1}{2}$ **(g)** $\frac{7}{2}$ **(h)** $\frac{5}{4}$ **71.** $g(x) = 5 - \frac{7}{2}x$ **73.** 4 **75.** $2x + h - 1$ **77.** $6x + 3h - 2$ **79.** $3x^2 + 3xh + h^2$ **81.** $A = -\frac{7}{2}$ **83.** $A = -4$
85. $A = 8$; undefined at $x = 3$ **87.** $A(x) = \frac{1}{2}x^2$ **89.** $G(x) = 10x$ **91. (a)** P is the dependent variable; a is the independent variable.
(b) $P(20) = 197.34$; In 2005, there are 197.34 million people 20 years of age or older. **(c)** $P(0) = 290.580$; In 2005, there are 290.580 million people.
93. (a) 15.1 m, 14.071 m, 12.944 m, 11.719 m **(b)** 1.01 s, 1.43 s, 1.75 s **(c)** 2.02 s **95. (a)** \$222 **(b)** \$225 **(c)** \$220 **(d)** \$230
97. $R(x) = \frac{L(x)}{P(x)}$ **99.** $H(x) = P(x) \cdot I(x)$ **101. (a)** $P(x) = -0.05x^3 + 0.8x^2 + 155x - 500$ **(b)** $P(15) = \$1836.25$
(c) When 15 hundred cell phones are sold, the profit is \$1836.25. **103.** Only $h(x) = 2x$ **107.** Square the real number t and then subtract 2.

2.2 Assess Your Understanding *(page 74)*

3. vertical **4.** 5; -3 **5.** $(-2, 7)$ **6.** F **7.** F **8.** T **9. (a)** $f(0) = 3$; $f(-6) = -3$ **(b)** $f(6) = 0$; $f(11) = 1$ **(c)** Positive **(d)** Negative
(e) -3, 6, and 10 **(f)** $-3 < x < 6$; $10 < x \leq 11$ **(g)** $\{x|-6 \leq x \leq 11\}$ **(h)** $\{y|-3 \leq y \leq 4\}$ **(i)** $-3, 6, 10$ **(j)** 3 **(k)** 3 times **(l)** Once
(m) 0, 4 **(n)** $-5, 8$ **11.** Not a function **13.** Function **(a)** Domain: $\{x|-\pi \leq x \leq \pi\}$; Range: $\{y|-1 \leq y \leq 1\}$ **(b)** $\left(-\frac{\pi}{2}, 0\right), \left(\frac{\pi}{2}, 0\right), (0, 1)$
(c) y-axis **15.** Not a function **17.** Function **(a)** Domain: $\{x|x > 0\}$; Range: all real numbers **(b)** $(1, 0)$ **(c)** None
19. Function **(a)** Domain: all real numbers; Range: $\{y|y \leq 2\}$ **(b)** $(-3, 0), (3, 0), (0, 2)$ **(c)** y-axis **21.** Function **(a)** Domain: all real numbers;
Range: $\{y|y \geq -3\}$ **(b)** $(1, 0), (3, 0), (0, 9)$ **(c)** None **23. (a)** Yes **(b)** $f(-2) = 9$; $(-2, 9)$ **(c)** $0, \frac{1}{2}$; $(0, -1), \left(\frac{1}{2}, -1\right)$ **(d)** All real numbers
(e) $-\frac{1}{2}, 1$ **(f)** -1 **25. (a)** No **(b)** $f(4) = -3$; $(4, -3)$ **(c)** 14; $(14, 2)$ **(d)** $\{x|x \neq 6\}$ **(e)** -2 **(f)** $-\frac{1}{3}$ **27. (a)** Yes **(b)** $f(2) = \frac{8}{17}$; $\left(2, \frac{8}{17}\right)$
(c) $-1, 1$; $(-1, 1), (1, 1)$ **(d)** All real numbers **(e)** 0 **(f)** 0

29. (a) Approximately 10.4 ft high **(b)** Approximately 9.9 ft high
(c)

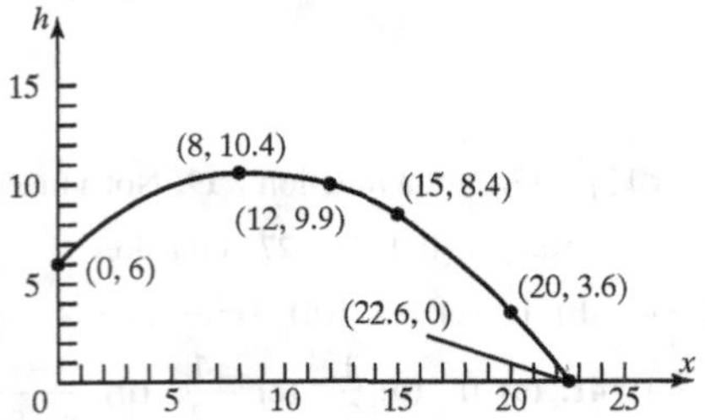

(d) The ball will not go through the hoop; $h(15) \approx 8.4$ ft.
If $v = 30$ ft/s, $h(15) = 10$ ft.

31. (a)

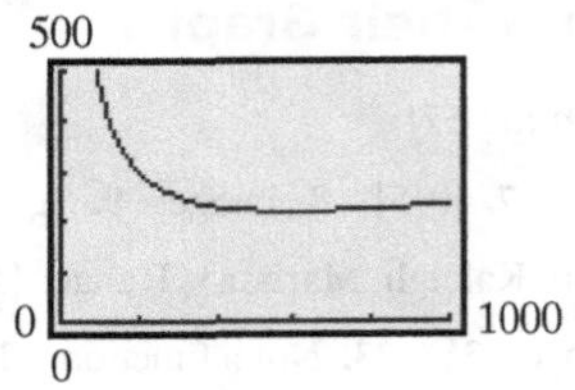

33. (a) 3 **(b)** -2 **(c)** -1 **(d)** 1 **(e)** 2 **(f)** $-\frac{1}{3}$ **35. (a)** \$80; it costs \$80 if you use 0 miniutes. **(b)** \$80; it costs \$80 if you use 1000 minutes. **(c)** \$210; it costs \$210 if you use 2000 minutes. **(d)** $\{m \mid 0 \le m \le 14{,}400\}$. There are at most 14,400 anytime minutes in a month.
37. The x-intercepts can number anywhere from 0 to infinitely many. There is at most one y-intercept. **39. (a)** III **(b)** IV **(c)** I **(d)** V **(e)** II
41.

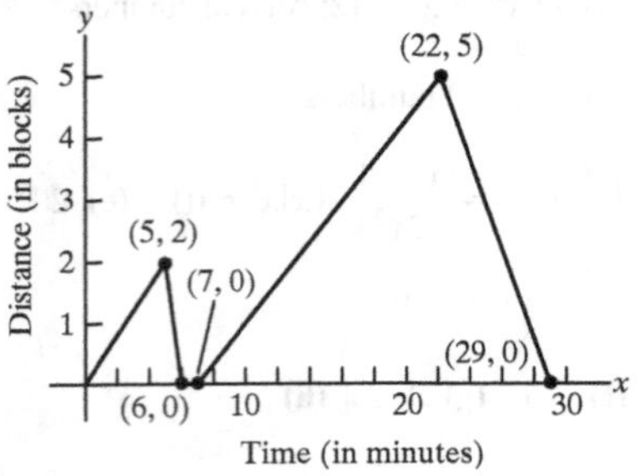

43. (a) 2 hr elapsed during which Kevin was between 0 and 3 mi from home. **(b)** 0.5 hr elapsed during which Kevin was 3 mi from home. **(c)** 0.3 hr elapsed during which Kevin was between 0 and 3 mi from home. **(d)** 0.2 hr elapsed during which Kevin was 0 mi from home. **(e)** 0.9 hr elapsed during which Kevin was between 0 and 2.8 mi from home. **(f)** 0.3 hr elapsed during which Kevin was 2.8 mi from home. **(g)** 1.1 hr elapsed during which Kevin was between 0 and 2.8 mi from home. **(h)** 3 mi **(i)** 2 times
45. No points whose x-coordinate is 5 or whose y-coordinate is 0 can be on the graph.

2.3 Assess Your Understanding *(page 86)*

6. increasing **7.** even; odd **9.** T **11.** Yes **13.** No **15.** $(-8, -2)$; $(0, 2)$; $(5, \infty)$ **17.** Yes; 10 **19.** $-2, 2$; $6, 10$
21. (a) $(-2, 0)$, $(0, 3)$, $(2, 0)$ **(b)** Domain: $\{x \mid -4 \le x \le 4\}$ or $[-4, 4]$; Range: $\{y \mid 0 \le y \le 3\}$ or $[0, 3]$
(c) Increasing on $(-2, 0)$ and $(2, 4)$; Decreasing on $(-4, -2)$ and $(0, 2)$ **(d)** Even
23. (a) $(0, 1)$ **(b)** Domain: all real numbers; Range: $\{y \mid y > 0\}$ or $(0, \infty)$
(c) Increasing on $(-\infty, \infty)$ **(d)** Neither
25. (a) $(-\pi, 0)$, $(0, 0)$, $(\pi, 0)$ **(b)** Domain: $\{x \mid -\pi \le x \le \pi\}$ or $[-\pi, \pi]$; Range: $\{y \mid -1 \le y \le 1\}$ or $[-1, 1]$
(c) Increasing on $\left(-\frac{\pi}{2}, \frac{\pi}{2}\right)$; Decreasing on $\left(-\pi, -\frac{\pi}{2}\right)$ and $\left(\frac{\pi}{2}, \pi\right)$ **(d)** Odd
27. (a) $\left(0, \frac{1}{2}\right)$, $\left(\frac{1}{3}, 0\right)$, $\left(\frac{5}{2}, 0\right)$ **(b)** Domain: $\{x \mid -3 \le x \le 3\}$ or $[-3, 3]$; Range: $\{y \mid -1 \le y \le 2\}$ or $[-1, 2]$
(c) Increasing on $(2, 3)$; Decreasing on $(-1, 1)$; Constant on $(-3, -1)$ and $(1, 2)$ **(d)** Neither
29. (a) 0; 3 **(b)** $-2, 2$; $0, 0$ **31. (a)** $\frac{\pi}{2}$; 1 **(b)** $-\frac{\pi}{2}$; -1 **33.** Odd **35.** Even **37.** Odd **39.** Neither **41.** Even **43.** Odd

45.

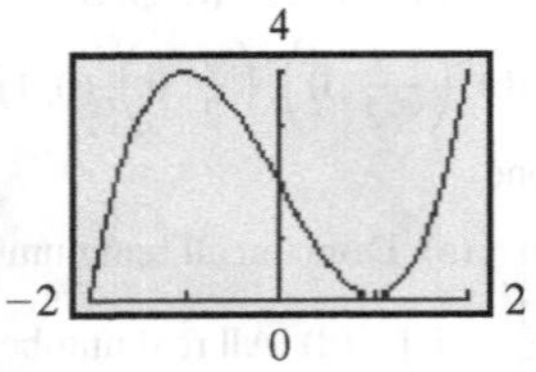

Increasing: $(-2, -1)$, $(1, 2)$
Decreasing: $(-1, 1)$
Local maximum: 4 at $x = -1$
Local minimum: 0 at $x = 1$

47.

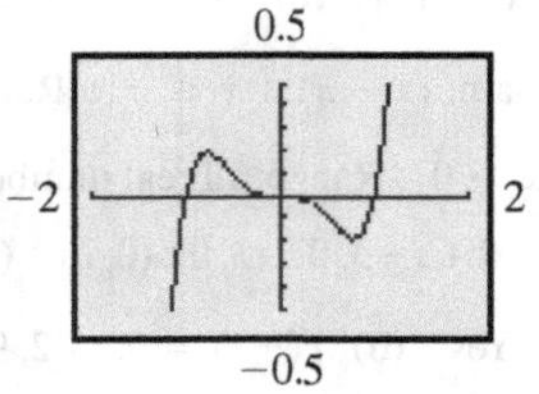

Increasing: $(-2, -0.77)$, $(0.77, 2)$
Decreasing: $(-0.77, 0.77)$
Local maximum: 0.19 at $x = -0.77$
Local minimum: -0.19 at $x = 0.77$

49.

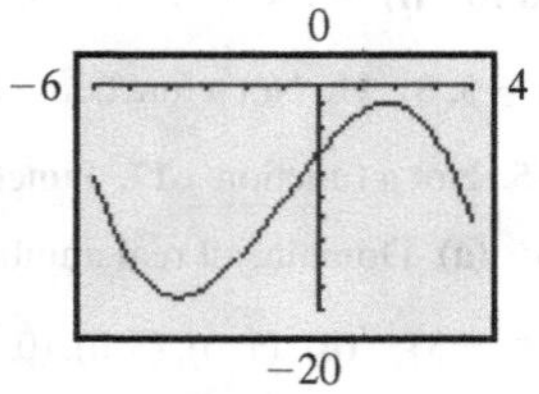

Increasing: $(-3.77, 1.77)$
Decreasing: $(-6, -3.77)$, $(1.77, 4)$
Local maximum: -1.91 at $x = 1.77$
Local minimum: -18.89 at $x = -3.77$

51.

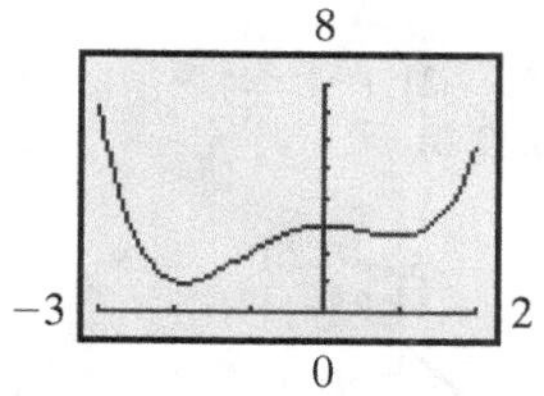

Increasing: $(-1.87, 0)$, $(0.97, 2)$
Decreasing: $(-3, -1.87)$, $(0, 0.97)$
Local maximum: 3 at $x = 0$
Local minimum: 0.95 at $x = -1.87$
Local minimum: 2.65 at $x = 0.97$

53. (a) -4 **(b)** -8 **(c)** -10 **55. (a)** 17 **(b)** -1 **(c)** 11
57. (a) 5 **(b)** $y = 5x - 2$ **59. (a)** -1; **(b)** $y = -x$
61. (a) 4 **(b)** $y = 4x - 8$

63. (a) Odd
(b)

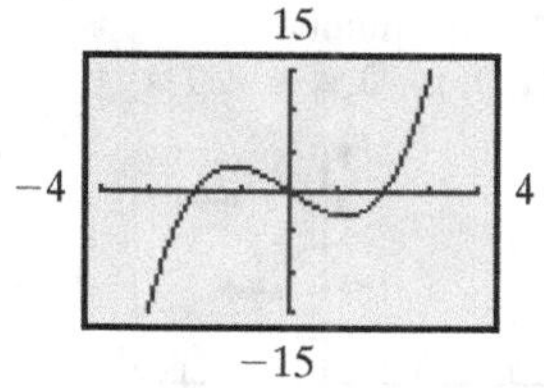

(c) Local minimum: -3.08 at $x = 1.15$
(d) Local maximum: 3.08 at $x = -1.15$

65. (a) Even
(b)

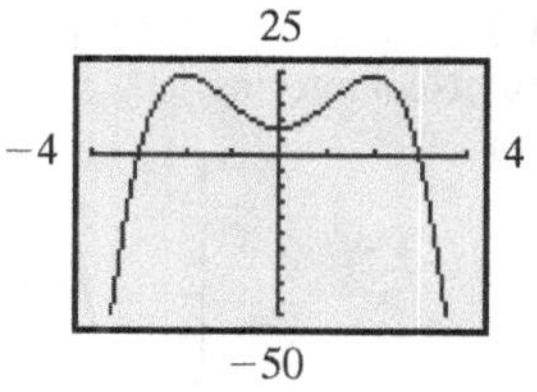

(c) Local maximum: 24 at $x = 2$
(d) Local maximum: 24 at $x = -2$
(e) 47.4 sq. units

67. (a)

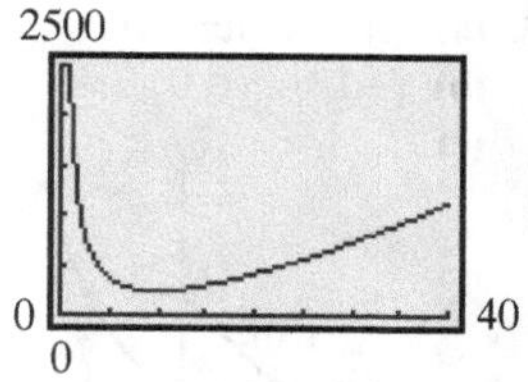

(b) 10 riding lawn mowers/hr
(c) \$239/mower

69. (a) On average, the population is increasing at a rate of 0.036 g/hr from 0 to 2.5 hr.
(b) On average, from 4.5 to 6 hr, the population is increasing at a rate of 0.1 g/hr. **(c)** The average rate of change is increasing over time.

71. (a) 1 **(b)** 0.5 **(c)** 0.1 **(d)** 0.01 **(e)** 0.001
(f)

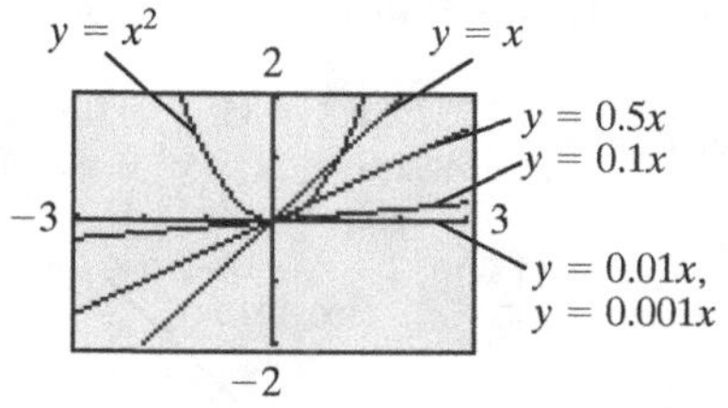

(g) They are getting closer to the tangent line at $(0, 0)$.
(h) They are getting closer to 0.

73. (a) 2 **(b)** 2; 2; 2; 2
(c) $y = 2x + 5$
(d)

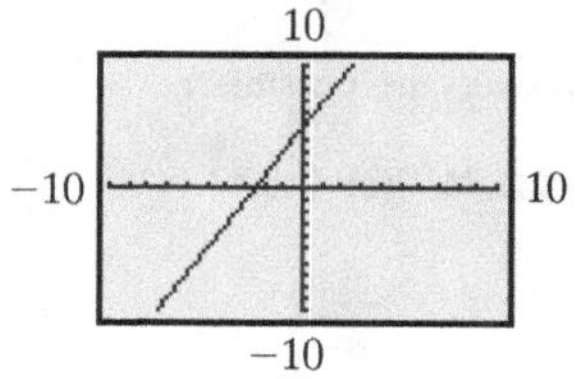

75. (a) $2x + h + 2$ **(b)** 4.5; 4.1; 4.01; 4
(c) $y = 4.01x - 1.01$
(d)

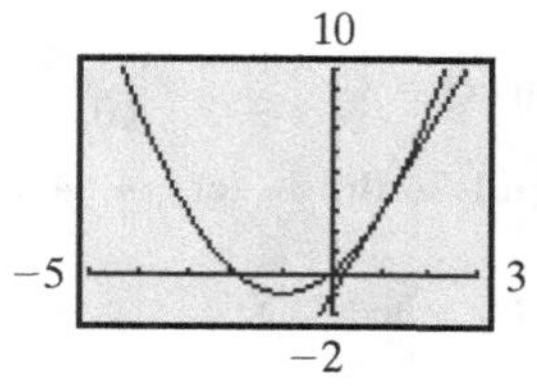

77. (a) $4x + 2h - 3$ **(b)** 2; 1.2; 1.02; 1
(c) $y = 1.02x - 1.02$
(d)

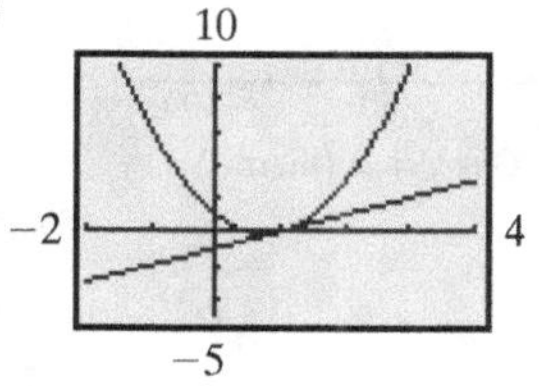

79. (a) $-\dfrac{1}{(x + h)x}$ **(b)** $-\dfrac{2}{3}; -\dfrac{10}{11}; -\dfrac{100}{101}; -1$ **(c)** $y = -\dfrac{100}{101}x + \dfrac{201}{101}$
(d)

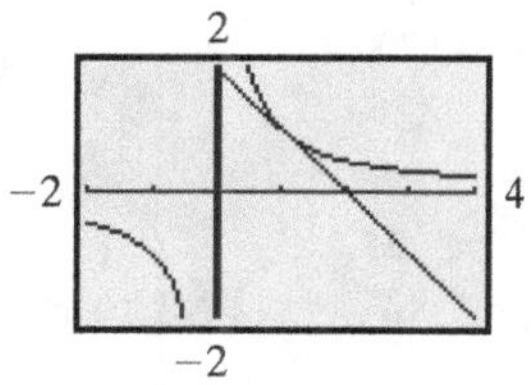

83. At most one **85.** Yes; the function $f(x) = 0$ is both even and odd.

2.4 Assess Your Understanding *(page 96)*

4. $(-\infty, 0)$ **5.** piecewise-defined **6.** T **7.** F **8.** F **9.** C **11.** E **13.** B **15.** F

17.

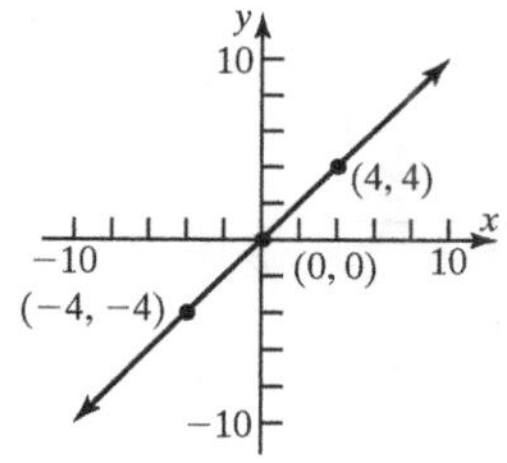

19.

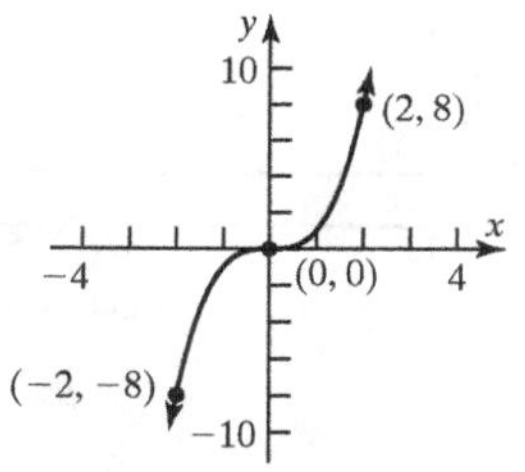

21.

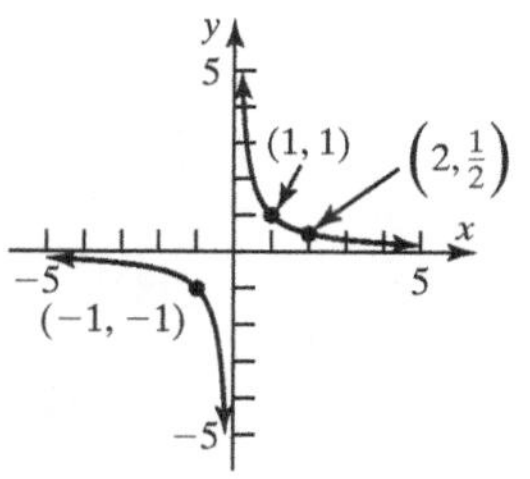

23.

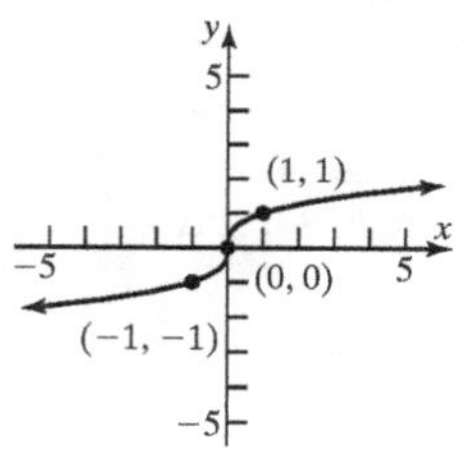

25. **(a)** 4 **(b)** 2 **(c)** 5 **27.** **(a)** −4 **(b)** −2 **(c)** 0 **(d)** 25

29. **(a)** All real numbers
(b) (0, 1)
(c)

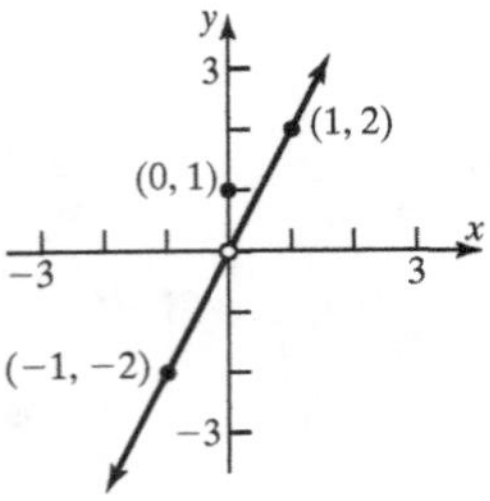

(d) $\{y \mid y \neq 0\}$; $(-\infty, 0) \cup (0, \infty)$
(e) Discontinuous at $x = 0$

31. **(a)** All real numbers
(b) (0, 3)
(c)

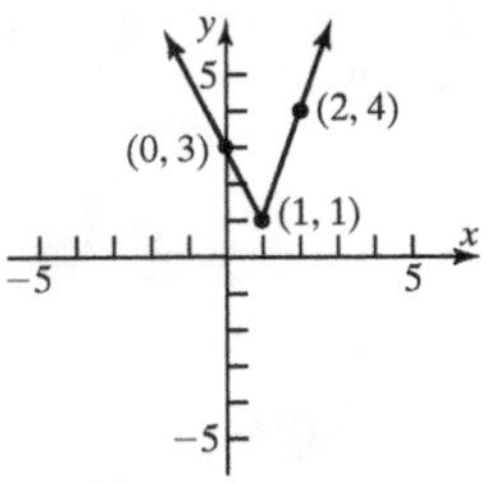

(d) $\{y \mid y \geq 1\}$; $[1, \infty)$
(e) Continuous

33. **(a)** $\{x \mid x \geq -2\}$; $[-2, \infty)$
(b) (0, 3), (2, 0)
(c)

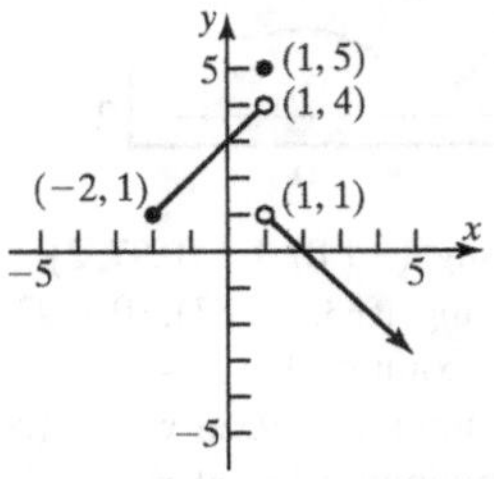

(d) $\{y \mid y < 4, y = 5\}$; $(-\infty, 4) \cup \{5\}$
(e) Discontinuous at $x = 1$

35. **(a)** All real numbers
(b) (−1, 0), (0, 0)
(c)

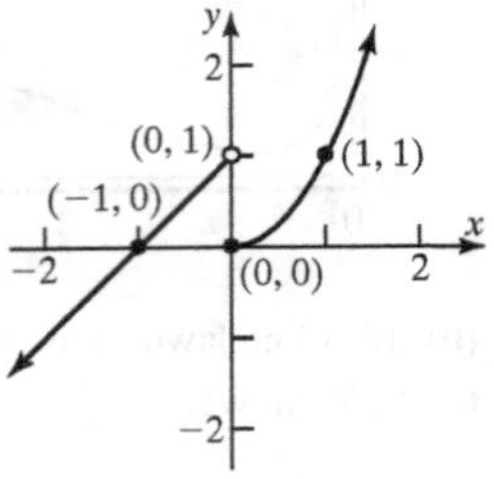

(d) All real numbers
(e) Discontinuous at $x = 0$

37. **(a)** $\{x \mid x \geq -2, x \neq 0\}$; $[-2, 0) \cup (0, \infty)$
(b) No intercepts
(c)

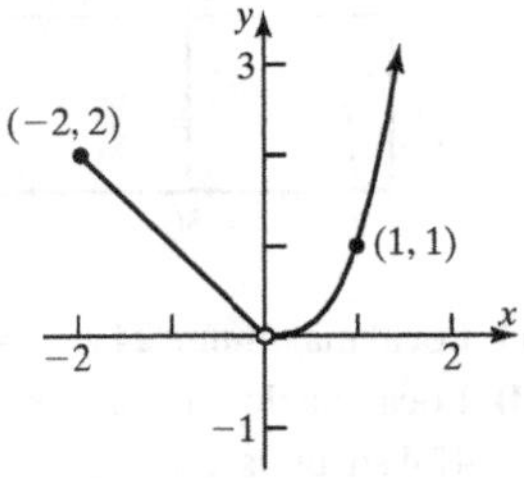

(d) $\{y \mid y > 0\}$; $(0, \infty)$
(e) Discontinuous at $x = 0$

39. **(a)** All real numbers
(b) $(x, 0)$ for $0 \leq x < 1$
(c)

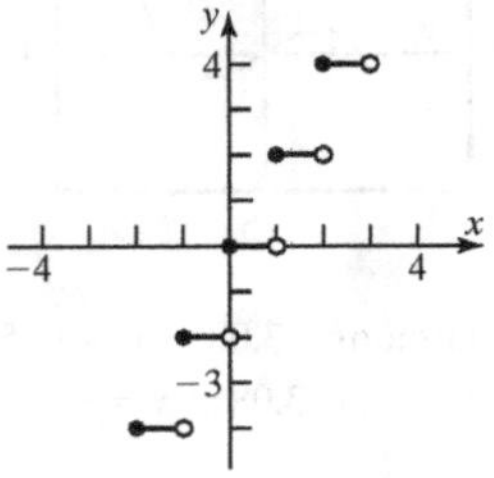

(d) Set of even integers
(e) Discontinuous at $\{x \mid x \text{ is an integer}\}$

41. $f(x) = \begin{cases} -x & \text{if } -1 \leq x \leq 0 \\ \frac{1}{2}x & \text{if } 0 < x \leq 2 \end{cases}$ (Other answers are possible.)

43. $f(x) = \begin{cases} -x & \text{if } x \leq 0 \\ -x + 2 & \text{if } 0 < x \leq 2 \end{cases}$ (Other answers are possible.)

45. **(a)** 2 **(b)** 3 **(c)** −4 **47.** **(a)** \$39.99 **(b)** \$46.74 **(c)** \$40.44

49. **(a)** \$71.33 **(b)** \$516.04

(c) $C(x) = \begin{cases} 1.23755x + 9.45 & \text{if } 0 \leq x \leq 50 \\ 0.98825x + 21.915 & \text{if } x > 50 \end{cases}$

(d)

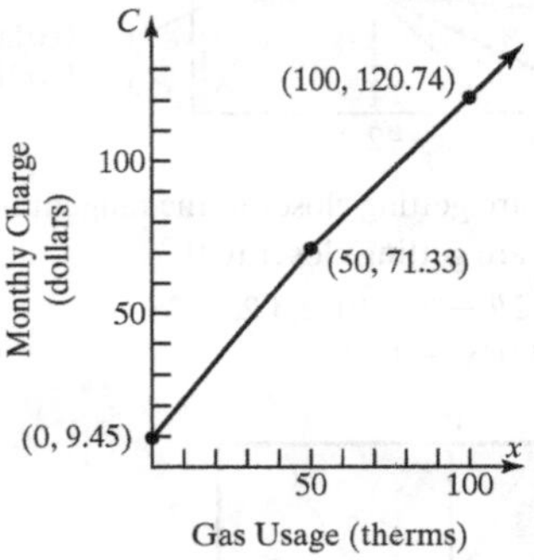

51. For schedule X:

$$f(x) = \begin{cases} 0.10x & \text{if } 0 < x \leq 7825 \\ 782.50 + 0.15(x - 7825) & \text{if } 7825 < x \leq 31{,}850 \\ 4386.25 + 0.25(x - 31{,}850) & \text{if } 31{,}850 < x \leq 77{,}100 \\ 15{,}698.75 + 0.28(x - 77{,}100) & \text{if } 77{,}100 < x \leq 160{,}850 \\ 39{,}148.75 + 0.33(x - 160{,}850) & \text{if } 160{,}850 < x \leq 349{,}700 \\ 101{,}469.25 + 0.35(x - 349{,}700) & \text{if } x > 349{,}700 \end{cases}$$

53. **(a)**

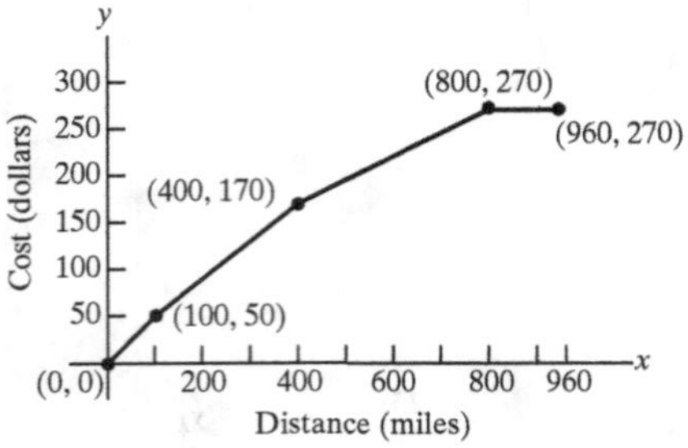

(b) $C(x) = 10 + 0.4x$

(c) $C(x) = 70 + 0.25x$

55.

$$f(x) = \begin{cases} x & \text{if } 0 \leq x < 10 \\ 10 & \text{if } 10 \leq x < 500 \\ 30 & \text{if } 500 \leq x < 1000 \\ 50 & \text{if } 1000 \leq x < 1500 \\ 70 & \text{if } 1500 \leq x \end{cases}$$

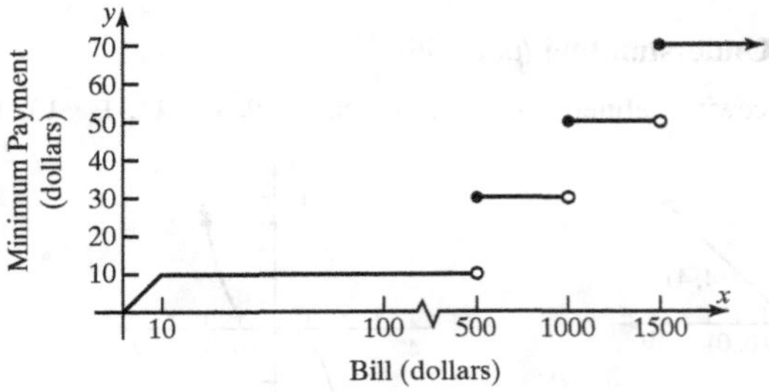

57. **(a)** 10°C
(b) 4°C
(c) −3°C
(d) −4°C
(e) The wind chill is equal to the air temperature.
(f) At wind speed greater than 20 m/s, the wind chill factor depends only on the air temperature.

59.

$$C(x) = \begin{cases} 0.80 & 0 < x \le 1 \\ 0.97 & 1 < x \le 2 \\ 1.14 & 2 < x \le 3 \\ 1.31 & 3 < x \le 4 \\ 1.48 & 4 < x \le 5 \\ 1.65 & 5 < x \le 6 \\ 1.82 & 6 < x \le 7 \\ 1.99 & 7 < x \le 8 \\ 2.16 & 8 < x \le 9 \\ 2.33 & 9 < x \le 10 \\ 2.50 & 10 < x \le 11 \\ 2.67 & 11 < x \le 12 \\ 2.84 & 12 < x \le 13 \end{cases}$$

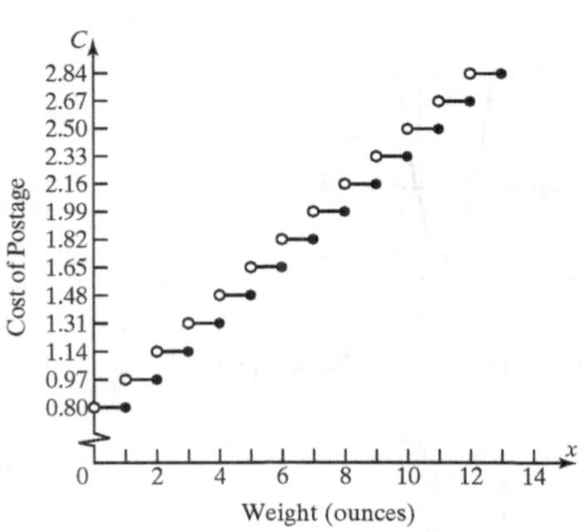

61. Each graph is that of $y = x^2$, but shifted horizontally. If $y = (x - k)^2, k > 0$, the shift is right k units; if $y = (x + k)^2, k > 0$, the shift is left k units. **63.** The graph of $y = -f(x)$ is the reflection about the x-axis of the graph of $y = f(x)$. **65.** Yes. The graph of $y = (x - 1)^3 + 2$ is the graph of $y = x^3$ shifted right 1 unit and up 2 units. **67.** They all have the same general shape. All three go through the points $(-1, -1)$, $(0, 0)$, and $(1, 1)$. As the exponent increases, the steepness of the curve increases (except near $x = 0$).

2.5 Assess Your Understanding *(page 108)*

1. horizontal; right **2.** y **3.** −5; −2; 2 **4.** T **5.** F **6.** T **7.** B **9.** H **11.** I **13.** L **15.** F **17.** G **19.** $y = (x - 4)^3$ **21.** $y = x^3 + 4$ **23.** $y = -x^3$ **25.** $y = 4x^3$ **27.** (1) $y = \sqrt{x} + 2$; (2) $y = -(\sqrt{x} + 2)$; (3) $y = -(\sqrt{-x} + 2)$ **29.** (1) $y = -\sqrt{x}$; (2) $y = -\sqrt{x} + 2$; (3) $y = -\sqrt{x + 3} + 2$ **31.** (c) **33.** (c) **35.** **(a)** −7 and 1 **(b)** −3 and 5 **(c)** −5 and 3 **(d)** −3 and 5 **37** **(a)** $(-3, 3)$ **(b)** $(4, 10)$ **(c)** Decreasing on $(-1, 5)$ **(d)** Decreasing on $(-5, 1)$

39.

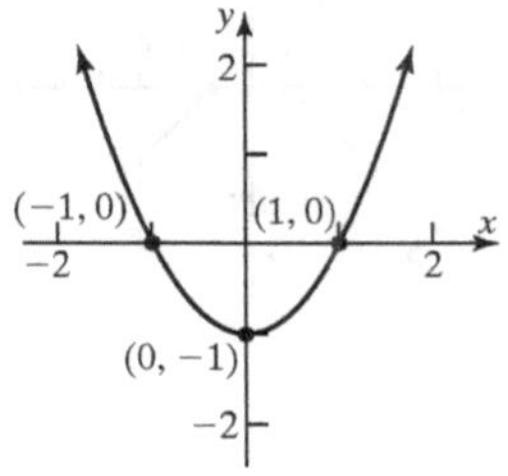

Domain: $(-\infty, \infty)$; Range: $[-1, \infty)$

41.

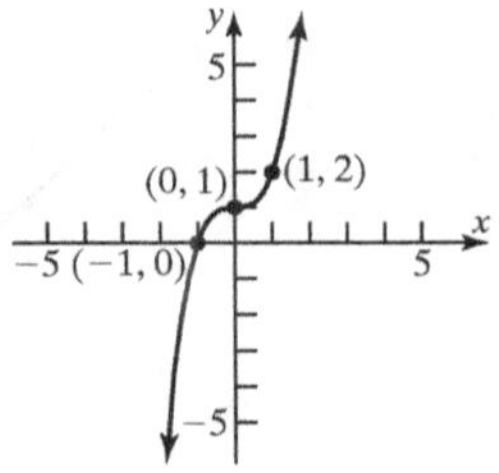

Domain: $(-\infty, \infty)$; Range: $(-\infty, \infty)$

43.

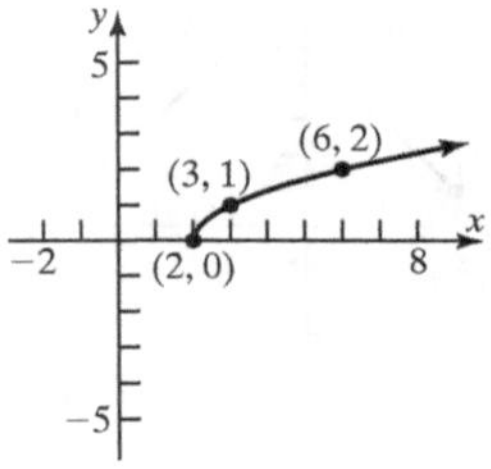

Domain: $[2, \infty)$; Range: $[0, \infty)$

45.

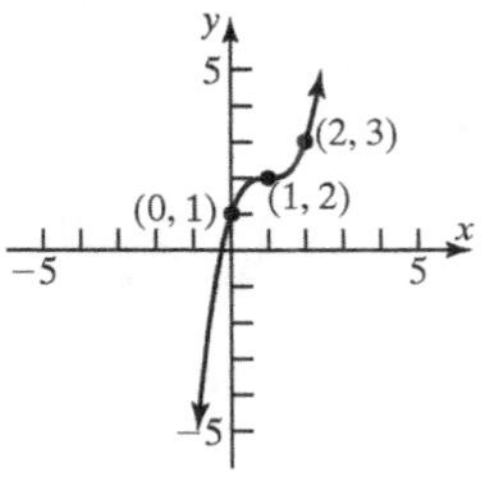

Domain: $(-\infty, \infty)$; Range: $(-\infty, \infty)$

47.

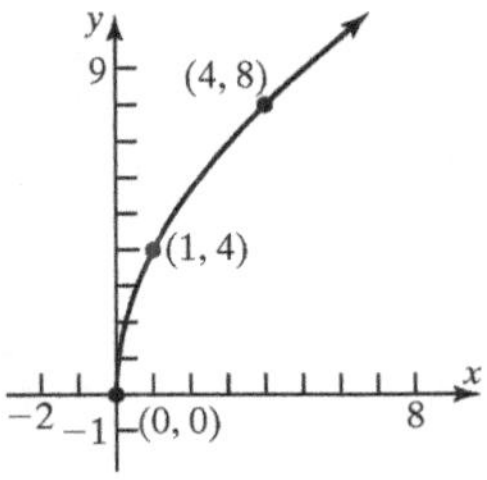

Domain: $[0, \infty)$; Range: $[0, \infty)$

49.

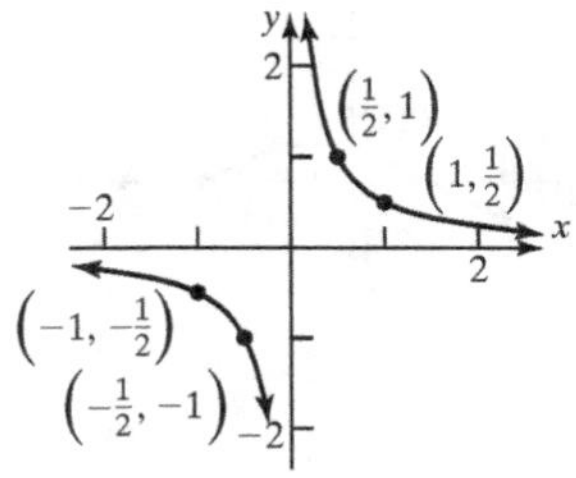

Domain: $(-\infty, 0) \cup (0, \infty)$

Range: $(-\infty, 0) \cup (0, \infty)$

51.

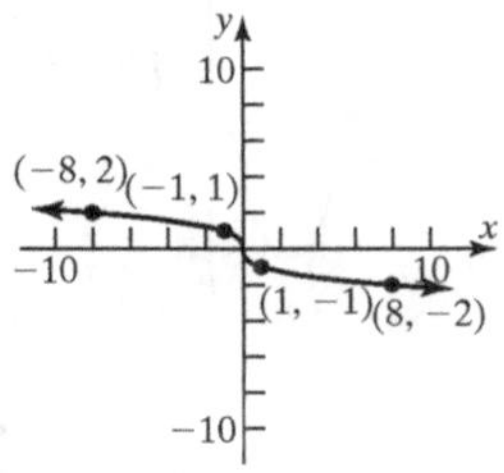

Domain: $(-\infty, \infty)$; Range: $(-\infty, \infty)$

53.

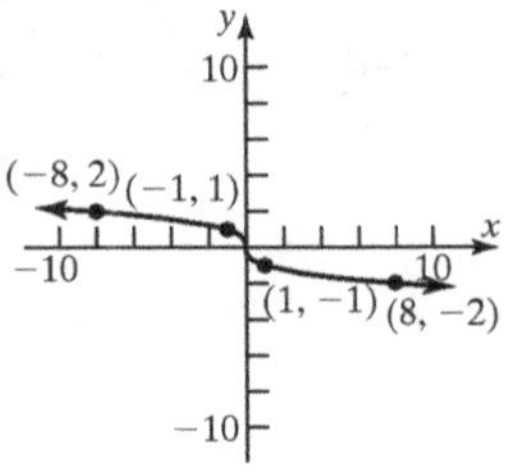

Domain: $(-\infty, \infty)$; Range: $(-\infty, \infty)$

55.

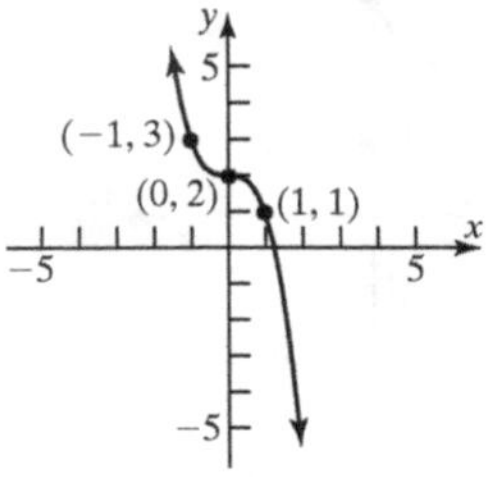

Domain: $(-\infty, \infty)$; Range: $(-\infty, \infty)$

57.

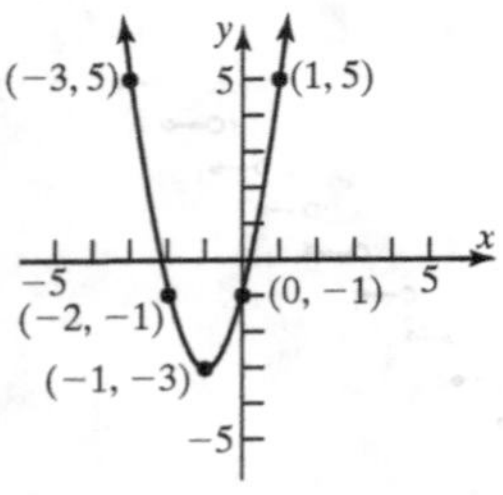

Domain: $(-\infty, \infty)$; Range: $[-3, \infty)$

59.

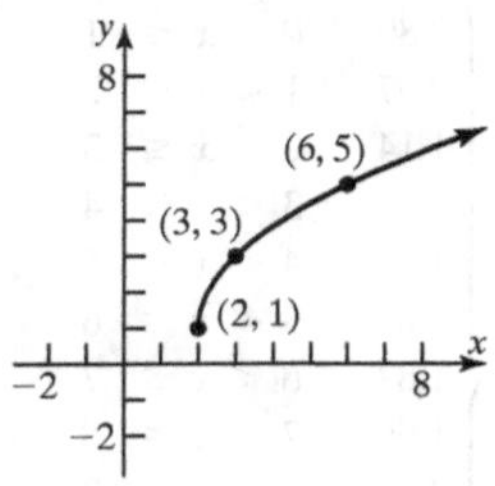

Domain: $[2, \infty)$; Range: $[1, \infty)$

61.

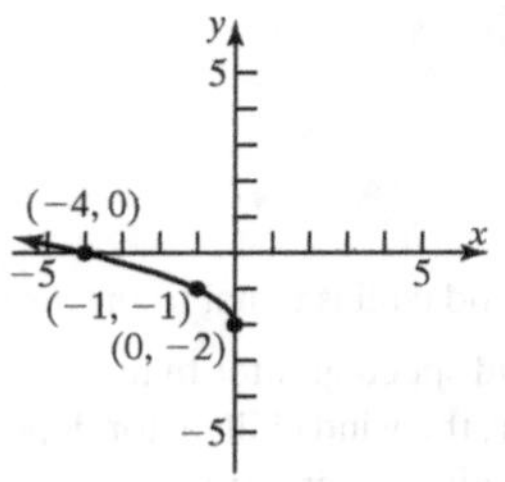

Domain: $(-\infty, 0]$; Range: $[-2, \infty)$

63.

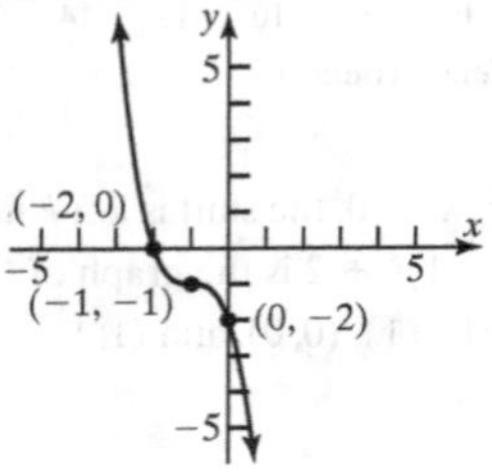

Domain: $(-\infty, \infty)$; Range: $(-\infty, \infty)$

65.

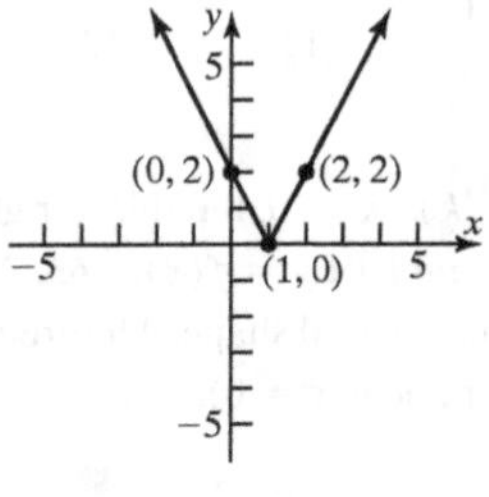

Domain: $(-\infty, \infty)$; Range: $[0, \infty)$

67.

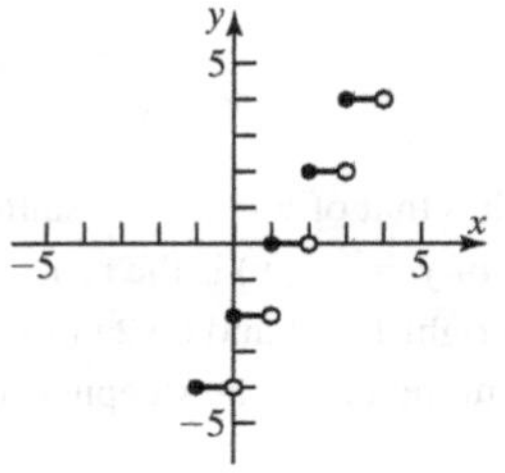

Domain: $(-\infty, \infty)$;
Range: $\{y \mid y \text{ is an even integer}\}$

69. (a) $F(x) = f(x) + 3$

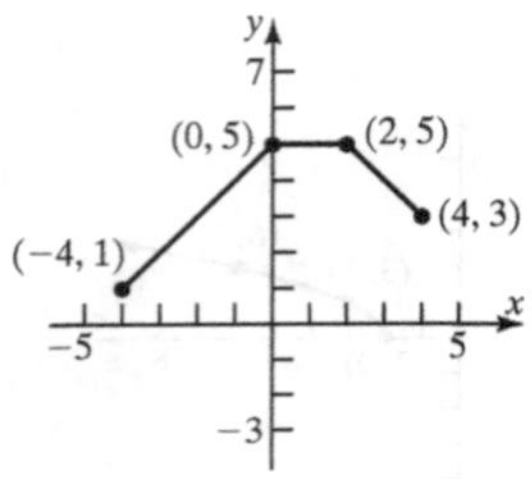

(b) $G(x) = f(x + 2)$

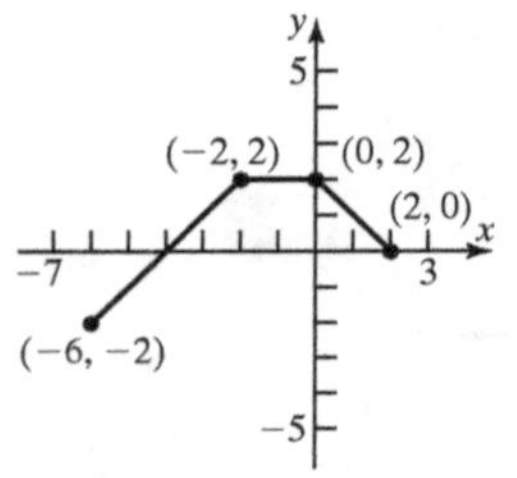

(c) $P(x) = -f(x)$

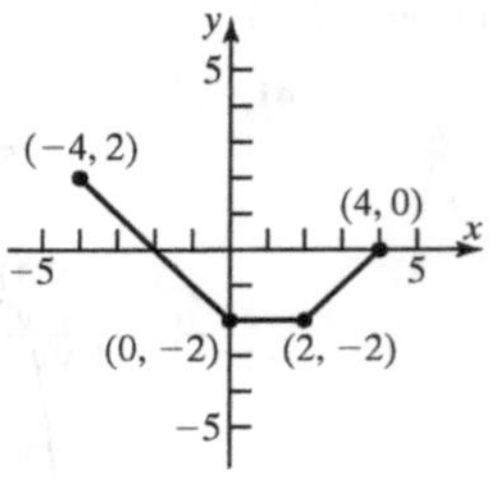

(d) $H(x) = f(x + 1) - 2$

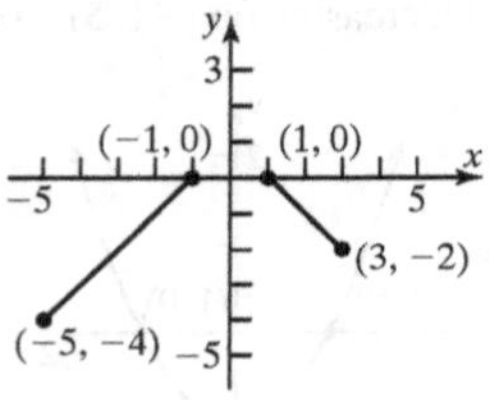

(e) $Q(x) = \frac{1}{2}f(x)$

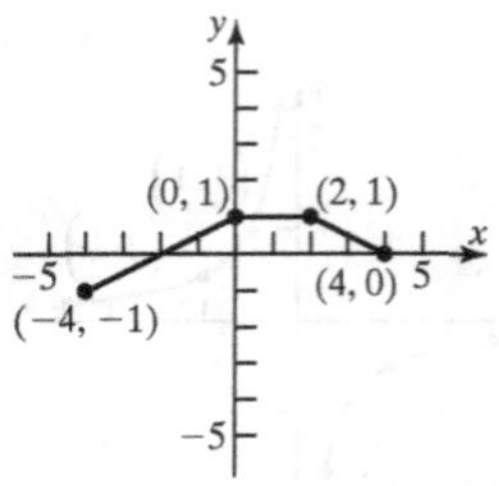

(f) $g(x) = f(-x)$

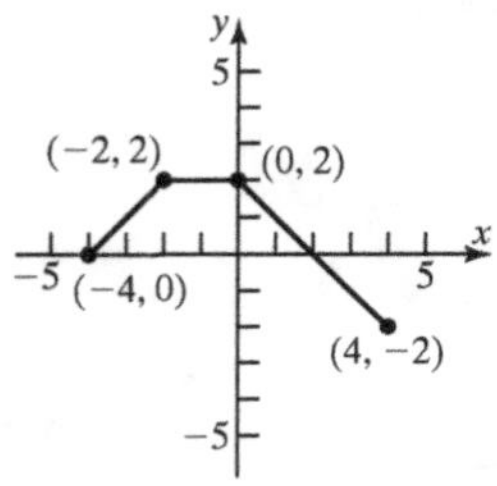

(g) $h(x) = f(2x)$

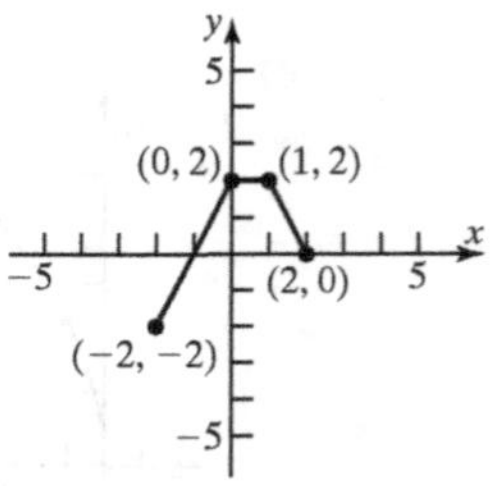

71. (a) $F(x) = f(x) + 3$

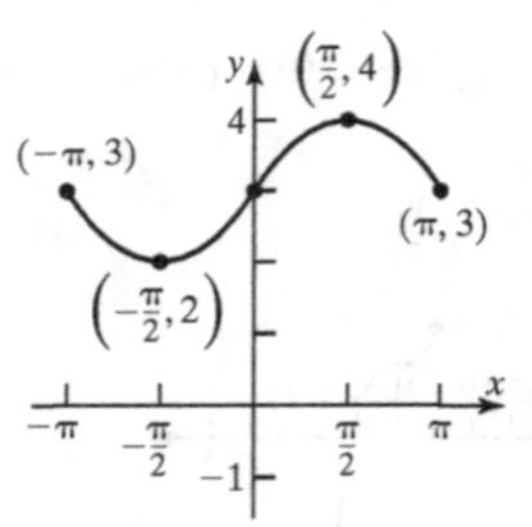

(b) $G(x) = f(x + 2)$

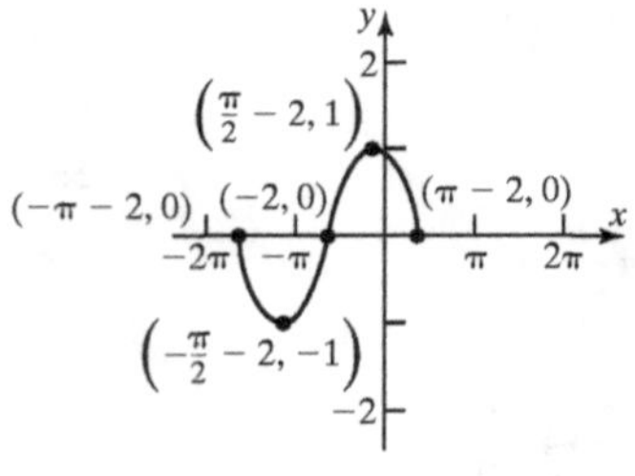

(c) $P(x) = -f(x)$

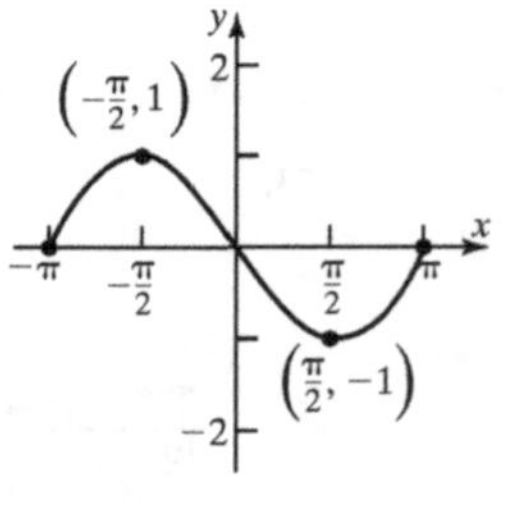

(d) $H(x) = f(x + 1) - 2$

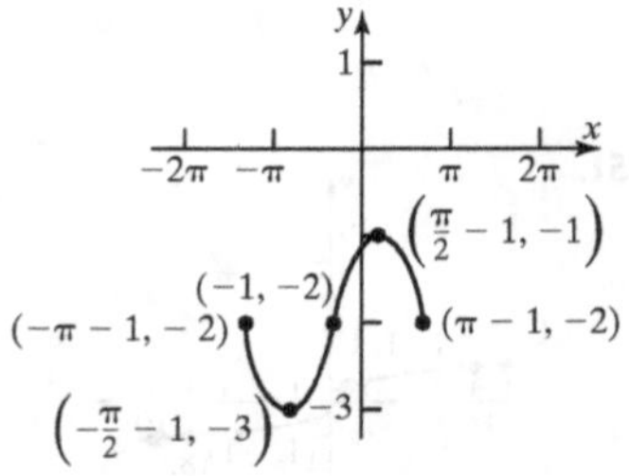

(e) $Q(x) = \frac{1}{2}f(x)$

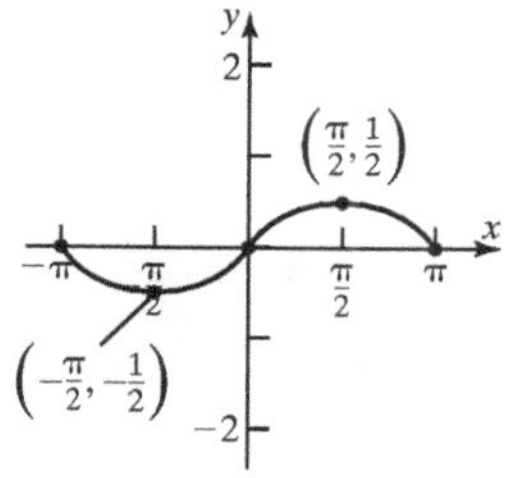

(f) $g(x) = f(-x)$

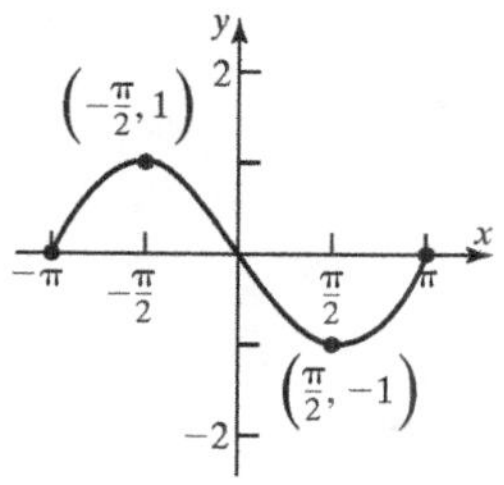

(g) $h(x) = f(2x)$

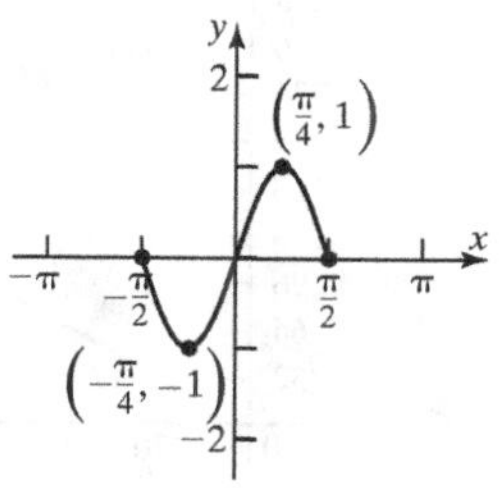

73. (a)

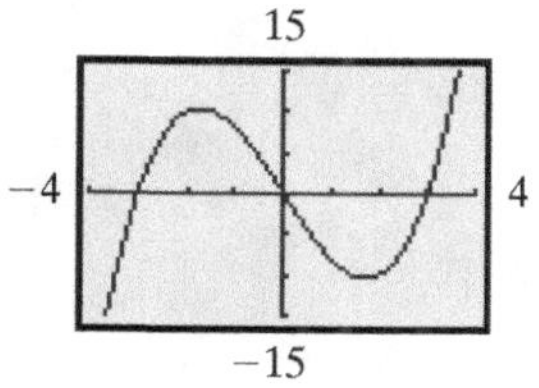

(b) −3, 0, 3

(c) Local maximum: 10.39 at $x = -1.73$
Local minimum: −10.39 at $x = 1.73$

(d) Increasing: (−4, −1.73), (1.73, 4)
Decreasing: (−1.73, 1.73)

(e) Intercepts: −5, −2, 1;
Local maximum: 10.39 at $x = -3.73$;
Local minimum: −10.39 at $x = -0.27$;
Increasing: (−6, −3.73), (−0.27, 2);
Decreasing: (−3.73, −0.27)

(f) Intercepts: −3, 0, 3;
Local maximum: 20.78 at $x = -1.73$;
Local minimum: −20.78 at $x = 1.73$;
Increasing: (−4, −1.73), (1.73, 4);
Decreasing: (−1.73, 1.73)

(g) Intercepts: −3, 0, 3;
Local maximum: 10.39 at $x = 1.73$;
Local minimum: −10.39 at $x = -1.73$;
Decreasing: (−4, −1.73), (1.73, 4);
Increasing: (−1.73, 1.73)

75. $f(x) = (x + 1)^2 - 1$

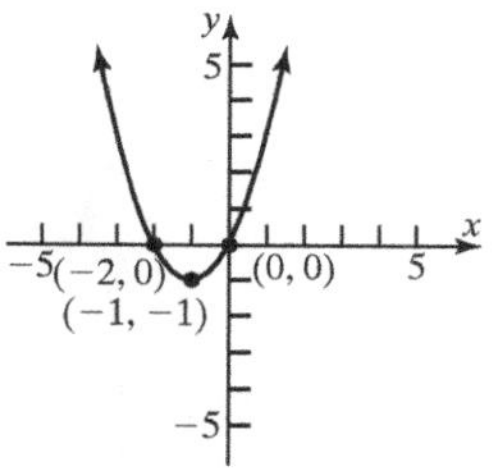

77. $f(x) = (x - 4)^2 - 15$

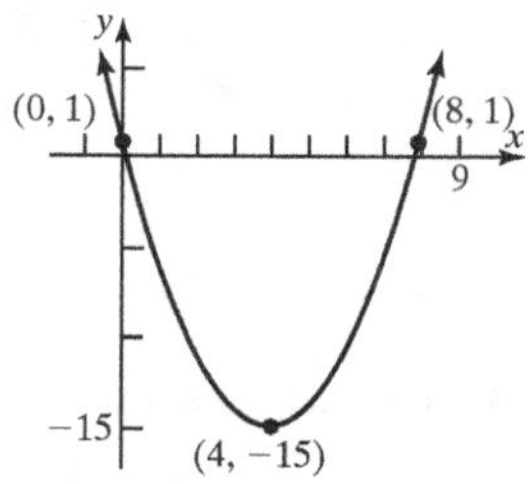

79. $f(x) = \left(x + \frac{1}{2}\right)^2 + \frac{3}{4}$

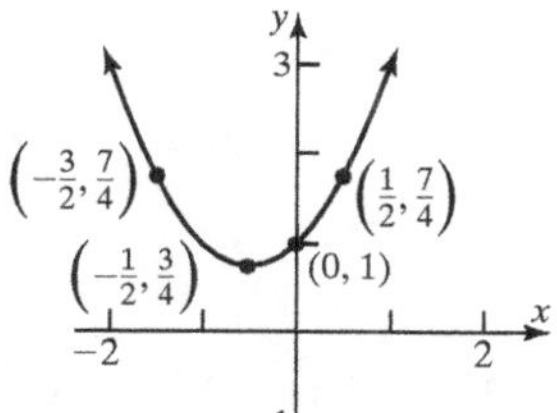

81. $f(x) = 2(x - 3)^2 + 1$

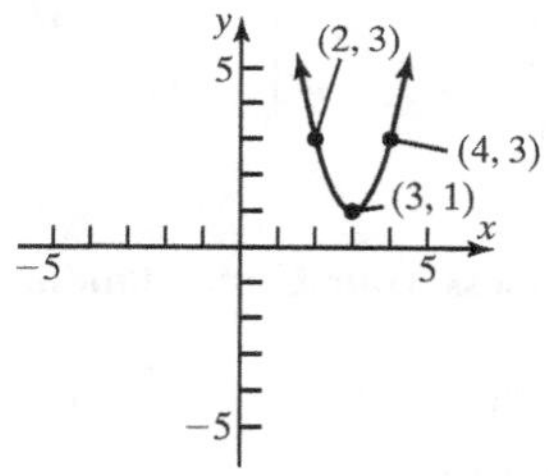

83. $f(x) = -3(x + 2)^2 - 5$

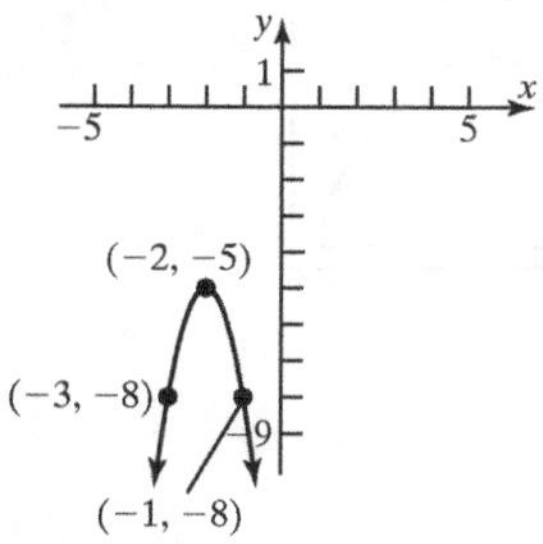

85.

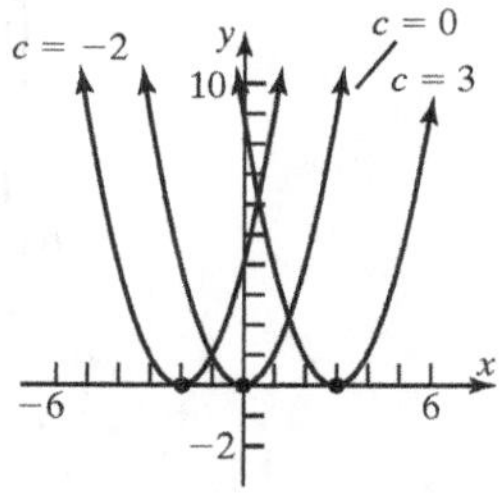

87. (a) 72°F; 65°F

(b) The temperature decreases by 2° to 70°F during the day and 63°F overnight

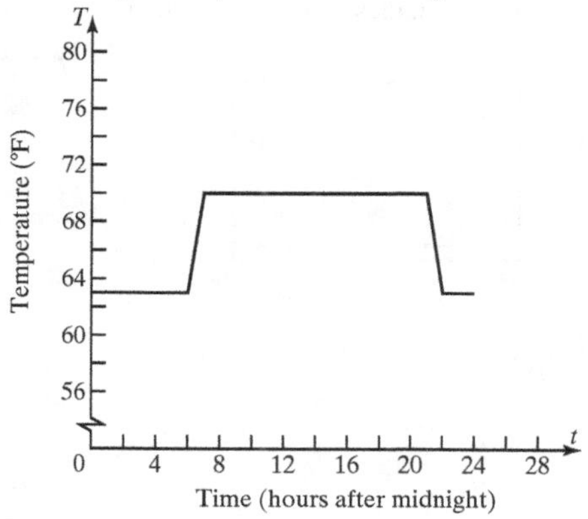

(c) The time at which the temperature adjusts between the daytime and overnight settings is moved to 1 hr sooner. It begins warming up at 5:00 AM instead of 6:00 AM, and it begins cooling down at 8:00 PM in stead of 9:00 PM.

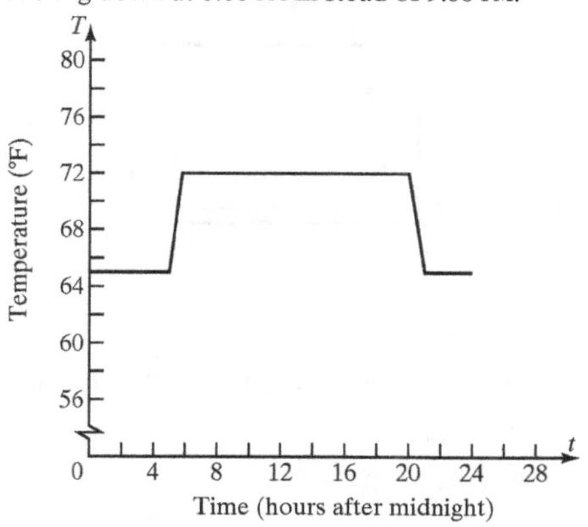

89.

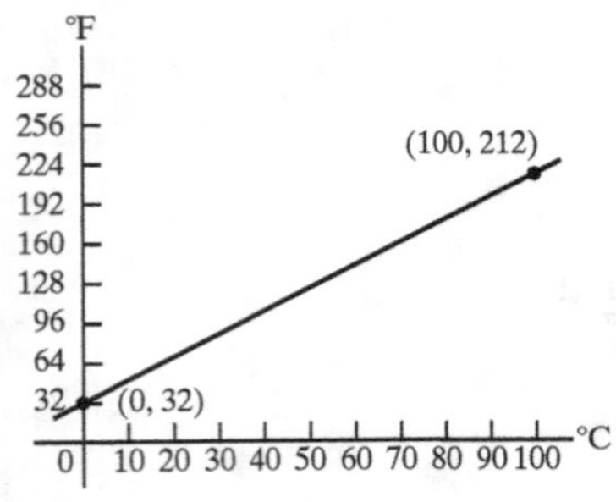

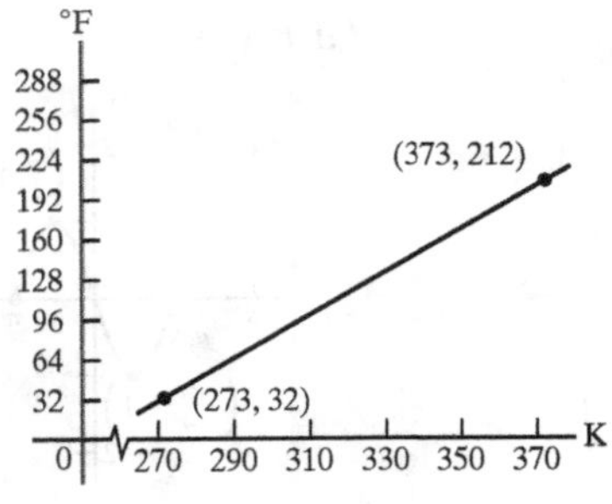

91. (a)

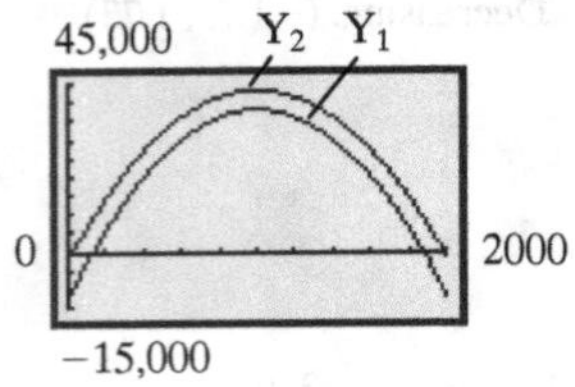

(b) 10% tax

(c) Y_1 is the graph of $p(x)$ shifted down vertically 10,000 units.
Y_2 is the graph of $p(x)$ vertically compressed by a factor of 0.9.

(d) 10% tax

93. (a)

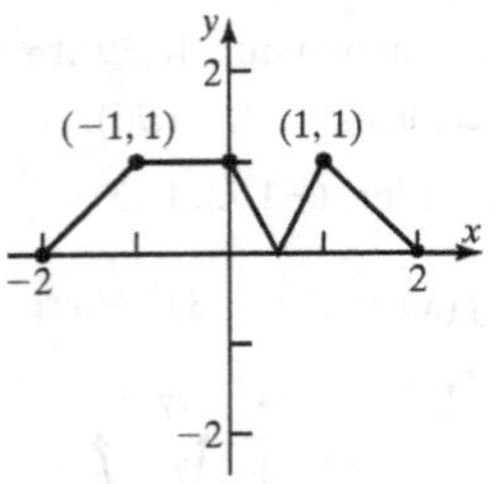

(b)

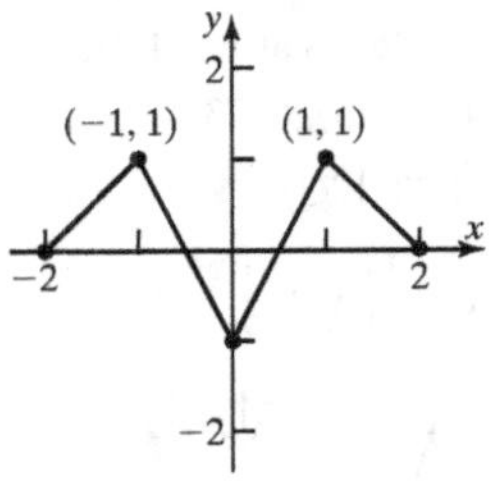

95. (a) $(-4, 2)$ **(b)** $(1, -12)$ **(c)** $(-4, 5)$ **97.** $\frac{16}{3}$ square units

2.6 Assess Your Understanding *(page 115)*

1. (a) $d(x) = \sqrt{x^4 - 15x^2 + 64}$

(b) $d(0) = 8$

(c) $d(1) = \sqrt{50} \approx 7.07$

(d)

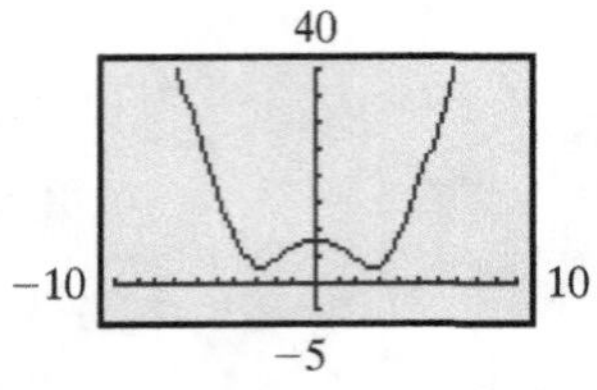

(e) d is smallest when $x \approx -2.74$ or $x \approx 2.74$.

3. (a) $d(x) = \sqrt{x^2 - x + 1}$

(b)

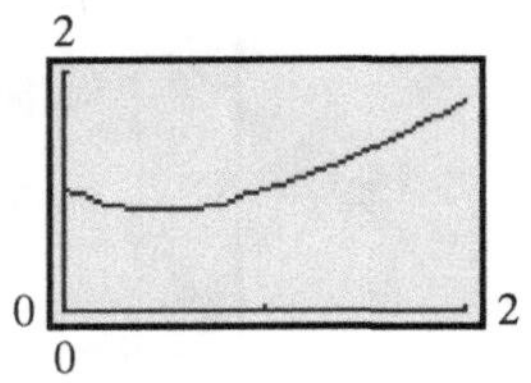

(c) d is smallest when $x = 0.5$.

5. $A(x) = \frac{1}{2}x^4$

7. (a) $A(x) = x(16 - x^2)$

(b) Domain: $\{x | 0 < x < 4\}$

(c) The area is largest when $x \approx 2.31$.

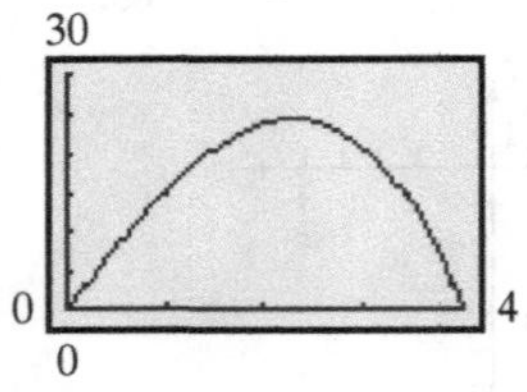

9. (a) $A(x) = 4x\sqrt{4 - x^2}$

(c) A is largest when $x \approx 1.41$.

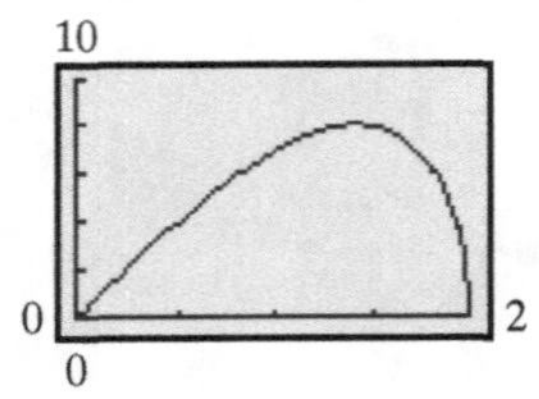

(b) $p(x) = 4x + 4\sqrt{4 - x^2}$

(d) p is largest when $x \approx 1.41$.

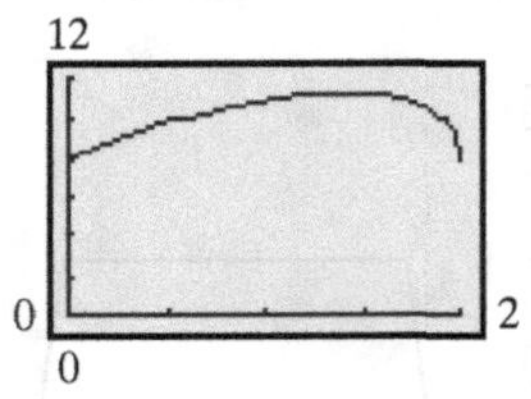

11. (a) $A(x) = x^2 + \frac{25 - 20x + 4x^2}{\pi}$

(b) Domain: $\{x | 0 < x < 2.5\}$

(c) A is smallest when $x \approx 1.40$ m.

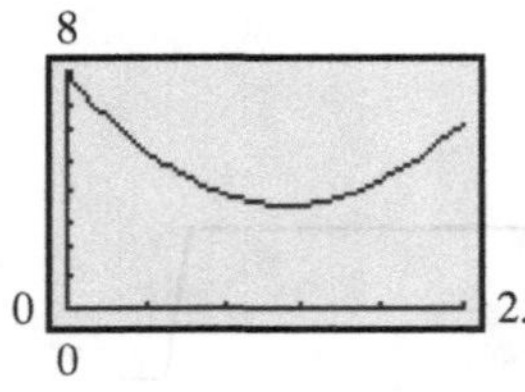

13. (a) $C(x) = x$ **(b)** $A(x) = \frac{x^2}{4\pi}$ **15. (a)** $A(r) = 2r^2$ **(b)** $p(r) = 6r$ **17.** $A(x) = \left(\frac{\pi}{3} - \frac{\sqrt{3}}{4}\right)x^2$

19. **(a)** $d(t) = \sqrt{2500t^2 - 360t + 13}$
(b) d is smallest when $t \approx 0.07$ hr.

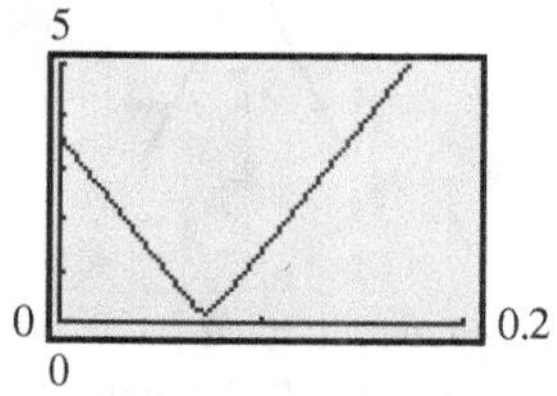

21. $V(r) = \dfrac{\pi H(R - r)r^2}{R}$

23. **(a)** $T(x) = \dfrac{12 - x}{5} + \dfrac{\sqrt{x^2 + 4}}{3}$
(b) $\{x | 0 \le x \le 12\}$
(c) 3.09 hr
(d) 3.55 hr

25. **(a)** $V(x) = x(24 - 2x)^2$
(b) 972 in.^{3} **(c)** 160 in.^{3}
(d) V is largest when $x = 4$.

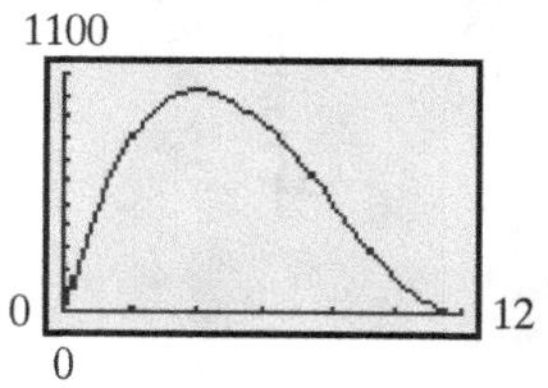

Review Exercises *(page 119)*

1. Function; domain $\{-1, 2, 4\}$, range $\{0, 3\}$ **3.** **(a)** 2 **(b)** -2 **(c)** $-\dfrac{3x}{x^2 - 1}$ **(d)** $-\dfrac{3x}{x^2 - 1}$ **(e)** $\dfrac{3(x - 2)}{x^2 - 4x + 3}$ **(f)** $\dfrac{6x}{4x^2 - 1}$

5. **(a)** 0 **(b)** 0 **(c)** $\sqrt{x^2 - 4}$ **(d)** $-\sqrt{x^2 - 4}$ **(e)** $\sqrt{x^2 - 4x}$ **(f)** $2\sqrt{x^2 - 1}$

7. **(a)** 0 **(b)** 0 **(c)** $\dfrac{x^2 - 4}{x^2}$ **(d)** $-\dfrac{x^2 - 4}{x^2}$ **(e)** $\dfrac{x(x - 4)}{(x - 2)^2}$ **(f)** $\dfrac{x^2 - 1}{x^2}$

9. $\{x | x \ne -3, x \ne 3\}$ **11.** $\{x | x \le 2\}$ **13.** $\{x | x > 0\}$ **15.** $\{x | x \ne -3, x \ne 1\}$

17. $(f + g)(x) = 2x + 3$; Domain: all real numbers
$(f - g)(x) = -4x + 1$; Domain: all real numbers
$(f \cdot g)(x) = -3x^2 + 5x + 2$; Domain: all real numbers
$\left(\dfrac{f}{g}\right)(x) = \dfrac{2 - x}{3x + 1}$; Domain: $\left\{x \middle| x \ne -\dfrac{1}{3}\right\}$

19. $(f + g)(x) = 3x^2 + 4x + 1$; Domain: all real numbers
$(f - g)(x) = 3x^2 - 2x + 1$; Domain: all real numbers
$(f \cdot g)(x) = 9x^3 + 3x^2 + 3x$; Domain: all real numbers
$\left(\dfrac{f}{g}\right)(x) = \dfrac{3x^2 + x + 1}{3x}$; Domain: $\{x | x \ne 0\}$

21. $(f + g)(x) = \dfrac{x^2 + 2x - 1}{x(x - 1)}$; Domain: $\{x | x \ne 0, x \ne 1\}$
$(f - g)(x) = \dfrac{x^2 + 1}{x(x - 1)}$; Domain: $\{x | x \ne 0, x \ne 1\}$
$(f \cdot g)(x) = \dfrac{x + 1}{x(x - 1)}$; Domain: $\{x | x \ne 0, x \ne 1\}$
$\left(\dfrac{f}{g}\right)(x) = \dfrac{x(x + 1)}{x - 1}$; Domain: $\{x | x \ne 0, x \ne 1\}$

23. $-4x + 1 - 2h$

25. **(a)** Domain: $\{x | -4 \le x \le 3\}$; Range: $\{y | -3 \le y \le 3\}$ **(b)** $(0, 0)$ **(c)** -1 **(d)** -4 **(e)** $\{x | 0 < x \le 3\}$

(f)

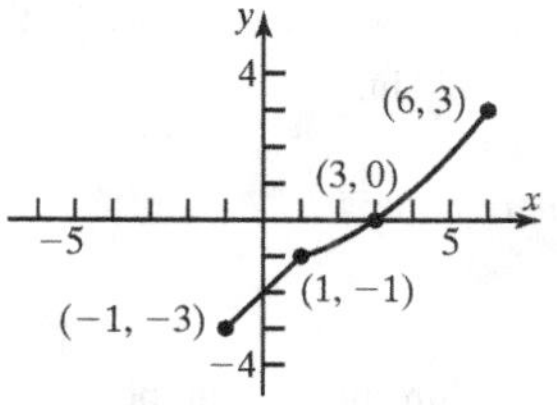

(g)

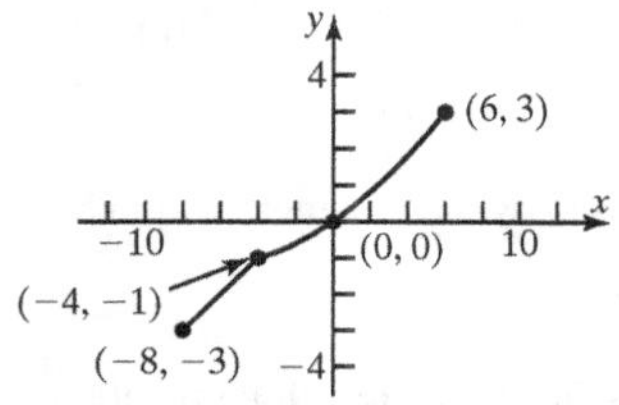

(h)

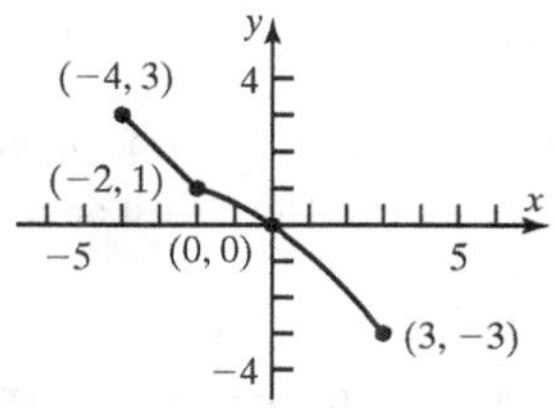

27. **(a)** Domain: $\{x | -4 \le x \le 4\}$ or $[-4, 4]$
Range: $\{y | -3 \le y \le 1\}$ or $[-3, 1]$
(b) Increasing on $(-4, -1)$ and $(3, 4)$
Decreasing on $(-1, 3)$
(c) Local maximum is 1 and occurs at $x = -1$.
Local minimum is -3 and occurs at $x = 3$.
(d) No symmetry
(e) Neither
(f) x-intercepts: $-2, 0, 4$; y-intercept: 0

29. Odd **31.** Even **33.** Neither **35.** Odd

37.

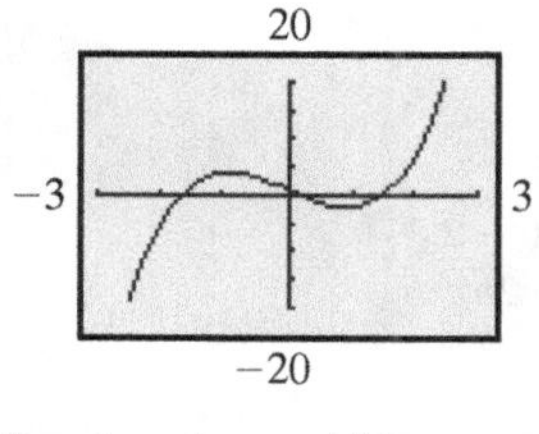

Local maximum: 4.04 at $x = -0.91$
Local minimum: -2.04 at $x = 0.91$

Increasing: $(-3, -0.91)$; $(0.91, 3)$
Decreasing: $(-0.91, 0.91)$

39.

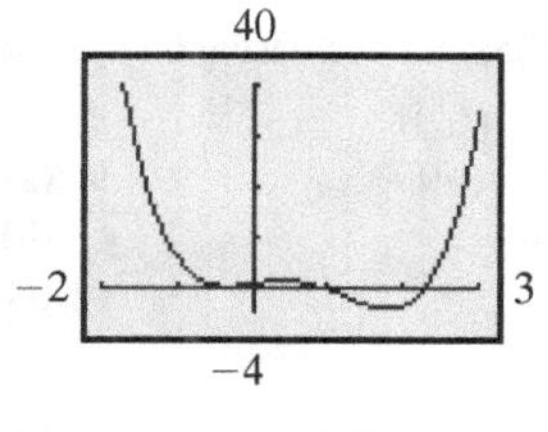

Local maximum: 1.53 at $x = 0.41$
Local minima: 0.54 at $x = -0.34$
and -3.56 at $x = 1.80$
Increasing: $(-0.34, 0.41)$; $(1.80, 3)$
Decreasing: $(-2, -0.34)$; $(0.41, 1.80)$

41. **(a)** 23 **(b)** 7 **(c)** 47
43. -5
45. -17
47. No
49. Yes

51.

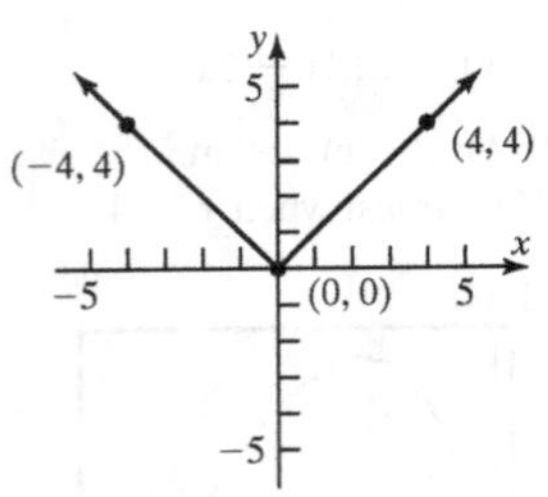

53.

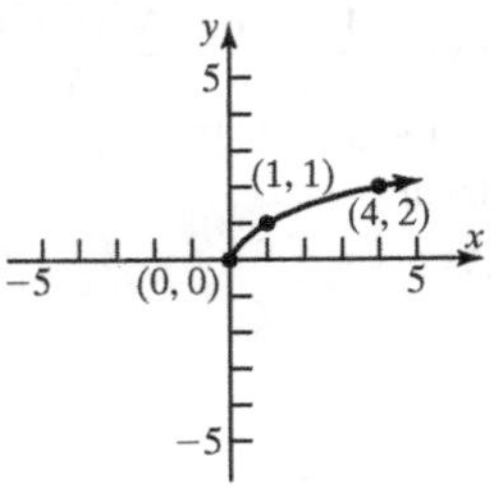

55.

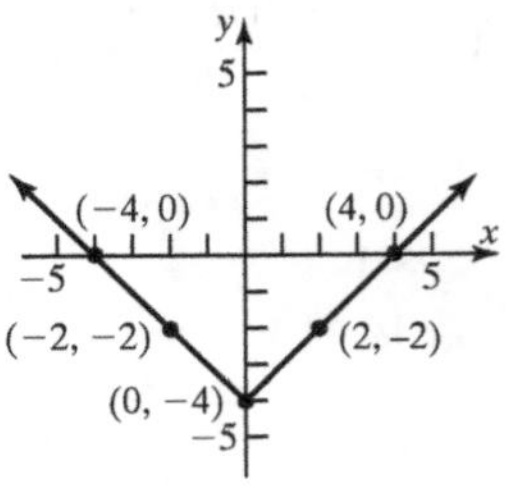

Intercepts: $(-4, 0)$, $(4, 0)$, $(0, -4)$
Domain: all real numbers
Range: $\{y \mid y \geq -4\}$ or $[-4, \infty)$

57.

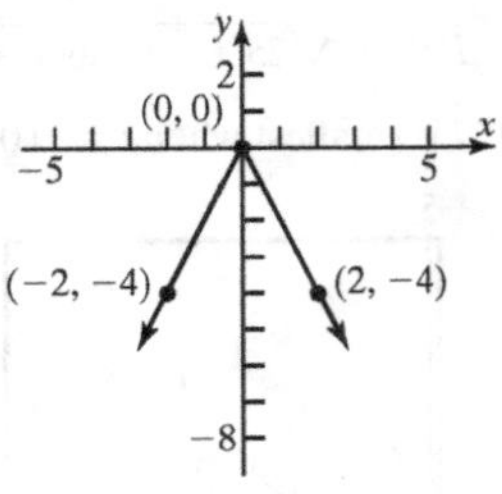

Intercept: $(0, 0)$
Domain: all real numbers
Range: $\{y \mid y \leq 0\}$ or $(-\infty, 0]$

59.

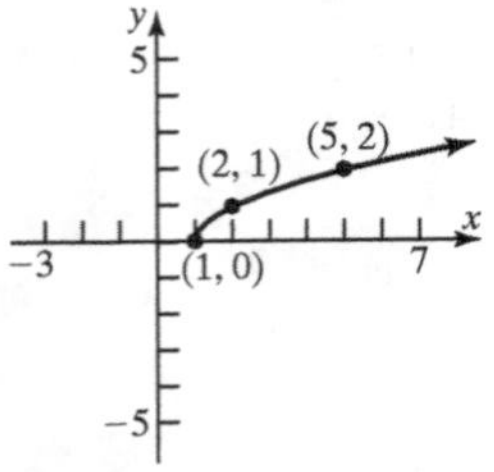

Intercept: $(1, 0)$

Domain: $\{x \mid x \geq 1\}$ or $[1, \infty)$
Range: $\{y \mid y \geq 0\}$ or $[0, \infty)$

61.

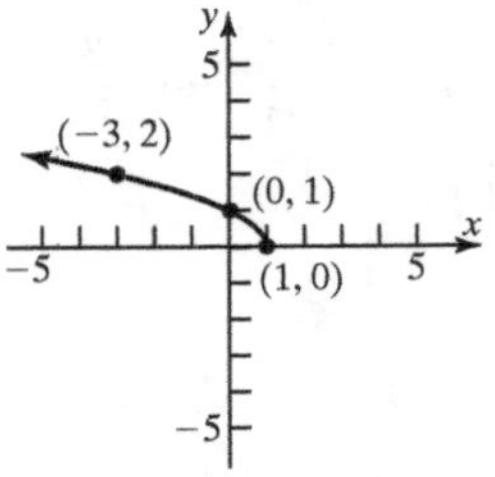

Intercepts: $(0, 1)$, $(1, 0)$

Domain: $\{x \mid x \leq 1\}$ or $(-\infty, 1]$
Range: $\{y \mid y \geq 0\}$ or $[0, \infty)$

63.

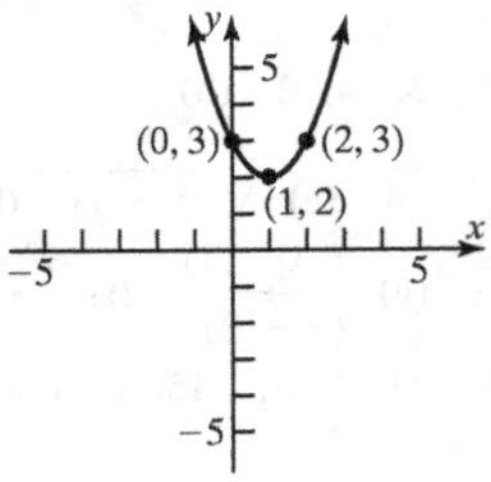

Intercept: $(0, 3)$

Domain: all real numbers
Range: $\{y \mid y \geq 2\}$ or $[2, \infty)$

65.

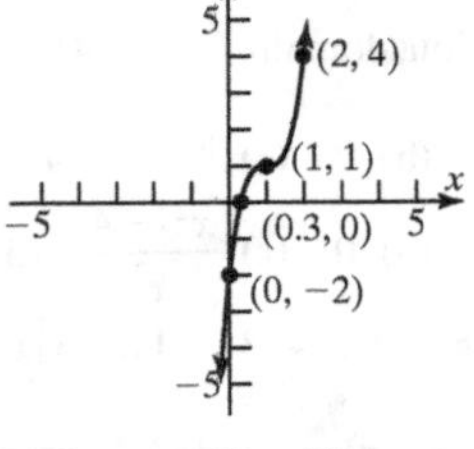

Intercepts: $(0, -2)$, $\left(1 - \frac{\sqrt[3]{9}}{3}, 0\right)$ or about $(0.3, 0)$
Domain: all real numbers
Range: all real numbers

67. (a) $\{x \mid x > -2\}$ or $(-2, \infty)$ **(b)** $(0, 0)$ **(c)**

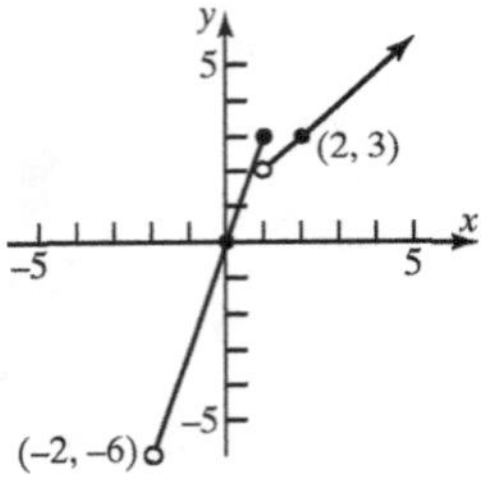

(d) $\{y \mid y > -6\}$ or $(-6, \infty)$
(e) Discontinuous at $x = 1$

69. (a) $\{x \mid x \geq -4\}$ or $[-4, \infty)$ **(b)** $(0, 1)$ **(c)**

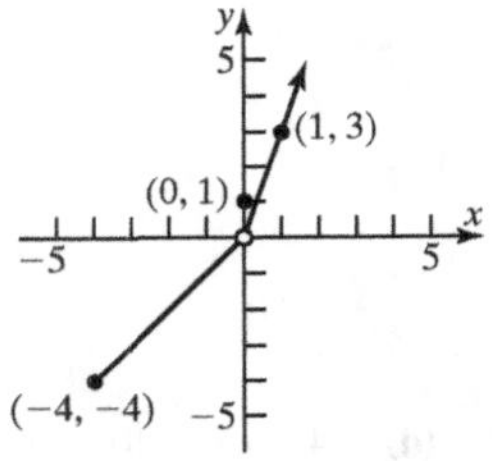

(d) $\{y \mid -4 \leq y < 0 \text{ or } y > 0\}$ or $[-4, 0) \cup (0, \infty)$
(e) Discontinuous at $x = 0$

71. $A = 11$

73. (a) $A(x) = (8.5 - 2x)(11 - 2x)$
(b) $0 \leq x < 4.25$, $0 < A \leq 93.5$
(c) $A(1) = 58.5 \text{ in.}^2$, $A(1.2) = 52.46 \text{ in.}^2$, $A(1.5) = 44 \text{ in.}^2$
(d)

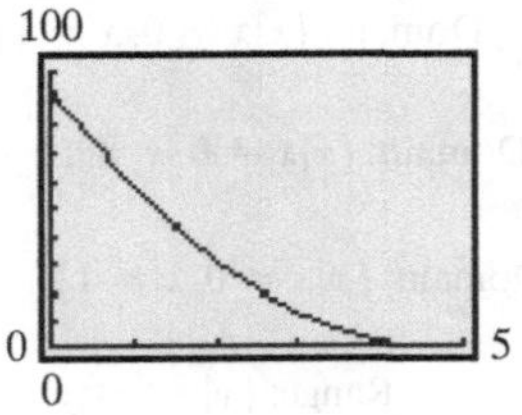

(e) $A(x) \approx 70$ when $x \approx 0.64$ in.; $A(x) \approx 50$ when $x \approx 1.28$ in.

75. (a) $A(x) = 10x - x^3$ **(b)** The largest area that can be enclosed by the rectangle is approximately 12.17 square units.

Chapter Test *(page 122)*

1. (a) Function; domain: $\{2, 4, 6, 8\}$; range: $\{5, 6, 7, 8\}$ **(b)** Not a function **(c)** Not a function **(d)** Function; domain: all real numbers; range: $\{y \mid y \geq 2\}$ **2.** Domain: $\left\{x \middle| x \leq \frac{4}{5}\right\}$; $f(-1) = 3$ **3.** Domain: $\{x \mid x \neq -2\}$; $g(-1) = 1$ **4.** Domain: $\{x \mid x \neq -9, x \neq 4\}$; $h(-1) = \frac{1}{8}$

5. (a) Domain: $\{x \mid -5 \leq x \leq 5\}$; range: $\{y \mid -3 \leq y \leq 3\}$ **(b)** $(0, 2)$, $(-2, 0)$, and $(2, 0)$ **(c)** $f(1) = 3$ **(d)** $x = -5$ and $x = 3$ **(e)** $\{x \mid -5 \leq x < -2 \text{ or } 2 < x \leq 5\}$ or $[-5, -2) \cup (2, 5]$ **6.** Local maxima: $f(-0.85) \approx -0.86$; $f(2.35) \approx 15.55$; local minima: $f(0) = -2$; the function is increasing on the intervals $(-5, -0.85)$ and $(0, 2.35)$ and decreasing on the intervals $(-0.85, 0)$ and $(2.35, 5)$.

7. (a)

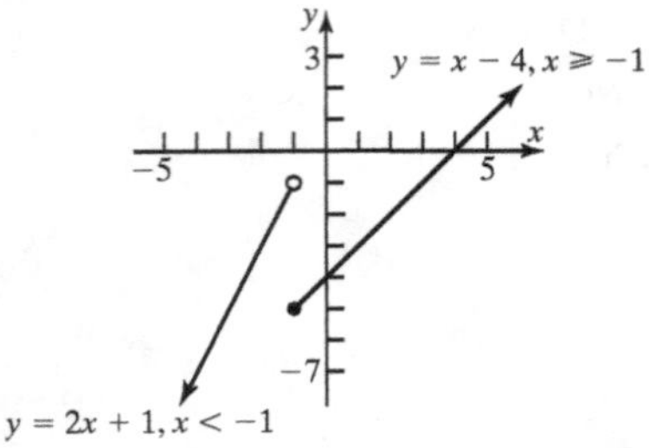

(b) $(0, -4)$, $(4, 0)$
(c) $g(-5) = -9$
(d) $g(2) = -2$

8. 19

9. (a) $(f - g) = 2x^2 - 3x + 3$
(b) $(f \cdot g) = 6x^3 - 4x^2 + 3x - 2$
(c) $f(x + h) - f(x) = 4xh + 2h^2$

10. (a)

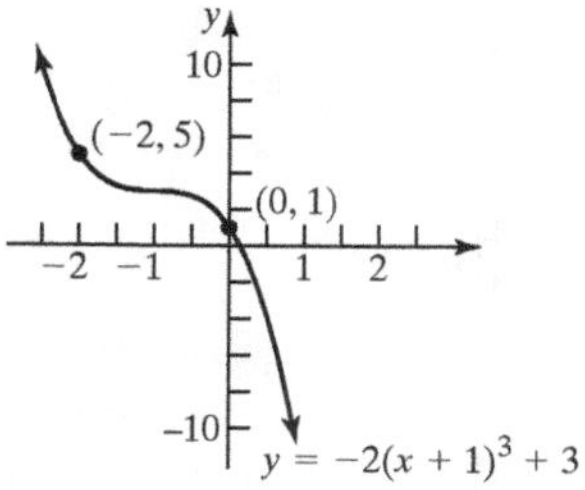

(b)

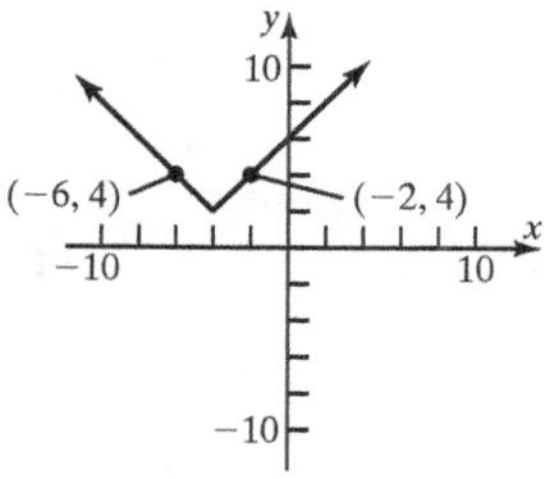

11. (a) 8.67% occurring in 1997 ($x \approx 5$)
(b) The model predicts that the interest rate will be −10.343%. This is not reasonable.

12. (a) $V(x) = \frac{x^2}{8} - \frac{5x}{4} + \frac{\pi x^2}{64}$ **(b)** 1297.61 ft^3

Cumulative Review *(page 123)*

1. $\left\{\frac{4}{5}\right\}$ **2.** {3, 4} **3.** $\left\{-\frac{1}{3}, 2\right\}$ **4.** $\left\{-\frac{1}{2}\right\}$ **5.** No real solution **6.** {−7} **7.** {−31} **8.** $\left\{\frac{1}{3}, 1\right\}$ **9.** $\left\{\frac{1-\sqrt{15}i}{4}, \frac{1+\sqrt{15}i}{4}\right\}$
10. $\{x \mid 1 < x < 4\}$

11.

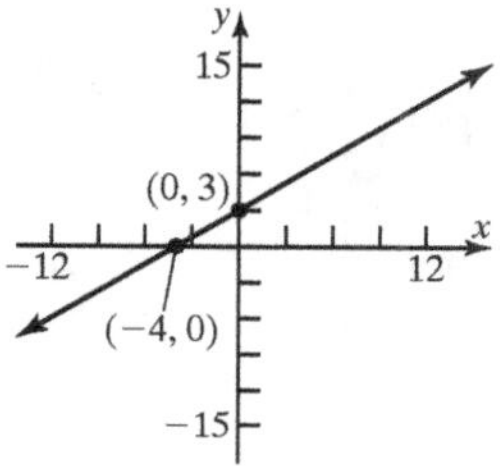

12.

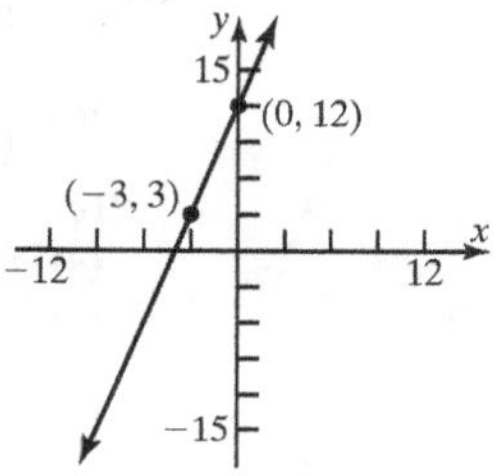

13.

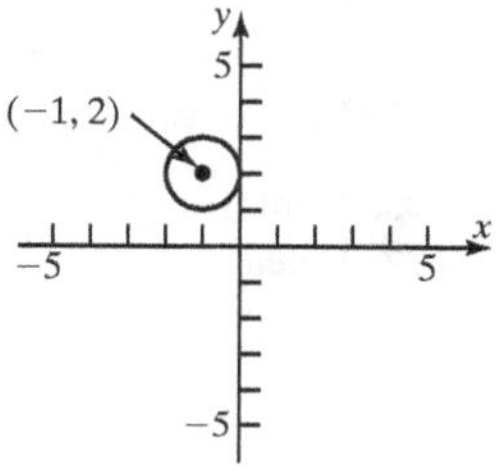

14.

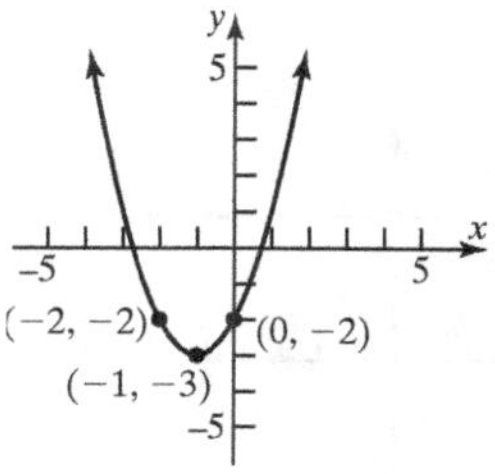

15. (a) Domain: $\{x \mid -4 \le x \le 4\}$; range: $\{y \mid -1 \le y \le 3\}$ **(b)** (−1, 0), (0, −1), (1, 0) **(c)** y-axis **(d)** 1 **(e)** −4 and 4 **(f)** $\{x \mid -1 < x < 1\}$

(g)

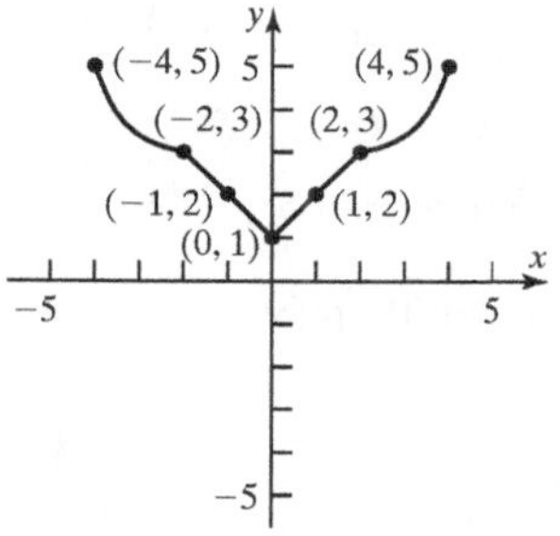

(h)

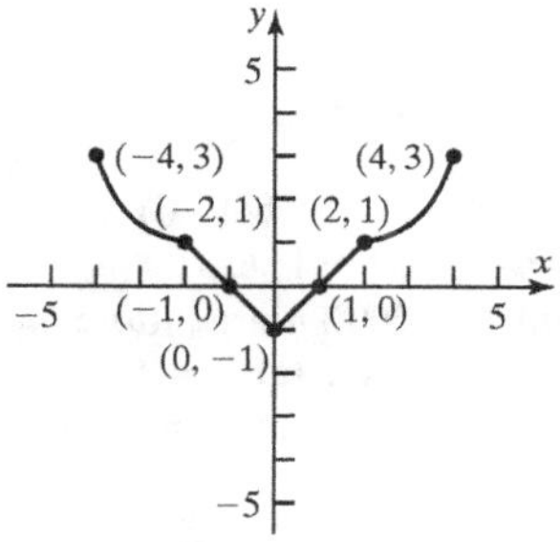

(i)

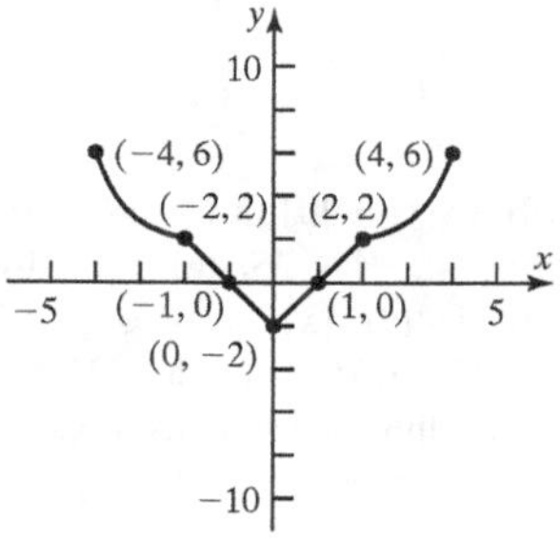

(j) even **(k)** (0, 4) **(l)** (−4, 0) **(m)** f has a local minimum of −1 at $x = 0$ **(n)** 1
16. $5\sqrt{2}$ **17.** (−2, −1) and (2, 3) are on the graph. **18.** x-intercepts: $-5, \frac{1}{3}$; y-intercept: −5 **19.** {−1.10, 0.26, 1.48, 2.36}

20. $y = -\frac{1}{2}x + \frac{13}{2}$

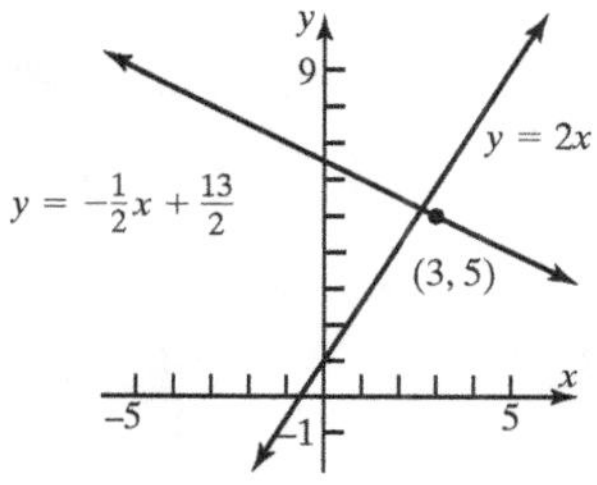

21. Yes, a function **22. (a)** −3 **(b)** $x^2 - 4x - 2$ **(c)** $x^2 + 4x + 1$ **(d)** $-x^2 + 4x - 1$ **(e)** $x^2 - 3$ **(f)** $2x + h - 4$ **23.** $\{z \mid z \ne -1, z \ne 7\}$ **24.** Yes, a function
25. (a) No **(b)** −1; (−2, −1) is on the graph. **(c)** −8; (−8, 2) is on the graph.
26. $2(x^2+1)^{1/2}(4x^2+1)$ **27.** $\frac{(3x+10)(x+5)^{1/2}}{x+5}$

CHAPTER 3 Linear and Quadratic Functions

3.1 Assess Your Understanding *(page 132)*

7. slope; y-intercept **8.** -4; 3 **9.** positive **10.** T **11.** F **12.** F

13. (a) $m = 2; b = 3$

(b)

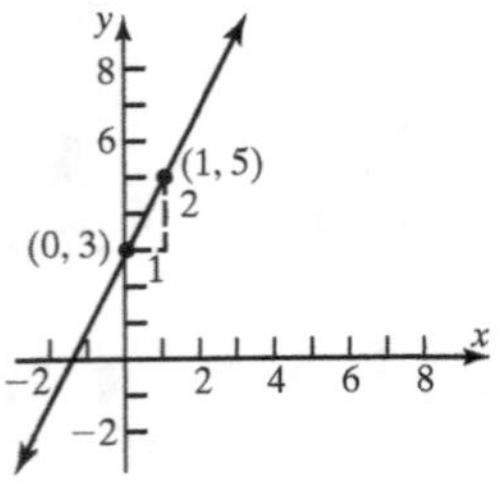

(c) Domain and Range: $(-\infty, \infty)$

(d) 2 **(e)** Increasing

15. (a) $m = -3; b = 4$

(b)

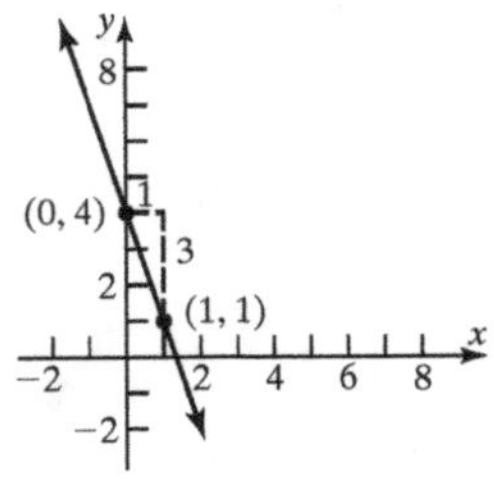

(c) Domain and Range: $(-\infty, \infty)$

(d) -3 **(e)** Decreasing

17. (a) $m = \frac{1}{4}; b = -3$

(b)

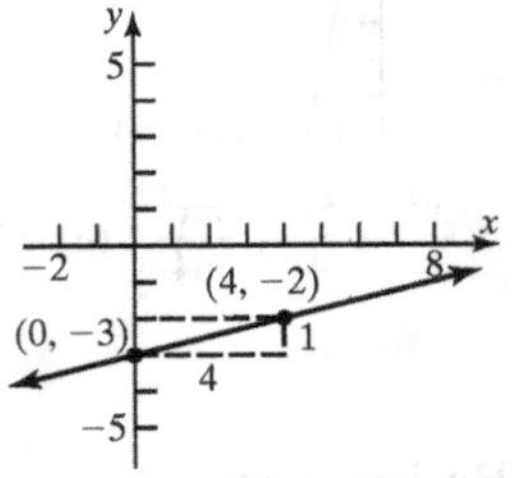

(c) Domain and Range: $(-\infty, \infty)$

(d) $\frac{1}{4}$ **(e)** Increasing

19. (a) $m = 0; b = 4$

(b)

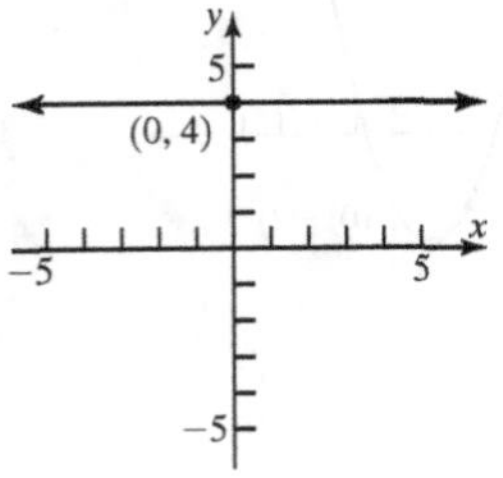

(c) Domain: $(-\infty, \infty)$

Range: $\{y \mid y = 4\}$

(d) 0 **(e)** Constant

21. Linear; $y = -3x - 2$

23. Nonlinear

25. Nonlinear

27. Linear; $y = 8$

29. (a) $\frac{1}{4}$

(b) $\left\{x \middle| x > \frac{1}{4}\right\}$ or $\left(\frac{1}{4}, \infty\right)$

(c) 1

(d) $\{x|x \le 1\}$ or $(-\infty, 1]$

(e)

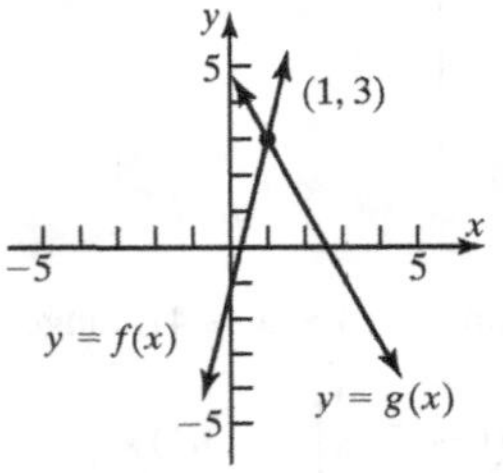

31. (a) 40 **(b)** 88 **(c)** -40 **(d)** $\{x|x > 40\}$ or $(40, \infty)$ **(e)** $\{x|x \le 88\}$ or $(-\infty, 88]$ **(f)** $\{x|-40 < x < 88\}$ or $(-40, 88)$

33. (a) -4 **(b)** $\{x|x < -4\}$ or $(-\infty, -4)$ **35. (a)** -6 **(b)** $\{x|-6 \le x < 5\}$ or $[-6, 5)$

37. (a) \$45 **(b)** 180 mi **(c)** 260 mi **(d)** $\{x|x \ge 0\}$ or $[0, \infty)$ **39. (a)** \$16; 600 T-shirts **(b)** $\$0 \le p < \$16$ **(c)** The price will increase.

41. (a) $\{x|7825 \le x \le 31{,}850\}$ or $[7825, 31{,}850]$ **(b)** \$2308.75

(c) The independent variable is adjusted gross income, x. The dependent variable is the tax bill, T.

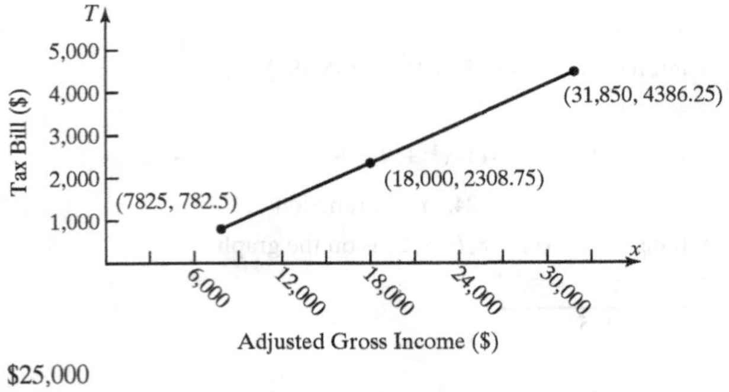

(e) \$25,000

43. (a) $x = 5000$

(b) $x > 5000$

45. (a) $V(x) = -1000x + 3000$ **(b)** $\{x|0 \le x \le 3\}$ or $[0, 3]$

(c)

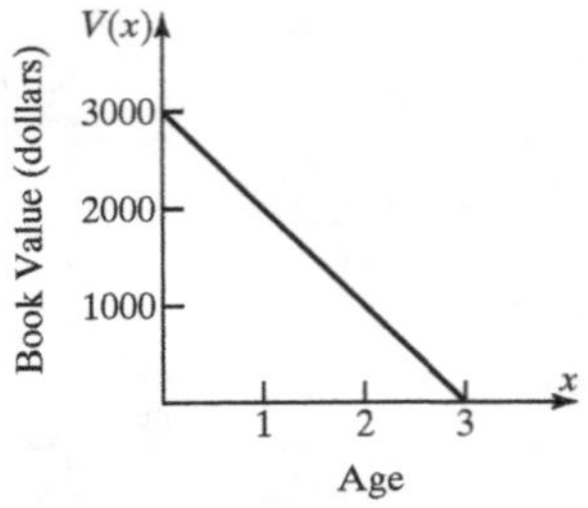

(d) \$1000 **(e)** After 1 year

47. (a) $C(x) = 90x + 1800$

(b)

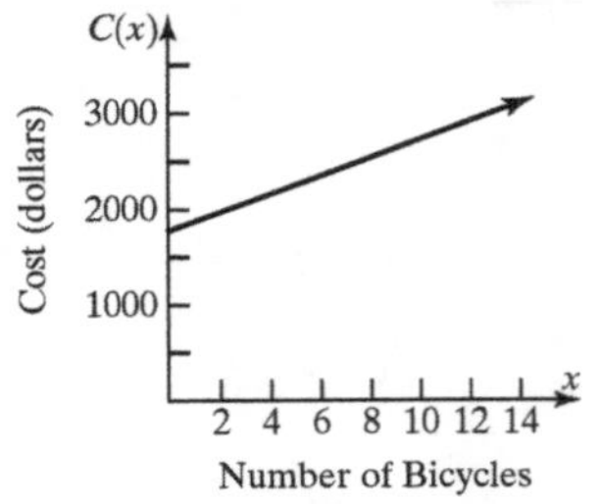

(c) \$3060 **(d)** 22 bicycles

49. **(a)** $C(x) = 0.07x + 29$ **(b)** \$36.70; \$45.10

51. **(a)**

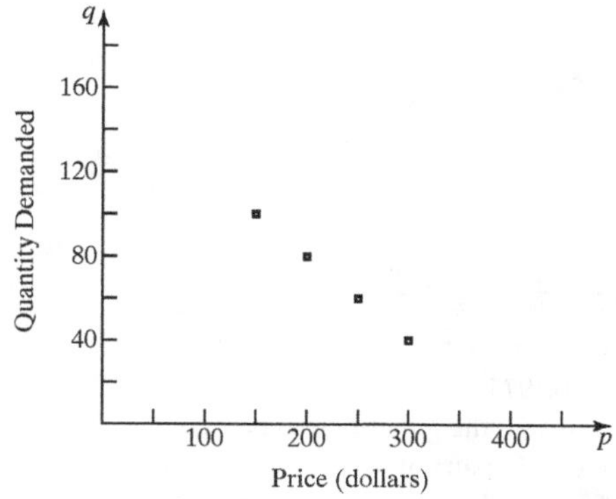

(b) Since each input (price) corresponds to a single output (quantity demanded), we know that quantity demanded is a function of price. Also, because the average rate of change is a constant −\$0.4 per MP3 player, the function is linear.
(c) $q(p) = -0.4p + 160$
(d) $\{p \mid 0 \le p \le 400\}$ or $[0, 400]$

(e)

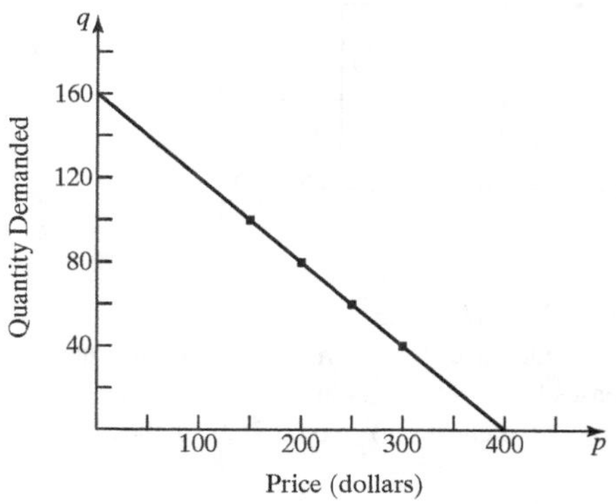

(f) If price increases by \$1, quantity demanded of MP3 players decreases by 0.4 player.
(g) q-intercept: When the price is \$0, 160 MP3 players will be demanded. p-intercept: There will be 0 MP3 players demanded when the price is \$400.

53. (d), (e) **55.** $b = 0$; yes

3.2 Assess Your Understanding *(page 139)*

3. scatter diagram **4.** T **5.** Linear relation, $m > 0$ **7.** Linear relation, $m < 0$ **9.** Nonlinear relation

11. **(a)**

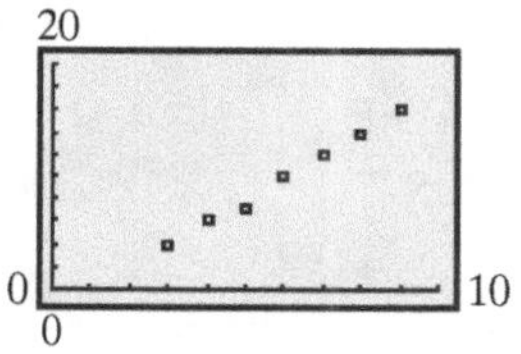

(b) Answers vary. Using (4, 6) and (8, 14), $y = 2x - 2$.

(c)

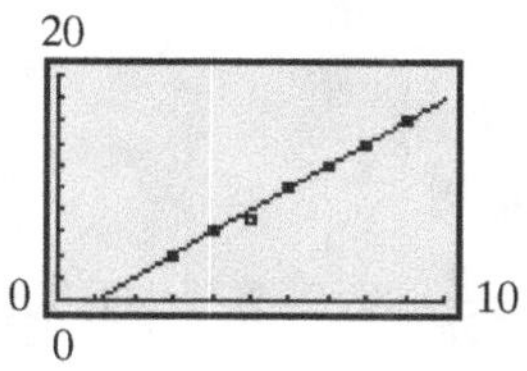

(d) $y = 2.0357x - 2.3571$

(e)

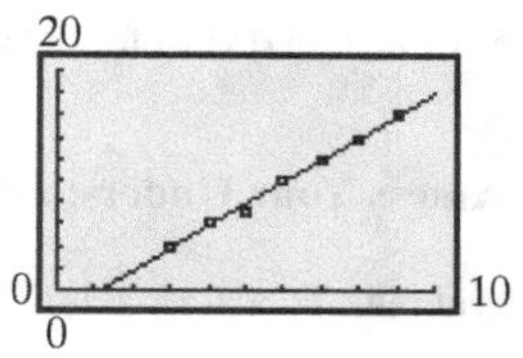

13. **(a)**

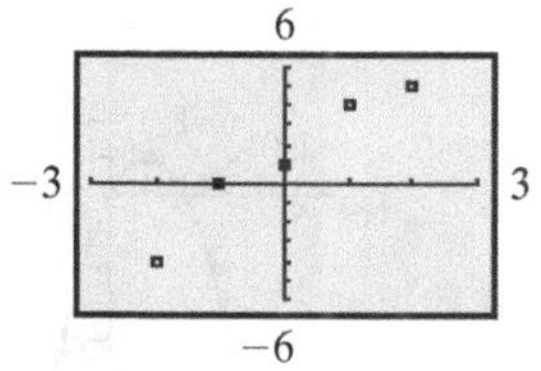

(b) Answers will vary. Using (−2, −4) and (2, 5), $y = \frac{9}{4}x + \frac{1}{2}$.

(c)

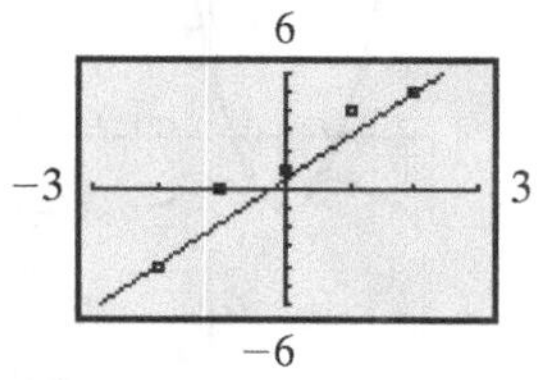

(d) $y = 2.2x + 1.2$

(e)

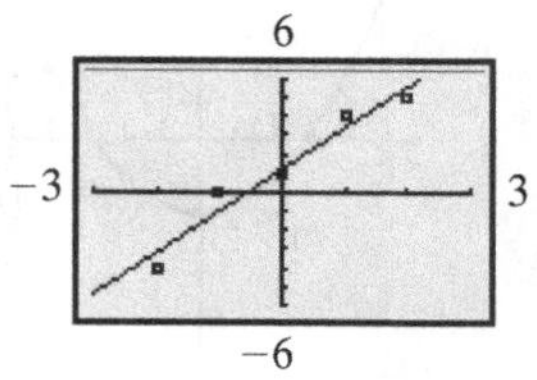

15. **(a)**

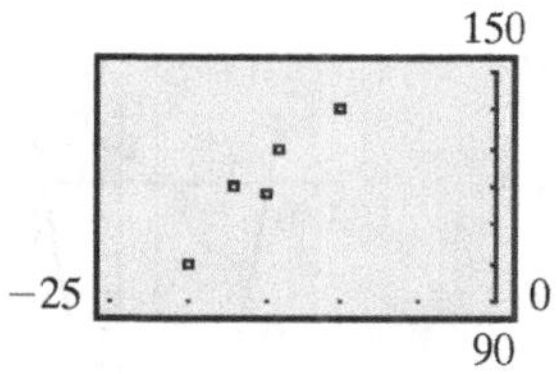

(b) Answers will vary. Using (−20, 100) and (−10, 140), $y = 4x + 180$

(c)

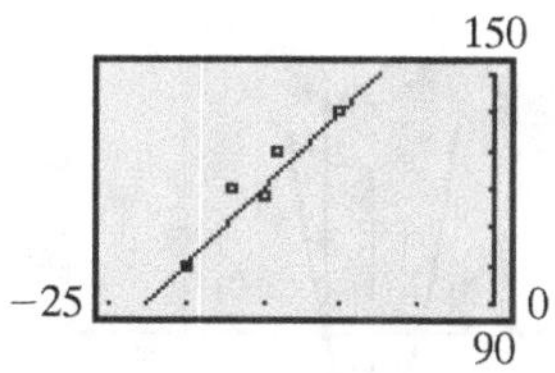

(d) $y = 3.8613x + 180.2920$

(e)

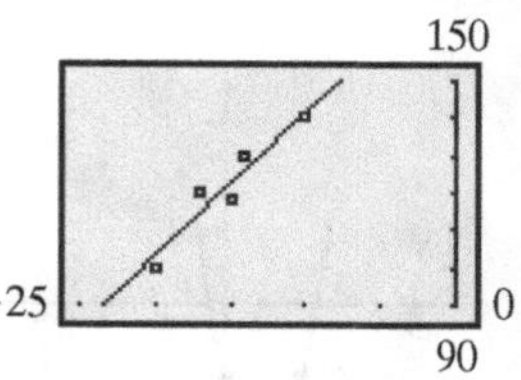

17. **(a)**

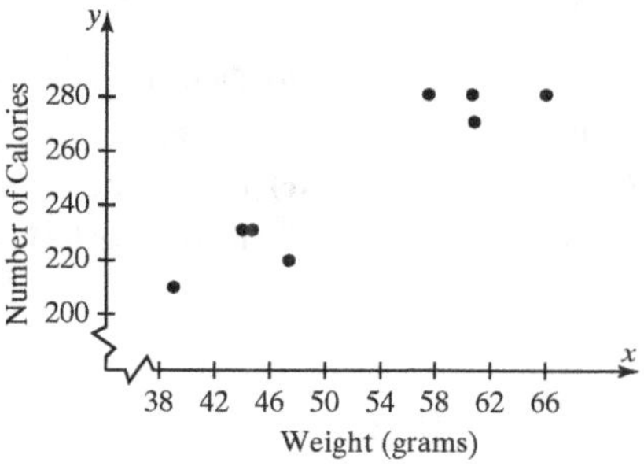

(b) Linear

(c) Answers will vary. Using the points (39.52, 210) and (66.45, 280), $y = 2.599x + 107.288$.

(d)

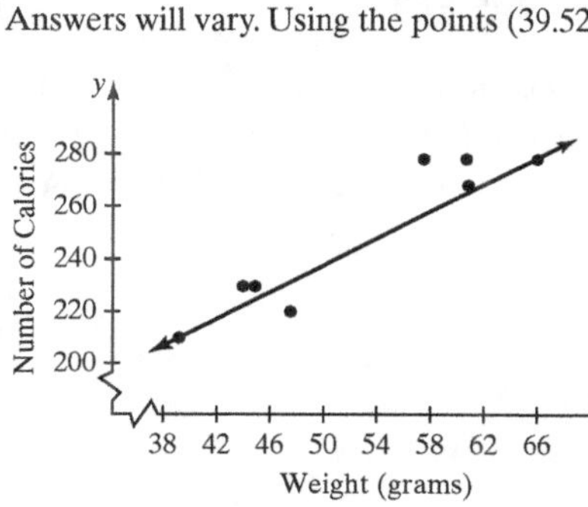

(e) 269 calories

(f) If the weight of a candy bar is increased by 1 gram, the number of calories will increase by 2.599.

19. (a)

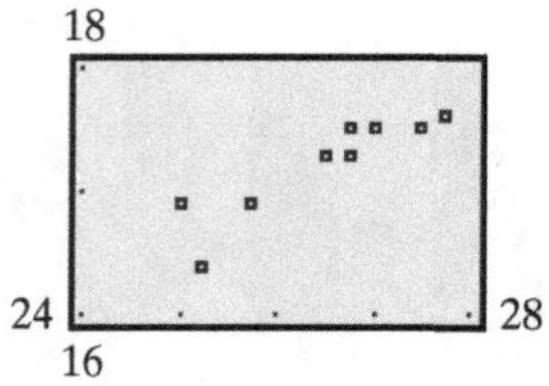

(b) $C(H) = 0.3734H + 7.3268$
(c) If height increases by 1 inch, head circumference increases by about 0.3734 inch.
(d) About 17.0 inches **(e)** About 26.98 inches

21. (a) No
(b)

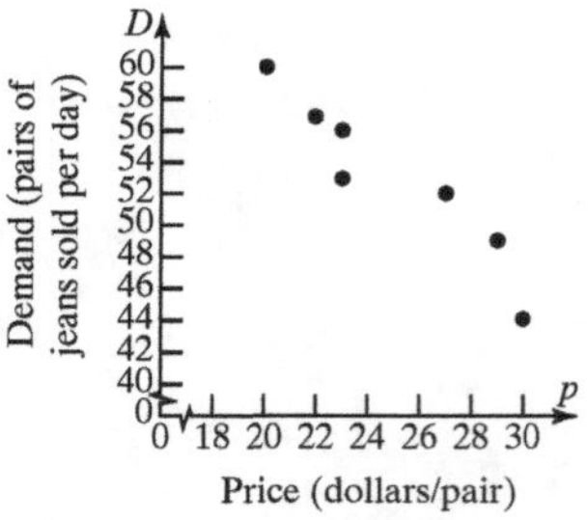

(c) $D = -1.3355p + 86.1974$
(d) If the price increases $1, the quantity sold per day decreases by about 1.34 pairs of jeans.
(e) $D(p) = -1.3355p + 86.1974$ **(f)** $\{p \mid 0 < p \leq 64\}$
(g) About 49 pairs

23.

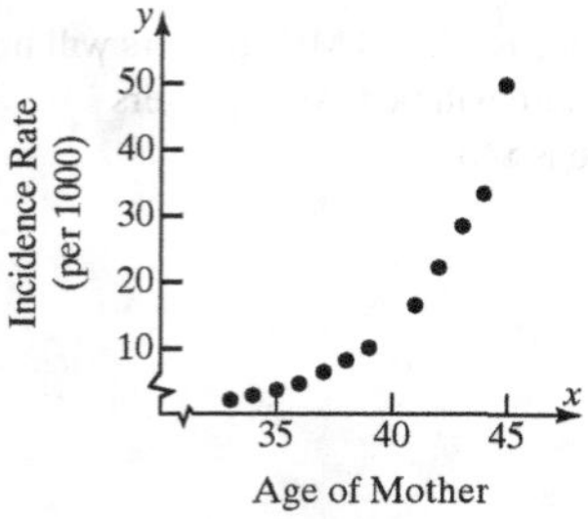

No, the data do not follow a linear pattern.

25. No linear relation

3.3 Assess Your Understanding *(page 151)*

5. parabola **6.** axis or axis of symmetry **7.** $-\dfrac{b}{2a}$ **8.** T **9.** T **10.** T **11.** C **13.** F **15.** G **17.** H

19.

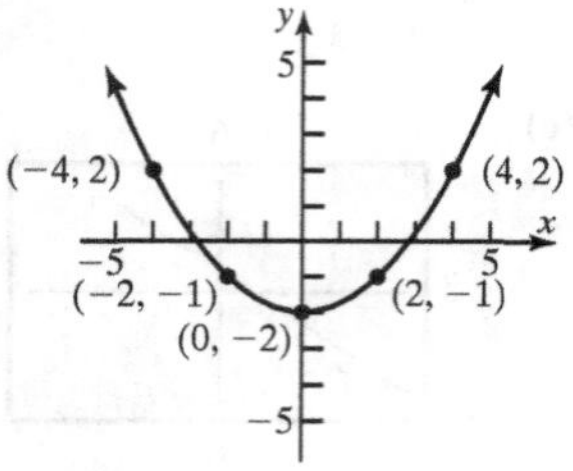

21.

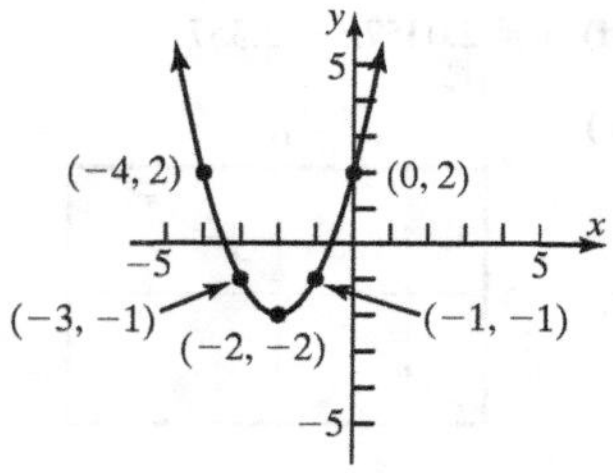

23.

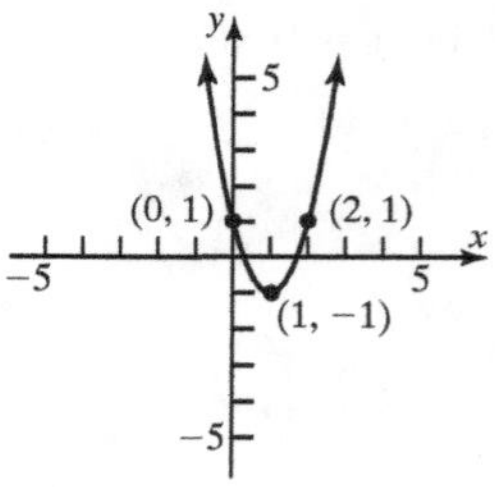

25. $f(x) = -(x + 1)^2 + 1$

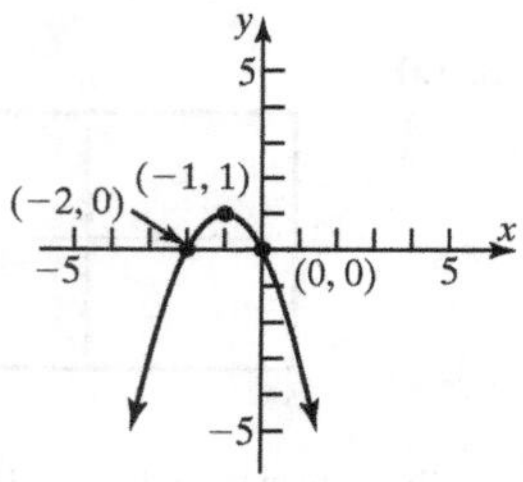

27. $f(x) = 2(x + 1)^2 - 4$

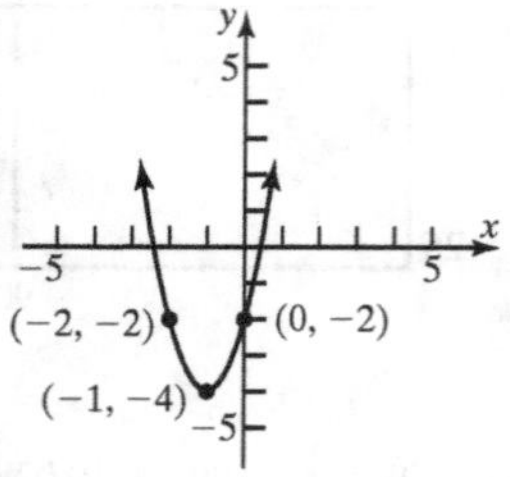

29. (a)

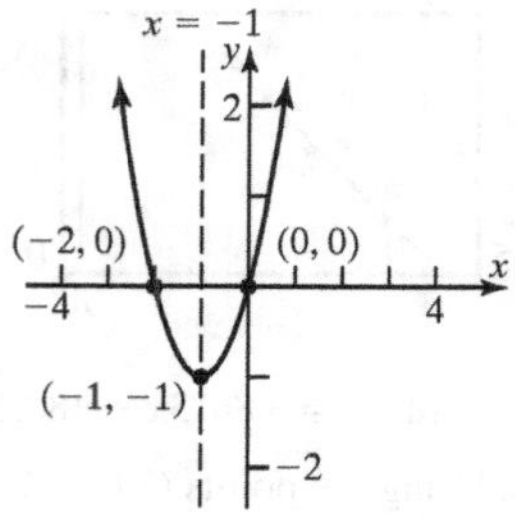

(b) Domain: $(-\infty, \infty)$
Range: $[-1, \infty)$
(c) Decreasing: $(-\infty, -1)$
Increasing: $(-1, \infty)$

31. (a)

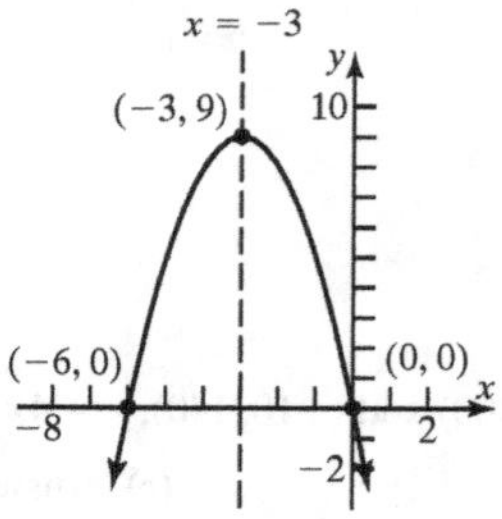

(b) Domain: $(-\infty, \infty)$
Range: $(-\infty, 9]$
(c) Increasing: $(-\infty, -3)$
Decreasing: $(-3, \infty)$

33. (a)

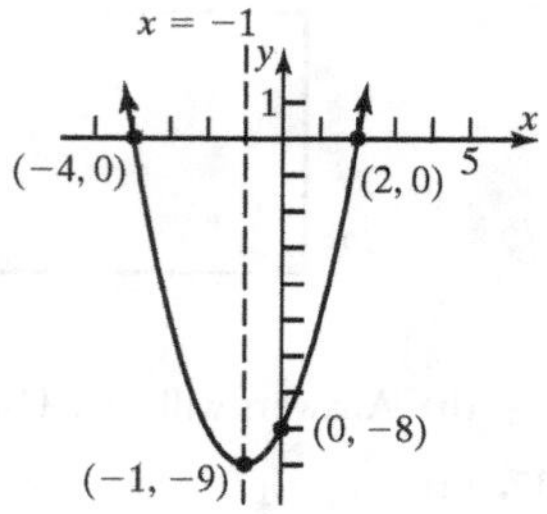

(b) Domain: $(-\infty, \infty)$
Range: $[-9, \infty)$
(c) Decreasing: $(-\infty, -1)$
Increasing: $(-1, \infty)$

35. (a)

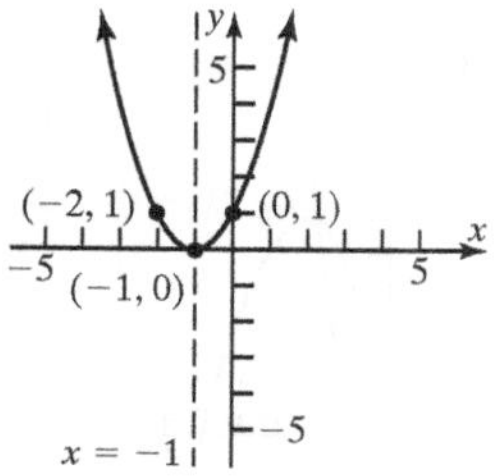

(b) Domain: $(-\infty, \infty)$

Range: $[0, \infty)$

(c) Decreasing: $(-\infty, -1)$

Increasing: $(-1, \infty)$

37. (a)

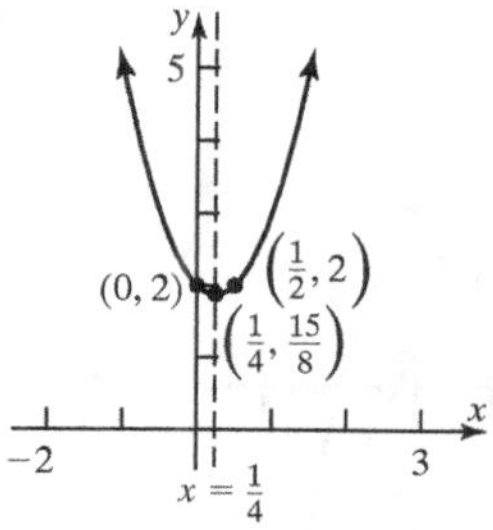

(b) Domain: $(-\infty, \infty)$

Range: $\left[\frac{15}{8}, \infty\right)$

(c) Decreasing: $\left(-\infty, \frac{1}{4}\right)$

Increasing: $\left(\frac{1}{4}, \infty\right)$

39. (a)

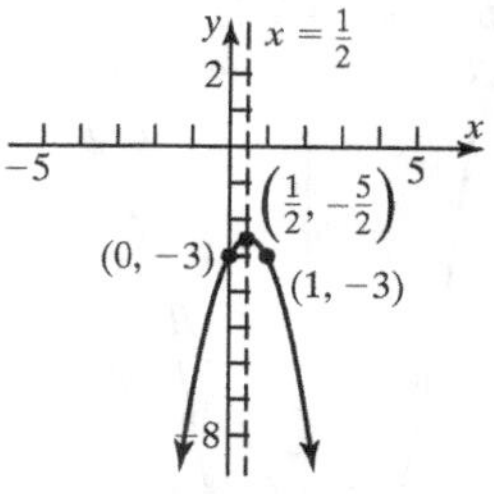

(b) Domain: $(-\infty, \infty)$

Range: $\left(-\infty, -\frac{5}{2}\right]$

(c) Increasing: $\left(-\infty, \frac{1}{2}\right)$

Decreasing: $\left(\frac{1}{2}, \infty\right)$

41. (a)

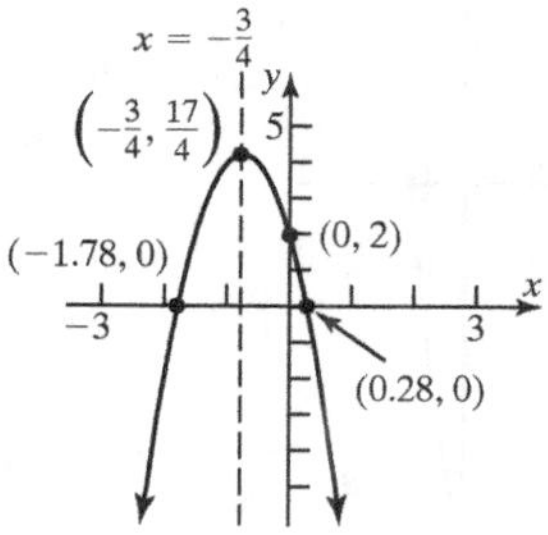

(b) Domain: $(-\infty, \infty)$

Range: $\left(-\infty, \frac{17}{4}\right]$

(c) Increasing: $\left(-\infty, -\frac{3}{4}\right)$

Decreasing: $\left(-\frac{3}{4}, \infty\right)$

43. $f(x) = (x + 1)^2 - 2 = x^2 + 2x - 1$

45. $f(x) = -(x + 3)^2 + 5 = -x^2 - 6x - 4$

47. $f(x) = 2(x - 1)^2 - 3 = 2x^2 - 4x - 1$

49. Minimum value; −18

51. Minimum value; −21

53. Maximum value; 21

55. Maximum value; 13

57. (a)

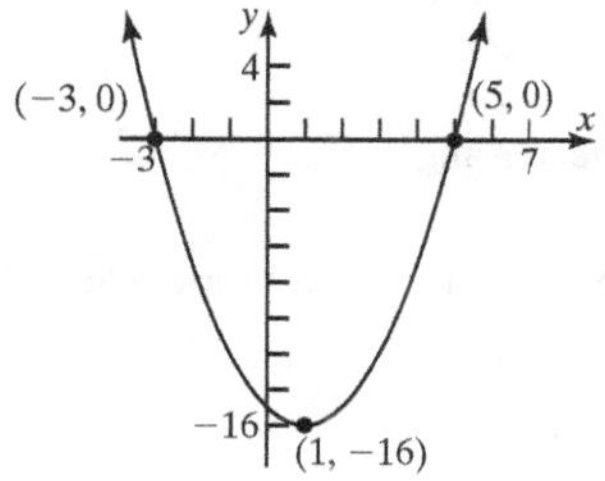

(b) Domain: $(-\infty, \infty)$
Range: $[-16, \infty)$
(c) Decreasing: $(-\infty, 1)$
Increasing: $(1, \infty)$

59. (a)

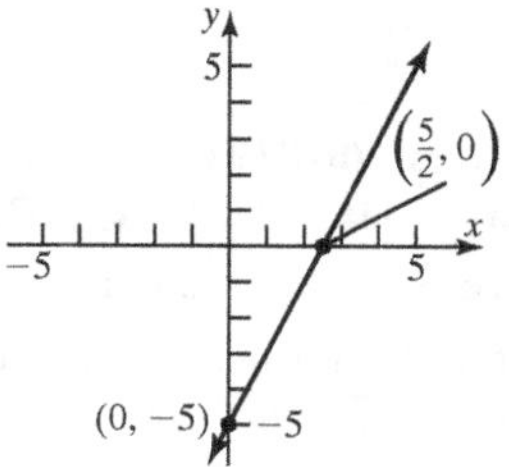

(b) Domain: $(-\infty, \infty)$
Range: $(-\infty, \infty)$
(c) Increasing: $(-\infty, \infty)$

61. (a)

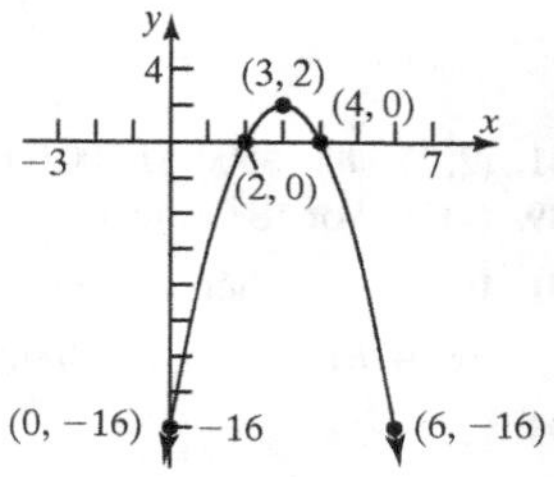

(b) Domain: $(-\infty, \infty)$
Range: $(-\infty, 2]$
(c) Increasing: $(-\infty, 3)$
Decreasing: $(3, \infty)$

63. (a)

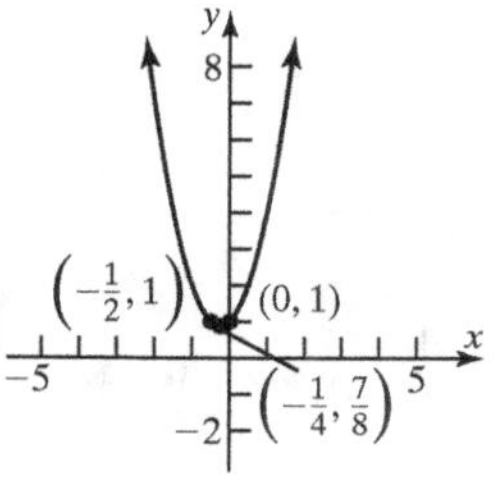

(b) Domain: $(-\infty, \infty)$

Range: $\left[\frac{7}{8}, \infty\right)$

(c) Decreasing: $\left(-\infty, -\frac{1}{4}\right)$

Increasing: $\left(-\frac{1}{4}, \infty\right)$

65. (a)

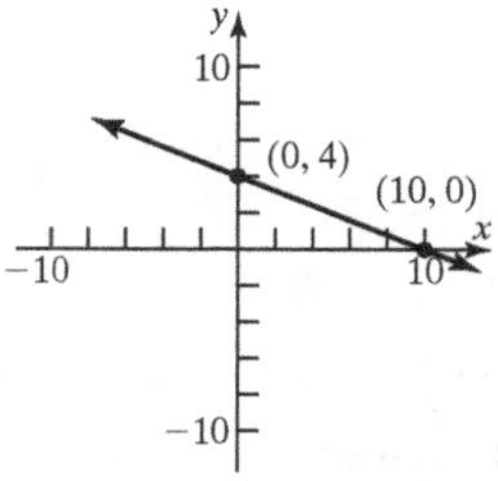

(b) Domain: $(-\infty, \infty)$

Range: $(-\infty, \infty)$

(c) Decreasing: $(-\infty, \infty)$

67. (a)

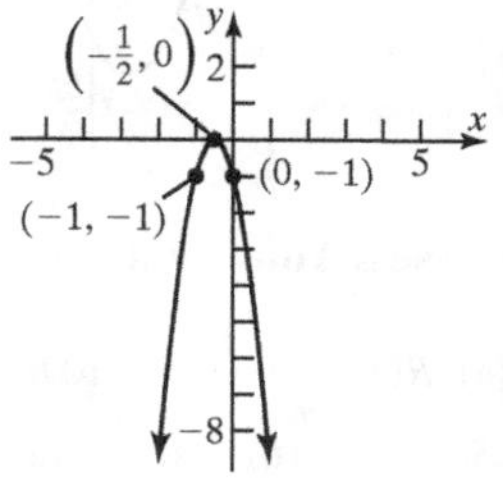

(b) Domain: $(-\infty, \infty)$

Range: $(-\infty, 0]$

(c) Increasing: $\left(-\infty, -\frac{1}{2}\right)$

Decreasing: $\left(-\frac{1}{2}, \infty\right)$

69. $a = 6, b = 0, c = 2$

71. **(a), (c), (d)**

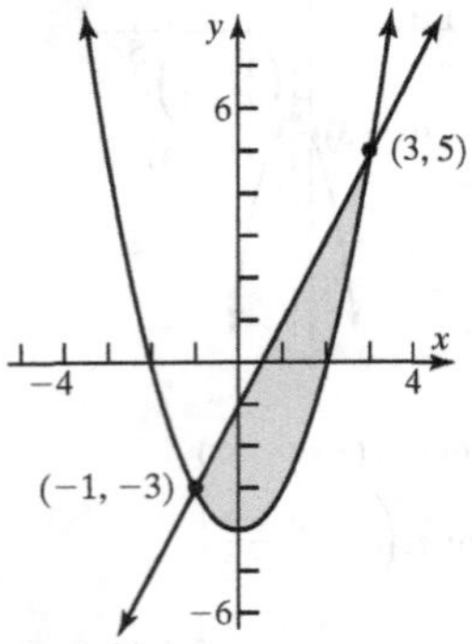

(b) $\{-1, 3\}$

73. **(a), (c), (d)**

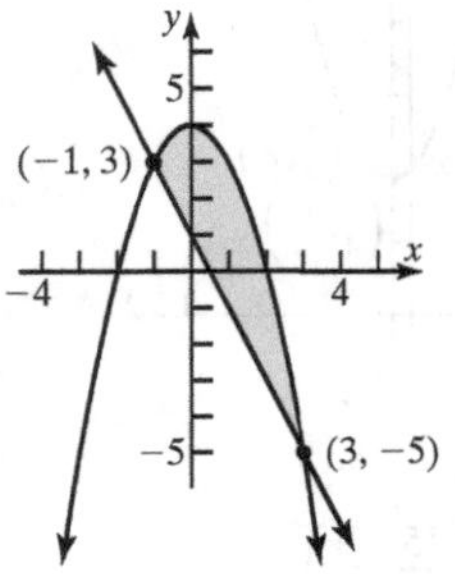

(b) $\{-1, 3\}$

75. **(a), (c), (d)**

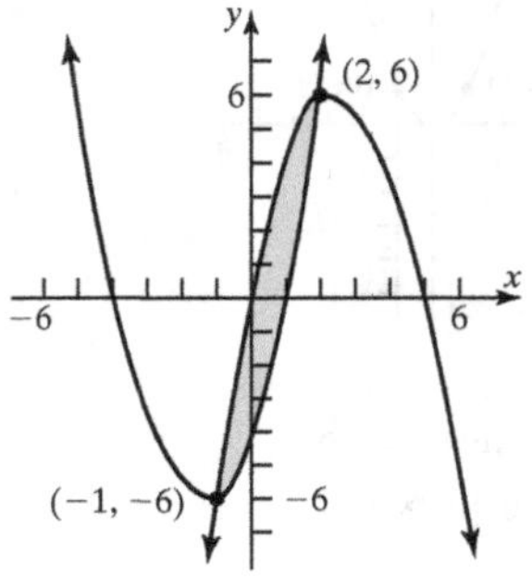

(b) $\{-1, 2\}$

77. **(a)** $a = 1: f(x) = (x + 3)(x - 1) = x^2 + 2x - 3$

$a = 2: f(x) = 2(x + 3)(x - 1) = 2x^2 + 4x - 6$

$a = -2: f(x) = -2(x + 3)(x - 1) = -2x^2 - 4x + 6$

$a = 5: f(x) = 5(x + 3)(x - 1) = 5x^2 + 10x - 15$

(b) The value of a does not affect the x-intercepts, but it changes the y-intercept by a factor of a.

(c) The value of a does not affect the axis of symmetry. It is $x = -1$ for all values of a.

(d) The value of a does not affect the x-coordinate of the vertex. However, the y-coordinate of the vertex is multiplied by a.

(e) The mean of the x-intercepts is the x-coordinate of the vertex.

79. **(a)** $(-2, -25)$ **(b)** $-7, 3$

(c) $-4, 0; (-4, -21), (0, -21)$

(d)

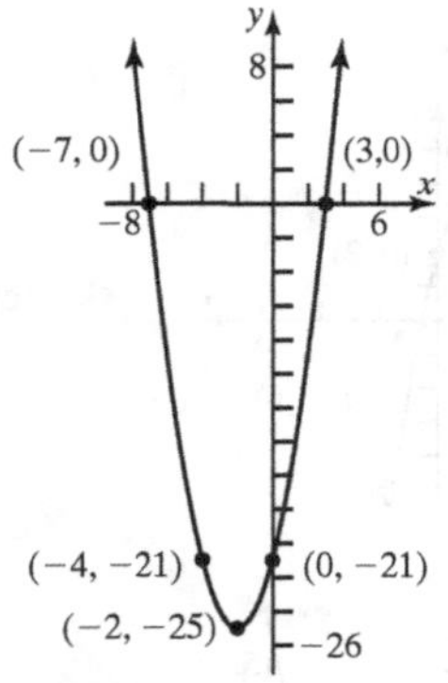

81. (2, 2) **83.** \$500; \$1,000,000 **85.** **(a)** 70,000 mp3 players **(b)** \$2500 **87.** **(a)** 37.4 years old; 3784 **(b)** Decreasing

89. **(a)** 187 or 188 watches; \$7031.20 **(b)** $P(x) = -0.2x^2 + 43x - 1750$ **(c)** 107 or 108 watches; \$561.20

91. If x is even, then ax^2 and bx are even and $ax^2 + bx$ is even, which means that $ax^2 + bx + c$ is odd. If x is odd, then ax^2 and bx are odd and $ax^2 + bx$ is even, which means that $ax^2 + bx + c$ is odd. In either case, $f(x)$ is odd.

93.

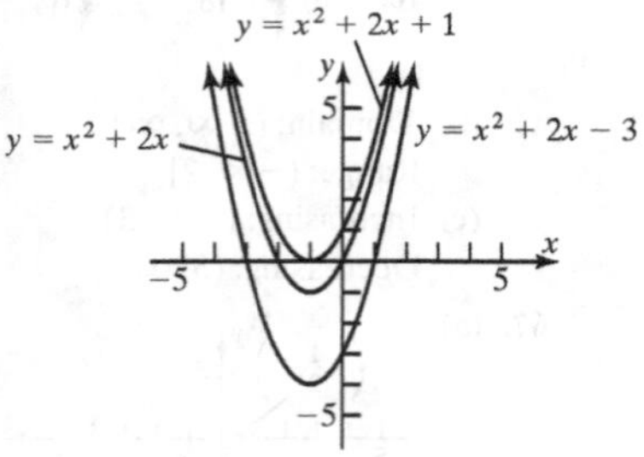

95. $b^2 - 4ac < 0$

97. No

3.4 Assess Your Understanding *(page 160)*

3. **(a)** $R(x) = -\frac{1}{6}x^2 + 100x$ **(b)** $\{x|0 \le x < 600\}$ **(c)** \$13,333.33 **(d)** 300; \$15,000 **(e)** \$50 **5.** **(a)** $R(x) = -\frac{1}{5}x^2 + 20x$ **(b)** \$255 **(c)** 50; \$500 **(d)** \$10 **7.** **(a)** $A(w) = -w^2 + 200w$ **(b)** A is largest when $w = 100$ yd. **(c)** 10,000 yd² **9.** 2,000,000 m²

11. **(a)** $\frac{625}{16} \approx 39$ ft **(b)** $\frac{7025}{32} \approx 219.5$ ft

(c) About 170 ft

(d)

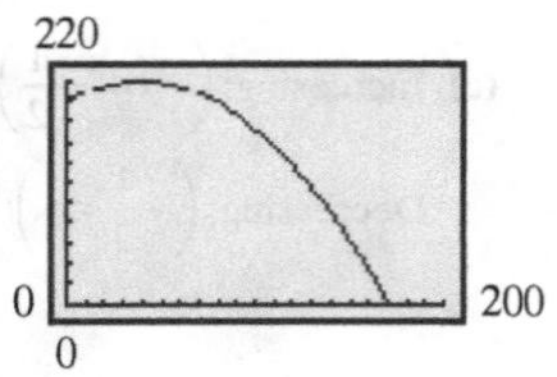

(f) When the height is 100 ft, the projectile is about 135.7 ft from the cliff.

13. 18.75 m

15. 3 in.

17. $\frac{750}{\pi} \approx 238.73$ m by 375 m

19. **(a)** 171 ft **(b)** 49 mph

21. $x = \frac{a}{2}$

23. $\frac{38}{3}$

25. $\frac{248}{3}$

27. (a)

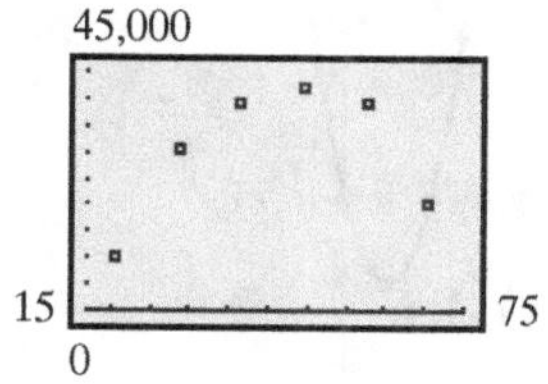

The data appear to follow a quadratic relation with $a < 0$.

(b) $I(x) = -43.384x^2 + 4089.654x - 53{,}244.570$
(c) About 47 years of age
(d) Approximately \$43,134
(e)

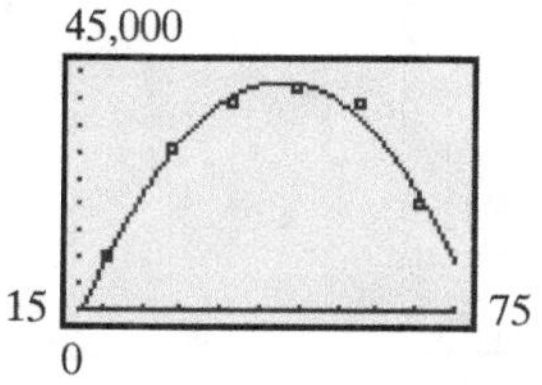

29. (a)

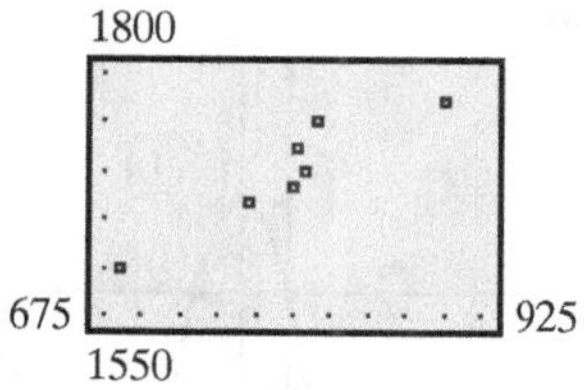

The data appear to be linearly related with positive slope.
(b) $R(x) = 0.836x + 1032.273$ **(c)** \$1743

31. (a)

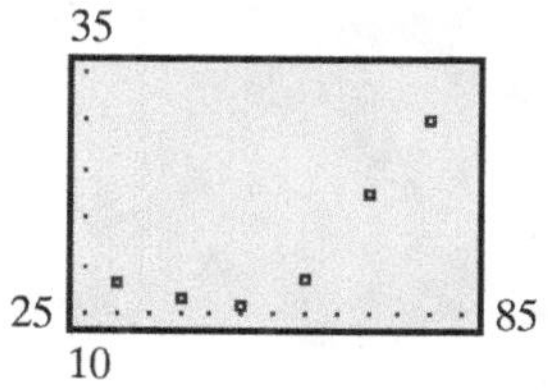

The data appear to follow a quadratic relation with $a > 0$.
(b) $P(a) = 0.015a^2 - 1.332a + 39.823$ **(c)** 11.6%

3.5 Assess Your Understanding *(page 166)*

3. (a) $\{x|x < -2 \text{ or } x > 2\}; (-\infty, -2) \cup (2, \infty)$ **(b)** $\{x|-2 \le x \le 2\}; [-2, 2]$

5. (a) $\{x|-2 \le x \le 1\}; [-2, 1]$ **(b)** $\{x|x < -2 \text{ or } x > 1\}; (-\infty, -2) \cup (1, \infty)$ **7.** $\{x|-2 \le x \le 5\}; [-2, 5]$

9. $\{x|x < 0 \text{ or } x > 4\}; (-\infty, 0) \cup (4, \infty)$ **11.** $\{x|-3 < x < 3\}; (-3, 3)$ **13.** $\{x|x < -4 \text{ or } x > 3\}; (-\infty, -4) \cup (3, \infty)$

15. $\left\{x\middle|-\frac{1}{2} \le x \le 3\right\}; \left[-\frac{1}{2}, 3\right]$ **17.** $\{x|x < -1 \text{ or } x > 8\}; (-\infty, -1) \cup (8, \infty)$ **19.** No real solution **21.** All real numbers; $(-\infty, \infty)$

23. $\{x|x \le -4 \text{ or } x \ge 4\}; (-\infty, -4] \cup [4, \infty)$ **25. (a)** $\{-1, 1\}$ **(b)** $\{-1\}$ **(c)** $\{-1, 4\}$ **(d)** $\{x|x < -1 \text{ or } x > 1\}; (-\infty, -1) \cup (1, \infty)$
(e) $\{x|x \le -1\}; (-\infty, -1]$ **(f)** $\{x|x < -1 \text{ or } x > 4\}; (-\infty, -1) \cup (4, \infty)$ **(g)** $\{x|x \le -\sqrt{2} \text{ or } x \ge \sqrt{2}\}; (-\infty, -\sqrt{2}] \cup [\sqrt{2}, \infty)$

27. (a) $\{-1, 1\}$ **(b)** $\left\{-\frac{1}{4}\right\}$ **(c)** $\{-4, 0\}$ **(d)** $\{x|-1 < x < 1\}; (-1, 1)$ **(e)** $\left\{x\middle|x \le -\frac{1}{4}\right\}$ or $\left(-\infty, -\frac{1}{4}\right]$ **(f)** $\{x|-4 < x < 0\}; (-4, 0)$
(g) $\{0\}$ **29. (a)** $\{-2, 2\}$ **(b)** $\{-2, 2\}$ **(c)** $\{-2, 2\}$ **(d)** $\{x|x < -2 \text{ or } x > 2\}; (-\infty, -2) \cup (2, \infty)$
(e) $\{x|x \le -2 \text{ or } x \ge 2\}; (-\infty, -2] \cup [2, \infty)$ **(f)** $\{x|x < -2 \text{ or } x > 2\}; (-\infty, -2) \cup (2, \infty)$
(g) $\{x|x \le -\sqrt{5} \text{ or } x \ge \sqrt{5}\}; (-\infty, -\sqrt{5}] \cup [\sqrt{5}, \infty)$ **31. (a)** $\{-1, 2\}$ **(b)** $\{-2, 1\}$ **(c)** $\{0\}$
(d) $\{x|x < -1 \text{ or } x > 2\}; (-\infty, -1) \cup (2, \infty)$ **(e)** $\{x|-2 \le x \le 1\}; [-2, 1]$ **(f)** $\{x|x < 0\}; (-\infty, 0)$

(g) $\left\{x\middle|x \le \frac{1 - \sqrt{13}}{2} \text{ or } x \ge \frac{1 + \sqrt{13}}{2}\right\}; \left(-\infty, \frac{1 - \sqrt{13}}{2}\right] \cup \left[\frac{1 + \sqrt{13}}{2}, \infty\right)$

33. (a) 5 sec **(b)** The ball is more than 96 ft above the ground from time t between 2 and 3 sec, $2 < t < 3$.
35. (a) \$0, \$1000 **(b)** The revenue is more than \$800,000 for prices between \$276.39 and \$723.61, $\$276.39 < p < \$723.61$.
37. (a) $\{c \mid 0.112 < c < 81.907\}; (0.112, 81.907)$ **(b)** It is possible to hit a target 75 km away if $c = 0.651$ or $c = 1.536$.

Review Exercises *(page 168)*

1. (a) $m = 2; b = -5$
(b)

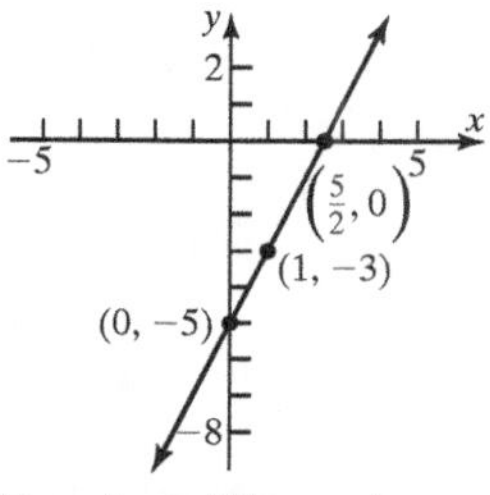

(c) Domain and Range: $(-\infty, \infty)$
(d) 2 **(e)** Increasing

3. (a) $m = \frac{4}{5}; b = -6$
(b)

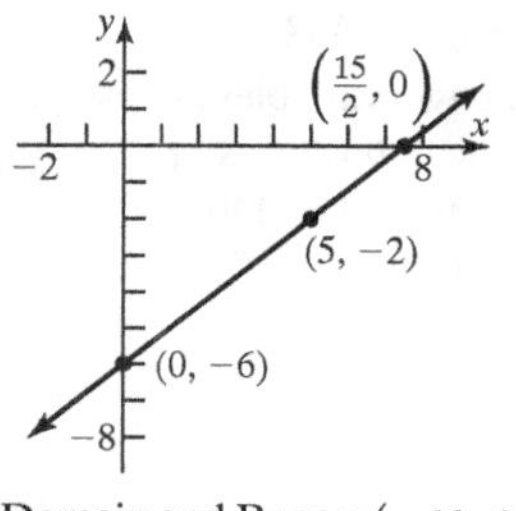

(c) Domain and Range: $(-\infty, \infty)$
(d) $\frac{4}{5}$ **(e)** Increasing

5. (a) $m = 0; b = 4$
(b)

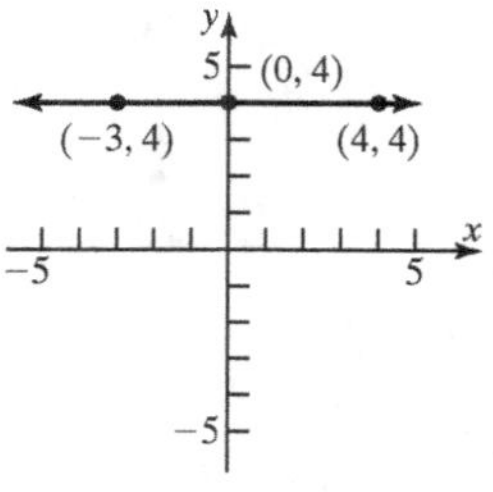

(c) Domain: $(-\infty, \infty)$
Range: $\{y \mid y = 4\}$
(d) 0 **(e)** Constant

7. Linear; $y = 5x + 3$

9.

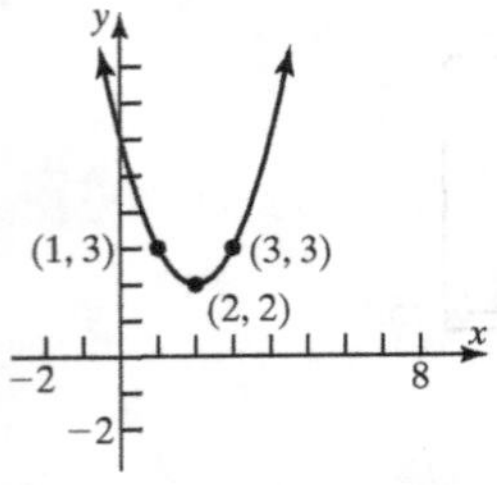

11.

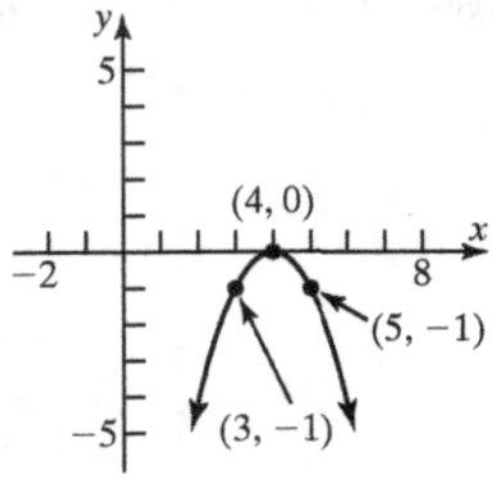

13.

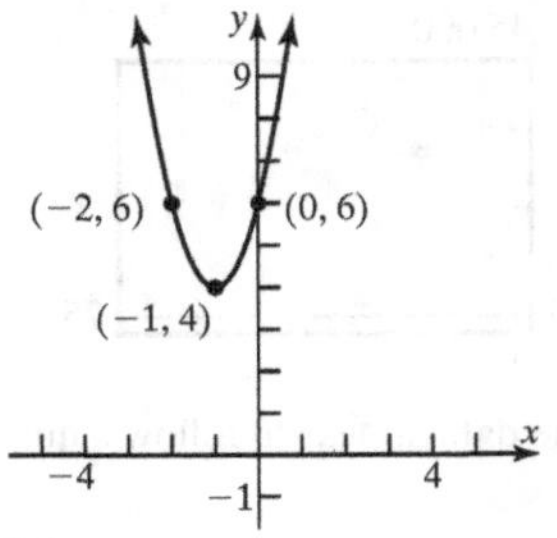

15. (a)

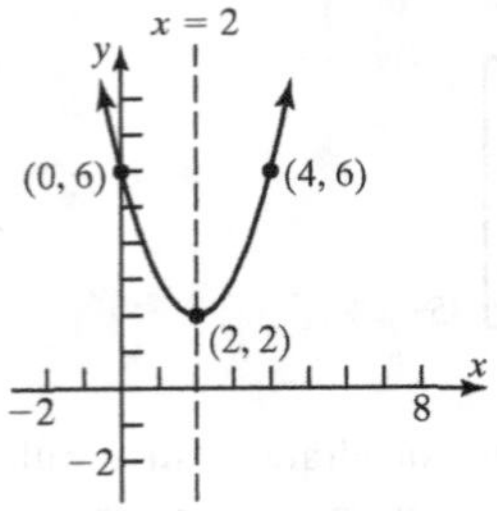

(b) Domain: $(-\infty, \infty)$
Range: $[2, \infty)$
(c) Decreasing: $(-\infty, 2)$
Increasing: $(2, \infty)$

17. (a)

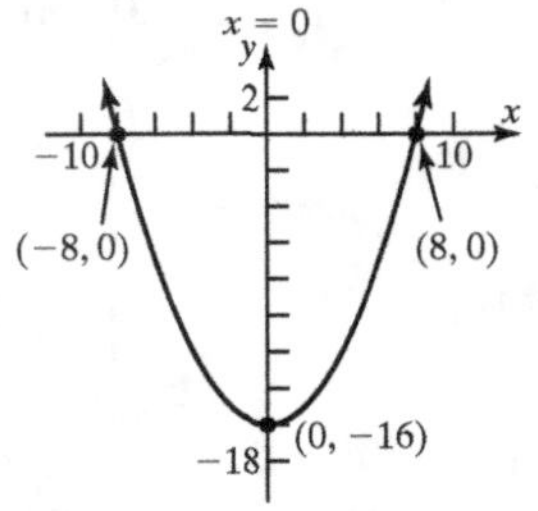

(b) Domain: $(-\infty, \infty)$
Range: $[-16, \infty)$
(c) Decreasing: $(-\infty, 0)$
Increasing: $(0, \infty)$

19. (a)

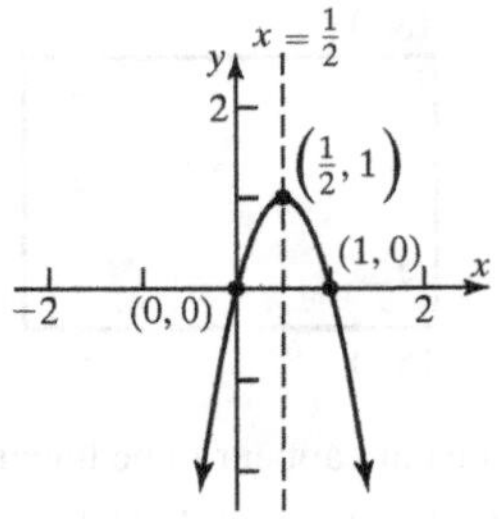

(b) Domain: $(-\infty, \infty)$
Range: $(-\infty, 1]$
(c) Increasing: $\left(-\infty, \frac{1}{2}\right)$
Decreasing: $\left(\frac{1}{2}, \infty\right)$

21. (a)

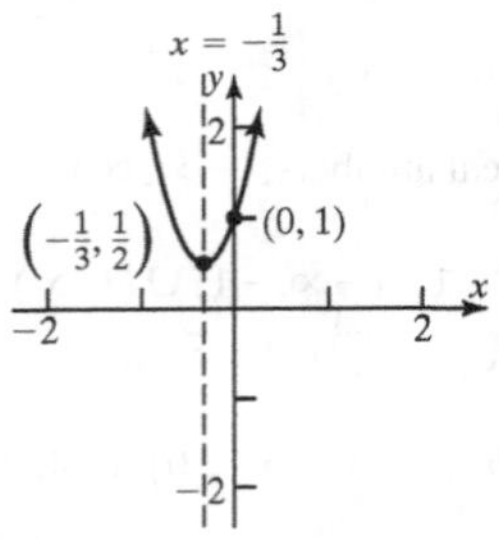

(b) Domain: $(-\infty, \infty)$
Range: $\left[\frac{1}{2}, \infty\right)$
(c) Decreasing: $\left(-\infty, -\frac{1}{3}\right)$
Increasing: $\left(-\frac{1}{3}, \infty\right)$

23. (a)

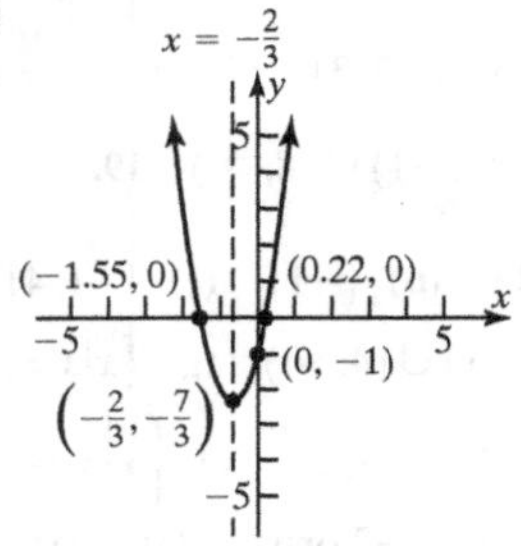

(b) Domain: $(-\infty, \infty)$
Range: $\left[-\frac{7}{3}, \infty\right)$
(c) Decreasing: $\left(-\infty, -\frac{2}{3}\right)$
Increasing: $\left(-\frac{2}{3}, \infty\right)$

25. Minimum value; 1 **27.** Maximum value; 12 **29.** Maximum value; 16 **31.** $\{x \mid -8 < x < 2\}$; $(-8, 2)$

33. $\left\{x \middle| x \le -\frac{1}{3} \text{ or } x \ge 5\right\}$; $\left(-\infty, -\frac{1}{3}\right] \cup [5, \infty)$ **35. (a)** Company A: $C(x) = 0.06x + 7$; Company B: $C(x) = 0.08x$ **(b)** 350 min **(c)** $0 \le x < 350$ **37. (a)** $R(x) = -\frac{1}{10}x^2 + 150x$ **(b)** \$14,000 **(c)** 750; \$56,250 **(d)** \$75 **39.** 4,166,666.7 m^2

41. (a) 63 clubs **(b)** \$151.90 **43.** $A(x) = -x^2 + 10x$, $0 < x < 10$; 25 units^2

45. (a)

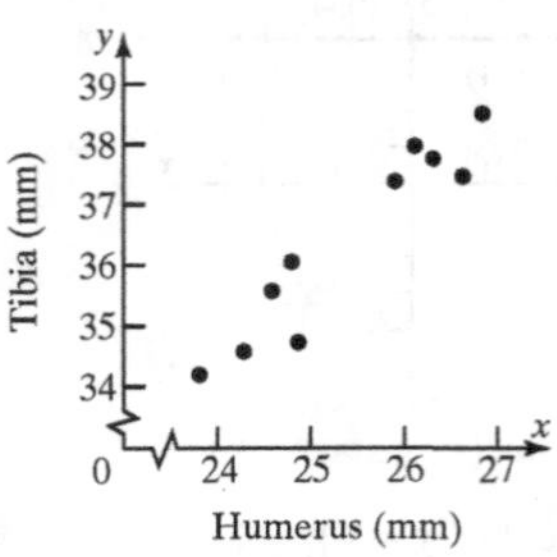

(b) Yes; the two variables appear to be linearly related with positive slope.
(c) $y = 1.3902x + 1.1140$
(d) 37.95 mm

Chapter Test *(page 171)*

1. (a) Slope: -4; y-intercept: 3
(b) Decreasing

(c)

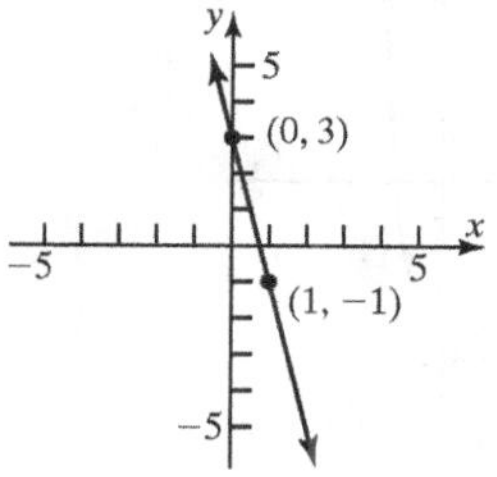

2. Linear; $y = -5x + 2$

3.

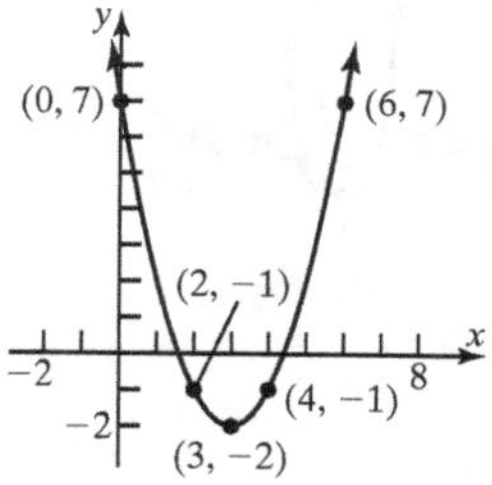

4. (a) Opens up
(b) $(2, -8)$
(c) $x = 2$
(d) x-intercepts: $\frac{6 - 2\sqrt{6}}{3}, \frac{6 + 2\sqrt{6}}{3}$;
y-intercept: 4

(e)

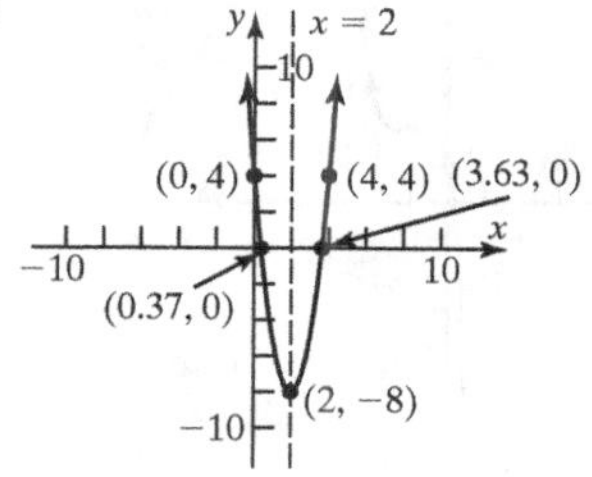

(f) Domain: All real numbers; $(-\infty, \infty)$
Range: $\{y \mid y \geq -8\}$; $[-8, \infty)$
(g) Decreasing: $(-\infty, 2)$; Increasing: $(2, \infty)$

5. (a) Opens down
(b) $(1, -3)$
(c) $x = 1$
(d) No x-intercepts: y-intercept: -5

(e)

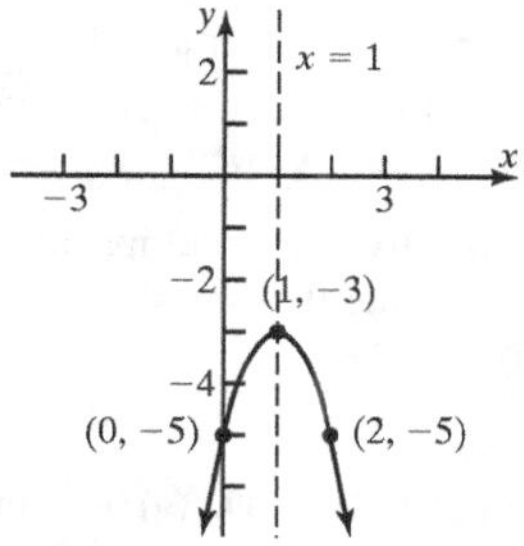

(f) Domain: All real numbers; $(-\infty, \infty)$
Range: $\{y \mid y \leq -3\}$; $(-\infty, -3]$
(g) Increasing: $(-\infty, 1)$; Decreasing: $(1, \infty)$

6. $f(x) = 2x^2 - 4x - 30$ **7.** Maximum value; 21 **8.** $\{x \mid x \leq 4 \text{ or } x \geq 6\}$; $(-\infty, 4] \cup [6, \infty)$

9. (a) $C(m) = 0.15m + 129.50$ **(b)** \$258.50 **(c)** 562 miles **10. (a)** $R(x) = -\frac{1}{10}x^2 + 1000x$ **(b)** \$384,000 **(c)** 5000 units; \$2,500,000 **(d)** \$500

11. (a)

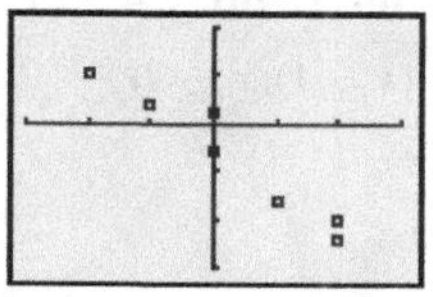

Linear with negative slope

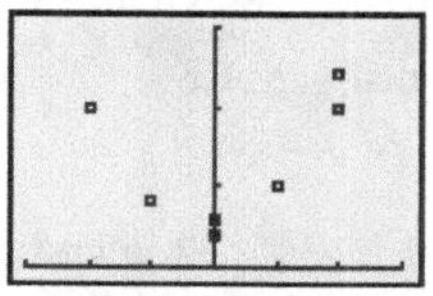

Quadratic that opens up

(b) $y = -4.234x - 2.362$ **(c)** $y = 1.993x^2 + 0.289x + 2.503$

Cumulative Review *(page 171)*

1. (a) -3 **(b)** $x^2 - 4x - 2$ **(c)** $x^2 + 4x + 1$ **(d)** $-x^2 + 4x - 1$ **(e)** $x^2 - 3$ **(f)** $2x + h - 4$ **2.** $\left\{z \middle| z \neq \frac{7}{6}\right\}$ **3.** Yes **4. (a)** No **(b)** -1; $(-2, -1)$ is on the graph. **(c)** -8; $(-8, 2)$ is on the graph. **5.** Neither **6.** Local maximum is 5.30 and occurs at $x = -1.29$. Local minimum is -3.30 and occurs at $x = 1.29$. Increasing: $(-4, -1.29)$ and $(1.29, 4)$; Decreasing: $(-1.29, 1.29)$ **7. (a)** $\{-4\}$ **(b)** $\{x \mid x > -4\}$ or $(-4, \infty)$ **8. (a)** $\{-1, 3\}$ **(b)** $\{x \mid x < -1 \text{ or } x > 3\}$ or $(-\infty, -1)$ h $(3, \infty)$

9. (a) Domain: $\{x \mid -4 \leq x \leq 4\}$ or $[-4, 4]$; Range: $\{y \mid -1 \leq y \leq 3\}$ or $[-1, 3]$ **(b)** $(-1, 0), (0, -1), (1, 0)$ **(c)** y-axis **(d)** 1 **(e)** -4 and 4 **(f)** $\{x \mid -1 < x < 1\}$

(g)

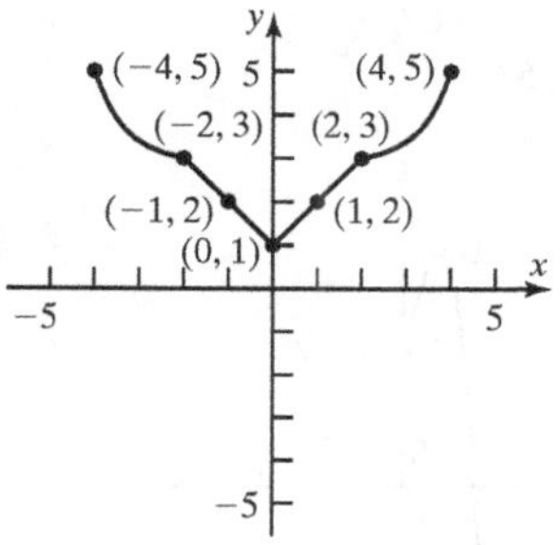

(h)

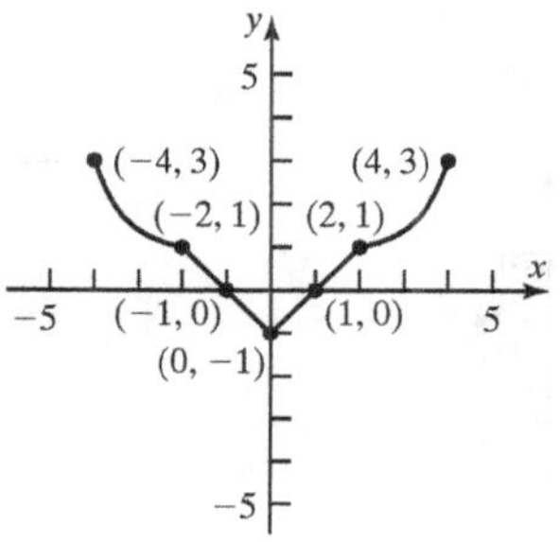

(i)

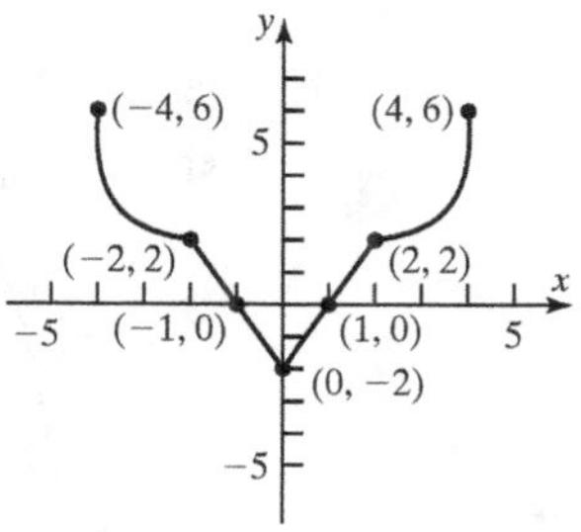

(j) Even **(k)** $(0, 4)$

CHAPTER 4 Polynomial and Rational Functions

4.1 Assess Your Understanding *(page 187)*

5. smooth; continuous **6.** zero or root **7.** touches **8.** T **9.** F **10.** F **11.** Yes; degree 3 **13.** Yes; degree 2 **15.** No; x is raised to the -1 power. **17.** No; x is raised to the $\frac{3}{2}$ power. **19.** Yes; degree 4 **21.** Yes; degree 4

23.

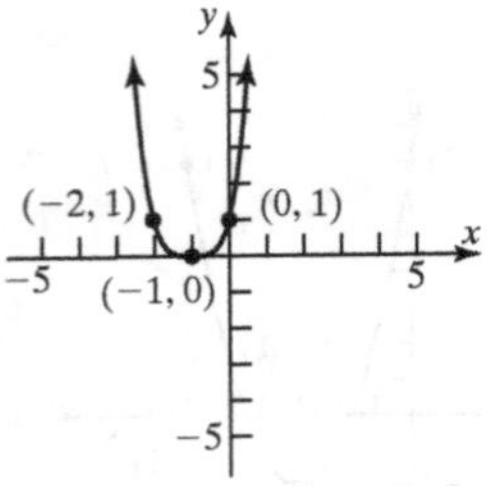

25.

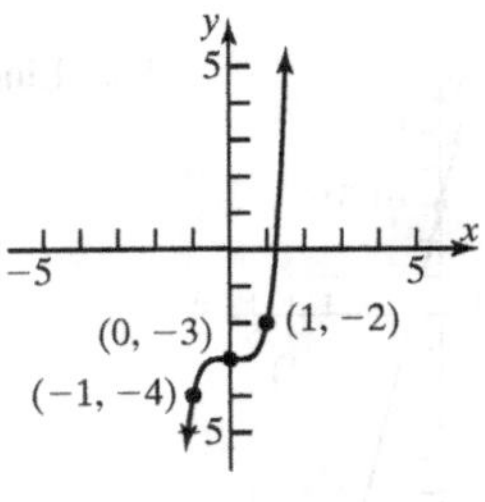

27.

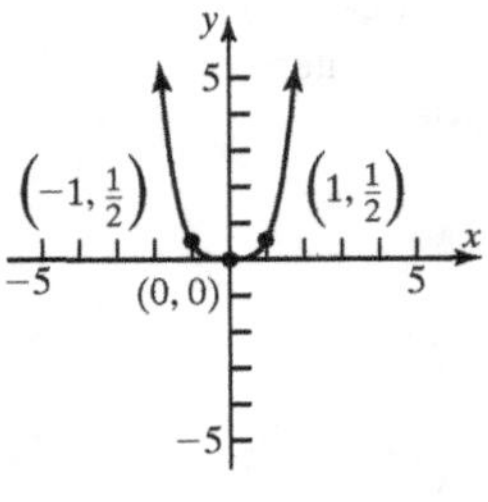

29.

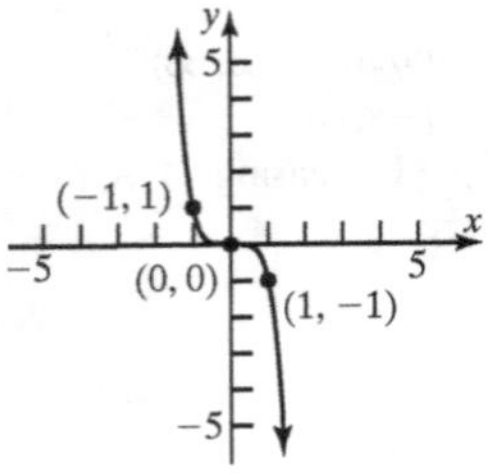

31.

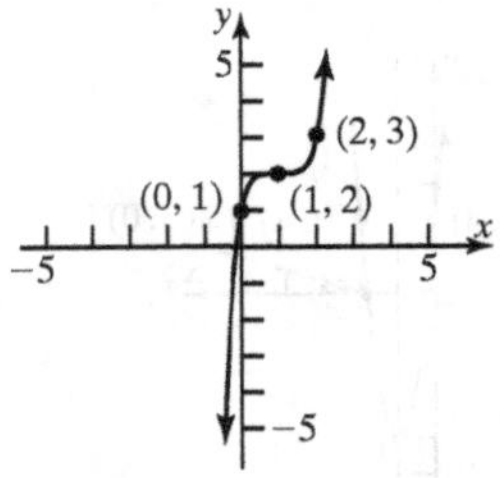

33.

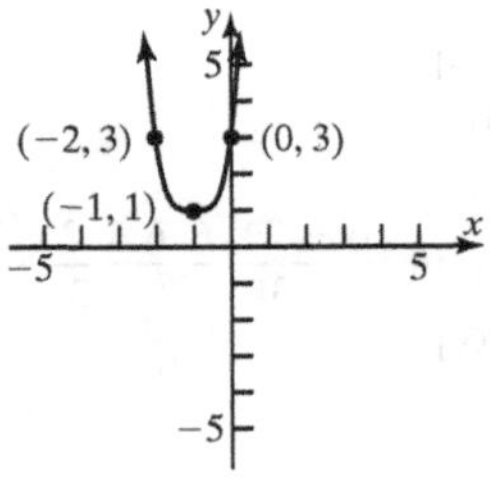

35.

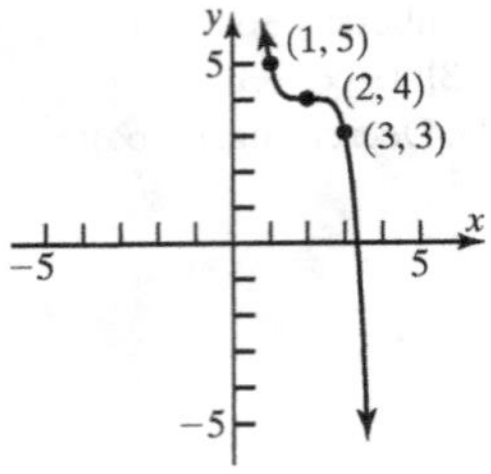

37. $f(x) = x^3 - 3x^2 - x + 3$ for $a = 1$
39. $f(x) = x^3 - x^2 - 12x$ for $a = 1$
41. $f(x) = x^4 - 15x^2 + 10x + 24$ for $a = 1$
43. $f(x) = x^3 - 5x^2 + 3x + 9$ for $a = 1$
45. **(a)** 7, multiplicity 1; −3, multiplicity 2
(b) Graph touches the x-axis at −3 and crosses it at 7.
(c) 2 **(d)** $y = 3x^3$

47. **(a)** 2, multiplicity 3 **(b)** Graph crosses the x-axis at 2 **(c)** 4 **(d)** $y = 4x^5$ **49.** **(a)** $-\frac{1}{2}$, multiplicity 2; −4, multiplicity 3 **(b)** Graph touches the x-axis at $-\frac{1}{2}$ and crosses it at −4. **(c)** 4 **(d)** $y = -2x^5$ **51.** **(a)** 5, multiplicity 3; −4, multiplicity 2 **(b)** Graph touches the x-axis at −4 and crosses it at 5. **(c)** 4 **(d)** $y = x^5$ **53.** **(a)** No real zeros **(b)** Graph neither crosses nor touches the x-axis. **(c)** 5 **(d)** $y = 3x^6$
55. **(a)** 0, multiplicity 2; $-\sqrt{2}$, $\sqrt{2}$, multiplicity 1 **(b)** Graph touches the x-axis at 0 and crosses it at $-\sqrt{2}$ and $\sqrt{2}$. **(c)** 3 **(d)** $y = -2x^4$
57. Could be; zeros: −1, 1, 2; least degree is 3. **59.** Cannot be the graph of a polynomial; gap at $x = -1$ **61.** $f(x) = x(x - 1)(x - 2)$
63. $f(x) = -\frac{1}{2}(x + 1)(x - 1)(x - 2)$

65. Step 1: $y = x^3$
Step 2: x-intercepts: 0, 3; y-intercept: 0
Step 3: 0: multiplicity 2; touches;
3: multiplicity 1; crosses
Step 4:

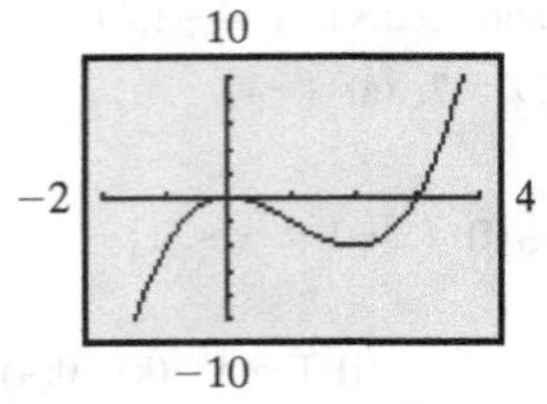

Step 5: (2, −4); (0, 0)
Step 6:

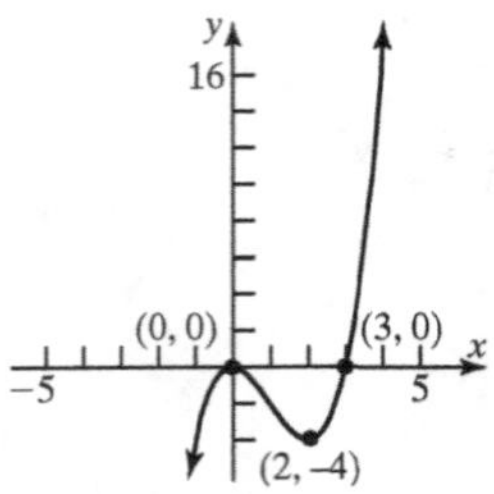

Step 7: Domain: $(-\infty, \infty)$;
Range: $(-\infty, \infty)$
Step 8: Increasing on $(-\infty, 0)$ and $(2, \infty)$
Decreasing on $(0, 2)$

67. Step 1: $y = x^3$
Step 2: x-intercepts: −4, 2
y-intercept: 16
Step 3: −4: multiplicity 1, crosses; 2: multiplicity 2, touches
Step 4:

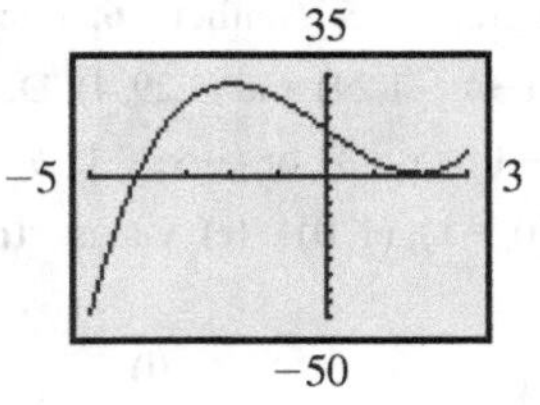

Step 5: (−2, 32); (2, 0)
Step 6:

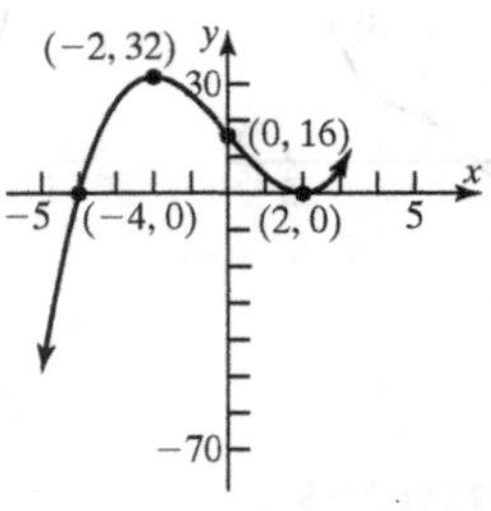

Step 7: Domain: $(-\infty, \infty)$; Range: $(-\infty, \infty)$
Step 8: Increasing on $(-\infty, -2)$ and $(2, \infty)$
Decreasing on $(-2, 2)$

69. Step 1: $y = -2x^4$
Step 2: x-intercepts: −2, 2
y-intercept: 32
Step 3: −2: multiplicity 1, crosses;
2: multiplicity 3, crosses
Step 4:

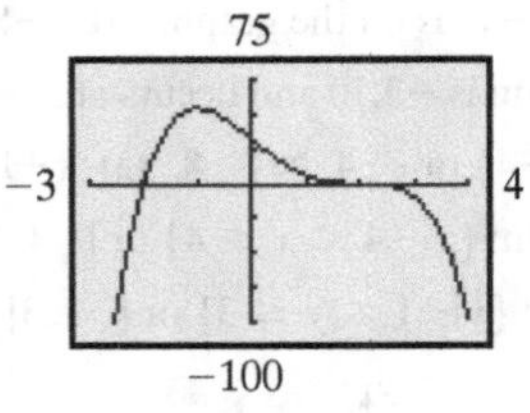

Step 5: (−1, 54)
Step 6:

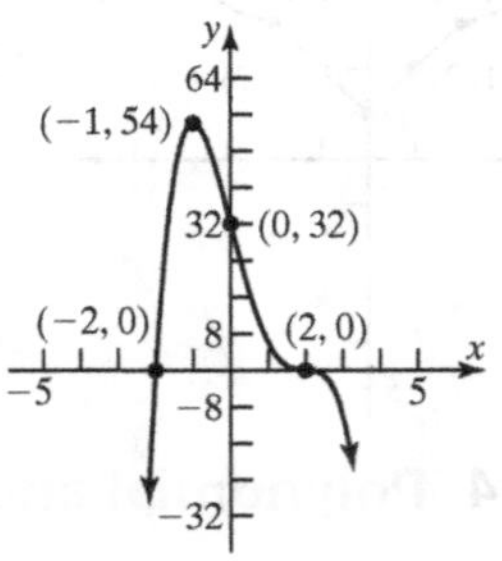

Step 7: Domain: $(-\infty, \infty)$; Range: $(-\infty, 54]$
Step 8: Increasing on $(-\infty, -1)$
Decreasing on $(-1, \infty)$

71. Step 1: $y = x^3$

Step 2: x-intercepts: $-4, -1, 2$ y-intercept: -8
Step 3: $-4, -1, 2$: multiplicity 1, crosses
Step 4:

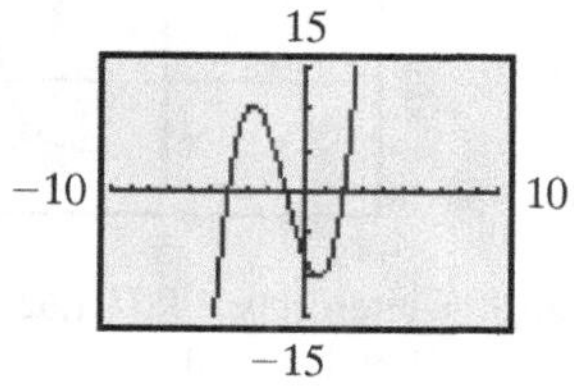

Step 5: $(-2.73, 10.39)$; $(0.73, -10.39)$

Step 6:

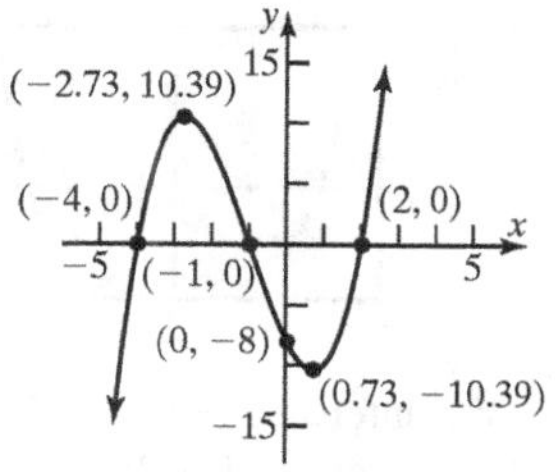

Step 7: Domain: $(-\infty, \infty)$; Range: $(-\infty, \infty)$
Step 8: Increasing on $(-\infty, -2.73)$ and $(0.73, \infty)$
Decreasing on $(-2.73, 0.73)$

73. Step 1: $y = x^4$
Step 2: x-intercepts: $-2, 0, 2$ y-intercept: 0
Step 3: $-2, 2$: multiplicity 1, crosses; 0: multiplicity 2, touches
Step 4:

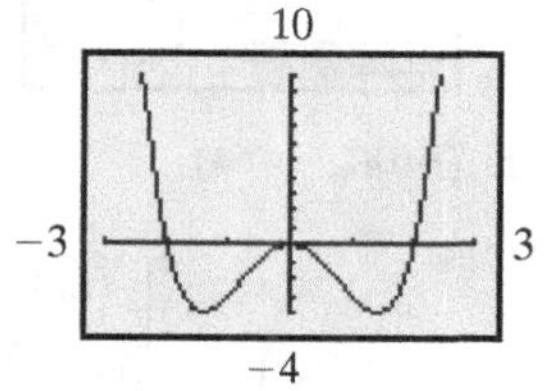

Step 5: $(-1.41, -4)$; $(1.41, -4)$; $(0, 0)$
Step 6:

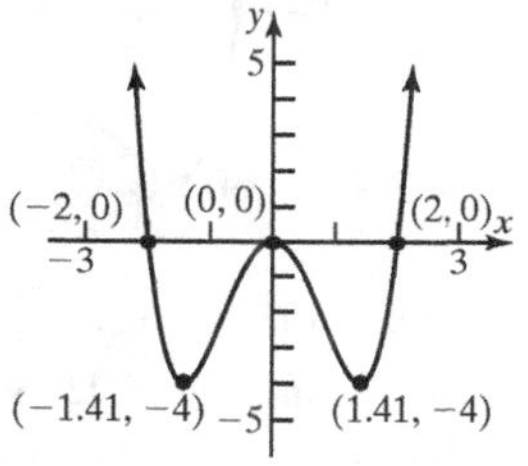

Step 7: Domain: $(-\infty, \infty)$; Range: $[-4, \infty)$
Step 8: Increasing on $(-1.41, 0)$ and $(1.41, \infty)$
Decreasing on $(-\infty, -1.41)$ and $(0, 1.41)$

75. Step 1: $y = x^4$
Step 2: x-intercepts: $-1, 2$ y-intercept: 4
Step 3: $-1, 2$: multiplicity 2, touches
Step 4:

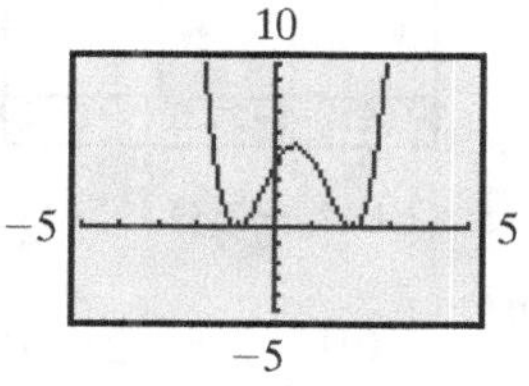

Step 5: $(-1, 0)$; $(2, 0)$; $(0.5, 5.06)$
Step 6:

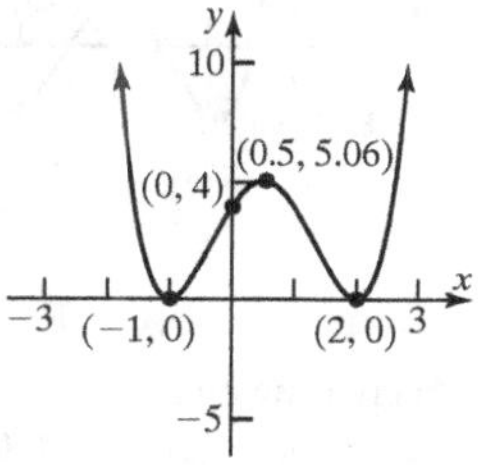

Step 7: Domain: $(-\infty, \infty)$; Range: $[0, \infty)$
Step 8: Increasing on $(-1, 0.5)$ and $(2, \infty)$
Decreasing on $(-\infty, -1)$ and $(0.5, 2)$

77. Step 1: $y = x^4$
Step 2: x-intercepts: $-1, 0, 3$; y-intercept: 0
Step 3: $-1, 3$: multiplicity 1, crosses; 0: multiplicity 2, touches
Step 4:

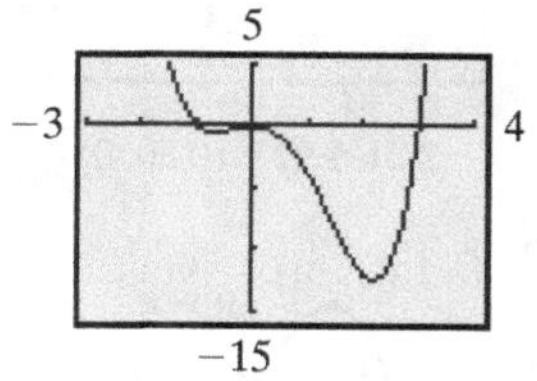

Step 5: $(-0.69, -0.54)$; $(2.19, -12.39)$; $(0, 0)$
Step 6:

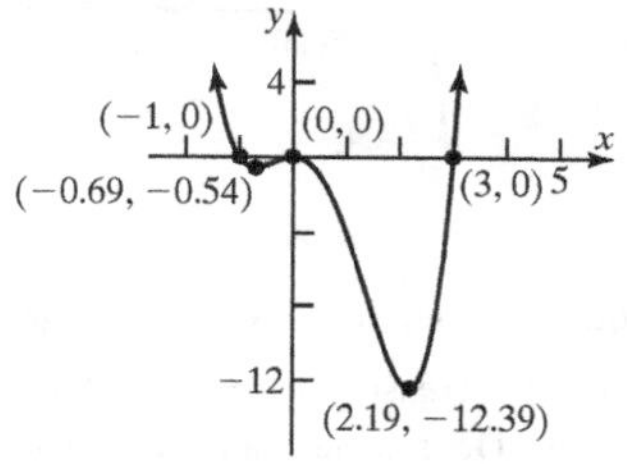

Step 7: Domain: $(-\infty, \infty)$; Range: $[-12.39, \infty)$
Step 8: Increasing on $(-0.69, 0)$ and $(2.19, \infty)$
Decreasing on $(-\infty, -0.69)$ and $(0, 2.19)$

79. Step 1: $y = x^4$
Step 2: x-intercepts: $-2, 4$; y-intercept: 64
Step 3: $-2, 4$: multiplicity 2, touches
Step 4:

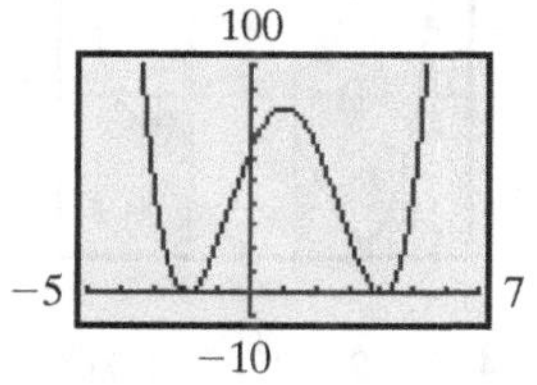

Step 5: $(-2, 0)$; $(4, 0)$; $(1, 81)$
Step 6:

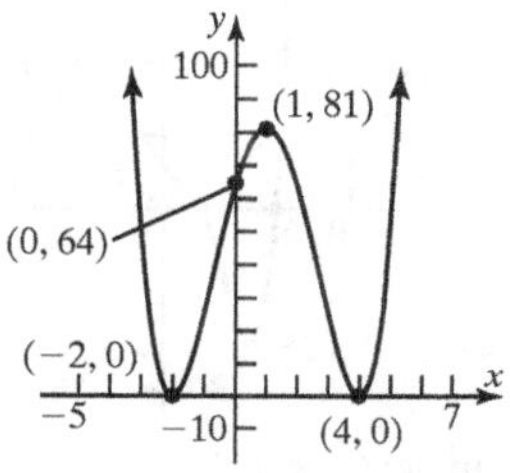

Step 7: Domain: $(-\infty, \infty)$; Range: $[0, \infty)$
Step 8: Increasing on $(-2, 1)$ and $(4, \infty)$
Decreasing on $(-\infty, -2)$ and $(1, 4)$

81. Step 1: $y = x^5$
Step 2: x-intercepts: 0, 2; y-intercept: 0
Step 3: 0: multiplicity 2, touches; 2: multiplicity 1, crosses
Step 4:

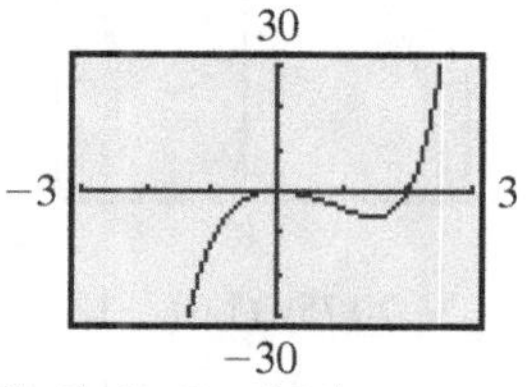

Step 5: $(0, 0)$; $(1.48, -5.91)$
Step 6:

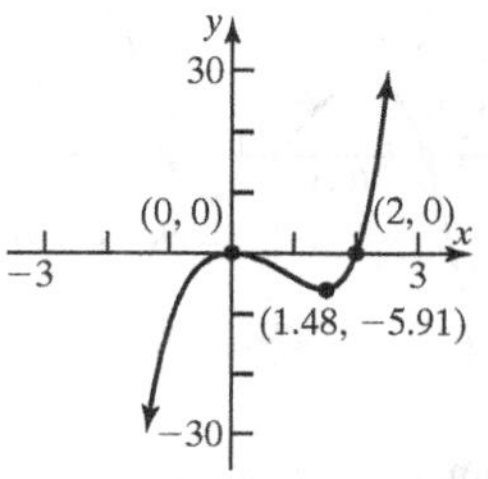

Step 7: Domain: $(-\infty, \infty)$; Range: $(-\infty, \infty)$
Step 8: Increasing on $(-\infty, 0)$ and $(1.48, \infty)$
Decreasing on $(0, 1.48)$

83. Step 1: $y = x^3$
Step 2:

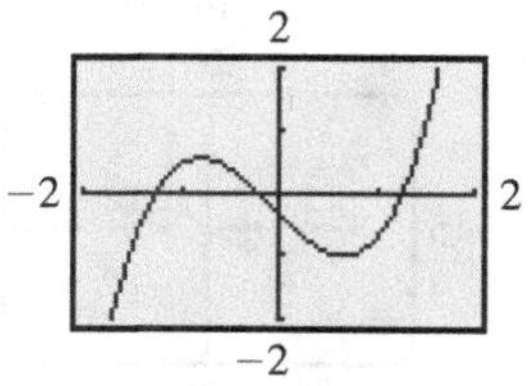

Step 3: x-intercepts: $-1.26, -0.20, 1.26$
y-intercept: -0.31752

Step 4:

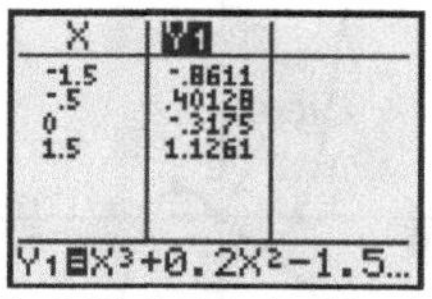

Step 5: $(-0.80, 0.57)$; $(0.66, -0.99)$
Step 6:

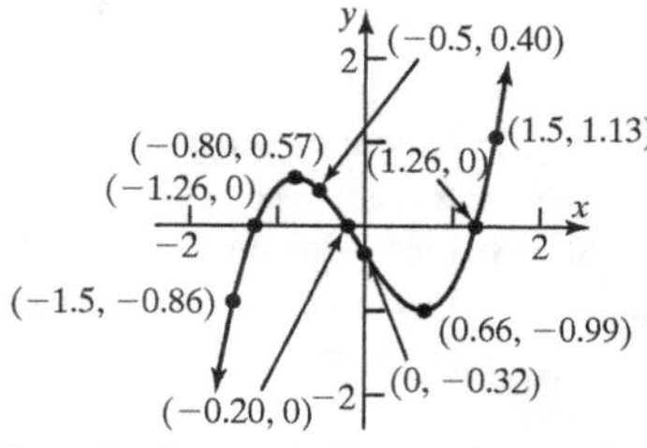

Step 7: Domain: $(-\infty, \infty)$; Range: $(-\infty, \infty)$
Step 8: Increasing on $(-\infty, -0.80)$ and $(0.66, \infty)$
Decreasing on $(-0.80, 0.66)$

85. Step 1: $y = x^3$

Step 2:

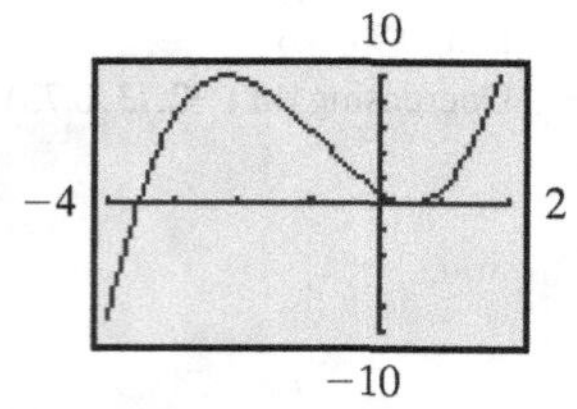

Step 3: x-intercepts: −3.56, 0.50
y-intercept: 0.89

Step 4:

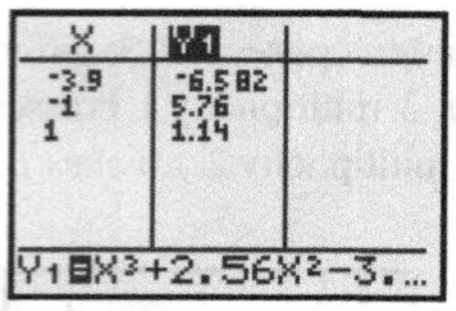

Step 5: (−2.21, 9.91); (0.50, 0)

Step 6:

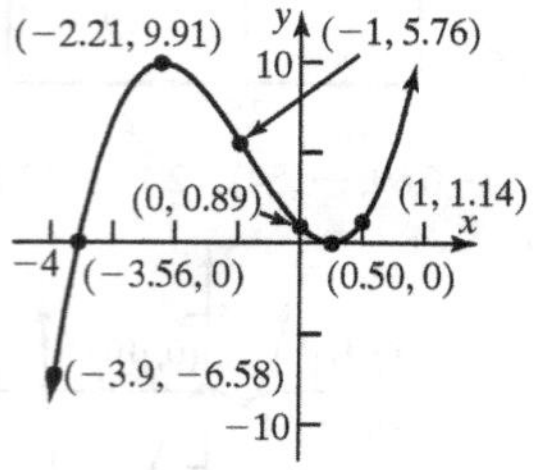

Step 7: Domain: $(-\infty, \infty)$; Range: $(-\infty, \infty)$

Step 8: Increasing on $(-\infty, -2.21)$ and $(0.50, \infty)$
Decreasing on $(-2.21, 0.50)$

87. Step 1: $y = x^3$

Step 2:

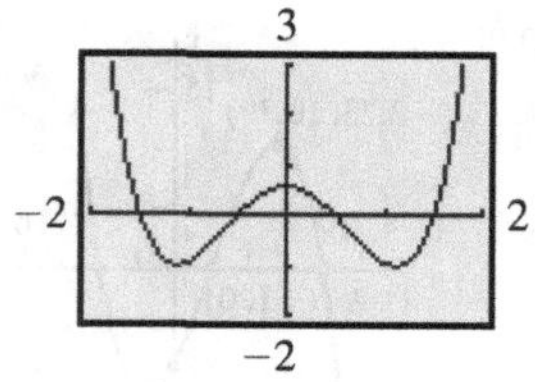

Step 3: x-intercepts: −1.5, −0.5, 0.5, 1.5
y-intercept: 0.5625

Step 4:

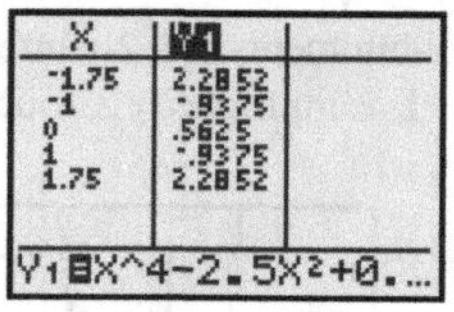

Step 5: (−1.12, −1); (1.12, −1); (0, 0.56)

Step 6:

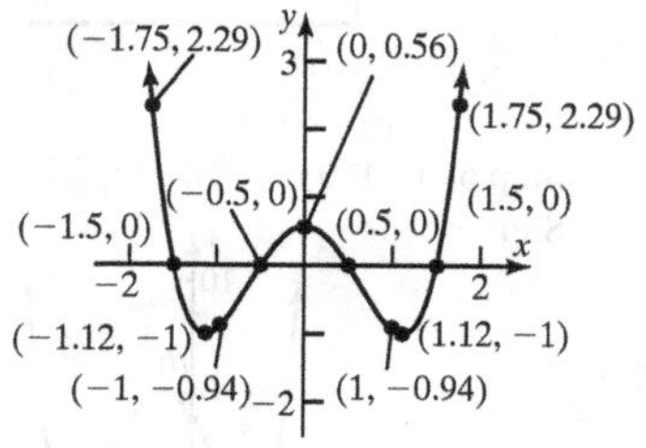

Step 7: Domain: $(-\infty, \infty)$; Range: $[-1, \infty)$

Step 8: Increasing on $(-1.12, 0)$ and $(1.12, \infty)$
Decreasing on $(-2.21, 0.50)$

89. Step 1: $y = 2x^4$

Step 2:

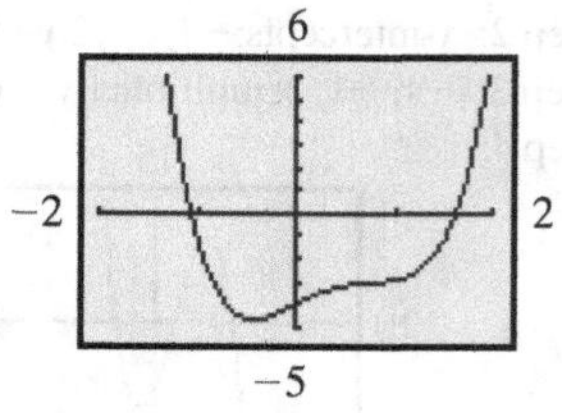

Step 3: x-intercepts: −1.07, 1.62
y-intercept: −4

Step 4:

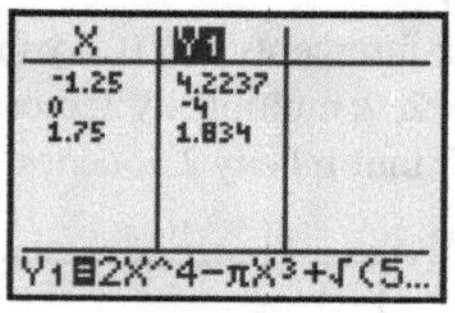

Step 5: (−0.42, −4.64)

Step 6:

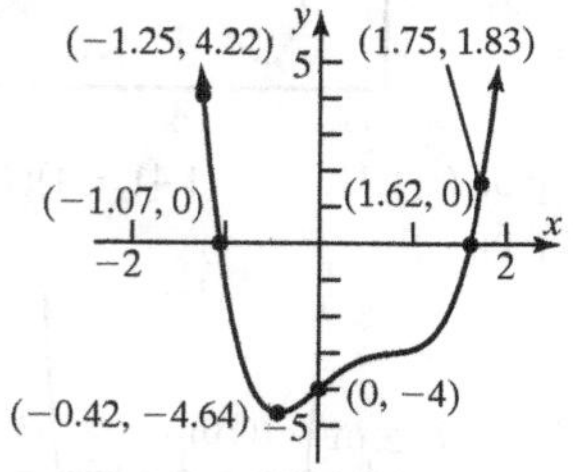

Step 7: Domain: $(-\infty, \infty)$; Range: $[-4.64, \infty)$

Step 8: Increasing on $(-0.42, \infty)$
Decreasing on $(-\infty, -0.42)$

91. $f(x) = -x(x + 2)(x - 2)$

Step 1: $y = -x^3$

Step 2: x-intercepts: −2, 0, 2; y-intercept: 0

Step 3: −2, 0, 2: multiplicity 1, crosses

Step 4:

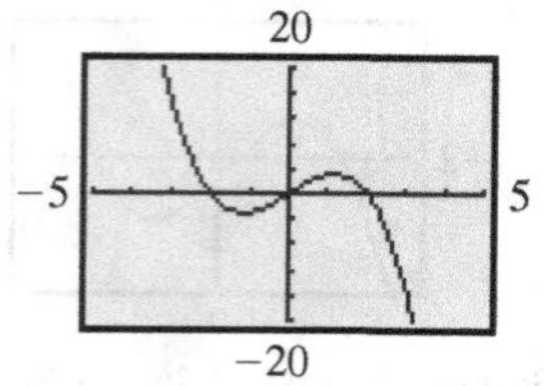

Step 5: (−1.15, −3.08); (1.15, 3.08)

Step 6:

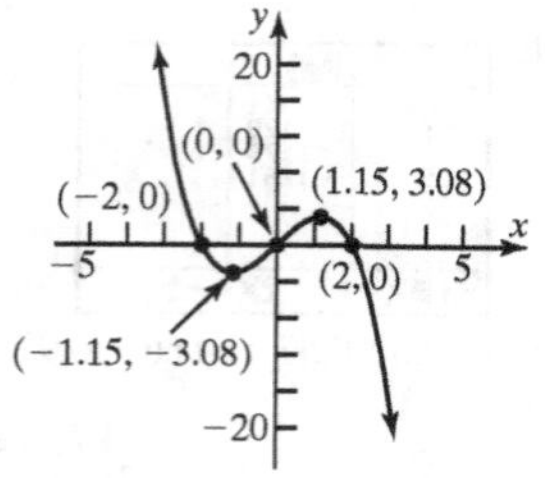

Step 7: Domain: $(-\infty, \infty)$;
Range: $(-\infty, \infty)$

Step 8: Increasing on $(-1.15, 1.15)$
Decreasing on $(-\infty, -1.15)$ and $(1.15, \infty)$

93. $f(x) = x(x + 4)(x - 3)$

Step 1: $y = x^3$

Step 2: x-intercepts: −4, 0, 3; y-intercept: 0

Step 3: −4, 0, 3: multiplicity 1, crosses

Step 4:

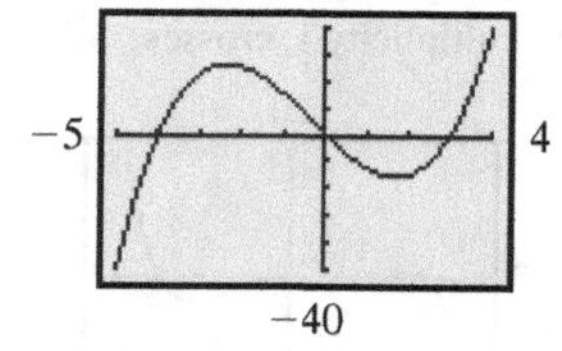

Step 5: (−2.36, 20.75); (1.69, −12.60)

Step 6:

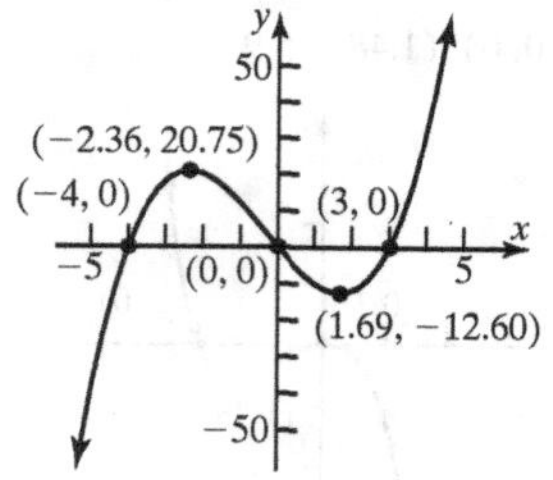

Step 7: Domain: $(-\infty, \infty)$;
Range: $(-\infty, \infty)$

Step 8: Increasing on $(-\infty, -2.36)$ and $(1.69, \infty)$
Decreasing on $(-2.36, 1.69)$

95. $f(x) = 2x(x + 6)(x - 2)(x + 2)$

Step 1: $y = 2x^4$

Step 2: x-intercepts: −6, −2, 0, 2; y-intercept: 0

Step 3: −6, −2, 0, 2: multiplicity 1, crosses

Step 4:

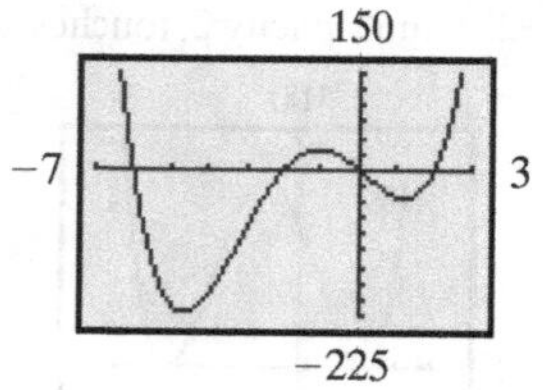

Step 5: (−4.65, −221.25); (−1.06, 30.12); (1.21, −44.25)

Step 6:

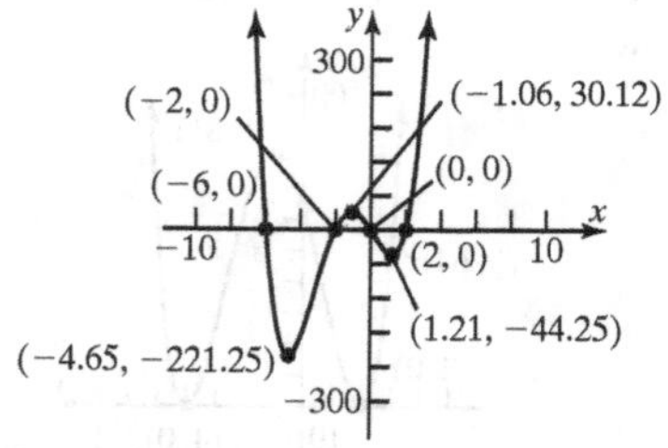

Step 7: Domain: $(-\infty, \infty)$;
Range: $[-221.25, \infty)$

Step 8: Decreasing on $(-\infty, -4.65)$ and $(-1.06, 1.21)$ and $(-1.06, 1.21)$
Increasing on $(-4.65, -1.06)$ and $(1.21, \infty)$

97. $f(x) = -x^2(x + 1)^2(x - 1)$

Step 1: $y = -x^5$

Step 2: x-intercepts: $-1, 0, 1$; y-intercept: 0

Step 3: 1: multiplicity 1, crosses; $-1, 0$: multiplicity 2, touches

Step 4:

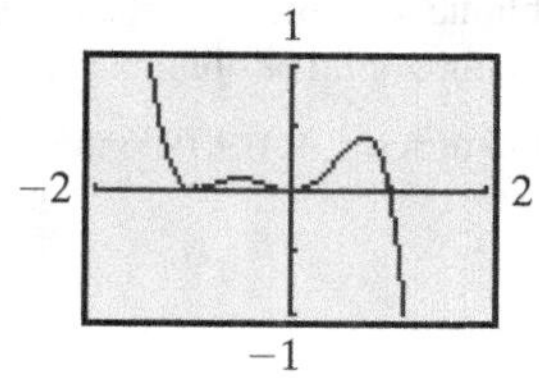

Step 5: $(-1, 0)$; $(-0.54, 0.10)$; $(0, 0)$; $(0.74, 0.43)$

Step 6:

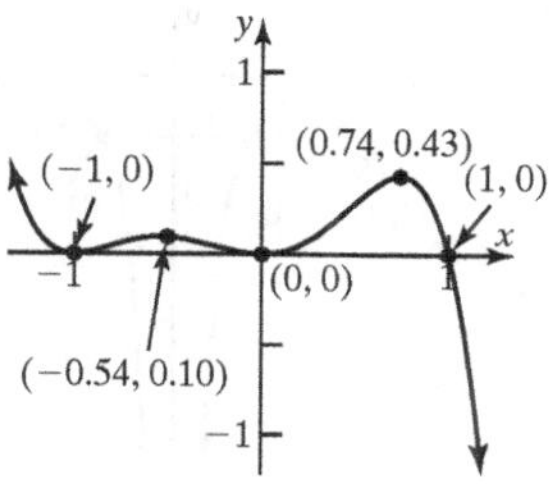

Step 7: Domain: $(-\infty, \infty)$; Range: $(-\infty, \infty)$

Step 8: Increasing on $(-1, -0.54)$ and $(0, 0.74)$
Decreasing on $(-\infty, -1)$, $(-0.54, 0)$ and $(0.74, \infty)$

99. **(a)** $T(r) = \underbrace{500(1 + r)(1 + r)}_{\text{Account value of deposit 1}} + \underbrace{500(1 + r)}_{\text{Account value of deposit 2}} + \underbrace{500}_{\text{Deposit 3}}$

$= 500(1 + 2r + r^2) + 500 + 500r + 500 = 500 + 1000r + 500r^2 + 500 + 500r + 500 = 500r^2 + 1500r + 1500$

(b) \$2155.06

101. **(a)**

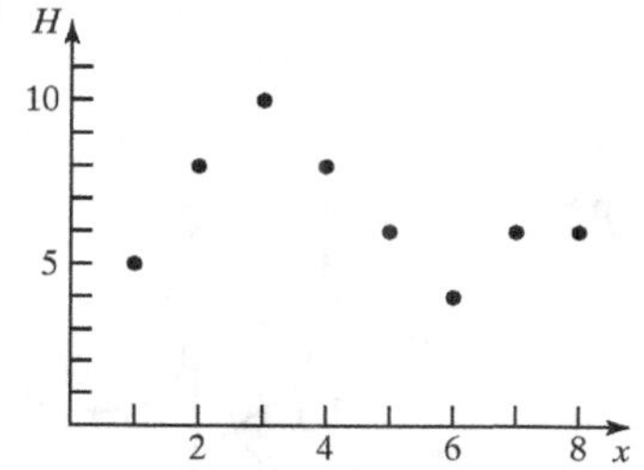

The relation appears to be cubic.

(b) $H(x) = 0.1591x^3 - 2.3203x^2 + 9.3301x - 2.2143$

(c) About 6 major hurricanes

(d)

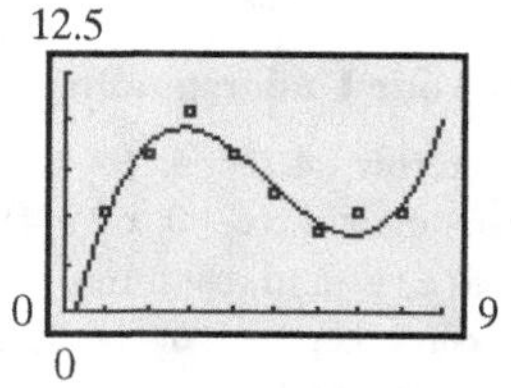

(e) Approximately 10 major hurricanes

103. **(a)**

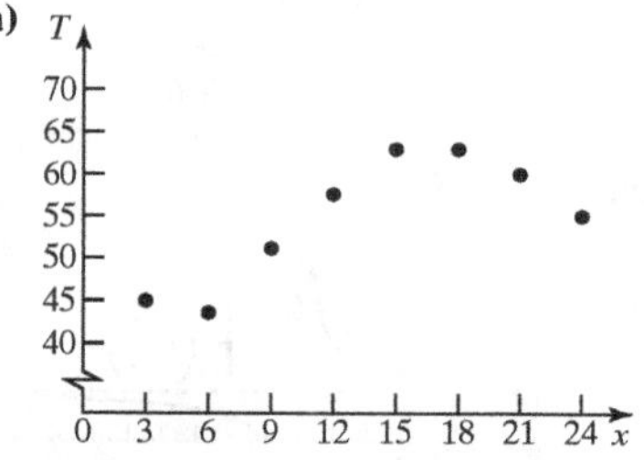

The relation appears to be cubic.

(b) Average rate of change: 2.27° /h

(c) Average rate of change: 0° /h

(d) $T(x) = -0.0103x^3 + 0.3174x^2 - 1.3742x + 45.3929$; The predicted temperature at 5 PM is 63.2°F.

(e)

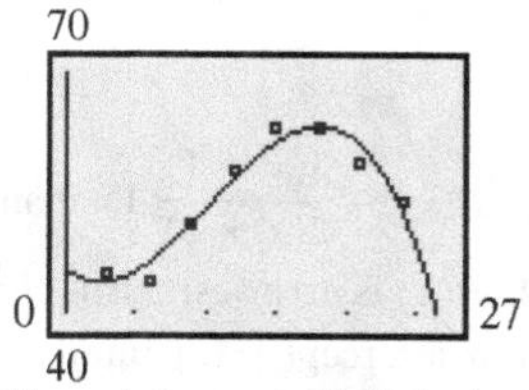

(f) The y-intercept, 45.4°, is the predicted temperature at midnight.

109. (a)–(d)

4.2 Assess Your Understanding *(page 200)*

5. $y = 1$ **6.** $x = -1$ **7.** Proper **8.** F **9.** T **10.** T **11.** All real numbers except 3; $\{x|x \neq 3\}$

13. All real numbers except 2 and -4; $\{x|x \neq 2, x \neq -4\}$ **15.** All real numbers except $-\frac{1}{2}$ and 3; $\left\{x \middle| x \neq -\frac{1}{2}, x \neq 3\right\}$

17. All real numbers except 2; $\{x|x \neq 2\}$ **19.** All real numbers **21.** All real numbers except -3 and 3; $\{x|x \neq -3, x \neq 3\}$

23. **(a)** Domain: $\{x|x \neq 2\}$; Range: $\{y|y \neq 1\}$ **(b)** $(0, 0)$ **(c)** $y = 1$ **(d)** $x = 2$ **(e)** None

25. **(a)** Domain: $\{x|x \neq 0\}$; Range: all real numbers **(b)** $(-1, 0)$, $(1, 0)$ **(c)** None **(d)** $x = 0$ **(e)** $y = 2x$

27. **(a)** Domain: $\{x|x \neq -2, x \neq 2\}$; Range: $\{y|y \leq 0, y > 1\}$ **(b)** $(0, 0)$ **(c)** $y = 1$ **(d)** $x = -2, x = 2$ **(e)** None

29.

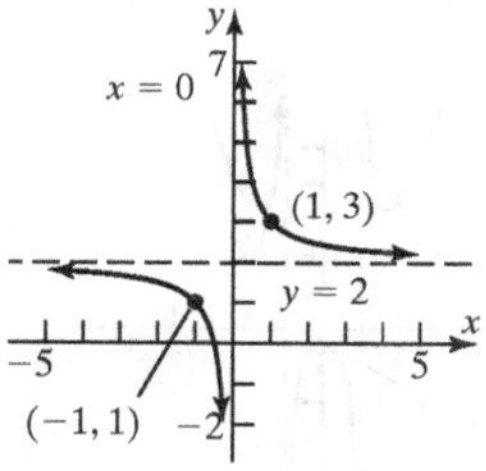

31.

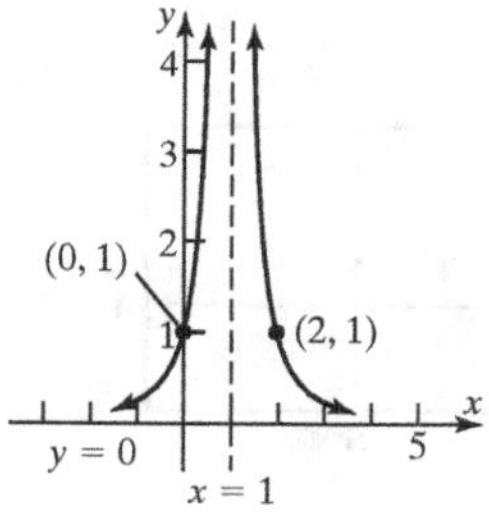

33.

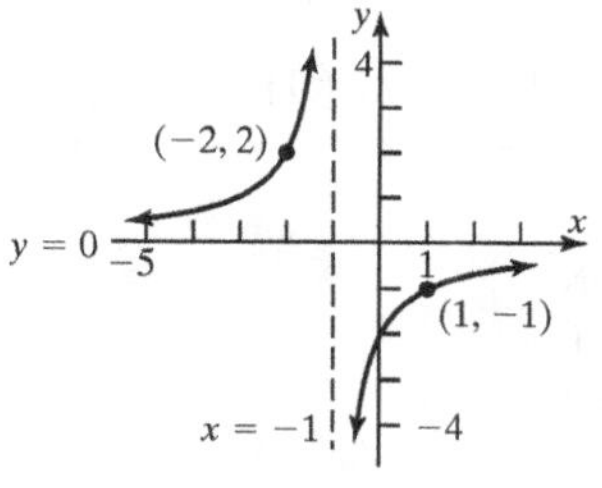

35.

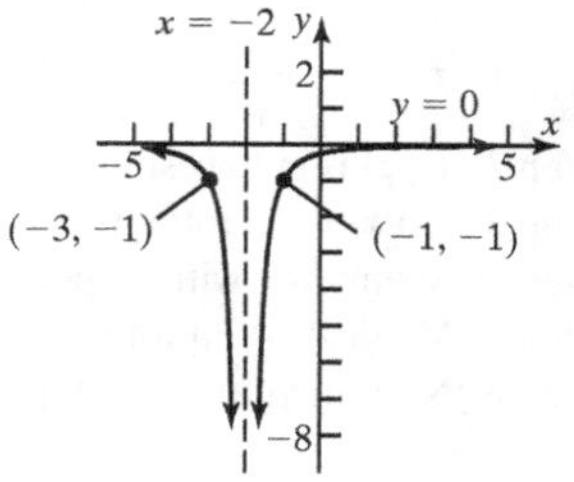

37.

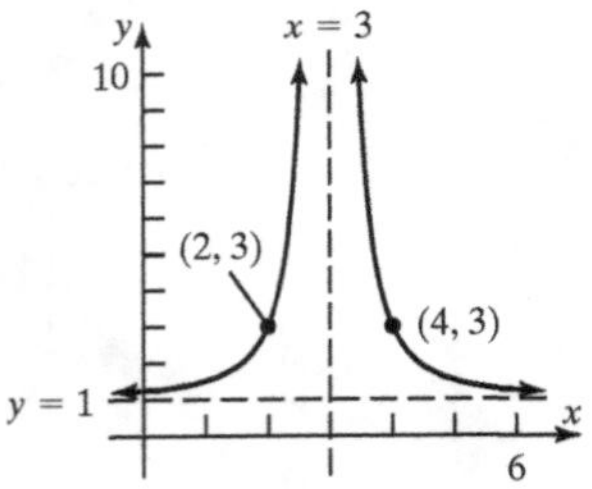

39.

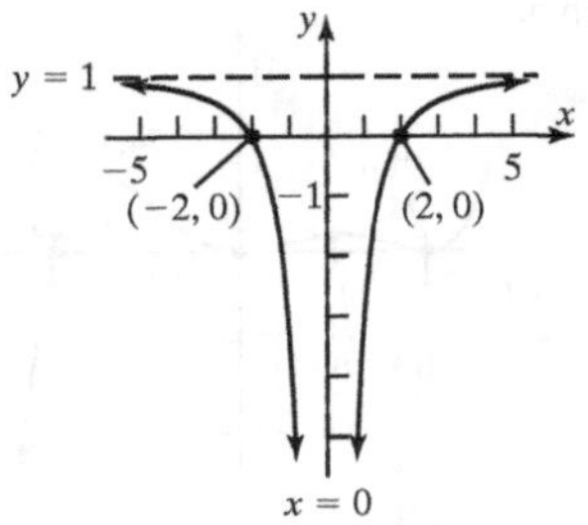

41. Vertical asymptote: $x = -4$; horizontal asymptote: $y = 3$
43. Vertical asymptote: $x = 3$; oblique asymptote: $y = x + 5$
45. Vertical asymptotes: $x = 1$, $x = -1$; horizontal asymptote: $y = 0$
47. Vertical asymptote: $x = -\frac{1}{3}$; horizontal asymptote: $y = \frac{2}{3}$
49. Vertical asymptote: none; oblique asymptote: $y = 2x - 1$
51. Vertical asymptote: $x = 0$; no horizontal or oblique asymptotes
53. **(a)** 9.8208 m/sec^2 **(b)** 9.8195 m/sec^2 **(c)** 9.7936 m/sec^2
(d) h-axis **(e)** $\varnothing$

55. **(a)**

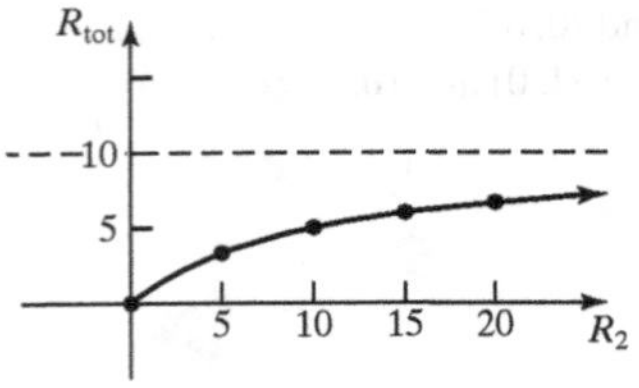

(b) Horizontal: $R_{tot} = 10$; as the resistance of R_2 increases without bound, the total resistance approaches 10 ohms, the resistance R_1.
(c) $R_1 \approx 103.5$ ohms

4.3 Assess Your Understanding *(page 210)*

3. in lowest terms **4.** F **5.** F **6.** T

7. Step 1: Domain: $\{x|x \neq 0, x \neq -4\}$
Step 2: $R(x)$ is in lowest terms.
Step 3: x-intercept: -1; no y-intercept
Step 4: No symmetry
Step 5: Vertical asymptotes: $x = 0$, $x = -4$
Step 6: Horizontal asymptote: $y = 0$, intersected at $(-1, 0)$

Step 7:

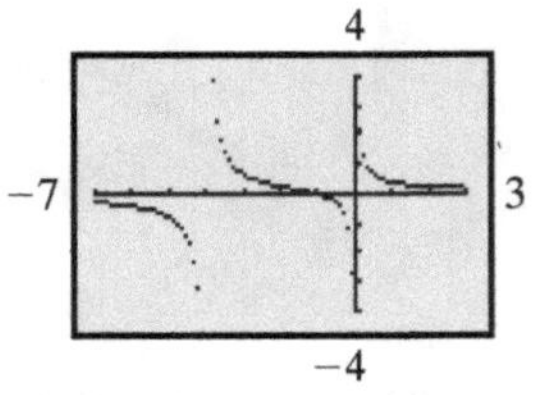

Step 8:

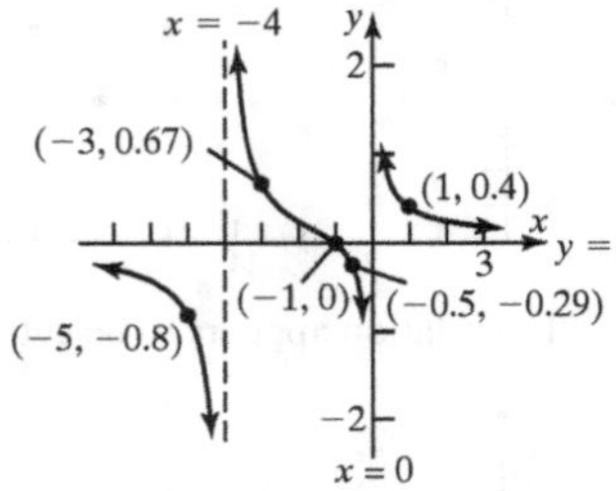

9. Step 1: $R(x) = \frac{3(x + 1)}{2(x + 2)}$; Domain: $\{x|x \neq -2\}$
Step 2: $R(x)$ is in lowest terms.
Step 3: x-intercept: -1; y-intercept: $\frac{3}{4}$
Step 4: No symmetry
Step 5: Vertical asymptote: $x = -2$
Step 6: Horizontal asymptote: $y = \frac{3}{2}$, not intersected

Step 7:

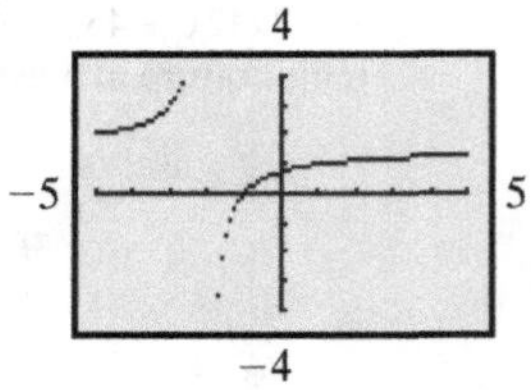

Step 8:

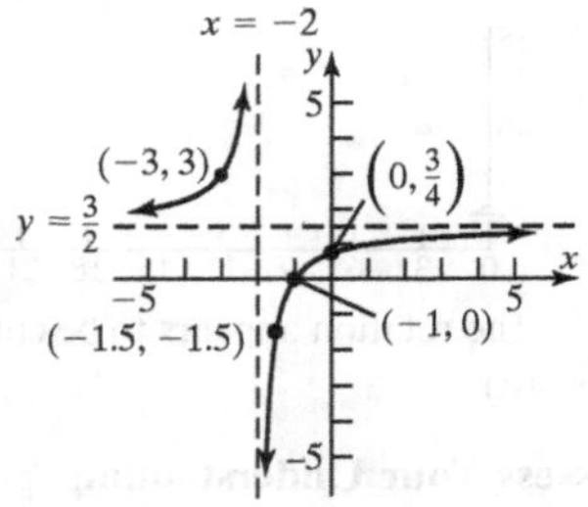

11. Step 1: $R(x) = \frac{3}{(x + 2)(x - 2)}$;
Domain: $\{x|x \neq -2, x \neq 2\}$
Step 2: $R(x)$ is in lowest terms.
Step 3: No x-intercept; y-intercept: $-\frac{3}{4}$
Step 4: Symmetric with respect to the y-axis
Step 5: Vertical asymptotes: $x = 2$, $x = -2$
Step 6: Horizontal asymptote: $y = 0$, not intersected

Step 7:

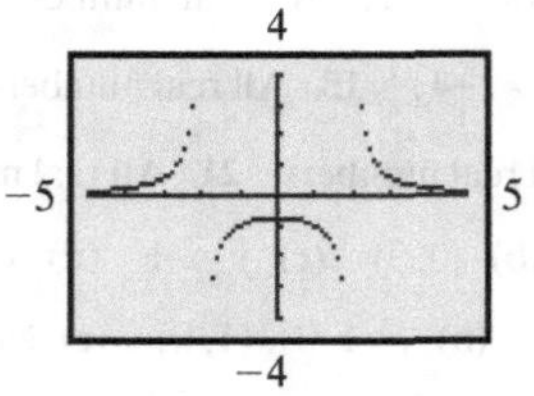

Step 8:

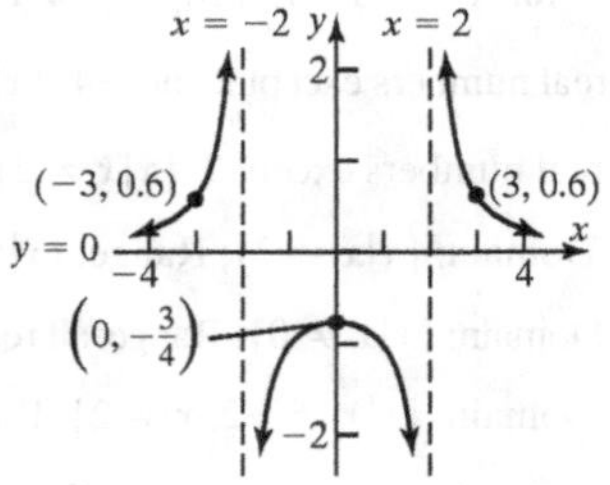

13. Step 1: $P(x) = \frac{x^4 + x^2 + 1}{(x + 1)(x - 1)}$; Domain: $\{x|x \neq -1, x \neq 1\}$
Step 2: $P(x)$ is in lowest terms.
Step 3: No x-intercept; y-intercept: -1
Step 4: Symmetric with respect to the y-axis
Step 5: Vertical asymptotes: $x = -1$, $x = 1$
Step 6: No horizontal or oblique asymptotes

Step 7:

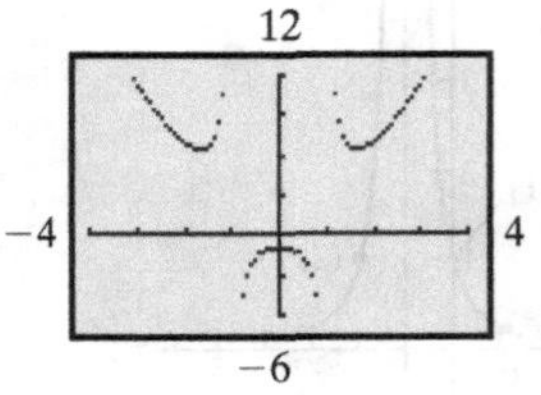

Step 8:

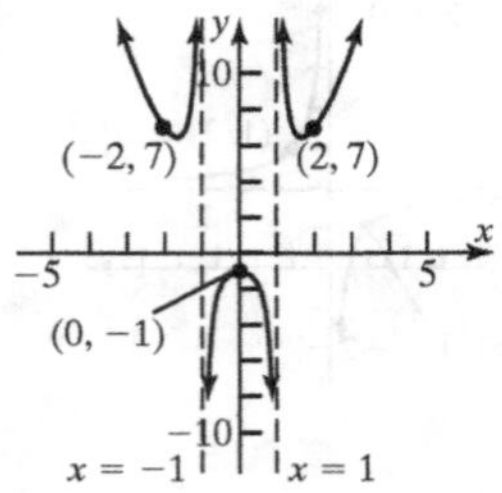

15. Step 1: $H(x) = \dfrac{(x-1)(x^2+x+1)}{(x+3)(x-3)}$;
Domain: $\{x|x \neq -3, x \neq 3\}$
Step 2: $H(x)$ is in lowest terms.
Step 3: x-intercept: 1; y-intercept: $\dfrac{1}{9}$
Step 4: No symmetry
Step 5: Vertical asymptotes: $x = 3$, $x = -3$
Step 6: Oblique asymptote: $y = x$, intersected at $\left(\dfrac{1}{9}, \dfrac{1}{9}\right)$

Step 7:

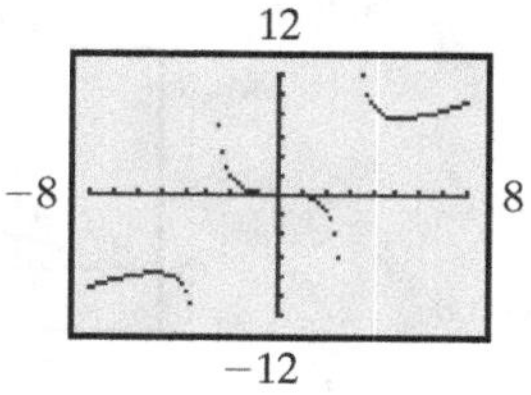

Step 8:

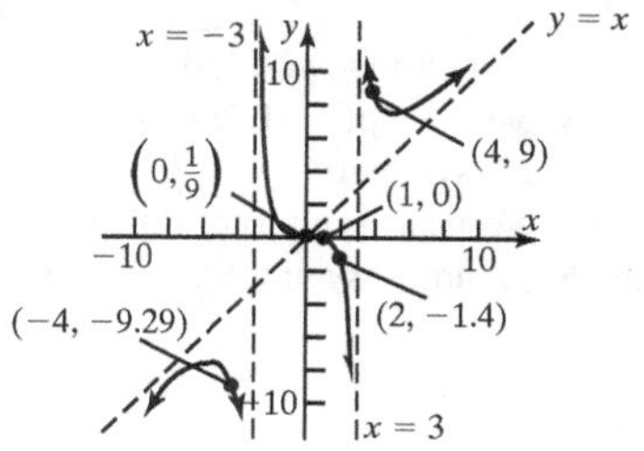

17. Step 1: $R(x) = \dfrac{x^2}{(x+3)(x-2)}$;
Domain: $\{x \neq -3, x \neq 2\}$
Step 2: $R(x)$ is in lowest terms.
Step 3: Intercept: (0, 0)
Step 4: No symmetry
Step 5: Vertical asymptotes: $x = 2$, $x = -3$
Step 6: Horizontal asymptote: $y = 1$, intersected at (6, 1)

Step 7:

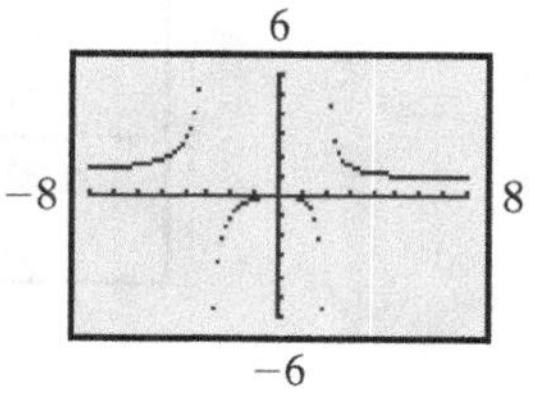

Step 8:

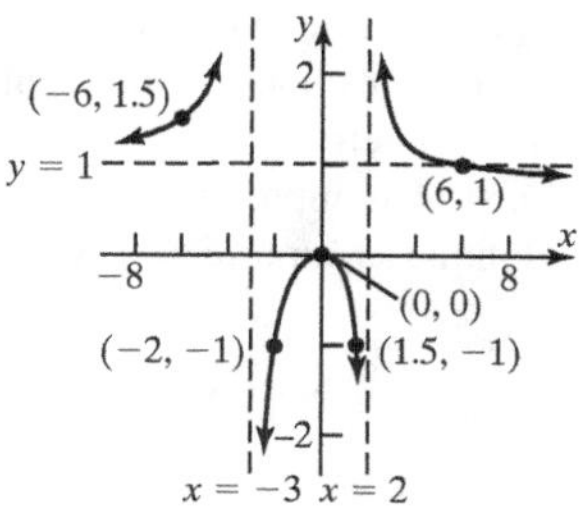

19. Step 1: $G(x) = \dfrac{x}{(x+2)(x-2)}$; Domain: $\{x|x \neq -2, x \neq 2\}$
Step 2: $G(x)$ is in lowest terms.
Step 3: Intercept: (0, 0)
Step 4: Symmetry with respect to the origin
Step 5: Vertical asymptotes: $x = -2$, $x = 2$
Step 6: Horizontal asymptote: $y = 0$, intersected at (0, 0)

Step 7:

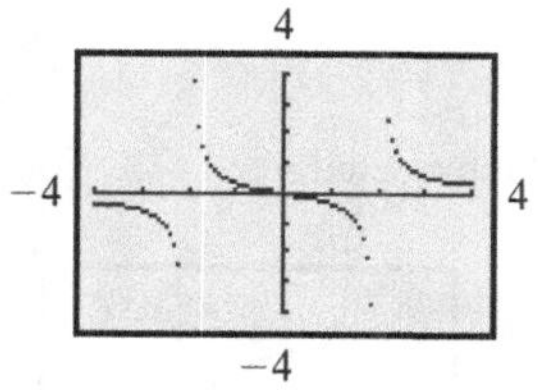

Step 8:

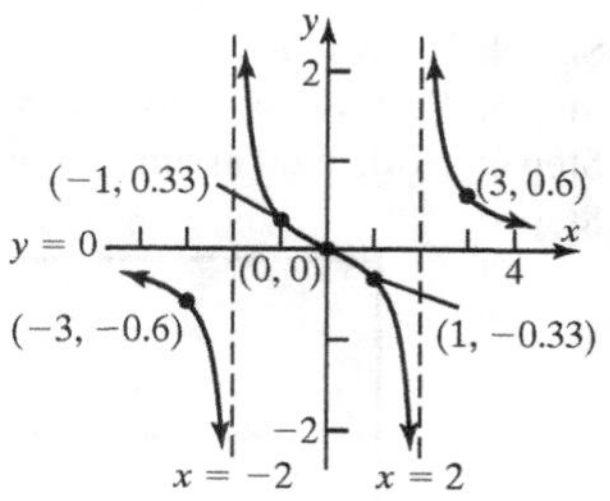

21. Step 1: $R(x) = \dfrac{3}{(x-1)(x-2)(x+2)}$;
Domain: $\{x|x \neq 1, x \neq -2, x \neq 2\}$
Step 2: $R(x)$ is in lowest terms.
Step 3: No x-intercept; y-intercept: $\dfrac{3}{4}$
Step 4: No symmetry
Step 5: Vertical asymptotes: $x = -2$, $x = 1$, $x = 2$
Step 6: Horizontal asymptote: $y = 0$, not intersected

Step 7:

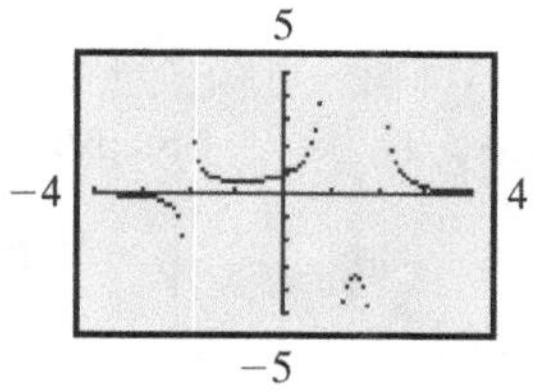

Step 8:

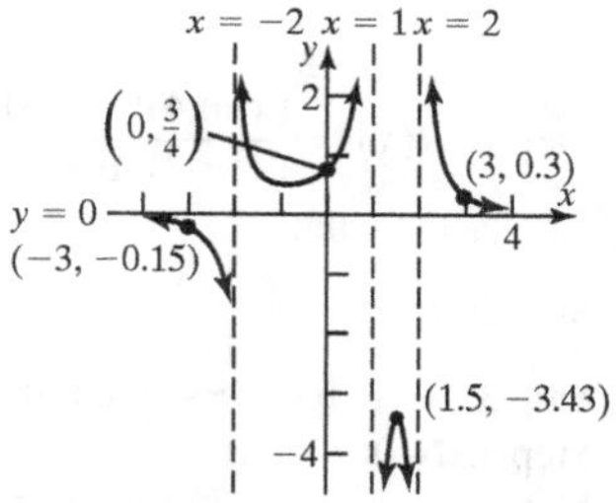

23. Step 1: $H(x) = \dfrac{4(x+1)(x-1)}{(x^2+4)(x+2)(x-2)}$;
Domain: $\{x|x \neq -2, x \neq 2\}$
Step 2: $H(x)$ is in lowest terms.
Step 3: x-intercepts: −1, 1; y-intercept: $\dfrac{1}{4}$
Step 4: Symmetry with respect to the y-axis
Step 5: Vertical asymptotes: $x = -2$, $x = 2$
Step 6: Horizontal asymptote: $y = 0$, intersected at (−1, 0) and (1, 0)

Step 7:

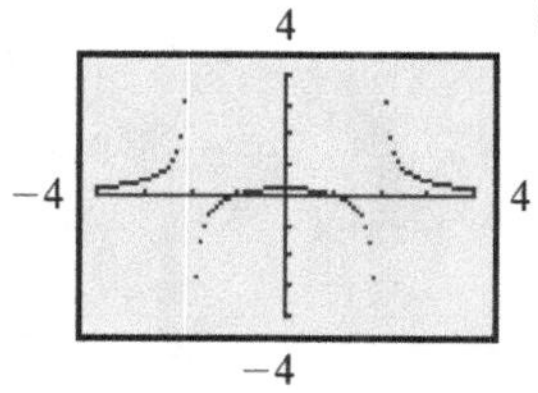

Step 8:

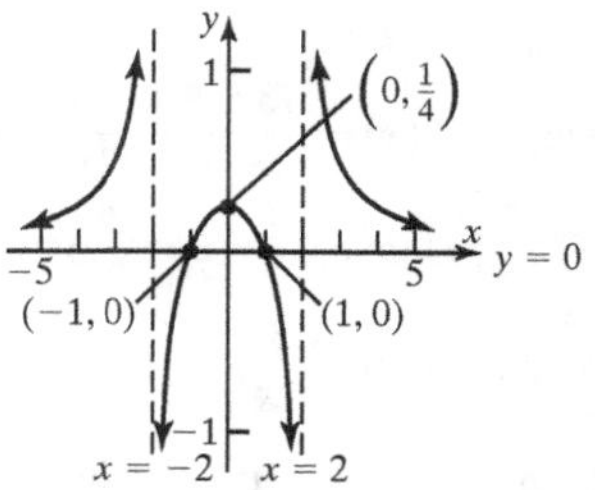

25. Step 1: $F(x) = \dfrac{(x-4)(x+1)}{x+2}$; Domain: $\{x|x \neq -2\}$
Step 2: $F(x)$ is in lowest terms.
Step 3: x-intercepts: −1, 4; y-intercept: −2
Step 4: No symmetry
Step 5: Vertical asymptote: $x = -2$
Step 6: Oblique asymptote: $y = x - 5$, not intersected

Step 7:

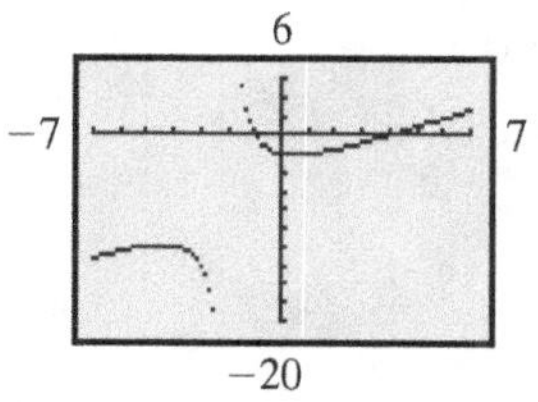

Step 8:

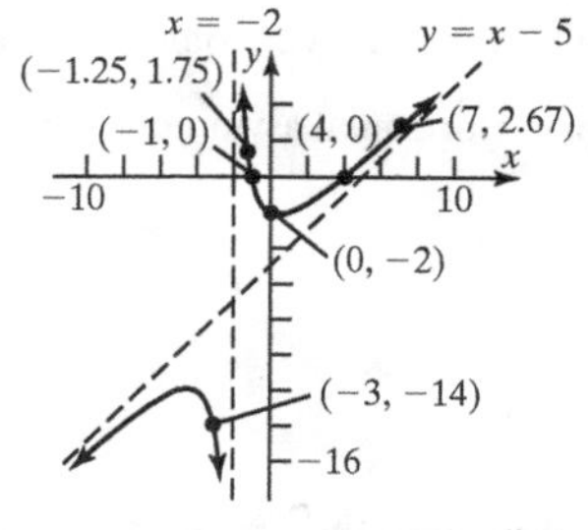

27. Step 1: $R(x) = \dfrac{(x+4)(x-3)}{x-4}$; Domain: $\{x \mid x \neq 4\}$
Step 2: $R(x)$ is in lowest terms.
Step 3: x-intercepts: $-4, 3$; y-intercept: 3
Step 4: No symmetry
Step 5: Vertical asymptote: $x = 4$
Step 6: Oblique asymptote: $y = x + 5$, not intersected

Step 7:

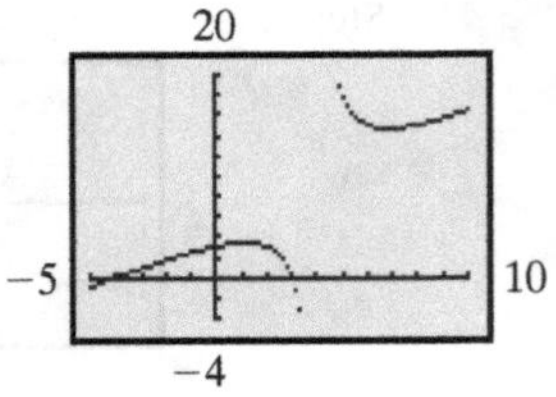

Step 8.

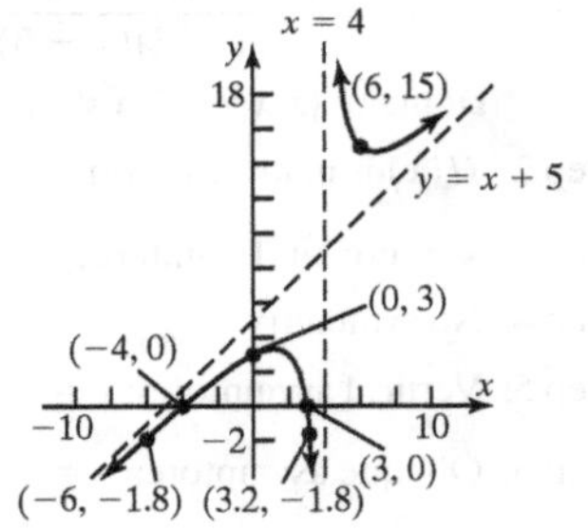

29. Step 1: $F(x) = \dfrac{(x+4)(x-3)}{x+2}$; Domain: $\{x \mid x \neq -2\}$
Step 2: $F(x)$ is in lowest terms.
Step 3: x-intercepts: $-4, 3$; y-intercept: -6
Step 4: No symmetry
Step 5: Vertical asymptote: $x = -2$
Step 6: Oblique asymptote: $y = x - 1$, not intersected

Step 7:

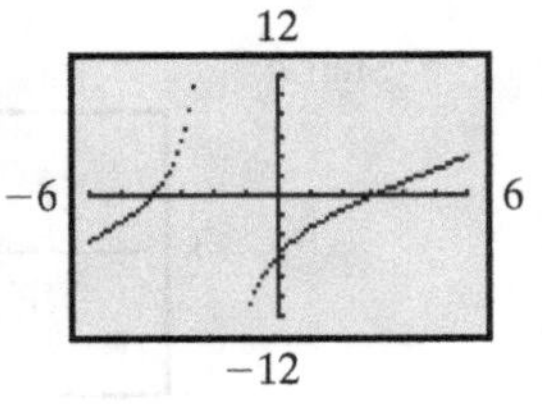

Step 8:

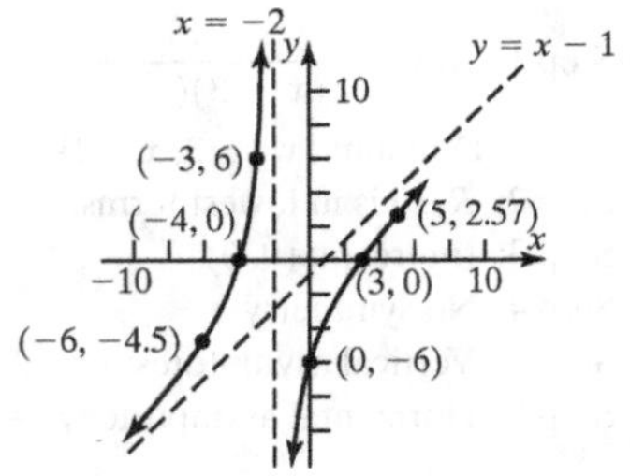

31. Step 1: Domain: $\{x \mid x \neq -3\}$
Step 2: $R(x)$ is in lowest terms.
Step 3: x-intercepts: 0, 1; y-intercept: 0
Step 4: No symmetry
Step 5: Vertical asymptote: $x = -3$
Step 6: Horizontal asymptote: $y = 1$, not intersected
Step 7:

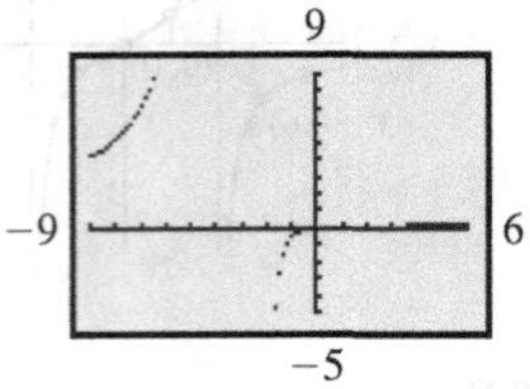

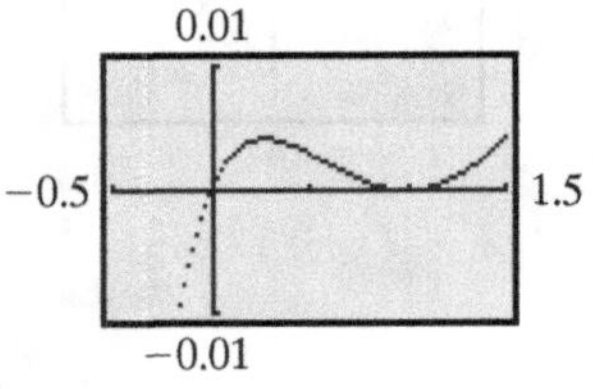

Step 8:

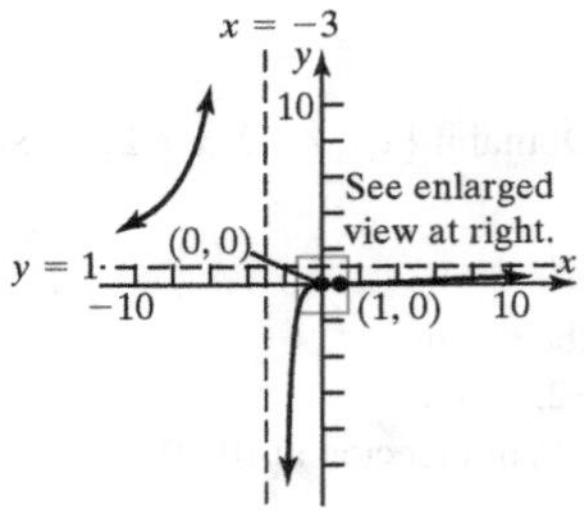

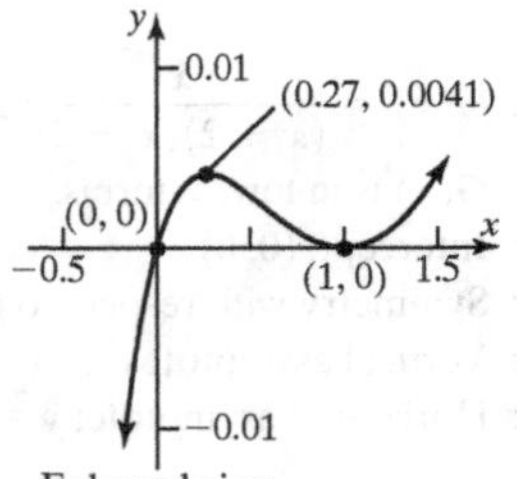

Enlarged view

33. Step 1: $R(x) = \dfrac{(x+4)(x-3)}{(x+2)(x-3)}$;
Domain: $\{x \mid x \neq -2, x \neq 3\}$
Step 2: $R(x) = \dfrac{x+4}{x+2}$
Step 3: x-intercept: -4; y-intercept: 2
Step 4: No symmetry
Step 5: Vertical asymptote: $x = -2$; hole at $\left(3, \dfrac{7}{5}\right)$
Step 6: Horizontal asymptote: $y = 1$, not intersected

Step 7:

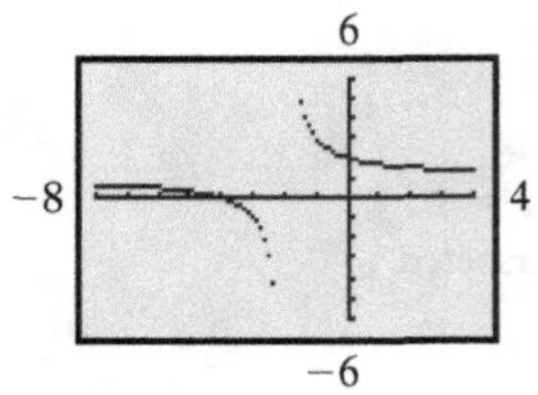

Step 8:

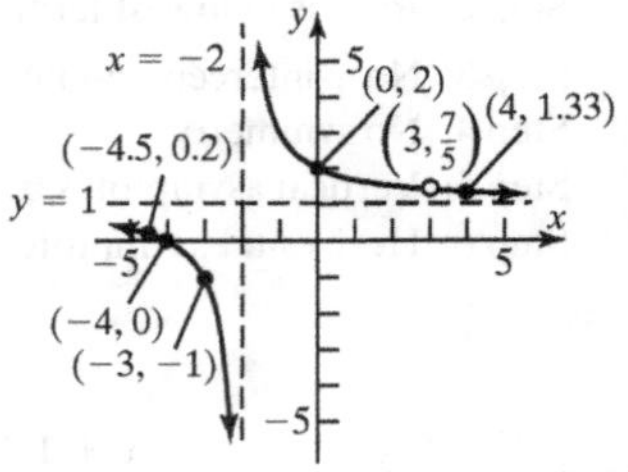

35. Step 1: $R(x) = \dfrac{(3x+1)(2x-3)}{(x-2)(2x-3)}$;
Domain: $\left\{x \,\middle|\, x \neq \dfrac{3}{2}, x \neq 2\right\}$
Step 2: $R(x) = \dfrac{3x+1}{x-2}$
Step 3: x-intercept: $-\dfrac{1}{3}$; y-intercept: $-\dfrac{1}{2}$
Step 4: No symmetry
Step 5: Vertical asymptote: $x = 2$; hole at $\left(\dfrac{3}{2}, -11\right)$
Step 6: Horizontal asymptote: $y = 3$, not intersected

Step 7:

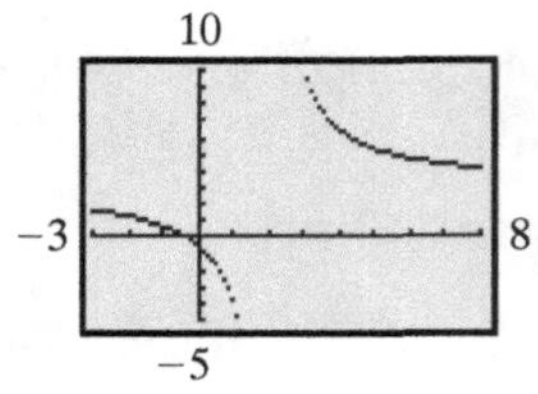

Step 8:

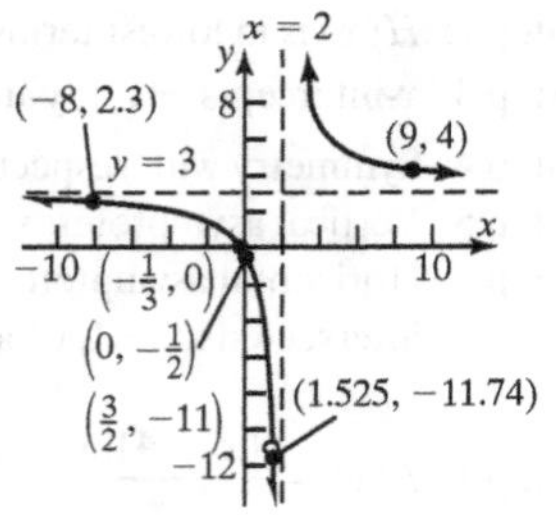

37. Step 1: $R(x) = \dfrac{(x+2)(x+3)}{(x+3)}$; Domain: $\{x \mid x \neq -3\}$
Step 2: $R(x) = x + 2$
Step 3: x-intercept: -2; y-intercept: 2
Step 4: No symmetry
Step 5: Vertical asymptote: none; hole at $(-3, -1)$
Step 6: Oblique asymptote: $y = x + 2$, intersected over entire domain

Step 7:

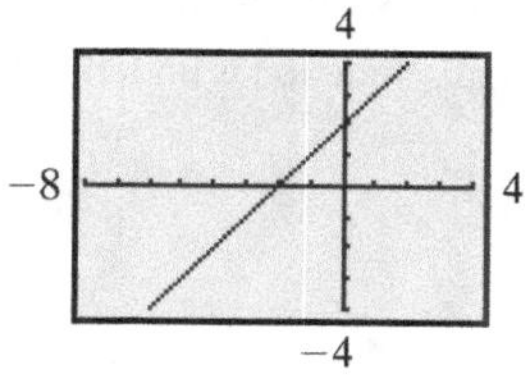

Step 8:

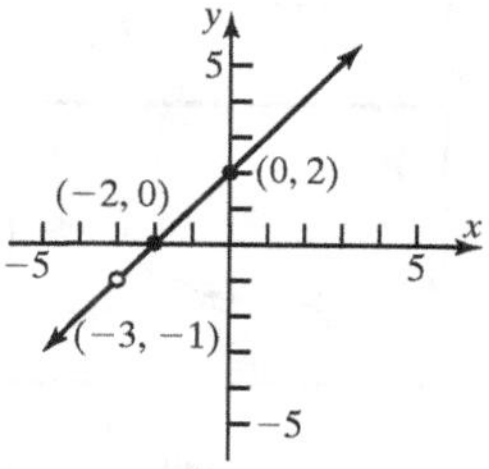

39. Step 1: $f(x) = \dfrac{x^2+1}{x}$; Domain: $\{x \mid x \neq 0\}$
Step 2: $f(x)$ is in lowest terms.
Step 3: No x-intercepts; no y-intercept
Step 4: Symmetric with respect to the origin
Step 5: Vertical asymptote: $x = 0$
Step 6: Oblique asymptote: $y = x$, not intersected

Step 7:

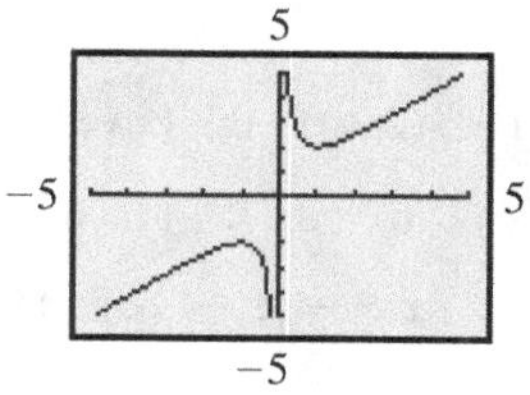

Step 8:

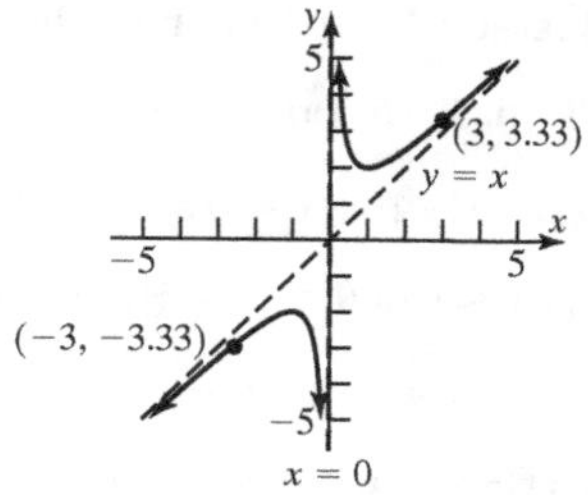

41. Step 1: $f(x) = \dfrac{x^3+1}{x} = \dfrac{(x+1)(x^2-x+1)}{x}$;
Domain: $\{x \mid x \neq 0\}$
Step 2: $f(x)$ is in lowest terms.
Step 3: x-intercept: -1; no y-intercept
Step 4: No symmetry
Step 5: Vertical asymptote: $x = 0$
Step 6: No horizontal or oblique asymptotes

Step 7:

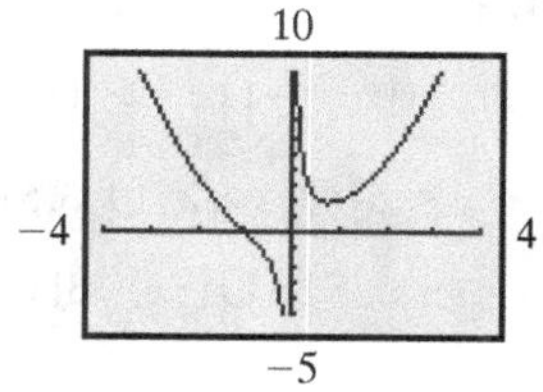

Step 8:

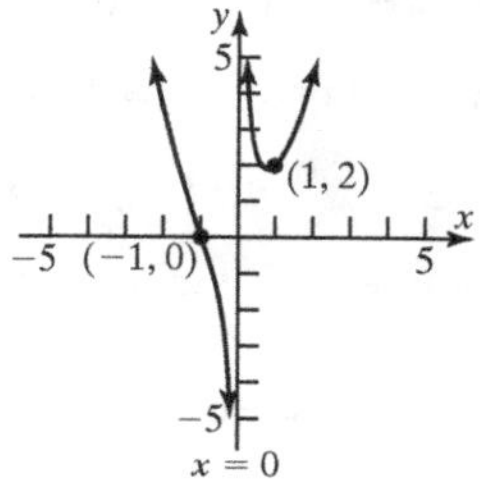

43. Step 1: $f(x) = \dfrac{x^4+1}{x^3}$; Domain: $\{x \mid x \neq 0\}$
Step 2: $f(x)$ is in lowest terms.
Step 3: No x-intercepts; no y-intercept
Step 4: Symmetric with respect to the origin
Step 5: Vertical asymptote: $x = 0$
Step 6: Oblique asymptote: $y = x$, not intersected.

Step 7:

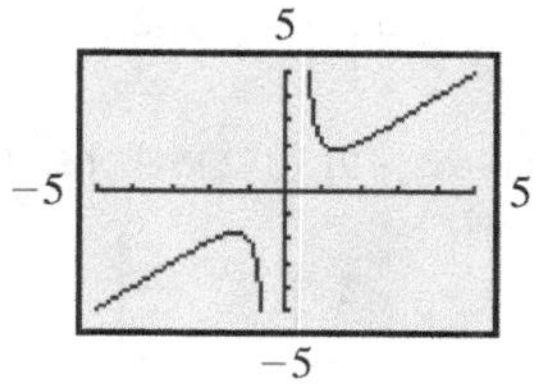

Step 8:

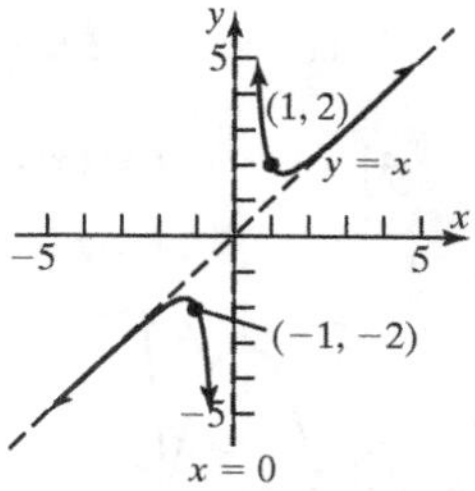

45. Minimum value: 2.00 at $x = 1.00$

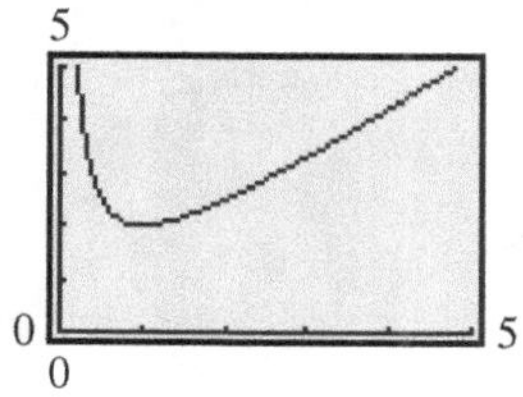

47. Minimum value: 1.89 at $x = 0.79$

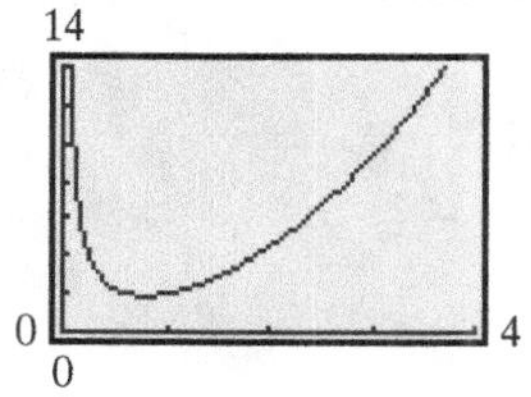

49. Minimum value: 1.75 at $x = 1.32$

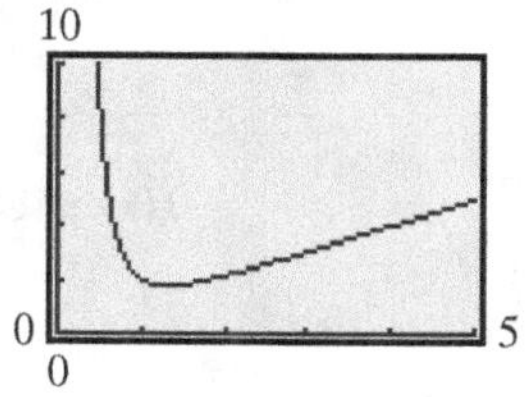

51. One possibility: $R(x) = \dfrac{x^2}{x^2 - 4}$

53. One possibility: $R(x) = \dfrac{(x-1)(x-3)\left(x^2 + \frac{4}{3}\right)}{(x+1)^2(x-2)^2}$

55. **(a)** t-axis; $C(t) \to 0$
(b)

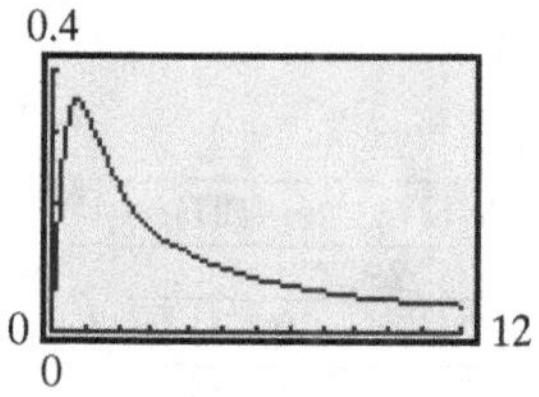

(c) 0.71 h after injection

57. **(a)** $C(x) = 16x + \dfrac{5000}{x} + 100$
(b) $x > 0$
(c)

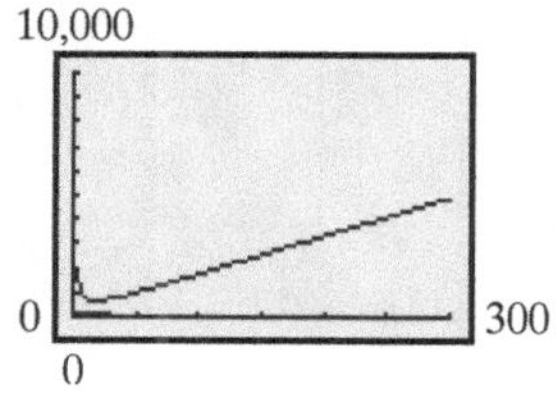

(d) Approximately 17.7 ft by 56.6 ft (longer side parallel to river)

59. **(a)** $S(x) = 2x^2 + \dfrac{40{,}000}{x}$
(b)

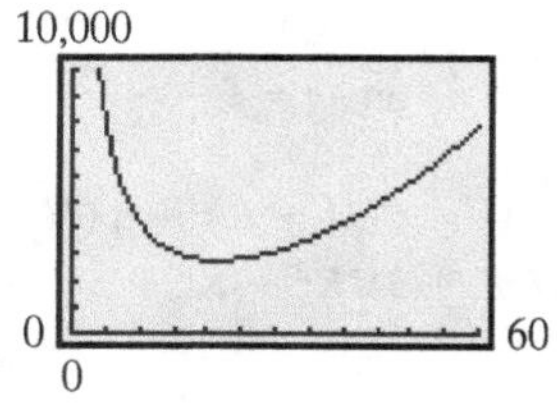

(c) 2784.95 in.^{2}
(d) 21.54 in. × 21.54 in. × 21.54 in.
(e) To minimize the cost of materials needed for construction

61. **(a)** $C(r) = 12\pi r^2 + \dfrac{4000}{r}$

(b)

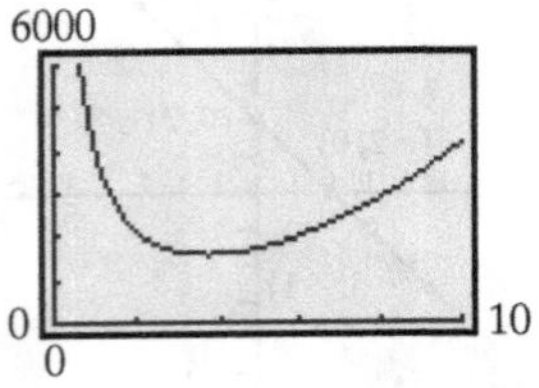

The cost is smallest when $r = 3.76$ cm.

63. No. Each function is a quotient of polynomials, but it is not written in lowest terms Each function is undefined for $x = 1$; each graph has a hole at $x = 1$.

4.4 Assess Your Understanding *(page 217)*

3. T **4.** F **5.** **(a)** $\{x|0 < x < 1 \text{ or } x > 2\}$; $(0, 1) \cup (2, \infty)$ **(b)** $\{x|x \le 0 \text{ or } 1 \le x \le 2\}$; $(-\infty, 0] \cup [1, 2]$

7. **(a)** $\{x|-1 < x < 0 \text{ or } x > 1\}$; $(-1, 0) \cup (1, \infty)$ **(b)** $\{x|x < -1 \text{ or } 0 \le x < 1\}$; $(-\infty, -1) \cup [0, 1)$

9. $\{x|x < 0 \text{ or } 0 < x < 3\}$; $(-\infty, 0) \cup (0, 3)$ **11.** $\{x|x \ge -4\}$; $[-4, \infty)$ **13.** $\{x|x \le -2 \text{ or } x \ge 2\}$; $(-\infty, -2] \cup [2, \infty)$

15. $\{x|-4 < x < -1 \text{ or } x > 0\}$; $(-4, -1) \cup (0, \infty)$ **17.** $\{x|-2 < x \le -1\}$; $(-2, -1]$ **19.** $\{x|x < -2\}$; $(-\infty, -2)$ **21.** $\{x|x > 4\}$; $(4, \infty)$

23. $\{x|-4 < x < 0 \text{ or } x > 0\}$; $(-4, 0) \cup (0, \infty)$ **25.** $\{x|x \le 1 \text{ or } 2 \le x \le 3\}$; $(-\infty, 1] \cup [2, 3]$ **27.** $\{x|-1 < x < 0 \text{ or } x > 3\}$; $(-1, 0) \cup (3, \infty)$

29. $\{x|x < -1 \text{ or } x > 1\}$; $(-\infty, -1) \cup (1, \infty)$ **31.** $\{x|x < -1 \text{ or } x > 1\}$; $(-\infty, -1) \cup (1, \infty)$ **33.** $\{x|x < -1 \text{ or } x > 1\}$; $(-\infty, -1) \cup (1, \infty)$

35. $\{x|x \le -1 \text{ or } 0 < x \le 1\}$; $(-\infty, -1] \cup (0, 1]$ **37.** $\{x|x < -1 \text{ or } x > 1\}$; $(-\infty, -1) \cup (1, \infty)$ **39.** $\{x|x < 2\}$; $(-\infty, 2)$

41. $\{x|-2 < x \le 9\}$; $(-2, 9]$ **43.** $\{x|x < 2 \text{ or } 3 < x < 5\}$; $(-\infty, 2) \cup (3, 5)$

45. $\{x|x < -5 \text{ or } -4 \le x \le -3 \text{ or } x = 0 \text{ or } x > 1\}$; $(-\infty, -5) \cup [-4, -3] \cup \{0\} \cup (1, \infty)$ **47.** $\left\{x\middle|-\dfrac{1}{2} < x < 1 \text{ or } x > 3\right\}$; $\left(-\dfrac{1}{2}, 1\right) \cup (3, \infty)$

49. $\{x|-1 < x < 3 \text{ or } x > 5\}$; $(-1, 3) \cup (5, \infty)$ **51.** $\left\{x\middle|x \le -4 \text{ or } x \ge \dfrac{1}{2}\right\}$; $(-\infty, -4] \cup \left[\dfrac{1}{2}, \infty\right)$ **53.** $\{x|x < 3 \text{ or } x \ge 7\}$; $(-\infty, 3) \cup [7, \infty)$

55. $\{x|x < 2\}$; $(-\infty, 2)$ **57.** $\left\{x\middle|x < -\dfrac{2}{3} \text{ or } 0 < x < \dfrac{3}{2}\right\}$; $\left(-\infty, -\dfrac{2}{3}\right) \cup \left(0, \dfrac{3}{2}\right)$ **59.** $\{x|x \le -3 \text{ or } 0 \le x \le 3\}$; $(-\infty, -3] \cup [0, 3]$

61. $\{x|x > 4\}$; $(4, \infty)$ **63.** $\{x|x \le -2 \text{ or } x \ge 2\}$; $(-\infty, -2] \cup [2, \infty)$ **65.** $\{x|x < -4 \text{ or } x \ge 2\}$; $(-\infty, -4) \cup [2, \infty)$

67.

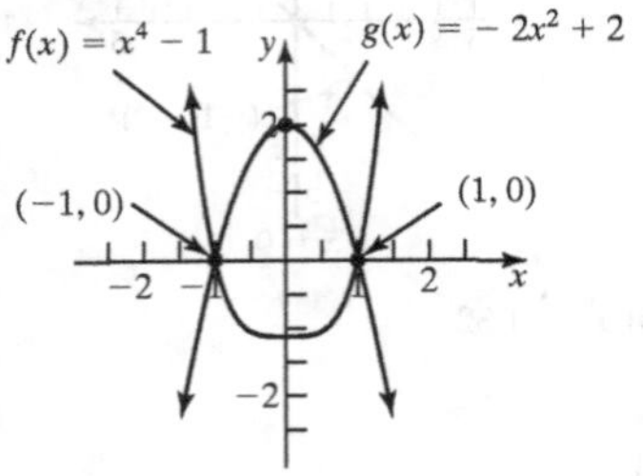

$f(x) \le g(x)$ if $-1 \le x \le 1$

69.

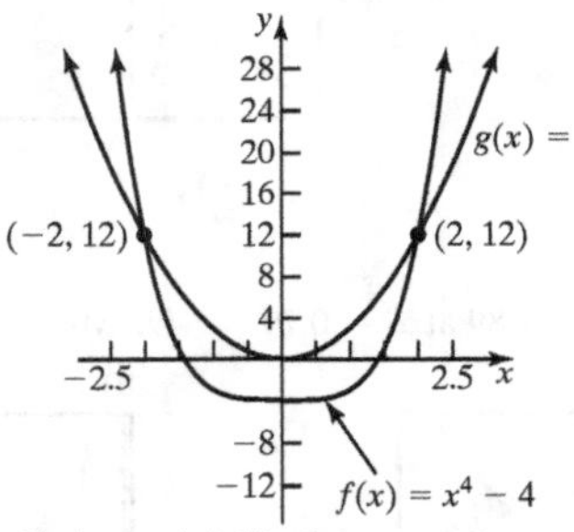

$f(x) \le g(x)$ if $-2 \le x \le 2$

71. Produce at least 250 bicycles

73. **(a)** The stretch is less than 39 ft.

(b) The ledge should be at least 84 ft above the ground for a 150-lb jumper.

75. At least 50 students must attend.

Historical Problems *(page 231)*

1.

$$\left(x - \frac{b}{3}\right)^3 + b\left(x - \frac{b}{3}\right)^2 + c\left(x - \frac{b}{3}\right) + d = 0$$

$$x^3 - bx^2 + \frac{b^2x}{3} - \frac{b^3}{27} + bx^2 - \frac{2b^2x}{3} + \frac{b^3}{9} + cx - \frac{bc}{3} + d = 0$$

$$x^3 + \left(c - \frac{b^2}{3}\right)x + \left(\frac{2b^3}{27} - \frac{bc}{3} + d\right) = 0$$

Let $p = c - \dfrac{b^2}{3}$ and $q = \dfrac{2b^3}{27} - \dfrac{bc}{3} + d$. Then $x^3 + px + q = 0$.

2.

$$(H + K)^3 + p(H + K) + q = 0$$

$$H^3 + 3H^2K + 3HK^2 + K^3 + pH + pK + q = 0$$

Let $3HK = -p$.

$$H^3 - pH - pK + K^3 + pH + pK + q = 0,$$

$$H^3 + K^3 = -q$$

3.

$$3HK = -p$$

$$K = -\frac{p}{3H}$$

$$H^3 + \left(-\frac{p}{3H}\right)^3 = -q$$

$$H^3 - \frac{p^3}{27H^3} = -q$$

$$27H^6 - p^3 = -27qH^3$$

$$27H^6 + 27qH^3 - p^3 = 0$$

$$H^3 = \frac{-27q \pm \sqrt{(27q)^2 - 4(27)(-p^3)}}{2 \cdot 27}$$

$$H^3 = \frac{-q}{2} \pm \sqrt{\frac{27^2q^2}{2^2(27^2)} + \frac{4(27)p^3}{2^2(27^2)}}$$

$$H^3 = \frac{-q}{2} \pm \sqrt{\frac{q^2}{4} + \frac{p^3}{27}}$$

$$H = \sqrt[3]{\frac{-q}{2} + \sqrt{\frac{q^2}{4} + \frac{p^3}{27}}}$$

Choose the positive root for now.

4. $H^3 + K^3 = -q$

$$K^3 = -q - H^3$$
$$K^3 = -q - \left[\frac{-q}{2} + \sqrt{\frac{q^2}{4} + \frac{p^3}{27}}\right]$$
$$K^3 = \frac{-q}{2} - \sqrt{\frac{q^2}{4} + \frac{p^3}{27}}$$
$$K = \sqrt[3]{\frac{-q}{2} - \sqrt{\frac{q^2}{4} + \frac{p^3}{27}}}$$

5. $x = H + K$

$$x = \sqrt[3]{\frac{-q}{2} + \sqrt{\frac{q^2}{4} + \frac{p^3}{27}}} + \sqrt[3]{\frac{-q}{2} - \sqrt{\frac{q^2}{4} + \frac{p^3}{27}}}$$

(Note that had we used the negative root in 3 the result would be the same.)

6. $x = 3$ **7.** $x = 2$ **8.** $x = 2$

4.5 Assess Your Understanding *(page 231)*

5. Remainder; Dividend **6.** $f(c)$ **7.** -4 **8.** F **9.** F **10.** T **11.** $R = f(2) = 8$; no **13.** $R = f(2) = 0$; yes; $f(x) = (x - 2)(3x^3 - 5)$ **15.** $R = f(-3) = 0$; yes; $f(x) = (x + 3)(3x^5 - 9x^4 + 27x^3 + x^2 - 3x + 9)$ **17.** $R = f(-4) = 1$; no **19.** $R = f\left(\frac{1}{2}\right) = 0$; yes; $f(x) = \left(x - \frac{1}{2}\right)(2x^3 + 2)$ **21.** 4; $\pm 1, \pm\frac{1}{3}$ **23.** 5; $\pm 1, \pm 3$ **25.** 3; $\pm 1, \pm 2, \pm\frac{1}{4}, \pm\frac{1}{2}$ **27.** 4; $\pm 1, \pm 3, \pm 9, \pm\frac{1}{2}, \pm\frac{1}{3}, \pm\frac{1}{6}, \pm\frac{3}{2}, \pm\frac{9}{2}$ **29.** 5; $\pm 1, \pm 2, \pm 3, \pm 4, \pm 6, \pm 12, \pm\frac{1}{2}, \pm\frac{3}{2}$ **31.** 4; $\pm 1, \pm 2, \pm 4, \pm 5, \pm 10, \pm 20, \pm\frac{1}{2}, \pm\frac{5}{2}, \pm\frac{1}{3}, \pm\frac{2}{3}, \pm\frac{4}{3}, \pm\frac{5}{3}, \pm\frac{10}{3}, \pm\frac{20}{3}, \pm\frac{1}{6}, \pm\frac{5}{6}$

33. -1 and 1

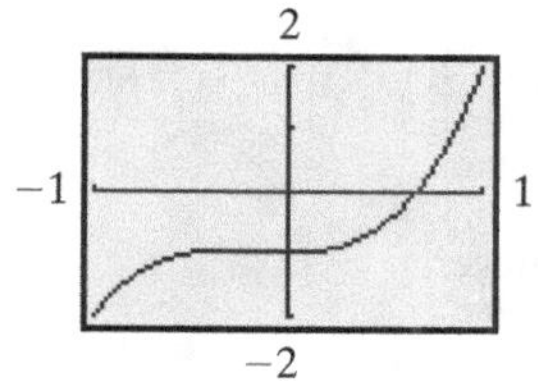

35. -12 and 12

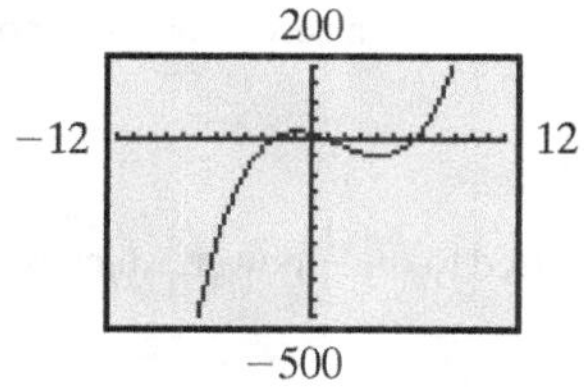

37. -10 and 10

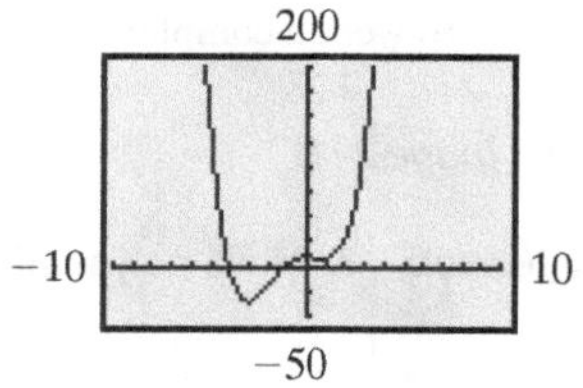

39. $-3, -1, 2$; $f(x) = (x + 3)(x + 1)(x - 2)$ **41.** $\frac{1}{2}, 3, 3$; $f(x) = (2x - 1)(x - 3)^2$ **43.** $-\frac{1}{3}$; $f(x) = (3x + 1)(x^2 + x + 1)$ **45.** $3, \frac{5 + \sqrt{17}}{2}, \frac{5 - \sqrt{17}}{2}$; $f(x) = (x - 3)\left(x - \left(\frac{5 + \sqrt{17}}{2}\right)\right)\left(x - \left(\frac{5 - \sqrt{17}}{2}\right)\right)$ **47.** $-2, -1, 1, 1$; $f(x) = (x + 2)(x + 1)(x - 1)^2$ **49.** $-5, -3, -\frac{3}{2}, 1$; $f(x) = (x + 5)(x + 3)(2x + 3)(x - 1)$ **51.** $-2, -\frac{3}{2}, 1, 4$; $f(x) = (x + 2)(2x + 3)(x - 1)(x - 4)$ **53.** $-\frac{1}{2}, \frac{1}{2}$; $f(x) = (2x + 1)(2x - 1)(x^2 + 2)$ **55.** $\frac{\sqrt{2}}{2}, -\frac{\sqrt{2}}{2}, 2$; $f(x) = (x - 2)(\sqrt{2}x - 1)(\sqrt{2}x + 1)(2x^2 + 1)$ **57.** $-5.9, -0.3, 3$ **59.** $-3.8, 4.5$ **61.** $-43.5, 1, 23$ **63.** $\{-1, 2\}$ **65.** $\left\{\frac{2}{3}, -1 + \sqrt{2}, -1 - \sqrt{2}\right\}$ **67.** $\left\{\frac{1}{3}, \sqrt{5}, -\sqrt{5}\right\}$ **69.** $\{-3, -2\}$ **71.** $\left\{-\frac{1}{3}\right\}$ **73.** $f(0) = -1$; $f(1) = 10$; Zero: 0.22 **75.** $f(-5) = -58$; $f(-4) = 2$; Zero: -4.05 **77.** $f(1.4) = -0.17536$; $f(1.5) = 1.40625$; Zero: 1.41

79. Step 1: $y = x^3$
Step 2: x-intercepts: $-3, -1, 2$;
y-intercept: -6
Step 3: $-3, -1, 2$: multiplicity 1, crosses
1: multiplicity 2, touches
Step 4:

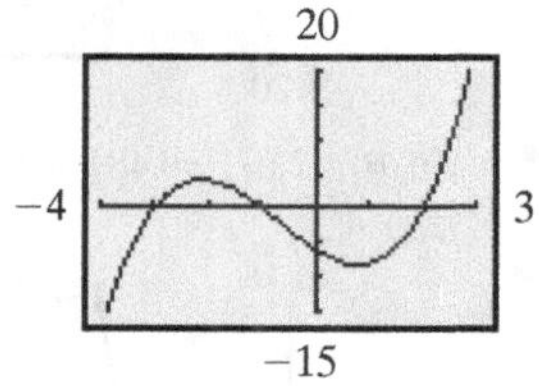

Step 5: $(-2.12, 4.06)$; $(0.79, -8.21)$
Step 6:

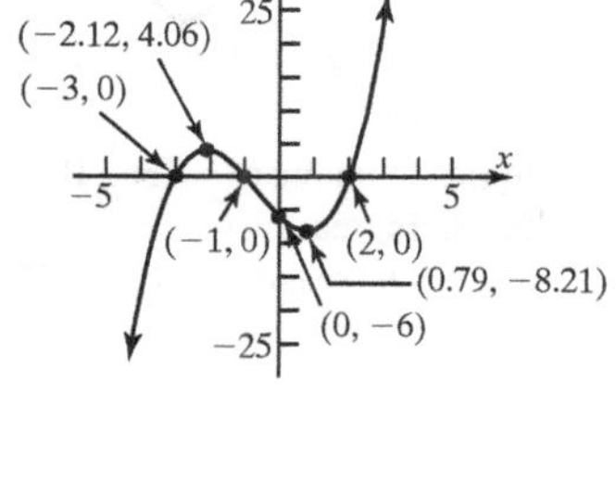

Step 7: Domain and Range: $(-\infty, \infty)$
Step 8: Increasing: $(-\infty, -2.12)$, $(0.79, \infty)$;
Decreasing: $(-2.12, 0.79)$

81. Step 1: $y = x^4$
Step 2: x-intercepts: $-2, -1, 1$;
y-intercept: 2
Step 3: $-2, -1$: multiplicity 1, crosses;
1: multiplicity 2, touches
Step 4:

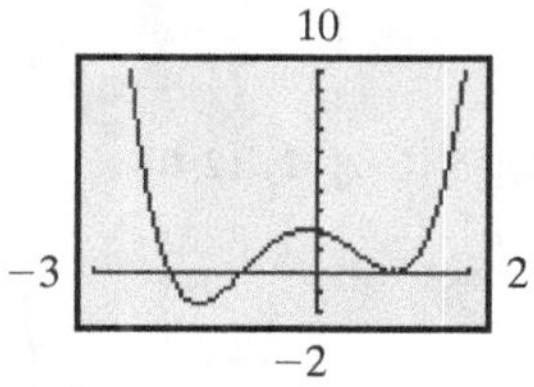

Step 5: $(-1.59, -1.62)$, $(-0.16, 2.08)$, $(1, 0)$
Step 6:

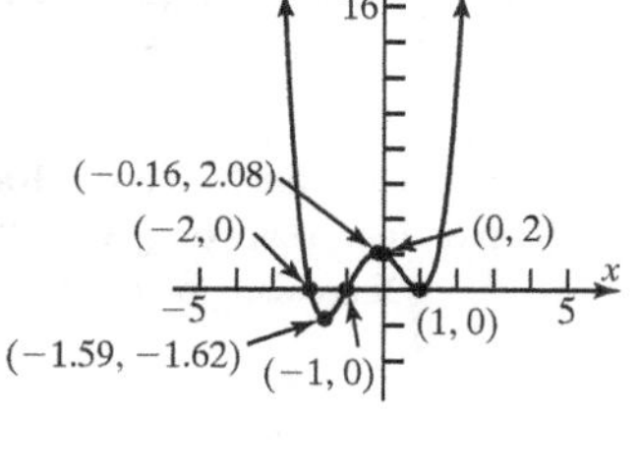

Step 7: Domain: $[-\infty, \infty)$; Range: $[-1.62, \infty)$
Step 8: Increasing: $(-1.59, -0.16)$, $(1, \infty)$;
Decreasing: $(-\infty, -1.59)$, $(-0.16, 1)$

83. Step 1: $y = 4x^5$
Step 2: x-intercepts: $-\frac{\sqrt{2}}{2}, \frac{\sqrt{2}}{2}, 2$;
y-intercept: 2
Step 3: $-\frac{\sqrt{2}}{2}, \frac{\sqrt{2}}{2}, 2$: multiplicity 1, crosses
Step 4:

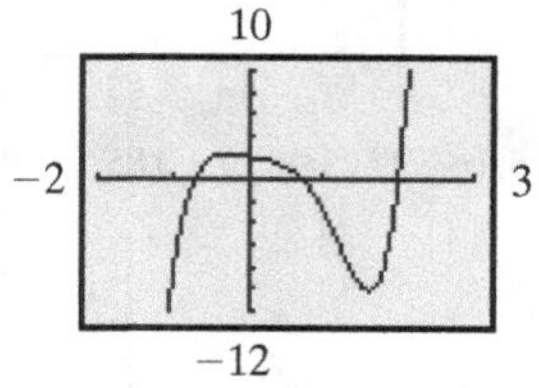

Step 5: $(-0.30, 2.23)$; $(1.61, -10.09)$
Step 6:

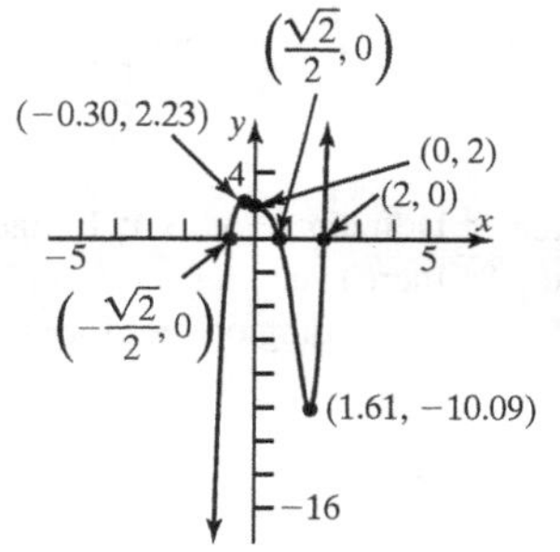

Step 7: Domain and range: $(-\infty, \infty)$
Step 8: Increasing: $(-\infty, -0.30)$, $(1.61, \infty)$;
Decreasing: $(-0.30, 1.61)$

85. $k = 5$ **87.** -7 **89.** If $f(x) = x^n - c^n$, then $f(c) = c^n - c^n = 0$; so $x - c$ is a factor of f.
91. 5 **93.** 7 in. **95.** All the potential rational zeros are integers, so r is either an integer or is not a rational zero (and is therefore irrational).
97. 0.215 **99.** No; by the Rational Zeros Theorem, $\frac{1}{3}$ is not a potential rational zero. **101.** No; by the Rational Zeros Theorem, $\frac{2}{3}$ is not a potential rational zero.

4.6 Assess Your Understanding *(page 238)*

3. one **4.** $3 - 4i$ **5.** T **6.** F **7.** $4 + i$ **9.** $-i, 1 - i$ **11.** $-i, -2i$ **13.** $-i$ **15.** $2 - i, -3 + i$
17. $f(x) = x^4 - 14x^3 + 77x^2 - 200x + 208; a = 1$ **19.** $f(x) = x^5 - 4x^4 + 7x^3 - 8x^2 + 6x - 4; a = 1$
21. $f(x) = x^4 - 6x^3 + 10x^2 - 6x + 9; a = 1$ **23.** $-2i, 4$ **25.** $2i, -3, \frac{1}{2}$ **27.** $3 + 2i, -2, 5$ **29.** $4i, -\sqrt{11}, \sqrt{11}, -\frac{2}{3}$
31. $1, -\frac{1}{2} - \frac{\sqrt{3}}{2}i, -\frac{1}{2} + \frac{\sqrt{3}}{2}i; f(x) = (x - 1)\left(x + \frac{1}{2} + \frac{\sqrt{3}}{2}i\right)\left(x + \frac{1}{2} - \frac{\sqrt{3}}{2}i\right)$
33. $2, 3 - 2i, 3 + 2i; f(x) = (x - 2)(x - 3 + 2i)(x - 3 - 2i)$ **35.** $-i, i, -2i, 2i;\ f(x) = (x + i)(x - i)(x + 2i)(x - 2i)$
37. $-5i, 5i, -3, 1; f(x) = (x + 5i)(x - 5i)(x + 3)(x - 1)$ **39.** $-4, \frac{1}{3}, 2 - 3i, 2 + 3i; f(x) = 3(x + 4)\left(x - \frac{1}{3}\right)(x - 2 + 3i)(x - 2 - 3i)$
41. Zeros that are complex numbers must occur in conjugate pairs; or a polynomial with real coefficients of odd degree must have at least one real zero.
43. If the remaining zero were a complex number, its conjugate would also be a zero, creating a polynomial of degree 5.

Review Exercises *(page 241)*

1. Polynomial of degree 5 **3.** Not a polynomial; The variable x is raised to the $\frac{1}{2}$ power, which is not a nonnegative integer.

5.

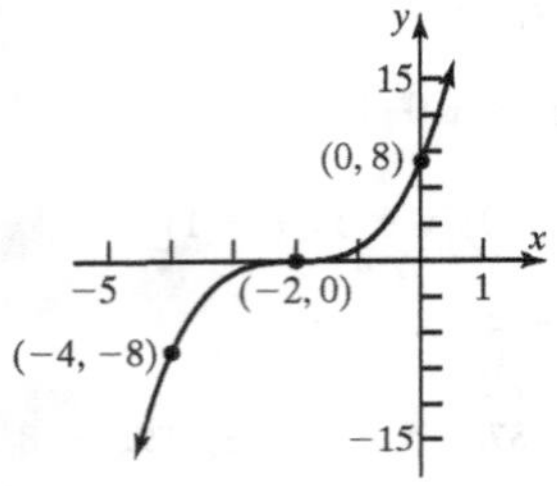

7.

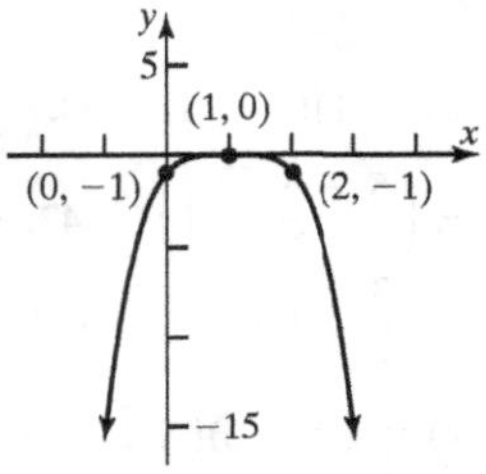

9.

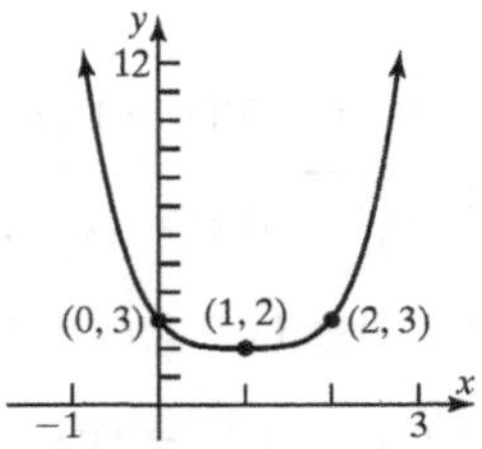

11. Step 1: $y = x^3$
Step 2: x-intercepts: $-4, -2, 0$; y-intercept: 0
Step 3: $-4, -2, 0$: multiplicity 1; crosses

Step 4:

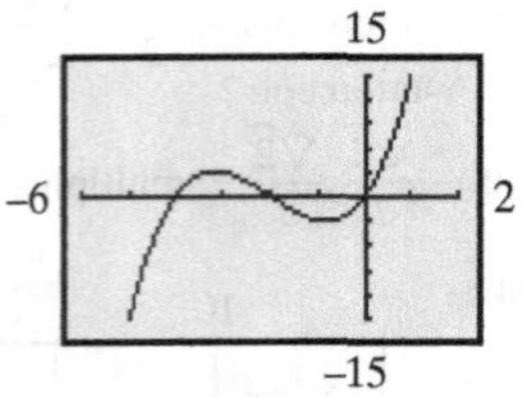

Step 5: $(-3.15, 3.08), (-0.85, -3.08)$
Step 6:

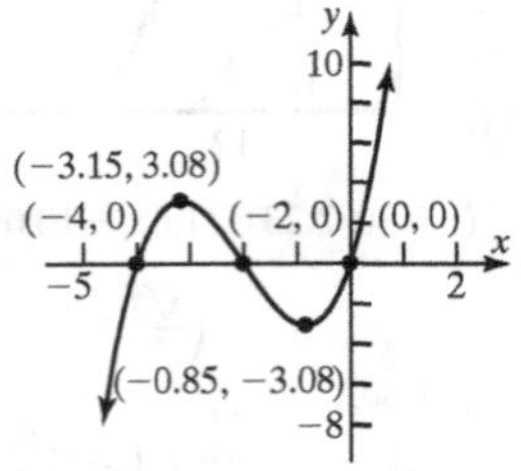

Step 7: Domain: $(-\infty, \infty)$; Range: $(-\infty, \infty)$
Step 8: Increasing on $(-\infty, -3.15)$ and $(-0.85, \infty)$
Decreasing on $(-3.15, -0.85)$

13. Step 1: $y = x^3$
Step 2: x-intercepts: $-4, 2$; y-intercept: 16
Step 3: -4: multiplicity 1; crosses;
2: multiplicity 2; touches

Step 4:

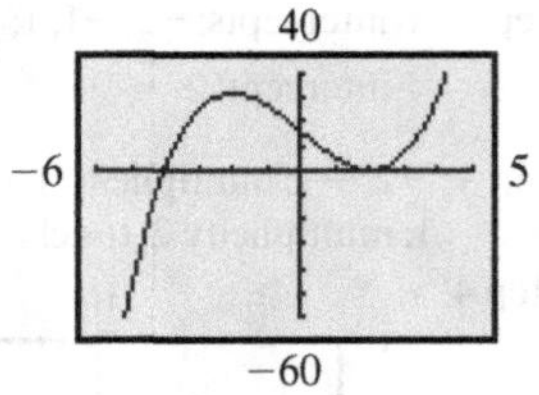

Step 5: $(-2, 32), (2, 0)$
Step 6:

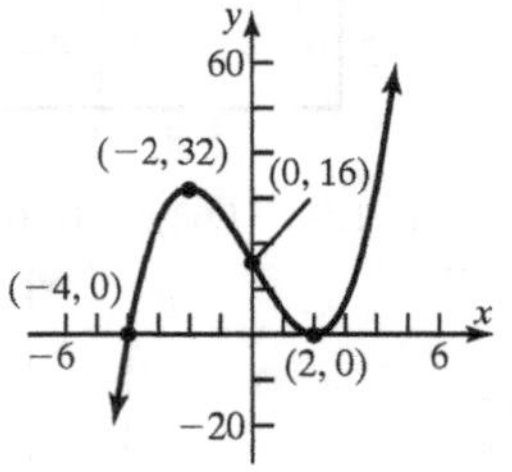

Step 7: Domain: $(-\infty, \infty)$; Range: $(-\infty, \infty)$
Step 8: Increasing on $(-\infty, 0.85)$ and $(3.15, \infty)$
Decreasing on $(0.85, 3.15)$

15. Step 1: $y = x^3$
Step 2: x-intercepts: 0, 4; y-intercept: 0
Step 3: 0: multiplicity 2; touches; 4: multiplicity 1; crosses

Step 4:

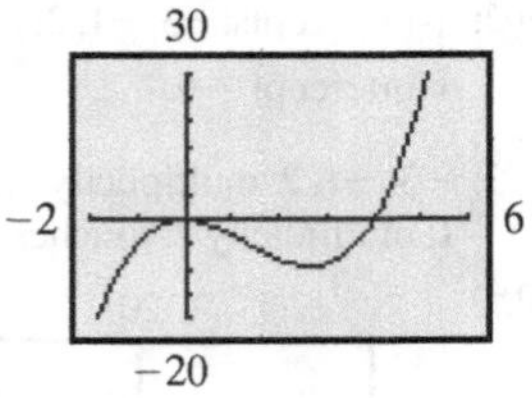

Step 5: $(0, 0), (2.67, -9.48)$
Step 6:

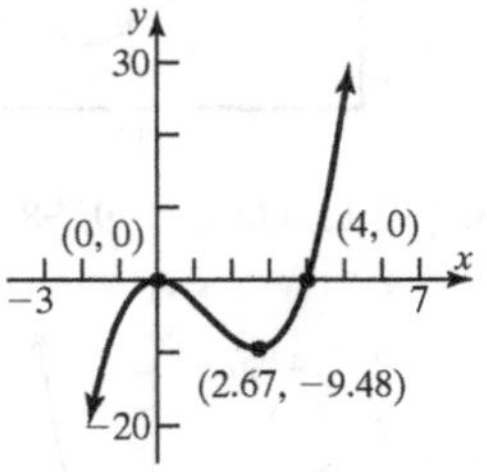

Step 7: Domain: $(-\infty, \infty)$; Range: $(-\infty, \infty)$
Step 8: Increasing on $(-\infty, 0)$ and $(2.67, \infty)$
Decreasing on $(0, 2.67)$

17. Step 1: $y = x^4$
Step 2: x-intercepts: $-3, -1, 1$; y-intercept: 3
Step 3: $-3, -1$: multiplicity 1; crosses; 1: multiplicity 2; touches
Step 4:

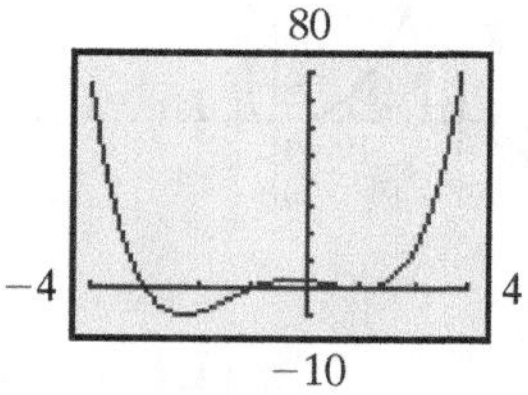

Step 5: $(-2.28, -9.91)$, $(-0.22, 3.23)$, $(1, 0)$
Step 6:

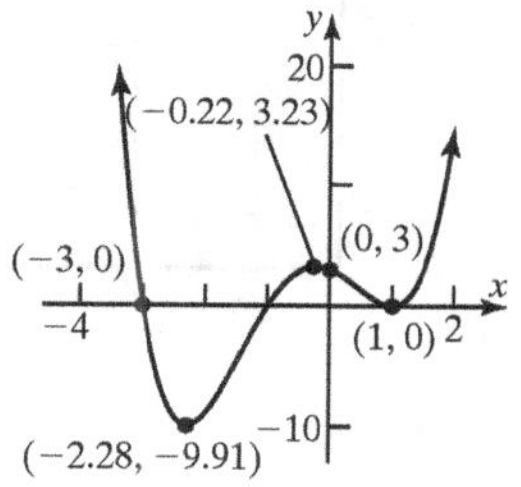

Step 7: Domain: $(-\infty, \infty)$; Range: $(-\infty, \infty)$
Step 8: Increasing on $(-2.28, -0.22)$ and $(1, \infty)$
Decreasing on $(-\infty, -2.28)$ and $(-0.22, 1)$

19. Domain: $\{x|x \neq -3, x \neq 3\}$; Horizontal asymptote: $y = 0$; Vertical asymptotes: $x = -3, x = 3$

21. Domain: $\{x|x \neq -2\}$; Horizontal asymptote: $y = 2$; Vertical asymptote: $x = -2$

23. Step 1: $R(x) = \dfrac{2(x-3)}{x}$; Domain: $\{x|x \neq 0\}$
Step 2: $R(x)$ is in lowest terms.
Step 3: x-intercept: 3; no y-intercept
Step 4: No symmetry
Step 5: Vertical asymptote: $x = 0$
Step 6: Horizontal asymptote: $y = 2$, not intersected
Step 7:

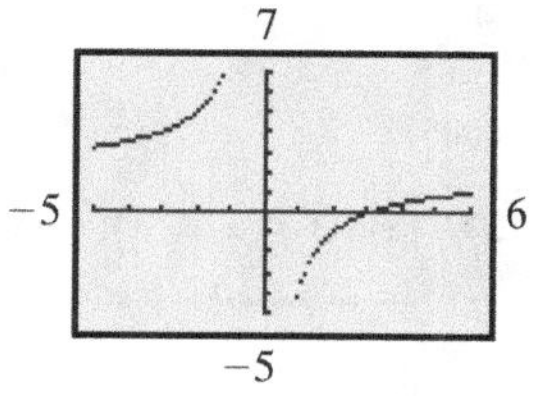

Step 8:

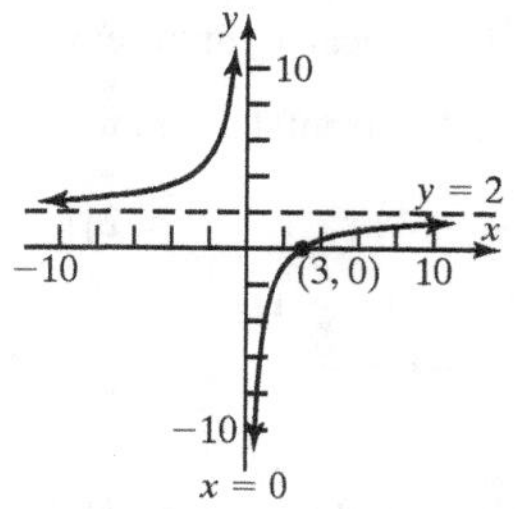

25. Step 1: Domain: $\{x|x \neq 0, x \neq 2\}$
Step 2: $H(x)$ is in lowest terms.
Step 3: x-intercept: -2; no y-intercept
Step 4: No symmetry
Step 5: Vertical asymptotes: $x = 0, x = 2$
Step 6: Horizontal asymptote: $y = 0$, intersected at $(-2, 0)$
Step 7:

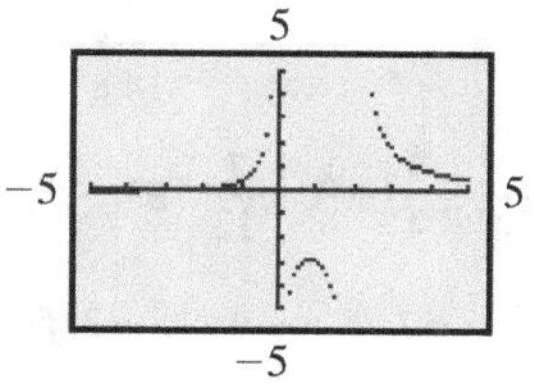

Step 8:

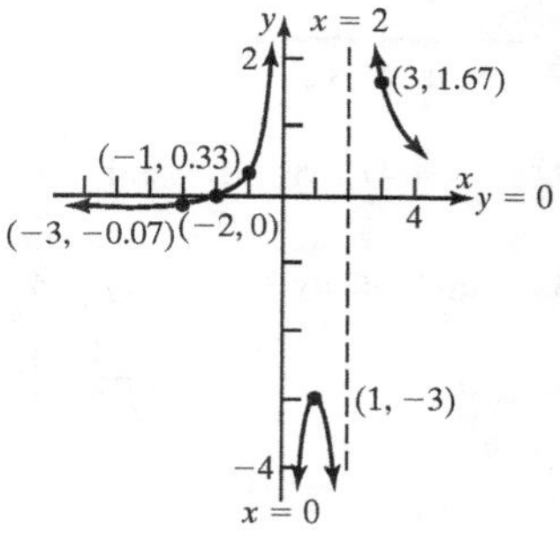

27. Step 1: $R(x) = \dfrac{(x+3)(x-2)}{(x-3)(x+2)}$;
Domain: $\{x|x \neq -2, x \neq 3\}$
Step 2: $R(x)$ is in lowest terms.
Step 3: x-intercepts: $-3, 2$; y-intercept: 1
Step 4: No symmetry
Step 5: Vertical asymptotes: $x = -2, x = 3$
Step 6: Horizontal asymptote: $y = 1$, intersected at $(0, 1)$
Step 7:

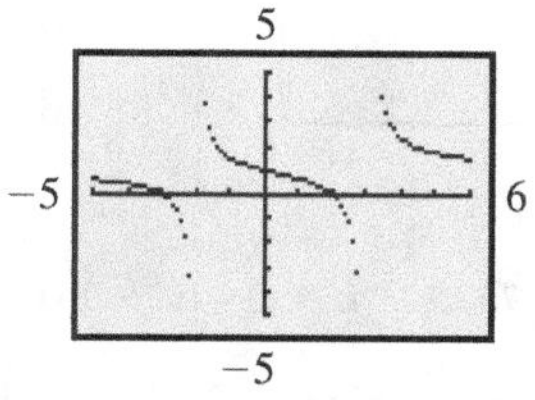

Step 8:

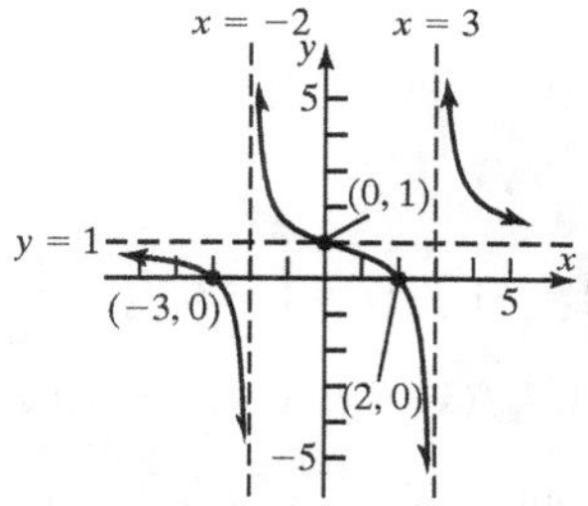

29. Step 1: $F(x) = \dfrac{x^3}{(x+2)(x-2)}$;
Domain: $\{x|x \neq -2, x \neq 2\}$
Step 2: $F(x)$ is in lowest terms.
Step 3: Intercept: $(0, 0)$
Step 4: Symmetric with respect to the origin
Step 5: Vertical asymptotes: $x = -2, x = 2$
Step 6: Oblique asymptote: $y = x$, intersected at $(0, 0)$
Step 7:

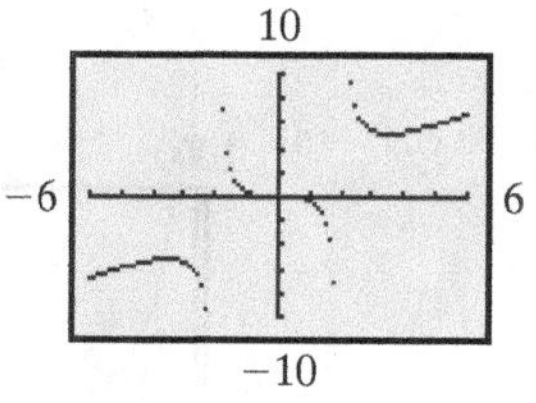

Step 8:

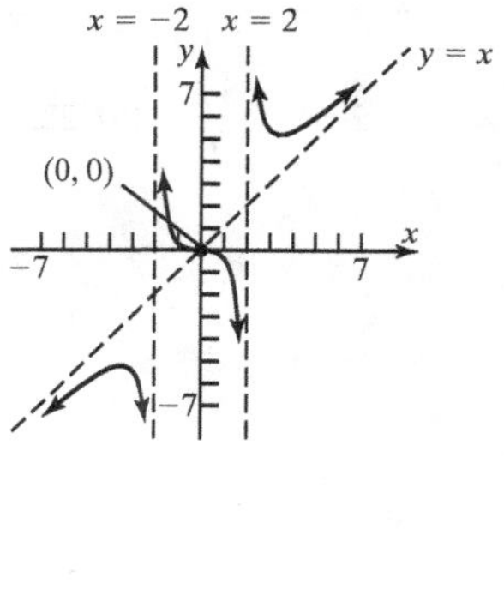

31. Step 1: Domain: $\{x|x \neq 1\}$
Step 2: $R(x)$ is in lowest terms.
Step 3: Intercept: $(0, 0)$
Step 4: No symmetry
Step 5: Vertical asymptote: $x = 1$
Step 6: No oblique or horizontal asymptote

Step 7:

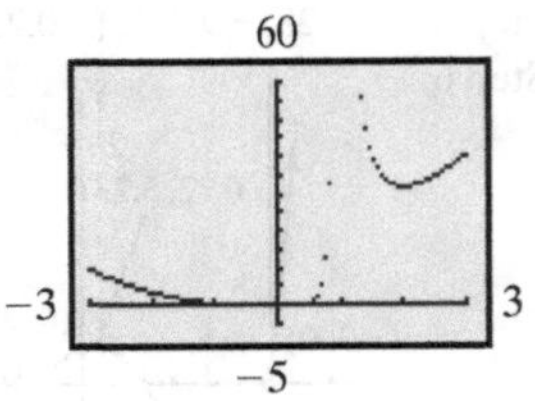

Step 8:

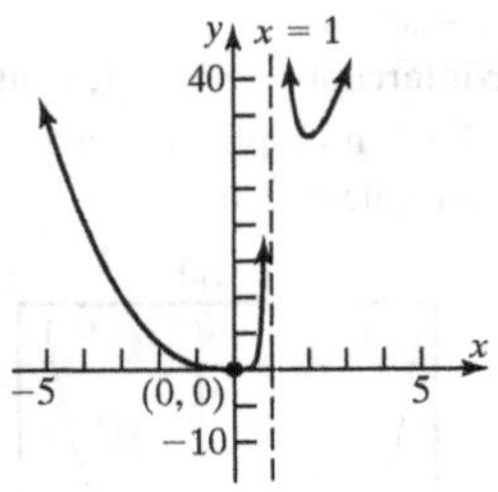

33. Step 1: $G(x) = \dfrac{(x+2)(x-2)}{(x+1)(x-2)}$;
Domain: $\{x|x \neq -1, x \neq 2\}$
Step 2: $G(x) = \dfrac{x+2}{x+1}$
Step 3: x-intercept: -2; y-intercept: 2
Step 4: No symmetry
Step 5: Vertical asymptote: $x = -1$; hole at $\left(2, \frac{4}{3}\right)$
Step 6: Horizontal asymptote: $y = 1$, not intersected

Step 7:

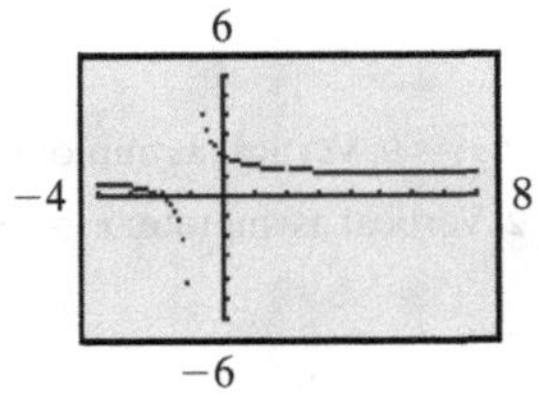

Step 8:

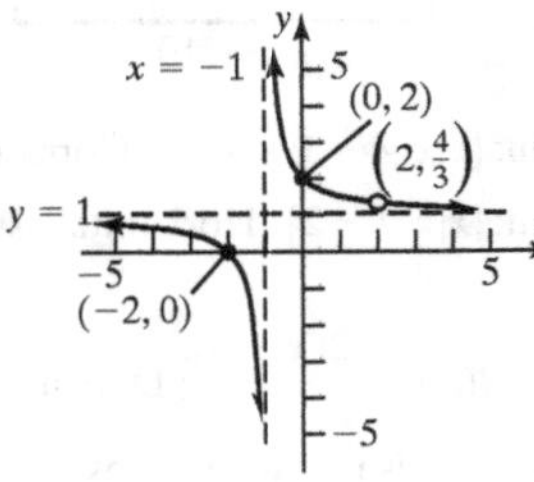

35. $\{x|x < -2 \text{ or } -1 < x < 2\}$; $(-\infty, -2) \cup (-1, 2)$

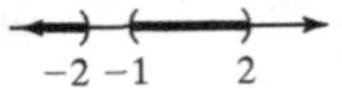

37. $\{x|-3 < x \leq 3\}$; $(-3, 3]$

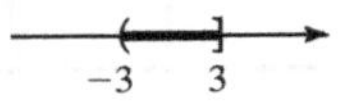

39. $\{x|x < 1 \text{ or } x > 2\}$; $(-\infty, 1) \cup (2, \infty)$

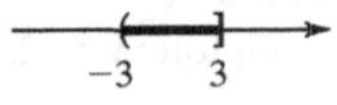

41. $\{x|1 \leq x \leq 2 \text{ or } x > 3\}$; $[1, 2] \cup (3, \infty)$

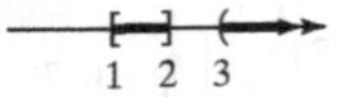

43. $\{x|x < -4 \text{ or } 2 < x < 4 \text{ or } x > 6\}$; $(-\infty, -4) \cup (2, 4) \cup (6, \infty)$

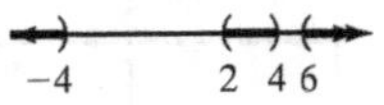

45. $R = 10$; g is not a factor of f.
47. $R = 0$; g is a factor of f.

49. $f(4) = 47{,}105$ **51.** 8; $\pm 1, \pm 3, \pm\frac{1}{2}, \pm\frac{3}{2}, \pm\frac{1}{3}, \pm\frac{1}{4}, \pm\frac{3}{4}, \pm\frac{1}{6}, \pm\frac{1}{12}$ **53.** $-2, 1, 4$; $f(x) = (x+2)(x-1)(x-4)$

55. $\frac{1}{2}$, multiplicity 2; -2; $f(x) = 4\left(x - \frac{1}{2}\right)^2(x+2)$ **57.** 2, multiplicity 2; $f(x) = (x-2)^2(x^2+5)$ **59.** $-2.5, 3.1, 5.32$ **61.** $-11.3, -0.6, 4, 9.33$

63. $\{-3, 2\}$ **65.** $\left\{-3, -1, -\frac{1}{2}, 1\right\}$ **67.** -5 and 5

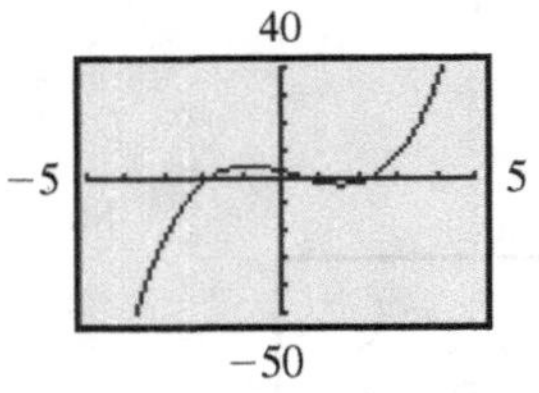

69. $-\frac{37}{2}$ and $\frac{37}{2}$

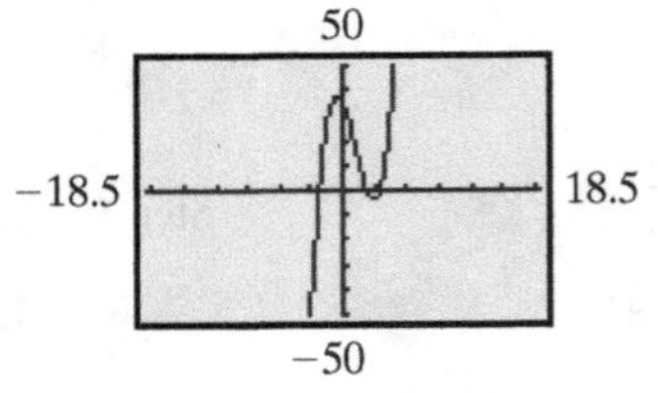

71. $f(0) = -1$; $f(1) = 1$ **73.** $f(0) = -1$; $f(1) = 1$ **75.** $4 - i$; $f(x) = x^3 - 14x^2 + 65x - 102$ **77.** $-i, 1 - i$; $f(x) = x^4 - 2x^3 + 3x^2 - 2x + 2$

79. $-2, 1, 4$; $f(x) = (x+2)(x-1)(x-4)$ **81.** $-2, \frac{1}{2}$ (multiplicity 2); $f(x) = 4(x+2)\left(x - \frac{1}{2}\right)^2$

83. 2 (multiplicity 2) $-\sqrt{5}i, \sqrt{5}i$; $f(x) = \left(x + \sqrt{5}i\right)\left(x - \sqrt{5}i\right)(x-2)^2$

85. $-3, 2, -\frac{\sqrt{2}}{2}i, \frac{\sqrt{2}}{2}i$; $f(x) = 2(x+3)(x-2)\left(x + \frac{\sqrt{2}}{2}i\right)\left(x - \frac{\sqrt{2}}{2}i\right)$

87. **(a)** $A(r) = 2\pi r^2 + \dfrac{500}{r}$ **(b)** 223.22 cm^2 **(c)** 257.08 cm^2 **(d)**

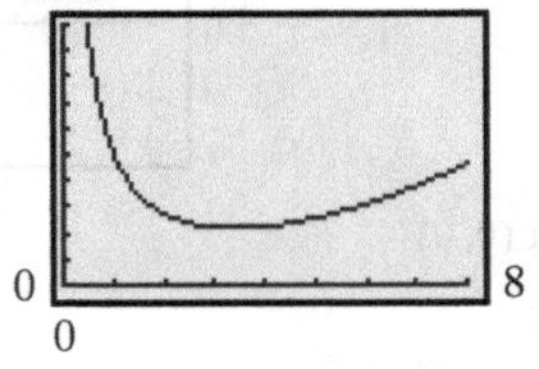

A is smallest when $r \approx 3.41$ cm.

Chapter Test (page 243)

1.

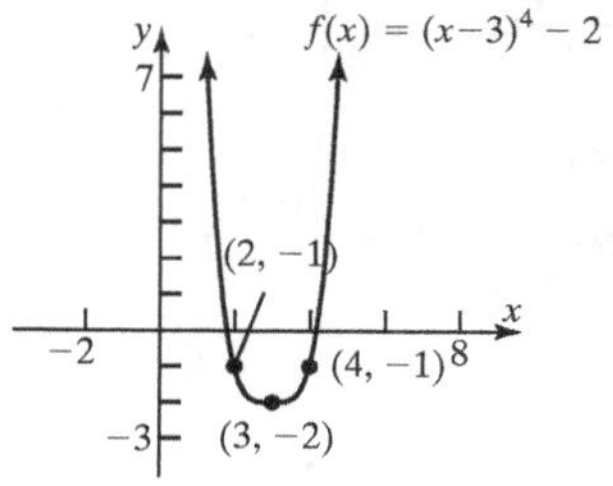

2. **(a)** 3 **(b)** Every zero of g lies between -15 and 15.

(c) $\pm\frac{1}{2}, \pm 1, \pm\frac{3}{2}, \pm\frac{5}{2}, \pm 3, \pm 5, \pm\frac{15}{2}, \pm 15$

(d) $-5, -\frac{1}{2}, 3$; $g(x) = (x+5)(2x+1)(x-3)$

(e) y-intercept: -15; x-intercepts: $-5, -\frac{1}{2}, 3$

(f) Crosses at $-5, -\frac{1}{2}, 3$ **(g)** $y = 2x^3$

(h) $(-3.15, 60.30)$, $(1.48, -39.00)$

(i)

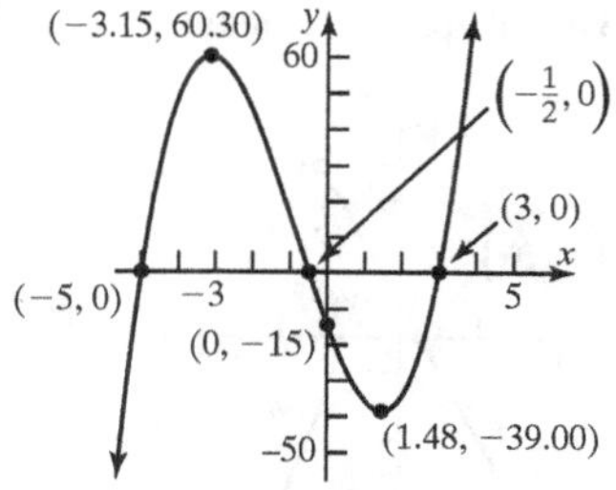

3. $4, -5i, 5i$ **4.** $\left\{1, \frac{5-\sqrt{61}}{6}, \frac{5+\sqrt{61}}{6}\right\}$ **5.** Domain: $\{x \mid x \neq -10, x \neq 4\}$; asymptotes: $x = -10$, $y = 2$

6. Domain: $\{x \mid x \neq -1\}$; asymptotes: $x = -1$, $y = x + 1$

7.

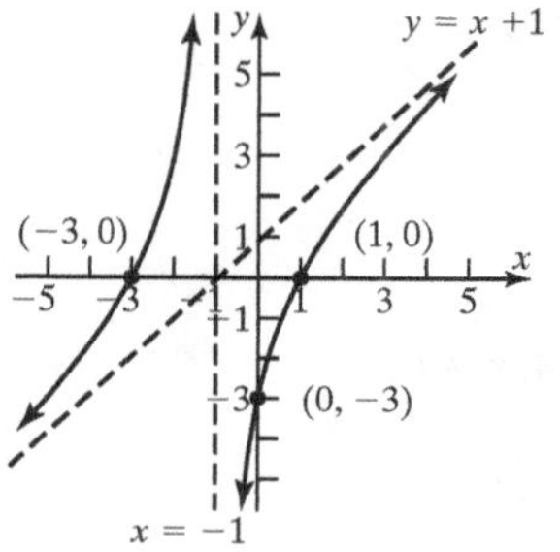

8. Answers may vary. One possibility is $f(x) = x^4 - 4x^3 - 2x^2 + 20x$.

9. Answers may vary. One possibility is $r(x) = \dfrac{2(x-9)(x-1)}{(x-4)(x-9)}$.

10. $f(0) = 8$; $f(4) = -36$

Since $f(0) = 8 > 0$ and $f(4) = -36 < 0$, the Intermediate Value Theorem guarantees that there is at least one real zero between 0 and 4.

11. $\{x \mid x < 3 \text{ or } x > 8\}$; $(-\infty, 3) \cup (8, \infty)$

Cumulative Review (page 243)

1. $\sqrt{26}$

2. $\{x \mid x \leq 0 \text{ or } x \geq 1\}$; $(-\infty, 0]$ or $[1, \infty)$

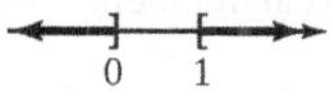

3. $\{x \mid -1 < x < 4\}$; $(-1, 4)$

4. $f(x) = -3x + 1$

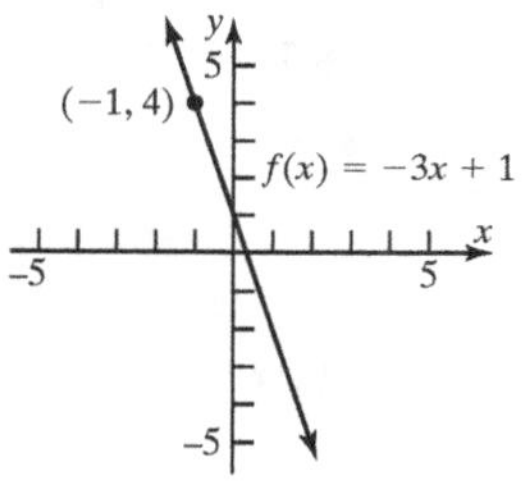

5. $y = 2x - 1$

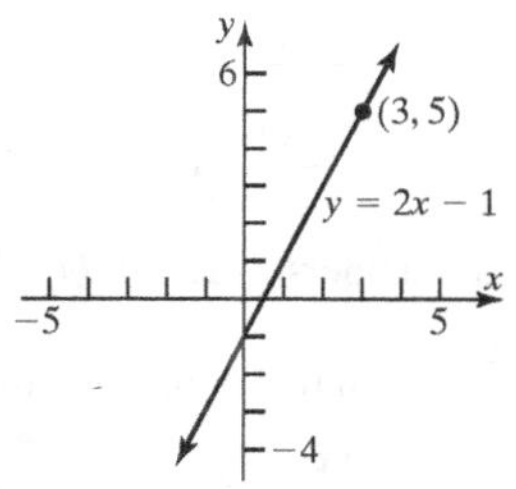

6.

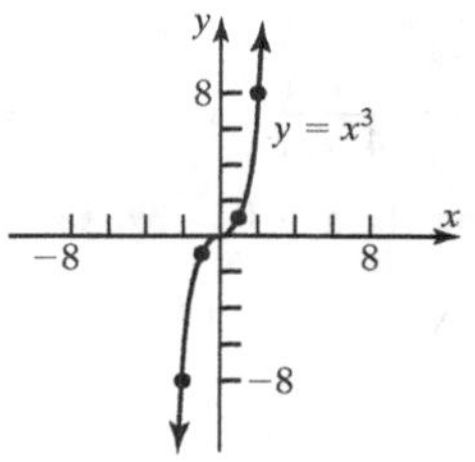

7. Not a function; 3 has two images. **8.** $\{0, 2, 4\}$ **9.** $\left\{x \,\middle|\, x \geq \frac{3}{2}\right\}$; $\left[\frac{3}{2}, \infty\right)$

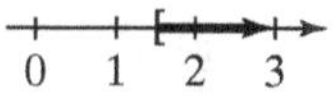

10. Center: $(-2, 1)$; radius: 3

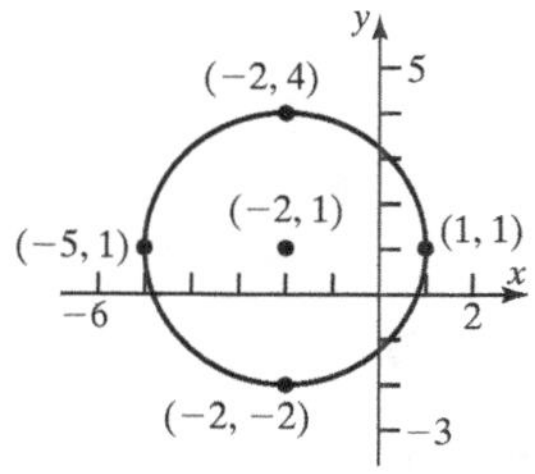

11. x-intercepts: $-3, 0, 3$; y-intercept: 0; symmetric with respect to the origin.

12. $y = -\frac{2}{3}x + \frac{17}{3}$

13. Not a function; it fails the vertical-line test.

14. **(a)** 22 **(b)** $x^2 - 5x - 2$ **(c)** $-x^2 - 5x + 2$ **(d)** $9x^2 + 15x - 2$ **(e)** $2x + h + 5$

15. **(a)** $\{x \mid x \neq 1\}$ **(b)** No; $(2, 7)$ is on the graph. **(c)** 4; $(3, 4)$ is on the graph.

(d) $\frac{7}{4}$; $\left(\frac{7}{4}, 9\right)$ is on the graph.

16.

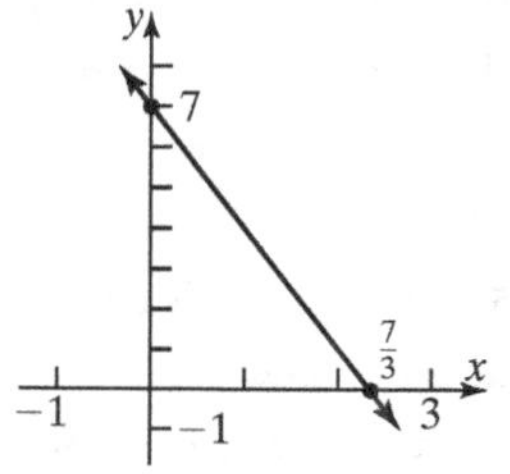

17.

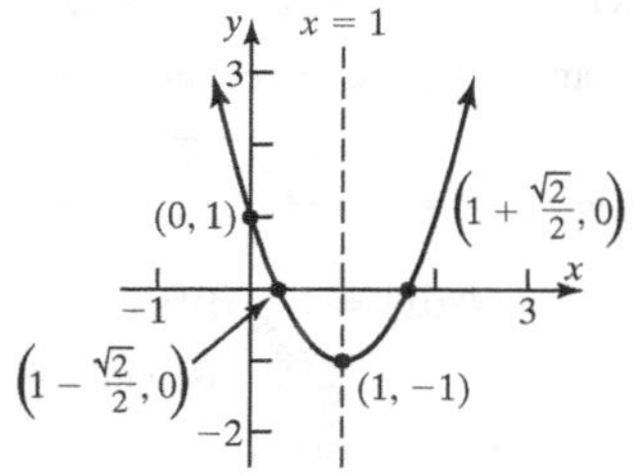

18. 6; $y = 6x - 1$

19. **(a)** x-intercepts: $-5, -1, 5$; y-intercept: -3

(b) No symmetry

(c) Neither

(d) Increasing: $(-\infty, -3)$ and $(2, \infty)$; Decreasing: $(-3, 2)$

(e) Local maximum is 5 and occurs at $x = -3$.

(f) Local minimum is -6 and occurs at $x = 2$.

20. Odd

21. **(a)** Domain: $\{x|x > -3\}$ or $(-3, \infty)$

(b) x-intercept: $-\frac{1}{2}$; y-intercept: 1

(c)

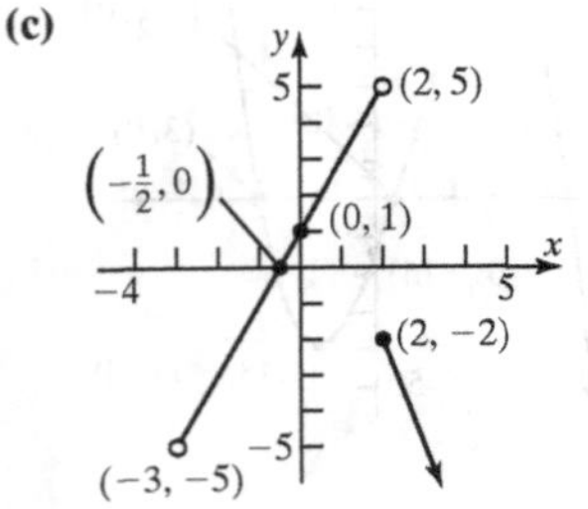

(d) Range: $\{y|y < 5\}$ or $(-\infty, 5)$

22.

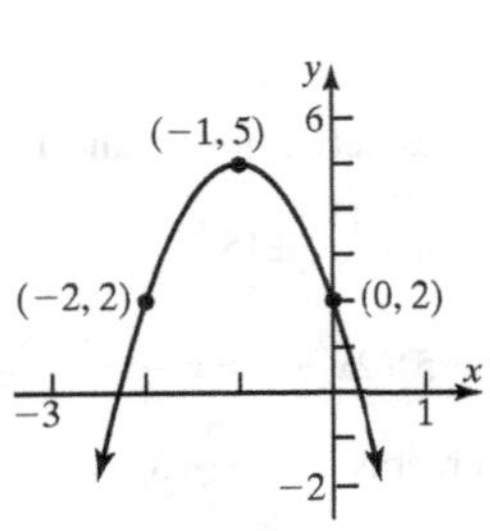

23. **(a)** $(f + g)(x) = x^2 - 9x - 6$; domain: all real numbers

(b) $\left(\frac{f}{g}\right)(x) = \frac{x^2 - 5x + 1}{-4x - 7}$; domain: $\left\{x \middle| x \neq -\frac{7}{4}\right\}$

24. **(a)** $R(x) = -\frac{1}{10}x^2 + 150x$ **(b)** $14,000 **(c)** 750; $56,250 **(d)** $75

CHAPTER 5 Exponential and Logarithmic Functions

5.1 Assess Your Understanding *(page 253)*

4. $(g \circ f)(x)$ **5.** F **6.** F **7.** **(a)** -1 **(b)** -1 **(c)** 8 **(d)** 0 **(e)** 8 **(f)** -7 **9.** **(a)** 4 **(b)** 5 **(c)** -1 **(d)** -2

11. **(a)** 98 **(b)** 49 **(c)** 4 **(d)** 4 **13.** **(a)** 97 **(b)** $-\frac{163}{2}$ **(c)** 1 **(d)** $-\frac{3}{2}$ **15.** **(a)** $2\sqrt{2}$ **(b)** $2\sqrt{2}$ **(c)** 1 **(d)** 0

17. **(a)** $\frac{1}{17}$ **(b)** $\frac{1}{5}$ **(c)** 1 **(d)** $\frac{1}{2}$ **19.** **(a)** $\frac{3}{\sqrt[3]{4} + 1}$ **(b)** 1 **(c)** $\frac{6}{5}$ **(d)** 0 **21.** $\{x|x \neq 0, x \neq 2\}$ **23.** $\{x|x \neq -4, x \neq 0\}$

25. $\left\{x \middle| x \geq -\frac{3}{2}\right\}$ **27.** $\{x|x \geq 1\}$ **29.** **(a)** $(f \circ g)(x) = 6x + 3$; all real numbers **(b)** $(g \circ f)(x) = 6x + 9$; all real numbers

(c) $(f \circ f)(x) = 4x + 9$; all real numbers **(d)** $(g \circ g)(x) = 9x$; all real numbers

31. **(a)** $(f \circ g)(x) = 3x^2 + 1$; all real numbers **(b)** $(g \circ f)(x) = 9x^2 + 6x + 1$; all real numbers **(c)** $(f \circ f)(x) = 9x + 4$; all real numbers

(d) $(g \circ g)(x) = x^4$; all real numbers **33.** **(a)** $(f \circ g)(x) = x^4 + 8x^2 + 16$; all real numbers **(b)** $(g \circ f)(x) = x^4 + 4$; all real numbers

(c) $(f \circ f)(x) = x^4$; all real numbers **(d)** $(g \circ g)(x) = x^4 + 8x^2 + 20$; all real numbers **35.** **(a)** $(f \circ g)(x) = \frac{3x}{2 - x}$; $\{x|x \neq 0, x \neq 2\}$

(b) $(g \circ f)(x) = \frac{2(x - 1)}{3}$; $\{x|x \neq 1\}$ **(c)** $(f \circ f)(x) = \frac{3(x - 1)}{4 - x}$; $\{x|x \neq 1, x \neq 4\}$ **(d)** $(g \circ g)(x) = x$; $\{x|x \neq 0\}$

37. **(a)** $(f \circ g)(x) = \frac{4}{4 + x}$; $\{x|x \neq -4, x \neq 0\}$ **(b)** $(g \circ f)(x) = \frac{-4(x - 1)}{x}$; $\{x|x \neq 0, x \neq 1\}$ **(c)** $(f \circ f)(x) = x$; $\{x|x \neq 1\}$

(d) $(g \circ g)(x) = x$; $\{x|x \neq 0\}$ **39.** **(a)** $(f \circ g)(x) = \sqrt{2x + 3}$; $\left\{x \middle| x \geq -\frac{3}{2}\right\}$ **(b)** $(g \circ f)(x) = 2\sqrt{x} + 3$; $\{x|x \geq 0\}$

(c) $(f \circ f)(x) = \sqrt[4]{x}$; $\{x|x \geq 0\}$ **(d)** $(g \circ g)(x) = 4x + 9$; all real numbers **41.** **(a)** $(f \circ g)(x) = x$; $\{x|x \geq 1\}$

(b) $(g \circ f)(x) = |x|$; all real numbers **(c)** $(f \circ f)(x) = x^4 + 2x^2 + 2$; all real numbers **(d)** $(g \circ g)(x) = \sqrt{\sqrt{x - 1} - 1}$; $\{x|x \geq 2\}$

43. **(a)** $(f \circ g)(x) = -\frac{4x - 17}{2x - 1}$; $\left\{x \middle| x \neq 3;\ x \neq \frac{1}{2}\right\}$ **(b)** $(g \circ f)(x) = -\frac{3x - 3}{2x + 8}$; $\{x|x \neq -4;\ x \neq -1\}$

(c) $(f \circ f)(x) = -\frac{2x + 5}{x - 2}$; $\{x|x \neq -1;\ x \neq 2\}$ **(d)** $(g \circ g)(x) = -\frac{3x - 4}{2x - 11}$; $\left\{x \middle| x \neq \frac{11}{2};\ x \neq 3\right\}$

45. $(f \circ g)(x) = f(g(x)) = f\left(\frac{1}{2}x\right) = 2\left(\frac{1}{2}x\right) = x$; $(g \circ f)(x) = g(f(x)) = g(2x) = \frac{1}{2}(2x) = x$

47. $(f \circ g)(x) = f(g(x)) = f\left(\sqrt[3]{x}\right) = \left(\sqrt[3]{x}\right)^3 = x$; $(g \circ f)(x) = g(f(x)) = g(x^3) = \sqrt[3]{x^3} = x$

49. $(f \circ g)(x) = f(g(x)) = f\left(\frac{1}{2}(x + 6)\right) = 2\left[\frac{1}{2}(x + 6)\right] - 6 = x + 6 - 6 = x$;

$(g \circ f)(x) = g(f(x)) = g(2x - 6) = \frac{1}{2}(2x - 6 + 6) = \frac{1}{2}(2x) = x$

51. $(f \circ g)(x) = f(g(x)) = f\left(\frac{1}{a}(x - b)\right) = a\left[\frac{1}{a}(x - b)\right] + b = x$; $(g \circ f)(x) = g(f(x)) = g(ax + b) = \frac{1}{a}(ax + b - b) = x$

53. $f(x) = x^4$; $g(x) = 2x + 3$ (Other answers are possible.) **55.** $f(x) = \sqrt{x}$; $g(x) = x^2 + 1$ (Other answers are possible.)

57. $f(x) = |x|$; $g(x) = 2x + 1$ (Other answers are possible.) **59.** $(f \circ g)(x) = 11$; $(g \circ f)(x) = 2$ **61.** $-3, 3$ **63.** **(a)** $(f \circ g)(x) = acx + ad + b$

(b) $(g \circ f)(x) = acx + bc + d$ **(c)** The domains of both $f \circ g$ and $g \circ f$ are all real numbers. **(d)** $f \circ g = g \circ f$ when $ad + b = bc + d$

65. $S(t) = \frac{16}{9}\pi t^6$ **67.** $C(t) = 15{,}000 + 800{,}000t - 40{,}000t^2$ **69.** $C(p) = \frac{2\sqrt{100 - p}}{25} + 600, 0 \leq p \leq 100$ **71.** $V(r) = 2\pi r^3$

73. **(a)** $f(x) = 0.7480x$ **(b)** $g(x) = 158.7160x$ **(c)** $g(f(x)) = g(0.7480x) = 118.719568x$ **(d)** 118,719.568 yen **75.** **(a)** $f(p) = p - 200$

(b) $g(p) = 0.8p$ **(c)** $(f \circ g)(p) = 0.8p - 200$; $(g \circ f)(p) = 0.8p - 160$; The 20% discount followed by the $200 rebate is the better deal.

77. f is an odd function, so $f(-x) = -f(x)$. g is an even function, so $g(-x) = g(x)$. Then $(f \circ g)(-x) = f(g(-x)) = f(g(x)) = (f \circ g)(x)$. So $f \circ g$ is even. Also, $(g \circ f)(-x) = g(f(-x)) = g(-f(x)) = g(f(x)) = (g \circ f)(x)$, so $g \circ f$ is even.

5.2 Assess Your Understanding *(page 265)*

4. one-to-one **5.** $y = x$ **6.** $[4, \infty)$ **7.** F **8.** T **9.** one-to-one **11.** not one-to-one **13.** not one-to-one **15.** one-to-one **17.** one-to-one **19.** not one-to-one **21.** one-to-one

23.

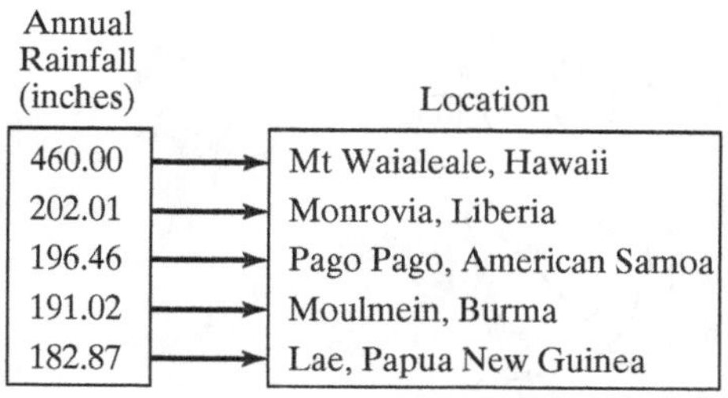

Domain: {460.00, 202.01, 196.46, 191.02, 182.87}
Range: {Mt Waialeale, Monrovia, Pago Pago, Moulmein, Lae}

25.

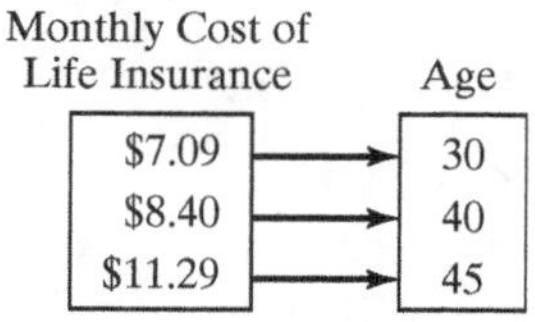

Domain: {$7.09, $8.40, $11.29}
Range: {30, 40, 45}

27. $\{(5, -3), (9, -2), (2, -1), (11, 0), (-5, 1)\}$
Domain: $\{5, 9, 2, 11, -5\}$
Range: $\{-3, -2, -1, 0, 1\}$

29. $\{(1, -2), (2, -3), (0, -10), (9, 1), (4, 2)\}$
Domain: $\{1, 2, 0, 9, 4\}$
Range: $\{-2, -3, -10, 1, 2\}$

31. $f(g(x)) = f\left(\frac{1}{3}(x-4)\right) = 3\left[\frac{1}{3}(x-4)\right] + 4 = (x-4) + 4 = x$

$g(f(x)) = g(3x+4) = \frac{1}{3}[(3x+4) - 4] = \frac{1}{3}(3x) = x$

33. $f(g(x)) = f\left(\frac{x}{4} + 2\right) = 4\left[\frac{x}{4} + 2\right] - 8 = (x+8) - 8 = x$

$g(f(x)) = g(4x - 8) = \frac{4x-8}{4} + 2 = (x-2) + 2 = x$

35. $f(g(x)) = f\left(\sqrt[3]{x+8}\right) = \left(\sqrt[3]{x+8}\right)^3 - 8 = (x+8) - 8 = x$

$g(f(x)) = g(x^3 - 8) = \sqrt[3]{(x^3-8)+8} = \sqrt[3]{x^3} = x$

37. $f(g(x)) = f\left(\frac{1}{x}\right) = \frac{1}{\left(\frac{1}{x}\right)} = x;\ g(f(x)) = g\left(\frac{1}{x}\right) = \frac{1}{\left(\frac{1}{x}\right)} = x$

39. $f(g(x)) = f\left(\frac{4x-3}{2-x}\right) = \frac{2\left(\frac{4x-3}{2-x}\right)+3}{\frac{4x-3}{2-x}+4}$

$= \frac{2(4x-3)+3(2-x)}{4x-3+4(2-x)} = \frac{5x}{5} = x,\ x \neq 2$

$g(f(x)) = g\left(\frac{2x+3}{x+4}\right) = \frac{4\left(\frac{2x+3}{x+4}\right)-3}{2-\frac{2x+3}{x+4}}$

$= \frac{4(2x+3)-3(x+4)}{2(x+4)-(2x+3)} = \frac{5x}{5} = x,\ x \neq -4$

41.

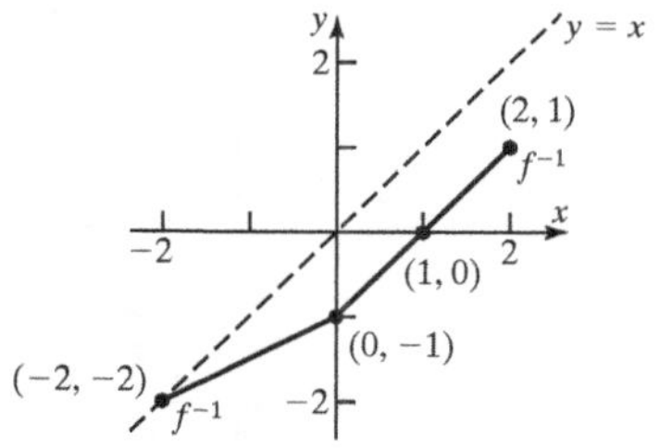

43.

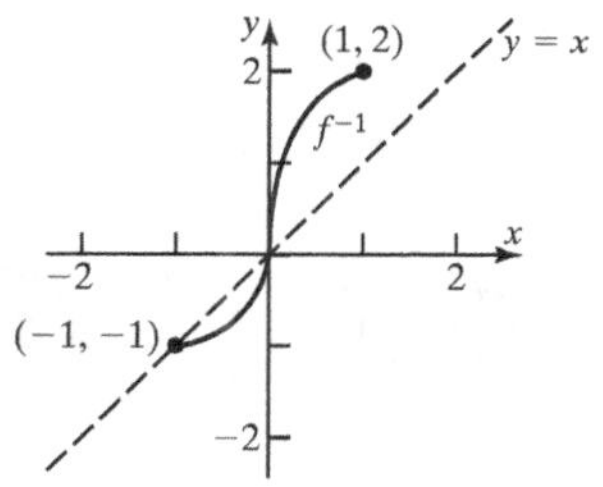

45.

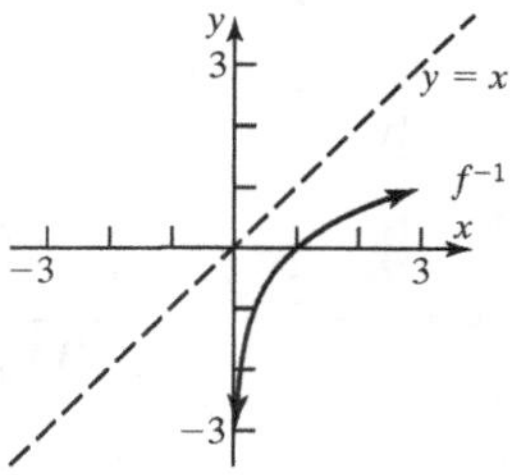

47. $f^{-1}(x) = \frac{1}{3}x$

$f(f^{-1}(x)) = f\left(\frac{1}{3}x\right) = 3\left(\frac{1}{3}x\right) = x$

$f^{-1}(f(x)) = f^{-1}(3x) = \frac{1}{3}(3x) = x$

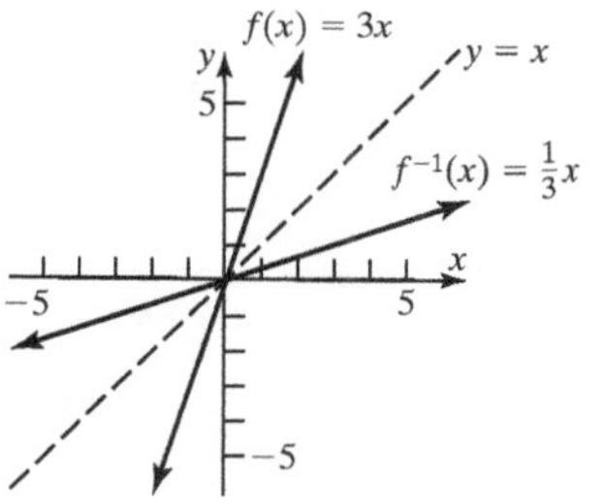

49. $f^{-1}(x) = \frac{x}{4} - \frac{1}{2}$

$f(f^{-1}(x)) = f\left(\frac{x}{4} - \frac{1}{2}\right) = 4\left(\frac{x}{4} - \frac{1}{2}\right) + 2$

$= (x-2) + 2 = x$

$f^{-1}(f(x)) = f^{-1}(4x+2) = \frac{4x+2}{4} - \frac{1}{2}$

$= \left(x + \frac{1}{2}\right) - \frac{1}{2} = x$

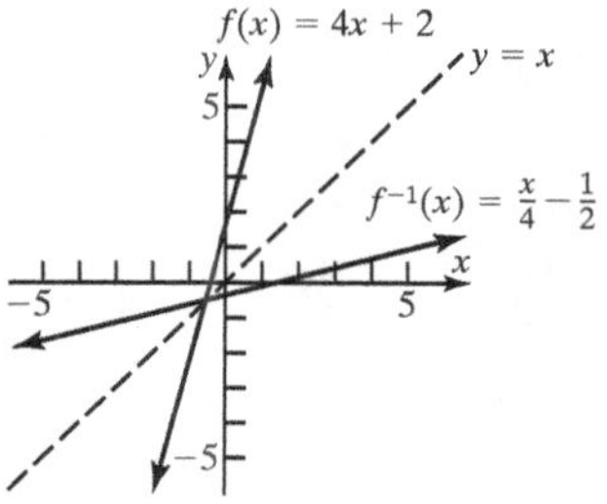

51. $f^{-1}(x) = \sqrt[3]{x+1}$

$f(f^{-1}(x)) = f\left(\sqrt[3]{x+1}\right)$

$= \left(\sqrt[3]{x+1}\right)^3 - 1 = x$

$f^{-1}(f(x)) = f^{-1}(x^3 - 1)$

$= \sqrt[3]{(x^3-1)+1} = x$

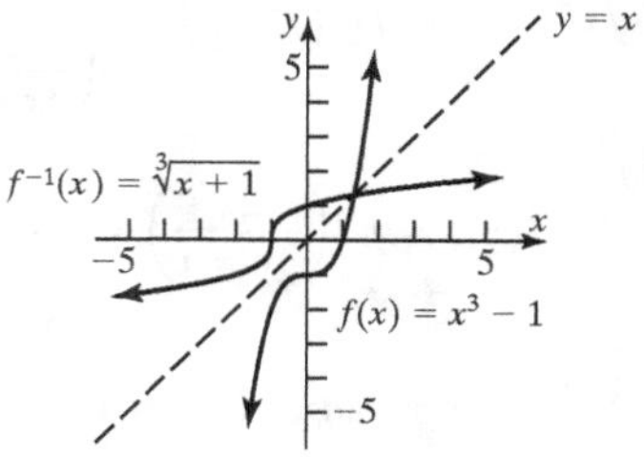

53. $f^{-1}(x) = \sqrt{x - 4}, x \geq 4$

$$f(f^{-1}(x)) = f(\sqrt{x-4}) = (\sqrt{x-4})^2 + 4 = x$$
$$f^{-1}(f(x)) = f^{-1}(x^2+4) = \sqrt{(x^2+4)-4} = \sqrt{x^2} = x, x \geq 0$$

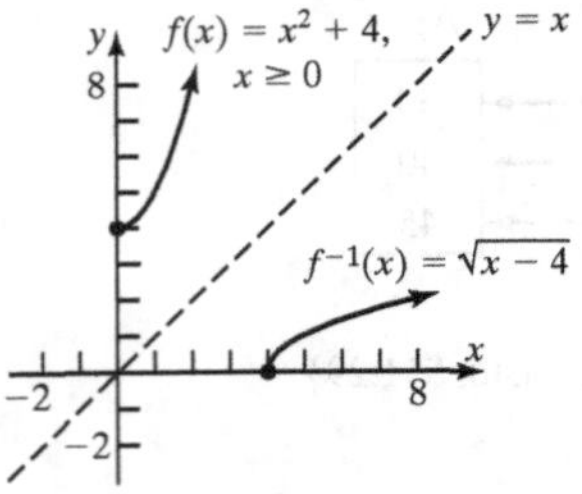

55. $f^{-1}(x) = \dfrac{4}{x}$

$$f(f^{-1}(x)) = f\left(\frac{4}{x}\right) = \frac{4}{\left(\frac{4}{x}\right)} = x$$
$$f^{-1}(f(x)) = f^{-1}\left(\frac{4}{x}\right) = \frac{4}{\left(\frac{4}{x}\right)} = x$$

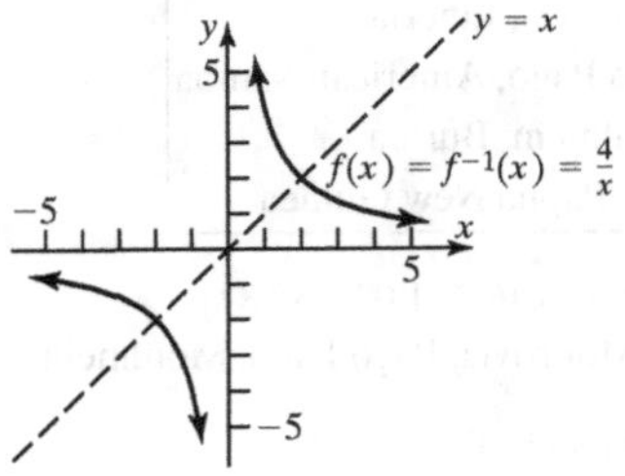

57. $f^{-1}(x) = \dfrac{2x+1}{x}$

$$f(f^{-1}(x)) = f\left(\frac{2x+1}{x}\right) = \frac{1}{\frac{2x+1}{x} - 2} = \frac{x}{(2x+1) - 2x} = x$$
$$f^{-1}(f(x)) = f^{-1}\left(\frac{1}{x-2}\right) = \frac{2\left(\frac{1}{x-2}\right) + 1}{\frac{1}{x-2}} = \frac{2 + (x-2)}{1} = x$$

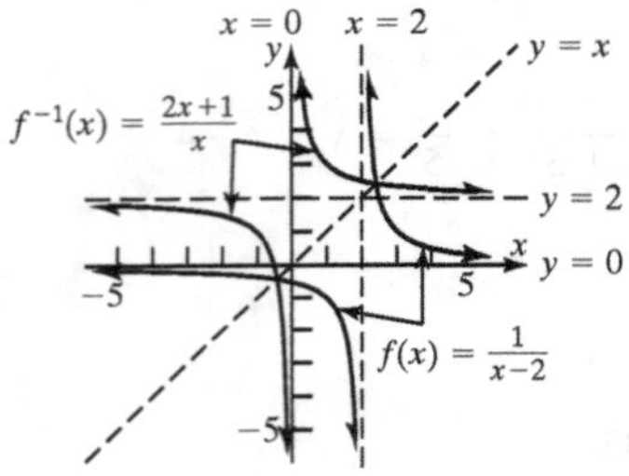

59. $f^{-1}(x) = \dfrac{2-3x}{x}$

$$f(f^{-1}(x)) = f\left(\frac{2-3x}{x}\right) = \frac{2}{3 + \frac{2-3x}{x}} = \frac{2x}{3x + 2 - 3x} = \frac{2x}{2} = x$$
$$f^{-1}(f(x)) = f^{-1}\left(\frac{2}{3+x}\right) = \frac{2 - 3\left(\frac{2}{3+x}\right)}{\frac{2}{3+x}} = \frac{2(3+x) - 3\cdot 2}{2} = \frac{2x}{2} = x$$

Domain f = range of f^{-1} = all real numbers except -3

Range f = domain f^{-1} = all real numbers except 0

61. $f^{-1}(x) = \dfrac{-2x}{x-3}$

$$f(f^{-1}(x)) = f\left(\frac{-2x}{x-3}\right) = \frac{3\left(\frac{-2x}{x-3}\right)}{\frac{-2x}{x-3} + 2} = \frac{3(-2x)}{-2x + 2(x-3)} = \frac{-6x}{-6} = x$$
$$f^{-1}(f(x)) = f^{-1}\left(\frac{3x}{x+2}\right) = \frac{-2\left(\frac{3x}{x+2}\right)}{\frac{3x}{x+2} - 3} = \frac{-2(3x)}{3x - 3(x+2)} = \frac{-6x}{-6} = x$$

Domain f = range of f^{-1} = all real numbers except -2

Range f = domain f^{-1} = all real numbers except 3

63. $f^{-1}(x) = \dfrac{x}{3x-2}$

$$f(f^{-1}(x)) = f\left(\frac{x}{3x-2}\right) = \frac{2\left(\frac{x}{3x-2}\right)}{3\left(\frac{x}{3x-2}\right) - 1} = \frac{2x}{3x - (3x-2)} = \frac{2x}{2} = x$$
$$f^{-1}(f(x)) = f^{-1}\left(\frac{2x}{3x-1}\right) = \frac{\frac{2x}{3x-1}}{3\left(\frac{2x}{3x-1}\right) - 2} = \frac{2x}{6x - 2(3x-1)} = \frac{2x}{2} = x$$

Domain f = range of f^{-1} = all real numbers except $\frac{1}{3}$

Range f = domain f^{-1} = all real numbers except $\frac{2}{3}$

65. $f^{-1}(x) = \dfrac{3x + 4}{2x - 3}$

$$f(f^{-1}(x)) = f\left(\frac{3x+4}{2x-3}\right) = \frac{3\left(\frac{3x+4}{2x-3}\right) + 4}{2\left(\frac{3x+4}{2x-3}\right) - 3} = \frac{3(3x+4) + 4(2x-3)}{2(3x+4) - 3(2x-3)} = \frac{17x}{17} = x$$

$$f^{-1}(f(x)) = f^{-1}\left(\frac{3x+4}{2x-3}\right) = \frac{3\left(\frac{3x+4}{2x-3}\right) + 4}{2\left(\frac{3x+4}{2x-3}\right) - 3} = \frac{3(3x+4) + 4(2x-3)}{2(3x+4) - 3(2x-3)} = \frac{17x}{17} = x$$

Domain f = range of f^{-1} = all real numbers except $\frac{3}{2}$

Range f = domain f^{-1} = all real numbers except $\frac{3}{2}$

67. $f^{-1}(x) = \dfrac{-2x + 3}{x - 2}$

$$f(f^{-1}(x)) = f\left(\frac{-2x+3}{x-2}\right) = \frac{2\left(\frac{-2x+3}{x-2}\right) + 3}{\frac{-2x+3}{x-2} + 2} = \frac{2(-2x+3) + 3(x-2)}{-2x + 3 + 2(x-2)} = \frac{-x}{-1} = x$$

$$f^{-1}(f(x)) = f^{-1}\left(\frac{2x+3}{x+2}\right) = \frac{-2\left(\frac{2x+3}{x+2}\right) + 3}{\frac{2x+3}{x+2} - 2} = \frac{-2(2x+3) + 3(x+2)}{2x + 3 - 2(x+2)} = \frac{-x}{-1} = x$$

Domain f = range of f^{-1} = all real numbers except -2

Range f = domain f^{-1} = all real numbers except 2

69. $f^{-1}(x) = \dfrac{2}{\sqrt{1 - 2x}}$

$$f(f^{-1}(x)) = f\left(\frac{2}{\sqrt{1-2x}}\right) = \frac{\frac{4}{1-2x} - 4}{2\cdot\frac{4}{1-2x}} = \frac{4 - 4(1-2x)}{2\cdot 4} = \frac{8x}{8} = x$$

$$f^{-1}(f(x)) = f^{-1}\left(\frac{x^2-4}{2x^2}\right) = \frac{2}{\sqrt{1 - 2\left(\frac{x^2-4}{2x^2}\right)}} = \frac{2}{\sqrt{\frac{4}{x^2}}} = \sqrt{x^2} = x, \text{ since } x > 0$$

Domain f = range of f^{-1} = $(0, \infty)$

Range f = domain f^{-1} = $\left(-\infty, \frac{1}{2}\right)$

71. **(a)** 0 **(b)** 2 **(c)** 0 **(d)** 1

73. 7 **75.** Domain of f^{-1}: $[-2, \infty)$; range of f^{-1}: $[5, \infty)$

77. Domain of g^{-1}: $[0, \infty)$; range of g^{-1}: all real numbers

79. Increasing on the interval $(f(0), f(5))$

81. $f^{-1}(x) = \dfrac{1}{m}(x - b), m \neq 0$

83. Quadrant I

85. Possible answer: $f(x) = |x|, x \geq 0$, is one-to-one; $f^{-1}(x) = x, x \geq 0$

87. **(a)** $r(d) = \dfrac{d + 90.39}{6.97}$

(b) $r(d(r)) = \dfrac{6.97r - 90.39 + 90.39}{6.97} = \dfrac{6.97r}{6.97} = r$

$d(r(d)) = 6.97\left(\dfrac{d + 90.39}{6.97}\right) - 90.39 = d + 90.39 - 90.39 = d$

(c) 56 miles per hour

89. **(a)** 77.6 kg **(b)** $h(W) = \dfrac{W - 50}{2.3} + 60 = \dfrac{W + 88}{2.3}$

(c) $h(W(h)) = \dfrac{50 + 2.3(h - 60) + 88}{2.3} = \dfrac{2.3h}{2.3} = h$

$W(h(W)) = 50 + 2.3\left(\dfrac{W + 88}{2.3} - 60\right) = 50 + W + 88 - 138 = W$

(d) 73 inches

91. **(a)** $\{g \mid 31{,}850 \leq g \leq 77{,}100\}$

(b) $\{T \mid 4386.25 \leq T \leq 15{,}698.75\}$

(c) $g(T) = \dfrac{T - 4386.25}{0.25} + 31{,}850$

Domain: $\{T \mid 4386.25 \leq T \leq 15{,}698.75\}$

Range: $\{g \mid 31{,}850 \leq g \leq 77{,}100\}$

93. **(a)** t represents time, so $t \geq 0$.

(b) $t(H) = \sqrt{\dfrac{H - 100}{-4.9}} = \sqrt{\dfrac{100 - H}{4.9}}$

(c) 2.02 seconds

95. $f^{-1}(x) = \dfrac{-dx + b}{cx - a}$; $f = f^{-1}$ if $a = -d$

99. No

5.3 Assess Your Understanding *(page 279)*

6. $\left(-1, \frac{1}{a}\right), (0, 1), (1, a)$ **7.** 1 **8.** 4 **9.** F **10.** F **11.** **(a)** 11.212 **(b)** 11.587 **(c)** 11.664 **(d)** 11.665 **13.** **(a)** 8.815 **(b)** 8.821 **(c)** 8.824 **(d)** 8.825 **15.** **(a)** 21.217 **(b)** 22.217 **(c)** 22.440 **(d)** 22.459 **17.** 3.320 **19.** 0.427 **21.** Neither **23.** Exponential; $H(x) = 4^x$ **25.** Exponential; $f(x) = 3(2^x)$ **27.** Linear; $H(x) = 2x + 4$ **29.** B **31.** D **33.** F **35.** E

37.

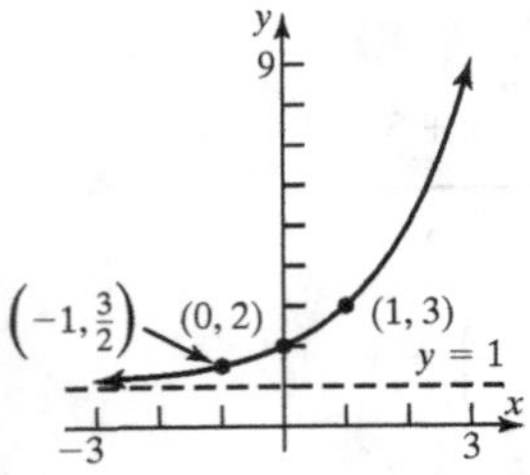

Domain: All real numbers
Range: $\{y | y > 1\}$ or $(1, \infty)$
Horizontal asymptote: $y = 1$

39.

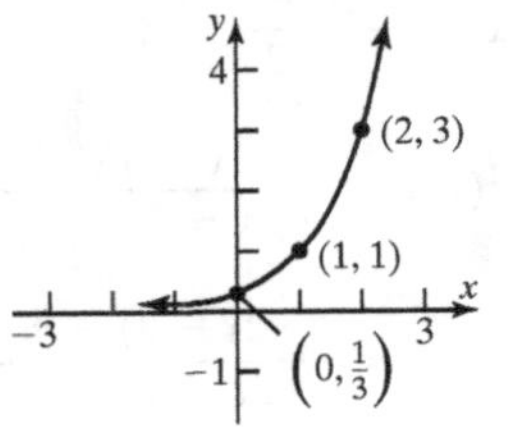

Domain: All real numbers
Range: $\{y | y > 0\}$ or $(0, \infty)$
Horizontal asymptote: $y = 0$

41.

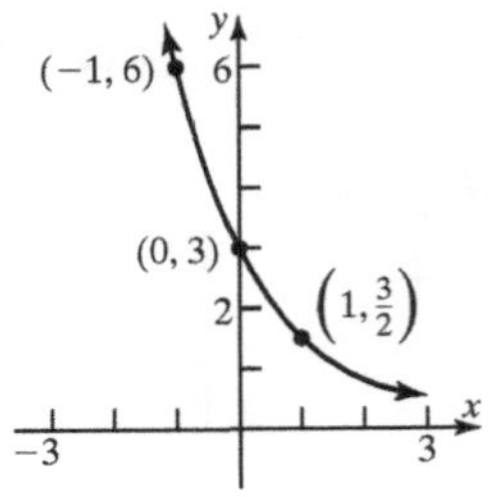

Domain: All real numbers
Range: $\{y | y > 0\}$ or $(0, \infty)$
Horizontal asymptote: $y = 0$

43.

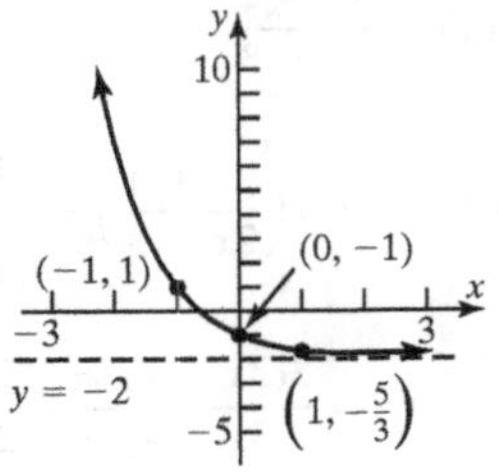

Domain: All real numbers
Range: $\{y | y > -2\}$ or $(-2, \infty)$
Horizontal asymptote: $y = -2$

45.

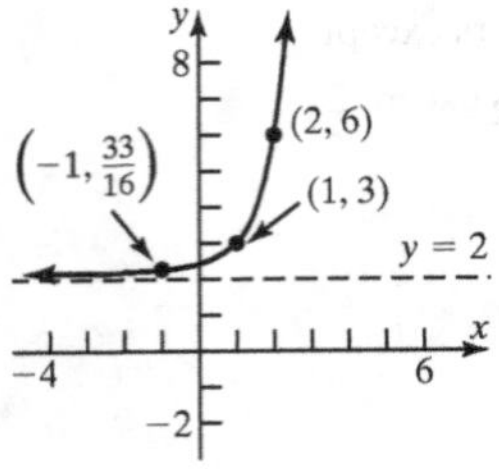

Domain: All real numbers
Range: $\{y | y > 2\}$ or $(2, \infty)$
Horizontal asymptote: $y = 2$

47.

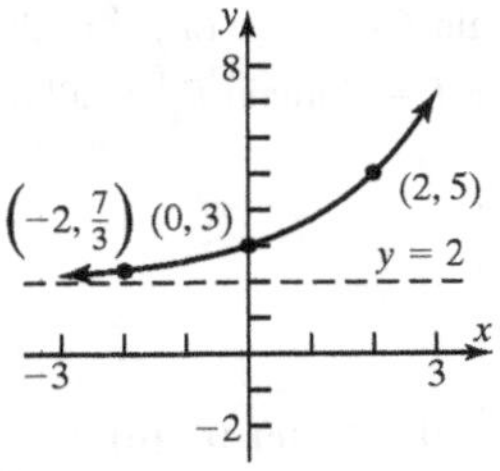

Domain: All real numbers
Range: $\{y | y > 2\}$ or $(2, \infty)$
Horizontal asymptote: $y = 2$

49.

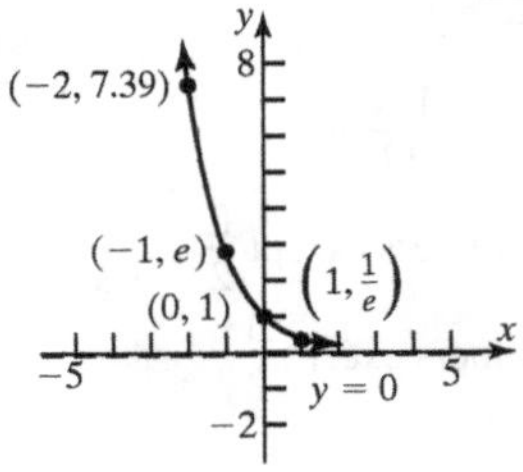

Domain: All real numbers
Range: $\{y | y > 0\}$ or $(0, \infty)$
Horizontal asymptote: $y = 0$

51.

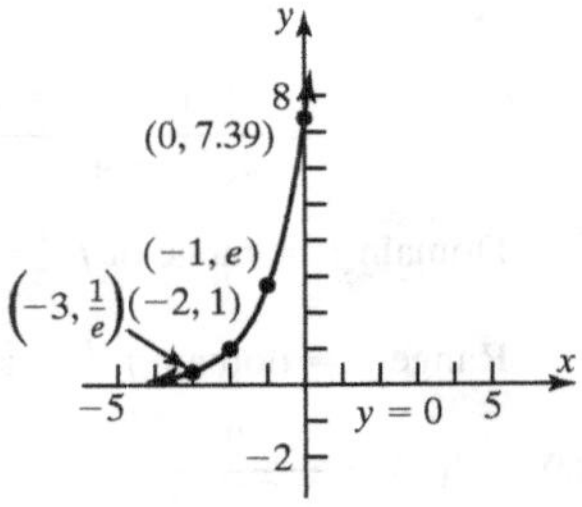

Domain: All real numbers
Range: $\{y | y > 0\}$ or $(0, \infty)$
Horizontal asymptote: $y = 0$

53.

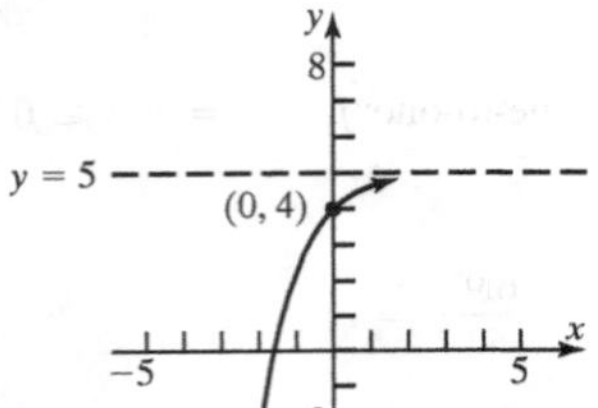

Domain: All real numbers
Range: $\{y | y < 5\}$ or $(-\infty, 5)$
Horizontal asymptote: $y = 5$

55.

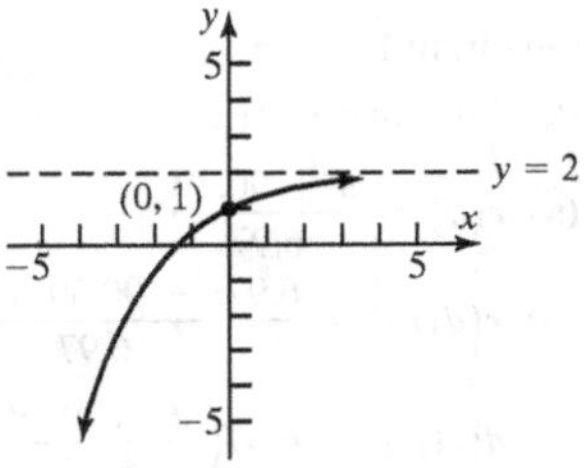

Domain: All real numbers
Range: $\{y | y < 2\}$ or $(-\infty, 2)$
Horizontal asymptote: $y = 2$

57. $\{3\}$ **59.** $\{-4\}$ **61.** $\{2\}$ **63.** $\left\{\frac{3}{2}\right\}$
65. $\{-\sqrt{2}, 0, \sqrt{2}\}$ **67.** $\{6\}$ **69.** $\{-1, 7\}$ **71.** $\{-4, 2\}$
73. $\{-4\}$ **75.** $\{1, 2\}$ **77.** $\frac{1}{49}$ **79.** $\frac{1}{4}$ **81.** $f(x) = 3^x$
83. $f(x) = -6^x$ **85. (a)** 16; (4, 16) **(b)** -4; $\left(-4, \frac{1}{16}\right)$
87. (a) $\frac{9}{4}$; $\left(-1, \frac{9}{4}\right)$ **(b)** 3; (3, 66)
89. (a) 60; $(-6, 60)$ **(b)** -4: $(-4, 12)$ **(c)** -2

91.

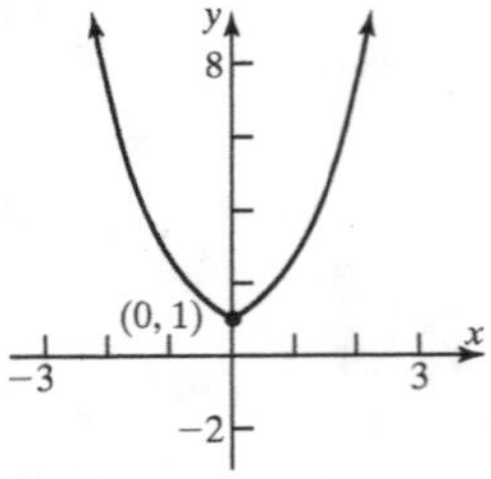

Domain: $(-\infty, \infty)$
Range: $[1, \infty)$
Intercept: (0, 1)

93.

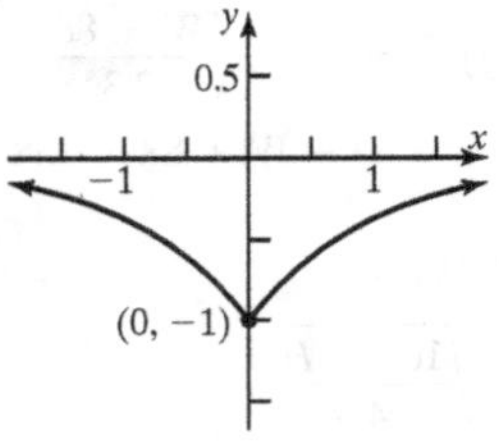

Domain: $(-\infty, \infty)$
Range: $[-1, 0)$
Intercept: $(0, -1)$

95. (a) 74% **(b)** 47%
97. (a) \$12,123 **(b)** \$6443
99. 3.35 mg; 0.45 mg

101. (a) 0.632 **(b)** 0.982 **(c)** 1
(d)

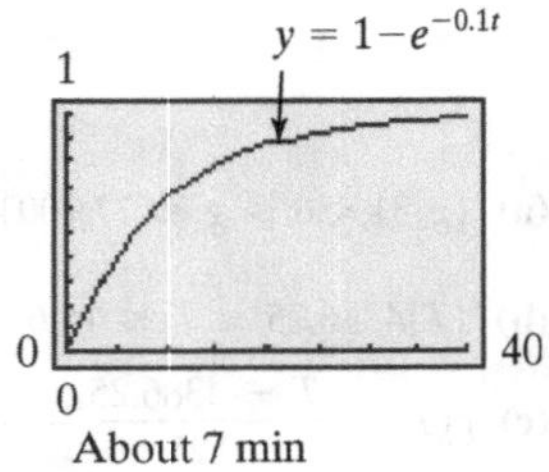

(e) About 7 min

103. (a) 0.0516 **(b)** 0.0888 **105. (a)** 70.95% **(b)** 72.62% **(c)** 100%
107. (a) 5.41 amp, 7.59 amp, 10.38 amp **(b)** 12 amp **(d)** 3.34 amp, 5.31 amp, 9.44 amp **(e)** 24 amp
(c), (f)

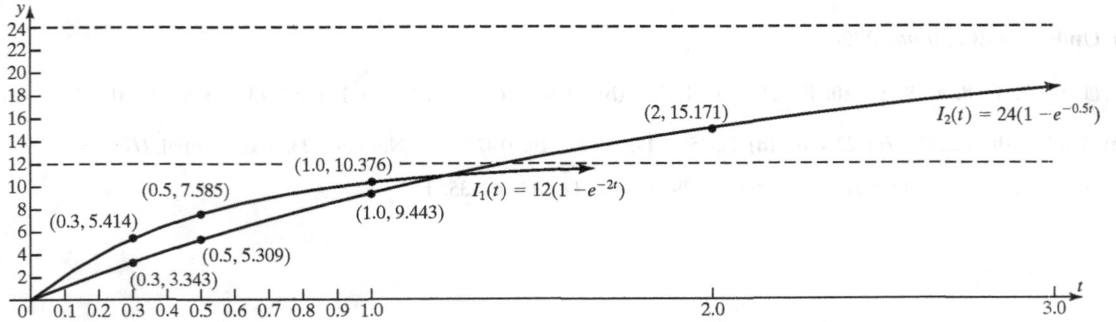

109. $n = 4$: 2.7083; $n = 6$: 2.7181; $n = 8$: 2.7182788; $n = 10$: 2.7182818

111. $\dfrac{f(x+h) - f(x)}{h} = \dfrac{a^{x+h} - a^x}{h} = \dfrac{a^x a^h - a^x}{h} = \dfrac{a^x(a^h - 1)}{h}$

113. $f(-x) = a^{-x} = \dfrac{1}{a^x} = \dfrac{1}{f(x)}$

115. **(a)** $f(-x) = \dfrac{1}{2}(e^{-x} - e^{-(-x)})$

$= \dfrac{1}{2}(e^{-x} - e^{x})$

$= -\dfrac{1}{2}(e^{x} - e^{-x})$

$= -f(x)$

(b)

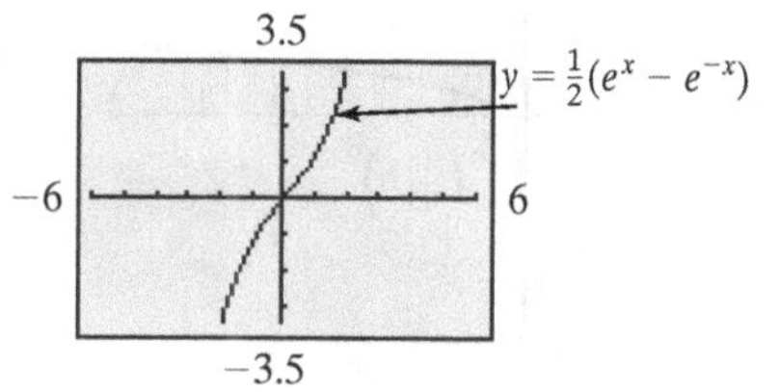

117. $f(1) = 5, f(2) = 17, f(3) = 257, f(4) = 65{,}537; f(5) = 4{,}294{,}967{,}297 = 641 \times 6{,}700{,}417$

5.4 Assess Your Understanding *(page 293)*

4. $\{x|x > 0\}$ or $(0, \infty)$ **5.** $\left(\frac{1}{a}, -1\right), (1, 0), (a, 1)$ **6.** 1 **7.** F **8.** T **9.** $2 = \log_3 9$ **11.** $2 = \log_a 1.6$ **13.** $x = \log_2 7.2$ **15.** $x = \ln 8$

17. $2^3 = 8$ **19.** $a^6 = 3$ **21.** $3^x = 2$ **23.** $e^x = 4$ **25.** 0 **27.** 2 **29.** −4 **31.** $\frac{1}{2}$ **33.** 4 **35.** $\frac{1}{2}$ **37.** $\{x|x > 3\}; (3, \infty)$

39. All real numbers except 0; $\{x|x \neq 0\}$ **41.** $\{x|x > 10\}; (10, \infty)$ **43.** $\{x|x > -1\}; (-1, \infty)$ **45.** $\{x|x < -1 \text{ or } x > 0\}; (-\infty, -1) \cup (0, \infty)$

47. $\{x|x \geq 1\}; [1, \infty)$ **49.** 0.511 **51.** 30.099 **53.** 2.303 **55.** −53.991 **57.** $\sqrt{2}$

59.

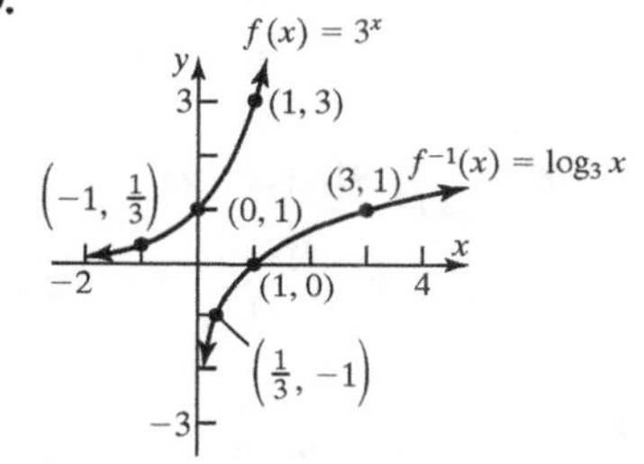

61.

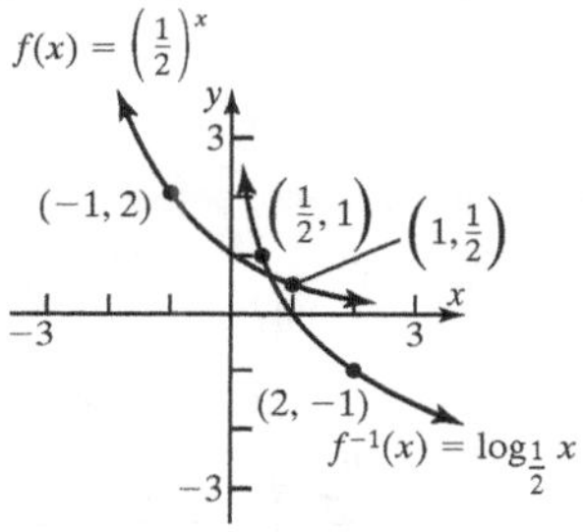

63. B **65.** D **67.** A **69.** E

71. **(a)** Domain: $(-4, \infty)$

(b)

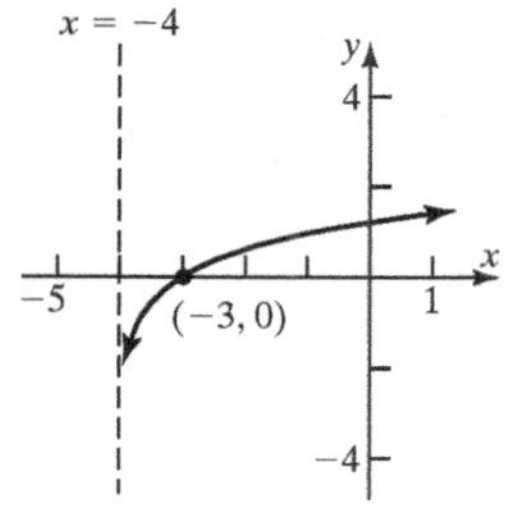

(c) Range: $(-\infty, \infty)$
Vertical asymptote: $x = -4$

(d) $f^{-1}(x) = e^x - 4$

(e) Range of f: $(-\infty, \infty)$
Range of f^{-1}: $(-4, \infty)$

(f)

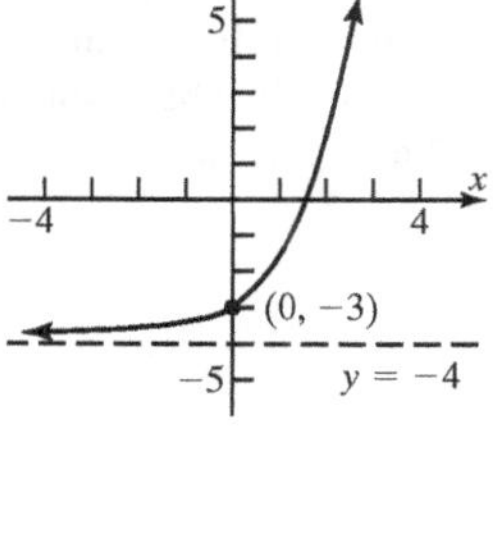

73. **(a)** Domain: $(0, \infty)$

(b)

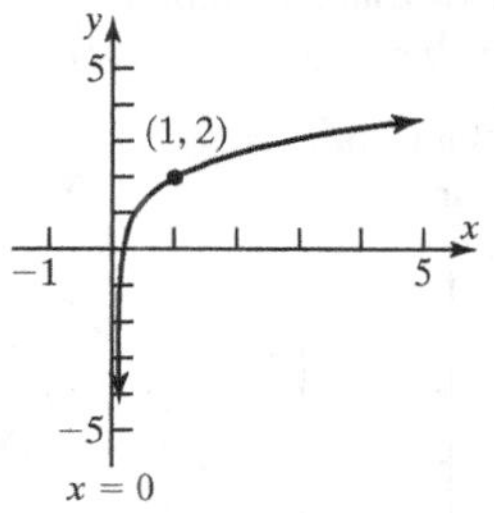

(c) Range: $(-\infty, \infty)$
Vertical asymptote: $x = 0$

(d) $f^{-1}(x) = e^{x-2}$

(e) Range of f: $(-\infty, \infty)$
Range of f^{-1}: $(0, \infty)$

(f)

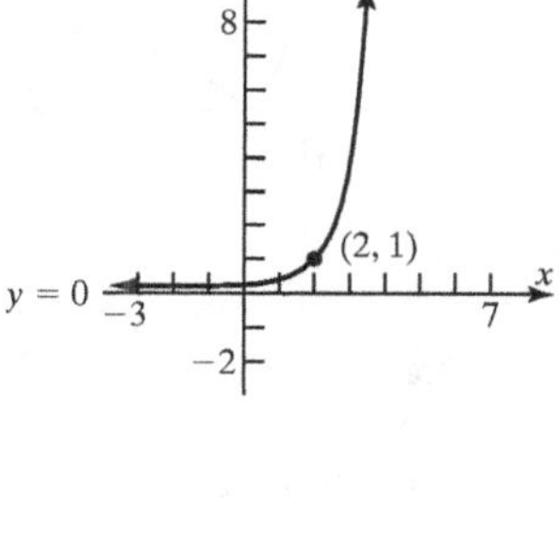

75. **(a)** Domain: $(0, \infty)$

(b)

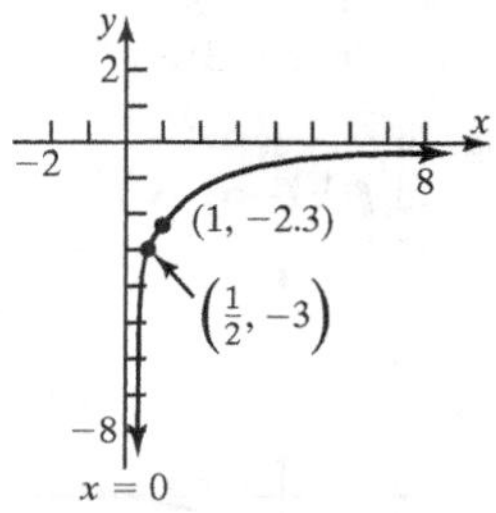

(c) Range: $(-\infty, \infty)$
Vertical asymptote: $x = 0$

(d) $f^{-1}(x) = \dfrac{1}{2}e^{x+3}$

(e) Range of f: $(-\infty, \infty)$
Range of f^{-1}: $(0, \infty)$

(f)

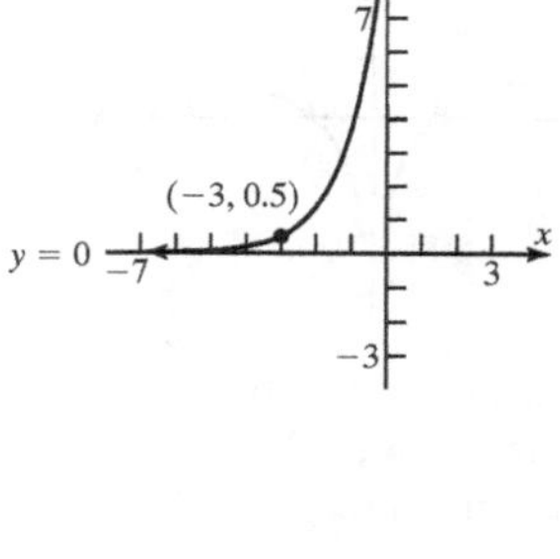

77. **(a)** Domain: $(4, \infty)$
(b)

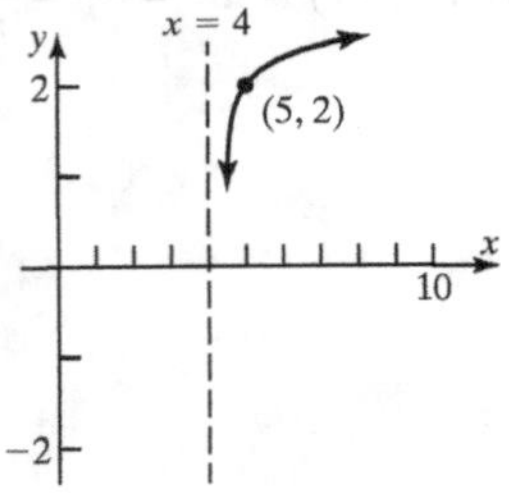

(c) Range: $(-\infty, \infty)$
Vertical asymptote: $x = 4$
(d) $f^{-1}(x) = 10^{x-2} + 4$
(e) Range of f: $(-\infty, \infty)$
Range of f^{-1}: $(4, \infty)$
(f)

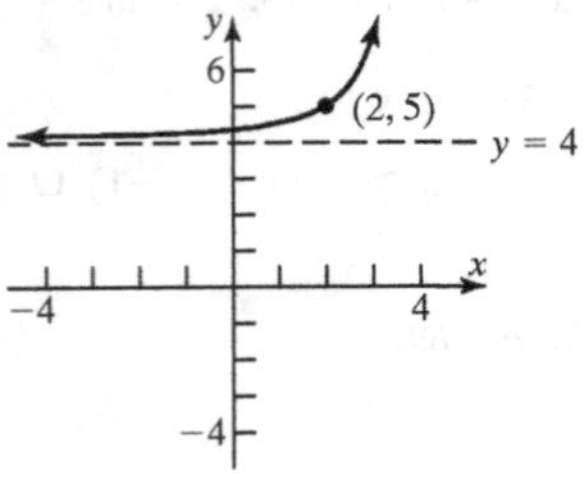

79. **(a)** Domain: $(0, \infty)$
(b)

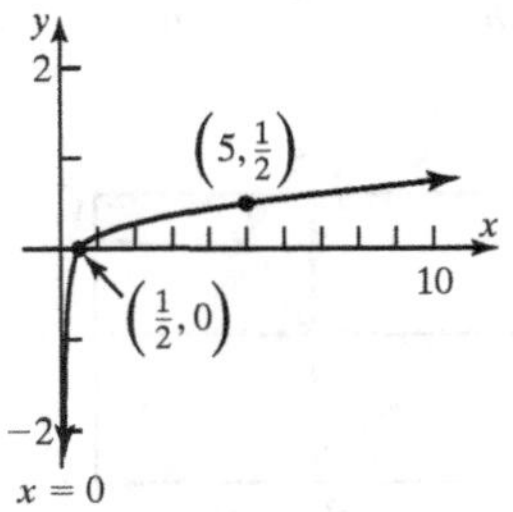

(c) Range: $(-\infty, \infty)$
Vertical asymptote: $x = 0$
(d) $f^{-1}(x) = \frac{1}{2} \cdot 10^{2x}$
(e) Range of f: $(-\infty, \infty)$
Range of f^{-1}: $(0,\infty)$
(f)

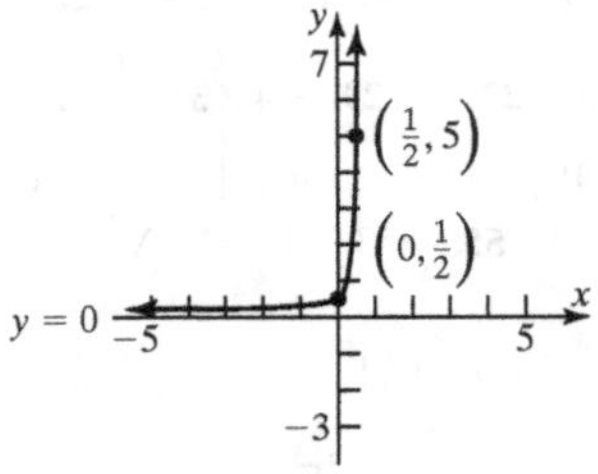

81. **(a)** Domain: $(-2, \infty)$
(b)

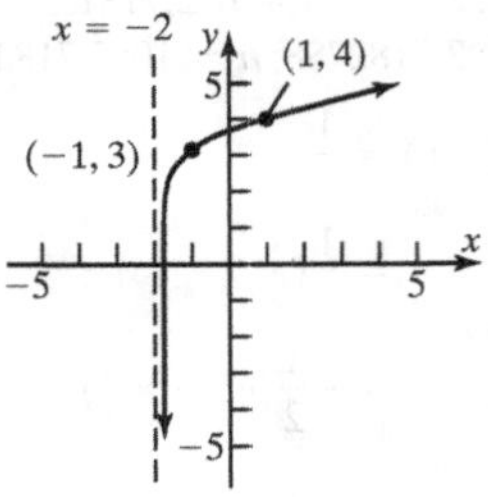

(c) Range: $(-\infty, \infty)$
Vertical asymptote: $x = -2$
(d) $f^{-1}(x) = 3^{x-3} - 2$
(e) Range of f: $(-\infty, \infty)$
Range of f^{-1}: $(-2, \infty)$
(f)

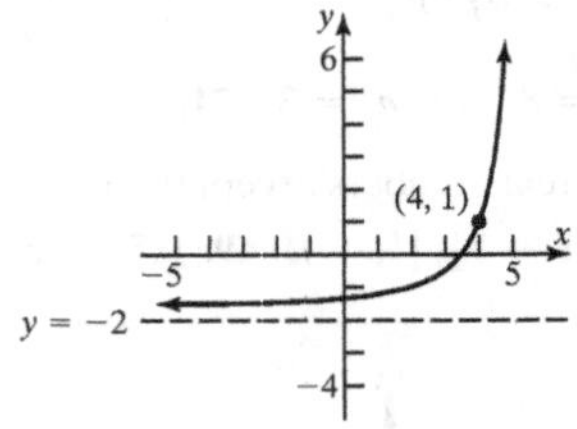

83. **(a)** Domain: $(-\infty, \infty)$
(b)

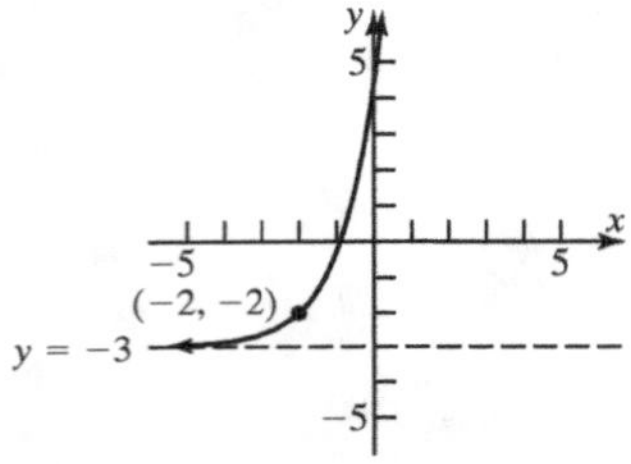

(c) Range: $(-3, \infty)$
Horizontal asymptote: $y = -3$
(d) $f^{-1}(x) = \ln(x + 3) - 2$
(e) Range of f: $(-3, \infty)$
Range of f^{-1}: $(-\infty, \infty)$
(f)

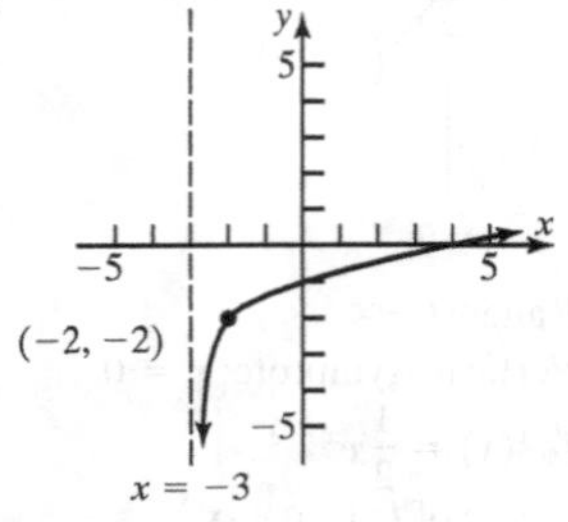

85. **(a)** Domain: $(-\infty, \infty)$
(b)

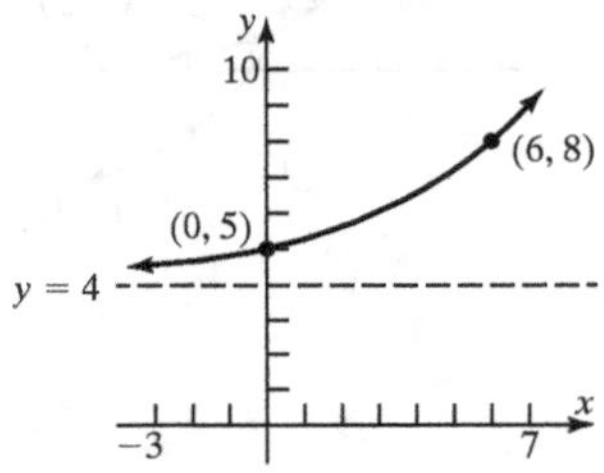

(c) Range: $(4, \infty)$
Horizontal asymptote: $y = 4$
(d) $f^{-1}(x) = 3 \log_2 (x - 4)$
(e) Range of f: $(4, \infty)$
Range of f^{-1}: $(-\infty, \infty)$
(f)

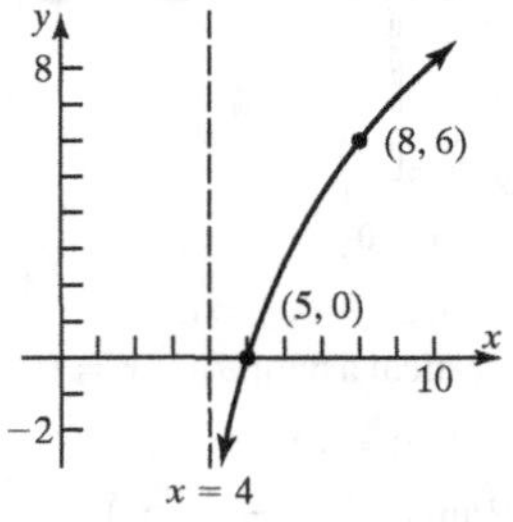

87. $\{9\}$ **89.** $\left\{\frac{7}{2}\right\}$ **91.** $\{2\}$ **93.** $\{5\}$
95. $\{3\}$ **97.** $\{2\}$ **99.** $\left\{\frac{\ln 10}{3}\right\}$
101. $\left\{\frac{\ln 8 - 5}{2}\right\}$
103. $\{-2\sqrt{2}, 2\sqrt{2}\}$ **105.** $\{-1\}$
107. $\left\{5 \ln \frac{7}{5}\right\}$ **109.** $\left\{2 - \log \frac{5}{2}\right\}$
111. **(a)** $\left\{x \middle| x > -\frac{1}{2}\right\}; \left(-\frac{1}{2}, \infty\right)$
(b) 2; (40, 2) **(c)** 121; (121, 3) **(d)** 4

113.

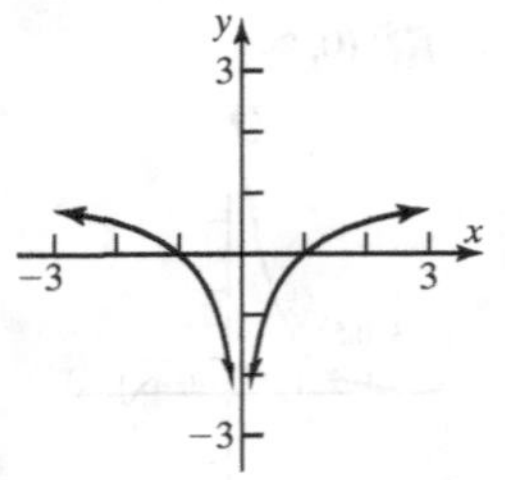

Domain: $\{x | x \neq 0\}$
Range: $(-\infty, \infty)$
Intercepts: $(-1, 0)$, $(1, 0)$

115.

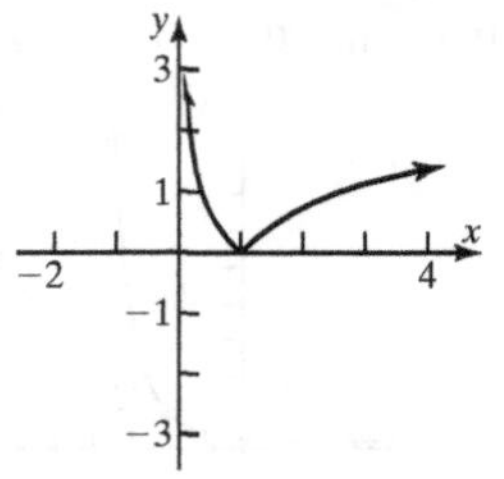

Domain: $\{x | x > 0\}$
Range: $\{y | y \geq 0\}$
Intercept: $(1, 0)$

117. **(a)** 1 **(b)** 2 **(c)** 3 **(d)** It increases.
(e) 0.000316 **(f)** 3.981×10^{-8}
119. **(a)** 5.97 km **(b)** 0.90 km
121. **(a)** 6.93 min **(b)** 16.09 min
123. $h \approx 2.29$, so the time between injections is about 2 h, 17 min.

125. 0.2695 s
0.8959 s

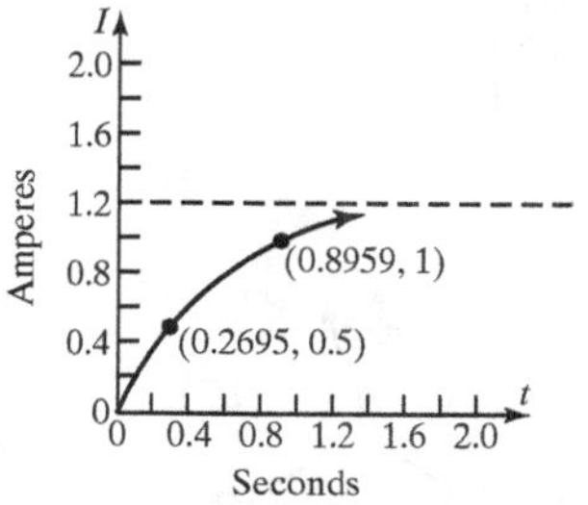

127. 50 decibels (dB) **129.** 90 dB **131.** 8.1
133. **(a)** $k \approx 11.216$ **(b)** 6.73 **(c)** 0.41% **(d)** 0.14%
135. Because $y = \log_1 x$ means $1^y = 1 = x$, which cannot be true for $x \neq 1$

5.5 Assess Your Understanding *(page 304)*

1. sum **2.** 7 **3.** $r \log_a M$ **4.** F **5.** F **6.** T **7.** 71 **9.** −4 **11.** 7 **13.** 1 **15.** 1 **17.** 2 **19.** $\frac{5}{4}$ **21.** 4 **23.** $a + b$ **25.** $b - a$ **27.** $3a$ **29.** $\frac{1}{5}(a+b)$ **31.** $2 + \log_5 x$ **33.** $3 \log_2 z$ **35.** $1 + \ln x$ **37.** $\ln x + x$ **39.** $2 \log_a u + 3 \log_a v$ **41.** $2 \ln x + \frac{1}{2}\ln(1-x)$ **43.** $3 \log_2 x - \log_2(x-3)$ **45.** $\log x + \log(x+2) - 2\log(x+3)$ **47.** $\frac{1}{3}\ln(x-2) + \frac{1}{3}\ln(x+1) - \frac{2}{3}\ln(x+4)$ **49.** $\ln 5 + \ln x + \frac{1}{2}\ln(1+3x) - 3\ln(x-4)$ **51.** $\log_5 u^3 v^4$ **53.** $\log_3\left(\frac{1}{x^{5/2}}\right)$ **55.** $\log_4\left[\frac{x-1}{(x+1)^4}\right]$ **57.** $-2\ln(x-1)$ **59.** $\log_2[x(3x-2)^4]$ **61.** $\log_a\left(\frac{25x^6}{\sqrt{2x+3}}\right)$ **63.** $\log_2\left[\frac{(x+1)^2}{(x+3)(x-1)}\right]$ **65.** 2.771 **67.** −3.880 **69.** 5.615 **71.** 0.874

73. $y = \frac{\log x}{\log 4}$

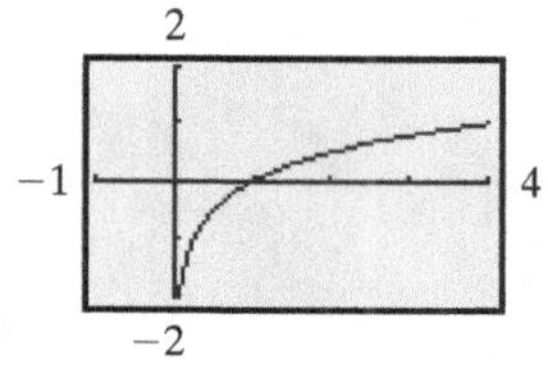

75. $y = \frac{\log(x+2)}{\log 2}$

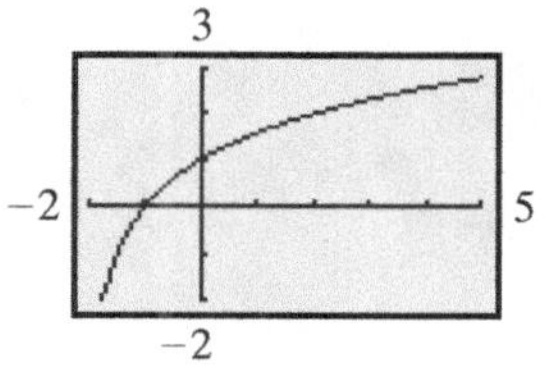

77. $y = \frac{\log(x+1)}{\log(x-1)}$

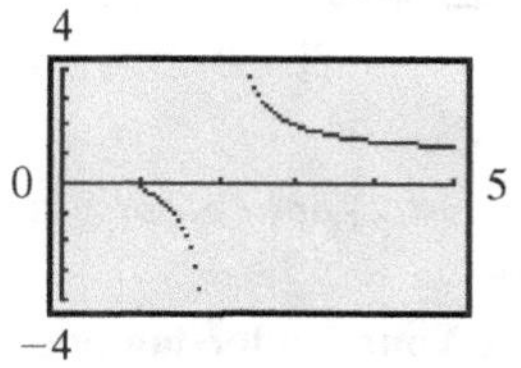

79. **(a)** $(f \circ g)(x) = x$; $\{x \mid x \text{ is any real number}\}$ or $(-\infty, \infty)$
(b) $(g \circ f)(x) = x$; $\{x \mid x > 0\}$ or $(0, \infty)$ **(c)** 5
(d) $(f \circ h)(x) = \ln x^2$; $\{x \mid x \neq 0\}$ or $(-\infty, 0) \cup (0, \infty)$ **(e)** 2

81. $y = Cx$ **83.** $y = Cx(x+1)$ **85.** $y = Ce^{3x}$ **87.** $y = Ce^{-4x} + 3$

89. $y = \frac{\sqrt[3]{C}(2x+1)^{1/6}}{(x+4)^{1/9}}$ **91.** 3 **93.** 1

95. $\log_a\left(x + \sqrt{x^2-1}\right) + \log_a\left(x - \sqrt{x^2-1}\right) = \log_a\left[\left(x + \sqrt{x^2-1}\right)\left(x - \sqrt{x^2-1}\right)\right] = \log_a[x^2 - (x^2-1)] = \log_a 1 = 0$

97. $\ln(1 + e^{2x}) = \ln[e^{2x}(e^{-2x} + 1)] = \ln e^{2x} + \ln(e^{-2x} + 1) = 2x + \ln(1 + e^{-2x})$

99. $y = f(x) = \log_a x$; $a^y = x$ implies $a^y = \left(\frac{1}{a}\right)^{-y} = x$, so $-y = \log_{1/a} x = -f(x)$.

101. $f(x) = \log_a x$; $f\left(\frac{1}{x}\right) = \log_a \frac{1}{x} = \log_a 1 - \log_a x = -f(x)$

103. $\log_a \frac{M}{N} = \log_a(M \cdot N^{-1}) = \log_a M + \log_a N^{-1} = \log_a M - \log_a N$, since $a^{\log_a N^{-1}} = N^{-1}$ implies $a^{-\log_a N^{-1}} = N$; i.e., $\log_a N = -\log_a N^{-1}$.

5.6 Assess Your Understanding *(page 310)*

5. {16} **7.** $\left\{\frac{16}{5}\right\}$ **9.** {6} **11.** {16} **13.** $\left\{\frac{1}{3}\right\}$ **15.** {3} **17.** {5} **19.** $\left\{\frac{21}{8}\right\}$ **21.** {−6} **23.** {−2} **25.** $\left\{-1 + \sqrt{1 + e^4}\right\} \approx \{6.456\}$ **27.** $\left\{\frac{-5 + 3\sqrt{5}}{2}\right\} \approx \{0.854\}$ **29.** {2} **31.** $\left\{\frac{9}{2}\right\}$ **33.** {8} **35.** $\{\log_2 10\} = \left\{\frac{\ln 10}{\ln 2}\right\} \approx \{3.322\}$ **37.** $\{-\log_8 1.2\} = \left\{-\frac{\ln 1.2}{\ln 8}\right\} \approx \{-0.088\}$ **39.** $\left\{\frac{1}{3}\log_2 \frac{8}{5}\right\} = \left\{\frac{\ln \frac{8}{5}}{3 \ln 2}\right\} \approx \{0.226\}$ **41.** $\left\{\frac{\ln 3}{2\ln 3 + \ln 4}\right\} \approx \{0.307\}$ **43.** $\left\{\frac{\ln 7}{\ln 0.6 + \ln 7}\right\} \approx \{1.356\}$ **45.** {0} **47.** $\left\{\frac{\ln \pi}{1 + \ln \pi}\right\} \approx \{0.534\}$ **49.** $\left\{\frac{\ln 3}{\ln 2}\right\} \approx \{1.585\}$ **51.** {0} **53.** $\left\{\log_4\left(-2 + \sqrt{7}\right)\right\} \approx \{-0.315\}$

55. $\{\log_5 4\} \approx \{0.861\}$ **57.** No real solution **59.** $\{\log_4 5\} \approx \{1.161\}$ **61.** $\{2.79\}$ **63.** $\{-0.57\}$ **65.** $\{-0.70\}$ **67.** $\{0.57\}$ **69.** $\{0.39, 1.00\}$

71. $\{1.32\}$ **73.** $\{1.31\}$ **75.** $\{1\}$ **77.** $\{16\}$ **79.** $\left\{-1, \frac{2}{3}\right\}$ **81.** $\{0\}$ **83.** $\{\ln(2 + \sqrt{5})\} \approx \{1.444\}$ **85.** $\left\{e^{\frac{\ln 5 \cdot \ln 3}{\ln 15}}\right\} \approx \{1.921\}$

87. (a) $\{5\}; (5, 3)$ **(b)** $\{5\}; (5, 4)$ **(c)** $\{1\}$; yes, at $(1, 2)$ **(d)** $\{5\}$ **(e)** $\left\{-\frac{1}{11}\right\}$

89. (a)

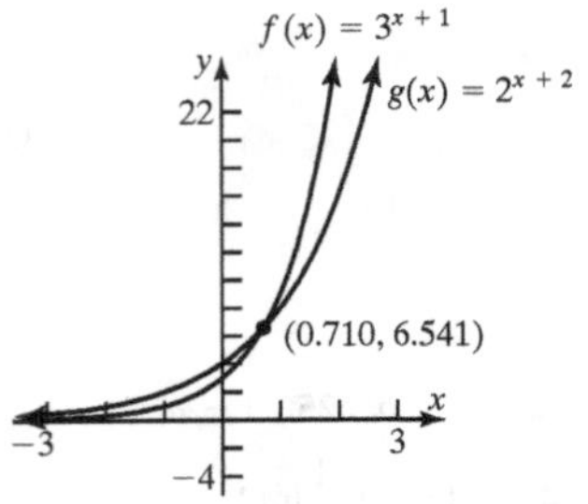

(b) $(0.710, 6.541)$
(c) $\{x \mid x > 0.710\}$ or $(0.710, \infty)$

91. (a), (b)

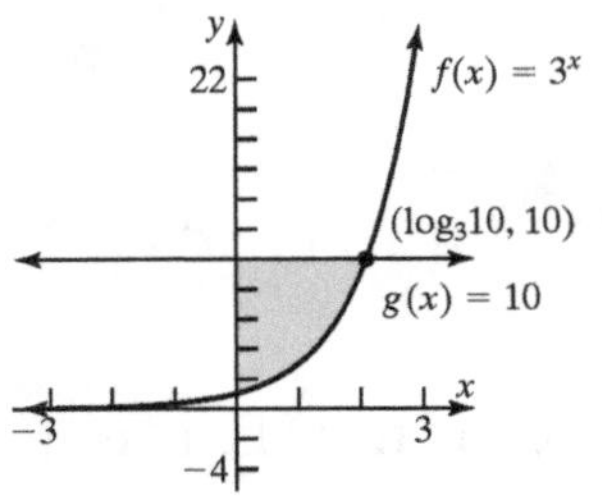

(c) $(\log_3 10, 10)$

93. (a), (b)

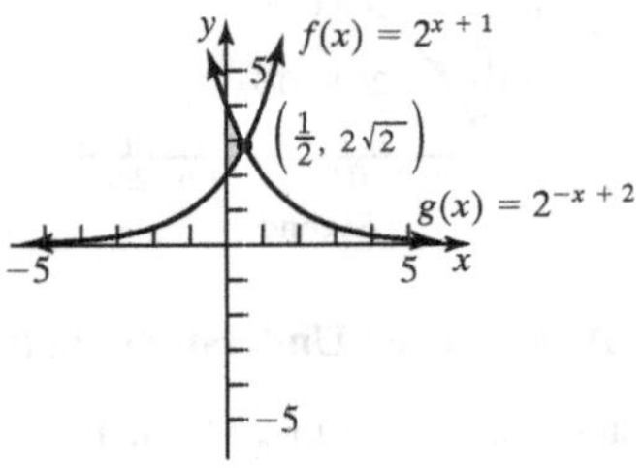

(c) $\left(\frac{1}{2}, 2\sqrt{2}\right)$

95. (a)

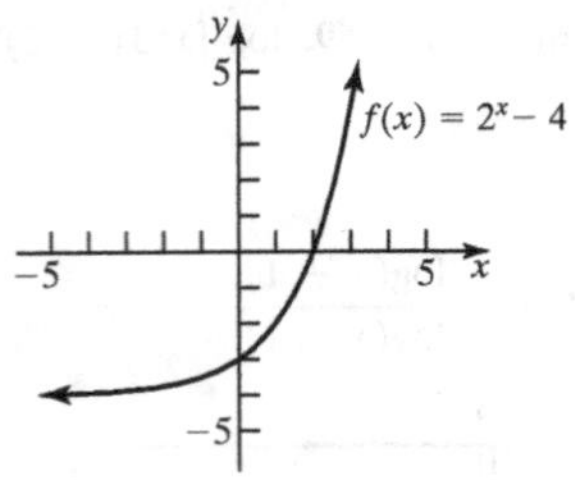

(b) 2
(c) $\{x \mid x < 2\}$ or $(-\infty, 2)$

97. (a) 2010 **(b)** 2027
99. (a) After 2.4 yr
(b) After 6.5 yr
(c) After 10 yr

5.7 Assess Your Understanding *(page 320)*

3. \$108.29 **5.** \$609.50 **7.** \$697.09 **9.** \$12.46 **11.** \$125.23 **13.** \$88.72 **15.** \$860.72 **17.** \$554.09 **19.** \$59.71 **21.** \$361.93 **23.** 5.095% **25.** 5.127% **27.** $6\frac{1}{4}$% compounded annually **29.** 9% compounded monthly **31.** 25.992% **33.** 24.573% **35. (a)** About 8.69 yr **(b)** About 8.66 yr **37.** 6.823% **39.** 5.09 yr; 5.07 yr **41.** 15.27 yr or 15 yr, 3 mo **43.** \$104,335 **45.** \$12,910.62 **47.** About \$30.17 per share or \$3017 **49.** Not quite. Jim will have \$1057.60. The second bank gives a better deal, since Jim will have \$1060.62 after 1 yr. **51.** Will has \$11,632.73; Henry has \$10,947.89. **53. (a)** \$49,581 **(b)** \$33,235 **55.** Approximately \$602 billion **57.** \$940.90 **59.** 2.53% **61.** 34.31 yr **63. (a)** \$1364.62 **(b)** \$1353.35 **65.** \$4631.93

67. (a) 6.12 yr
(b) 18.45 yr
(c)
$$mP = P\left(1 + \frac{r}{n}\right)^{nt}$$
$$m = \left(1 + \frac{r}{n}\right)^{nt}$$
$$\ln m = \ln\left(1 + \frac{r}{n}\right)^{nt} = nt \ln\left(1 + \frac{r}{n}\right)$$
$$t = \frac{\ln m}{n \ln\left(1 + \frac{r}{n}\right)}$$

69. (a) 2.51% **(b)** In 2022 or after 27 yr **71.** 22.7 yr

5.8 Assess Your Understanding *(page 331)*

1. (a) 500 insects
(b) $0.02 = 2\%$
(c)

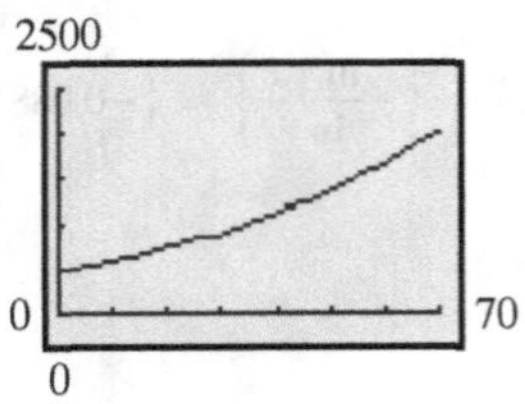

(d) About 611 insects
(e) After about 23.5 days
(f) After about 34.7 days

3. (a) $-0.0244 = -2.44\%$
(b)

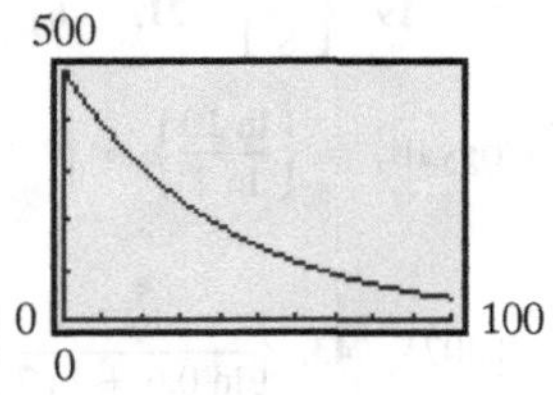

(c) About 391.7 g
(d) After about 9.1 yr
(e) 28.4 yr

5. (a) $N(t) = N_0 e^{kt}$
(b) 5832
(c) 3.9 days
7. (a) $N(t) = N_0 e^{kt}$
(b) 25,198
9. 9.797 g

11. **(a)** 9727 yr ago
(b)

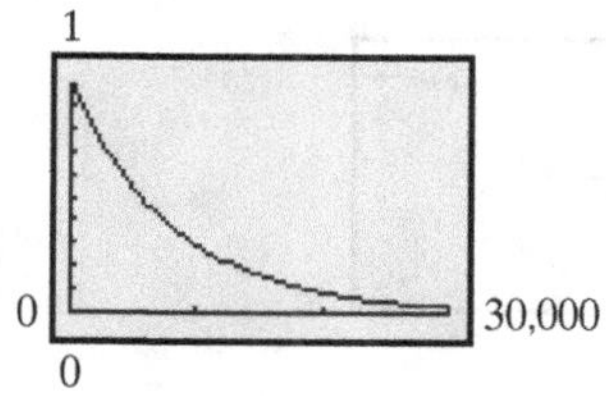

(c) 5600 yr

13. **(a)** About 5:18 PM
(b)

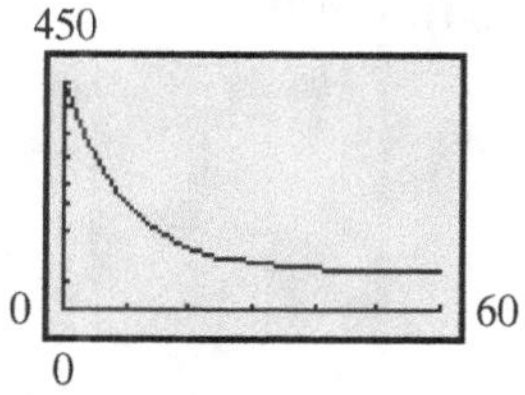

(c) About 14.3 min
(d) The temperature of the pizza approaches 70°F.

15. **(a)** 18.63°C; 25.07°C
(b)

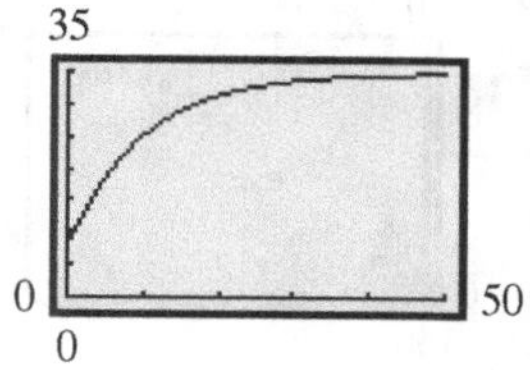

17. 1.7 ppm; 7.17 days or 172 h **19.** 0.26 mol; 6.58 h or 395 min **21.** 26.6 days

23. **(a)** 1000 g **(b)** 43.9% **(c)** 30 g
(d)

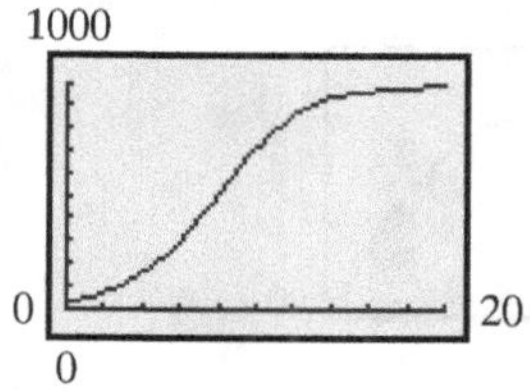

(e) 616.6 g **(f)** After 9.85 h
(g) About 7.9 h

25. **(a)** 9.23×10^{-3}, or about 0
(b) 0.81, or about 1
(c) 5.01, or about 5
(d) 57.91°, 43.99°, 30.07°

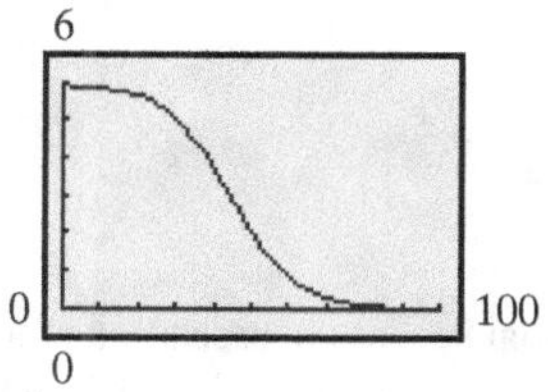

27. **(a)** In 1984, 91.8% of households did not own a personal computer.
(b)

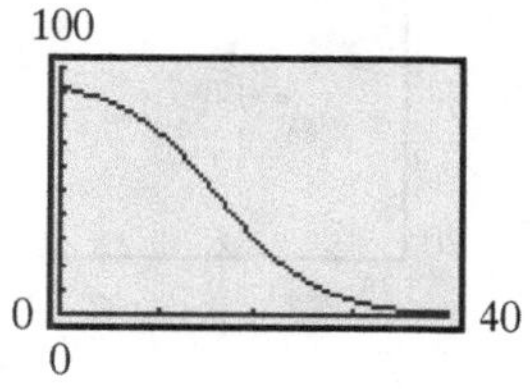

(c) 70.6% **(d)** During 2011

29. **(a)**

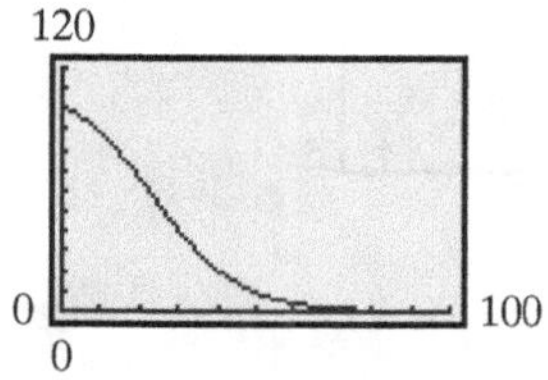

(b) 0.78 or 78% **(c)** 50 people
(d) As n increases, the probability decreases.

5.9 Assess Your Understanding *(page 339)*

1. **(a)**

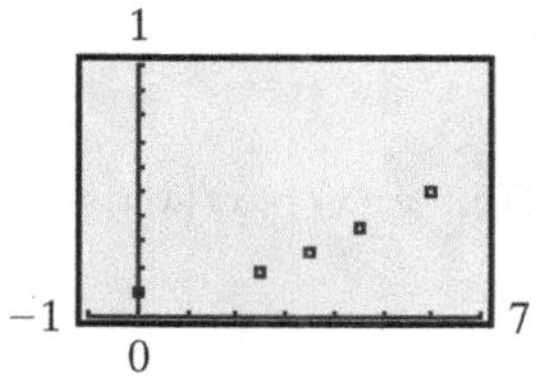

(b) $y = 0.0903(1.3384)^x$
(c) $N(t) = 0.0903e^{0.2915t}$

(d)

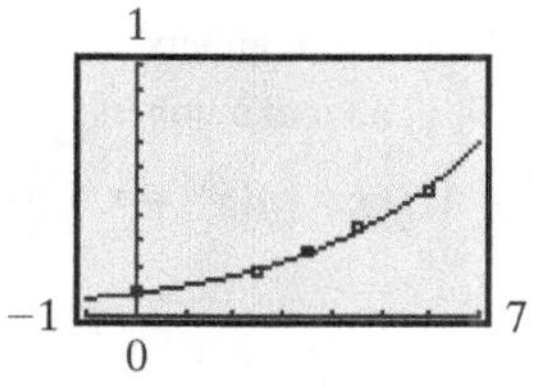

(e) 0.69
(f) After about 7.26 hr

3. **(a)**

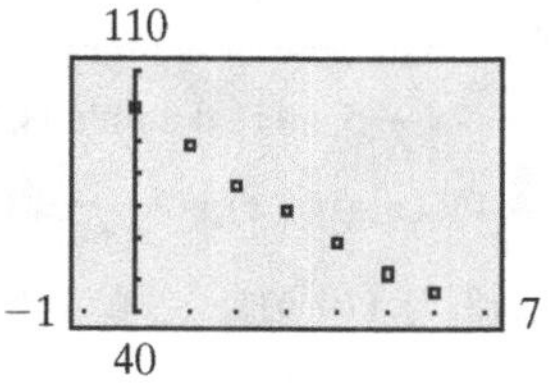

(b) $y = 100.326(0.8769)^x$
(c) $A(t) = 100.326e^{-0.1314t}$

(d)

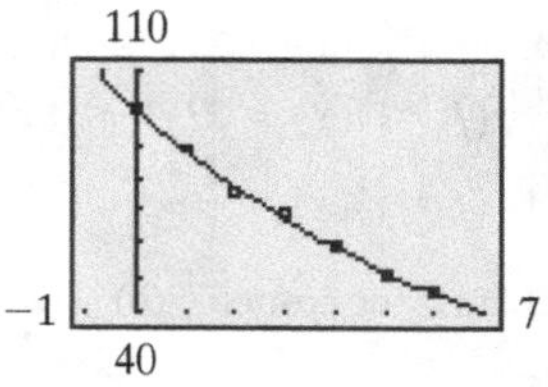

(e) 5.3 weeks **(f)** 0.14 g
(g) After about 12.3 weeks

5. **(a)**

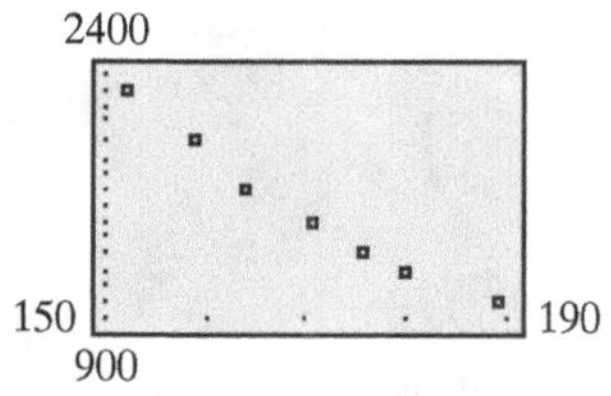

(b) $y = 32{,}741.02 - 6070.96 \ln x$

(c)

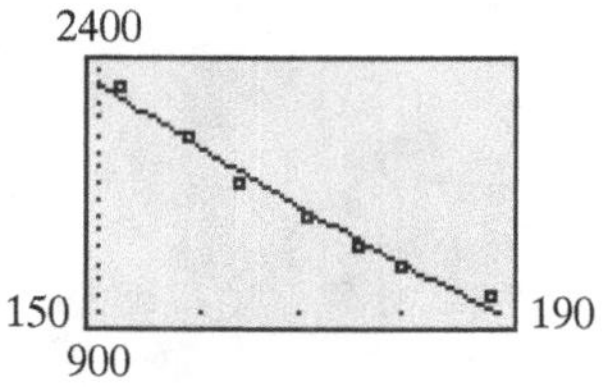

(d) Approximately 168 computers

7. **(a)**

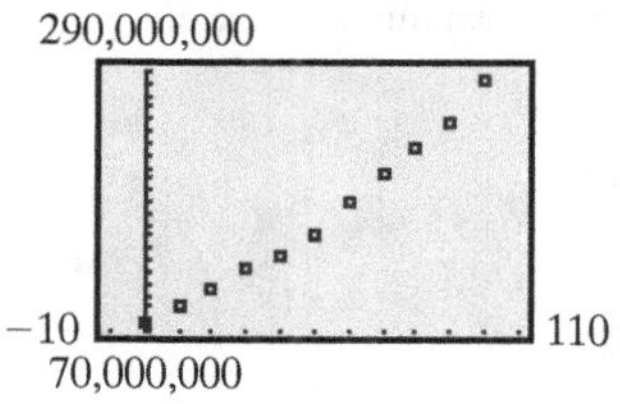

(b) $y = \dfrac{799{,}475{,}916.5}{1 + 9.1968e^{-0.0160x}}$

(c)

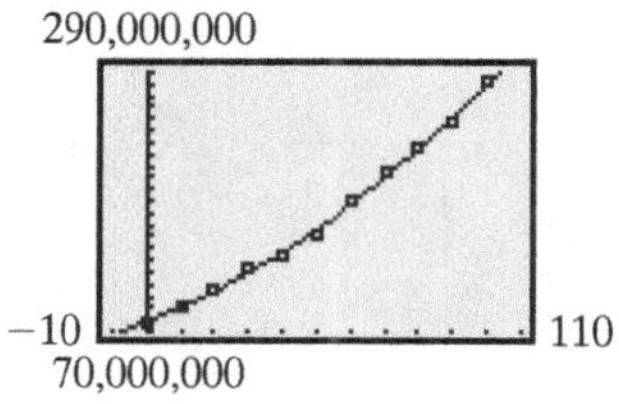

(d) 799,475,917
(e) Approximately 291,599,733
(f) 2006

9. (a)

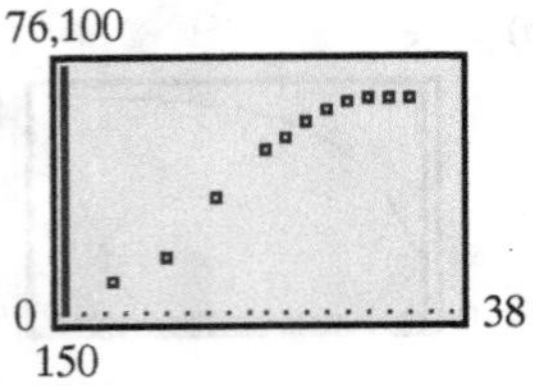

(b) $y = \dfrac{68{,}684.8}{1 + 18.9416e^{-0.1974x}}$

(c)

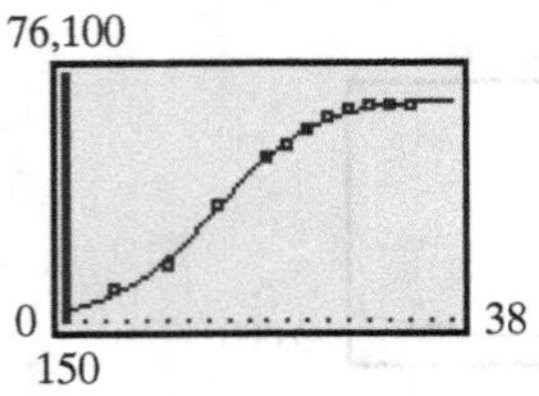

(d) About 68,685,000 subscribers

(e) About 68,505,000 subscribers

11. (a)

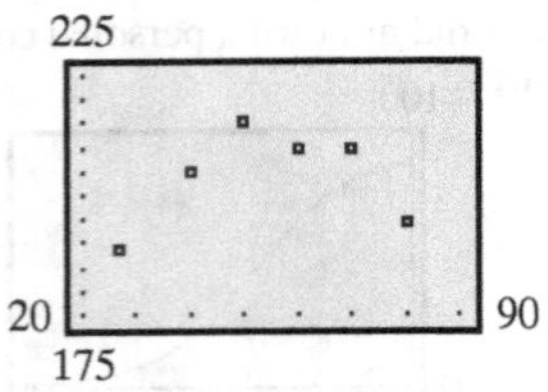

(b) Quadratic with $a < 0$ because of the "upside down U-shape" of the data

(c) $y = -0.0311x^2 + 3.4444x + 118.2493$

(d)

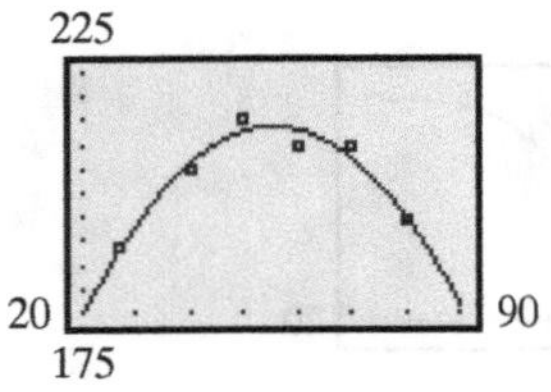

(e) 201

13. (a)

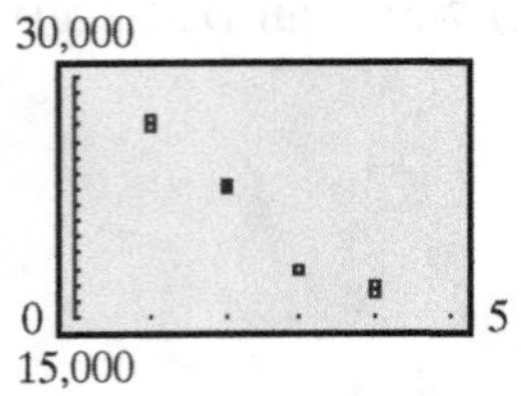

(b) Exponential because depreciation of a car is described by exponential models in the theory of finance

(c) $y = 31{,}808.51\,(0.8474)^x$

(d)

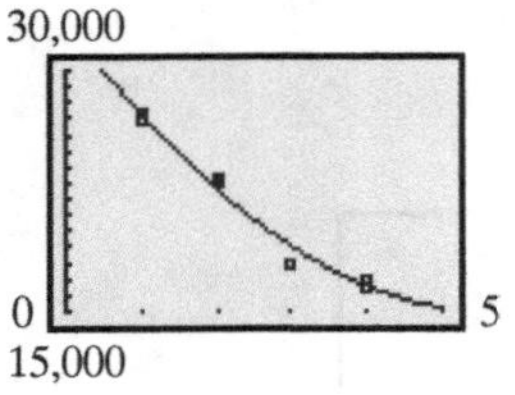

(e) \$13,899

Review Exercises *(page 344)*

1. (a) -26 **(b)** -241 **(c)** 16 **(d)** -1 **3. (a)** $\sqrt{11}$ **(b)** 1 **(c)** $\sqrt{\sqrt{6}+2}$ **(d)** 19 **5. (a)** e^4 **(b)** $3e^{-2} - 2$ **(c)** e^{e^4} **(d)** -17

7. $(f \circ g)(x) = 1 - 3x$, all real numbers; $(g \circ f)(x) = 7 - 3x$, all real numbers; $(f \circ f)(x) = x$, all real numbers; $(g \circ g)(x) = 9x + 4$, all real numbers

9. $(f \circ g)(x) = 27x^2 + 3|x| + 1$, all real numbers; $(g \circ f)(x) = 3|3x^2 + x + 1|$, all real numbers; $(f \circ f)(x) = 27x^4 + 18x^3 + 24x^2 + 7x + 5$, all real numbers; $(g \circ g)(x) = 9|x|$, all real numbers

11. $(f \circ g)(x) = \dfrac{1+x}{1-x}$, $\{x \mid x \neq 0, x \neq 1\}$; $(g \circ f)(x) = \dfrac{x-1}{x+1}$, $\{x \mid x \neq -1, x \neq 1\}$; $(f \circ f)(x) = x$, $\{x \mid x \neq 1\}$; $(g \circ g)(x) = x$, $\{x \mid x \neq 0\}$

13. (a) one-to-one **(b)** $\{(2, 1), (5, 3), (8, 5), (10, 6)\}$

15.

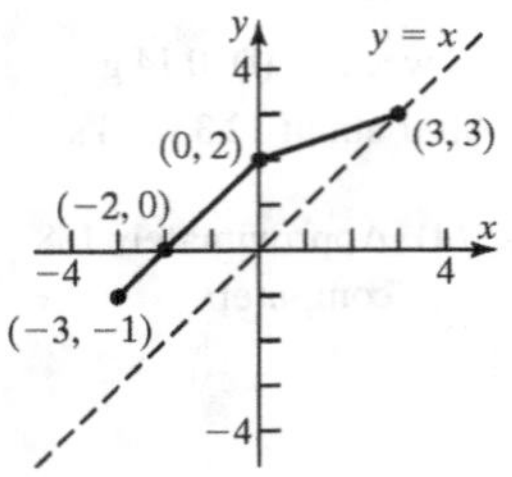

17. $f^{-1}(x) = \dfrac{2x+3}{5x-2}$

$$f(f^{-1}(x)) = \frac{2\left(\dfrac{2x+3}{5x-2}\right) + 3}{5\left(\dfrac{2x+3}{5x-2}\right) - 2} = x$$

$$f^{-1}(f(x)) = \frac{2\left(\dfrac{2x+3}{5x-2}\right) + 3}{5\left(\dfrac{2x+3}{5x-2}\right) - 2} = x$$

Domain of f = range of f^{-1} = all real numbers except $\frac{2}{5}$

Range of f = domain of f^{-1} = all real numbers except $\frac{2}{5}$

19. $f^{-1}(x) = \dfrac{x+1}{x}$

$$f(f^{-1}(x)) = \frac{1}{\dfrac{x+1}{x} - 1} = x$$

$$f^{-1}(f(x)) = \frac{\dfrac{1}{x-1} + 1}{\dfrac{1}{x-1}} = x$$

Domain of f = range of f^{-1} = all real numbers except 1

Range of f = domain of f^{-1} = all real numbers except 0

21. $f^{-1}(x) = \dfrac{27}{x^3}$

$f(f^{-1}(x)) = \dfrac{3}{\left(\dfrac{27}{x^3}\right)^{1/3}} = x$

$f^{-1}(f(x)) = \dfrac{27}{\left(\dfrac{3}{x^{1/3}}\right)^3} = x$

Domain of f = range of f^{-1} = all real numbers except 0

Range of f = domain of f^{-1} = all real numbers except 0

23. **(a)** 81 **(b)** 2 **(c)** $\frac{1}{9}$ **(d)** -3 **25.** $\log_5 z = 2$ **27.** $5^{13} = u$

29. $\left\{x \middle| x > \frac{2}{3}\right\}; \left(\frac{2}{3}, \infty\right)$ **31.** $\{x|x < 1 \text{ or } x > 2\}; (-\infty, 1)$ *h* $(2, \infty)$

33. -3 **35.** $\sqrt{2}$ **37.** 0.4 **39.** $\log_3 u + 2\log_3 v - \log_3 w$

41. $2\log x + \frac{1}{2}\log(x^3 + 1)$ **43.** $\ln x + \frac{1}{3}\ln(x^2 + 1) - \ln(x - 3)$

45. $\frac{25}{4}\log_4 x$ **47.** $-2\ln(x + 1)$ **49.** $\log\left(\dfrac{4x^3}{[(x + 3)(x - 2)]^{1/2}}\right)$

51. 2.124

53.

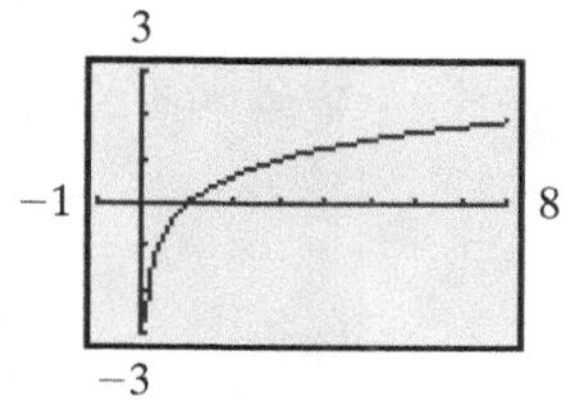

55. **(a)** Domain of f: $(-\infty, \infty)$

(b)

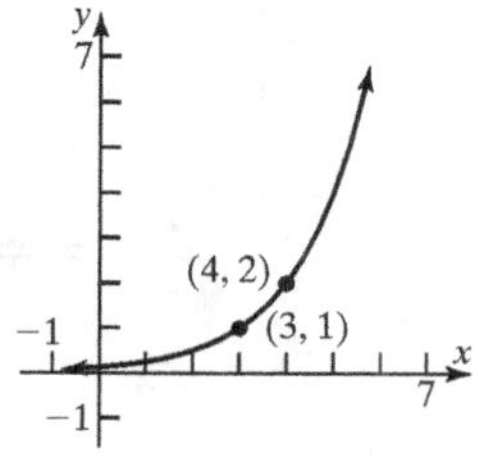

(c) Range of f: $(0, \infty)$

Horizontal asymptote: $y = 0$

(d) $f^{-1}(x) = 3 + \log_2 x$

(e) Range of f: $(0, \infty)$

(f)

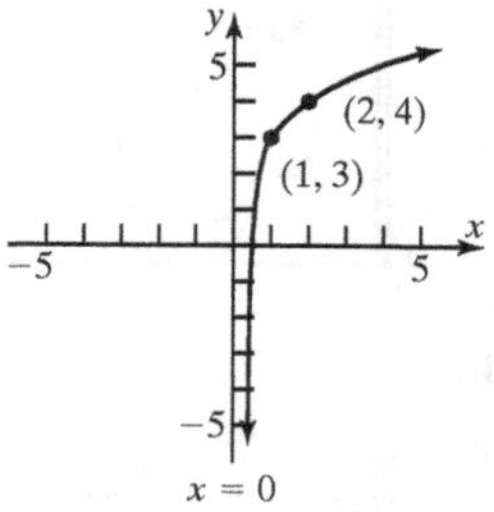

57. **(a)** Domain of f: $(-\infty, \infty)$

(b)

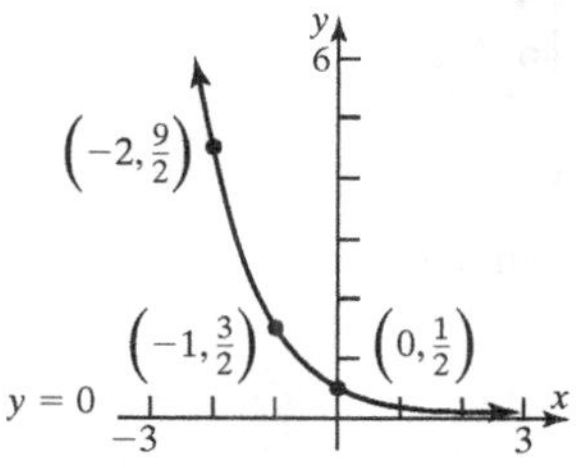

(c) Range of f: $(0, \infty)$

Horizontal asymptote: $y = 0$

(d) $f^{-1}(x) = -\log_3(2x)$

(e) Range of f: $(0, \infty)$

(f)

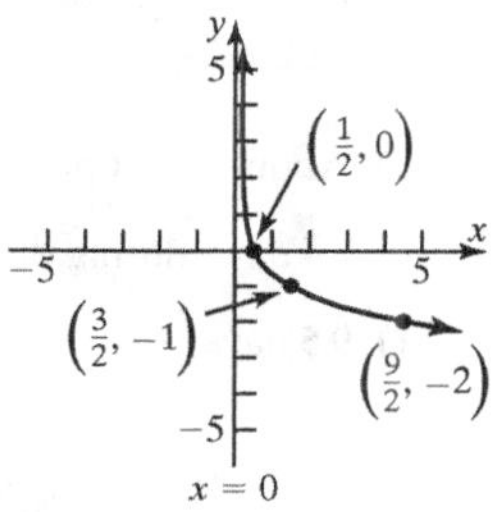

59. **(a)** Domain of f: $(-\infty, \infty)$

(b)

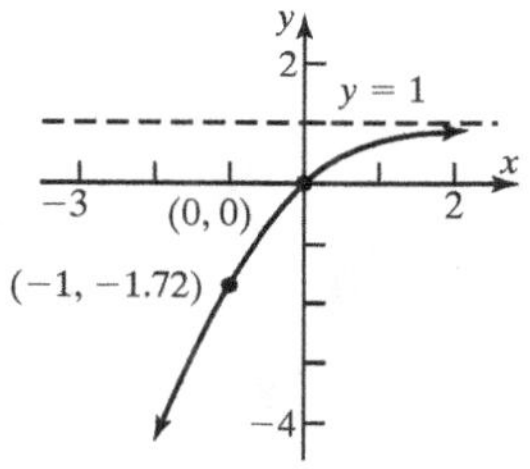

(c) Range of f: $(-\infty, 1)$

Horizontal asymptote: $y = 1$

(d) $f^{-1}(x) = -\ln(1 - x)$

(e) Range of f: $(-\infty, 1)$

(f)

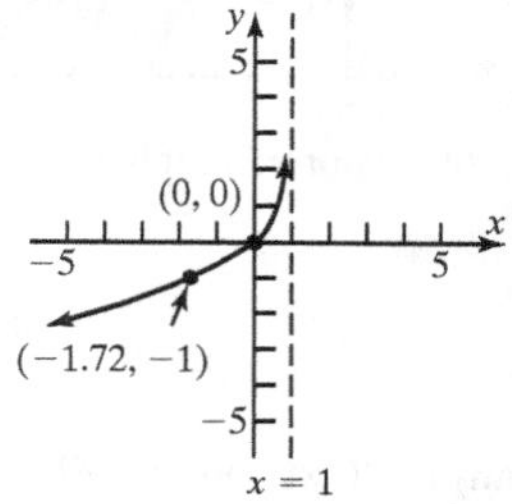

61. **(a)** Domain of f: $(-3, \infty)$

(b)

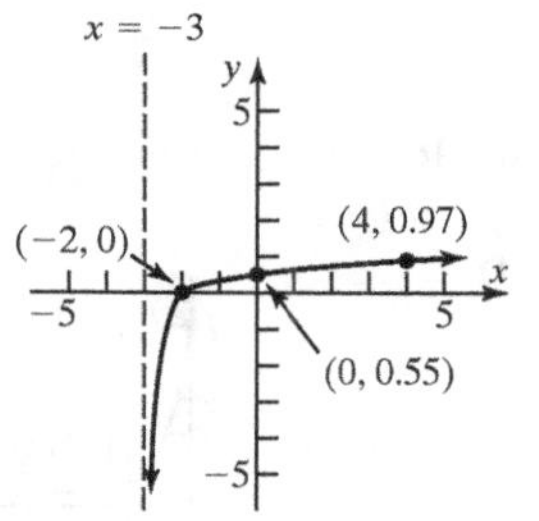

(c) Range of f: $(-\infty, \infty)$

Vertical asymptote: $x = -3$

(d) $f^{-1}(x) = e^{2x} - 3$

(e) Range of f: $(-\infty, \infty)$

(f)

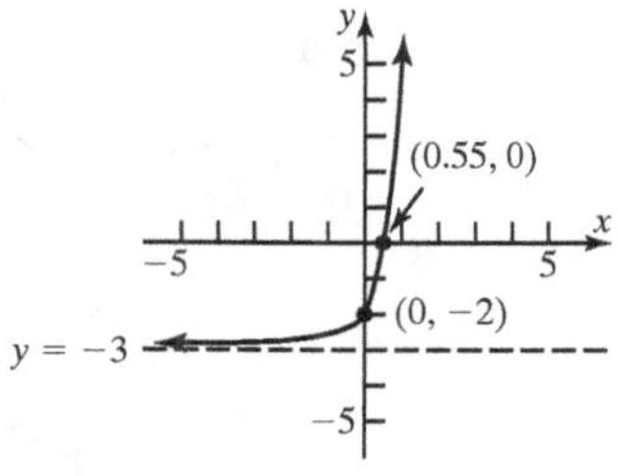

63. $\left\{\frac{1}{4}\right\}$ **65.** $\left\{\dfrac{-1 - \sqrt{3}}{2}, \dfrac{-1 + \sqrt{3}}{2}\right\} \approx \{-1.366, 0.366\}$ **67.** $\left\{\frac{1}{4}\right\}$ **69.** $\left\{\dfrac{2\ln 3}{\ln 5 - \ln 3}\right\} \approx \{4.301\}$ **71.** $\left\{\frac{12}{5}\right\}$ **73.** $\{83\}$ **75.** $\left\{\frac{1}{2}, -3\right\}$

77. $\{-1\}$ **79.** $\{1 - \ln 5\} \approx \{-0.609\}$ **81.** $\left\{\log_3\left(-2 + \sqrt{7}\right)\right\} = \left\{\dfrac{\ln\left(-2+\sqrt{7}\right)}{\ln 3}\right\} \approx \{-0.398\}$

83. **(a), (e)**

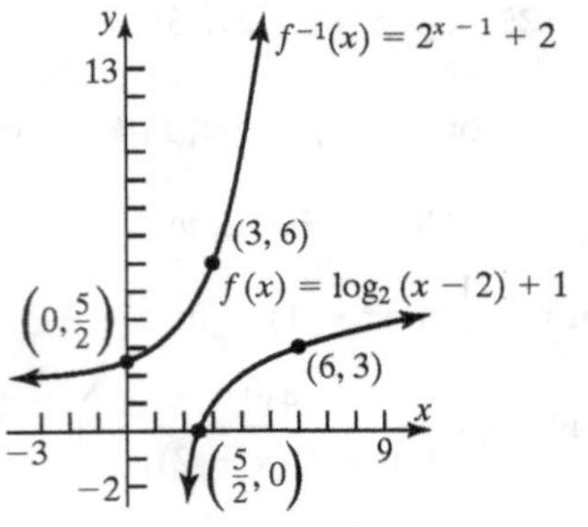

(b) 3; (6, 3) **(c)** 10; (10, 4)
(d) $\left\{x \middle| x > \frac{5}{2}\right\}$ or $\left(\frac{5}{2}, \infty\right)$
(e) $f^{-1}(x) = 2^{x-1} + 2$

85. 3229.5 m **87.** **(a)** 37.3 W **(b)** 6.9 dB **89.** **(a)** 9.85 yr **(b)** 4.27 yr **91.** $41,668.97 **93.** 24,203 yr ago **95.** 7,237,271,501 **97.** $483.67 billion

99. **(a)**

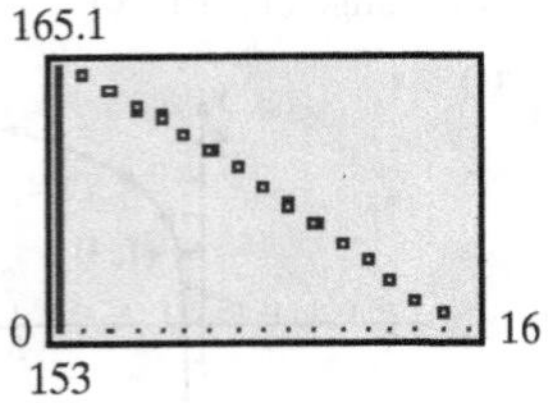

(b) $y = 165.73(0.9951)^x$

(c)

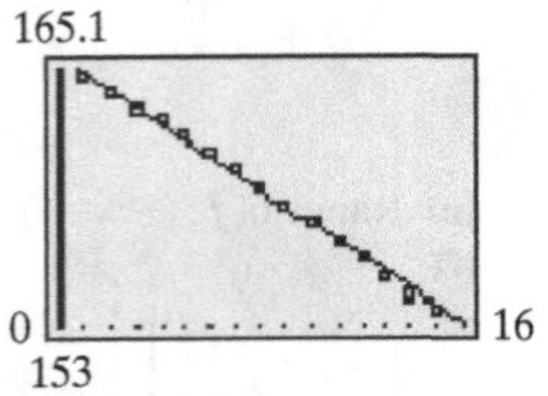

(d) Approximately 83 s

101. **(a)**

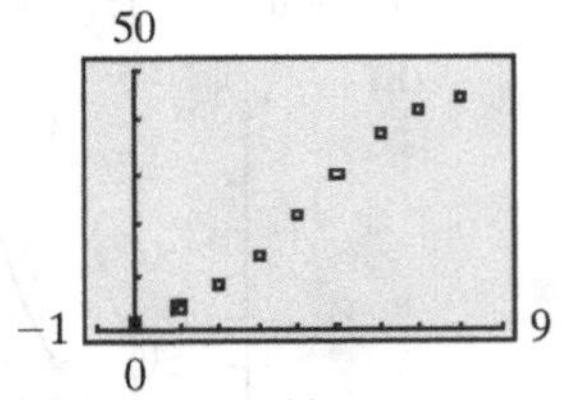

(b) $C = \dfrac{46.93}{1 + 21.273e^{-0.7306t}}$

(c)

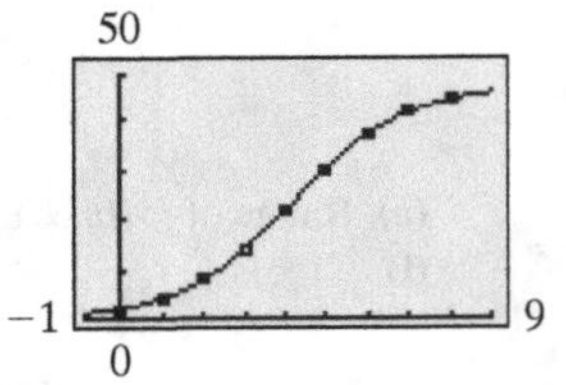

(d) About 47 people; 50 people

(e) 2.4 days; during the tenth hour of day 3

(f) 9.5 days

Chapter Test *(page 348)*

1. **(a)** $f \circ g = \dfrac{2x + 7}{2x + 3}$; domain: $\left\{x \middle| x \neq -\frac{3}{2}\right\}$ **(b)** $(g \circ f)(-2) = 5$ **(c)** $(f \circ g)(-2) = -3$

2. **(a)** The function is not one-to-one. **(b)** The function is one-to-one.

3. $f^{-1}(x) = \dfrac{2 + 5x}{3x}$; domain of $f = \left\{x \middle| x \neq \frac{5}{3}\right\}$, range of $f = \{y \mid y \neq 0\}$; domain of $f^{-1} = \{x \mid x \neq 0\}$; range of $f^{-1} = \left\{y \middle| y \neq \frac{5}{3}\right\}$

4. The point $(-5, 3)$ must be on the graph of f^{-1}. **5.** $x = 5$ **6.** $b = 4$ **7.** $x = 625$ **8.** $e^3 + 2 \approx 22.086$ **9.** $\log 20 \approx 1.301$

10. $\log_3 21 = \dfrac{\ln 21}{\ln 3} \approx 2.771$ **11.** $\ln 133 \approx 4.890$

12. **(a)** Domain of f: $\{x \mid -\infty < x < \infty\}$ or $(-\infty, \infty)$ **(e)** Range of f: $\{y \mid y > -2\}$ or $(-2, \infty)$

(b)

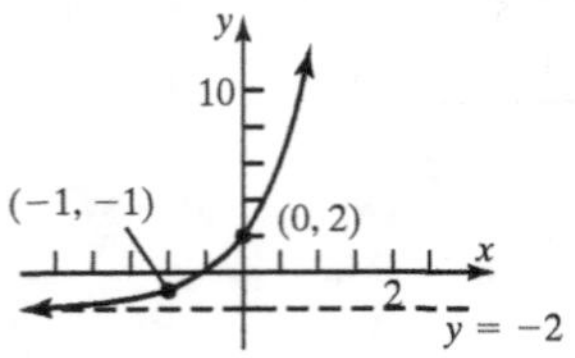

(f)

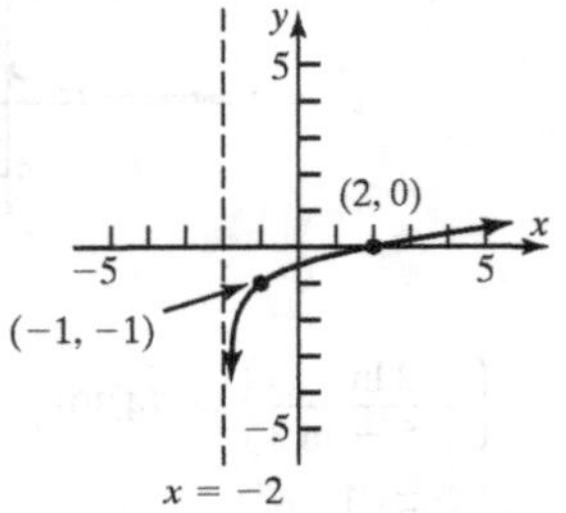

(c) Range of f: $\{y \mid y > -2\}$ or $(-2, \infty)$;
Horizontal asymptote: $y = -2$

(d) $f^{-1}(x) = \log_4(x + 2) - 1$

13. **(a)** Domain of f: $\{x \mid x > 2\}$ or $(2, \infty)$ **(e)** Range of f: $\{y \mid -\infty < y < \infty\}$ or $(-\infty, \infty)$

(b)

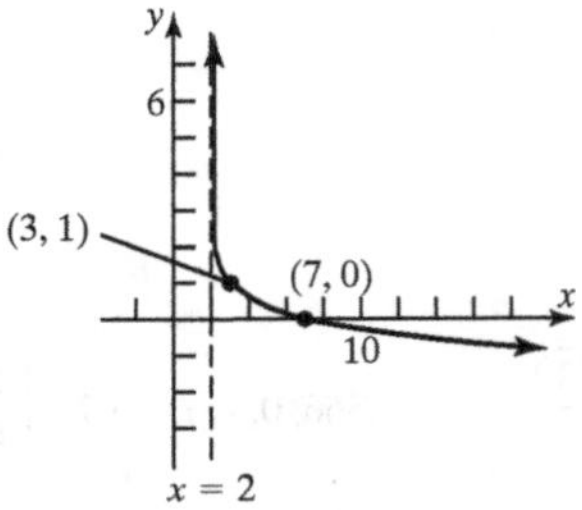

(f)

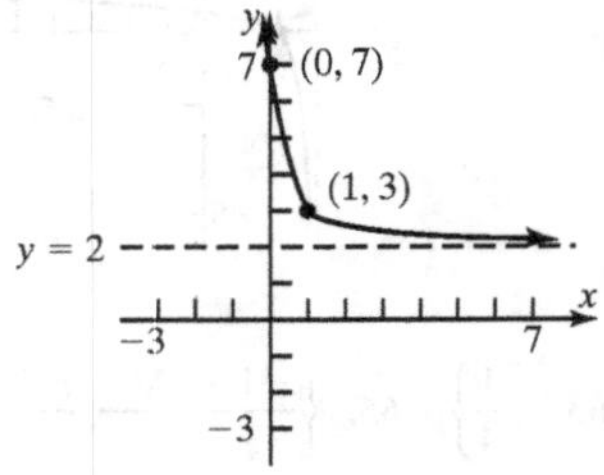

(c) Range of f: $\{y \mid -\infty < y < \infty\}$ or $(-\infty, \infty)$; vertical asymptote: $x = 2$

(d) $f^{-1}(x) = 5^{1-x} + 2$

14. {1} **15.** {91} **16.** $\{-\ln 2\} \approx \{-0.693\}$ **17.** $\left\{\dfrac{1 - \sqrt{13}}{2}, \dfrac{1 + \sqrt{13}}{2}\right\} \approx \{-1.303, 2.303\}$ **18.** $\left\{\dfrac{3 \ln 7}{1 - \ln 7}\right\} \approx \{-6.172\}$ **19.** $\{2\sqrt{6}\} \approx \{4.899\}$

20. $2 + 3\log_2 x - \log_2(x-6) - \log_2(x+3)$ **21.** About 250.39 days **22. (a)** \$1033.82 **(b)** \$963.42 **(c)** 11.9 yr
23. (a) About 83 dB **(b)** The pain threshold will be exceeded if 31,623 people shouted at the same time.

Cumulative Review *(page 348)*

1. Yes; no **2. (a)** 10 **(b)** $2x^2 + 3x + 1$ **(c)** $2x^2 + 4xh + 2h^2 - 3x - 3h + 1$ **3.** $\left(\frac{1}{2}, \frac{\sqrt{3}}{2}\right)$ is on the graph. **4.** $\{-26\}$

5.

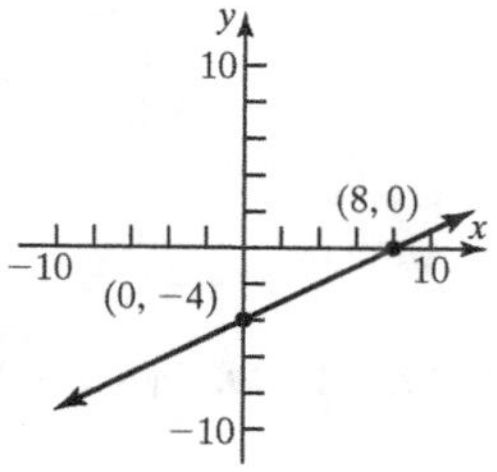

6. (a)

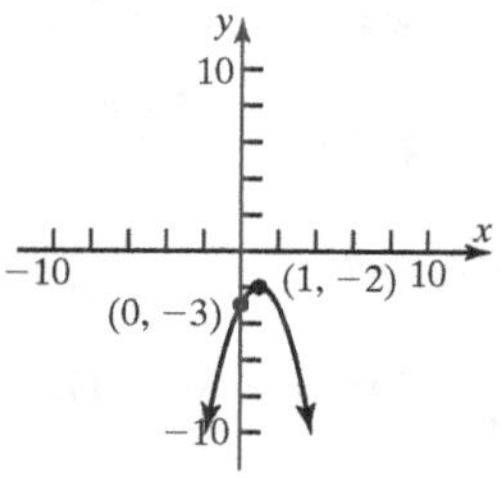

(b) $\{x \mid -\infty < x < \infty\}$

7. $f(x) = 2(x-4)^2 - 8 = 2x^2 - 16x + 24$
8.

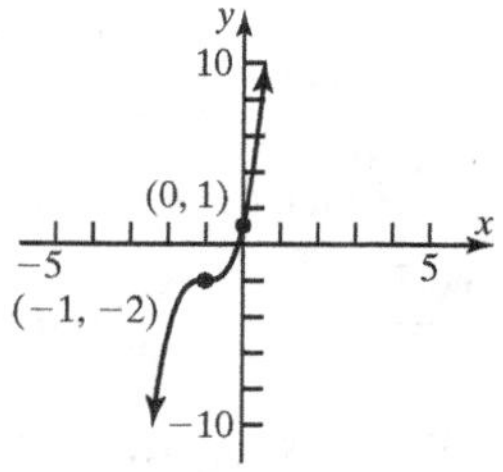

9. $f(g(x)) = \dfrac{4}{(x-3)^2} + 2;$

domain: $\{x \mid x \neq 3\}$; 3

10. (a) Zeros: $-4, -\frac{1}{4}, 2$

(b) *x*-intercepts: $-4, -\frac{1}{4}, 2$; *y*-intercept: -8

(c) Local maximum of 60.75 occurs at $x = -2.5$.

Local minimum of -25 occurs at $x = 1$.

(d)

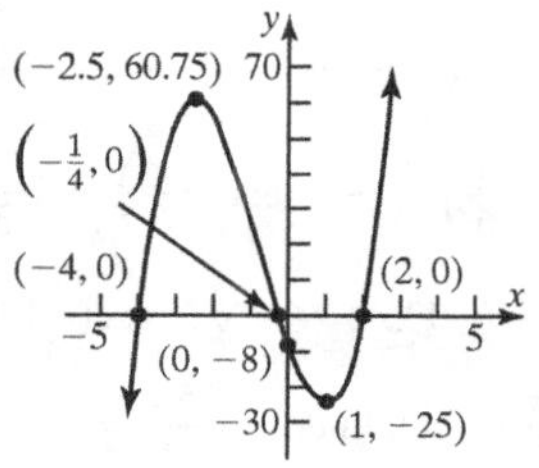

11. (a), (c)

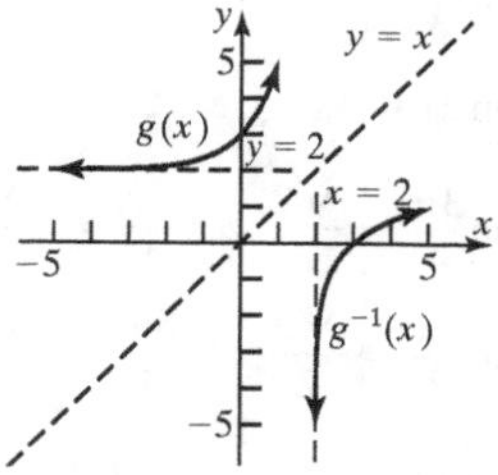

Domain g = range $g^{-1} = (-\infty, \infty)$
Range g = domain $g^{-1} = (2, \infty)$

(b) $g^{-1}(x) = \log_3(x-2)$

12. $\left\{-\frac{3}{2}\right\}$ **13.** $\{2\}$ **14. (a)** $\{-1\}$ **(b)** $\{x \mid x > -1\}$ or $(-1, \infty)$ **(c)** $\{25\}$ **15. (a)**

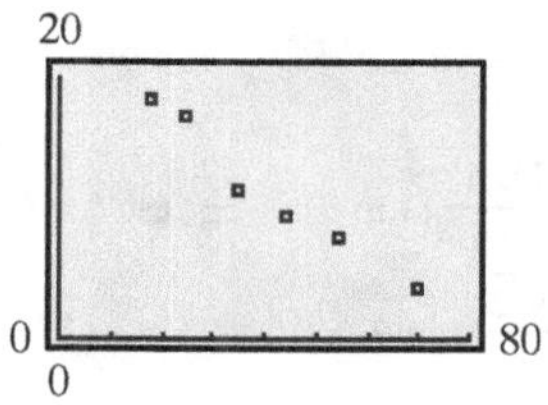

CHAPTER 6 Trigonometric Functions

6.1 Assess Your Understanding *(page 361)*

3. standard position **4.** $r\theta; \frac{1}{2}r^2\theta$ **5.** $\frac{s}{t}; \frac{\theta}{t}$ **6.** F **7.** T **8.** T **9.** T **10.** F

11.

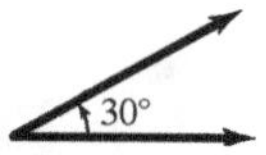

13.

15.

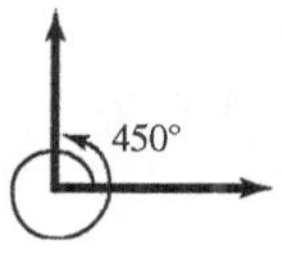

17.

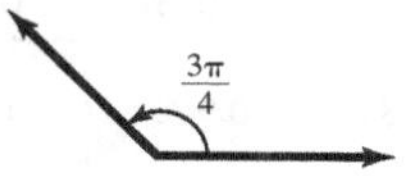

19.

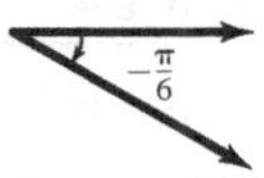

21.

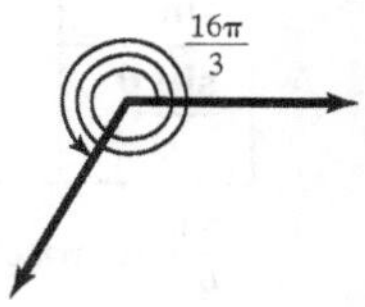

23. 40.17° **25.** 1.03° **27.** 9.15° **29.** 40°19′12″ **31.** 18°15′18″ **33.** 19°59′24″ **35.** $\frac{\pi}{6}$ **37.** $\frac{4\pi}{3}$ **39.** $-\frac{\pi}{3}$ **41.** π **43.** $-\frac{3\pi}{4}$ **45.** $-\frac{\pi}{2}$
47. 60° **49.** −225° **51.** 90° **53.** 15° **55.** −90° **57.** −30° **59.** 0.30 **61.** −0.70 **63.** 2.18 **65.** 179.91° **67.** 114.59° **69.** 362.11°
71. 5 m **73.** 6 ft **75.** 0.6 radian **77.** $\frac{\pi}{3} \approx 1.047$ in. **79.** 25 m^2 **81.** $2\sqrt{3} \approx 3.464$ ft **83.** 0.24 radian **85.** $\frac{\pi}{3} \approx 1.047$ in.^{2}
87. $s = 2.094$ ft; $A = 2.094$ ft^2 **89.** $s = 14.661$ yd; $A = 87.965$ yd^2 **91.** $3\pi \approx 9.42$ in; $5\pi \approx 15.71$ in. **93.** $2\pi \approx 6.28$ m^2
95. $\frac{675\pi}{2} \approx 1060.29$ ft^2 **97.** $\omega = \frac{1}{60}$ radian/s; $v = \frac{1}{12}$ cm/s **99.** Approximately 452.5 rpm **101.** Approximately 359 mi

103. Approximately 898 mi/h **105.** Approximately 2292 mi/h **107.** $\frac{3}{4}$rpm **109.** Approximately 2.86 mi/h **111.** Approximately 31.47 rpm
113. Approximately 1037 mi/h **115.** Radius $\approx$ 3979 mi; circumference $\approx$ 25,000 mi **117.** $v_1 = r_1\omega_1$, $v_2 = r_2\omega_2$, and $v_1 = v_2$, so $r_1\omega_1 = r_2\omega_2 \Rightarrow \frac{r_1}{r_2} = \frac{\omega_2}{\omega_1}$.

6.2 Assess Your Understanding *(page 378)*

7. $\frac{3}{2}$ **8.** 0.91 **9.** T **10.** F **11.** $\sin t = \frac{1}{2}$; $\cos t = \frac{\sqrt{3}}{2}$; $\tan t = \frac{\sqrt{3}}{3}$; $\csc t = 2$; $\sec t = \frac{2\sqrt{3}}{3}$; $\cot t = \sqrt{3}$
13. $\sin t = \frac{\sqrt{21}}{5}$; $\cos t = -\frac{2}{5}$; $\tan t = -\frac{\sqrt{21}}{2}$; $\csc t = \frac{5\sqrt{21}}{21}$; $\sec t = -\frac{5}{2}$; $\cot t = -\frac{2\sqrt{21}}{21}$
15. $\sin t = \frac{\sqrt{2}}{2}$; $\cos t = -\frac{\sqrt{2}}{2}$; $\tan t = -1$; $\csc t = \sqrt{2}$; $\sec t = -\sqrt{2}$; $\cot t = -1$
17. $\sin t = -\frac{1}{3}$; $\cos t = \frac{2\sqrt{2}}{3}$; $\tan t = -\frac{\sqrt{2}}{4}$; $\csc t = -3$; $\sec t = \frac{3\sqrt{2}}{4}$; $\cot t = -2\sqrt{2}$ **19.** -1 **21.** 0 **23.** -1 **25.** 0 **27.** -1 **29.** $\frac{1}{2}(\sqrt{2} + 1)$
31. 2 **33.** $\frac{1}{2}$ **35.** $\sqrt{6}$ **37.** 4 **39.** 0 **41.** $2\sqrt{2} + \frac{4\sqrt{3}}{3}$ **43.** 1
45. $\sin\frac{2\pi}{3} = \frac{\sqrt{3}}{2}$; $\cos\frac{2\pi}{3} = -\frac{1}{2}$; $\tan\frac{2\pi}{3} = -\sqrt{3}$; $\csc\frac{2\pi}{3} = \frac{2\sqrt{3}}{3}$; $\sec\frac{2\pi}{3} = -2$; $\cot\frac{2\pi}{3} = -\frac{\sqrt{3}}{3}$
47. $\sin 210° = -\frac{1}{2}$; $\cos 210° = -\frac{\sqrt{3}}{2}$; $\tan 210° = \frac{\sqrt{3}}{3}$; $\csc 210° = -2$; $\sec 210° = -\frac{2\sqrt{3}}{3}$; $\cot 210° = \sqrt{3}$
49. $\sin\frac{3\pi}{4} = \frac{\sqrt{2}}{2}$; $\cos\frac{3\pi}{4} = -\frac{\sqrt{2}}{2}$; $\tan\frac{3\pi}{4} = -1$; $\csc\frac{3\pi}{4} = \sqrt{2}$; $\sec\frac{3\pi}{4} = -\sqrt{2}$; $\cot\frac{3\pi}{4} = -1$
51. $\sin\frac{8\pi}{3} = \frac{\sqrt{3}}{2}$; $\cos\frac{8\pi}{3} = -\frac{1}{2}$; $\tan\frac{8\pi}{3} = -\sqrt{3}$; $\csc\frac{8\pi}{3} = \frac{2\sqrt{3}}{3}$; $\sec\frac{8\pi}{3} = -2$; $\cot\frac{8\pi}{3} = -\frac{\sqrt{3}}{3}$
53. $\sin 405° = \frac{\sqrt{2}}{2}$; $\cos 405° = \frac{\sqrt{2}}{2}$; $\tan 405° = 1$; $\csc 405° = \sqrt{2}$; $\sec 405° = \sqrt{2}$; $\cot 405° = 1$
55. $\sin\left(-\frac{\pi}{6}\right) = -\frac{1}{2}$; $\cos\left(-\frac{\pi}{6}\right) = \frac{\sqrt{3}}{2}$; $\tan\left(-\frac{\pi}{6}\right) = -\frac{\sqrt{3}}{3}$; $\csc\left(-\frac{\pi}{6}\right) = -2$; $\sec\left(-\frac{\pi}{6}\right) = \frac{2\sqrt{3}}{3}$; $\cot\left(-\frac{\pi}{6}\right) = -\sqrt{3}$
57. $\sin(-135°) = -\frac{\sqrt{2}}{2}$; $\cos(-135°) = -\frac{\sqrt{2}}{2}$; $\tan(-135°) = 1$; $\csc(-135°) = -\sqrt{2}$; $\sec(-135°) = -\sqrt{2}$; $\cot(-135°) = 1$
59. $\sin\frac{5\pi}{2} = 1$; $\cos\frac{5\pi}{2} = 0$; $\tan\frac{5\pi}{2}$ is undefined; $\csc\frac{5\pi}{2} = 1$; $\sec\frac{5\pi}{2}$ is undefined; $\cot\frac{5\pi}{2} = 0$
61. $\sin 720° = 0$; $\cos 720° = 1$; $\tan 720° = 0$; $\csc 720°$ is undefined; $\sec 720° = 1$; $\cot 720°$ is undefined **63.** 0.47 **65.** 1.07 **67.** 0.32 **69.** 3.73
71. 0.84 **73.** 0.02 **75.** $\sin\theta = \frac{4}{5}$; $\cos\theta = -\frac{3}{5}$; $\tan\theta = -\frac{4}{3}$; $\csc\theta = \frac{5}{4}$; $\sec\theta = -\frac{5}{3}$; $\cot\theta = -\frac{3}{4}$
77. $\sin\theta = -\frac{3\sqrt{13}}{13}$; $\cos\theta = \frac{2\sqrt{13}}{13}$; $\tan\theta = -\frac{3}{2}$; $\csc\theta = -\frac{\sqrt{13}}{3}$; $\sec\theta = \frac{\sqrt{13}}{2}$; $\cot\theta = -\frac{2}{3}$
79. $\sin\theta = -\frac{\sqrt{2}}{2}$; $\cos\theta = -\frac{\sqrt{2}}{2}$; $\tan\theta = 1$; $\csc\theta = -\sqrt{2}$; $\sec\theta = -\sqrt{2}$; $\cot\theta = 1$
81. $\sin\theta = \frac{3}{5}$; $\cos\theta = \frac{4}{5}$; $\tan\theta = \frac{3}{4}$; $\csc\theta = \frac{5}{3}$; $\sec\theta = \frac{5}{4}$; $\cot\theta = \frac{4}{3}$ **83.** 0 **85.** 0 **87.** -0.1 **89.** 3 **91.** 5 **93.** $\frac{\sqrt{3}}{2}$ **95.** $\frac{1}{2}$ **97.** $\frac{3}{4}$ **99.** $\frac{\sqrt{3}}{2}$
101. $\sqrt{3}$ **103.** $-\frac{\sqrt{3}}{2}$ **105.** $\frac{1 + \sqrt{3}}{2}$ **107.** $-\frac{1}{2}$ **109.** $\frac{\sqrt{3}}{2}$ **111.** $\frac{\sqrt{2}}{4}$ **113.** **(a)** $\frac{\sqrt{2}}{2}$; $\left(\frac{\pi}{4}, \frac{\sqrt{2}}{2}\right)$ **(b)** $\left(\frac{\sqrt{2}}{2}, \frac{\pi}{4}\right)$ **(c)** $\left(0, \frac{\sqrt{2}}{2} - 3\right)$
115.

θ	0.5	0.4	0.2	0.1	0.01	0.001	0.0001	0.00001
$\sin\theta$	0.4794	0.3894	0.1987	0.0998	0.0100	0.0010	0.0001	0.00001
$\frac{\sin\theta}{\theta}$	0.9589	0.9735	0.9933	0.9983	1.0000	1.0000	1.0000	1.0000

$\frac{\sin\theta}{\theta}$ approaches 1 as θ approaches 0.

117. $R \approx 310.56$ ft; $H \approx 77.64$ ft **119.** $R \approx 19{,}541.95$ m; $H \approx 2278.14$ m **121.** **(a)** 1.20 sec **(b)** 1.12 sec **(c)** 1.20 sec
123. **(a)** 1.9 hr; 0.57 hr **(b)** 1.69 hr; 0.75 hr **(c)** 1.63 hr; 0.86 hr **(d)** 1.67 hr; tan 90° is undefined
125. **(a)** 16.56 ft **(b)**

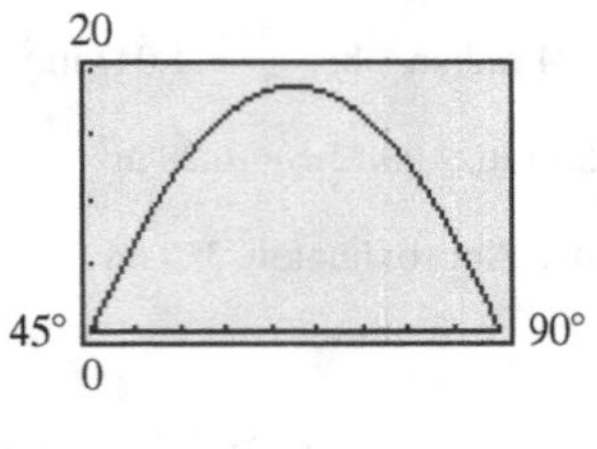

(c) 67.5° **127.** **(a)** values estimated to the nearest tenth: $\sin 1 \approx 0.8$; $\cos 1 \approx 0.5$; $\tan 1 \approx 1.6$; $\csc 1 \approx 1.3$; $\sec 1 \approx 2.0$; $\cot 1 \approx 0.6$; actual values to the nearest tenth: $\sin 1 \approx 0.8$; $\cos 1 \approx 0.5$; $\tan 1 \approx 1.6$; $\csc 1 \approx 1.2$; $\sec 1 \approx 1.9$; $\cot 1 \approx 0.6$
(b) values estimated to the nearest tenth: $\sin 5.1 \approx -0.9$; $\cos 5.1 \approx 0.4$; $\tan 5.1 \approx -2.3$; $\csc 5.1 \approx -1.1$; $\sec 5.1 \approx 2.5$; $\cot 5.1 \approx -0.4$; actual values to the nearest tenth: $\sin 5.1 \approx -0.9$; $\cos 5.1 \approx 0.4$; $\tan 5.1 \approx -2.4$; $\csc 5.1 \approx -1.1$; $\sec 5.1 \approx 2.6$; $\cot 5.1 \approx -0.4$

6.3 Assess Your Understanding *(page 392)*

5. 2π; π **6.** all real numbers except odd multiples of $\frac{\pi}{2}$ **7.** $[-1, 1]$ **8.** T **9.** F **10.** F **11.** $\frac{\sqrt{2}}{2}$ **13.** 1 **15.** 1 **17.** $\sqrt{3}$ **19.** $\frac{\sqrt{2}}{2}$ **21.** 0 **23.** $\sqrt{2}$ **25.** $\frac{\sqrt{3}}{3}$ **27.** II **29.** IV **31.** IV **33.** II **35.** $\tan\theta = -\frac{3}{4}$; $\cot\theta = -\frac{4}{3}$; $\sec\theta = \frac{5}{4}$; $\csc\theta = -\frac{5}{3}$ **37.** $\tan\theta = 2$; $\cot\theta = \frac{1}{2}$; $\sec\theta = \sqrt{5}$; $\csc\theta = \frac{\sqrt{5}}{2}$ **39.** $\tan\theta = \frac{\sqrt{3}}{3}$; $\cot\theta = \sqrt{3}$; $\sec\theta = \frac{2\sqrt{3}}{3}$; $\csc\theta = 2$ **41.** $\tan\theta = -\frac{\sqrt{2}}{4}$; $\cot\theta = -2\sqrt{2}$; $\sec\theta = \frac{3\sqrt{2}}{4}$; $\csc\theta = -3$ **43.** $\cos\theta = -\frac{5}{13}$; $\tan\theta = -\frac{12}{5}$; $\csc\theta = \frac{13}{12}$; $\sec\theta = -\frac{13}{5}$; $\cot\theta = -\frac{5}{12}$ **45.** $\sin\theta = -\frac{3}{5}$; $\tan\theta = \frac{3}{4}$; $\csc\theta = -\frac{5}{3}$; $\sec\theta = -\frac{5}{4}$; $\cot\theta = \frac{4}{3}$ **47.** $\cos\theta = -\frac{12}{13}$; $\tan\theta = -\frac{5}{12}$; $\csc\theta = \frac{13}{5}$; $\sec\theta = -\frac{13}{12}$; $\cot\theta = -\frac{12}{5}$ **49.** $\sin\theta = \frac{2\sqrt{2}}{3}$; $\tan\theta = -2\sqrt{2}$; $\csc\theta = \frac{3\sqrt{2}}{4}$; $\sec\theta = -3$; $\cot\theta = -\frac{\sqrt{2}}{4}$ **51.** $\cos\theta = -\frac{\sqrt{5}}{3}$; $\tan\theta = -\frac{2\sqrt{5}}{5}$; $\csc\theta = \frac{3}{2}$; $\sec\theta = -\frac{3\sqrt{5}}{5}$; $\cot\theta = -\frac{\sqrt{5}}{2}$ **53.** $\sin\theta = -\frac{\sqrt{3}}{2}$; $\cos\theta = \frac{1}{2}$; $\tan\theta = -\sqrt{3}$; $\csc\theta = -\frac{2\sqrt{3}}{3}$; $\cot\theta = -\frac{\sqrt{3}}{3}$ **55.** $\sin\theta = -\frac{3}{5}$; $\cos\theta = -\frac{4}{5}$; $\csc\theta = -\frac{5}{3}$; $\sec\theta = -\frac{5}{4}$; $\cot\theta = \frac{4}{3}$ **57.** $\sin\theta = \frac{\sqrt{10}}{10}$; $\cos\theta = -\frac{3\sqrt{10}}{10}$; $\csc\theta = \sqrt{10}$; $\sec\theta = -\frac{\sqrt{10}}{3}$; $\cot\theta = -3$ **59.** $-\frac{\sqrt{3}}{2}$ **61.** $-\frac{\sqrt{3}}{3}$ **63.** 2 **65.** -1 **67.** -1 **69.** $\frac{\sqrt{2}}{2}$ **71.** 0 **73.** $-\sqrt{2}$ **75.** $\frac{2\sqrt{3}}{3}$ **77.** 1 **79.** 1 **81.** 0 **83.** 1 **85.** -1 **87.** 0 **89.** 0.9 **91.** 9 **93.** 0 **95.** All real numbers **97.** Odd multiples of $\frac{\pi}{2}$ **99.** Odd multiples of $\frac{\pi}{2}$ **101.** $-1 \le y \le 1$

103. All real numbers **105.** $|y| \ge 1$ **107.** Odd; yes; origin **109.** Odd; yes; origin **111.** Even; yes; y-axis **113. (a)** $-\frac{1}{3}$ **(b)** 1 **115. (a)** -2 **(b)** 6 **117. (a)** -4 **(b)** -12 **119.** About 15.81 min **121.** Let a be a real number and $P = (x, y)$ be the point on the unit circle that corresponds to t. Consider the equation $\tan t = \frac{y}{x} = a$. Then $y = ax$. But $x^2 + y^2 = 1$, so $x^2 + a^2x^2 = 1$. So, $x = \pm\frac{1}{\sqrt{1 + a^2}}$ and $y = \pm\frac{a}{\sqrt{1 + a^2}}$; that is, for any real number a, there is a point $P = (x, y)$ on the unit circle for which $\tan t = a$. In other words, the range of the tangent function is the set of all real numbers. **123.** Suppose that there is a number p, $0 < p < 2\pi$, for which $\sin(\theta + p) = \sin\theta$ for all θ. If $\theta = 0$, then $\sin(0 + p) = \sin p = \sin 0 = 0$, so $p = \pi$. If $\theta = \frac{\pi}{2}$, then $\sin\left(\frac{\pi}{2} + p\right) = \sin\left(\frac{\pi}{2}\right)$. But $p = \pi$. Thus, $\sin\left(\frac{3\pi}{2}\right) = -1 = \sin\left(\frac{\pi}{2}\right) = 1$. This is impossible. Therefore, the smallest positive number p for which $\sin(\theta + p) = \sin\theta$ for all θ is 2π. **125.** $\sec\theta = \frac{1}{\cos\theta}$; since $\cos\theta$ has period 2π, so does $\sec\theta$. **127.** If $P = (a, b)$ is the point on the unit circle corresponding to θ, then $Q = (-a, -b)$ is the point on the unit circle corresponding to $\theta + \pi$. Thus, $\tan(\theta + \pi) = \frac{-b}{-a} = \frac{b}{a} = \tan\theta$. Suppose that there exists a number p, $0 < p < \pi$, for which $\tan(\theta + p) = \tan\theta$ for all θ. Then, if $\theta = 0$, then $\tan p = \tan 0 = 0$. But this means that p is a multiple of π. Since no multiple of π exists in the interval $(0, \pi)$, this is a contradiction. Therefore, the period of $f(\theta) = \tan\theta$ is π.

129. Let $P = (a, b)$ be the point on the unit circle corresponding to θ. Then $\csc\theta = \frac{1}{b} = \frac{1}{\sin\theta}$; $\sec\theta = \frac{1}{a} = \frac{1}{\cos\theta}$; $\cot\theta = \frac{a}{b} = \frac{1}{b/a} = \frac{1}{\tan\theta}$.

131. $(\sin\theta\cos\phi)^2 + (\sin\theta\sin\phi)^2 + \cos^2\theta = \sin^2\theta\cos^2\phi + \sin^2\theta\sin^2\phi + \cos^2\theta$

$$= \sin^2\theta(\cos^2\phi + \sin^2\phi) + \cos^2\theta = \sin^2\theta + \cos^2\theta = 1$$

6.4 Assess Your Understanding *(page 406)*

3. 1; $\frac{\pi}{2} + 2\pi k$, k any integer **4.** 3; π **5.** 3; $\frac{\pi}{3}$ **6.** T **7.** F **8.** T **9.** 0 **11.** $-\frac{\pi}{2} < x < \frac{\pi}{2}$ **13.** 1 **15.** $0, \pi, 2\pi$ **17.** $\sin x = 1$ for $x = -\frac{3\pi}{2}, \frac{\pi}{2}$; $\sin x = -1$ for $x = -\frac{\pi}{2}, \frac{3\pi}{2}$ **19.** Amplitude $= 2$; period $= 2\pi$ **21.** Amplitude $= 4$; period $= \pi$ **23.** Amplitude $= 6$; period $= 2$ **25.** Amplitude $= \frac{1}{2}$; period $= \frac{4\pi}{3}$ **27.** Amplitude $= \frac{5}{3}$; period $= 3$ **29.** F **31.** A **33.** H **35.** C **37.** J **39.** A **41.** B

43.

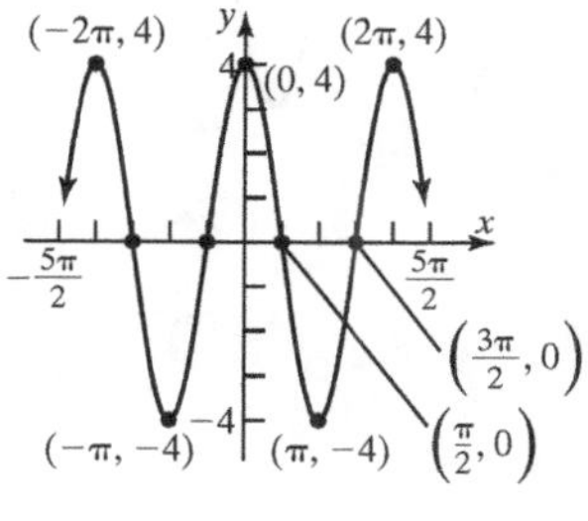

Domain: $(-\infty, \infty)$

Range: $[-4, 4]$

45.

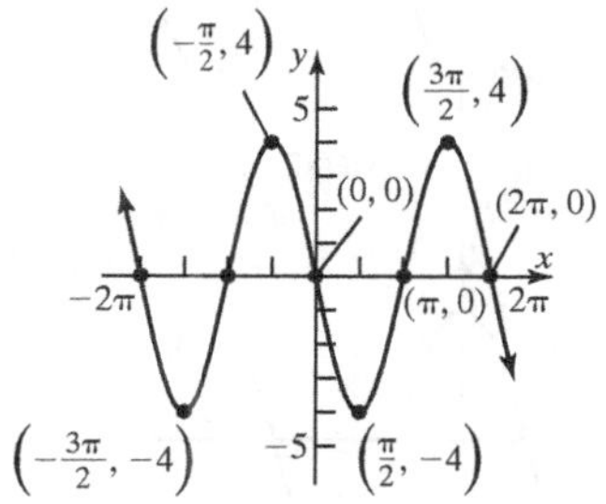

Domain: $(-\infty, \infty)$

Range: $[-4, 4]$

47.

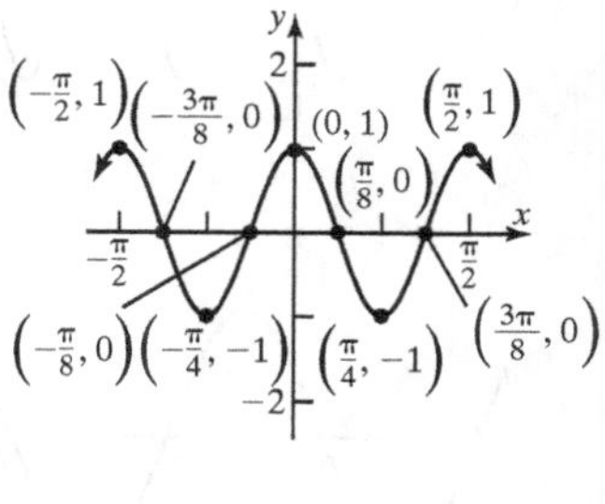

Domain: $(-\infty, \infty)$

Range: $[-1, 1]$

49.

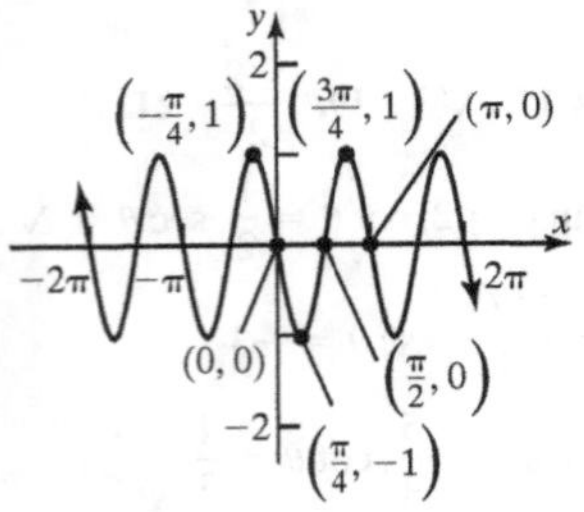

Domain: $(-\infty, \infty)$

Range: $[-1, 1]$

51.

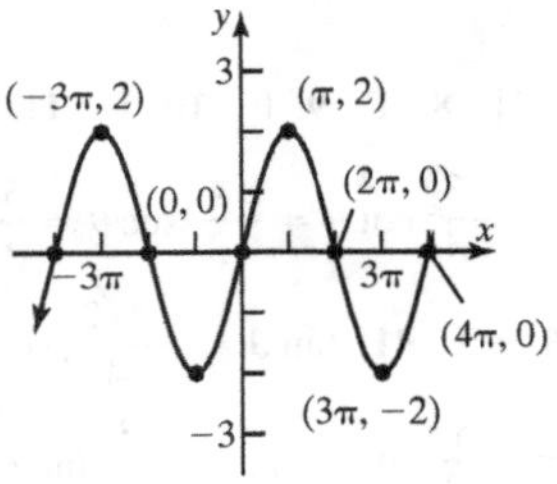

Domain: $(-\infty, \infty)$

Range: $[-2, 2]$

53.

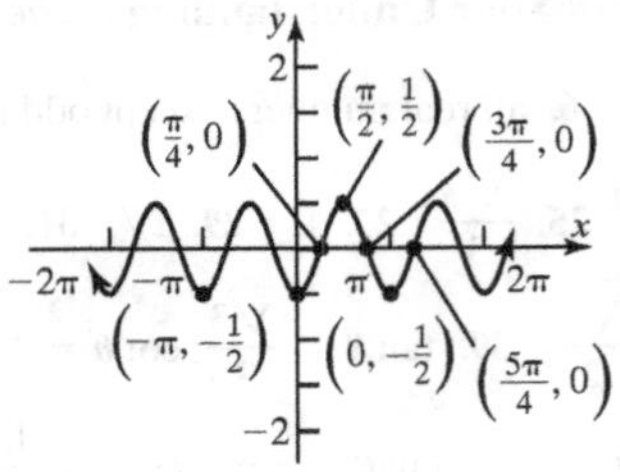

Domain: $(-\infty, \infty)$

Range: $\left[-\frac{1}{2}, \frac{1}{2}\right]$

55.

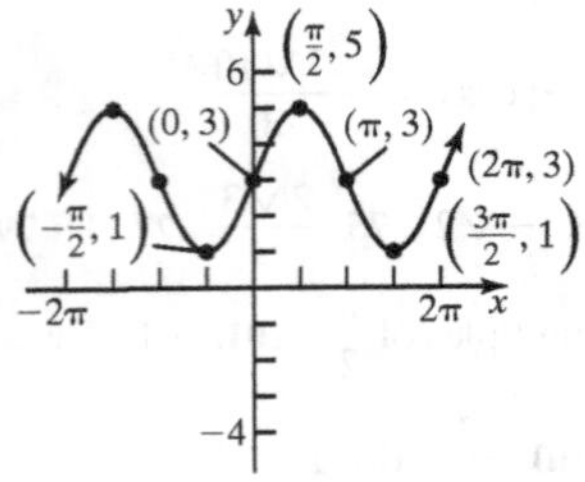

Domain: $(-\infty, \infty)$

Range: $[1, 5]$

57.

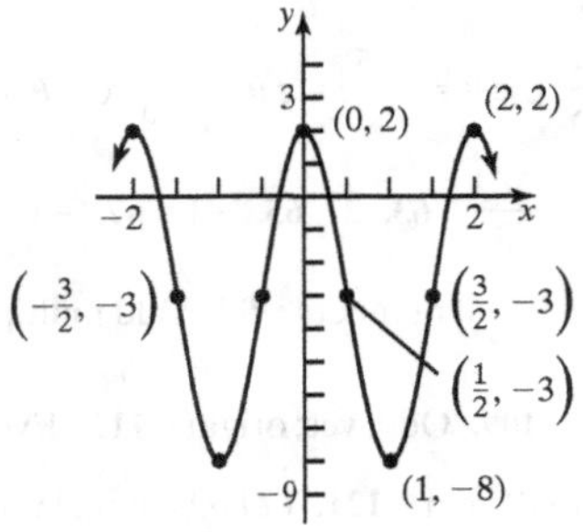

Domain: $(-\infty, \infty)$

Range: $[-8, 2]$

59.

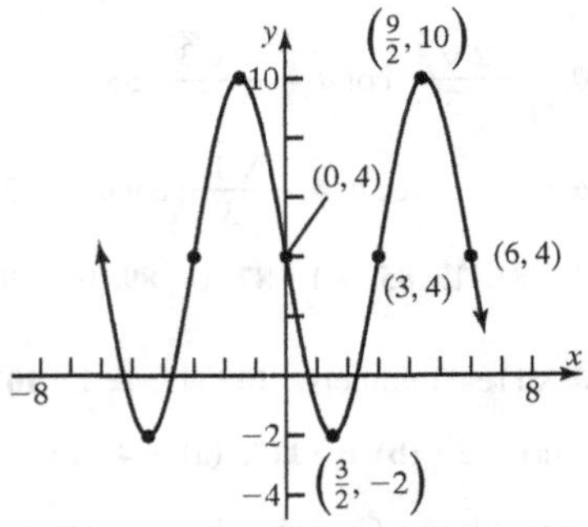

Domain: $(-\infty, \infty)$

Range: $[-2, 10]$

61.

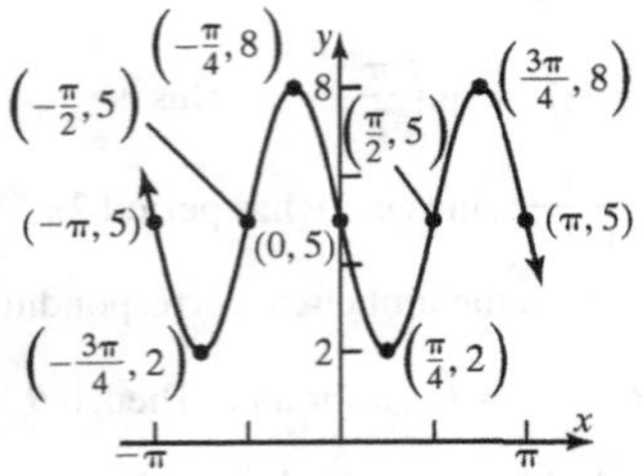

Domain: $(-\infty, \infty)$

Range: $[2, 8]$

63.

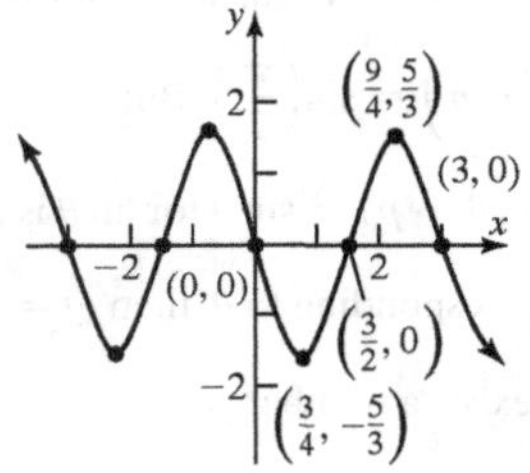

Domain: $(-\infty, \infty)$

Range: $\left[-\frac{5}{3}, \frac{5}{3}\right]$

65.

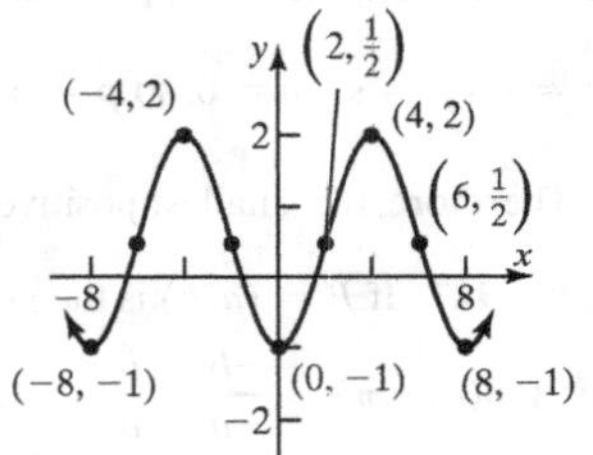

Domain: $(-\infty, \infty)$

Range: $[-1, 2]$

67. $y = \pm 3\sin(2x)$ **69.** $y = \pm 3\sin(\pi x)$ **71.** $y = 5\cos\left(\frac{\pi}{4}x\right)$ **73.** $y = -3\cos\left(\frac{1}{2}x\right)$ **75.** $y = \frac{3}{4}\sin(2\pi x)$ **77.** $y = -\sin\left(\frac{3}{2}x\right)$

79. $y = -\cos\left(\frac{4\pi}{3}x\right) + 1$ **81.** $y = 3\sin\left(\frac{\pi}{2}x\right)$ **83.** $y = -4\cos(3x)$ **85.** $\frac{2}{\pi}$ **87.** $\frac{\sqrt{2}}{\pi}$

89. $(f \circ g)(x) = \sin(4x)$

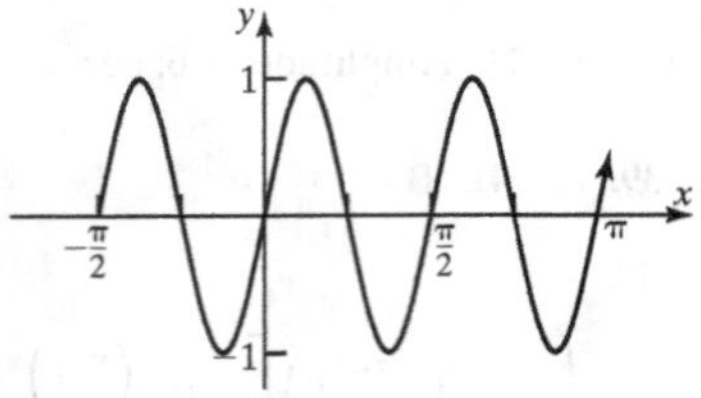

$(g \circ f)(x) = 4\sin x$

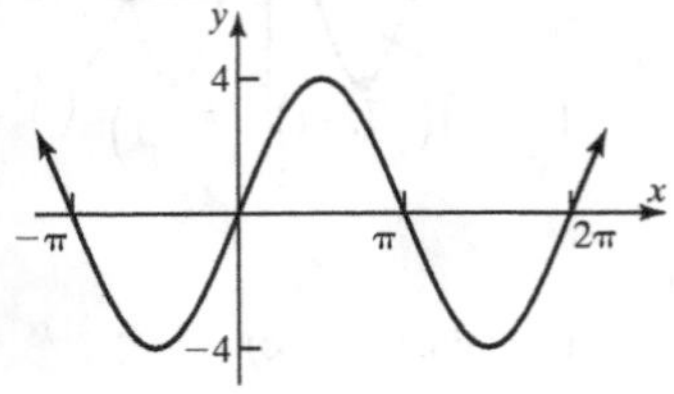

91. $(f \circ g)(x) = -2\cos x$

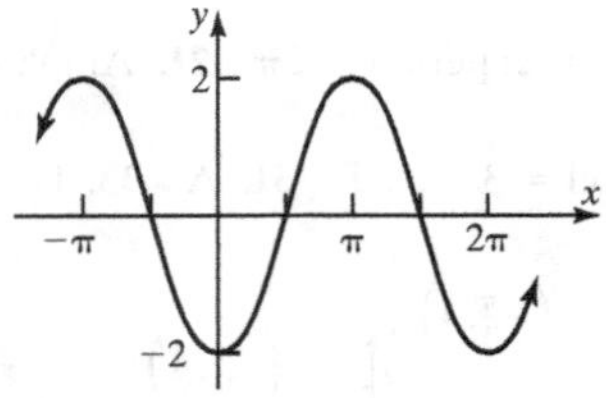

$(g \circ f)(x) = \cos(-2x)$

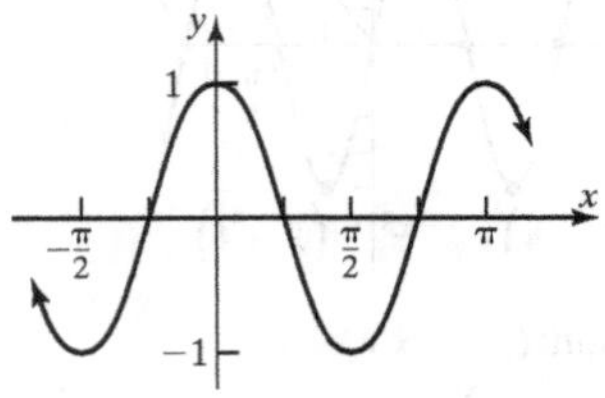

93. Period $= \frac{1}{30}$ s; amplitude $= 220$ amp

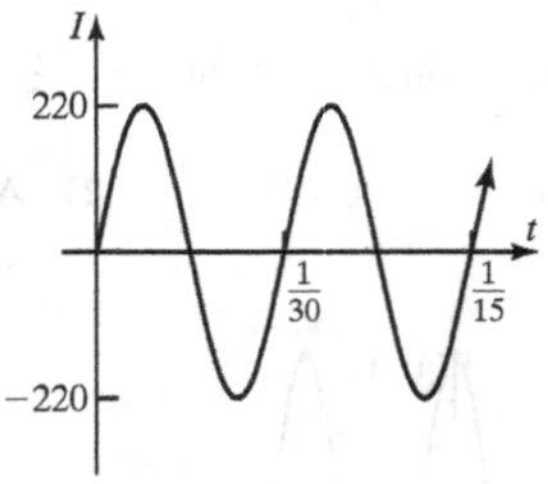

95. (a) Amplitude = 220 V; period = $\frac{1}{60}$ s

(b), (e)

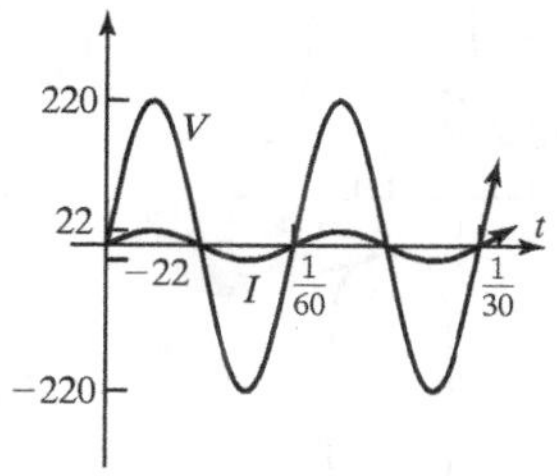

(c) $I(t) = 22\sin(120\pi t)$

(d) Amplitude = 22 amp; period = $\frac{1}{60}$ s

97. (a) $P(t) = \frac{[V_0 \sin(2\pi f t)]^2}{R} = \frac{V_0^2}{R}\sin^2(2\pi f t)$

(b) Since the graph of P has amplitude $\frac{V_0^2}{2R}$ and period $\frac{1}{2f}$ and is of the form $y = A\cos(\omega t) + B$, then $A = -\frac{V_0^2}{2R}$ and $B = \frac{V_0^2}{2R}$. Since $\frac{1}{2f} = \frac{2\pi}{\omega}$, then $\omega = 4\pi f$. Therefore,

$$P(t) = -\frac{V_0^2}{2R}\cos(4\pi f t) + \frac{V_0^2}{2R} = \frac{V_0^2}{2R}[1 - \cos(4\pi f t)].$$

99. (a) Physical potential: $\omega = \frac{2\pi}{23}$; emotional potential: $\omega = \frac{\pi}{14}$; intellectual potential: $\omega = \frac{2\pi}{33}$

(b)

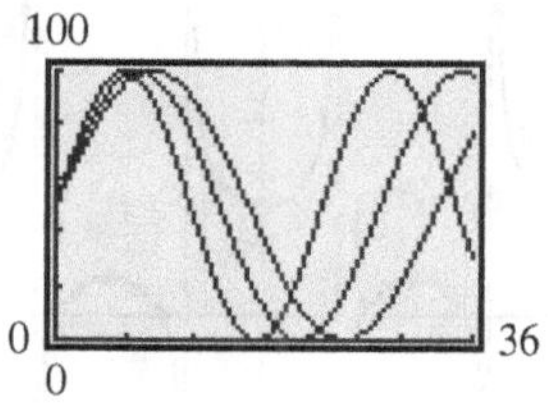

(c) No

(d) Physical potential peaks at 15 days after 20th birthday. Emotional potential is 50% at 17 days, with a maximum at 10 days and a minimum at 24 days. Intellectual potential starts fairly high, drops to a minimum at 13 days, and rises to a maximum at 29 days.

101.

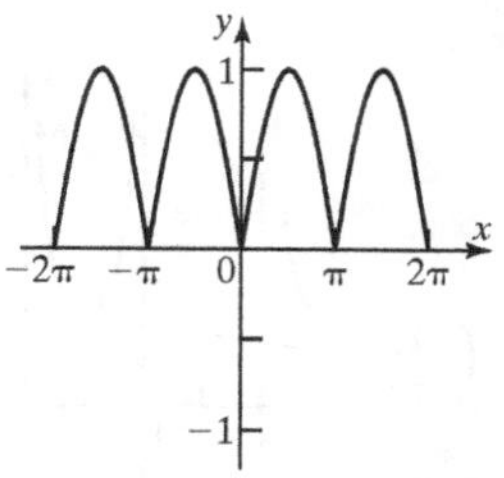

6.5 Assess Your Understanding *(page 417)*

3. origin; odd multiples of $\frac{\pi}{2}$ **4.** y-axis; odd multiples of $\frac{\pi}{2}$ **5.** $y = \cos x$ **6.** T **7.** 0 **9.** 1

11. $\sec x = 1$ for $x = -2\pi, 0, 2\pi$; $\sec x = -1$ for $x = -\pi, \pi$ **13.** $-\frac{3\pi}{2}, -\frac{\pi}{2}, \frac{\pi}{2}, \frac{3\pi}{2}$ **15.** $-\frac{3\pi}{2}, -\frac{\pi}{2}, \frac{\pi}{2}, \frac{3\pi}{2}$

17.

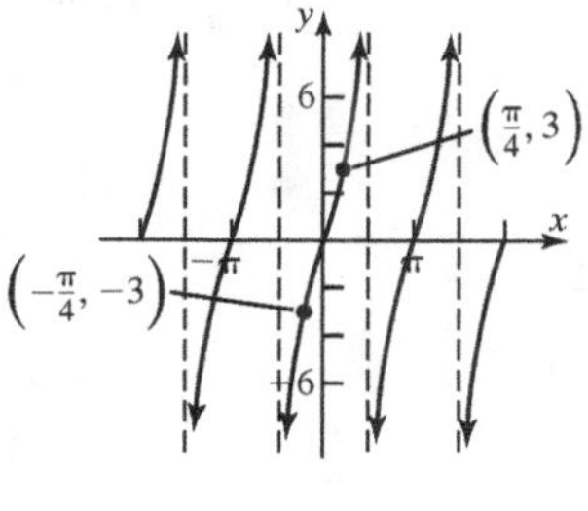

Domain: $\left\{x \mid x \neq \frac{k\pi}{2}, k \text{ is an odd integer}\right\}$
Range: $(-\infty, \infty)$

19.

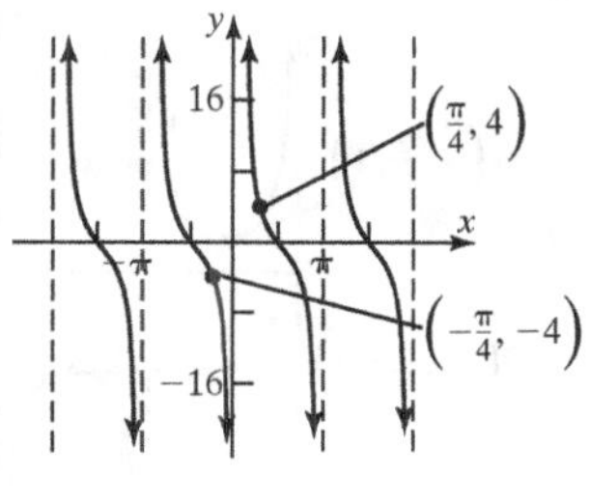

Domain: $\{x \mid x \neq k\pi, k \text{ is an integer}\}$
Range: $(-\infty, \infty)$

21.

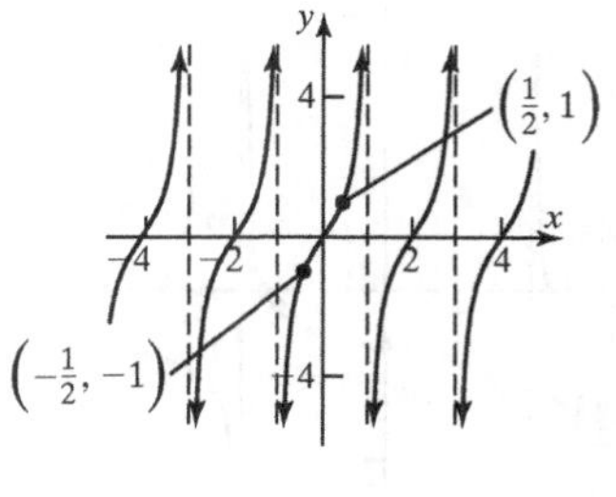

Domain: $\{x \mid x \text{ does not equal an odd integer}\}$
Range: $(-\infty, \infty)$

23.

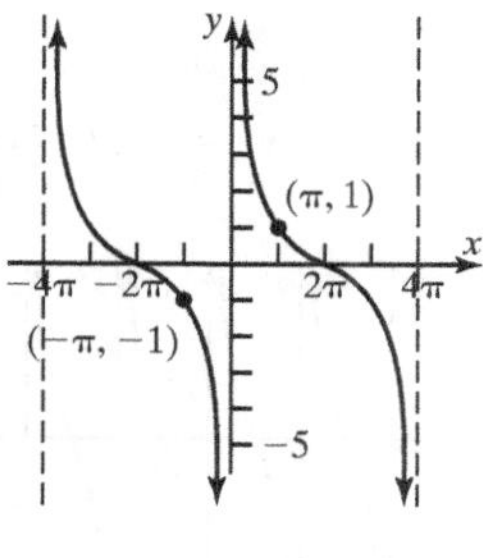

Domain: $\{x \mid x \neq 4k\pi, k \text{ is an integer}\}$

Range: $(-\infty, \infty)$

25.

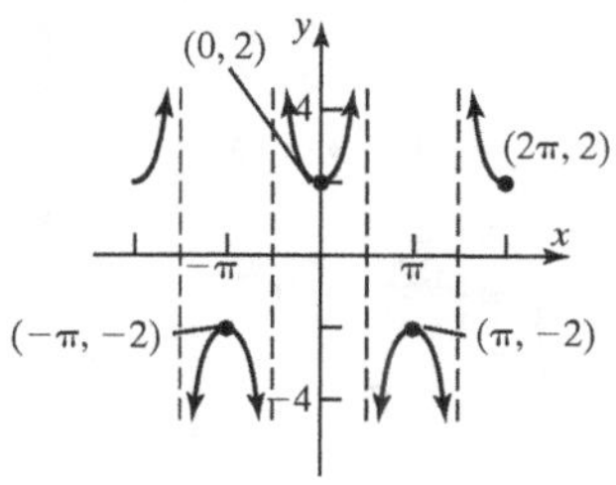

Domain: $\left\{x \mid x \neq \frac{k\pi}{2}, k \text{ is an odd integer}\right\}$

Range: $\{y \mid y \leq -2 \text{ or } y \geq 2\}$

27.

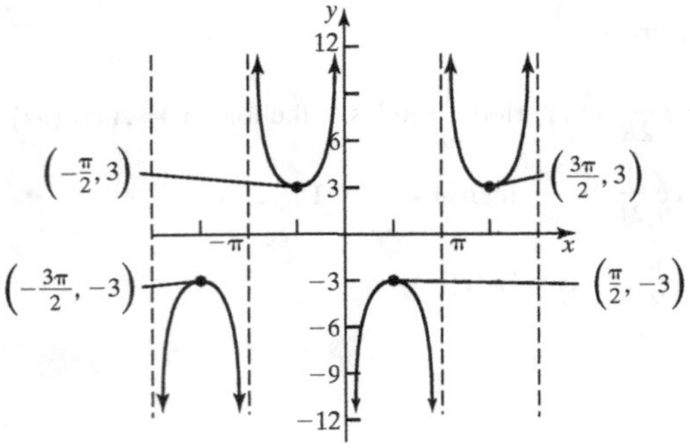

Domain: $\{x|x \neq k\pi, k \text{ is an integer}\}$

Range: $\{y|y \leq -3 \text{ or } y \geq 3\}$

29.

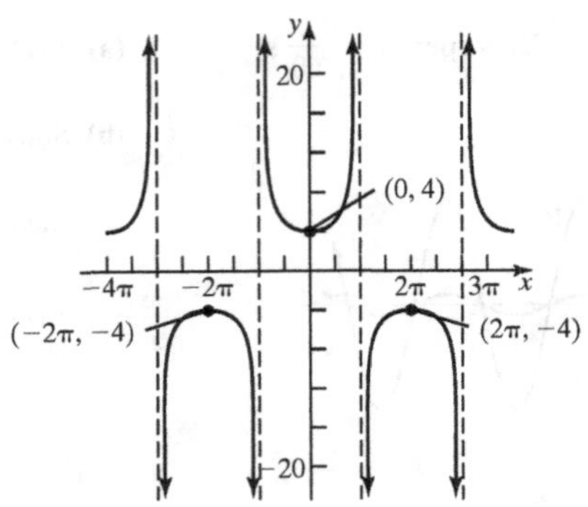

Domain: $\{x|x \neq k\pi, k \text{ is an odd integer}\}$

Range: $\{y|y \leq -4 \text{ or } y \geq 4\}$

31.

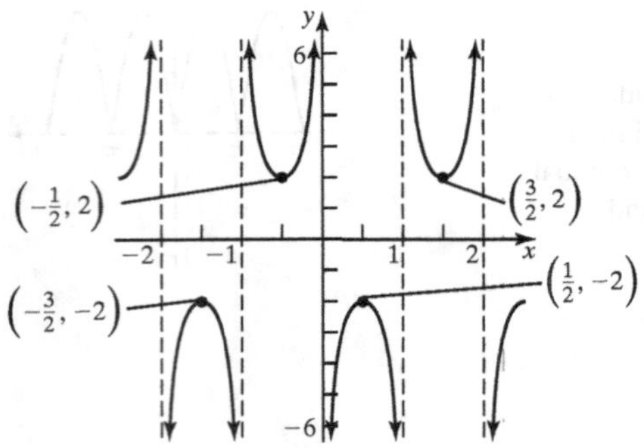

Domain: $\{x|x \text{ does not equal an integer}\}$

Range: $\{y|y \leq -2 \text{ or } y \geq 2\}$

33.

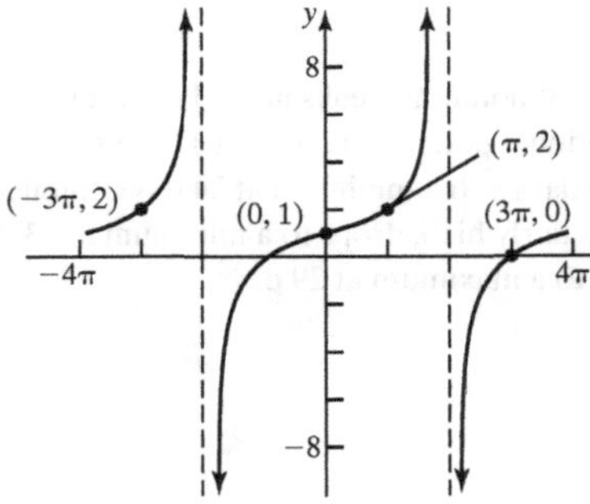

Domain: $\{x|x \neq 2\pi k, k \text{ is an odd integer}\}$

Range: $(-\infty, \infty)$

35.

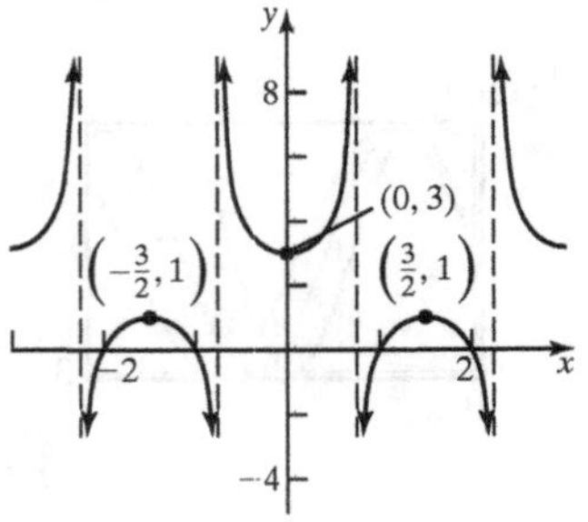

Domain: $\left\{x|x \neq \frac{3}{4}k, k \text{ is an odd integer}\right\}$

Range: $\{y|y \leq 1 \text{ or } y \geq 3\}$

37.

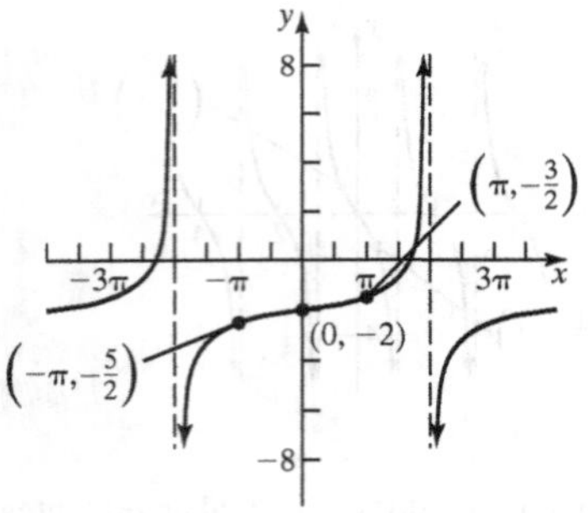

Domain: $\{x|x \neq 2\pi k, k \text{ is an odd integer}\}$

Range: $(-\infty, \infty)$

39.

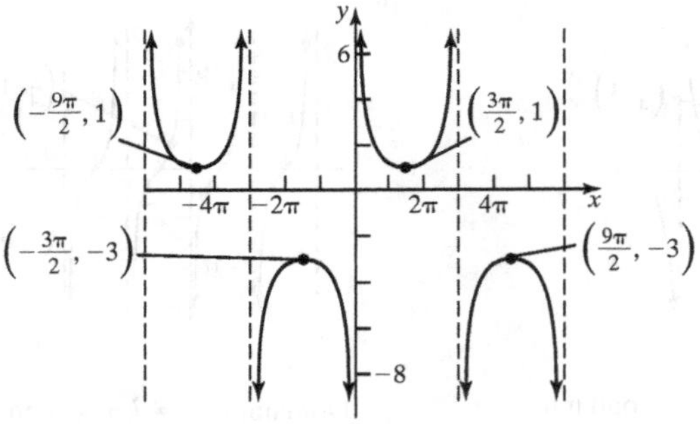

Domain: $\{x|x \neq 3\pi k, k \text{ is an integer}\}$

Range: $\{y|y \leq -3 \text{ or } y \geq 1\}$

41. $\frac{2\sqrt{3}}{\pi}$ **43.** $\frac{6\sqrt{3}}{\pi}$

45. $(f \circ g)(x) = \tan(4x)$

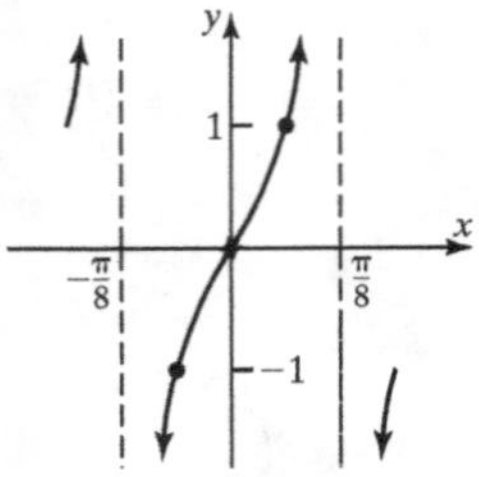

$(g \circ f)(x) = 4 \tan x$

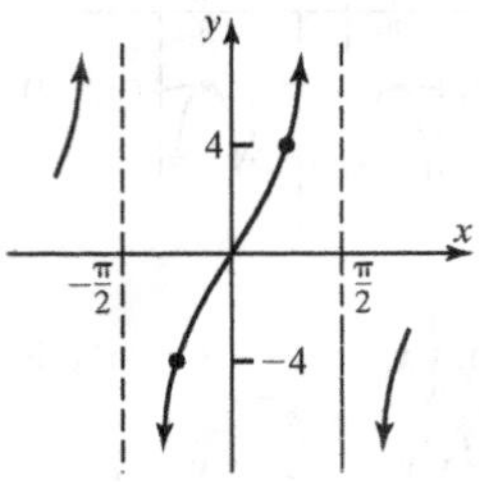

47. $(f \circ g)(x) = -2 \cot x$

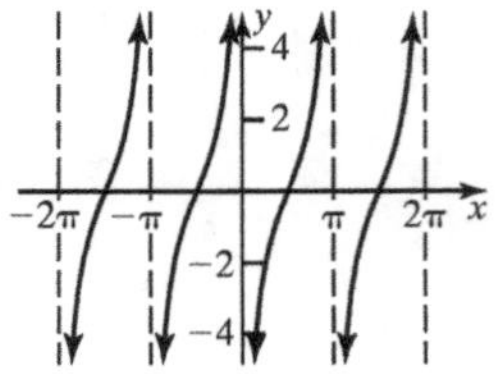

$(g \circ f)(x) = \cot(-2x)$

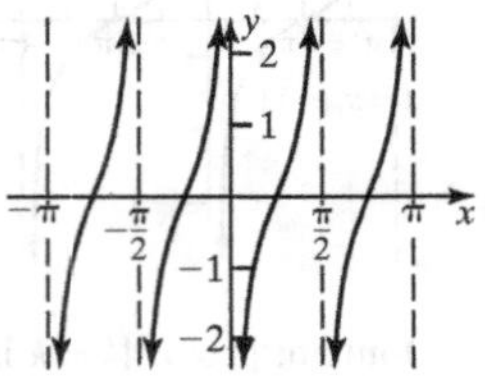

49. **(a)** $L(\theta) = \dfrac{3}{\cos\theta} + \dfrac{4}{\sin\theta} = 3\sec\theta + 4\csc\theta$
(c) Approximately 0.83
(d) Approximately 9.86 ft

(b)

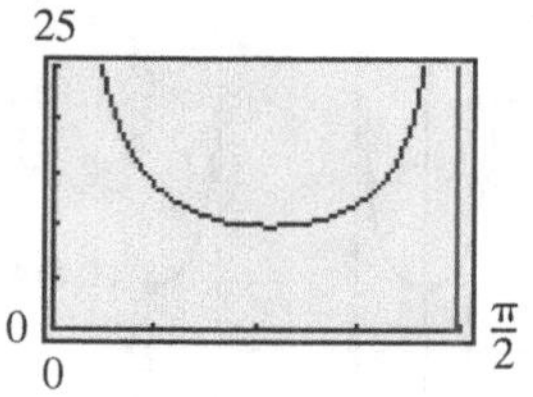

51.

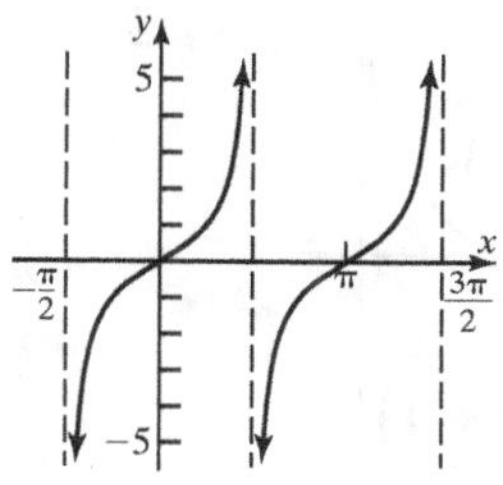

$y = \tan x$

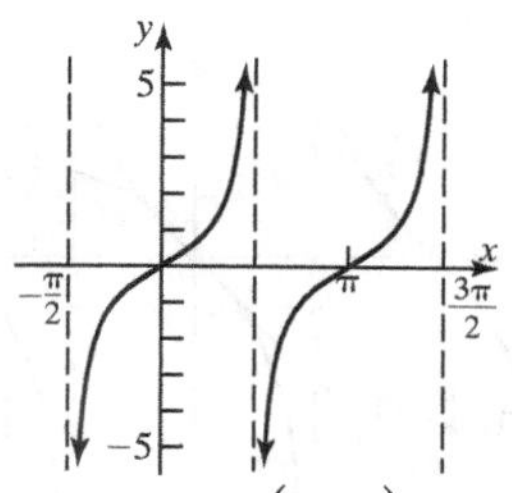

$y = -\cot\left(x + \frac{\pi}{2}\right)$

6.6 Assess Your Understanding *(page 427)*

1. phase shift **2.** F

3. Amplitude = 4

Period = π

Phase shift = $\dfrac{\pi}{2}$

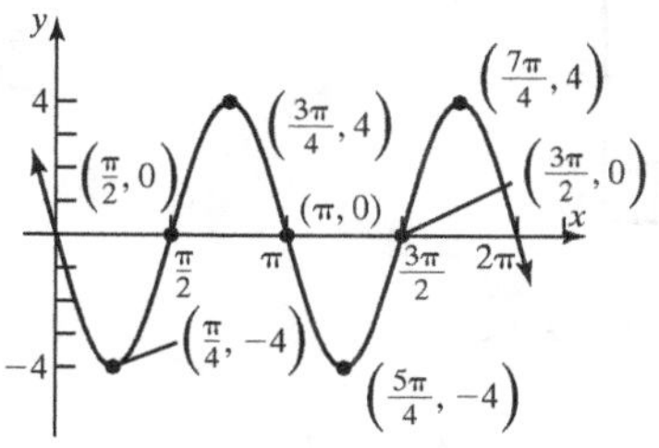

5. Amplitude = 2

Period = $\dfrac{2\pi}{3}$

Phase shift = $-\dfrac{\pi}{6}$

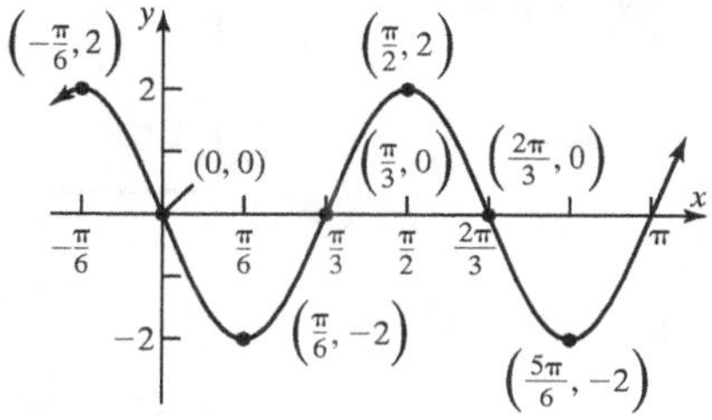

7. Amplitude = 3

Period = π

Phase shift = $-\dfrac{\pi}{4}$

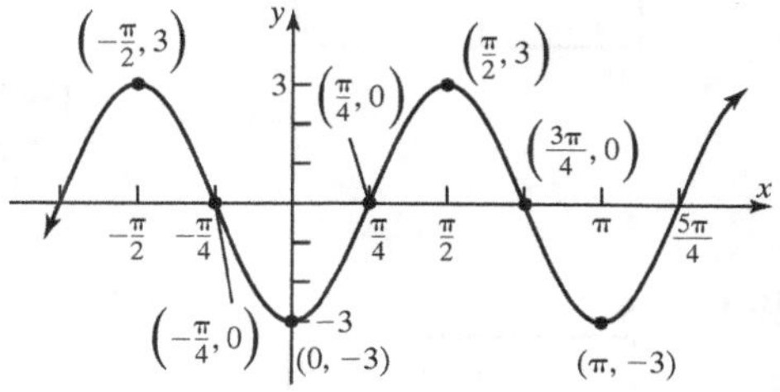

9. Amplitude = 4

Period = 2

Phase shift = $-\dfrac{2}{\pi}$

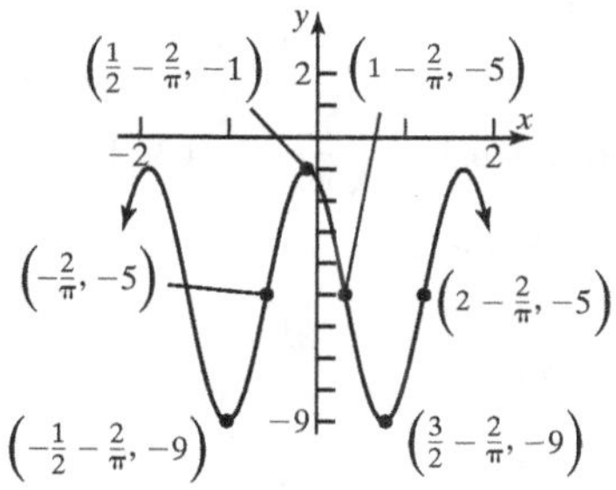

11. Amplitude = 3

Period = 2

Phase shift = $\dfrac{2}{\pi}$

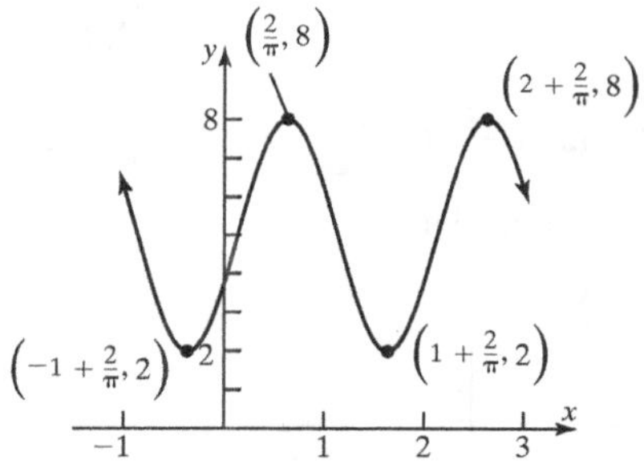

13. Amplitude = 3

Period = π

Phase shift = $\dfrac{\pi}{4}$

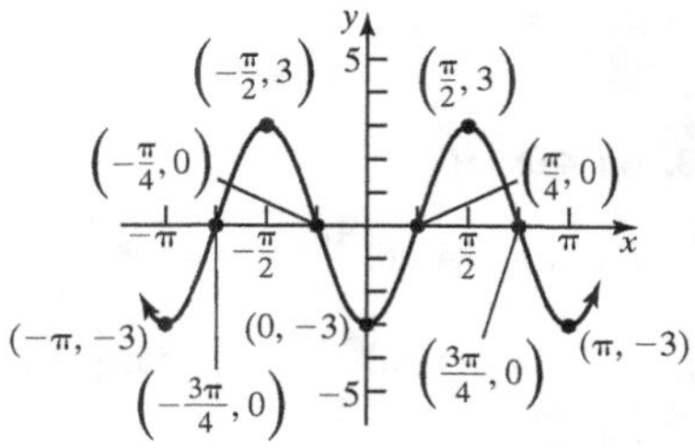

15. $y = 2\sin\left[2\left(x - \frac{1}{2}\right)\right]$ or $y = 2\sin(2x - 1)$ **17.** $y = 3\sin\left[\frac{2}{3}\left(x + \frac{1}{3}\right)\right]$ or $y = 3\sin\left(\frac{2}{3}x + \frac{2}{9}\right)$

19.

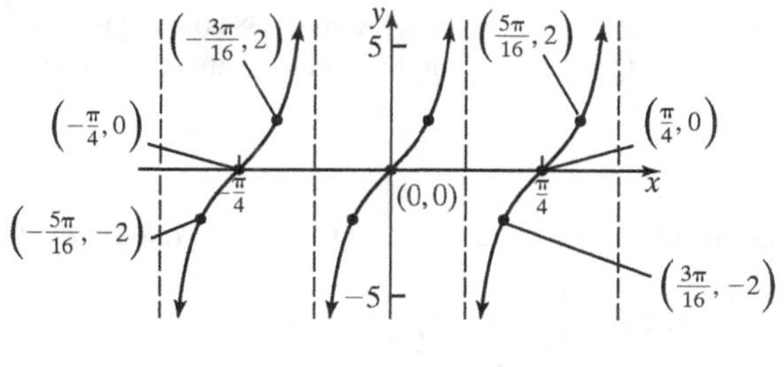

21.

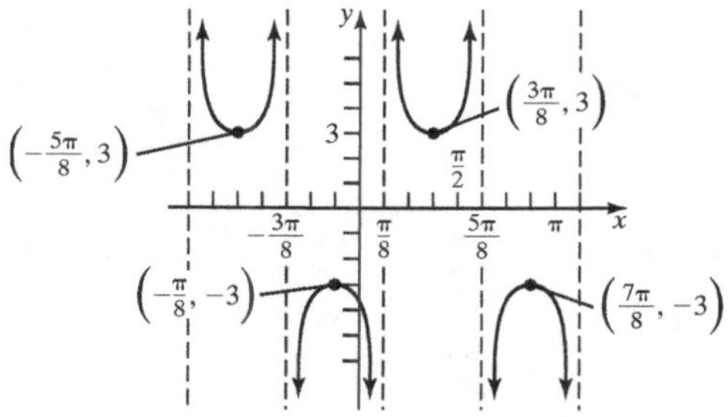

23.

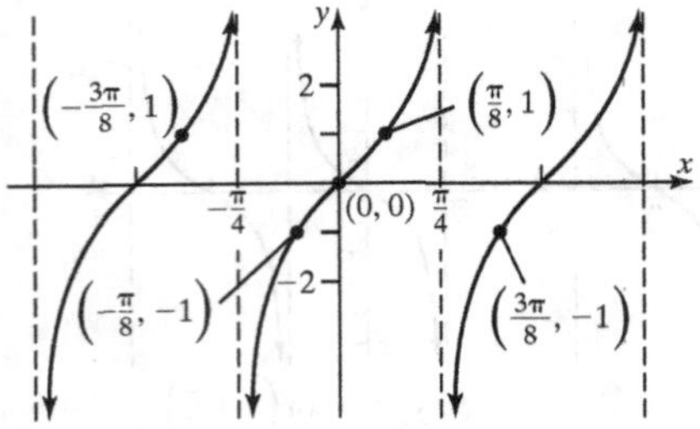

25.

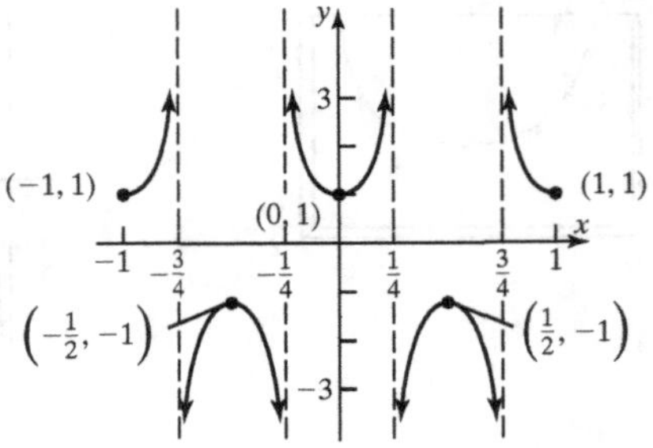

27. Period $= \frac{1}{15}$ s; amplitude $= 120$ amp; phase shift $= \frac{1}{90}$ s

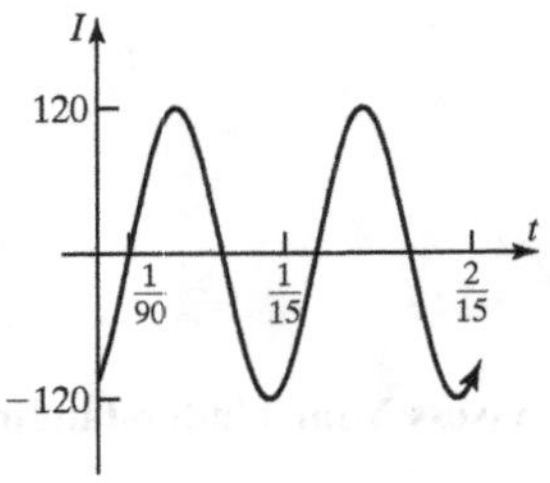

29. (a)

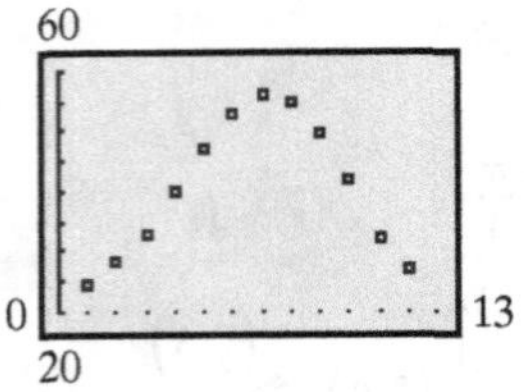

(b) $y = 15.9 \sin\left[\frac{\pi}{6}(x - 4)\right] + 40.1$ or $y = 15.9 \sin\left(\frac{\pi}{6}x - \frac{2\pi}{3}\right) + 40.1$

(c)

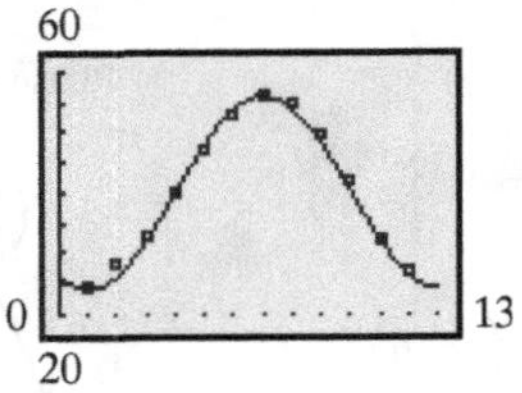

(d) $y = 15.62 \sin(0.517x - 2.096) + 40.377$

(e)

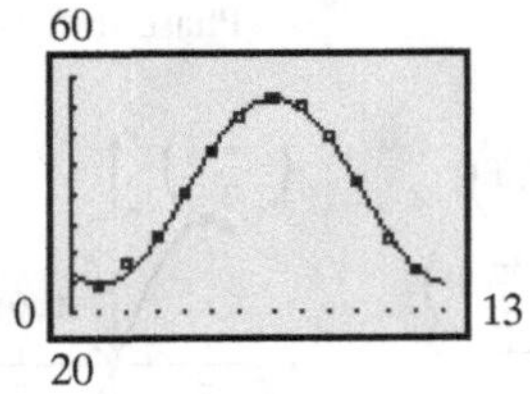

31. (a)

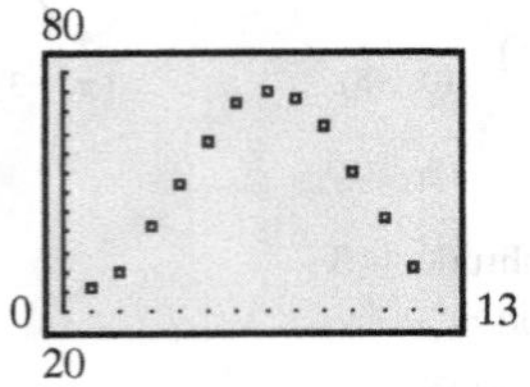

(b) $y = 24.95 \sin\left[\frac{\pi}{6}(x - 4)\right] + 50.45$ or $y = 24.95 \sin\left(\frac{\pi}{6}x - \frac{2\pi}{3}\right) + 50.45$

(c)

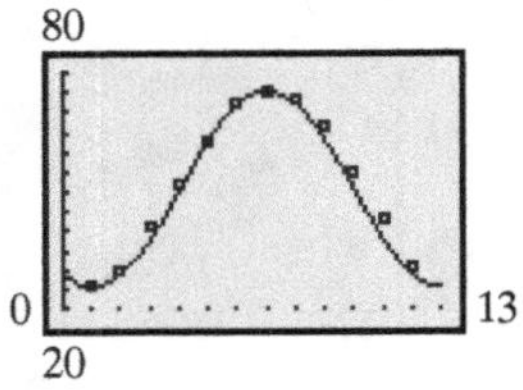

(d) $y = 25.693 \sin(0.476x - 1.814) + 49.854$

(e)

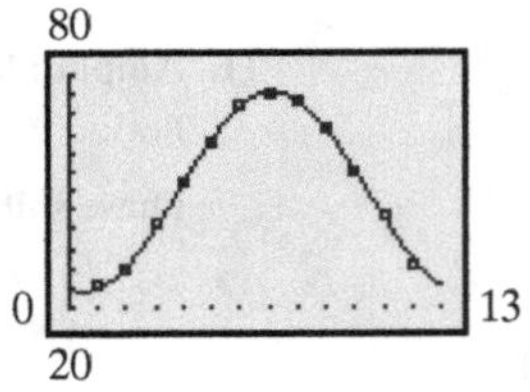

33. (a) 4:08 PM

(b) $y = 4.4 \sin\left[\frac{4\pi}{25}(x - 0.5083)\right] + 3.8$ or

$y = 4.4 \sin\left[\frac{4\pi}{25}x - 0.2555\right] + 3.8$

(c)

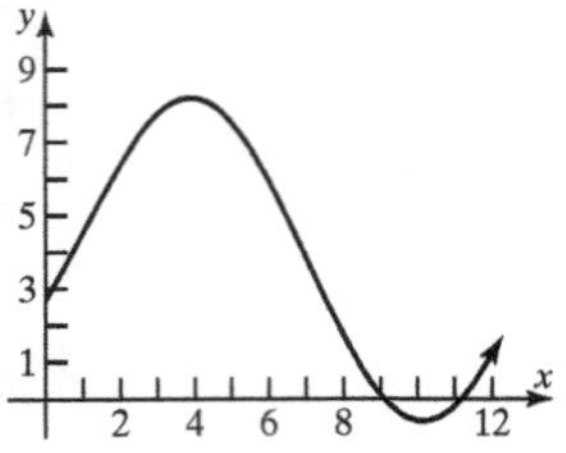

(d) 8.2 ft

35. (a) $y = 1.6 \sin\left(\frac{2\pi}{365}x - 1.39\right) + 12.15$

(b) 12.43 h

(c)

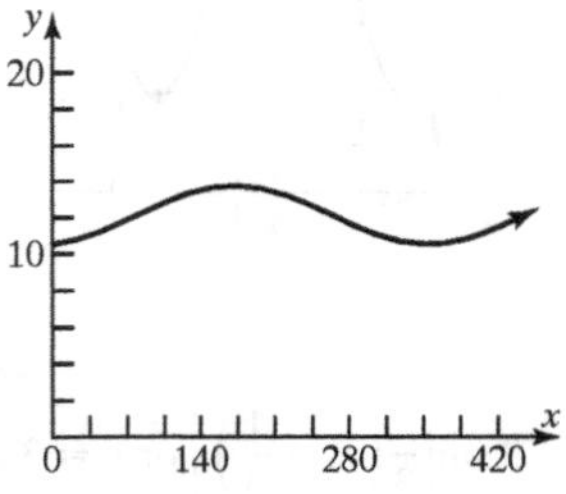

(d) The actual hours of sunlight on April 1, 2007, were 12.43 hours. This is the same as the predicted amount.

37. (a) $y = 6.97 \sin\left(\frac{2\pi}{365}x - 1.39\right) + 12.45$

(b) 13.67 h

(c)

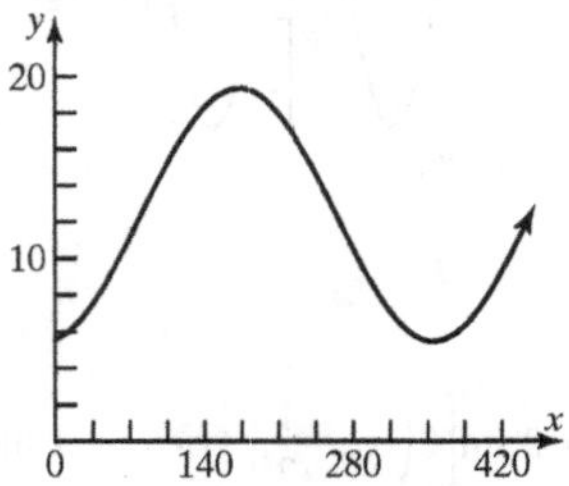

(d) The actual hours of sunlight on April 1 2007, were 13.38 hours. This is close to the predicted amount of 13.67 hours.

Review Exercises *(page 433)*

1. $\frac{3\pi}{4}$ **3.** $\frac{\pi}{10}$ **5.** $135°$ **7.** $-450°$ **9.** $\frac{1}{2}$ **11.** $\frac{3\sqrt{2}}{2} - \frac{4\sqrt{3}}{3}$ **13.** $-3\sqrt{2} - 2\sqrt{3}$ **15.** 3 **17.** 0 **19.** 0 **21.** 1 **23.** 1 **25.** 1 **27.** -1 **29.** 1

31. $\cos\theta = \frac{3}{5}$; $\tan\theta = \frac{4}{3}$; $\csc\theta = \frac{5}{4}$; $\sec\theta = \frac{5}{3}$; $\cot\theta = \frac{3}{4}$ **33.** $\sin\theta = -\frac{12}{13}$; $\cos\theta = -\frac{5}{13}$; $\csc\theta = -\frac{13}{12}$; $\sec\theta = -\frac{13}{5}$; $\cot\theta = \frac{5}{12}$

35. $\sin\theta = \frac{3}{5}$; $\cos\theta = -\frac{4}{5}$; $\tan\theta = -\frac{3}{4}$; $\csc\theta = \frac{5}{3}$; $\cot\theta = -\frac{4}{3}$ **37.** $\cos\theta = -\frac{5}{13}$; $\tan\theta = -\frac{12}{5}$; $\csc\theta = \frac{13}{12}$; $\sec\theta = -\frac{13}{5}$; $\cot\theta = -\frac{5}{12}$

39. $\cos\theta = \frac{12}{13}$; $\tan\theta = -\frac{5}{12}$; $\csc\theta = -\frac{13}{5}$; $\sec\theta = \frac{13}{12}$; $\cot\theta = -\frac{12}{5}$ **41.** $\sin\theta = -\frac{\sqrt{10}}{10}$; $\cos\theta = -\frac{3\sqrt{10}}{10}$; $\csc\theta = -\sqrt{10}$; $\sec\theta = -\frac{\sqrt{10}}{3}$; $\cot\theta = 3$

43. $\sin\theta = -\frac{2\sqrt{2}}{3}$; $\cos\theta = \frac{1}{3}$; $\tan\theta = -2\sqrt{2}$; $\csc\theta = -\frac{3\sqrt{2}}{4}$; $\cot\theta = -\frac{\sqrt{2}}{4}$

45. $\sin\theta = \frac{\sqrt{5}}{5}$; $\cos\theta = -\frac{2\sqrt{5}}{5}$; $\tan\theta = -\frac{1}{2}$; $\csc\theta = \sqrt{5}$; $\sec\theta = -\frac{\sqrt{5}}{2}$

47.

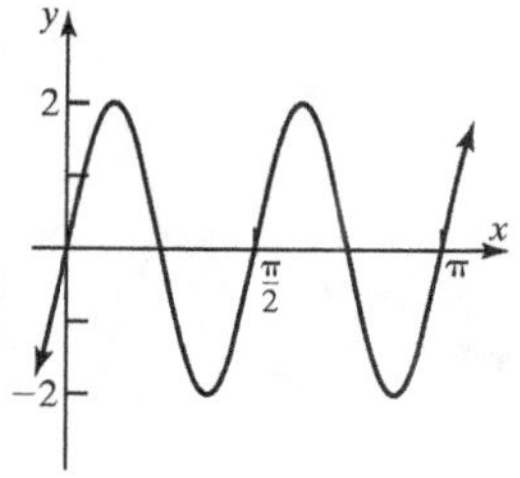

49.

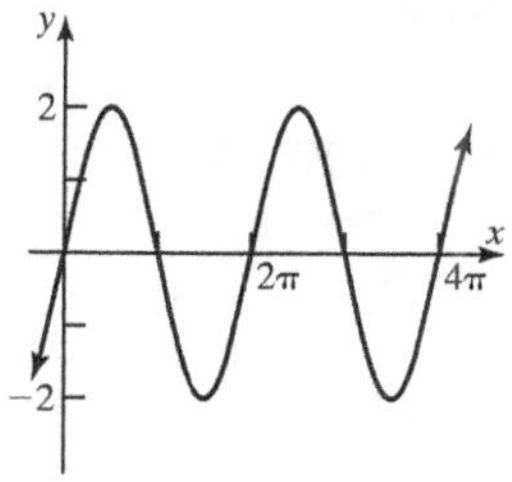

51.

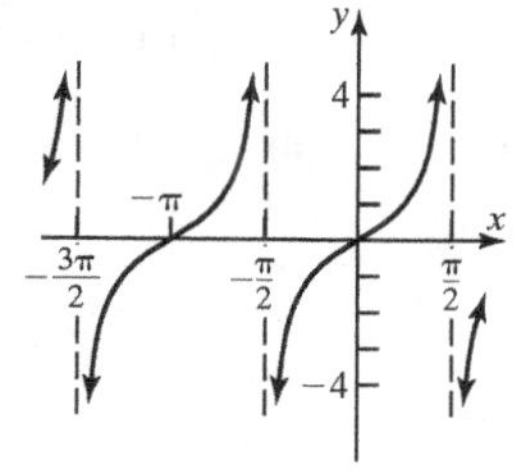

53.

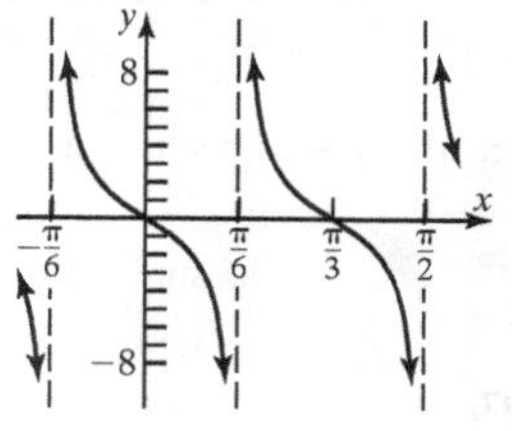

55.

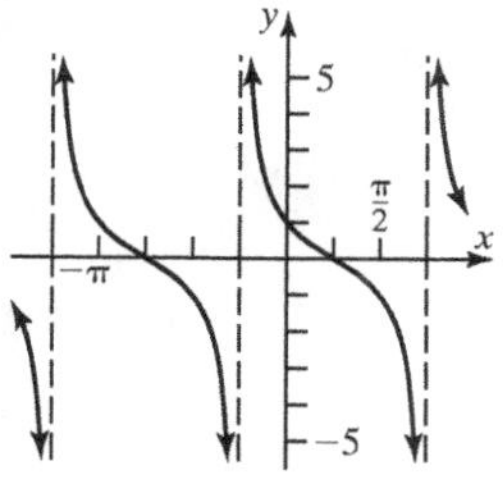

57.

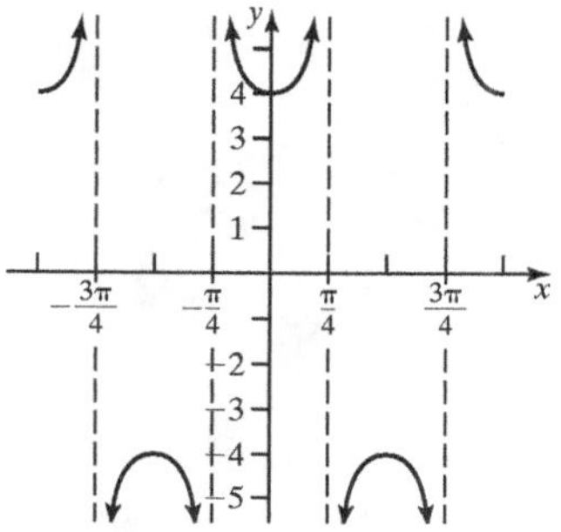

59.

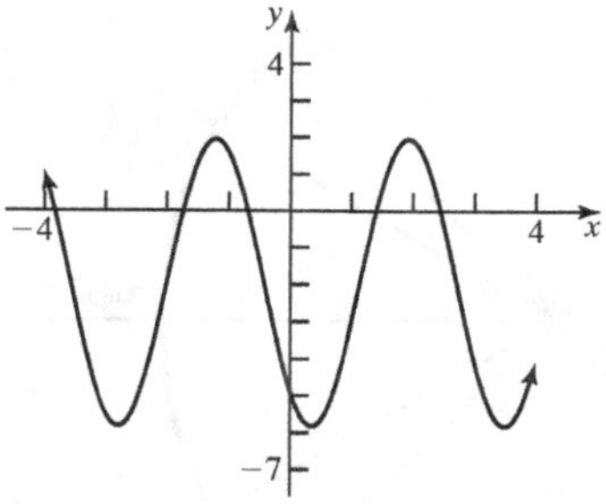

61.

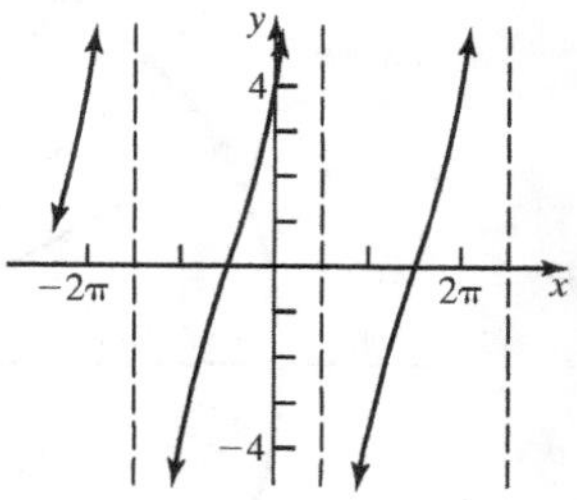

63. Amplitude = 4; period = 2π **65.** Amplitude = 8; period = 4

67. Amplitude = 4

Period = $\frac{2\pi}{3}$

Phase shift = 0

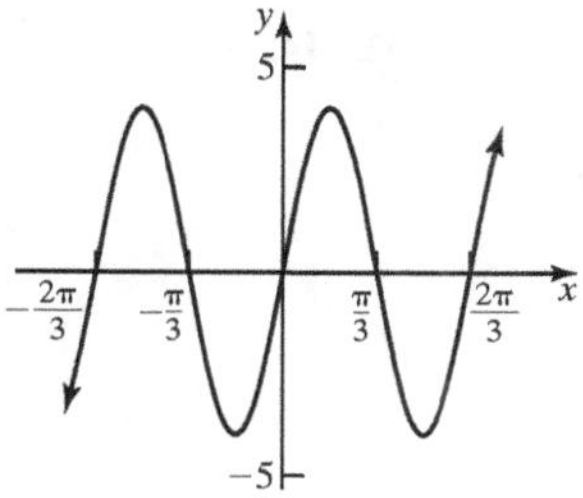

69. Amplitude = 2

Period = π

Phase shift = $\frac{\pi}{2}$

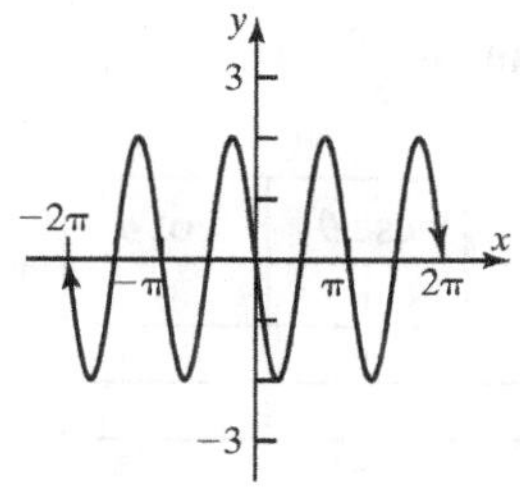

71. Amplitude = $\frac{1}{2}$

Period = $\frac{4\pi}{3}$

Phase shift = $\frac{2\pi}{3}$

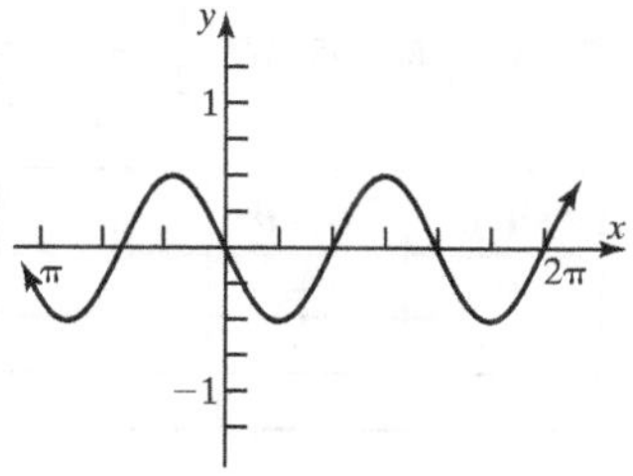

73. Amplitude = $\frac{2}{3}$

Period = 2

Phase shift = $\frac{6}{\pi}$

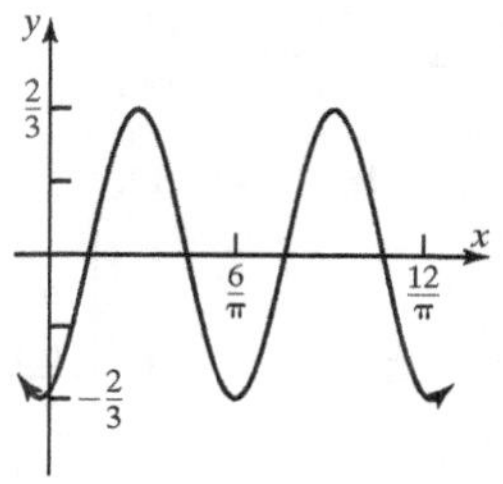

75. $y = 5\cos\frac{x}{4}$ **77.** $y = -6\cos\left(\frac{\pi}{4}x\right)$ **79.** 0.38 **81.** Sine, cosine, cosecant and secant: negative; tangent and cotangent: positive

83. $\sin\theta = \frac{2\sqrt{2}}{3}$; $\cos\theta = -\frac{1}{3}$; $\tan\theta = -2\sqrt{2}$; $\csc\theta = \frac{3\sqrt{2}}{4}$; $\sec\theta = -3$; $\cot\theta = -\frac{\sqrt{2}}{4}$

85. Domain: $\left\{x \,\middle|\, x \neq \text{odd multiple of } \frac{\pi}{2}\right\}$; range: $\{y \mid |y| \geq 1\}$; period = $2(\pi)$ **87.** $\frac{\pi}{3} \approx 1.05$ ft; $\frac{\pi}{3} \approx 1.05$ ft^2

89. Approximately 114.59 revolutions/hr **91.** 0.1 revolution/sec = $\frac{\pi}{5}$ radian/sec **93.** **(a)** 120 **(b)** $\frac{1}{60}$ **(c)**

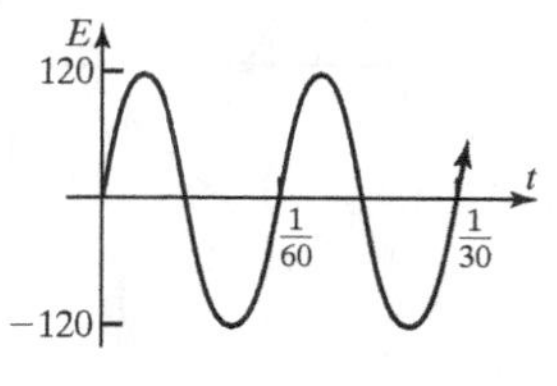

95. **(a)**

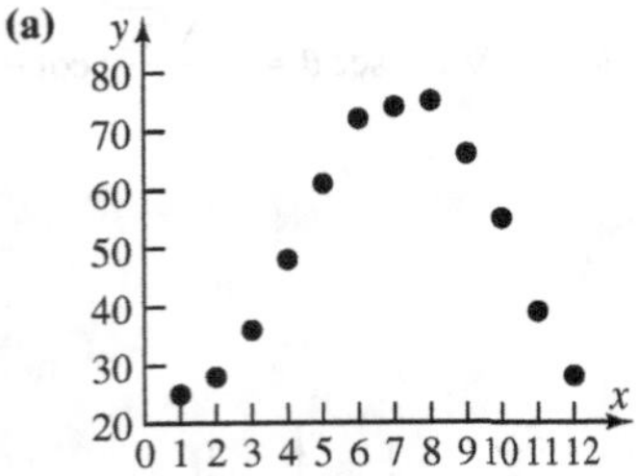

(b) $y = 19.5 \sin\left[\frac{\pi}{6}(x - 4)\right] + 70.5$ or

$y = 19.5 \sin\left(\frac{\pi}{6}x - \frac{2\pi}{3}\right) + 70.5$

(c)

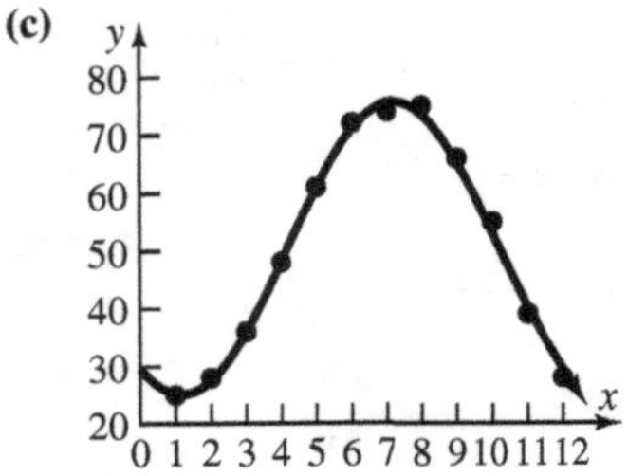

(d) $y = 19.52 \sin(0.54x - 2.28) + 71.01$

(e)

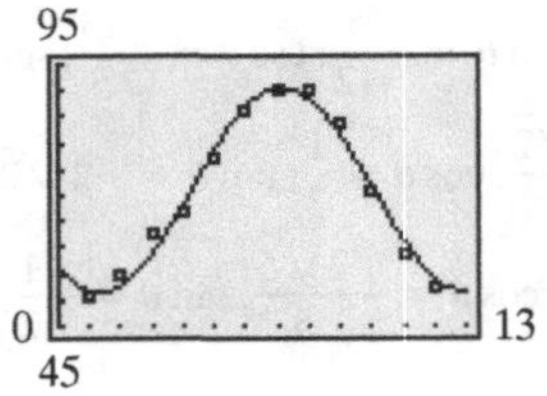

97.

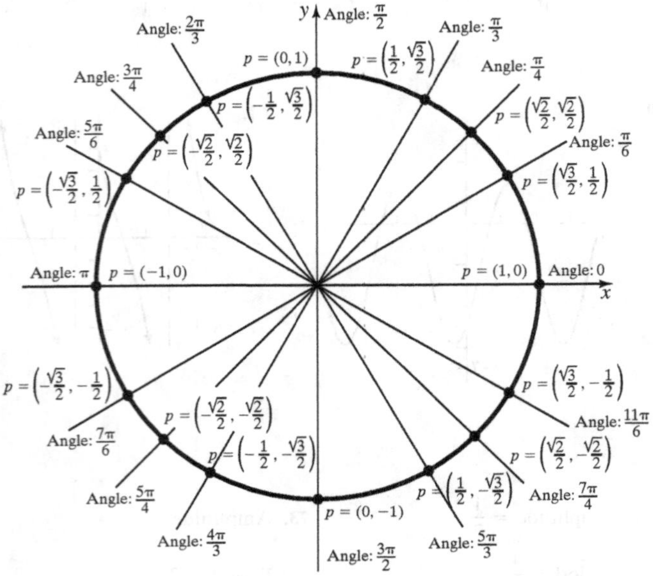

Chapter Test *(page 436)*

1. $\frac{13\pi}{9}$ **2.** $-\frac{20\pi}{9}$ **3.** $\frac{13\pi}{180}$ **4.** $-22.5°$ **5.** $810°$ **6.** $135°$ **7.** $\frac{1}{2}$ **8.** 0 **9.** $-\frac{1}{2}$ **10.** $-\frac{\sqrt{3}}{3}$ **11.** 2 **12.** $\frac{3(1 - \sqrt{2})}{2}$ **13.** 0.292 **14.** 0.309 **15.** −1.524 **16.** 2.747 **17.**

	$\sin\theta$	$\cos\theta$	$\tan\theta$	$\sec\theta$	$\csc\theta$	$\cot\theta$
θ in QI	+	+	+	+	+	+
θ in QII	+	−	−	−	+	−
θ in QIII	−	−	+	−	−	+
θ in QIV	−	+	−	+	−	−

18. $-\frac{3}{5}$

19. $\cos\theta = -\frac{2\sqrt{6}}{7}$; $\tan\theta = -\frac{5\sqrt{6}}{12}$; $\csc\theta = \frac{7}{5}$; $\sec\theta = -\frac{7\sqrt{6}}{12}$; $\cot\theta = -\frac{2\sqrt{6}}{5}$ **20.** $\sin\theta = -\frac{\sqrt{5}}{3}$; $\tan\theta = -\frac{\sqrt{5}}{2}$; $\csc\theta = -\frac{3\sqrt{5}}{5}$; $\sec\theta = \frac{3}{2}$; $\cot\theta = -\frac{2\sqrt{5}}{5}$ **21.** $\sin\theta = \frac{12}{13}$; $\cos\theta = -\frac{5}{13}$; $\csc\theta = \frac{13}{12}$; $\sec\theta = -\frac{13}{5}$; $\cot\theta = -\frac{5}{12}$ **22.** $\frac{7\sqrt{53}}{53}$ **23.** $-\frac{5\sqrt{146}}{146}$ **24.** $-\frac{1}{2}$

25.

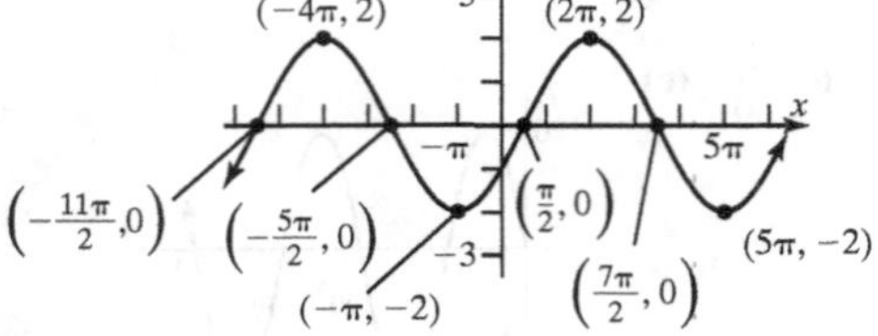

26.

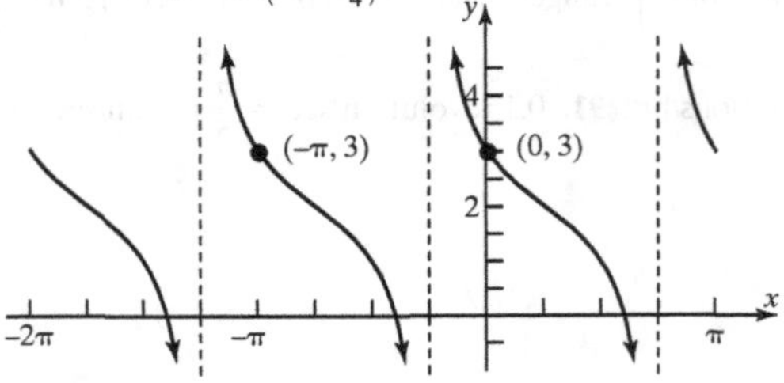

27. $y = -3\sin\left(3x + \frac{3\pi}{4}\right)$

28. 78.93 ft^2 **29.** 143.5 rpm

Cumulative Review *(page 436)*

1. $\left\{-1, \frac{1}{2}\right\}$ **2.** $y - 5 = -3(x + 2)$ or $y = -3x - 1$ **3.** $x^2 + (y + 2)^2 = 16$

4. A line; slope $\frac{2}{3}$; intercepts $(6, 0)$ and $(0, -4)$

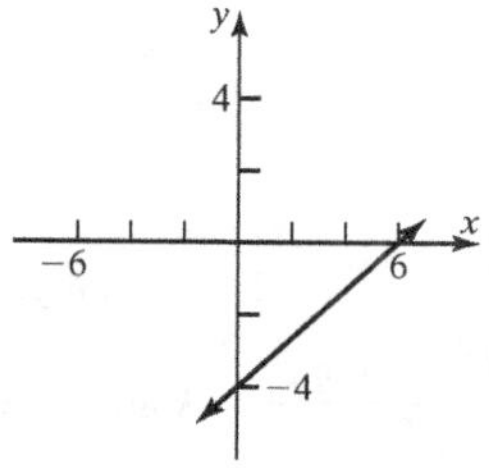

5. A circle; center $(1, -2)$; radius 3

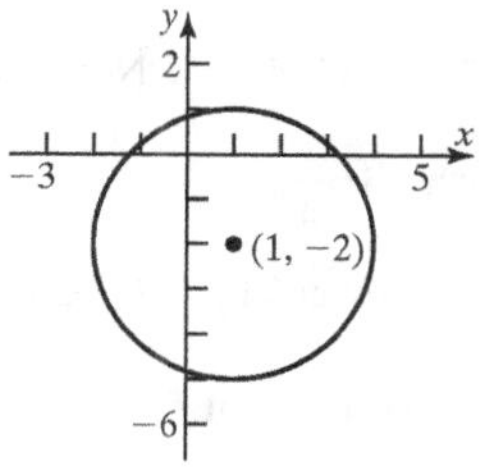

6.

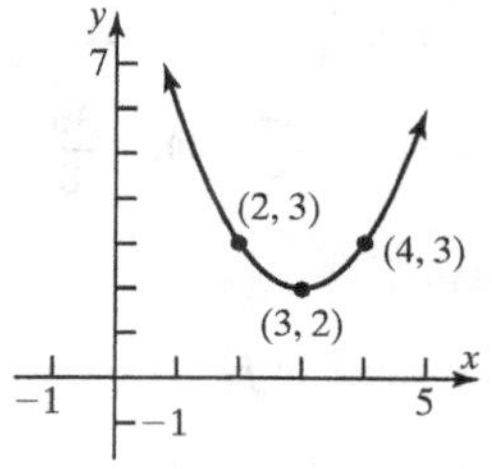

7. (a)

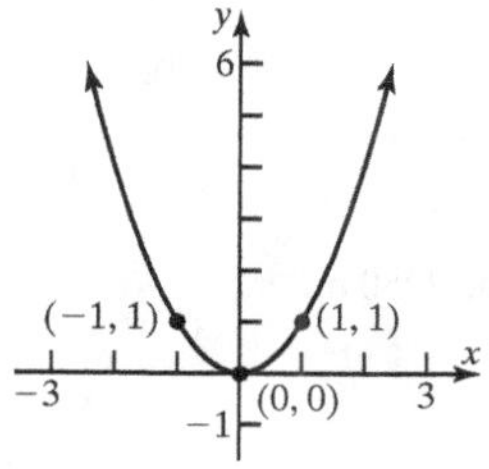

(b)

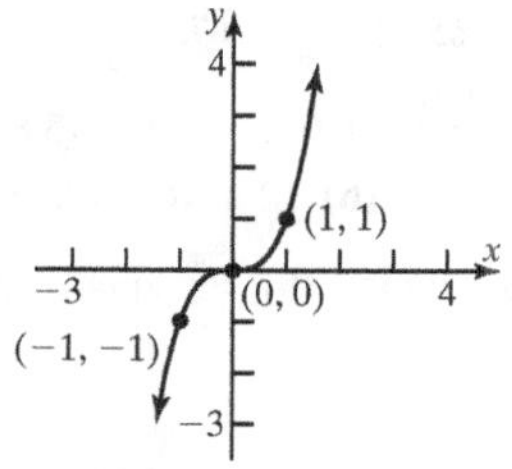

(c)

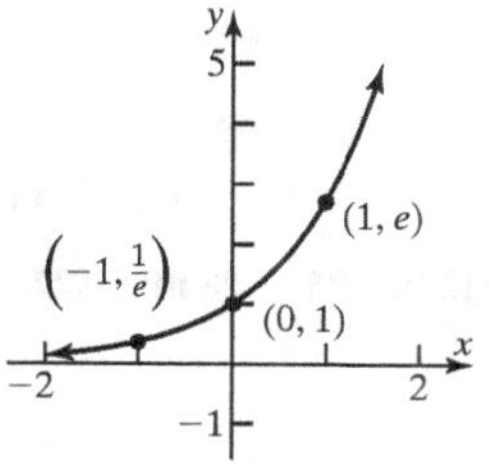

(d)

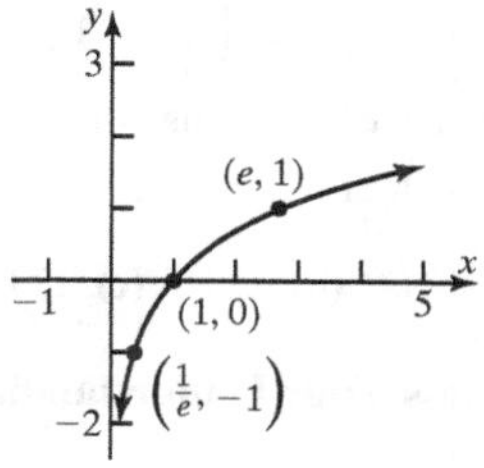

(e)

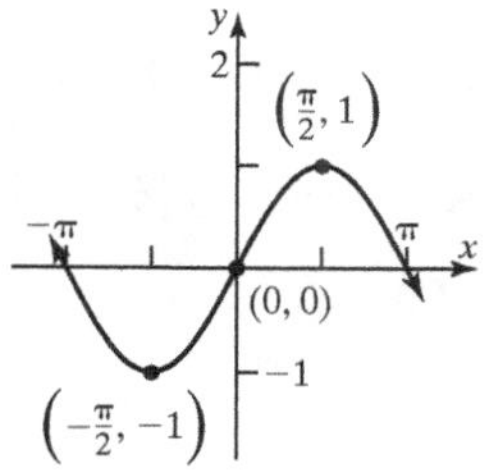

(f)

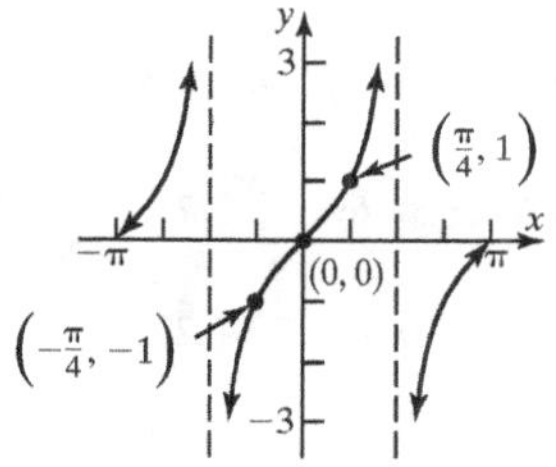

8. $f^{-1}(x) = \frac{1}{3}(x + 2)$

9. -2

10.

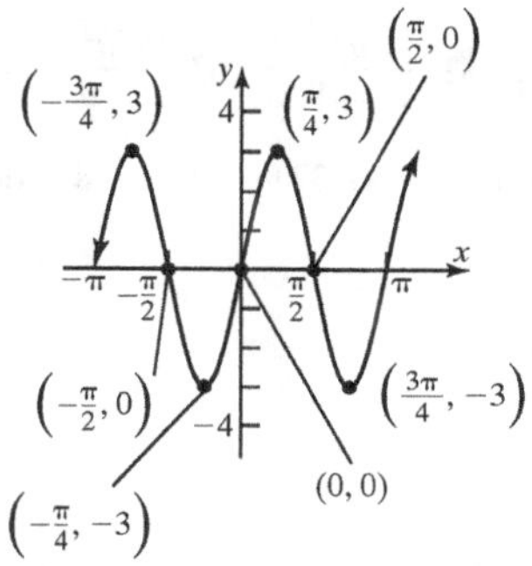

11. $3 - \frac{3\sqrt{3}}{2}$

12. $y = 2(3^x)$

13. $y = 3\cos\left(\frac{\pi}{6}x\right)$

14. (a) $f(x) = -3x - 3$; $m = -3$; $(-1, 0)$, $(0, -3)$

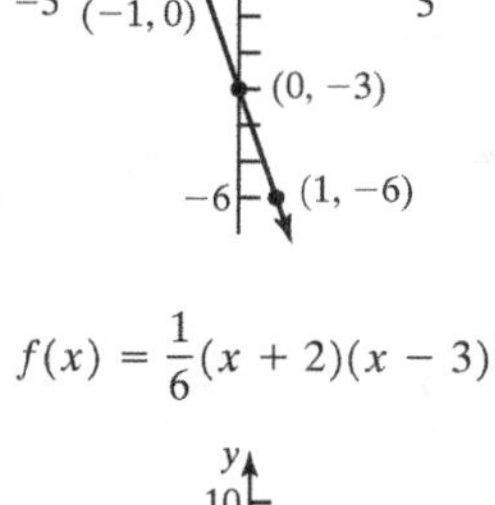

(b) $f(x) = (x - 1)^2 - 6$; $(0, -5)$, $\left(-\sqrt{6} + 1, 0\right)$, $\left(\sqrt{6} + 1, 0\right)$

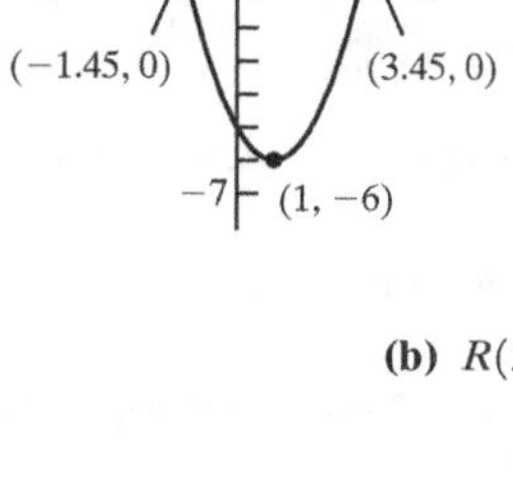

(c) We have that $y = 3$ when $x = -2$ and $y = -6$ when $x = 1$. Both points satisfy $y = ae^x$. Therefore, for $(-2, 3)$ we have $3 = ae^{-2}$, which implies that $a = 3e^2$. But for $(1, -6)$ we have $-6 = ae^1$, which implies that $a = -6e^{-1}$. Therefore, there is no exponential function $y = ae^x$ that contains $(-2, 3)$ and $(1, -6)$.

15. (a) $f(x) = \frac{1}{6}(x + 2)(x - 3)(x - 5)$

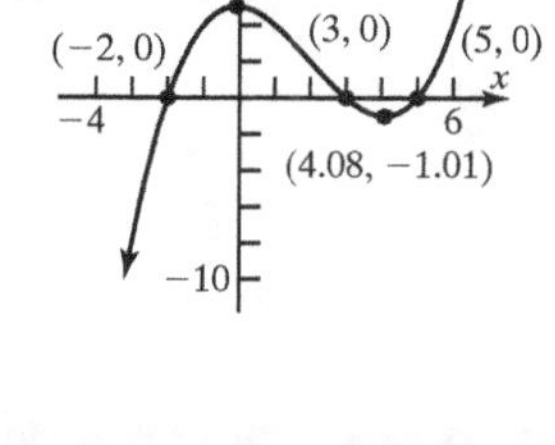

(b) $R(x) = \dfrac{(x + 2)(x - 3)(x - 5)}{3(x - 2)}$

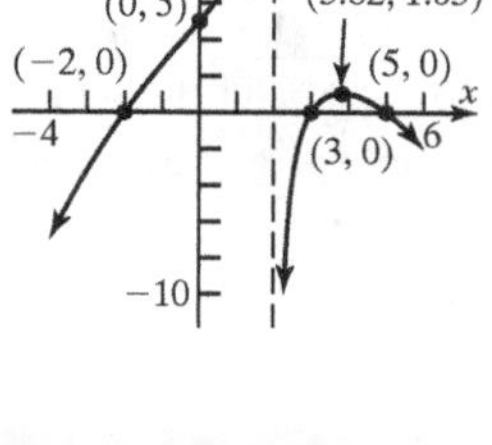

CHAPTER 7 Analytic Trigonometry

7.1 Assess Your Understanding *(page 450)*

7. $x = \sin y$ **8.** $\frac{\pi}{2}$ **9.** $\frac{\pi}{5}$ **10.** F **11.** T **12.** T **13.** 0 **15.** $-\frac{\pi}{2}$ **17.** 0 **19.** $\frac{\pi}{4}$ **21.** $\frac{\pi}{3}$ **23.** $\frac{5\pi}{6}$ **25.** 0.10 **27.** 1.37 **29.** 0.51 **31.** −0.38 **33.** −0.12 **35.** 1.08 **37.** $\frac{4\pi}{5}$ **39.** $-\frac{3\pi}{8}$ **41.** $-\frac{\pi}{8}$ **43.** $-\frac{\pi}{5}$ **45.** $\frac{1}{4}$ **47.** 4 **49.** Not defined **51.** π

53. $f^{-1}(x) = \sin^{-1}\frac{x-2}{5}$
Domain of f = range of f^{-1}: $(-\infty, \infty)$
Domain of f^{-1} = range of f: $[-3, 7]$

55. $f^{-1}(x) = \frac{1}{3}\cos^{-1}\left(-\frac{x}{2}\right)$
Domain of f = range of f^{-1}: $(-\infty, \infty)$
Domain of f^{-1} = range of f: $[-2, 2]$

57. $f^{-1}(x) = -\tan^{-1}(x+3) - 1$
Domain of f: $x \neq \frac{(2k+1)\pi}{2} - 1$, k an integer
Range of f^{-1}: $y \neq \frac{(2k+1)\pi}{2} - 1$, k an integer
Domain of f^{-1} = range of f: $(-\infty, \infty)$

59. $f^{-1}(x) = \frac{1}{2}\left[\sin^{-1}\left(\frac{x}{3}\right) - 1\right]$
Domain of f = range of f^{-1}: $(-\infty, \infty)$
Domain of f^{-1} = range of f: $[-3, 3]$

61. $\left\{\frac{\sqrt{2}}{2}\right\}$ **63.** $\left\{-\frac{1}{4}\right\}$ **65.** $\{\sqrt{3}\}$ **67.** $\{-1\}$
69. (a) 13.92 h or 13 h, 55 min **(b)** 12 h **(c)** 13.85 h or 13 h, 51 min
71. (a) 13.3 h or 13 h, 18 min **(b)** 12 h **(c)** 13.26 h or 13 h, 15 min

73. (a) 12 h **(b)** 12 h **(c)** 12 h **(d)** It is 12 h. **75.** 3.28 min **77. (a)** $\frac{\pi}{3}$ square units **(b)** $\frac{5\pi}{12}$ square units **79.** 4250 mi

7.2 Assess Your Understanding *(page 457)*

4. $x = \sec y$; ≥ 1; 0; π **5.** $\frac{\sqrt{2}}{2}$ **6.** F **7.** T **8.** T **9.** $\frac{\sqrt{2}}{2}$ **11.** $-\frac{\sqrt{3}}{3}$ **13.** 2 **15.** $\sqrt{2}$ **17.** $-\frac{\sqrt{2}}{2}$ **19.** $\frac{2\sqrt{3}}{3}$ **21.** $\frac{3\pi}{4}$ **23.** $\frac{\pi}{6}$ **25.** $\frac{\sqrt{2}}{4}$ **27.** $\frac{\sqrt{5}}{2}$ **29.** $-\frac{\sqrt{14}}{2}$ **31.** $-\frac{3\sqrt{10}}{10}$ **33.** $\sqrt{5}$ **35.** $-\frac{\pi}{4}$ **37.** $\frac{\pi}{6}$ **39.** $-\frac{\pi}{2}$ **41.** $\frac{\pi}{6}$ **43.** $\frac{2\pi}{3}$ **45.** 1.32 **47.** 0.46 **49.** −0.34 **51.** 2.72 **53.** −0.73 **55.** 2.55 **57.** $\frac{1}{\sqrt{1+u^2}}$ **59.** $\frac{u}{\sqrt{1-u^2}}$ **61.** $\frac{\sqrt{u^2-1}}{|u|}$ **63.** $\frac{\sqrt{u^2-1}}{u}$ **65.** $\frac{1}{u}$ **67.** $\frac{5}{13}$ **69.** $\frac{3\pi}{4}$ **71.** $-\frac{3}{4}$ **73.** $\frac{5}{13}$ **75.** $\frac{\pi}{6}$ **77.** $-\sqrt{15}$

79. (a) $\theta = 31.89°$ **(b)** 54.64 ft in diameter **(c)** 37.96 ft high **81. (a)** $\theta = 22.3°$ **(b)** $v_0 = 2940.23$ ft/s

83.

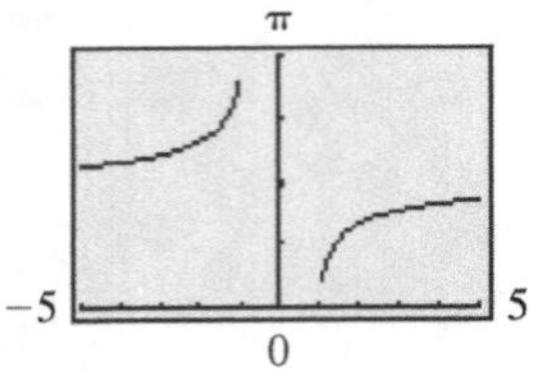

7.3 Assess Your Understanding *(page 463)*

3. identity; conditional **4.** −1 **5.** 0 **6.** T **7.** F **8.** T **9.** $\frac{1}{\cos\theta}$ **11.** $\frac{1+\sin\theta}{\cos\theta}$ **13.** $\frac{1}{\sin\theta\cos\theta}$ **15.** 2 **17.** $\frac{3\sin\theta+1}{\sin\theta+1}$

19. $\csc\theta \cdot \cos\theta = \frac{1}{\sin\theta}\cdot\cos\theta = \frac{\cos\theta}{\sin\theta} = \cot\theta$ **21.** $1 + \tan^2(-\theta) = 1 + (-\tan\theta)^2 = 1 + \tan^2\theta = \sec^2\theta$

23. $\cos\theta(\tan\theta + \cot\theta) = \cos\theta\left(\frac{\sin\theta}{\cos\theta} + \frac{\cos\theta}{\sin\theta}\right) = \cos\theta\left(\frac{\sin^2\theta + \cos^2\theta}{\cos\theta\sin\theta}\right) = \cos\theta\left(\frac{1}{\cos\theta\sin\theta}\right) = \frac{1}{\sin\theta} = \csc\theta$

25. $\tan u \cot u - \cos^2 u = \tan u \cdot \frac{1}{\tan u} - \cos^2 u = 1 - \cos^2 u = \sin^2 u$ **27.** $(\sec\theta - 1)(\sec\theta + 1) = \sec^2\theta - 1 = \tan^2\theta$

29. $(\sec\theta + \tan\theta)(\sec\theta - \tan\theta) = \sec^2\theta - \tan^2\theta = 1$ **31.** $\cos^2\theta(1 + \tan^2\theta) = \cos^2\theta\sec^2\theta = \cos^2\theta\cdot\frac{1}{\cos^2\theta} = 1$

33. $(\sin\theta + \cos\theta)^2 + (\sin\theta - \cos\theta)^2 = \sin^2\theta + 2\sin\theta\cos\theta + \cos^2\theta + \sin^2\theta - 2\sin\theta\cos\theta + \cos^2\theta$
$= \sin^2\theta + \cos^2\theta + \sin^2\theta + \cos^2\theta = 1 + 1 = 2$

35. $\sec^4\theta - \sec^2\theta = \sec^2\theta(\sec^2\theta - 1) = (1 + \tan^2\theta)\tan^2\theta = \tan^4\theta + \tan^2\theta$

37. $\sec u - \tan u = \frac{1}{\cos u} - \frac{\sin u}{\cos u} = \frac{1-\sin u}{\cos u}\cdot\frac{1+\sin u}{1+\sin u} = \frac{1-\sin^2 u}{\cos u(1+\sin u)} = \frac{\cos^2 u}{\cos u(1+\sin u)} = \frac{\cos u}{1+\sin u}$

39. $3\sin^2\theta + 4\cos^2\theta = 3\sin^2\theta + 3\cos^2\theta + \cos^2\theta = 3(\sin^2\theta + \cos^2\theta) + \cos^2\theta = 3 + \cos^2\theta$

41. $1 - \frac{\cos^2\theta}{1+\sin\theta} = 1 - \frac{1-\sin^2\theta}{1+\sin\theta} = 1 - \frac{(1+\sin\theta)(1-\sin\theta)}{1+\sin\theta} = 1 - (1 - \sin\theta) = \sin\theta$

43. $\dfrac{1+\tan v}{1-\tan v} = \dfrac{1+\dfrac{1}{\cot v}}{1-\dfrac{1}{\cot v}} = \dfrac{\dfrac{\cot v+1}{\cot v}}{\dfrac{\cot v-1}{\cot v}} = \dfrac{\cot v+1}{\cot v-1}$ **45.** $\dfrac{\sec\theta}{\csc\theta} + \dfrac{\sin\theta}{\cos\theta} = \dfrac{\dfrac{1}{\cos\theta}}{\dfrac{1}{\sin\theta}} + \tan\theta = \dfrac{\sin\theta}{\cos\theta} + \tan\theta = \tan\theta + \tan\theta = 2\tan\theta$

47. $\dfrac{1+\sin\theta}{1-\sin\theta} = \dfrac{1+\dfrac{1}{\csc\theta}}{1-\dfrac{1}{\csc\theta}} = \dfrac{\dfrac{\csc\theta+1}{\csc\theta}}{\dfrac{\csc\theta-1}{\csc\theta}} = \dfrac{\csc\theta+1}{\csc\theta-1}$

49. $\dfrac{1-\sin v}{\cos v} + \dfrac{\cos v}{1-\sin v} = \dfrac{(1-\sin v)^2+\cos^2 v}{\cos v(1-\sin v)} = \dfrac{1-2\sin v+\sin^2 v+\cos^2 v}{\cos v(1-\sin v)} = \dfrac{2-2\sin v}{\cos v(1-\sin v)} = \dfrac{2(1-\sin v)}{\cos v(1-\sin v)} = \dfrac{2}{\cos v} = 2\sec v$

51. $\dfrac{\sin\theta}{\sin\theta-\cos\theta} = \dfrac{1}{\dfrac{\sin\theta-\cos\theta}{\sin\theta}} = \dfrac{1}{1-\dfrac{\cos\theta}{\sin\theta}} = \dfrac{1}{1-\cot\theta}$

53. $(\sec\theta-\tan\theta)^2 = \sec^2\theta - 2\sec\theta\tan\theta + \tan^2\theta = \dfrac{1}{\cos^2\theta} - \dfrac{2\sin\theta}{\cos^2\theta} + \dfrac{\sin^2\theta}{\cos^2\theta} = \dfrac{1-2\sin\theta+\sin^2\theta}{\cos^2\theta} = \dfrac{(1-\sin\theta)^2}{1-\sin^2\theta} = \dfrac{(1-\sin\theta)^2}{(1-\sin\theta)(1+\sin\theta)}$
$= \dfrac{1-\sin\theta}{1+\sin\theta}$

55. $\dfrac{\cos\theta}{1-\tan\theta} + \dfrac{\sin\theta}{1-\cot\theta} = \dfrac{\cos\theta}{1-\dfrac{\sin\theta}{\cos\theta}} + \dfrac{\sin\theta}{1-\dfrac{\cos\theta}{\sin\theta}} = \dfrac{\cos\theta}{\dfrac{\cos\theta-\sin\theta}{\cos\theta}} + \dfrac{\sin\theta}{\dfrac{\sin\theta-\cos\theta}{\sin\theta}} = \dfrac{\cos^2\theta}{\cos\theta-\sin\theta} + \dfrac{\sin^2\theta}{\sin\theta-\cos\theta}$
$= \dfrac{\cos^2\theta-\sin^2\theta}{\cos\theta-\sin\theta} = \dfrac{(\cos\theta-\sin\theta)(\cos\theta+\sin\theta)}{\cos\theta-\sin\theta} = \sin\theta+\cos\theta$

57. $\tan\theta + \dfrac{\cos\theta}{1+\sin\theta} = \dfrac{\sin\theta}{\cos\theta} + \dfrac{\cos\theta}{1+\sin\theta} = \dfrac{\sin\theta(1+\sin\theta)+\cos^2\theta}{\cos\theta(1+\sin\theta)} = \dfrac{\sin\theta+\sin^2\theta+\cos^2\theta}{\cos\theta(1+\sin\theta)} = \dfrac{\sin\theta+1}{\cos\theta(1+\sin\theta)} = \dfrac{1}{\cos\theta} = \sec\theta$

59. $\dfrac{\tan\theta+\sec\theta-1}{\tan\theta-\sec\theta+1} = \dfrac{\tan\theta+(\sec\theta-1)}{\tan\theta-(\sec\theta-1)}\cdot\dfrac{\tan\theta+(\sec\theta-1)}{\tan\theta+(\sec\theta-1)} = \dfrac{\tan^2\theta+2\tan\theta(\sec\theta-1)+\sec^2\theta-2\sec\theta+1}{\tan^2\theta-(\sec^2\theta-2\sec\theta+1)}$
$= \dfrac{\sec^2\theta-1+2\tan\theta(\sec\theta-1)+\sec^2\theta-2\sec\theta+1}{\sec^2\theta-1-\sec^2\theta+2\sec\theta-1} = \dfrac{2\sec^2\theta-2\sec\theta+2\tan\theta(\sec\theta-1)}{-2+2\sec\theta}$
$= \dfrac{2\sec\theta(\sec\theta-1)+2\tan\theta(\sec\theta-1)}{2(\sec\theta-1)} = \dfrac{2(\sec\theta-1)(\sec\theta+\tan\theta)}{2(\sec\theta-1)} = \tan\theta+\sec\theta$

61. $\dfrac{\tan\theta-\cot\theta}{\tan\theta+\cot\theta} = \dfrac{\dfrac{\sin\theta}{\cos\theta}-\dfrac{\cos\theta}{\sin\theta}}{\dfrac{\sin\theta}{\cos\theta}+\dfrac{\cos\theta}{\sin\theta}} = \dfrac{\dfrac{\sin^2\theta-\cos^2\theta}{\cos\theta\sin\theta}}{\dfrac{\sin^2\theta+\cos^2\theta}{\cos\theta\sin\theta}} = \dfrac{\sin^2\theta-\cos^2\theta}{1} = \sin^2\theta-\cos^2\theta$

63. $\dfrac{\tan u-\cot u}{\tan u+\cot u}+1 = \dfrac{\dfrac{\sin u}{\cos u}-\dfrac{\cos u}{\sin u}}{\dfrac{\sin u}{\cos u}+\dfrac{\cos u}{\sin u}}+1 = \dfrac{\dfrac{\sin^2 u-\cos^2 u}{\cos u\sin u}}{\dfrac{\sin^2 u+\cos^2 u}{\cos u\sin u}}+1 = \sin^2 u-\cos^2 u+1 = \sin^2 u+(1-\cos^2 u) = 2\sin^2 u$

65. $\dfrac{\sec\theta+\tan\theta}{\cot\theta+\cos\theta} = \dfrac{\dfrac{1}{\cos\theta}+\dfrac{\sin\theta}{\cos\theta}}{\dfrac{\cos\theta}{\sin\theta}+\cos\theta} = \dfrac{\dfrac{1+\sin\theta}{\cos\theta}}{\dfrac{\cos\theta+\cos\theta\sin\theta}{\sin\theta}} = \dfrac{1+\sin\theta}{\cos\theta}\cdot\dfrac{\sin\theta}{\cos\theta(1+\sin\theta)} = \dfrac{\sin\theta}{\cos\theta}\cdot\dfrac{1}{\cos\theta} = \tan\theta\sec\theta$

67. $\dfrac{1-\tan^2\theta}{1+\tan^2\theta}+1 = \dfrac{1-\tan^2\theta+1+\tan^2\theta}{1+\tan^2\theta} = \dfrac{2}{1+\tan^2\theta} = \dfrac{2}{\sec^2\theta} = 2\cos^2\theta$

69. $\dfrac{\sec\theta-\csc\theta}{\sec\theta\csc\theta} = \dfrac{\sec\theta}{\sec\theta\csc\theta} - \dfrac{\csc\theta}{\sec\theta\csc\theta} = \dfrac{1}{\csc\theta} - \dfrac{1}{\sec\theta} = \sin\theta-\cos\theta$

71. $\sec\theta-\cos\theta = \dfrac{1}{\cos\theta}-\cos\theta = \dfrac{1-\cos^2\theta}{\cos\theta} = \dfrac{\sin^2\theta}{\cos\theta} = \sin\theta\cdot\dfrac{\sin\theta}{\cos\theta} = \sin\theta\tan\theta$

73. $\dfrac{1}{1-\sin\theta}+\dfrac{1}{1+\sin\theta} = \dfrac{1+\sin\theta+1-\sin\theta}{(1+\sin\theta)(1-\sin\theta)} = \dfrac{2}{1-\sin^2\theta} = \dfrac{2}{\cos^2\theta} = 2\sec^2\theta$

75. $\dfrac{\sec\theta}{1-\sin\theta} = \dfrac{\sec\theta}{1-\sin\theta}\cdot\dfrac{1+\sin\theta}{1+\sin\theta} = \dfrac{\sec\theta(1+\sin\theta)}{1-\sin^2\theta} = \dfrac{\sec\theta(1+\sin\theta)}{\cos^2\theta} = \dfrac{1+\sin\theta}{\cos^3\theta}$

77. $\dfrac{(\sec v-\tan v)^2+1}{\csc v(\sec v-\tan v)} = \dfrac{\sec^2 v-2\sec v\tan v+\tan^2 v+1}{\dfrac{1}{\sin v}\left(\dfrac{1}{\cos v}-\dfrac{\sin v}{\cos v}\right)} = \dfrac{2\sec^2 v-2\sec v\tan v}{\dfrac{1}{\sin v}\left(\dfrac{1-\sin v}{\cos v}\right)} = \dfrac{\dfrac{2}{\cos^2 v}-\dfrac{2\sin v}{\cos^2 v}}{\dfrac{1-\sin v}{\sin v\cos v}} = \dfrac{2-2\sin v}{\cos^2 v}\cdot\dfrac{\sin v\cos v}{1-\sin v}$
$= \dfrac{2(1-\sin v)}{\cos v}\cdot\dfrac{\sin v}{1-\sin v} = \dfrac{2\sin v}{\cos v} = 2\tan v$

79. $\dfrac{\sin\theta+\cos\theta}{\cos\theta} - \dfrac{\sin\theta-\cos\theta}{\sin\theta} = \dfrac{\sin\theta}{\cos\theta}+1-1+\dfrac{\cos\theta}{\sin\theta} = \dfrac{\sin^2\theta+\cos^2\theta}{\cos\theta\sin\theta} = \dfrac{1}{\cos\theta\sin\theta} = \sec\theta\csc\theta$

81. $\dfrac{\sin^3\theta + \cos^3\theta}{\sin\theta + \cos\theta} = \dfrac{(\sin\theta + \cos\theta)(\sin^2\theta - \sin\theta\cos\theta + \cos^2\theta)}{\sin\theta + \cos\theta} = \sin^2\theta + \cos^2\theta - \sin\theta\cos\theta = 1 - \sin\theta\cos\theta$

83. $\dfrac{\cos^2\theta - \sin^2\theta}{1 - \tan^2\theta} = \dfrac{\cos^2\theta - \sin^2\theta}{1 - \dfrac{\sin^2\theta}{\cos^2\theta}} = \dfrac{\cos^2\theta - \sin^2\theta}{\dfrac{\cos^2\theta - \sin^2\theta}{\cos^2\theta}} = \cos^2\theta$

85. $\dfrac{(2\cos^2\theta - 1)^2}{\cos^4\theta - \sin^4\theta} = \dfrac{[2\cos^2\theta - (\sin^2\theta + \cos^2\theta)]^2}{(\cos^2\theta - \sin^2\theta)(\cos^2\theta + \sin^2\theta)} = \dfrac{(\cos^2\theta - \sin^2\theta)^2}{\cos^2\theta - \sin^2\theta} = \cos^2\theta - \sin^2\theta = (1 - \sin^2\theta) - \sin^2\theta = 1 - 2\sin^2\theta$

87. $\dfrac{1 + \sin\theta + \cos\theta}{1 + \sin\theta - \cos\theta} = \dfrac{(1 + \sin\theta) + \cos\theta}{(1 + \sin\theta) - \cos\theta}\cdot\dfrac{(1 + \sin\theta) + \cos\theta}{(1 + \sin\theta) + \cos\theta} = \dfrac{1 + 2\sin\theta + \sin^2\theta + 2(1 + \sin\theta)\cos\theta + \cos^2\theta}{1 + 2\sin\theta + \sin^2\theta - \cos^2\theta}$

$= \dfrac{1 + 2\sin\theta + \sin^2\theta + 2(1 + \sin\theta)(\cos\theta) + (1 - \sin^2\theta)}{1 + 2\sin\theta + \sin^2\theta - (1 - \sin^2\theta)} = \dfrac{2 + 2\sin\theta + 2(1 + \sin\theta)(\cos\theta)}{2\sin\theta + 2\sin^2\theta}$

$= \dfrac{2(1 + \sin\theta) + 2(1 + \sin\theta)(\cos\theta)}{2\sin\theta(1 + \sin\theta)} = \dfrac{2(1 + \sin\theta)(1 + \cos\theta)}{2\sin\theta(1 + \sin\theta)} = \dfrac{1 + \cos\theta}{\sin\theta}$

89. $(a\sin\theta + b\cos\theta)^2 + (a\cos\theta - b\sin\theta)^2 = a^2\sin^2\theta + 2ab\sin\theta\cos\theta + b^2\cos^2\theta + a^2\cos^2\theta - 2ab\sin\theta\cos\theta + b^2\sin^2\theta$

$= a^2(\sin^2\theta + \cos^2\theta) + b^2(\cos^2\theta + \sin^2\theta) = a^2 + b^2$

91. $\dfrac{\tan\alpha + \tan\beta}{\cot\alpha + \cot\beta} = \dfrac{\tan\alpha + \tan\beta}{\dfrac{1}{\tan\alpha} + \dfrac{1}{\tan\beta}} = \dfrac{\tan\alpha + \tan\beta}{\dfrac{\tan\beta + \tan\alpha}{\tan\alpha\tan\beta}} = (\tan\alpha + \tan\beta)\cdot\dfrac{\tan\alpha\tan\beta}{\tan\alpha + \tan\beta} = \tan\alpha\tan\beta$

93. $(\sin\alpha + \cos\beta)^2 + (\cos\beta + \sin\alpha)(\cos\beta - \sin\alpha) = (\sin^2\alpha + 2\sin\alpha\cos\beta + \cos^2\beta) + (\cos^2\beta - \sin^2\alpha)$

$= 2\cos^2\beta + 2\sin\alpha\cos\beta = 2\cos\beta(\cos\beta + \sin\alpha) = 2\cos\beta(\sin\alpha + \cos\beta)$

95. $\ln|\sec\theta| = \ln|\cos\theta|^{-1} = -\ln|\cos\theta|$ **97.** $\ln|1 + \cos\theta| + \ln|1 - \cos\theta| = \ln(|1 + \cos\theta||1 - \cos\theta|) = \ln|1 - \cos^2\theta| = \ln|\sin^2\theta| = 2\ln|\sin\theta|$

99. $g(x) = \sec x - \cos x = \dfrac{1}{\cos x} - \cos x = \dfrac{1}{\cos x} - \dfrac{\cos^2 x}{\cos x} = \dfrac{1 - \cos^2 x}{\cos x} = \dfrac{\sin^2 x}{\cos x} = \sin x\cdot\dfrac{\sin x}{\cos x} = \sin x\cdot\tan x = f(x)$

101. $f(\theta) = \dfrac{1 - \sin\theta}{\cos\theta} - \dfrac{\cos\theta}{1 + \sin\theta} = \dfrac{1 - \sin\theta}{\cos\theta}\cdot\dfrac{1 + \sin\theta}{1 + \sin\theta} - \dfrac{\cos\theta}{1 + \sin\theta}\cdot\dfrac{\cos\theta}{\cos\theta} = \dfrac{1 - \sin^2\theta}{\cos\theta(1 + \sin\theta)} - \dfrac{\cos^2\theta}{\cos\theta(1 + \sin\theta)}$

$= \dfrac{\cos^2\theta}{\cos\theta(1 + \sin\theta)} - \dfrac{\cos^2\theta}{\cos\theta(1 + \sin\theta)} = 0 = g(\theta)$

103. $1200\sec\theta\,(2\sec^2\theta - 1) = 1200\dfrac{1}{\cos\theta}\left(\dfrac{2}{\cos^2\theta} - 1\right) = 1200\dfrac{1}{\cos\theta}\left(\dfrac{2}{\cos^2\theta} - \dfrac{\cos^2\theta}{\cos^2\theta}\right) = 1200\dfrac{1}{\cos\theta}\left(\dfrac{2 - \cos^2\theta}{\cos^2\theta}\right) = \dfrac{1200\,(1 + 1 - \cos^2\theta)}{\cos^3\theta}$

$= \dfrac{1200\,(1 + \sin^2\theta)}{\cos^3\theta}$

7.4 Assess Your Understanding *(page 473)*

4. – **5.** – **6.** F **7.** F **8.** F **9.** $\frac{1}{4}(\sqrt{6} + \sqrt{2})$ **11.** $\frac{1}{4}(\sqrt{2} - \sqrt{6})$ **13.** $-\frac{1}{4}(\sqrt{2} + \sqrt{6})$ **15.** $2 - \sqrt{3}$ **17.** $-\frac{1}{4}(\sqrt{6} + \sqrt{2})$

19. $\sqrt{6} - \sqrt{2}$ **21.** $\frac{1}{2}$ **23.** 0 **25.** 1 **27.** −1 **29.** $\frac{1}{2}$ **31. (a)** $\frac{2\sqrt{5}}{25}$ **(b)** $\frac{11\sqrt{5}}{25}$ **(c)** $\frac{2\sqrt{5}}{5}$ **(d)** 2

33. (a) $\frac{4 - 3\sqrt{3}}{10}$ **(b)** $\frac{-3 - 4\sqrt{3}}{10}$ **(c)** $\frac{4 + 3\sqrt{3}}{10}$ **(d)** $\frac{25\sqrt{3} + 48}{39}$

35. (a) $-\frac{5 + 12\sqrt{3}}{26}$ **(b)** $\frac{12 - 5\sqrt{3}}{26}$ **(c)** $\frac{-5 + 12\sqrt{3}}{26}$ **(d)** $\frac{-240 + 169\sqrt{3}}{69}$

37. (a) $-\frac{2\sqrt{2}}{3}$ **(b)** $\frac{-2\sqrt{2} + \sqrt{3}}{6}$ **(c)** $\frac{-2\sqrt{2} + \sqrt{3}}{6}$ **(d)** $\frac{9 - 4\sqrt{2}}{7}$ **39.** $\frac{1 - 2\sqrt{6}}{6}$ **41.** $\frac{\sqrt{3} - 2\sqrt{2}}{6}$ **43.** $\frac{8\sqrt{2} - 9\sqrt{3}}{5}$

45. $\sin\left(\frac{\pi}{2} + \theta\right) = \sin\frac{\pi}{2}\cos\theta + \cos\frac{\pi}{2}\sin\theta = 1\cdot\cos\theta + 0\cdot\sin\theta = \cos\theta$

47. $\sin(\pi - \theta) = \sin\pi\cos\theta - \cos\pi\sin\theta = 0\cdot\cos\theta - (-1)\sin\theta = \sin\theta$

49. $\sin(\pi + \theta) = \sin\pi\cos\theta + \cos\pi\sin\theta = 0\cdot\cos\theta + (-1)\sin\theta = -\sin\theta$

51. $\tan(\pi - \theta) = \dfrac{\tan\pi - \tan\theta}{1 + \tan\pi\tan\theta} = \dfrac{0 - \tan\theta}{1 + 0\cdot\tan\theta} = -\tan\theta$ **53.** $\sin\left(\frac{3\pi}{2} + \theta\right) = \sin\frac{3\pi}{2}\cos\theta + \cos\frac{3\pi}{2}\sin\theta = (-1)\cos\theta + 0\cdot\sin\theta = -\cos\theta$

55. $\sin(\alpha + \beta) + \sin(\alpha - \beta) = \sin\alpha\cos\beta + \cos\alpha\sin\beta + \sin\alpha\cos\beta - \cos\alpha\sin\beta = 2\sin\alpha\cos\beta$

57. $\dfrac{\sin(\alpha + \beta)}{\sin\alpha\cos\beta} = \dfrac{\sin\alpha\cos\beta + \cos\alpha\sin\beta}{\sin\alpha\cos\beta} = \dfrac{\sin\alpha\cos\beta}{\sin\alpha\cos\beta} + \dfrac{\cos\alpha\sin\beta}{\sin\alpha\cos\beta} = 1 + \cot\alpha\tan\beta$

59. $\dfrac{\cos(\alpha + \beta)}{\cos\alpha\cos\beta} = \dfrac{\cos\alpha\cos\beta - \sin\alpha\sin\beta}{\cos\alpha\cos\beta} = \dfrac{\cos\alpha\cos\beta}{\cos\alpha\cos\beta} - \dfrac{\sin\alpha\sin\beta}{\cos\alpha\cos\beta} = 1 - \tan\alpha\tan\beta$

61. $\dfrac{\sin(\alpha+\beta)}{\sin(\alpha-\beta)} = \dfrac{\sin\alpha\cos\beta + \cos\alpha\sin\beta}{\sin\alpha\cos\beta - \cos\alpha\sin\beta} = \dfrac{\dfrac{\sin\alpha\cos\beta + \cos\alpha\sin\beta}{\cos\alpha\cos\beta}}{\dfrac{\sin\alpha\cos\beta - \cos\alpha\sin\beta}{\cos\alpha\cos\beta}} = \dfrac{\dfrac{\sin\alpha\cos\beta}{\cos\alpha\cos\beta} + \dfrac{\cos\alpha\sin\beta}{\cos\alpha\cos\beta}}{\dfrac{\sin\alpha\cos\beta}{\cos\alpha\cos\beta} - \dfrac{\cos\alpha\sin\beta}{\cos\alpha\cos\beta}} = \dfrac{\tan\alpha + \tan\beta}{\tan\alpha - \tan\beta}$

63. $\cot(\alpha+\beta) = \dfrac{\cos(\alpha+\beta)}{\sin(\alpha+\beta)} = \dfrac{\cos\alpha\cos\beta - \sin\alpha\sin\beta}{\sin\alpha\cos\beta + \cos\alpha\sin\beta} = \dfrac{\dfrac{\cos\alpha\cos\beta - \sin\alpha\sin\beta}{\sin\alpha\sin\beta}}{\dfrac{\sin\alpha\cos\beta + \cos\alpha\sin\beta}{\sin\alpha\sin\beta}} = \dfrac{\dfrac{\cos\alpha\cos\beta}{\sin\alpha\sin\beta} - \dfrac{\sin\alpha\sin\beta}{\sin\alpha\sin\beta}}{\dfrac{\sin\alpha\cos\beta}{\sin\alpha\sin\beta} + \dfrac{\cos\alpha\sin\beta}{\sin\alpha\sin\beta}} = \dfrac{\cot\alpha\cot\beta - 1}{\cot\beta + \cot\alpha}$

65. $\sec(\alpha+\beta) = \dfrac{1}{\cos(\alpha+\beta)} = \dfrac{1}{\cos\alpha\cos\beta - \sin\alpha\sin\beta} = \dfrac{\dfrac{1}{\sin\alpha\sin\beta}}{\dfrac{\cos\alpha\cos\beta - \sin\alpha\sin\beta}{\sin\alpha\sin\beta}} = \dfrac{\dfrac{1}{\sin\alpha}\cdot\dfrac{1}{\sin\beta}}{\dfrac{\cos\alpha\cos\beta}{\sin\alpha\sin\beta} - \dfrac{\sin\alpha\sin\beta}{\sin\alpha\sin\beta}} = \dfrac{\csc\alpha\csc\beta}{\cot\alpha\cot\beta - 1}$

67. $\sin(\alpha-\beta)\sin(\alpha+\beta) = (\sin\alpha\cos\beta - \cos\alpha\sin\beta)(\sin\alpha\cos\beta + \cos\alpha\sin\beta) = \sin^2\alpha\cos^2\beta - \cos^2\alpha\sin^2\beta$
$= (\sin^2\alpha)(1-\sin^2\beta) - (1-\sin^2\alpha)(\sin^2\beta) = \sin^2\alpha - \sin^2\beta$

69. $\sin(\theta + k\pi) = \sin\theta\cos k\pi + \cos\theta\sin k\pi = (\sin\theta)(-1)^k + (\cos\theta)(0) = (-1)^k\sin\theta$, k any integer

71. $\dfrac{\sqrt{3}}{2}$ **73.** $-\dfrac{24}{25}$ **75.** $-\dfrac{33}{65}$ **77.** $\dfrac{63}{65}$ **79.** $\dfrac{48+25\sqrt{3}}{39}$ **81.** $\dfrac{4}{3}$ **83.** $u\sqrt{1-v^2} - v\sqrt{1-u^2}$: $-1 \le u \le 1$; $-1 \le v \le 1$

85. $\dfrac{u\sqrt{1-v^2} - v}{\sqrt{1+u^2}}$: $-\infty < u < \infty$; $-1 \le v \le 1$ **87.** $\dfrac{uv - \sqrt{1-u^2}\sqrt{1-v^2}}{v\sqrt{1-u^2} + u\sqrt{1-v^2}}$: $-1 \le u \le 1$; $-1 \le v \le 1$

89. Let $\alpha = \sin^{-1} v$ and $\beta = \cos^{-1} v$. Then $\sin\alpha = \cos\beta = v$, and since $\sin\alpha = \cos\left(\dfrac{\pi}{2} - \alpha\right)$, $\cos\left(\dfrac{\pi}{2} - \alpha\right) = \cos\beta$.

If $v \ge 0$, then $0 \le \alpha \le \dfrac{\pi}{2}$, so $\left(\dfrac{\pi}{2} - \alpha\right)$ and β both lie on $\left[0, \dfrac{\pi}{2}\right]$. If $v < 0$, then $-\dfrac{\pi}{2} \le \alpha < 0$, so $\left(\dfrac{\pi}{2} - \alpha\right)$ and β both lie on $\left(\dfrac{\pi}{2}, \pi\right]$.

Either way, $\cos\left(\dfrac{\pi}{2} - \alpha\right) = \cos\beta$ implies $\dfrac{\pi}{2} - \alpha = \beta$, or $\alpha + \beta = \dfrac{\pi}{2}$.

91. Let $\alpha = \tan^{-1}\dfrac{1}{v}$ and $\beta = \tan^{-1} v$. Because $v \ne 0$, $\alpha, \beta \ne 0$. Then $\tan\alpha = \dfrac{1}{v} = \dfrac{1}{\tan\beta} = \cot\beta$, and since

$\tan\alpha = \cot\left(\dfrac{\pi}{2} - \alpha\right)$, $\cot\left(\dfrac{\pi}{2} - \alpha\right) = \cot\beta$. Because $v > 0$, $0 < \alpha < \dfrac{\pi}{2}$, and so $\left(\dfrac{\pi}{2} - \alpha\right)$ and β both lie on $\left(0, \dfrac{\pi}{2}\right)$.

Then $\cot\left(\dfrac{\pi}{2} - \alpha\right) = \cot\beta$ implies $\dfrac{\pi}{2} - \alpha = \beta$, or $\alpha = \dfrac{\pi}{2} - \beta$.

93. $\sin(\sin^{-1} v + \cos^{-1} v) = \sin(\sin^{-1} v)\cos(\cos^{-1} v) + \cos(\sin^{-1} v)\sin(\cos^{-1} v) = (v)(v) + \sqrt{1-v^2}\sqrt{1-v^2} = v^2 + 1 - v^2 = 1$

95. $\dfrac{\sin(x+h) - \sin x}{h} = \dfrac{\sin x\cos h + \cos x\sin h - \sin x}{h} = \dfrac{\cos x\sin h - \sin x(1-\cos h)}{h} = \cos x \cdot \dfrac{\sin h}{h} - \sin x \cdot \dfrac{1-\cos h}{h}$

97. **(a)** $\tan(\tan^{-1}1 + \tan^{-1}2 + \tan^{-1}3) = \tan((\tan^{-1}1 + \tan^{-1}2) + \tan^{-1}3) = \dfrac{\tan(\tan^{-1}1 + \tan^{-1}2) + \tan(\tan^{-1}3)}{1 - \tan(\tan^{-1}1 + \tan^{-1}2)\tan(\tan^{-1}3)}$

$$= \dfrac{\dfrac{\tan(\tan^{-1}1) + \tan(\tan^{-1}2)}{1 - \tan(\tan^{-1}1)\tan(\tan^{-1}2)} + 3}{1 - \dfrac{\tan(\tan^{-1}1) + \tan(\tan^{-1}2)}{1 - \tan(\tan^{-1}1)\tan(\tan^{-1}2)}\cdot 3} = \dfrac{\dfrac{1+2}{1-1\cdot 2} + 3}{1 - \dfrac{1+2}{1-1\cdot 2}\cdot 3} = \dfrac{\dfrac{3}{-1} + 3}{1 - \dfrac{3}{-1}\cdot 3} = \dfrac{-3+3}{1+9} = \dfrac{0}{10} = 0$$

(b) From the definition of the inverse tangent function $0 < \tan^{-1}1 < \dfrac{\pi}{2}$, $0 < \tan^{-1}2 < \dfrac{\pi}{2}$, and $0 < \tan^{-1}3 < \dfrac{\pi}{2}$, so $0 < \tan^{-1}1 + \tan^{-1}2 + \tan^{-1}3 < \dfrac{3\pi}{2}$.

On the interval $\left(0, \dfrac{3\pi}{2}\right)$, $\tan\theta = 0$ if and only if $\theta = \pi$. Therefore, from part (a), $\tan^{-1}1 + \tan^{-1}2 + \tan^{-1}3 = \pi$.

99. $\tan\theta = \tan(\theta_2 - \theta_1) = \dfrac{\tan\theta_2 - \tan\theta_1}{1 + \tan\theta_1\tan\theta_2} = \dfrac{m_2 - m_1}{1 + m_1 m_2}$

101. $2\cot(\alpha - \beta) = \dfrac{2}{\tan(\alpha-\beta)} = 2\left(\dfrac{1 + \tan\alpha\tan\beta}{\tan\alpha - \tan\beta}\right) = 2\left(\dfrac{1 + (x+1)(x-1)}{(x+1) - (x-1)}\right) = 2\left(\dfrac{1 + x^2 - 1}{x + 1 - x + 1}\right) = \dfrac{2x^2}{2} = x^2$

103. $\tan\dfrac{\pi}{2}$ is not defined; $\tan\left(\dfrac{\pi}{2} - \theta\right) = \dfrac{\sin\left(\dfrac{\pi}{2} - \theta\right)}{\cos\left(\dfrac{\pi}{2} - \theta\right)} = \dfrac{\cos\theta}{\sin\theta} = \cot\theta$.

7.5 Assess Your Understanding *(page 482)*

1. $\sin^2\theta$; $2\cos^2\theta$; $2\sin^2\theta$ **2.** $1 - \cos\theta$ **3.** $\sin\theta$ **4.** T **5.** F **6.** F **7. (a)** $\dfrac{24}{25}$ **(b)** $\dfrac{7}{25}$ **(c)** $\dfrac{\sqrt{10}}{10}$ **(d)** $\dfrac{3\sqrt{10}}{10}$

9. (a) $\dfrac{24}{25}$ **(b)** $-\dfrac{7}{25}$ **(c)** $\dfrac{2\sqrt{5}}{5}$ **(d)** $-\dfrac{\sqrt{5}}{5}$ **11. (a)** $-\dfrac{2\sqrt{2}}{3}$ **(b)** $\dfrac{1}{3}$ **(c)** $\sqrt{\dfrac{3+\sqrt{6}}{6}}$ **(d)** $\sqrt{\dfrac{3-\sqrt{6}}{6}}$

13. **(a)** $\frac{4\sqrt{2}}{9}$ **(b)** $-\frac{7}{9}$ **(c)** $\frac{\sqrt{3}}{3}$ **(d)** $\frac{\sqrt{6}}{3}$ **15.** **(a)** $-\frac{4}{5}$ **(b)** $\frac{3}{5}$ **(c)** $\sqrt{\frac{5+2\sqrt{5}}{10}}$ **(d)** $\sqrt{\frac{5-2\sqrt{5}}{10}}$

17. **(a)** $-\frac{3}{5}$ **(b)** $-\frac{4}{5}$ **(c)** $\frac{1}{2}\sqrt{\frac{10-\sqrt{10}}{5}}$ **(d)** $-\frac{1}{2}\sqrt{\frac{10+\sqrt{10}}{5}}$ **19.** $\frac{\sqrt{2-\sqrt{2}}}{2}$ **21.** $1-\sqrt{2}$ **23.** $-\frac{\sqrt{2+\sqrt{3}}}{2}$

25. $\frac{2}{\sqrt{2+\sqrt{2}}} = (2-\sqrt{2})\sqrt{2+\sqrt{2}}$ **27.** $-\frac{\sqrt{2-\sqrt{2}}}{2}$ **29.** $-\frac{4}{5}$ **31.** $\frac{\sqrt{10(5-\sqrt{5})}}{10}$ **33.** $\frac{4}{3}$ **35.** $-\frac{7}{8}$ **37.** $\frac{\sqrt{10}}{4}$ **39.** $-\frac{\sqrt{15}}{3}$

41. $\sin^4\theta = (\sin^2\theta)^2 = \left(\frac{1-\cos(2\theta)}{2}\right)^2 = \frac{1}{4}[1 - 2\cos(2\theta) + \cos^2(2\theta)] = \frac{1}{4} - \frac{1}{2}\cos(2\theta) + \frac{1}{4}\cos^2(2\theta)$

$= \frac{1}{4} - \frac{1}{2}\cos(2\theta) + \frac{1}{4}\left(\frac{1+\cos(4\theta)}{2}\right) = \frac{1}{4} - \frac{1}{2}\cos(2\theta) + \frac{1}{8} + \frac{1}{8}\cos(4\theta) = \frac{3}{8} - \frac{1}{2}\cos(2\theta) + \frac{1}{8}\cos(4\theta)$

43. $\cos(3\theta) = 4\cos^3\theta - 3\cos\theta$ **45.** $\sin(5\theta) = 16\sin^5\theta - 20\sin^3\theta + 5\sin\theta$ **47.** $\cos^4\theta - \sin^4\theta = (\cos^2\theta + \sin^2\theta)(\cos^2\theta - \sin^2\theta) = \cos(2\theta)$

49. $\cot(2\theta) = \frac{1}{\tan(2\theta)} = \frac{1-\tan^2\theta}{2\tan\theta} = \frac{1 - \frac{1}{\cot^2\theta}}{2\left(\frac{1}{\cot\theta}\right)} = \frac{\frac{\cot^2\theta - 1}{\cot^2\theta}}{\frac{2}{\cot\theta}} = \frac{\cot^2\theta - 1}{\cot^2\theta}\cdot\frac{\cot\theta}{2} = \frac{\cot^2\theta - 1}{2\cot\theta}$

51. $\sec(2\theta) = \frac{1}{\cos(2\theta)} = \frac{1}{2\cos^2\theta - 1} = \frac{1}{\frac{2}{\sec^2\theta} - 1} = \frac{1}{\frac{2-\sec^2\theta}{\sec^2\theta}} = \frac{\sec^2\theta}{2-\sec^2\theta}$ **53.** $\cos^2(2u) - \sin^2(2u) = \cos[2(2u)] = \cos(4u)$

55. $\frac{\cos(2\theta)}{1+\sin(2\theta)} = \frac{\cos^2\theta - \sin^2\theta}{1 + 2\sin\theta\cos\theta} = \frac{(\cos\theta - \sin\theta)(\cos\theta + \sin\theta)}{\sin^2\theta + \cos^2\theta + 2\sin\theta\cos\theta} = \frac{(\cos\theta - \sin\theta)(\cos\theta + \sin\theta)}{(\sin\theta + \cos\theta)(\sin\theta + \cos\theta)} = \frac{\cos\theta - \sin\theta}{\cos\theta + \sin\theta}$

$= \frac{\frac{\cos\theta - \sin\theta}{\sin\theta}}{\frac{\cos\theta + \sin\theta}{\sin\theta}} = \frac{\frac{\cos\theta}{\sin\theta} - \frac{\sin\theta}{\sin\theta}}{\frac{\cos\theta}{\sin\theta} + \frac{\sin\theta}{\sin\theta}} = \frac{\cot\theta - 1}{\cot\theta + 1}$

57. $\sec^2\frac{\theta}{2} = \frac{1}{\cos^2\left(\frac{\theta}{2}\right)} = \frac{1}{\frac{1+\cos\theta}{2}} = \frac{2}{1+\cos\theta}$

59. $\cot^2\frac{v}{2} = \frac{1}{\tan^2\left(\frac{v}{2}\right)} = \frac{1}{\frac{1-\cos v}{1+\cos v}} = \frac{1+\cos v}{1-\cos v} = \frac{1 + \frac{1}{\sec v}}{1 - \frac{1}{\sec v}} = \frac{\frac{\sec v + 1}{\sec v}}{\frac{\sec v - 1}{\sec v}} = \frac{\sec v + 1}{\sec v}\cdot\frac{\sec v}{\sec v - 1} = \frac{\sec v + 1}{\sec v - 1}$

61. $\frac{1 - \tan^2\left(\frac{\theta}{2}\right)}{1 + \tan^2\left(\frac{\theta}{2}\right)} = \frac{1 - \frac{1-\cos\theta}{1+\cos\theta}}{1 + \frac{1-\cos\theta}{1+\cos\theta}} = \frac{\frac{1+\cos\theta - (1-\cos\theta)}{1+\cos\theta}}{\frac{1+\cos\theta+1-\cos\theta}{1+\cos\theta}} = \frac{2\cos\theta}{1+\cos\theta}\cdot\frac{1+\cos\theta}{2} = \cos\theta$

63. $\frac{\sin(3\theta)}{\sin\theta} - \frac{\cos(3\theta)}{\cos\theta} = \frac{\sin(3\theta)\cos\theta - \cos(3\theta)\sin\theta}{\sin\theta\cos\theta} = \frac{\sin(3\theta - \theta)}{\frac{1}{2}(2\sin\theta\cos\theta)} = \frac{2\sin(2\theta)}{\sin(2\theta)} = 2$

65. $\tan(3\theta) = \tan(\theta + 2\theta) = \frac{\tan\theta + \tan(2\theta)}{1 - \tan\theta\tan(2\theta)} = \frac{\tan\theta + \frac{2\tan\theta}{1-\tan^2\theta}}{1 - \frac{\tan\theta(2\tan\theta)}{1-\tan^2\theta}} = \frac{\tan\theta - \tan^3\theta + 2\tan\theta}{1 - \tan^2\theta - 2\tan^2\theta} = \frac{3\tan\theta - \tan^3\theta}{1 - 3\tan^2\theta}$

67. $\frac{1}{2}(\ln|1 - \cos(2\theta)| - \ln 2) = \ln\left(\frac{|1-\cos(2\theta)|}{2}\right)^{1/2} = \ln|\sin^2\theta|^{1/2} = \ln|\sin\theta|$ **69.** $\frac{\sqrt{3}}{2}$ **71.** $\frac{7}{25}$ **73.** $\frac{24}{7}$ **75.** $\frac{24}{25}$ **77.** $\frac{1}{5}$ **79.** $\frac{25}{7}$

81. **(a)** $W = 2D(\csc\theta - \cot\theta) = 2D\left(\frac{1}{\sin\theta} - \frac{\cos\theta}{\sin\theta}\right) = 2D\frac{1-\cos\theta}{\sin\theta} = 2D\tan\frac{\theta}{2}$ **(b)** $\theta = 24.45°$

83. **(a)** $R = \frac{v_0^2\sqrt{2}}{16}\cos\theta(\sin\theta - \cos\theta)$

$= \frac{v_0^2\sqrt{2}}{32}(2\cos\theta\sin\theta - 2\cos^2\theta)$

$= \frac{v_0^2\sqrt{2}}{32}[\sin(2\theta) - \cos(2\theta) - 1]$

(b)

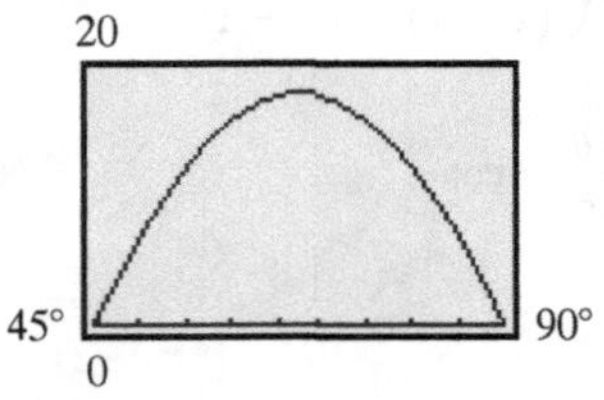

(c) $\theta = 67.5°$ makes R largest.

85. $A = \frac{1}{2}h(\text{base}) = h\left(\frac{1}{2}\text{base}\right) = s\cos\frac{\theta}{2}\cdot s\sin\frac{\theta}{2} = \frac{1}{2}s^2\sin\theta$ **87.** $\sin(2\theta) = \frac{4x}{4+x^2}$ **89.** $-\frac{1}{4}$

91. $\dfrac{2z}{1+z^2} = \dfrac{2\tan\left(\frac{\alpha}{2}\right)}{1+\tan^2\left(\frac{\alpha}{2}\right)} = \dfrac{2\tan\left(\frac{\alpha}{2}\right)}{\sec^2\left(\frac{\alpha}{2}\right)} = \dfrac{\dfrac{2\sin\left(\frac{\alpha}{2}\right)}{\cos\left(\frac{\alpha}{2}\right)}}{\dfrac{1}{\cos^2\left(\frac{\alpha}{2}\right)}} = 2\sin\left(\frac{\alpha}{2}\right)\cos\left(\frac{\alpha}{2}\right) = \sin\left(2\cdot\frac{\alpha}{2}\right) = \sin\alpha$

93.

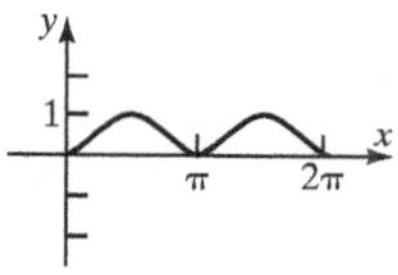

95. $\sin\dfrac{\pi}{24} = \dfrac{\sqrt{2}}{4}\sqrt{4-\sqrt{6}-\sqrt{2}}$

$\cos\dfrac{\pi}{24} = \dfrac{\sqrt{2}}{4}\sqrt{4+\sqrt{6}+\sqrt{2}}$

97. $\sin^3\theta + \sin^3(\theta+120°) + \sin^3(\theta+240°) = \sin^3\theta + (\sin\theta\cos 120° + \cos\theta\sin 120°)^3 + (\sin\theta\cos 240° + \cos\theta\sin 240°)^3$

$= \sin^3\theta + \left(-\dfrac{1}{2}\sin\theta + \dfrac{\sqrt{3}}{2}\cos\theta\right)^3 + \left(-\dfrac{1}{2}\sin\theta - \dfrac{\sqrt{3}}{2}\cos\theta\right)^3$

$= \sin^3\theta + \dfrac{1}{8}\left(3\sqrt{3}\cos^3\theta - 9\cos^2\theta\sin\theta + 3\sqrt{3}\cos\theta\sin^2\theta - \sin^3\theta\right) - \dfrac{1}{8}\left(\sin^3\theta + 3\sqrt{3}\sin^2\theta\cos\theta + 9\sin\theta\cos^2\theta + 3\sqrt{3}\cos^3\theta\right)$

$= \dfrac{3}{4}\sin^3\theta - \dfrac{9}{4}\cos^2\theta\sin\theta = \dfrac{3}{4}[\sin^3\theta - 3\sin\theta(1-\sin^2\theta)] = \dfrac{3}{4}(4\sin^3\theta - 3\sin\theta) = -\dfrac{3}{4}\sin(3\theta)$ (from Example 2)

7.6 Assess Your Understanding *(page 487)*

1. $\frac{1}{2}[\cos(2\theta) - \cos(6\theta)]$ **3.** $\frac{1}{2}[\sin(6\theta) + \sin(2\theta)]$ **5.** $\frac{1}{2}[\cos(2\theta) + \cos(8\theta)]$ **7.** $\frac{1}{2}[\cos\theta - \cos(3\theta)]$ **9.** $\frac{1}{2}[\sin(2\theta) + \sin\theta]$ **11.** $2\sin\theta\cos(3\theta)$

13. $2\cos(3\theta)\cos\theta$ **15.** $2\sin(2\theta)\cos\theta$ **17.** $2\sin\theta\sin\frac{\theta}{2}$ **19.** $\dfrac{\sin\theta + \sin(3\theta)}{2\sin(2\theta)} = \dfrac{2\sin(2\theta)\cos\theta}{2\sin(2\theta)} = \cos\theta$

21. $\dfrac{\sin(4\theta)+\sin(2\theta)}{\cos(4\theta)+\cos(2\theta)} = \dfrac{2\sin(3\theta)\cos\theta}{2\cos(3\theta)\cos\theta} = \dfrac{\sin(3\theta)}{\cos(3\theta)} = \tan(3\theta)$ **23.** $\dfrac{\cos\theta - \cos(3\theta)}{\sin\theta + \sin(3\theta)} = \dfrac{2\sin(2\theta)\sin\theta}{2\sin(2\theta)\cos\theta} = \dfrac{\sin\theta}{\cos\theta} = \tan\theta$

25. $\sin\theta[\sin\theta + \sin(3\theta)] = \sin\theta[2\sin(2\theta)\cos\theta] = \cos\theta[2\sin(2\theta)\sin\theta] = \cos\theta\left[2\cdot\frac{1}{2}[\cos\theta - \cos(3\theta)]\right] = \cos\theta[\cos\theta - \cos(3\theta)]$

27. $\dfrac{\sin(4\theta)+\sin(8\theta)}{\cos(4\theta)+\cos(8\theta)} = \dfrac{2\sin(6\theta)\cos(2\theta)}{2\cos(6\theta)\cos(2\theta)} = \dfrac{\sin(6\theta)}{\cos(6\theta)} = \tan(6\theta)$

29. $\dfrac{\sin(4\theta)+\sin(8\theta)}{\sin(4\theta)-\sin(8\theta)} = \dfrac{2\sin(6\theta)\cos(-2\theta)}{2\sin(-2\theta)\cos(6\theta)} = \dfrac{\sin(6\theta)}{\cos(6\theta)}\cdot\dfrac{\cos(2\theta)}{-\sin(2\theta)} = \tan(6\theta)[-\cot(2\theta)] = -\dfrac{\tan(6\theta)}{\tan(2\theta)}$

31. $\dfrac{\sin\alpha + \sin\beta}{\sin\alpha - \sin\beta} = \dfrac{2\sin\dfrac{\alpha+\beta}{2}\cos\dfrac{\alpha-\beta}{2}}{2\sin\dfrac{\alpha-\beta}{2}\cos\dfrac{\alpha+\beta}{2}} = \dfrac{\sin\dfrac{\alpha+\beta}{2}}{\cos\dfrac{\alpha+\beta}{2}}\cdot\dfrac{\cos\dfrac{\alpha-\beta}{2}}{\sin\dfrac{\alpha-\beta}{2}} = \tan\dfrac{\alpha+\beta}{2}\cot\dfrac{\alpha-\beta}{2}$

33. $\dfrac{\sin\alpha + \sin\beta}{\cos\alpha + \cos\beta} = \dfrac{2\sin\dfrac{\alpha+\beta}{2}\cos\dfrac{\alpha-\beta}{2}}{2\cos\dfrac{\alpha+\beta}{2}\cos\dfrac{\alpha-\beta}{2}} = \dfrac{\sin\dfrac{\alpha+\beta}{2}}{\cos\dfrac{\alpha+\beta}{2}} = \tan\dfrac{\alpha+\beta}{2}$

35. $1 + \cos(2\theta) + \cos(4\theta) + \cos(6\theta) = [1 + \cos(6\theta)] + [\cos(2\theta) + \cos(4\theta)] = 2\cos^2(3\theta) + 2\cos(3\theta)\cos(-\theta)$
$= 2\cos(3\theta)[\cos(3\theta) + \cos\theta] = 2\cos(3\theta)[2\cos(2\theta)\cos\theta] = 4\cos\theta\cos(2\theta)\cos(3\theta)$

37. **(a)** $y = 2\sin(2061\pi t)\cos(357\pi t)$ **(b)** $y_{max} = 2$ **(c)**

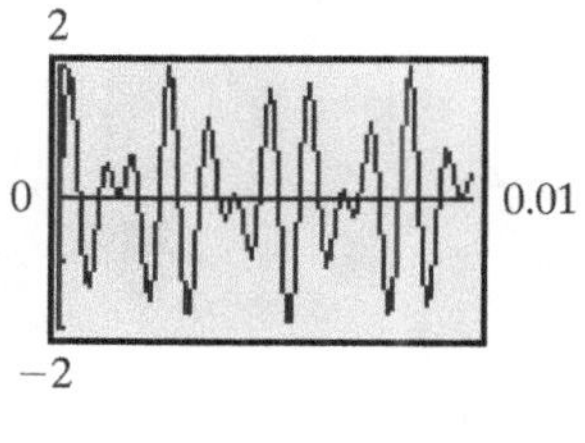

39. $I_u = I_x\cos^2\theta + I_y\sin^2\theta - 2I_{xy}\sin\theta\cos\theta = I_x\cos^2\theta + I_y\sin^2\theta - I_{xy}\sin 2\theta$

$= I_x\left(\dfrac{\cos 2\theta + 1}{2}\right) + I_y\left(\dfrac{1 - \cos 2\theta}{2}\right) - I_{xy}\sin 2\theta$

$= \dfrac{I_x}{2}\cos 2\theta + \dfrac{I_x}{2} + \dfrac{I_y}{2} - \dfrac{I_y}{2}\cos 2\theta - I_{xy}\sin 2\theta$

$= \dfrac{I_x + I_y}{2} + \dfrac{I_x - I_y}{2}\cos 2\theta - I_{xy}\sin 2\theta$

$I_v = I_x\sin^2\theta + I_y\cos^2\theta + 2I_{xy}\sin\theta\cos\theta = I_x\left(\dfrac{1 - \cos 2\theta}{2}\right) + I_y\left(\dfrac{\cos 2\theta + 1}{2}\right) + I_{xy}\sin 2\theta$

$= \dfrac{I_x}{2} - \dfrac{I_x}{2}\cos 2\theta + \dfrac{I_y}{2}\cos 2\theta + \dfrac{I_y}{2} + I_{xy}\sin 2\theta$

$= \dfrac{I_x + I_y}{2} - \dfrac{I_x - I_y}{2}\cos 2\theta + I_{xy}\sin 2\theta$

41. $\sin(2\alpha) + \sin(2\beta) + \sin(2\gamma) = 2\sin(\alpha + \beta)\cos(\alpha - \beta) + \sin(2\gamma) = 2\sin(\alpha + \beta)\cos(\alpha - \beta) + 2\sin\gamma\cos\gamma$

$= 2\sin(\pi - \gamma)\cos(\alpha - \beta) + 2\sin\gamma\cos\gamma = 2\sin\gamma\cos(\alpha - \beta) + 2\sin\gamma\cos\gamma = 2\sin\gamma[\cos(\alpha - \beta) + \cos\gamma]$

$= 2\sin\gamma\left(2\cos\dfrac{\alpha - \beta + \gamma}{2}\cos\dfrac{\alpha - \beta - \gamma}{2}\right) = 4\sin\gamma\cos\dfrac{\pi - 2\beta}{2}\cos\dfrac{2\alpha - \pi}{2} = 4\sin\gamma\cos\left(\dfrac{\pi}{2} - \beta\right)\cos\left(\alpha - \dfrac{\pi}{2}\right)$

$= 4\sin\gamma\sin\beta\sin\alpha = 4\sin\alpha\sin\beta\sin\gamma$

43.

$$\sin(\alpha - \beta) = \sin\alpha\cos\beta - \cos\alpha\sin\beta$$
$$\sin(\alpha + \beta) = \sin\alpha\cos\beta + \cos\alpha\sin\beta$$
$$\sin(\alpha - \beta) + \sin(\alpha + \beta) = 2\sin\alpha\cos\beta$$
$$\sin\alpha\cos\beta = \frac{1}{2}[\sin(\alpha + \beta) + \sin(\alpha - \beta)]$$

45. $2\cos\dfrac{\alpha + \beta}{2}\cos\dfrac{\alpha - \beta}{2} = 2\cdot\dfrac{1}{2}\left[\cos\left(\dfrac{\alpha + \beta}{2} + \dfrac{\alpha - \beta}{2}\right) + \cos\left(\dfrac{\alpha + \beta}{2} - \dfrac{\alpha - \beta}{2}\right)\right] = \cos\dfrac{2\alpha}{2} + \cos\dfrac{2\beta}{2} = \cos\alpha + \cos\beta$

7.7 Assess Your Understanding *(page 492)*

3. $\dfrac{\pi}{6}; \dfrac{5\pi}{6}$ **4.** $\left\{\theta \,\middle|\, \theta = \dfrac{\pi}{6} + 2\pi k, \theta = \dfrac{5\pi}{6} + 2\pi k, k \text{ is any integer}\right\}$ **5.** F **6.** F **7.** $\left\{\dfrac{7\pi}{6}, \dfrac{11\pi}{6}\right\}$ **9.** $\left\{\dfrac{\pi}{3}, \dfrac{2\pi}{3}, \dfrac{4\pi}{3}, \dfrac{5\pi}{3}\right\}$ **11.** $\left\{\dfrac{\pi}{4}, \dfrac{3\pi}{4}, \dfrac{5\pi}{4}, \dfrac{7\pi}{4}\right\}$

13. $\left\{\dfrac{\pi}{2}, \dfrac{7\pi}{6}, \dfrac{11\pi}{6}\right\}$ **15.** $\left\{\dfrac{\pi}{3}, \dfrac{2\pi}{3}, \dfrac{4\pi}{3}, \dfrac{5\pi}{3}\right\}$ **17.** $\left\{\dfrac{4\pi}{9}, \dfrac{8\pi}{9}, \dfrac{16\pi}{9}\right\}$ **19.** $\left\{\dfrac{7\pi}{6}, \dfrac{11\pi}{6}\right\}$ **21.** $\left\{\dfrac{3\pi}{4}, \dfrac{7\pi}{4}\right\}$ **23.** $\left\{\dfrac{2\pi}{3}, \dfrac{4\pi}{3}\right\}$ **25.** $\left\{\dfrac{3\pi}{4}, \dfrac{5\pi}{4}\right\}$

27. $\left\{\dfrac{3\pi}{4}, \dfrac{7\pi}{4}\right\}$ **29.** $\left\{\dfrac{11\pi}{6}\right\}$ **31.** $\left\{\theta \,\middle|\, \theta = \dfrac{\pi}{6} + 2k\pi, \theta = \dfrac{5\pi}{6} + 2k\pi\right\}; \dfrac{\pi}{6}, \dfrac{5\pi}{6}, \dfrac{13\pi}{6}, \dfrac{17\pi}{6}, \dfrac{25\pi}{6}, \dfrac{29\pi}{6}$

33. $\left\{\theta \,\middle|\, \theta = \dfrac{5\pi}{6} + k\pi\right\}; \dfrac{5\pi}{6}, \dfrac{11\pi}{6}, \dfrac{17\pi}{6}, \dfrac{23\pi}{6}, \dfrac{29\pi}{6}, \dfrac{35\pi}{6}$ **35.** $\left\{\theta \,\middle|\, \theta = \dfrac{\pi}{2} + 2k\pi, \theta = \dfrac{3\pi}{2} + 2k\pi\right\}; \dfrac{\pi}{2}, \dfrac{3\pi}{2}, \dfrac{5\pi}{2}, \dfrac{7\pi}{2}, \dfrac{9\pi}{2}, \dfrac{11\pi}{2}$

37. $\left\{\theta \,\middle|\, \theta = \dfrac{\pi}{3} + k\pi, \theta = \dfrac{2\pi}{3} + k\pi\right\}; \dfrac{\pi}{3}, \dfrac{2\pi}{3}, \dfrac{4\pi}{3}, \dfrac{5\pi}{3}, \dfrac{7\pi}{3}, \dfrac{8\pi}{3}$ **39.** $\left\{\theta \,\middle|\, \theta = \dfrac{8\pi}{3} + 4k\pi, \theta = \dfrac{10\pi}{3} + 4k\pi\right\}; \dfrac{8\pi}{3}, \dfrac{10\pi}{3}, \dfrac{20\pi}{3}, \dfrac{22\pi}{3}, \dfrac{32\pi}{3}, \dfrac{34\pi}{3}$

41. $\{0.41, 2.73\}$ **43.** $\{1.37, 4.51\}$ **45.** $\{2.69, 3.59\}$ **47.** $\{1.82, 4.46\}$ **49.** $\{2.08, 5.22\}$ **51.** $\{0.73, 2.41\}$ **53.** $\dfrac{\pi}{3}, \dfrac{2\pi}{3}, \dfrac{4\pi}{3}, \dfrac{5\pi}{3}$

55. (a) $-2\pi, -\pi, 0, \pi, 2\pi, 3\pi, 4\pi$

(b)

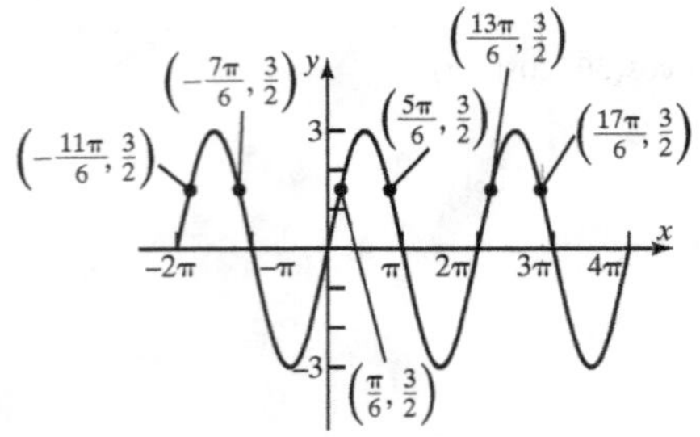

(c) $\left\{-\dfrac{11\pi}{6}, -\dfrac{7\pi}{6}, \dfrac{\pi}{6}, \dfrac{5\pi}{6}, \dfrac{13\pi}{6}, \dfrac{17\pi}{6}\right\}$

(d) $\left\{x \,\middle|\, -\dfrac{11\pi}{6} < x < -\dfrac{7\pi}{6} \text{ or } \dfrac{\pi}{6} < x < \dfrac{5\pi}{6} \text{ or } \dfrac{13\pi}{6} < x < \dfrac{17\pi}{6}\right\}$

57. (a) $\left\{x \,\middle|\, x = -\dfrac{\pi}{4} + k\pi, k \text{ is any integer}\right\}$

(b) $-\dfrac{\pi}{2} < x < -\dfrac{\pi}{4}$ or $\left(-\dfrac{\pi}{2}, -\dfrac{\pi}{4}\right)$

59. (a), (d)

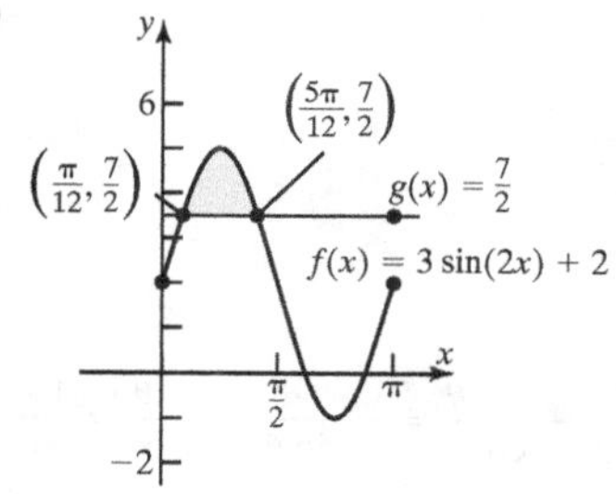

(b) $\left\{\frac{\pi}{12}, \frac{5\pi}{12}\right\}$

(c) $\left\{x \middle| \frac{\pi}{12} < x < \frac{5\pi}{12}\right\}$ or $\left(\frac{\pi}{12}, \frac{5\pi}{12}\right)$

61. (a), (d)

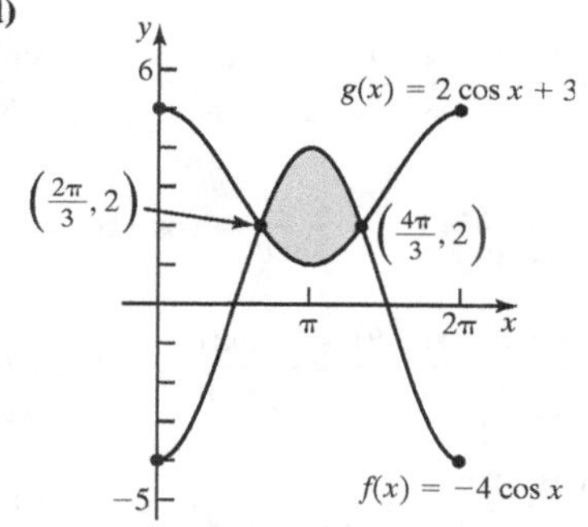

(b) $\left\{\frac{2\pi}{3}, \frac{4\pi}{3}\right\}$

(c) $\left\{x \middle| \frac{2\pi}{3} < x < \frac{4\pi}{3}\right\}$ or $\left(\frac{2\pi}{3}, \frac{4\pi}{3}\right)$

63. (a) 0 s, 0.43 s, 0.86 s **(b)** 0.21 s **(c)** [0, 0.03] ∪ [0.39, 0.43] ∪ [0.86, 0.89]

65. (a) 150 mi **(b)** 6.06, 8.44, 15.72, 18.11 min **(c)** Before 6.06 min, between 8.44 and 15.72 min, and after 18.11 min **(d)** No

67. 28.90° **69.** Yes; it varies from 1.25 to 1.34. **71.** 1.47

73. If θ is the original angle of incidence and ϕ is the angle of refraction, then $\frac{\sin\theta}{\sin\phi} = n_2$.
The angle of incidence of the emerging beam is also ϕ, and the index of refraction is $\frac{1}{n_2}$.
Thus, θ is the angle of refraction of the emerging beam.

7.8 Assess Your Understanding *(page 500)*

5. $\left\{\frac{\pi}{2}, \frac{2\pi}{3}, \frac{4\pi}{3}, \frac{3\pi}{2}\right\}$ **7.** $\left\{\frac{\pi}{2}, \frac{7\pi}{6}, \frac{11\pi}{6}\right\}$ **9.** $\left\{0, \frac{\pi}{4}, \frac{5\pi}{4}\right\}$ **11.** $\left\{\frac{\pi}{2}, \frac{2\pi}{3}, \frac{4\pi}{3}, \frac{3\pi}{2}\right\}$ **13.** $\{\pi\}$ **15.** $\left\{\frac{\pi}{3}, \frac{2\pi}{3}, \frac{4\pi}{3}, \frac{5\pi}{3}\right\}$ **17.** $\left\{\frac{\pi}{4}, \frac{5\pi}{4}\right\}$

19. $\left\{0, \frac{\pi}{3}, \pi, \frac{5\pi}{3}\right\}$ **21.** $\left\{\frac{\pi}{2}, \frac{3\pi}{2}\right\}$ **23.** $\left\{0, \frac{2\pi}{3}, \frac{4\pi}{3}\right\}$ **25.** $\left\{0, \frac{\pi}{3}, \frac{\pi}{2}, \frac{2\pi}{3}, \pi, \frac{4\pi}{3}, \frac{3\pi}{2}, \frac{5\pi}{3}\right\}$ **27.** $\left\{0, \frac{\pi}{5}, \frac{2\pi}{5}, \frac{3\pi}{5}, \frac{4\pi}{5}, \pi, \frac{6\pi}{5}, \frac{7\pi}{5}, \frac{8\pi}{5}, \frac{9\pi}{5}\right\}$

29. $\left\{\frac{\pi}{6}, \frac{5\pi}{6}, \frac{3\pi}{2}\right\}$ **31.** $\left\{\frac{\pi}{2}\right\}$ **33.** $\{0\}$ **35.** $\left\{\frac{\pi}{3}, \frac{5\pi}{3}\right\}$ **37.** No real solution **39.** No real solution **41.** $\left\{\frac{\pi}{2}, \frac{7\pi}{6}\right\}$ **43.** $\left\{0, \frac{\pi}{3}, \pi, \frac{5\pi}{3}\right\}$

45. $\left\{\frac{\pi}{4}\right\}$ **47.** −1.31, 1.98, 3.84 **49.** 0.52 **51.** 1.26 **53.** −1.02, 1.02 **55.** 0, 2.15 **57.** 0.76, 1.35 **59.** $\frac{\pi}{3}, \frac{2\pi}{3}, \frac{4\pi}{3}, \frac{5\pi}{3}$ **61.** $0, \frac{\pi}{3}, \pi, \frac{5\pi}{3}$ **63.** π

65. (a) 60° **(b)** 60°
(c) $A(60°) = 12\sqrt{3}$ in.^{2}
(d)

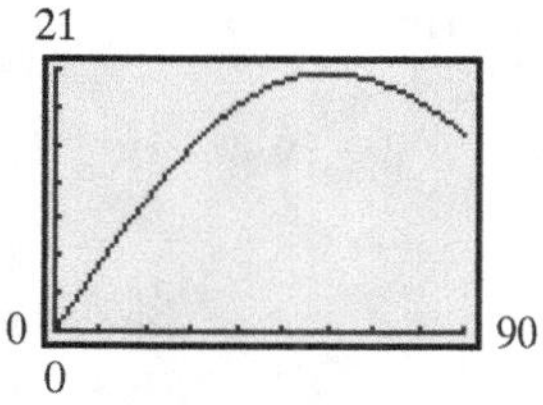

$\theta_{max} = 60°$
Maximum area = 20.78 in.^{2}

67. 2.03, 4.91

69. (a) 30°, 60° **(b)** 123.6 m
(c)

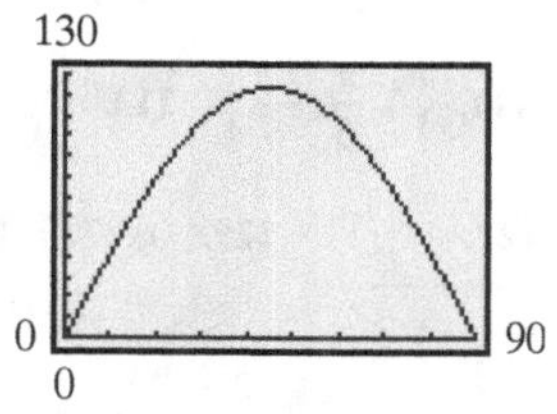

Review Exercises *(page 504)*

1. $\frac{\pi}{2}$ **3.** $\frac{\pi}{4}$ **5.** $\frac{5\pi}{6}$ **7.** $\frac{\pi}{4}$ **9.** $\frac{3\pi}{8}$ **11.** $-\frac{\pi}{3}$ **13.** $\frac{\pi}{7}$ **15.** 0.9 **17.** −0.3 **19.** Not defined **21.** $-\frac{\pi}{6}$ **23.** $-\frac{\pi}{4}$ **25.** $-\sqrt{3}$ **27.** $\frac{2\sqrt{3}}{3}$

29. $\frac{4}{5}$ **31.** $-\frac{4}{3}$ **33.** $f^{-1}(x) = \frac{1}{3}\sin^{-1}\left(\frac{x}{2}\right)$; Domain of f = range of f^{-1}: $(-\infty, \infty)$; Domain of f^{-1} = range of f: $[-2, 2]$

35. $f^{-1}(x) = \cos^{-1}(3 - x)$; Domain of f = range of f^{-1}: $(-\infty, \infty)$; Domain of f^{-1} = range of f: $[2, 4]$

37. $\sqrt{1 - u^2}$ **39.** $\frac{1}{u}$ **41.** $\tan\theta\cot\theta - \sin^2\theta = 1 - \sin^2\theta = \cos^2\theta$ **43.** $\sin^2\theta(1 + \cot^2\theta) = \sin^2\theta\csc^2\theta = 1$

45. $5\cos^2\theta + 3\sin^2\theta = 2\cos^2\theta + 3(\cos^2\theta + \sin^2\theta) = 3 + 2\cos^2\theta$

47. $\frac{1 - \cos\theta}{\sin\theta} + \frac{\sin\theta}{1 - \cos\theta} = \frac{(1 - \cos\theta)^2 + \sin^2\theta}{\sin\theta(1 - \cos\theta)} = \frac{1 - 2\cos\theta + \cos^2\theta + \sin^2\theta}{\sin\theta(1 - \cos\theta)} = \frac{2(1 - \cos\theta)}{\sin\theta(1 - \cos\theta)} = 2\csc\theta$

49. $\frac{\cos\theta}{\cos\theta - \sin\theta} = \frac{\frac{\cos\theta}{\cos\theta}}{\frac{\cos\theta - \sin\theta}{\cos\theta}} = \frac{1}{1 - \frac{\sin\theta}{\cos\theta}} = \frac{1}{1 - \tan\theta}$

51. $\dfrac{\csc\theta}{1+\csc\theta} = \dfrac{\frac{1}{\sin\theta}}{1+\frac{1}{\sin\theta}} = \dfrac{1}{1+\sin\theta} = \dfrac{1}{1+\sin\theta}\cdot\dfrac{1-\sin\theta}{1-\sin\theta} = \dfrac{1-\sin\theta}{1-\sin^2\theta} = \dfrac{1-\sin\theta}{\cos^2\theta}$

53. $\csc\theta - \sin\theta = \dfrac{1}{\sin\theta} - \sin\theta = \dfrac{1-\sin^2\theta}{\sin\theta} = \dfrac{\cos^2\theta}{\sin\theta} = \cos\theta\cdot\dfrac{\cos\theta}{\sin\theta} = \cos\theta\cot\theta$

55. $\dfrac{1-\sin\theta}{\sec\theta} = \cos\theta(1-\sin\theta)\cdot\dfrac{1+\sin\theta}{1+\sin\theta} = \dfrac{\cos\theta(1-\sin^2\theta)}{1+\sin\theta} = \dfrac{\cos^3\theta}{1+\sin\theta}$ **57.** $\cot\theta - \tan\theta = \dfrac{\cos\theta}{\sin\theta} - \dfrac{\sin\theta}{\cos\theta} = \dfrac{\cos^2\theta-\sin^2\theta}{\sin\theta\cos\theta} = \dfrac{1-2\sin^2\theta}{\sin\theta\cos\theta}$

59. $\dfrac{\cos(\alpha+\beta)}{\cos\alpha\sin\beta} = \dfrac{\cos\alpha\cos\beta - \sin\alpha\sin\beta}{\cos\alpha\sin\beta} = \dfrac{\cos\alpha\cos\beta}{\cos\alpha\sin\beta} - \dfrac{\sin\alpha\sin\beta}{\cos\alpha\sin\beta} = \cot\beta - \tan\alpha$

61. $\dfrac{\cos(\alpha-\beta)}{\cos\alpha\cos\beta} = \dfrac{\cos\alpha\cos\beta + \sin\alpha\sin\beta}{\cos\alpha\cos\beta} = \dfrac{\cos\alpha\cos\beta}{\cos\alpha\cos\beta} + \dfrac{\sin\alpha\sin\beta}{\cos\alpha\cos\beta} = 1 + \tan\alpha\tan\beta$

63. $(1+\cos\theta)\left(\tan\dfrac{\theta}{2}\right) = (1+\cos\theta)\cdot\dfrac{\sin\theta}{1+\cos\theta} = \sin\theta$

65. $2\cot\theta\cot 2\theta = 2\left(\dfrac{\cos\theta}{\sin\theta}\right)\left(\dfrac{\cos 2\theta}{\sin 2\theta}\right) = \dfrac{2\cos\theta(\cos^2\theta - \sin^2\theta)}{2\sin^2\theta\cos\theta} = \dfrac{\cos^2\theta-\sin^2\theta}{\sin^2\theta} = \cot^2\theta - 1$

67. $1 - 8\sin^2\theta\cos^2\theta = 1 - 2(2\sin\theta\cos\theta)^2 = 1 - 2\sin^2(2\theta) = \cos(4\theta)$ **69.** $\dfrac{\sin(2\theta)+\sin(4\theta)}{\cos(2\theta)+\cos(4\theta)} = \dfrac{2\sin(3\theta)\cos(-\theta)}{2\cos(3\theta)\cos(-\theta)} = \tan(3\theta)$

71. $\dfrac{\cos(2\theta)-\cos(4\theta)}{\cos(2\theta)+\cos(4\theta)} - \tan\theta\tan(3\theta) = \dfrac{-2\sin(3\theta)\sin(-\theta)}{2\cos(3\theta)\cos(-\theta)} - \tan\theta\tan(3\theta) = \tan(3\theta)\tan\theta - \tan\theta\tan(3\theta) = 0$

73. $\frac{1}{4}(\sqrt{6}-\sqrt{2})$ **75.** $\frac{1}{4}(\sqrt{6}-\sqrt{2})$ **77.** $\frac{1}{2}$ **79.** $\sqrt{2}-1$ **81.** **(a)** $-\frac{33}{65}$ **(b)** $-\frac{56}{65}$ **(c)** $-\frac{63}{65}$ **(d)** $\frac{33}{56}$ **(e)** $\frac{24}{25}$ **(f)** $\frac{119}{169}$ **(g)** $\frac{5\sqrt{26}}{26}$ **(h)** $\frac{2\sqrt{5}}{5}$

83. **(a)** $-\frac{16}{65}$ **(b)** $-\frac{63}{65}$ **(c)** $-\frac{56}{65}$ **(d)** $\frac{16}{63}$ **(e)** $\frac{24}{25}$ **(f)** $\frac{119}{169}$ **(g)** $\frac{\sqrt{26}}{26}$ **(h)** $-\frac{\sqrt{10}}{10}$ **85.** **(a)** $-\frac{63}{65}$ **(b)** $\frac{16}{65}$ **(c)** $\frac{33}{65}$ **(d)** $-\frac{63}{16}$ **(e)** $\frac{24}{25}$
(f) $-\frac{119}{169}$ **(g)** $\frac{2\sqrt{13}}{13}$ **(h)** $-\frac{\sqrt{10}}{10}$ **87.** **(a)** $\frac{-\sqrt{3}-2\sqrt{2}}{6}$ **(b)** $\frac{1-2\sqrt{6}}{6}$ **(c)** $\frac{-\sqrt{3}+2\sqrt{2}}{6}$ **(d)** $\frac{8\sqrt{2}+9\sqrt{3}}{23}$ **(e)** $-\frac{\sqrt{3}}{2}$ **(f)** $-\frac{7}{9}$
(g) $\frac{\sqrt{3}}{3}$ **(h)** $\frac{\sqrt{3}}{2}$ **89.** **(a)** 1 **(b)** 0 **(c)** $-\frac{1}{9}$ **(d)** Not defined **(e)** $\frac{4\sqrt{5}}{9}$ **(f)** $-\frac{1}{9}$ **(g)** $\frac{\sqrt{30}}{6}$ **(h)** $-\frac{\sqrt{6}\sqrt{3-\sqrt{5}}}{6}$

91. $\frac{4+3\sqrt{3}}{10}$ **93.** $-\frac{48+25\sqrt{3}}{39}$ **95.** $-\frac{24}{25}$ **97.** $\left\{\frac{\pi}{3}, \frac{5\pi}{3}\right\}$ **99.** $\left\{\frac{3\pi}{4}, \frac{5\pi}{4}\right\}$ **101.** $\left\{\frac{3\pi}{4}, \frac{7\pi}{4}\right\}$ **103.** $\left\{0, \frac{\pi}{2}, \pi, \frac{3\pi}{2}\right\}$ **105.** $\left\{\frac{\pi}{3}, \frac{2\pi}{3}, \frac{4\pi}{3}, \frac{5\pi}{3}\right\}$

107. $\{0, \pi\}$ **109.** $\left\{0, \frac{2\pi}{3}, \pi, \frac{4\pi}{3}\right\}$ **111.** $\left\{0, \frac{\pi}{6}, \frac{5\pi}{6}\right\}$ **113.** $\left\{\frac{\pi}{6}, \frac{\pi}{2}, \frac{5\pi}{6}\right\}$ **115.** $\left\{\frac{\pi}{3}, \frac{5\pi}{3}\right\}$ **117.** $\left\{\frac{\pi}{4}, \frac{\pi}{2}, \frac{3\pi}{4}, \frac{3\pi}{2}\right\}$ **119.** $\left\{\frac{\pi}{2}, \pi\right\}$

121. 0.78 **123.** −1.11 **125.** 1.23 **127.** {1.11} **129.** {0.87} **131.** {2.22} **133.** $\left\{-\frac{\sqrt{3}}{2}\right\}$

135. $\sin 15° = \sqrt{\dfrac{1-\cos 30°}{2}} = \sqrt{\dfrac{1-\frac{\sqrt{3}}{2}}{2}} = \sqrt{\dfrac{2-\sqrt{3}}{4}} = \dfrac{\sqrt{2-\sqrt{3}}}{2}$;

$\sin 15° = \sin(45° - 30°) = \sin 45°\cos 30° - \cos 45°\sin 30° = \dfrac{\sqrt{2}}{2}\cdot\dfrac{\sqrt{3}}{2} - \dfrac{\sqrt{2}}{2}\cdot\dfrac{1}{2} = \dfrac{\sqrt{6}}{4} - \dfrac{\sqrt{2}}{4} = \dfrac{\sqrt{6}-\sqrt{2}}{4}$;

$\left[\dfrac{\sqrt{2-\sqrt{3}}}{2}\right]^2 = \dfrac{2-\sqrt{3}}{4} = \dfrac{4(2-\sqrt{3})}{4\cdot 4} = \dfrac{8-4\sqrt{3}}{16} = \dfrac{6-2\sqrt{12}+2}{16} = \left(\dfrac{\sqrt{6}-\sqrt{2}}{4}\right)^2$

Chapter Test *(page 506)*

1. $\frac{\pi}{6}$ **2.** $-\frac{\pi}{4}$ **3.** $\frac{\pi}{5}$ **4.** $\frac{7}{3}$ **5.** 3 **6.** $-\frac{4}{3}$ **7.** 0.39 **8.** 0.78 **9.** 1.25 **10.** 0.20

11. $\dfrac{\csc\theta+\cot\theta}{\sec\theta+\tan\theta} = \dfrac{\csc\theta+\cot\theta}{\sec\theta+\tan\theta}\cdot\dfrac{\csc\theta-\cot\theta}{\csc\theta-\cot\theta} = \dfrac{\csc^2\theta-\cot^2\theta}{(\sec\theta+\tan\theta)(\csc\theta-\cot\theta)} = \dfrac{1}{(\sec\theta+\tan\theta)(\csc\theta-\cot\theta)}$

$= \dfrac{1}{(\sec\theta+\tan\theta)(\csc\theta-\cot\theta)}\cdot\dfrac{\sec\theta-\tan\theta}{\sec\theta-\tan\theta} = \dfrac{\sec\theta-\tan\theta}{(\sec^2\theta-\tan^2\theta)(\csc\theta-\cot\theta)} = \dfrac{\sec\theta-\tan\theta}{\csc\theta-\cot\theta}$

12. $\sin\theta\tan\theta + \cos\theta = \sin\theta\cdot\dfrac{\sin\theta}{\cos\theta} + \cos\theta = \dfrac{\sin^2\theta}{\cos\theta} + \dfrac{\cos^2\theta}{\cos\theta} = \dfrac{\sin^2\theta+\cos^2\theta}{\cos\theta} = \dfrac{1}{\cos\theta} = \sec\theta$

13. $\tan\theta + \cot\theta = \dfrac{\sin\theta}{\cos\theta} + \dfrac{\cos\theta}{\sin\theta} = \dfrac{\sin^2\theta}{\sin\theta\cos\theta} + \dfrac{\cos^2\theta}{\sin\theta\cos\theta} = \dfrac{\sin^2\theta+\cos^2\theta}{\sin\theta\cos\theta} = \dfrac{1}{\sin\theta\cos\theta} = \dfrac{2}{2\sin\theta\cos\theta} = \dfrac{2}{\sin(2\theta)} = 2\csc(2\theta)$

14. $\dfrac{\sin(\alpha+\beta)}{\tan\alpha+\tan\beta}=\dfrac{\sin\alpha\cos\beta+\cos\alpha\sin\beta}{\dfrac{\sin\alpha}{\cos\alpha}+\dfrac{\sin\beta}{\cos\beta}}=\dfrac{\sin\alpha\cos\beta+\cos\alpha\sin\beta}{\dfrac{\sin\alpha\cos\beta}{\cos\alpha\cos\beta}+\dfrac{\cos\alpha\sin\beta}{\cos\alpha\cos\beta}}=\dfrac{\sin\alpha\cos\beta+\cos\alpha\sin\beta}{\dfrac{\sin\alpha\cos\beta+\cos\alpha\sin\beta}{\cos\alpha\cos\beta}}$ $=\dfrac{\sin\alpha\cos\beta+\cos\alpha\sin\beta}{1}\cdot\dfrac{\cos\alpha\cos\beta}{\sin\alpha\cos\beta+\cos\alpha\sin\beta}=\cos\alpha\cos\beta$

15. $\sin(3\theta)=\sin(\theta+2\theta)=\sin\theta\cos(2\theta)+\cos\theta\sin(2\theta)=\sin\theta\cdot(\cos^2\theta-\sin^2\theta)+\cos\theta\cdot 2\sin\theta\cos\theta=\sin\theta\cos^2\theta-\sin^3\theta+2\sin\theta\cos^2\theta$ $=3\sin\theta\cos^2\theta-\sin^3\theta=3\sin\theta(1-\sin^2\theta)-\sin^3\theta=3\sin\theta-3\sin^3\theta-\sin^3\theta=3\sin\theta-4\sin^3\theta$

16. $\dfrac{\tan\theta-\cot\theta}{\tan\theta+\cot\theta}=\dfrac{\dfrac{\sin\theta}{\cos\theta}-\dfrac{\cos\theta}{\sin\theta}}{\dfrac{\sin\theta}{\cos\theta}+\dfrac{\cos\theta}{\sin\theta}}=\dfrac{\dfrac{\sin^2\theta-\cos^2\theta}{\sin\theta\cos\theta}}{\dfrac{\sin^2\theta+\cos^2\theta}{\sin\theta\cos\theta}}=\dfrac{\sin^2\theta-\cos^2\theta}{\sin^2\theta+\cos^2\theta}=\dfrac{-\cos(2\theta)}{1}=-(2\cos^2\theta-1)=1-2\cos^2\theta$ **17.** $\frac{1}{4}(\sqrt{6}+\sqrt{2})$

18. $2+\sqrt{3}$ **19.** $\dfrac{\sqrt{5}}{5}$ **20.** $\dfrac{12\sqrt{85}}{49}$ **21.** $\dfrac{2\sqrt{13}(\sqrt{5}-3)}{39}$ **22.** $\dfrac{2+\sqrt{3}}{4}$ **23.** $\dfrac{\sqrt{6}}{2}$ **24.** $\dfrac{\sqrt{2}}{2}$ **25.** $\left\{\dfrac{\pi}{3},\dfrac{2\pi}{3},\dfrac{4\pi}{3},\dfrac{5\pi}{3}\right\}$ **26.** $\{0, 1.911, \pi, 4.373\}$

27. $\left\{\dfrac{3\pi}{8},\dfrac{7\pi}{8},\dfrac{11\pi}{8},\dfrac{15\pi}{8}\right\}$ **28.** $\{0.285, 3.427\}$ **29.** $\{0.253, 2.889\}$ **30.** The change in elevation during the time trial was about 1.18 km.

Cumulative Review *(page 506)*

1. $\left\{\dfrac{-1-\sqrt{13}}{6},\dfrac{-1+\sqrt{13}}{6}\right\}$ **2.** $y+1=-1(x-4)$ or $x+y=3$; $6\sqrt{2}$; $(1,2)$ **3.** x-axis symmetry; $(0,-3)$, $(0,3)$, $(3,0)$

4.

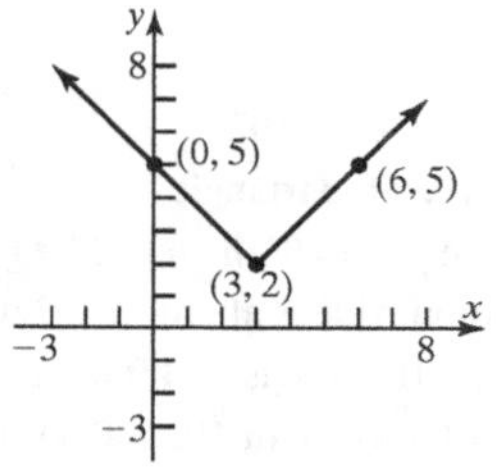

5.

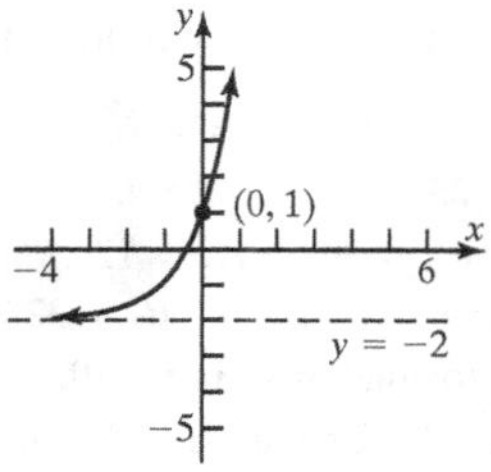

6.

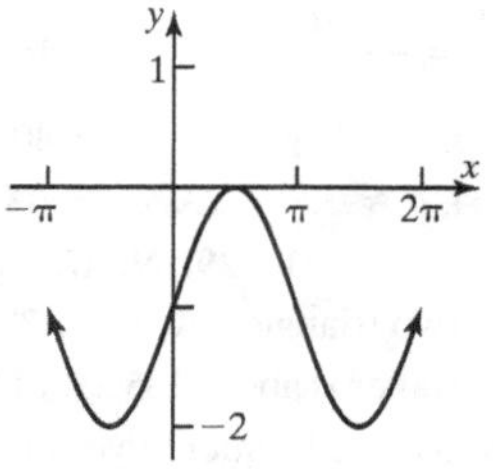

7. (a)

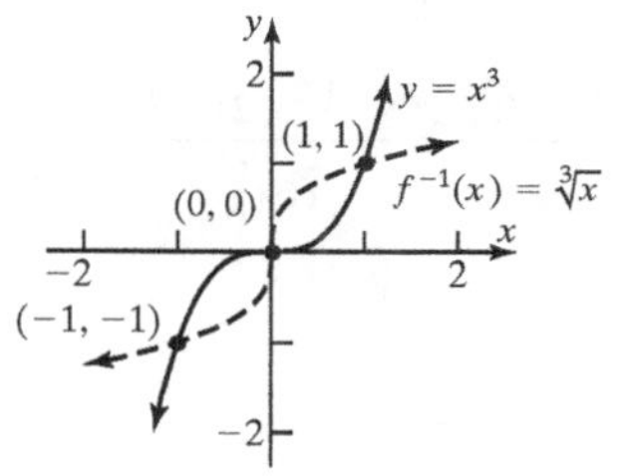

(b)

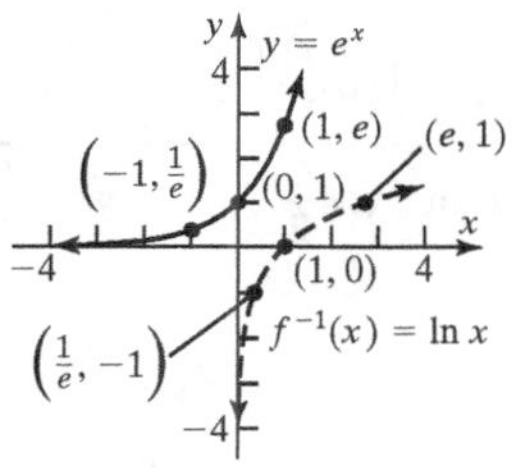

(c)

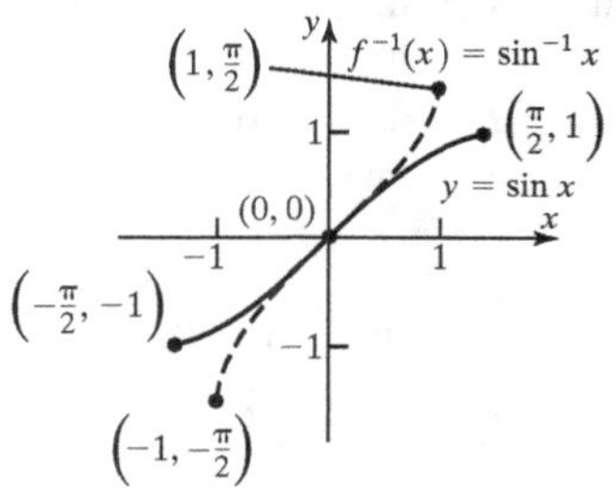

(d)

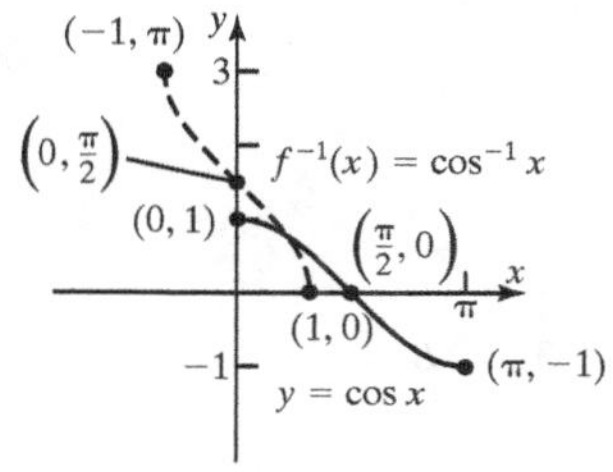

8. (a) $-\dfrac{2\sqrt{2}}{3}$ **(b)** $\dfrac{\sqrt{2}}{4}$ **(c)** $\dfrac{4\sqrt{2}}{9}$ **(d)** $\dfrac{7}{9}$ **(e)** $\sqrt{\dfrac{3+2\sqrt{2}}{6}}$ **(f)** $-\sqrt{\dfrac{3-2\sqrt{2}}{6}}$

9. $\dfrac{\sqrt{5}}{5}$ **10. (a)** $-\dfrac{2\sqrt{2}}{3}$ **(b)** $-\dfrac{2\sqrt{2}}{3}$ **(c)** $\dfrac{7}{9}$ **(d)** $\dfrac{4\sqrt{2}}{9}$ **(e)** $\dfrac{\sqrt{6}}{3}$

11. (a) $f(x)=(2x-1)(x-1)^2(x+1)^2$; $\dfrac{1}{2}$ multiplicity 1; 1 and -1 multiplicity 2

(b) $(0,-1)$; $\left(\dfrac{1}{2},0\right)$; $(-1,0)$; $(1,0)$

(c) $y=2x^5$

(d)

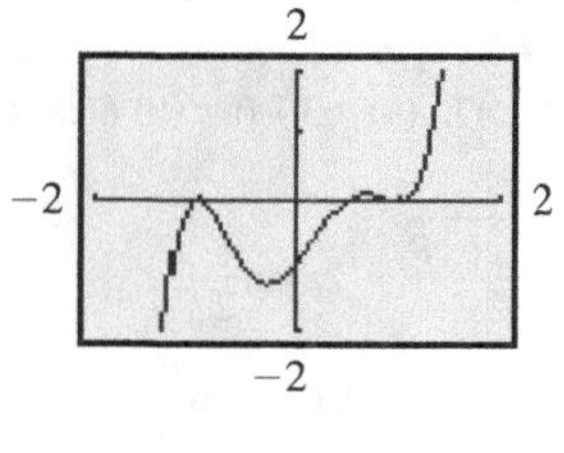

(f)

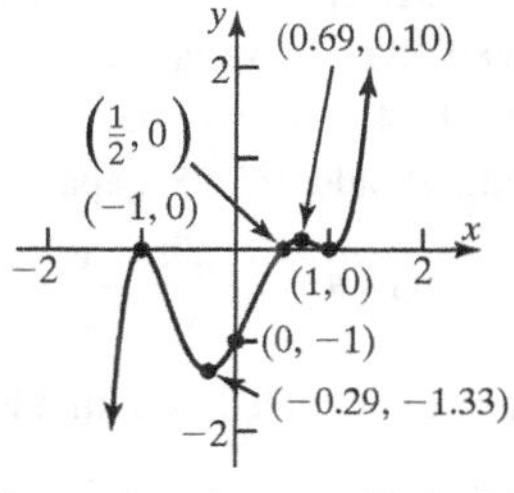

12. (a) $\left\{-1,-\dfrac{1}{2}\right\}$

(b) $\{-1, 1\}$

(c) $(-\infty,-1)\cup\left(-\dfrac{1}{2},\infty\right)$

(d) $(-\infty,-1]\cup[1,\infty)$

(e) Minima at $(-0.29,-1.33)$, $(1,0)$
Maxima at $(-1,0)$, $(0.69,0.10)$

(g) Increasing: $(-\infty,-1)$, $(-0.29,0.69)$, $(1,\infty)$
Decreasing: $(-1,-0.29)$, $(0.69,1)$

CHAPTER 8 Applications of Trigonometric Functions

8.1 Assess Your Understanding *(page 517)*

4. F **5.** T **6.** angle of elevation **7.** T **8.** F **9.** $\sin\theta = \frac{5}{13}$; $\cos\theta = \frac{12}{13}$; $\tan\theta = \frac{5}{12}$; $\cot\theta = \frac{12}{5}$; $\sec\theta = \frac{13}{12}$; $\csc\theta = \frac{13}{5}$

11. $\sin\theta = \frac{2\sqrt{13}}{13}$; $\cos\theta = \frac{3\sqrt{13}}{13}$; $\tan\theta = \frac{2}{3}$; $\cot\theta = \frac{3}{2}$; $\sec\theta = \frac{\sqrt{13}}{3}$; $\csc\theta = \frac{\sqrt{13}}{2}$

13. $\sin\theta = \frac{\sqrt{3}}{2}$; $\cos\theta = \frac{1}{2}$; $\tan\theta = \sqrt{3}$; $\cot\theta = \frac{\sqrt{3}}{3}$; $\sec\theta = 2$; $\csc\theta = \frac{2\sqrt{3}}{3}$

15. $\sin\theta = \frac{\sqrt{6}}{3}$; $\cos\theta = \frac{\sqrt{3}}{3}$; $\tan\theta = \sqrt{2}$; $\cot\theta = \frac{\sqrt{2}}{2}$; $\sec\theta = \sqrt{3}$; $\csc\theta = \frac{\sqrt{6}}{2}$

17. $\sin\theta = \frac{\sqrt{5}}{5}$; $\cos\theta = \frac{2\sqrt{5}}{5}$; $\tan\theta = \frac{1}{2}$; $\cot\theta = 2$; $\sec\theta = \frac{\sqrt{5}}{2}$; $\csc\theta = \sqrt{5}$

19. 0 **21.** 1 **23.** 0 **25.** 0 **27.** 1 **29.** $a \approx 13.74, c \approx 14.62, A = 70°$ **31.** $b \approx 5.03, c \approx 7.83, A = 50°$ **33.** $a \approx 0.71, c \approx 4.06, B = 80°$ **35.** $b \approx 10.72, c \approx 11.83, B = 65°$ **37.** $b \approx 3.08, a \approx 8.46, A = 70°$ **39.** $c \approx 5.83, A \approx 59.0°, B \approx 31.0°$ **41.** $b \approx 4.58, A \approx 23.6°, B \approx 66.4°$ **43.** 23.6° and 66.4° **45.** 4.59 in.;6.55 in. **47. (a)** 5.52 in. or 11.83 in. **49.** 70.02 ft **51.** 985.91 ft **53.** 137.37 m **55.** 80.5° **57. (a)** 111.96 ft/sec or 76.3 mi/hr **(b)** 82.42 ft/sec or 56.2 mi/hr **(c)** Under 18.8° **59. (a)** 2.4898×10^{13} miles **(b)** 0.000214° **61.** 554.52 ft **63.** S76.6°E **65.** The embankment is 30.5 m high. **67.** 3.83 mi **69.** 1978.09 ft **71.** 60.27 ft **73.** The buildings are 7984 ft apart. **75.** 69.0° **77.** 38.9° **79.** The white ball should hit the top cushion 4.125 ft from the upper left corner.

8.2 Assess Your Understanding *(page 529)*

4. oblique **5.** $\frac{\sin A}{a} = \frac{\sin B}{b} = \frac{\sin C}{c}$ **6.** F **7.** T **8.** F **9.** $a \approx 3.23, b \approx 3.55, A = 40°$ **11.** $a \approx 3.25, c \approx 4.23, B = 45°$ **13.** $C = 95°, c \approx 9.86, a \approx 6.36$ **15.** $A = 40°, a = 2, c \approx 3.06$ **17.** $C = 120°, b \approx 1.06, c \approx 2.69$ **19.** $A = 100°, a \approx 5.24, c \approx 0.92$ **21.** $B = 40°, a \approx 5.64, b \approx 3.86$ **23.** $C = 100°, a \approx 1.31, b \approx 1.31$ **25.** One triangle; $B \approx 30.7°, C \approx 99.3°, c \approx 3.86$ **27.** One triangle; $C \approx 36.2°, A \approx 43.8°, a \approx 3.51$ **29.** No triangle **31.** Two triangles; $C_1 \approx 30.9°, A_1 \approx 129.1°, a_1 \approx 9.07$ or $C_2 \approx 149.1°, A_2 \approx 10.9°, a_2 \approx 2.20$ **33.** No triangle **35.** Two triangles; $A_1 \approx 57.7°, B_1 \approx 97.3°, b_1 \approx 2.35$ or $A_2 \approx 122.3°, B_2 \approx 32.7°, b_2 \approx 1.28$ **37. (a)** Station Able is about 143.33 mi from the ship: Station Baker is about 135.58 mi from the ship. **(b)** Approximately 41 min **39.** 1490.48 ft **41.** 381.69 ft **43.** The tree is 39.4 ft high. **45.** Adam receives 88.3 more frequent flyer miles. **47.** 84.7°; 183.72 ft **49.** 2.64 mi **51.** 38.5 in. **53.** 449.36 ft **55.** 187,600,000 km or 101,440,000 km **57.** The diameter is 252 ft.

59. $$\frac{a-b}{c} = \frac{a}{c} - \frac{b}{c} = \frac{\sin A}{\sin C} - \frac{\sin B}{\sin C} = \frac{\sin A - \sin B}{\sin C} = \frac{2\sin\left(\frac{A-B}{2}\right)\cos\left(\frac{A+B}{2}\right)}{2\sin\frac{C}{2}\cos\frac{C}{2}} = \frac{\sin\left(\frac{A-B}{2}\right)\cos\left(\frac{\pi}{2} - \frac{C}{2}\right)}{\sin\frac{C}{2}\cos\frac{C}{2}} = \frac{\sin\left(\frac{A-B}{2}\right)}{\cos\frac{C}{2}}$$

61. $$\frac{a-b}{a+b} = \frac{\frac{a-b}{c}}{\frac{a+b}{c}} = \frac{\dfrac{\sin\left[\frac{1}{2}(A-B)\right]}{\cos\frac{C}{2}}}{\dfrac{\cos\left[\frac{1}{2}(A-B)\right]}{\sin\frac{C}{2}}} = \frac{\tan\left[\frac{1}{2}(A-B)\right]}{\cot\frac{C}{2}} = \frac{\tan\left[\frac{1}{2}(A-B)\right]}{\tan\left(\frac{\pi}{2} - \frac{C}{2}\right)} = \frac{\tan\left[\frac{1}{2}(A-B)\right]}{\tan\left[\frac{1}{2}(A+B)\right]}$$

8.3 Assess Your Understanding *(page 537)*

3. Cosines **4.** Sines **5.** Cosines **6.** F **7.** F **8.** T **9.** $b \approx 2.95, A \approx 28.7°, C \approx 106.3°$ **11.** $c \approx 3.75, A \approx 32.1°, B \approx 52.9°$ **13.** $A \approx 48.5°, B \approx 38.6°, C \approx 92.9°$ **15.** $A \approx 127.2°, B \approx 32.1°, C \approx 20.7°$ **17.** $c \approx 2.57, A \approx 48.6°, B \approx 91.4°$ **19.** $a \approx 2.99, B \approx 19.2°, C \approx 80.8°$ **21.** $b \approx 4.14, A \approx 43.0°, C \approx 27.0°$ **23.** $c \approx 1.69, A = 65.0°, B = 65.0°$ **25.** $A \approx 67.4°, B = 90°, C \approx 22.6°$ **27.** $A = 60°, B = 60°, C = 60°$ **29.** $A \approx 33.6°, B \approx 62.2°, C \approx 84.3°$ **31.** $A \approx 97.9°, B \approx 52.4°, C \approx 29.7°$ **33.** $A = 85°, a = 14.56, c = 14.12$ **35.** $A = 40.8°, B = 60.6°, C = 78.6°$ **37.** $A = 80°, b = 8.74, c = 13.80$ **39.** Two triangles: $B_1 = 35.4°, C_1 = 134.6°, c_1 = 12.29$; $B_2 = 144.6°, C_2 = 25.4°, c_2 = 7.40$ **41.** $B = 24.5°, C = 95.5°, a = 10.44$ **43.** 165 yd **45. (a)** 26.4° **(b)** 30.8 h **47. (a)** 63.7 ft **(b)** 66.8 ft **(c)** 92.8° **49. (a)** 492.6 ft **(b)** 269.3 ft **51.** 342.33 ft **53.** The footings should be 7.65 ft apart.

55. Suppose $0 < \theta < \pi$. Then by the Law of Cosines, $d^2 = r^2 + r^2 - 2r^2\cos\theta = 4r^2\left(\frac{1-\cos\theta}{2}\right) \Rightarrow d = 2r\sqrt{\frac{1-\cos\theta}{2}} = 2r\sin\frac{\theta}{2}$.

Since for any angle in $(0, \pi)$, d is strictly less than the length of the arc subtended by θ, that is, $d < r\theta$, then $2r\sin\frac{\theta}{2} < r\theta$, or $2\sin\frac{\theta}{2} < \theta$.

Since $\cos\frac{\theta}{2} < 1$, then, for $0 < \theta < \pi$, $\sin\theta = 2\sin\frac{\theta}{2}\cos\frac{\theta}{2} < 2\sin\frac{\theta}{2} < \theta$. If $\theta \geq \pi$, then since $\sin\theta \leq 1$, $\sin\theta < \theta$. Thus $\sin\theta < \theta$ for all $\theta > 0$.

57. $\sin\frac{C}{2} = \sqrt{\frac{1-\cos C}{2}} = \sqrt{\frac{1 - \frac{a^2+b^2-c^2}{2ab}}{2}} = \sqrt{\frac{2ab - a^2 - b^2 + c^2}{4ab}} = \sqrt{\frac{c^2-(a-b)^2}{4ab}} = \sqrt{\frac{(c+a-b)(c+b-a)}{4ab}}$

$= \sqrt{\frac{(2s-2b)(2s-2a)}{4ab}} = \sqrt{\frac{(s-a)(s-b)}{ab}}$

8.4 Assess Your Understanding *(page 542)*

2. Heron's **3.** F **4.** T **5.** 2.83 **7.** 2.99 **9.** 14.98 **11.** 9.56 **13.** 3.86 **15.** 1.48 **17.** 2.82 **19.** 30 **21.** 1.73 **23.** 19.90

25. $K = \frac{1}{2}ab\sin C = \frac{1}{2}a\sin C\left(\frac{a\sin B}{\sin A}\right) = \frac{a^2\sin B\sin C}{2\sin A}$ **27.** 0.92 **29.** 2.27 **31.** 5.44 **33.** 9.03 sq ft **35.** \$5446.38

37. The area of home plate is about 216.5 in^2. **39.** $K = \frac{1}{2}r^2(\theta + \sin\theta)$ **41.** The ground area is 7517.4 ft^2.

43. **(a)** Area $\Delta OAC = \frac{1}{2}|OC||AC| = \frac{1}{2}\cdot\frac{|OC|}{1}\cdot\frac{|AC|}{1} = \frac{1}{2}\sin\alpha\cos\alpha$

(b) Area $\Delta OCB = \frac{1}{2}|BC||OC| = \frac{1}{2}|OB|^2\frac{|BC|}{|OB|}\cdot\frac{|OC|}{|OB|} = \frac{1}{2}|OB|^2\sin\beta\cos\beta$

(c) Area $\Delta OAB = \frac{1}{2}|BD||OA| = \frac{1}{2}|OB|\frac{|BD|}{|OB|} = \frac{1}{2}|OB|\sin(\alpha+\beta)$

(d) $\frac{\cos\alpha}{\cos\beta} = \frac{\frac{|OC|}{1}}{\frac{|OC|}{|OB|}} = |OB|$

(e) Area ΔOAB = Area ΔOAC + Area ΔOCB

$\frac{1}{2}|OB|\sin(\alpha+\beta) = \frac{1}{2}\sin\alpha\cos\alpha + \frac{1}{2}|OB|^2\sin\beta\cos\beta$

$\sin(\alpha+\beta) = \frac{1}{|OB|}\sin\alpha\cos\alpha + |OB|\sin\beta\cos\beta$

$\sin(\alpha+\beta) = \frac{\cos\beta}{\cos\alpha}\sin\alpha\cos\alpha + \frac{\cos\alpha}{\cos\beta}\sin\beta\cos\beta$

$\sin(\alpha+\beta) = \sin\alpha\cos\beta + \cos\alpha\sin\beta$

45. 31,145 ft^2 **47.** **(a)** The perimeter and area are both 36. **(b)** The perimeter and area are both 60.

49. $K = \frac{1}{2}ah = \frac{1}{2}ab\sin C \Rightarrow h = b\sin C = \frac{a\sin B\sin C}{\sin A}$

51. $\cot\frac{C}{2} = \frac{\cos\frac{C}{2}}{\sin\frac{C}{2}} = \frac{\frac{c\sin\frac{A}{2}\sin\frac{B}{2}}{r}}{\sqrt{\frac{(s-a)(s-b)}{ab}}} = \frac{c\sqrt{\frac{(s-b)(s-c)}{bc}}\sqrt{\frac{(s-a)(s-c)}{ac}}}{r\sqrt{\frac{(s-a)(s-b)}{ab}}} = \frac{c}{r}\sqrt{\frac{(s-c)^2}{c^2}} = \frac{s-c}{r}$

53. K = area of triangle QOR + area of ROP + area of POQ $= \frac{1}{2}ar + \frac{1}{2}br + \frac{1}{2}cr = r\frac{1}{2}(a+b+c) = rs$, so

$r = \frac{K}{s} = \frac{\sqrt{s(s-a)(s-b)(s-c)}}{s} = \sqrt{\frac{(s-a)(s-b)(s-c)}{s}}$.

8.5 Assess Your Understanding *(page 552)*

2. simple harmonic; amplitude **3.** simple harmonic; damped **4.** T **5.** $d = -5\cos(\pi t)$ **7.** $d = -6\cos(2t)$ **9.** $d = -5\sin(\pi t)$ **11.** $d = -6\sin(2t)$

13. **(a)** simple harmonic **(b)** 5 m **(c)** $\frac{2\pi}{3}$ s **(d)** $\frac{3}{2\pi}$ oscillation/s **15.** **(a)** simple harmonic **(b)** 6 m **(c)** 2 s **(d)** $\frac{1}{2}$ oscillation/s

17. **(a)** simple harmonic **(b)** 3 m **(c)** 4π s **(d)** $\frac{1}{4\pi}$ oscillation/s **19.** **(a)** simple harmonic **(b)** 2 m **(c)** 1 s **(d)** 1 oscillation/s

21. **(a)** $d = -10e^{-0.7t/50}\cos\left(\sqrt{\frac{4\pi^2}{25} - \frac{0.49}{2500}}\,t\right)$

(b)

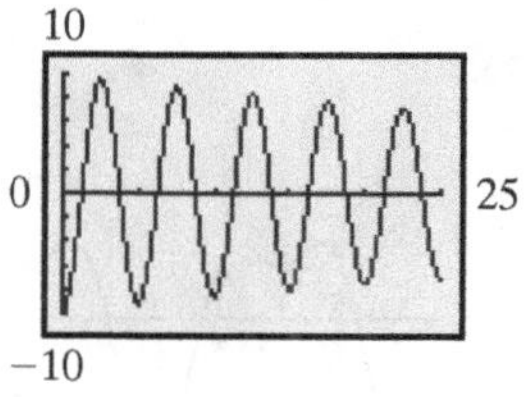

23. **(a)** $d = -18e^{-0.6t/60}\cos\left(\sqrt{\frac{\pi^2}{4} - \frac{0.36}{3600}}\,t\right)$

(b)

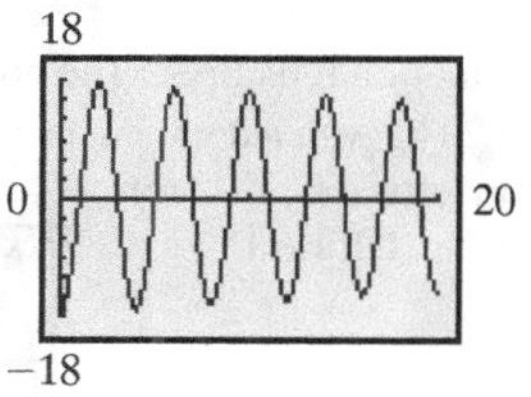

25. **(a)** $d = -5e^{-0.8t/20}\cos\left(\sqrt{\frac{4\pi^2}{9} - \frac{0.64}{400}}\,t\right)$

(b)

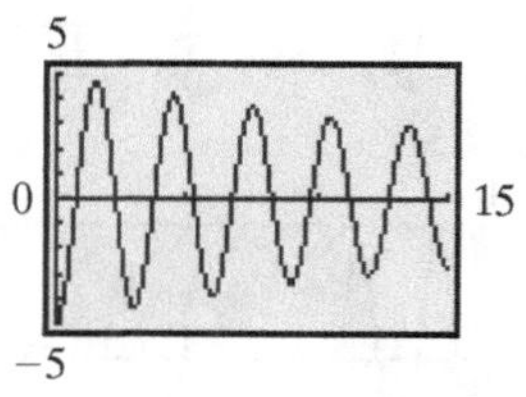

27. **(a)** The motion is damped. The bob has mass $m = 20$ kg with a damping factor of 0.7 kg/s. **(b)** 20 m leftward **(c)**

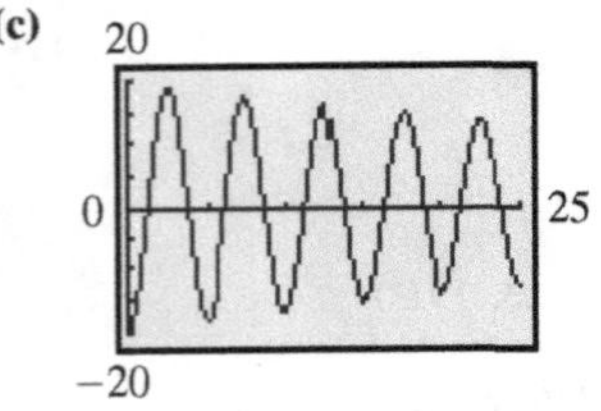

(d) 18.33 m leftward **(e)** $d \to 0$

29. **(a)** The motion is damped. The bob has mass $m = 40$ kg with a damping factor of 0.6 kg/s. **(b)** 30 m leftward **(c)**

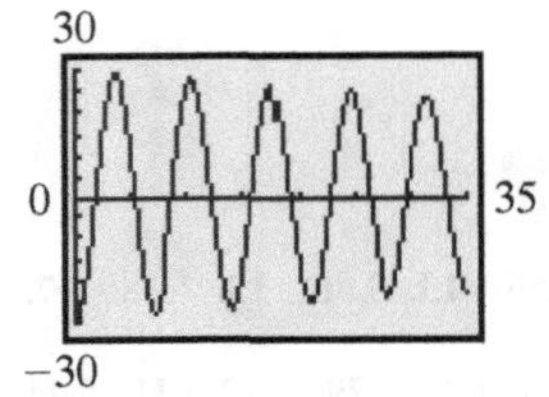

(d) 28.47 m leftward **(e)** $d \to 0$

31. **(a)** The motion is damped. The bob has mass $m = 15$ kg with a damping factor of 0.9 kg/s. **(b)** 15 m leftward **(c)**

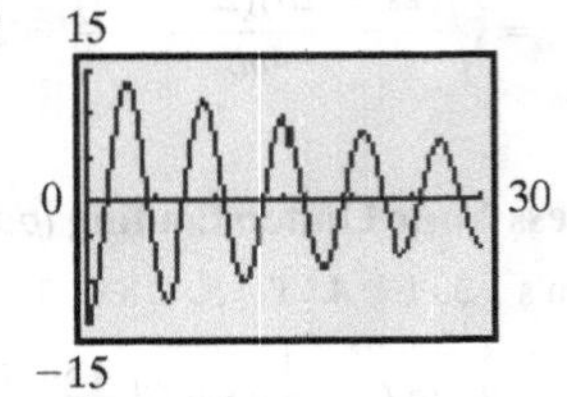

(d) 12.53 m leftward **(e)** $d \to 0$

33.

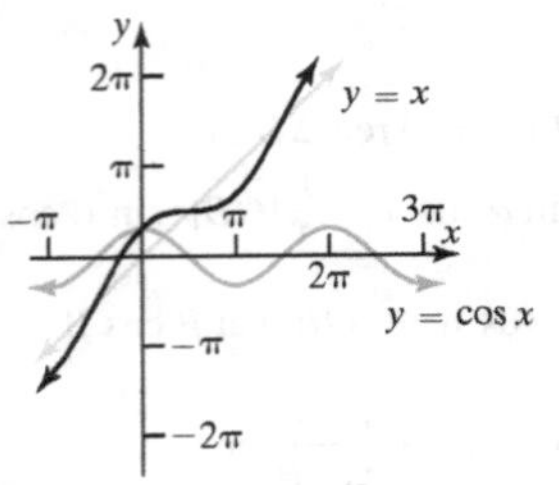

35.

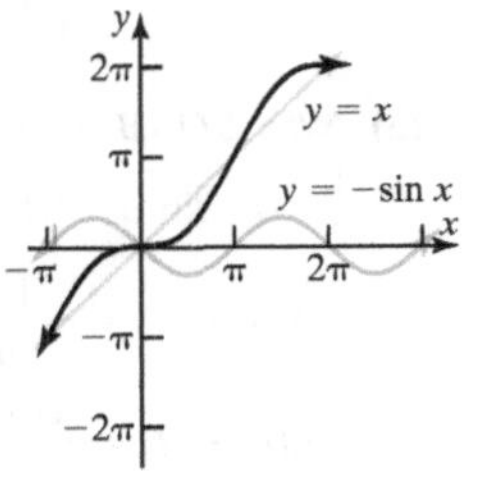

37.

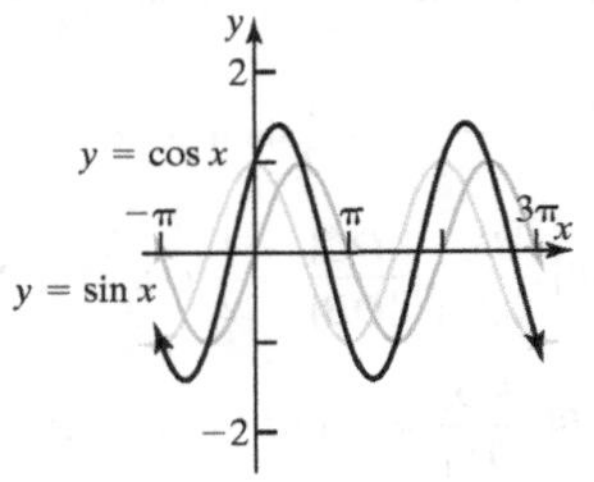

39.

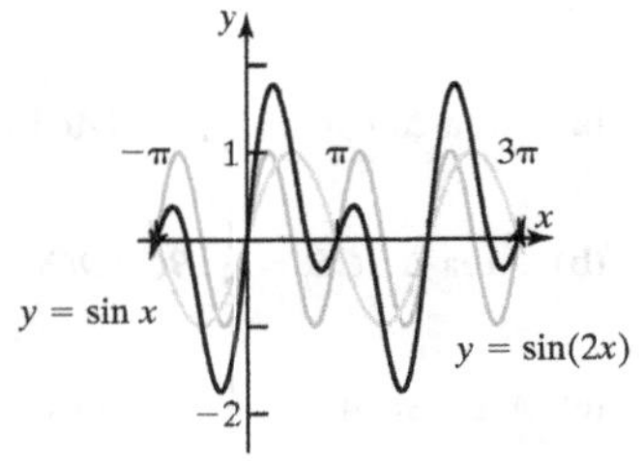

41. $\omega = 1040\pi$; $d = 0.80 \cos(1040\pi t)$

43. $\omega = 880\pi$; $d = 0.01 \sin(880\pi t)$

45. **(a)**

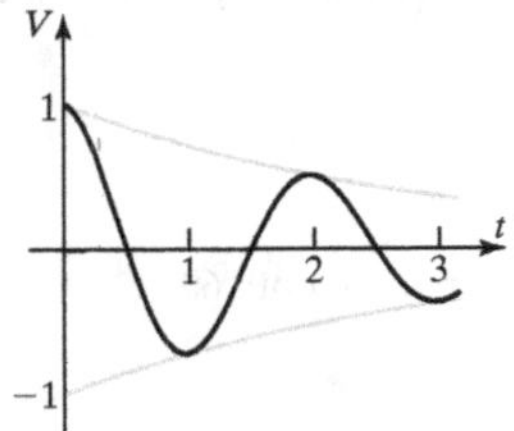

(b) At $t = 0, 2$; at $t = 1, t = 3$

(c) During the approximate intervals $0.35 < t < 0.67$, $1.29 < t < 1.75$, and $2.19 < t \leq 3$

47.

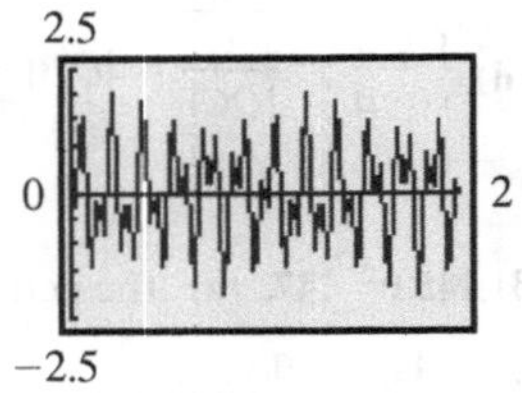

51.

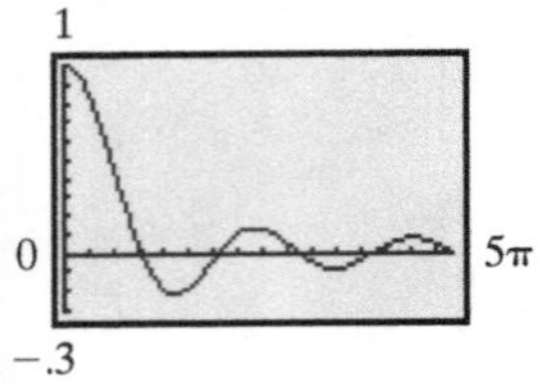

53. $y = \dfrac{1}{x}\sin x$

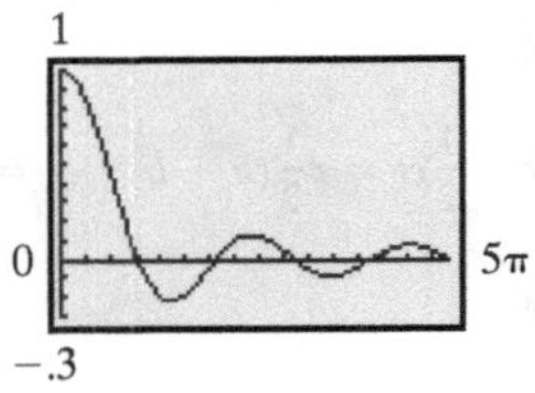

$y = \dfrac{1}{x^2}\sin x$

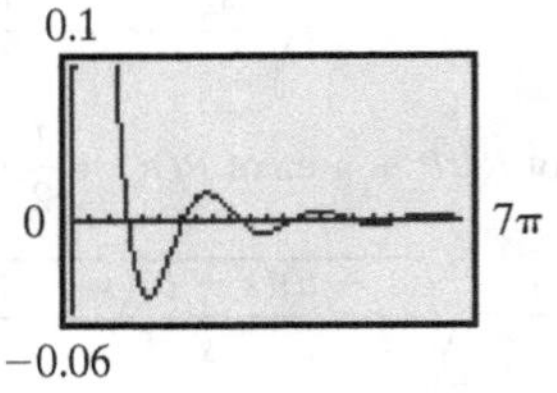

$y = \dfrac{1}{x^3}\sin x$

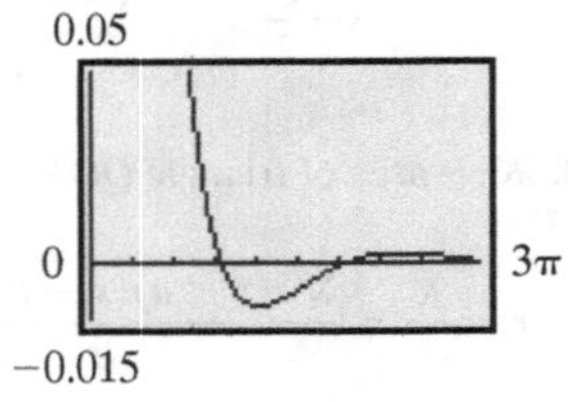

Review Exercises *(page 555)*

1. $\sin\theta = \frac{4}{3}$; $\cos\theta = \frac{3}{5}$; $\tan\theta = \frac{4}{3}$; $\cot\theta = \frac{3}{4}$; $\sec\theta = \frac{5}{3}$; $\csc\theta = \frac{5}{4}$ **3.** $\sin\theta = \frac{\sqrt{3}}{2}$; $\cos\theta = \frac{1}{2}$; $\tan\theta = \sqrt{3}$; $\cot\theta = \frac{\sqrt{3}}{3}$; $\sec\theta = 2$; $\csc\theta = \frac{2\sqrt{3}}{3}$
5. 0 **7.** 1 **9.** 1 **11.** $A = 70°, b \approx 3.42, a \approx 9.40$ **13.** $a \approx 4.58, A \approx 66.4°, B \approx 23.6°$ **15.** $C = 100°, b \approx 0.65, c \approx 1.29$
17. $B \approx 56.8°, C \approx 23.2°, b \approx 4.25$ **19.** No triangle **21.** $b \approx 3.32, A \approx 62.8°, C \approx 17.2°$ **23.** No triangle **25.** $c \approx 2.32, A \approx 16.1°, B \approx 123.9°$
27. $B \approx 36.2°, C \approx 63.8°, c \approx 4.55$ **29.** $A \approx 39.6°, B \approx 18.6°, C \approx 121.9°$ **31.** Two triangles: $B_1 \approx 13.4°, C_1 \approx 156.6°, c_1 \approx 6.86$ or $B_2 \approx 166.6°$, $C_2 \approx 3.4°, c_2 \approx 1.02$ **33.** $a \approx 5.23, B \approx 46.0°, C \approx 64.0°$ **35.** 1.93 **37.** 18.79 **39.** 6 **41.** 3.80 **43.** 0.32 **45.** 1.92 in^2
47. 23.32 ft **49.** 2.15 mi **51.** 132.55 ft/min **53.** 29.97 ft **55.** 6.22 mi **57.** 71.12 ft **59.** $222,983.51 **61.** 76.94 in. **63.** $d = -3\cos\left(\frac{\pi}{2}t\right)$
65. **(a)** Simple harmonic **(b)** 6 ft **(c)** π sec **(d)** $\frac{1}{\pi}$ oscillation/sec **67.** **(a)** Simple harmonic **(b)** 2 ft **(c)** 2 sec **(d)** $\frac{1}{2}$ oscillation/sec

69. **(a)** $d = -15e^{-0.75t/80}\cos\left(\sqrt{\frac{4\pi^2}{25} - \frac{0.5625}{6400}}\,t\right)$

(b)

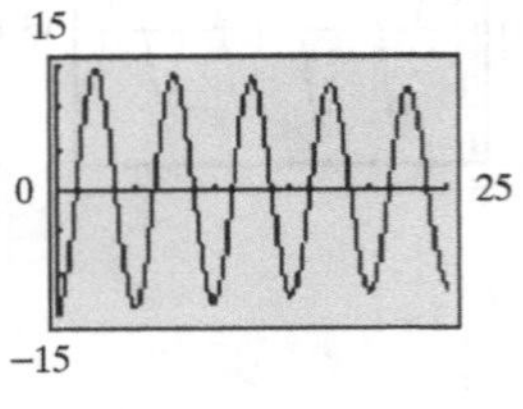

71. **(a)** The motion is damped. The bob has mass $m = 20$ kg with a damping factor of 0.6 kg/sec.
(b) 15 m leftward
(c)

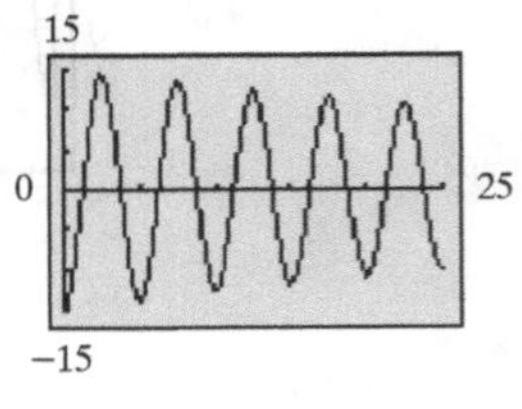

(d) 13.92 m leftward
(e) $d \to 0$

73.

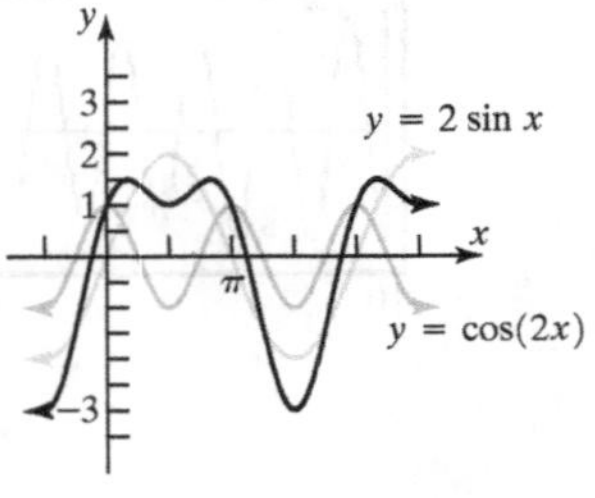

Chapter Test *(page 558)*

1. $\sin\theta = \frac{\sqrt{5}}{5}$; $\cos\theta = \frac{2\sqrt{5}}{5}$; $\tan\theta = \frac{1}{2}$; $\csc\theta = \sqrt{5}$; $\sec\theta = \frac{\sqrt{5}}{2}$; $\cot\theta = 2$ **2.** 0 **3.** $a = 15.88$, $B \approx 57.5°$, $C \approx 70.5°$ **4.** $b \approx 6.85$, $C = 117°$, $c \approx 16.30$ **5.** $A \approx 52.4°$, $B \approx 29.7°$, $C \approx 97.9°$ **6.** $b \approx 4.72$, $c \approx 1.67$, $B = 105°$ **7.** No triangle **8.** $c \approx 7.62$, $A \approx 80.5°$, $B \approx 29.5°$ **9.** 15.04 square units **10.** 19.81 square units **11.** 61.0° **12.** 1.3° **13.** The area of the shaded region is 9.26 cm^2. **14.** 54.15 square units **15.** Madison will have to swim about 2.23 miles. **16.** 12.63 square units **17.** The lengths of the sides are 15, 18, and 21. **18.** $d = 5(\sin 42°)\sin\left(\frac{\pi t}{3}\right)$ or $d \approx 3.346\sin\left(\frac{\pi t}{3}\right)$

Cumulative Review *(page 559)*

1. $\left\{\frac{1}{3}, 1\right\}$ **2.** $(x + 5)^2 + (y - 1)^2 = 9$

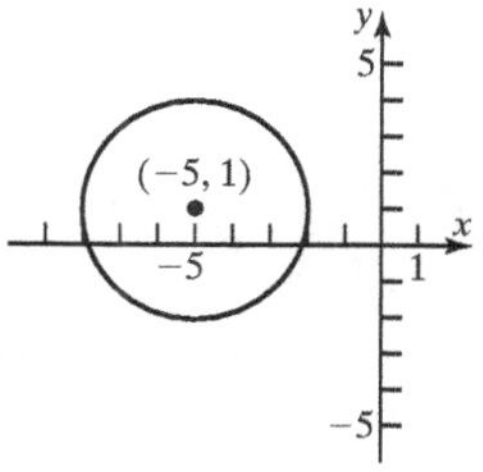

3. $\{x \mid x \le -1 \text{ or } x \ge 4\}$ **4.**

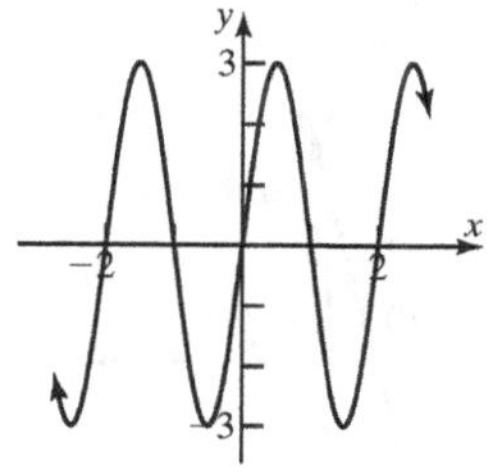

5.

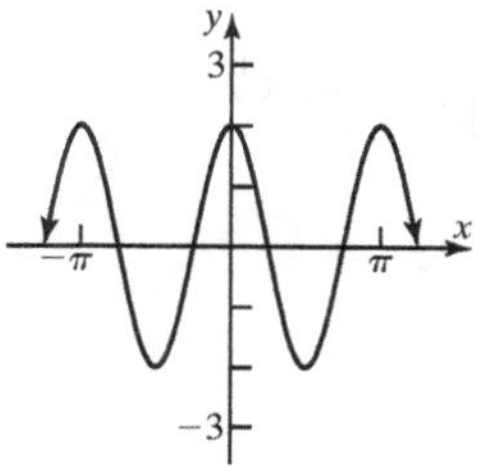

6. (a) $-\frac{2\sqrt{5}}{5}$ **(b)** $\frac{\sqrt{5}}{5}$ **(c)** $-\frac{4}{5}$ **(d)** $-\frac{3}{5}$ **(e)** $\sqrt{\frac{5-\sqrt{5}}{10}}$ **(f)** $-\sqrt{\frac{5+\sqrt{5}}{10}}$

7. (a)

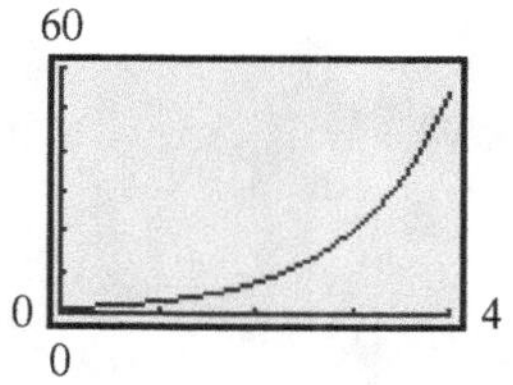

(b)

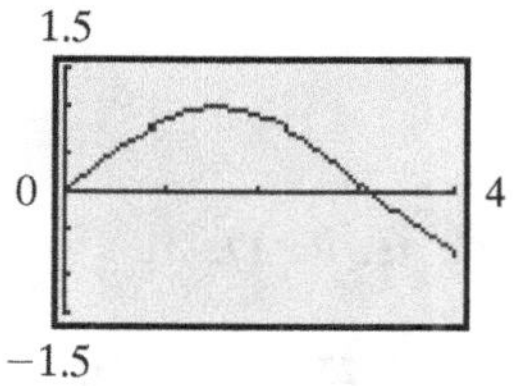

(c)

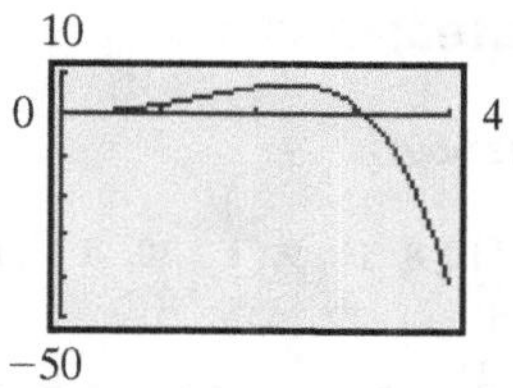

(d)

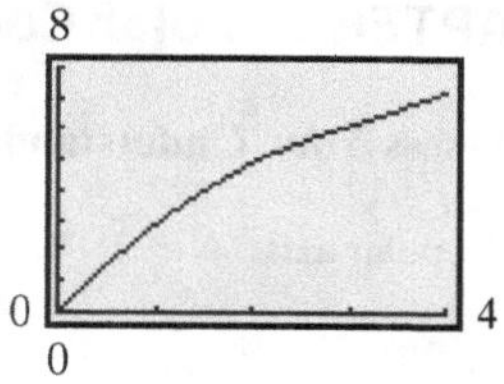

8. (a)

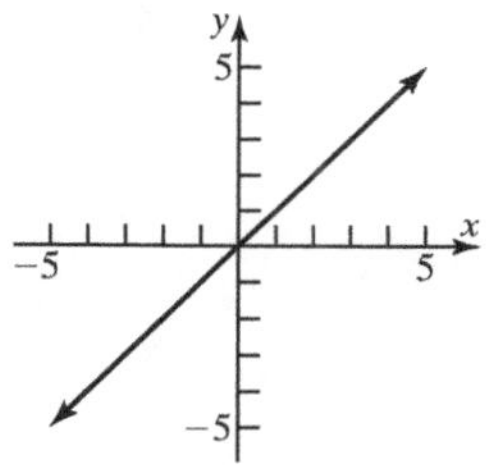

(b)

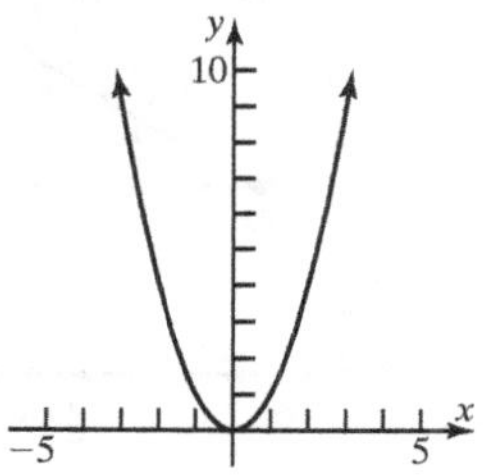

(c)

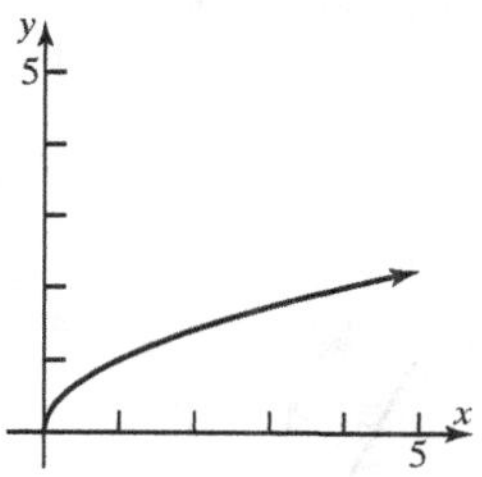

(d)

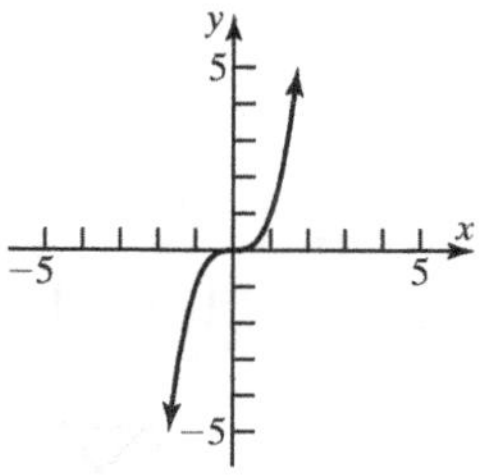

(e)

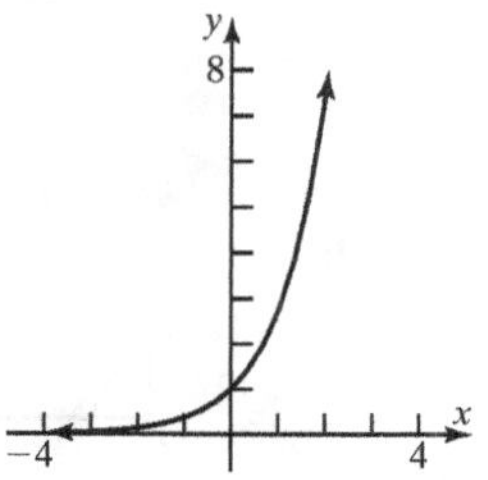

(f)

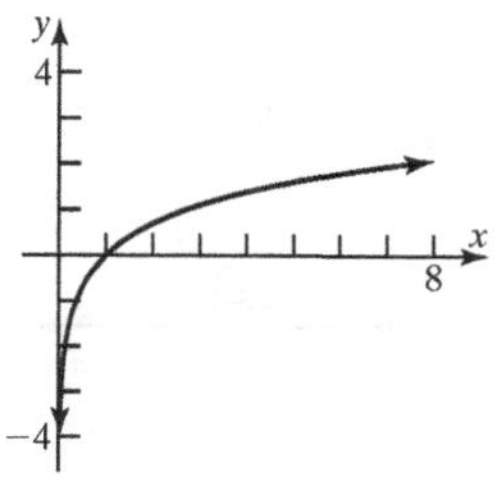

(g)

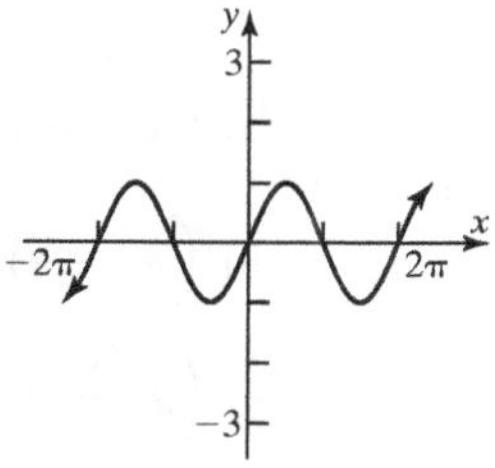

(h)

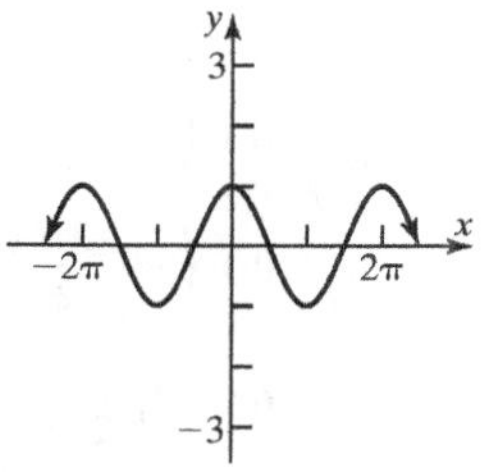

(i)

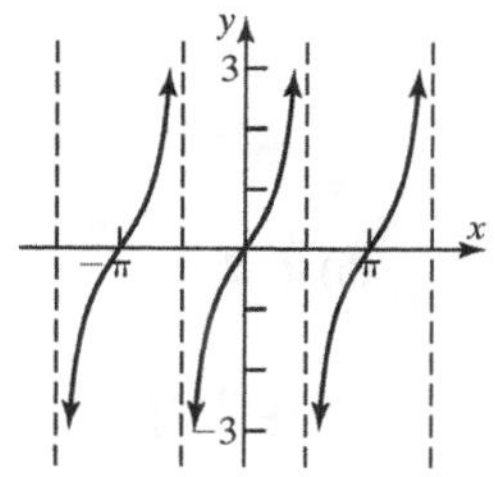

9. Two triangles: $A_1 \approx 59.0°$, $B_1 \approx 81.0°$, $b_1 \approx 23.05$ or $A_2 \approx 121.0°$, $B_2 \approx 19.0°$, $b_2 \approx 7.59$ **10.** $\left\{-2i, 2i, \frac{1}{3}, 1, 2\right\}$

11. $R(x) = \dfrac{(2x+1)(x-4)}{(x+5)(x-3)}$; domain: $\{x \mid x \neq -5, x \neq 3\}$

Intercepts: $\left(-\frac{1}{2}, 0\right)$, $(4, 0)$, $\left(0, \frac{4}{15}\right)$

No symmetry

Vertical asymptotes: $x = -5$, $x = 3$

Horizontal asymptote: $y = 2$

Intersects: $\left(\frac{26}{11}, 2\right)$

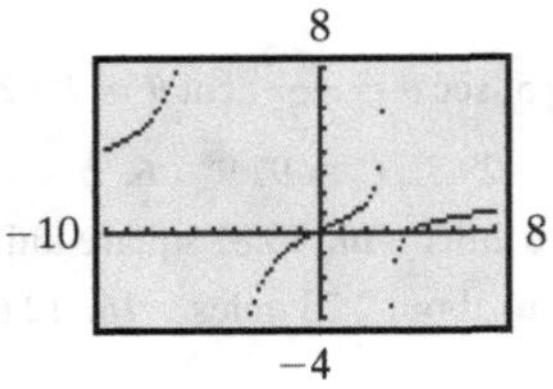

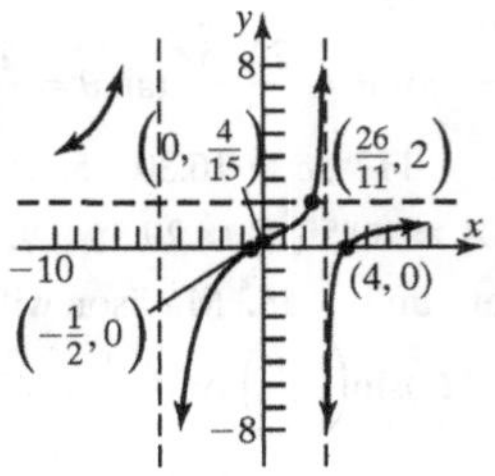

12. $\{2.26\}$ **13.** $\{1\}$ **14. (a)** $\left\{-\frac{5}{4}\right\}$ **(b)** $\{2\}$ **(c)** $\left\{\frac{-1-3\sqrt{13}}{2}, \frac{-1+3\sqrt{13}}{2}\right\}$ **(d)** $\left\{x \,\middle|\, x > -\frac{5}{4}\right\}$ or $\left(-\frac{5}{4}, \infty\right)$

(e) $\left\{x \,\middle|\, -8 \leq x \leq 3\right\}$ or $[-8, 3]$ **(f)**

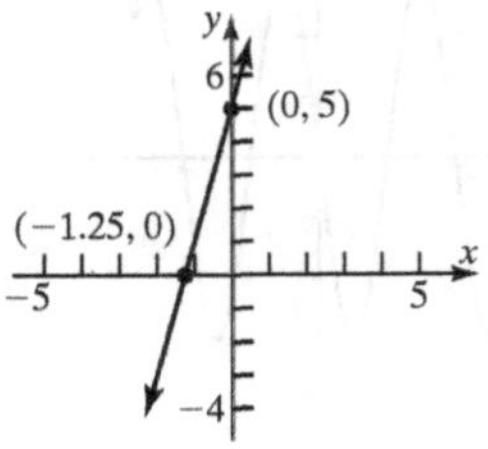

(g)

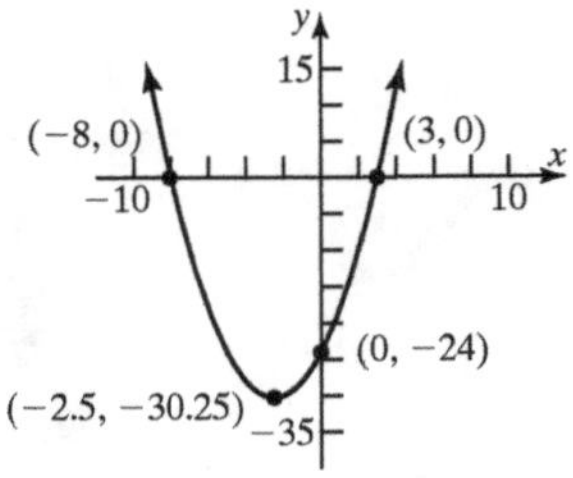

CHAPTER 9 Polar Coordinates; Vectors

9.1 Assess Your Understanding *(page 569)*

5. pole; polar axis **6.** -2 **7.** $(-\sqrt{3}, -1)$ **8.** F **9.** T **10.** T **11.** *A* **13.** *C* **15.** *B* **17.** *A*

19.

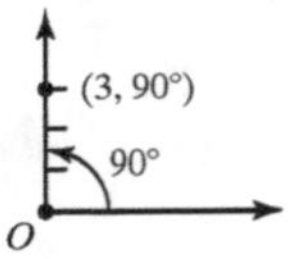

21.

23.

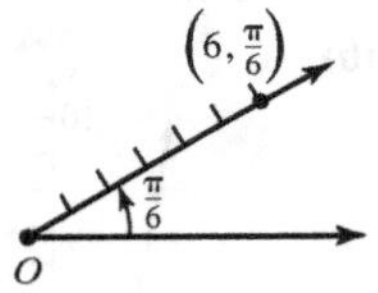

25.

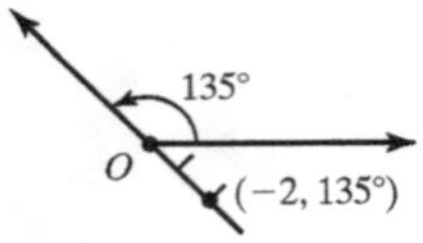

27.

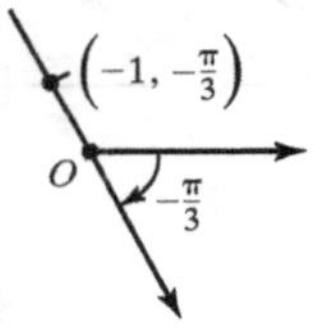

29.

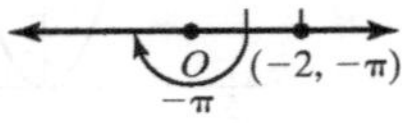

31.

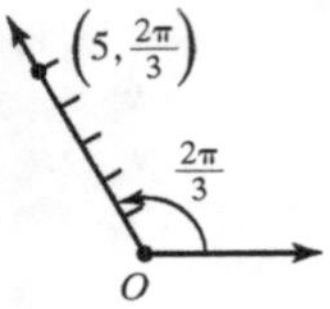

(a) $\left(5, -\frac{4\pi}{3}\right)$

(b) $\left(-5, \frac{5\pi}{3}\right)$

(c) $\left(5, \frac{8\pi}{3}\right)$

33.

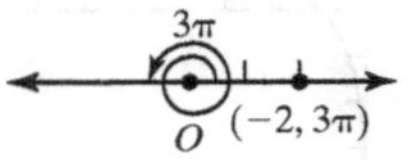

(a) $(2, -2\pi)$

(b) $(-2, \pi)$

(c) $(2, 2\pi)$

35.

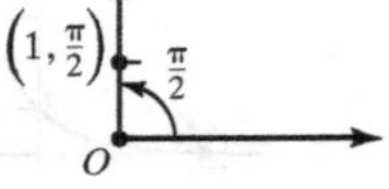

(a) $\left(1, -\frac{3\pi}{2}\right)$

(b) $\left(-1, \frac{3\pi}{2}\right)$

(c) $\left(1, \frac{5\pi}{2}\right)$

37.

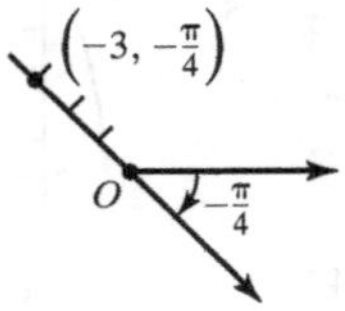

(a) $\left(3, -\frac{5\pi}{4}\right)$

(b) $\left(-3, \frac{7\pi}{4}\right)$

(c) $\left(3, \frac{11\pi}{4}\right)$

39. $(0, 3)$ **41.** $(-2, 0)$ **43.** $(-3\sqrt{3}, 3)$ **45.** $(\sqrt{2}, -\sqrt{2})$ **47.** $\left(-\frac{1}{2}, \frac{\sqrt{3}}{2}\right)$ **49.** $(2, 0)$ **51.** $(-2.57, 7.05)$ **53.** $(-4.98, -3.85)$ **55.** $(3, 0)$

57. $(1, \pi)$ **59.** $\left(\sqrt{2}, -\frac{\pi}{4}\right)$ **61.** $\left(2, \frac{\pi}{6}\right)$ **63.** $(2.47, -1.02)$ **65.** $(9.30, 0.47)$ **67.** $r^2 = \frac{3}{2}$ or $r = \frac{\sqrt{6}}{2}$ **69.** $r^2 \cos^2 \theta - 4r \sin \theta = 0$

71. $r^2 \sin 2\theta = 1$ **73.** $r \cos \theta = 4$ **75.** $x^2 + y^2 - x = 0$ or $\left(x - \frac{1}{2}\right)^2 + y^2 = \frac{1}{4}$ **77.** $(x^2 + y^2)^{3/2} - x = 0$ **79.** $x^2 + y^2 = 4$

81. $y^2 = 8(x + 2)$ **83. (a)** $(-10, 36)$ **(b)** $\left(2\sqrt{349}, 180° + \tan^{-1}\left(-\frac{18}{5}\right)\right) \approx (37.36, 105.5°)$ **(c)** $(-3, -35)$

(d) $\left(\sqrt{1234}, 180° + \tan^{-1}\left(\frac{35}{3}\right)\right) \approx (35.13, 265.1°)$

9.2 Assess Your Understanding *(page 586)*

7. polar equation **8.** $r = 2\cos\theta$ **9.** $-r$ **10.** F **11.** F **12.** F

13. $x^2 + y^2 = 16$; circle, radius 4, center at pole

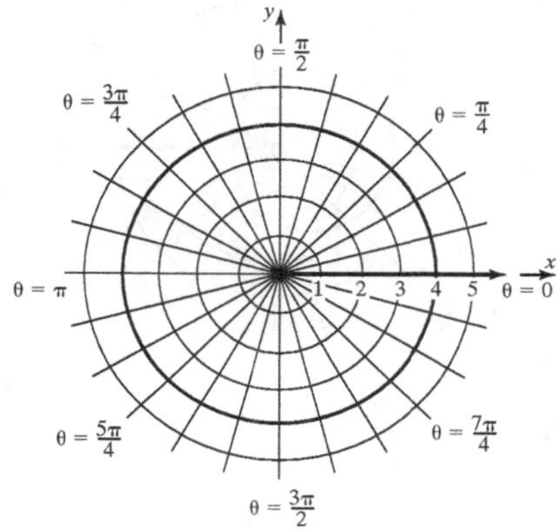

15. $y = \sqrt{3}x$; line through pole, making an angle of $\frac{\pi}{3}$ with polar axis

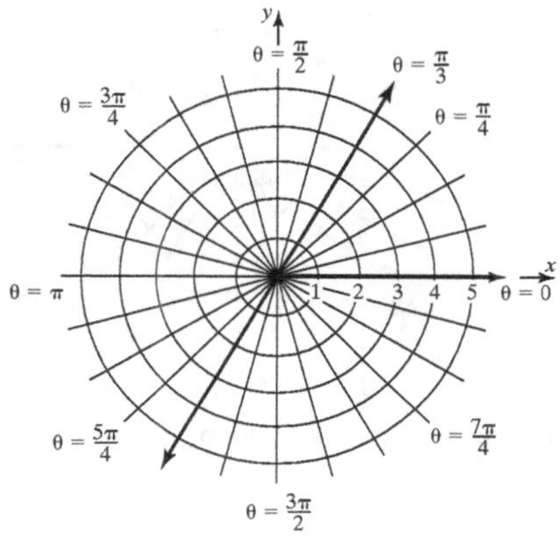

17. $y = 4$; horizontal line 4 units above the pole

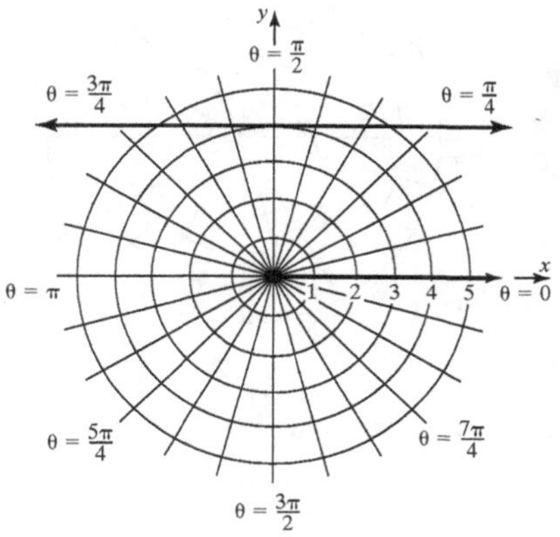

19. $x = -2$; vertical line 2 units to the left of the pole

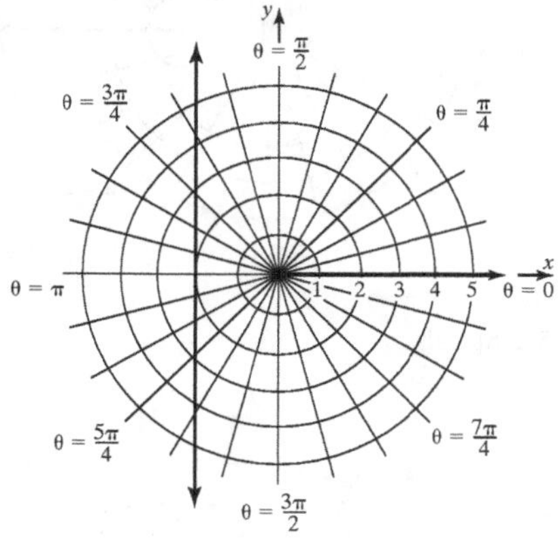

21. $(x - 1)^2 + y^2 = 1$; circle, radius 1, center $(1, 0)$ in rectangular coordinates

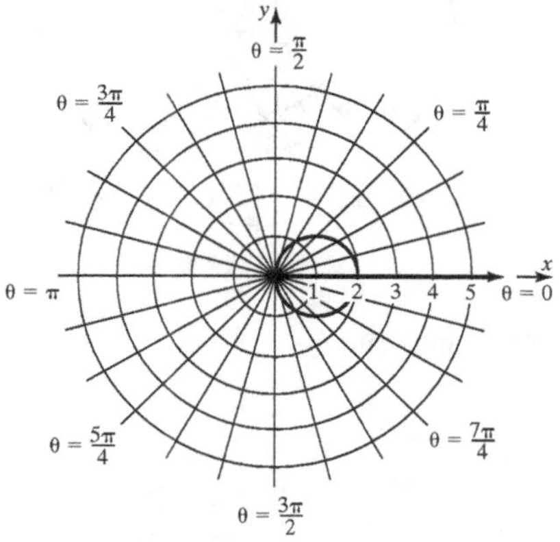

23. $x^2 + (y + 2)^2 = 4$; circle, radius 2, center at $(0, -2)$ in rectangular coordinates

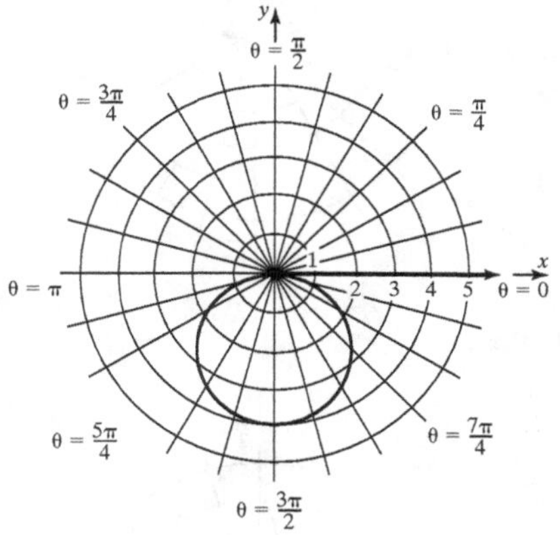

25. $(x-2)^2 + y^2 = 4$; circle, radius 2, center at $(2, 0)$ in rectangular coordinates

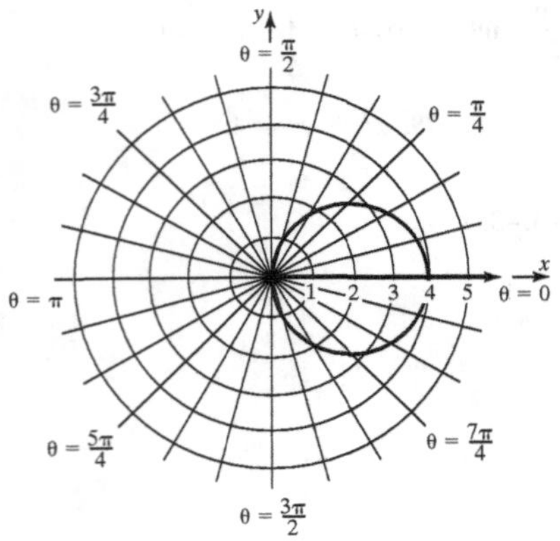

27. $x^2 + (y+1)^2 = 1$; circle, radius 1, center at $(0, -1)$ in rectangular coordinates

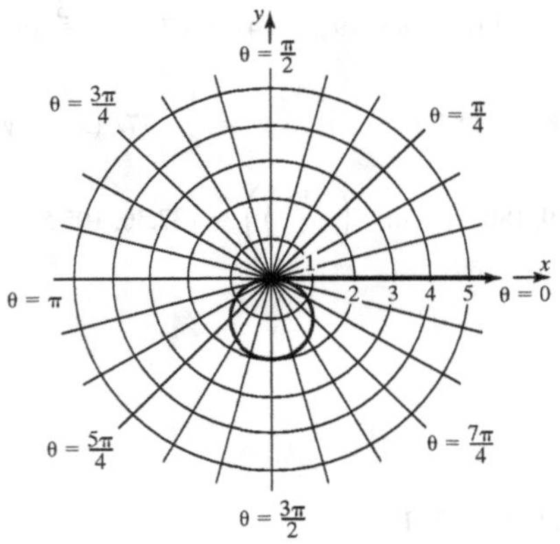

29. *E* **31.** *F* **33.** *H* **35.** *D*

37. Cardioid

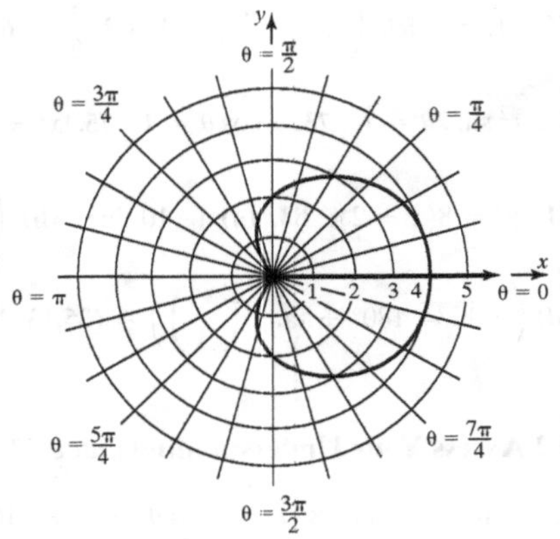

39. Cardioid

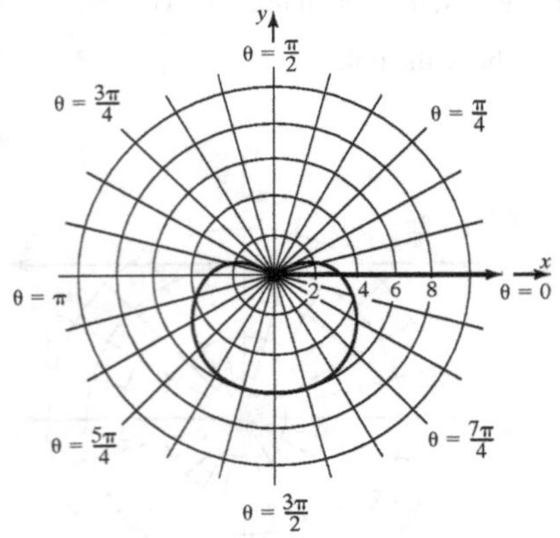

41. Limaçon without inner loop

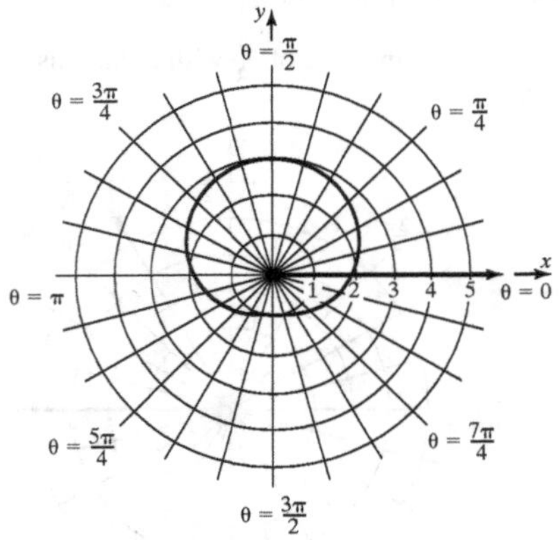

43. Limaçon without inner loop

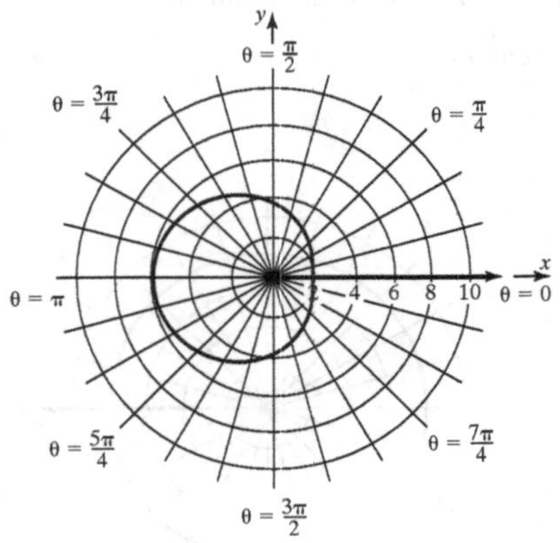

45. Limaçon with inner loop

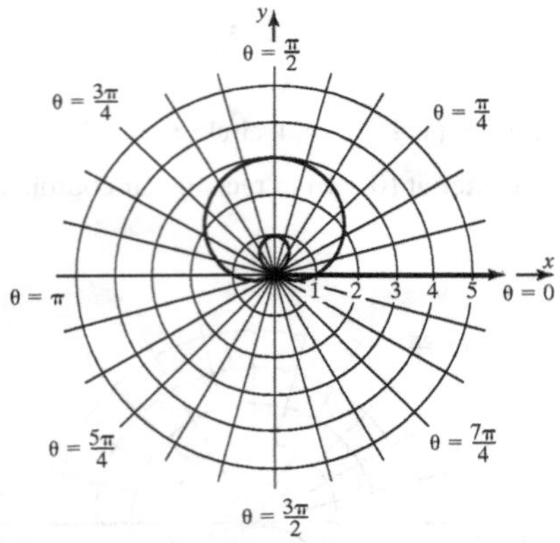

47. Limaçon with inner loop

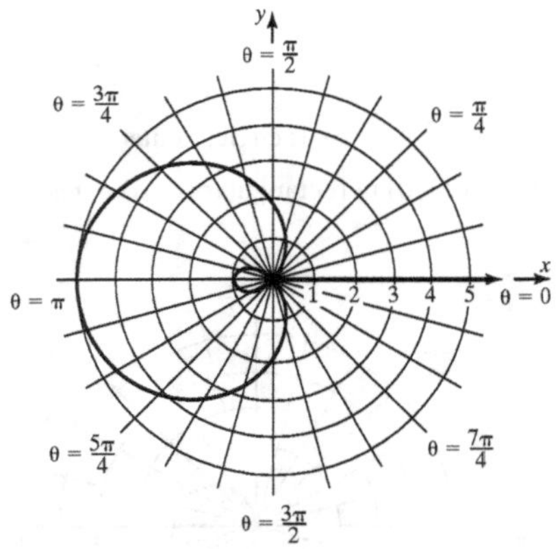

49. Rose

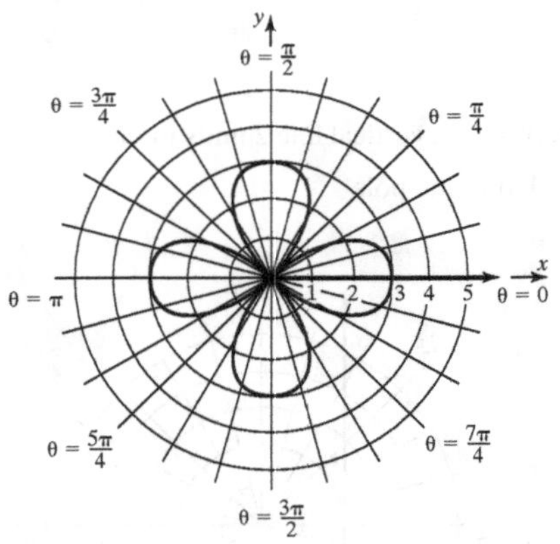

51. Rose

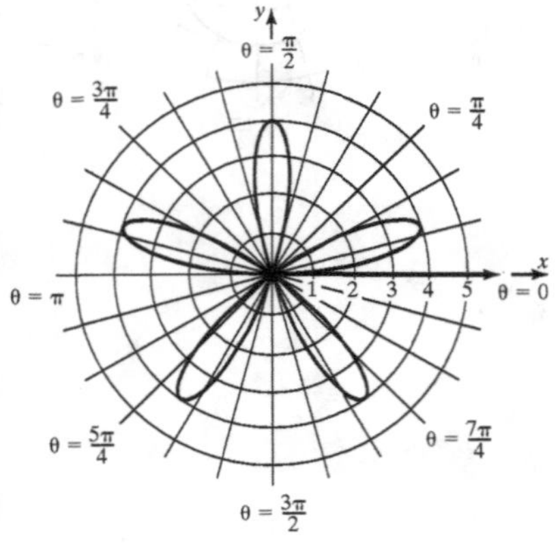

53. Lemniscate

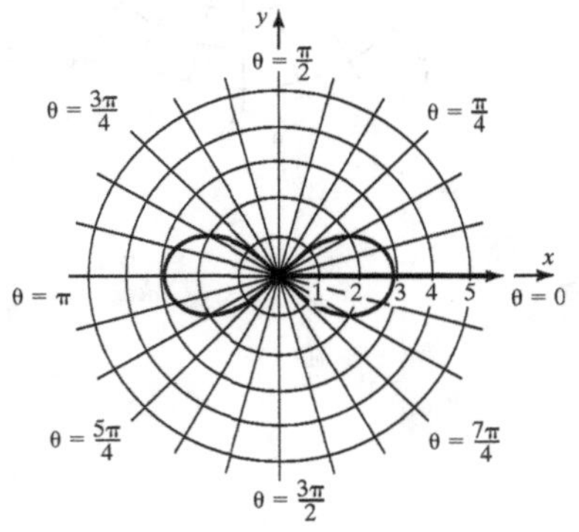

55. Spiral

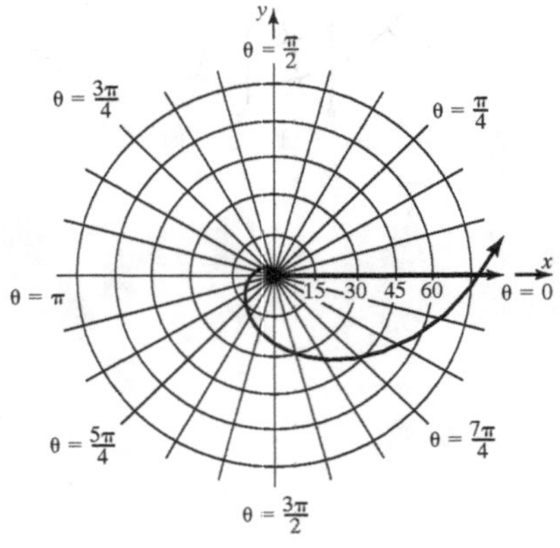

57. Cardioid

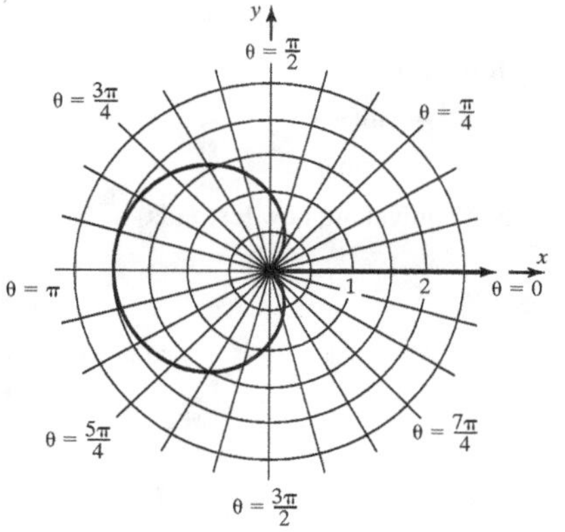

59. Limaçon with inner loop

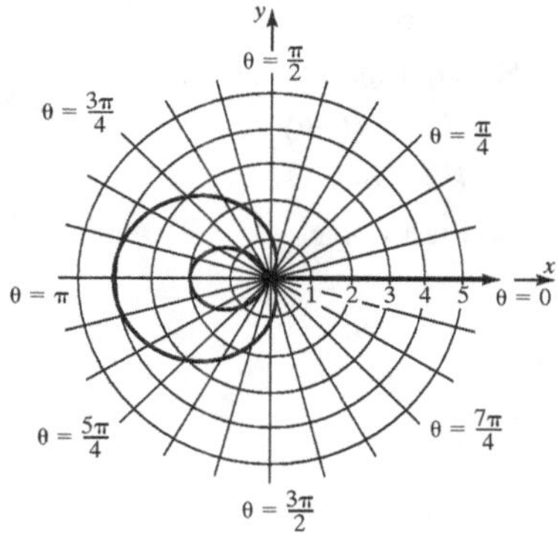

61.

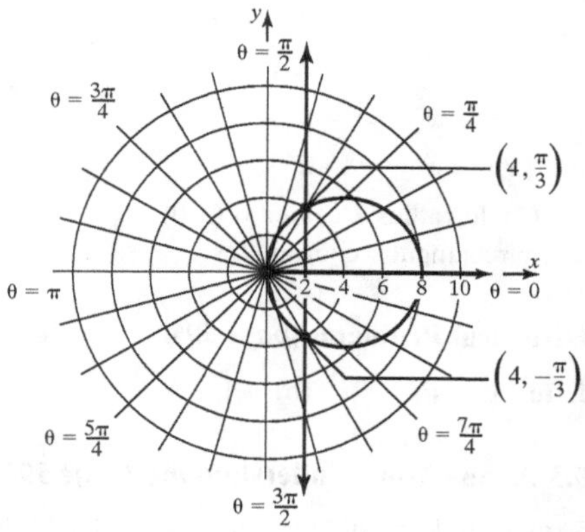

63.

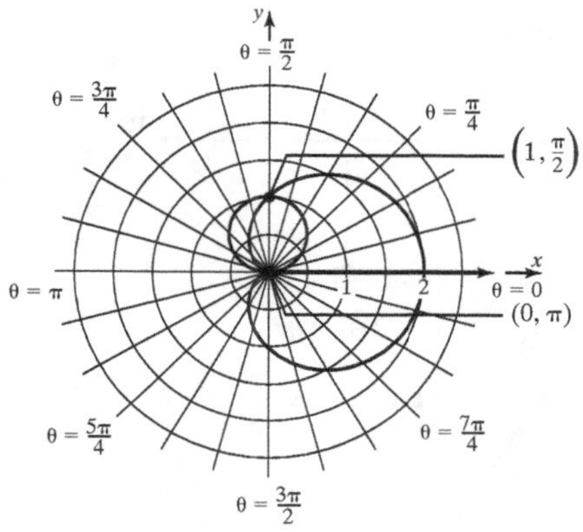

65.

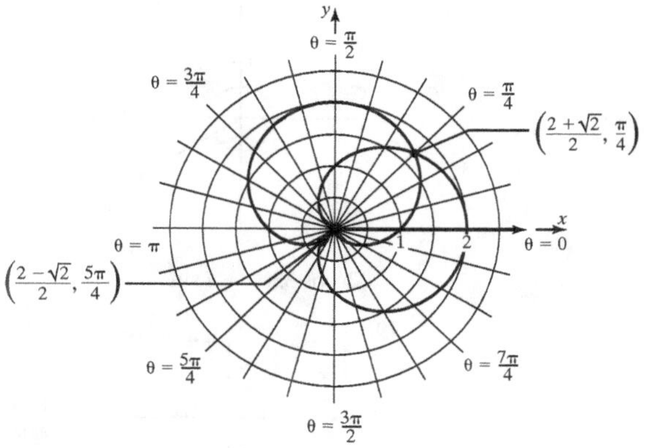

67. $r = 3 + 3\cos\theta$

69. $r = 4 + \sin\theta$

71.

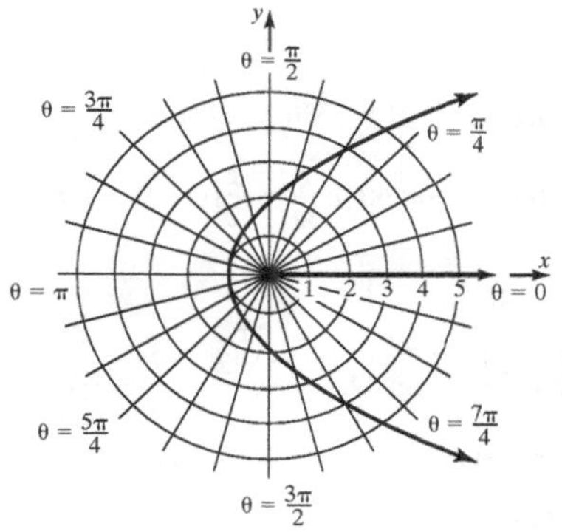

73.

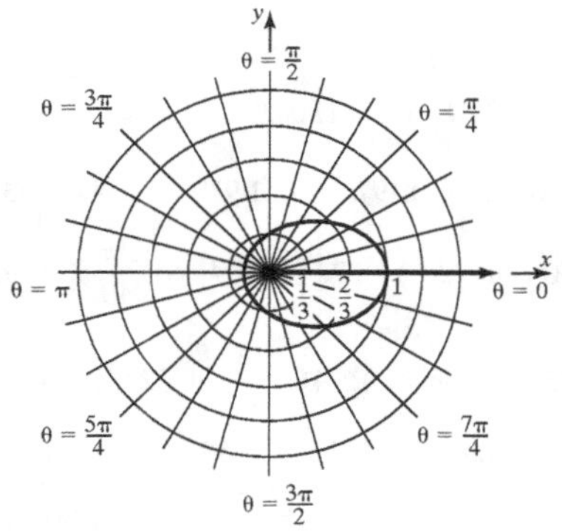

75.

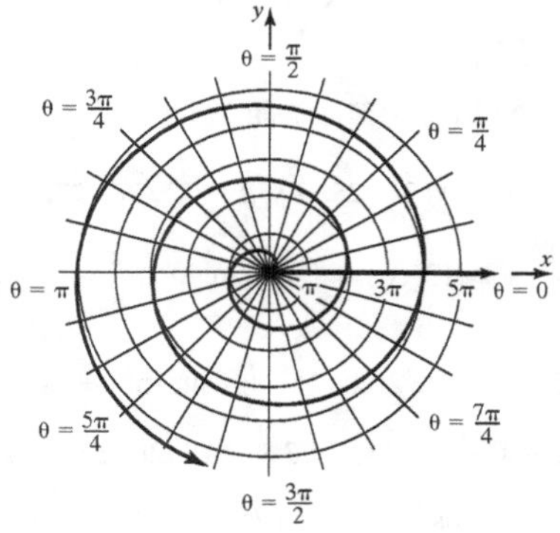

77.

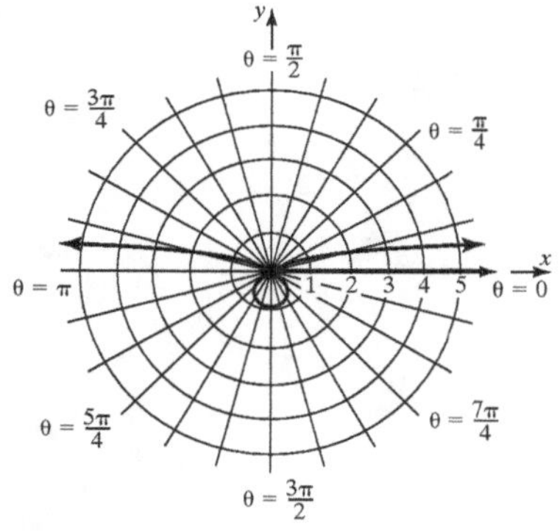

79.

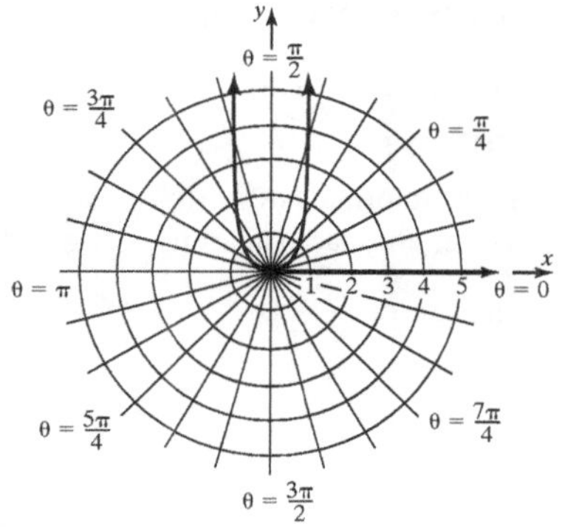

81. $r\sin\theta = a$

$y = a$

83.

$$\begin{aligned} r &= 2a\sin\theta \\ r^2 &= 2ar\sin\theta \\ x^2 + y^2 &= 2ay \\ x^2 + y^2 - 2ay &= 0 \\ x^2 + (y - a)^2 &= a^2 \end{aligned}$$

Circle, radius a, center at $(0, a)$ in rectangular coordinates

85.
$$r = 2a\cos\theta$$
$$r^2 = 2ar\cos\theta$$
$$x^2 + y^2 = 2ax$$
$$x^2 - 2ax + y^2 = 0$$
$$(x - a)^2 + y^2 = a^2$$
Circle, radius a, center at $(a, 0)$ in rectangular coordinates

87. (a) $r^2 = \cos\theta$: $r^2 = \cos(\pi - \theta)$
$$r^2 = -\cos\theta$$
Not equivalent; test fails.
$$(-r)^2 = \cos(-\theta)$$
$$r^2 = \cos\theta$$
New test works.

(b) $r^2 = \sin\theta$: $r^2 = \sin(\pi - \theta)$
$$r^2 = \sin\theta$$
Test works.
$$(-r)^2 = \sin(-\theta)$$
$$r^2 = -\sin\theta$$
Not equivalent; new test fails.

Historical Problems *(page 595)*

1. (a) $1 + 4i, 1 + i$ **(b)** $-1, 2 + i$.

9.3 Assess Your Understanding *(page 595)*

5. magnitude; modulus; argument **6.** De Moivre's **7.** three **8.** T **9.** F **10.** T

11.

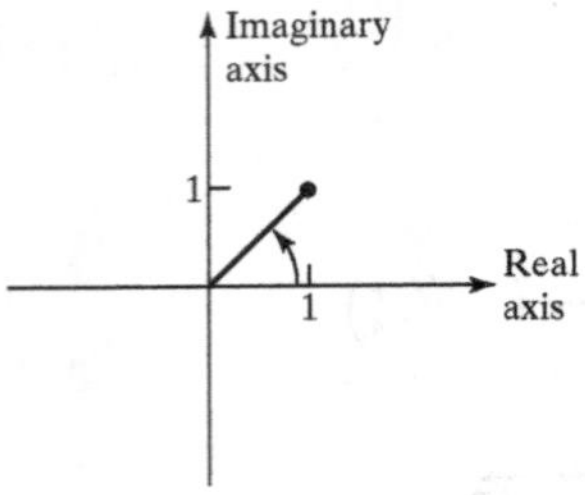

$\sqrt{2}(\cos 45° + i\sin 45°)$

13.

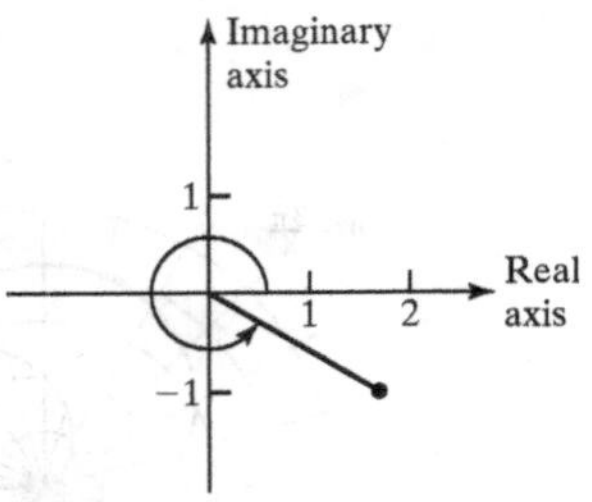

$2(\cos 330° + i\sin 330°)$

15.

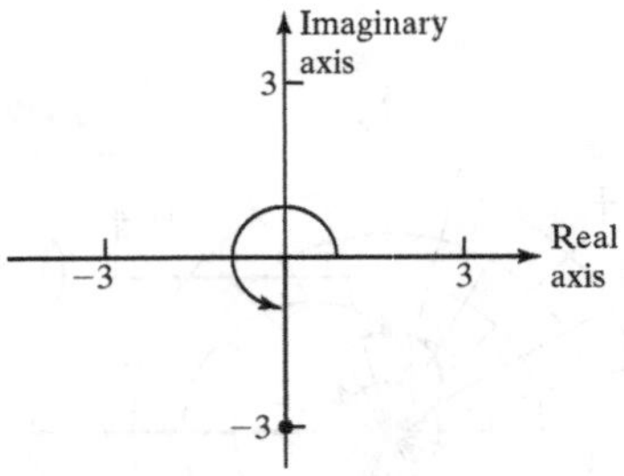

$3(\cos 270° + i\sin 270°)$

17.

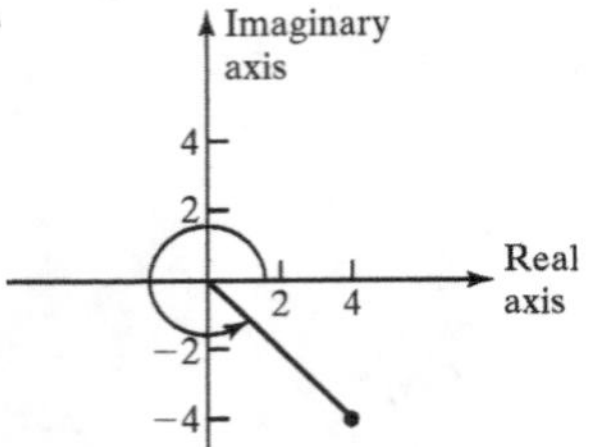

$4\sqrt{2}(\cos 315° + i\sin 315°)$

19.

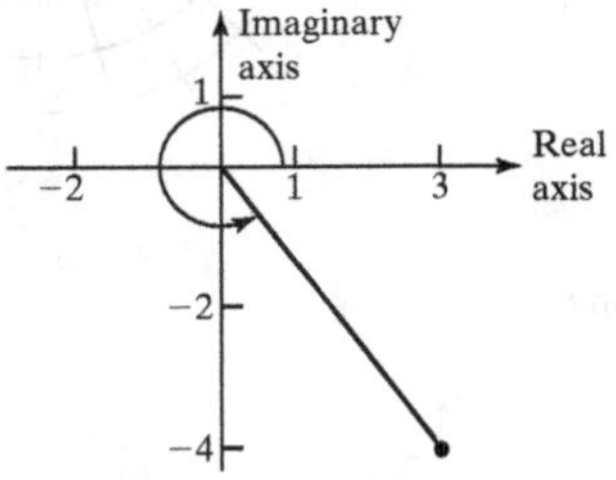

$5(\cos 306.9° + i\sin 306.9°)$

21.

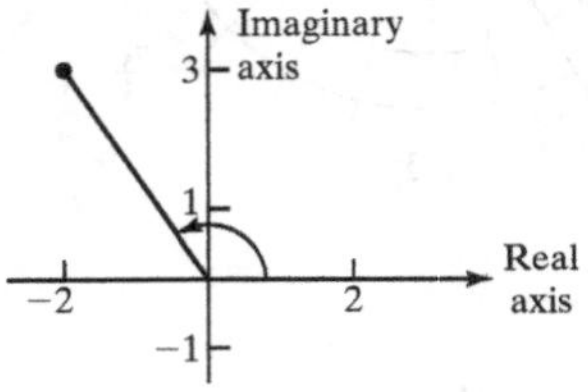

$\sqrt{13}(\cos 123.7° + i\sin 123.7°)$

23. $-1 + \sqrt{3}i$ **25.** $2\sqrt{2} - 2\sqrt{2}i$ **27.** $-3i$ **29.** $-0.035 + 0.197i$ **31.** $1.970 + 0.347i$ **33.** $zw = 8(\cos 60° + i\sin 60°)$; $\frac{z}{w} = \frac{1}{2}(\cos 20° + i\sin 20°)$

35. $zw = 12(\cos 40° + i\sin 40°)$; $\frac{z}{w} = \frac{3}{4}(\cos 220° + i\sin 220°)$ **37.** $zw = 4\left(\cos\frac{9\pi}{40} + i\sin\frac{9\pi}{40}\right)$; $\frac{z}{w} = \cos\frac{\pi}{40} + i\sin\frac{\pi}{40}$

39. $zw = 4\sqrt{2}(\cos 15° + i\sin 15°)$; $\frac{z}{w} = \sqrt{2}(\cos 75° + i\sin 75°)$ **41.** $-32 + 32\sqrt{3}i$ **43.** $32i$ **45.** $\frac{27}{2} + \frac{27\sqrt{3}}{2}i$ **47.** $-\frac{25\sqrt{2}}{2} + \frac{25\sqrt{2}}{2}i$

49. $-4 + 4i$ **51.** $-23 + 14.142i$ **53.** $\sqrt[6]{2}(\cos 15° + i\sin 15°)$, $\sqrt[6]{2}(\cos 135° + i\sin 135°)$, $\sqrt[6]{2}(\cos 255° + i\sin 255°)$

55. $\sqrt[4]{8}(\cos 75° + i\sin 75°)$, $\sqrt[4]{8}(\cos 165° + i\sin 165°)$, $\sqrt[4]{8}(\cos 255° + i\sin 255°)$, $\sqrt[4]{8}(\cos 345° + i\sin 345°)$

57. $2(\cos 67.5° + i\sin 67.5°)$, $2(\cos 157.5° + i\sin 157.5°)$, $2(\cos 247.5° + i\sin 247.5°)$, $2(\cos 337.5° + i\sin 337.5°)$

59. $\cos 18° + i\sin 18°$, $\cos 90° + i\sin 90°$, $\cos 162° + i\sin 162°$, $\cos 234° + i\sin 234°$, $\cos 306° + i\sin 306°$

61. $1, i, -1, -i$

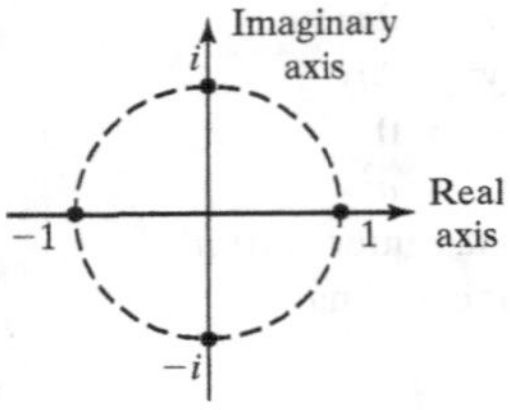

63. Look at formula (8); $|z_k| = \sqrt[n]{r}$ for all k.

65. Look at formula (8). The z_k are spaced apart by an angle of $\frac{2\pi}{n}$.

67. (a)

$z = a_0$	a_1	a_2	a_3	a_4	a_5	a_6
$0.1 - 0.4i$	$-0.05 - 0.48i$	$-0.13 - 0.35i$	$-0.01 - 0.31i$	$0.01 - 0.35i$	$0.2 - 0.41i$	$0.07 - 0.42i$
$0.5 + 0.8i$	$0.11 + 1.6i$	$-2.05 + 1.15i$	$3.37 - 3.92i$	$-3.52 - 25.6i$	$-641.9 + 181.1i$	$379290 - 232509i$
$-0.9 + 0.7i$	$-0.58 - 0.56i$	$0.87 + 1.35i$	$-1.95 - 1.67i$	$0.13 + 7.21i$	$-52.88 + 2.56i$	$2788.5 - 269.6i$
$-1.1 + 0.1i$	$0.1 - 0.12i$	$-1.10 + 0.76i$	$0.11 - 0.068i$	$-1.09 + 0.085i$	$0.085 - 0.85i$	$-1.10 + 0.086i$
$0 - 1.3i$	$-1.69 - 1.3i$	$1.17 + 3.09i$	$-8.21 + 5.92i$	$32.46 - 98.47i$	$-8643.6 - 6393.7i$	$33833744 + 110529134.4i$
$1 + 1i$	$1 + 3i$	$-7 + 7i$	$1 - 97i$	$-9407 - 193i$	$88454401 + 3631103i$	$7.8 \times 10^{15} + 6.4 \times 10^{14}i$

(b) z_1 and z_4 are in the Mandlebrot set. a_6 for the complex numbers not in the set have very large components.

(c)

z	$\lvert z\rvert$	$\lvert a_6\rvert$
$0.1 - 0.4i$	0.4	0.4
$0.5 + 0.8i$	0.9	444884
$-0.9 + 0.7i$	1.1	2802
$-1.1 + 0.1i$	1.1	1.1
$0 - 1.3i$	1.3	115591573
$1 + 1i$	1.4	7.8×10^{15}

The numbers that are in the Mandlebrot set satisfy the condition $|a_n| \le 2$.

9.4 Assess Your Understanding *(page 606)*

1. unit **2.** scalar **3.** horizontal; vertical **4.** T **5.** T **6.** F

7.

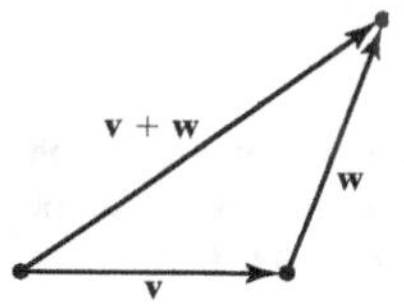

9.

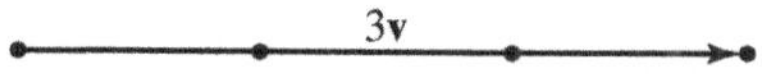

11.

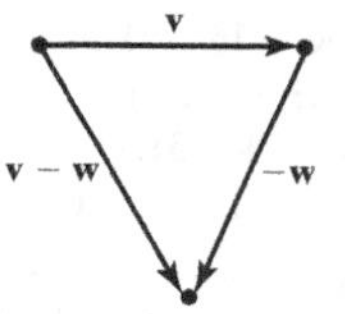

13.

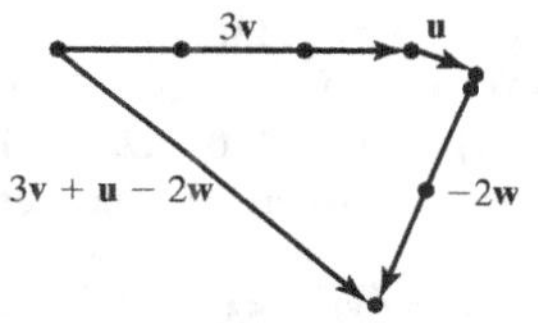

15. T **17.** F **19.** F **21.** T **23.** 12 **25.** $\mathbf{v} = 3\mathbf{i} + 4\mathbf{j}$ **27.** $\mathbf{v} = 2\mathbf{i} + 4\mathbf{j}$ **29.** $\mathbf{v} = 8\mathbf{i} - \mathbf{j}$ **31.** $\mathbf{v} = -\mathbf{i} + \mathbf{j}$ **33.** 5 **35.** $\sqrt{2}$ **37.** $\sqrt{13}$ **39.** $-\mathbf{j}$ **41.** $\sqrt{89}$ **43.** $\sqrt{34} - \sqrt{13}$ **45.** $\mathbf{i}$ **47.** $\frac{3}{5}\mathbf{i} - \frac{4}{5}\mathbf{j}$ **49.** $\frac{\sqrt{2}}{2}\mathbf{i} - \frac{\sqrt{2}}{2}\mathbf{j}$ **51.** $\mathbf{v} = \frac{8\sqrt{5}}{5}\mathbf{i} + \frac{4\sqrt{5}}{5}\mathbf{j}$ or $\mathbf{v} = -\frac{8\sqrt{5}}{5}\mathbf{i} - \frac{4\sqrt{5}}{5}\mathbf{j}$

53. $\{-2 + \sqrt{21}, -2 - \sqrt{21}\}$ **55.** $\mathbf{v} = \frac{5}{2}\mathbf{i} + \frac{5\sqrt{3}}{2}\mathbf{j}$ **57.** $\mathbf{v} = -7\mathbf{i} + 7\sqrt{3}\mathbf{j}$ **59.** $\mathbf{v} = \frac{25\sqrt{3}}{2}\mathbf{i} - \frac{25}{2}\mathbf{j}$

61. (a) $(-1, 4)$ **(b)**

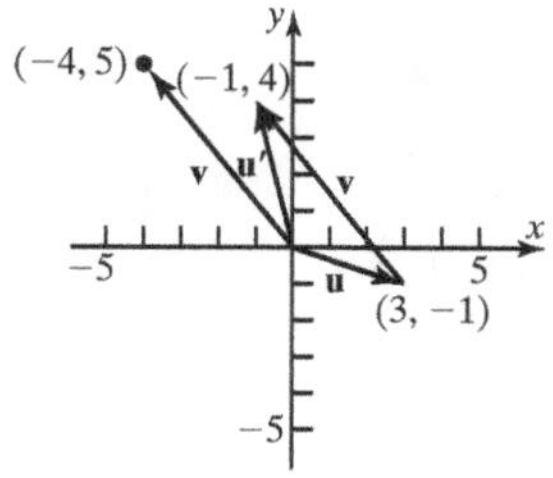

63. $\mathbf{F} = 20\sqrt{3}\mathbf{i} + 20\mathbf{j}$

65. $\mathbf{F} = (20\sqrt{3} + 30\sqrt{2})\mathbf{i} + (20 - 30\sqrt{2})\mathbf{j}$

67. Tension in right cable: 1000 lb; tension in left cable: 845.2 lb

69. Tension in right part: 1088.4 lb; tension in left part: 1089.1 lb

71. The truck must pull with a force of 4635.2 lb.

73.

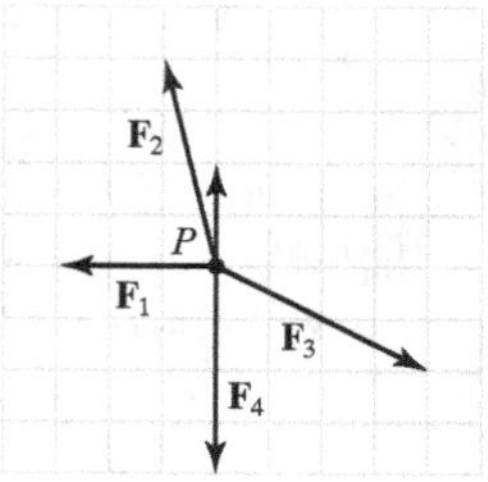

Historical Problem *(page 614)*

$(a\mathbf{i} + b\mathbf{j}) \cdot (c\mathbf{i} + d\mathbf{j}) = ac + bd$

Real part $[(\overline{a + bi})(c + di)]$ = real part$[(a - bi)(c + di)]$ = real part$[ac + adi - bci - bdi^2] = ac + bd$

9.5 Assess Your Understanding *(page 614)*

2. orthogonal **3.** parallel **4.** F **5.** T **6.** F **7. (a)** 0 **(b)** 90° **(c)** orthogonal **9. (a)** 0 **(b)** 90° **(c)** orthogonal **11. (a)** $\sqrt{3} - 1$ **(b)** 75° **(c)** neither **13. (a)** −50 **(b)** 180° **(c)** parallel **15. (a)** 0 **(b)** 90° **(c)** orthogonal **17.** $\frac{2}{3}$ **19.** $\mathbf{v}_1 = \frac{5}{2}\mathbf{i} - \frac{5}{2}\mathbf{j}$, $\mathbf{v}_2 = -\frac{1}{2}\mathbf{i} - \frac{1}{2}\mathbf{j}$ **21.** $\mathbf{v}_1 = -\frac{1}{5}\mathbf{i} - \frac{2}{5}\mathbf{j}$, $\mathbf{v}_2 = \frac{6}{5}\mathbf{i} - \frac{3}{5}\mathbf{j}$ **23.** $\mathbf{v}_1 = \frac{14}{5}\mathbf{i} + \frac{7}{5}\mathbf{j}$, $\mathbf{v}_2 = \frac{1}{5}\mathbf{i} - \frac{2}{5}\mathbf{j}$ **25.** 9 ft-lb **27. (a)** $\|\mathbf{I}\| = 0.022$; the intensity of the sun's rays is approximately 0.022 W/cm^2. $\|\mathbf{A}\| = 500$; the area of the solar panel is 500 cm^2. **(b)** $W = 10$; ten watts of energy is collected. **(c)** Vectors **I** and **A** should be parallel with the solar panels facing the sun. **29.** 496.7 mi/h; 38.5° west of south **31.** 8.6° off direct heading across the current, upstream; 1.52 min **33.** Force required to keep Sienna from rolling down the hill: 737.6 lb; force perpendicular to the hill: 5248.4 lb **35.** $\mathbf{v} = (250\sqrt{2} - 30)\mathbf{i} + (250\sqrt{2} + 30\sqrt{3})\mathbf{j}$; 518.8 km/h; N38.6°E **37.** Timmy must exert 85.5 lb. **39.** 60° **41.** Let $\mathbf{v} = a\mathbf{i} + b\mathbf{j}$. Then $\mathbf{0} \cdot \mathbf{v} = 0a + 0b = 0$. **43.** $\mathbf{v} = \cos\alpha\mathbf{i} + \sin\alpha\mathbf{j}, 0 \le \alpha \le \pi$; $\mathbf{w} = \cos\beta\mathbf{i} + \sin\beta\mathbf{j}, 0 \le \beta \le \pi$. If θ is the angle between **v** and **w**, then $\mathbf{v} \cdot \mathbf{w} = \cos\theta$, since $\|\mathbf{v}\| = 1$ and $\|\mathbf{w}\| = 1$. Now $\theta = \alpha - \beta$ or $\theta = \beta - \alpha$. Since the cosine function is even, $\mathbf{v} \cdot \mathbf{w} = \cos(\alpha - \beta)$. Also, $\mathbf{v} \cdot \mathbf{w} = \cos\alpha\cos\beta + \sin\alpha\sin\beta$. So $\cos(\alpha - \beta) = \cos\alpha\cos\beta + \sin\alpha\sin\beta$.

45. (a) If $\mathbf{u} = a_1\mathbf{i} + b_1\mathbf{j}$ and $\mathbf{v} = a_2\mathbf{i} + b_2\mathbf{j}$, then, since $\|\mathbf{u}\| = \|\mathbf{v}\|$, $a_1^2 + b_1^2 = \|\mathbf{u}\|^2 = \|\mathbf{v}\|^2 = a_2^2 + b_2^2$, and
$(\mathbf{u} + \mathbf{v})\cdot(\mathbf{u} - \mathbf{v}) = (a_1 + a_2)(a_1 - a_2) + (b_1 + b_2)(b_1 - b_2) = (a_1^2 + b_1^2) - (a_2^2 + b_2^2) = 0.$
(b) The legs of the angle can be made to correspond to vectors $\mathbf{u} + \mathbf{v}$ and $\mathbf{u} - \mathbf{v}$.

47. $(\|\mathbf{w}\|\mathbf{v} + \|\mathbf{v}\|\mathbf{w})\cdot(\|\mathbf{w}\|\mathbf{v} - \|\mathbf{v}\|\mathbf{w}) = \|\mathbf{w}\|^2\mathbf{v}\cdot\mathbf{v} - \|\mathbf{w}\|\|\mathbf{v}\|\mathbf{v}\cdot\mathbf{w} + \|\mathbf{v}\|\|\mathbf{w}\|\mathbf{w}\cdot\mathbf{v} - \|\mathbf{v}\|^2\mathbf{w}\cdot\mathbf{w} = \|\mathbf{w}\|^2\mathbf{v}\cdot\mathbf{v} - \|\mathbf{v}\|^2\mathbf{w}\cdot\mathbf{w} = \|\mathbf{w}\|^2\|\mathbf{v}\|^2 - \|\mathbf{v}\|^2\|\mathbf{w}\|^2 = 0$

49. $\|\mathbf{u} + \mathbf{v}\|^2 - \|\mathbf{u} - \mathbf{v}\|^2 = (\mathbf{u} + \mathbf{v})\cdot(\mathbf{u} + \mathbf{v}) - (\mathbf{u} - \mathbf{v})\cdot(\mathbf{u} - \mathbf{v}) = (\mathbf{u}\cdot\mathbf{u} + \mathbf{u}\cdot\mathbf{v} + \mathbf{v}\cdot\mathbf{u} + \mathbf{v}\cdot\mathbf{v}) - (\mathbf{u}\cdot\mathbf{u} - \mathbf{u}\cdot\mathbf{v} - \mathbf{v}\cdot\mathbf{u} + \mathbf{v}\cdot\mathbf{v})$
$= 2(\mathbf{u}\cdot\mathbf{v}) + 2(\mathbf{v}\cdot\mathbf{u}) = 4(\mathbf{u}\cdot\mathbf{v})$

9.6 Assess Your Understanding *(page 624)*

2. xy-plane **3.** components **4.** 1 **5.** F **6.** T **7.** All points of the form $(x, 0, z)$ **9.** All points of the form $(x, y, 2)$ **11.** All points of the form $(-4, y, z)$ **13.** All points of the form $(1, 2, z)$ **15.** $\sqrt{21}$ **17.** $\sqrt{33}$ **19.** $\sqrt{26}$ **21.** $(2,0,0); (2,1,0); (0,1,0); (2,0,3); (0,1,3); (0,0,3)$ **23.** $(1,4,3); (3,2,3); (3,4,3); (3,2,5); (1,4,5); (1,2,5)$ **25.** $(-1,2,2); (4,0,2); (4,2,2); (-1,2,5); (4,0,5); (-1,0,5)$ **27.** $\mathbf{v} = 3\mathbf{i} + 4\mathbf{j} - \mathbf{k}$ **29.** $\mathbf{v} = 2\mathbf{i} + 4\mathbf{j} + \mathbf{k}$ **31.** $\mathbf{v} = 8\mathbf{i} - \mathbf{j}$ **33.** 7 **35.** $\sqrt{3}$ **37.** $\sqrt{22}$ **39.** $-\mathbf{j} - 2\mathbf{k}$ **41.** $\sqrt{105}$ **43.** $\sqrt{38} - \sqrt{17}$ **45.** $\mathbf{i}$ **47.** $\frac{3}{7}\mathbf{i} - \frac{6}{7}\mathbf{j} - \frac{2}{7}\mathbf{k}$ **49.** $\frac{\sqrt{3}}{3}\mathbf{i} + \frac{\sqrt{3}}{3}\mathbf{j} + \frac{\sqrt{3}}{3}\mathbf{k}$ **51.** $\mathbf{v}\cdot\mathbf{w} = 0; \theta = 90°$ **53.** $\mathbf{v}\cdot\mathbf{w} = -2, \theta \approx 100.3°$ **55.** $\mathbf{v}\cdot\mathbf{w} = 0; \theta = 90°$ **57.** $\mathbf{v}\cdot\mathbf{w} = 52; \theta = 0°$
59. $\alpha \approx 64.6°; \beta \approx 149.0°; \gamma \approx 106.6°; \mathbf{v} = 7(\cos 64.6°\mathbf{i} + \cos 149.0°\mathbf{j} + \cos 106.6°\mathbf{k})$
61. $\alpha = \beta = \gamma \approx 54.7°; \mathbf{v} = \sqrt{3}(\cos 54.7°\mathbf{i} + \cos 54.7°\mathbf{j} + \cos 54.7°\mathbf{k})$ **63.** $\alpha = \beta = 45°; \gamma = 90°; \mathbf{v} = \sqrt{2}(\cos 45°\mathbf{i} + \cos 45°\mathbf{j} + \cos 90°\mathbf{k})$
65. $\alpha \approx 60.9°; \beta \approx 144.2°; \gamma \approx 71.1°; \mathbf{v} = \sqrt{38}(\cos 60.9°\mathbf{i} + \cos 144.2°\mathbf{j} + \cos 71.1°\mathbf{k})$ **67. (a)** $\mathbf{d} = \mathbf{a} + \mathbf{b} + \mathbf{c} = \langle 7, 1, 5\rangle$ **(b)** 8.66 ft
69. $(x - 3)^2 + (y - 1)^2 + (z - 1)^2 = 1$ **71.** Radius = 2, center $(-1, 1, 0)$ **73.** Radius = 3, center $(2, -2, -1)$
75. Radius $= \frac{3\sqrt{2}}{2}$, center $(2, 0, -1)$ **77.** 2 newton-meters = 2 joules **79.** 9 newton-meters = 9 joules

9.7 Assess Your Understanding *(page 630)*

1. T **2.** T **3.** T **4.** F **5.** F **6.** T **7.** 2 **9.** 4 **11.** $-11A + 2B + 5C$ **13.** $-6A + 23B - 15C$ **15. (a)** $5\mathbf{i} + 5\mathbf{j} + 5\mathbf{k}$ **(b)** $-5\mathbf{i} - 5\mathbf{j} - 5\mathbf{k}$ **(c)** 0 **(d)** 0 **17. (a)** $\mathbf{i} - \mathbf{j} - \mathbf{k}$ **(b)** $-\mathbf{i} + \mathbf{j} + \mathbf{k}$ **(c)** 0 **(d)** 0 **19. (a)** $-\mathbf{i} + 2\mathbf{j} + 2\mathbf{k}$ **(b)** $\mathbf{i} - 2\mathbf{j} - 2\mathbf{k}$ **(c)** 0 **(d)** 0 **21. (a)** $3\mathbf{i} - \mathbf{j} + 4\mathbf{k}$ **(b)** $-3\mathbf{i} + \mathbf{j} - 4\mathbf{k}$ **(c)** 0 **(d)** 0 **23.** $-9\mathbf{i} - 7\mathbf{j} - 3\mathbf{k}$ **25.** $9\mathbf{i} + 7\mathbf{j} + 3\mathbf{k}$ **27.** 0 **29.** $-27\mathbf{i} - 21\mathbf{j} - 9\mathbf{k}$ **31.** $-18\mathbf{i} - 14\mathbf{j} - 6\mathbf{k}$ **33.** 0 **35.** -25 **37.** 25 **39.** 0 **41.** Any vector of the form $c(-9\mathbf{i} - 7\mathbf{j} - 3\mathbf{k})$, where c is a nonzero scalar **43.** Any vector of the form $c(-\mathbf{i} + \mathbf{j} + 5\mathbf{k})$, where c is a nonzero scalar **45.** $\sqrt{166}$ **47.** $\sqrt{555}$ **49.** $\sqrt{34}$ **51.** $\sqrt{998}$ **53.** $\frac{11\sqrt{19}}{57}\mathbf{i} + \frac{\sqrt{19}}{57}\mathbf{j} + \frac{7\sqrt{19}}{57}\mathbf{k}$ or $-\frac{11\sqrt{19}}{57}\mathbf{i} - \frac{\sqrt{19}}{57}\mathbf{j} - \frac{7\sqrt{19}}{57}\mathbf{k}$
55. 98 cubic units

57. $$\mathbf{u}\times\mathbf{v} = \begin{vmatrix} \mathbf{i} & \mathbf{j} & \mathbf{k} \\ a_1 & b_1 & c_1 \\ a_2 & b_2 & c_2 \end{vmatrix} = (b_1c_2 - b_2c_1)\mathbf{i} - (a_1c_2 - a_2c_1)\mathbf{j} + (a_1b_2 - a_2b_1)\mathbf{k}$$
$$\|\mathbf{u}\times\mathbf{v}\|^2 = \left(\sqrt{(b_1c_2 - b_2c_1)^2 + (a_1c_2 - a_2c_1)^2 + (a_1b_2 - a_2b_1)^2}\right)^2$$
$$= b_1^2c_2^2 - 2b_1b_2c_1c_2 + b_2^2c_1^2 + a_1^2c_2^2 - 2a_1a_2c_1c_2 + a_2^2c_1^2 + a_1^2b_2^2 - 2a_1a_2b_1b_2 + a_2^2b_1^2$$
$$\|\mathbf{u}\|^2 = a_1^2 + b_1^2 + c_1^2, \|\mathbf{v}\|^2 = a_2^2 + b_2^2 + c_2^2$$
$$\|\mathbf{u}\|^2\|\mathbf{v}\|^2 = (a_1^2 + b_1^2 + c_1^2)(a_2^2 + b_2^2 + c_2^2) = a_1^2a_2^2 + a_1^2b_2^2 + a_1^2c_2^2 + b_1^2a_2^2 + b_1^2b_2^2 + b_1^2c_2^2 + a_2^2c_1^2 + b_2^2c_1^2 + c_1^2c_2^2$$
$$(\mathbf{u}\cdot\mathbf{v})^2 = (a_1a_2 + b_1b_2 + c_1c_2)^2 = (a_1a_2 + b_1b_2 + c_1c_2)(a_1a_2 + b_1b_2 + c_1c_2)$$
$$= a_1^2a_2^2 + a_1a_2b_1b_2 + a_1a_2c_1c_2 + b_1b_2c_1c_2 + b_1b_2a_1a_2 + b_1^2b_2^2 + b_1b_2c_1c_2 + a_1a_2c_1c_2 + c_1^2c_2^2$$
$$= a_1^2a_2^2 + b_1^2b_2^2 + c_1^2c_2^2 + 2a_1a_2b_1b_2 + 2b_1b_2c_1c_2 + 2a_1a_2c_1c_2$$
$\|\mathbf{u}\|^2\|\mathbf{v}\|^2 - (\mathbf{u}\cdot\mathbf{v})^2 = a_1^2b_2^2 + a_1^2c_2^2 + b_1^2a_2^2 + a_2^2c_1^2 + b_2^2c_1^2 + b_1^2c_2^2 - 2a_1a_2b_1b_2 - 2b_1b_2c_1c_2 - 2a_1a_2c_1c_2$, which equals $\|\mathbf{u}\times\mathbf{v}\|^2$.

59. By Problem 58, since $\mathbf{u}$ and $\mathbf{v}$ are orthogonal, $\|\mathbf{u}\times\mathbf{v}\| = \|\mathbf{u}\|\|\mathbf{v}\|$. If, in addition, $\mathbf{u}$ and $\mathbf{v}$ are unit vectors, $\|\mathbf{u}\times\mathbf{v}\| = 1\cdot 1 = 1$.

61. Assume that $\mathbf{u} = a\mathbf{i} + b\mathbf{j} + c\mathbf{k}$, $\mathbf{v} = d\mathbf{i} + e\mathbf{j} + f\mathbf{k}$, and $\mathbf{w} = l\mathbf{i} + m\mathbf{j} + n\mathbf{k}$. Then $\mathbf{u}\times\mathbf{v} = (bf - ec)\mathbf{i} - (af - dc)\mathbf{j} + (ae - db)\mathbf{k}$,
$\mathbf{u}\times\mathbf{w} = (bn - mc)\mathbf{i} - (an - lc)\mathbf{j} + (am - lb)\mathbf{k}$, and $\mathbf{v} + \mathbf{w} = (d + l)\mathbf{i} + (e + m)\mathbf{j} + (f + n)\mathbf{k}$. Therefore,
$(\mathbf{u}\times\mathbf{v}) + (\mathbf{u}\times\mathbf{w}) = (bf - ec + bn - mc)\mathbf{i} - (af - dc + an - lc)\mathbf{j} + (ae - db + am - lb)\mathbf{k}$ and
$\mathbf{u}\times(\mathbf{v} + \mathbf{w}) = [b(f + n) - (e + m)c]\mathbf{i} - [a(f + n) - (d + l)c]\mathbf{j} + [a(e + m) - (d + l)b]\mathbf{k}$
$= (bf - ec + bn - mc)\mathbf{i} - (af - dc + an - lc)\mathbf{j} + (ae - db + am - lb)\mathbf{k}$, which equals $(\mathbf{u}\times\mathbf{v}) + (\mathbf{u}\times\mathbf{w})$.

Review Exercises *(page 632)*

1. $\left(\frac{3\sqrt{3}}{2}, \frac{3}{2}\right)$

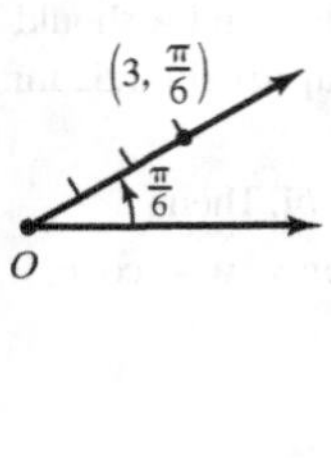

3. $(1, \sqrt{3})$

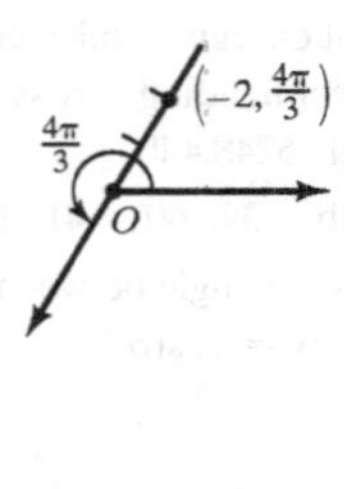

5. $(0, 3)$

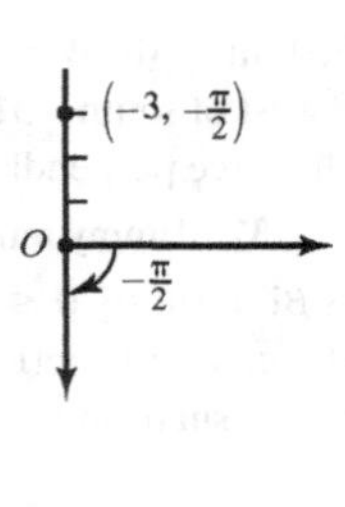

7. $\left(3\sqrt{2}, \frac{3\pi}{4}\right), \left(-3\sqrt{2}, -\frac{\pi}{4}\right)$
9. $\left(2, -\frac{\pi}{2}\right), \left(-2, \frac{\pi}{2}\right)$
11. $(5, 0.93), (-5, 4.07)$

13. **(a)** $x^2 + (y - 1)^2 = 1$ **(b)** circle, radius 1, center $(0, 1)$ in rectangular coordinates

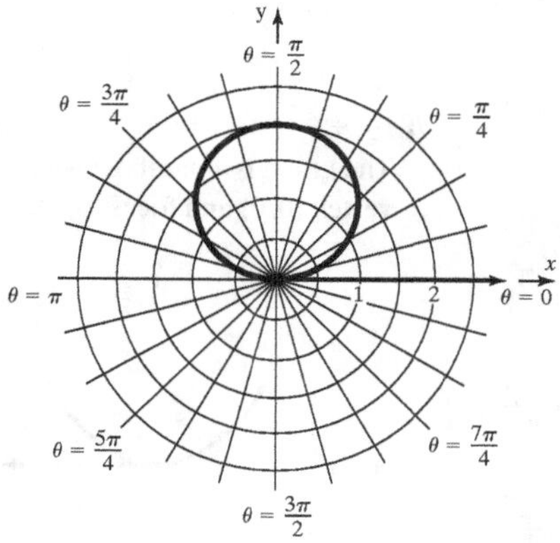

15. **(a)** $x^2 + y^2 = 25$ **(b)** circle, radius 5, center at pole

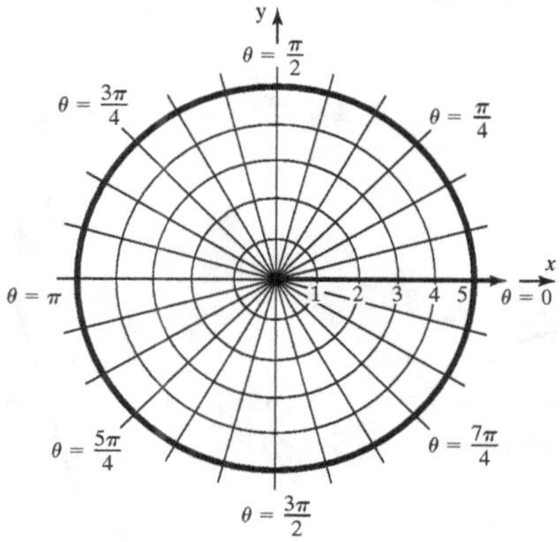

17. **(a)** $x + 3y = 6$ **(b)** line through $(6, 0)$ and $(0, 2)$ in rectangular coordinates

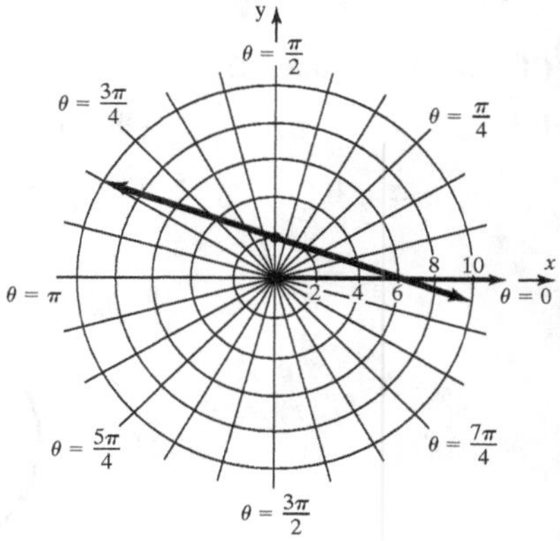

19. Circle; radius 2, center at $(2, 0)$ in rectangular coordinates; symmetric with respect to the polar axis

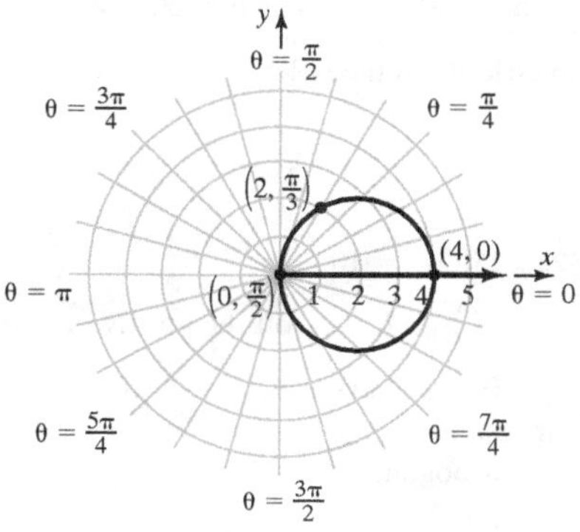

21. Cardioid; symmetric with respect to the line $\theta = \dfrac{\pi}{2}$

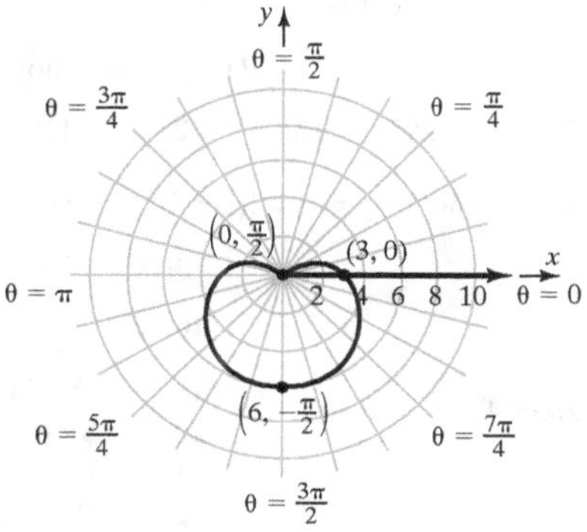

23. Limaçon without inner loop; symmetric with respect to the polar axis

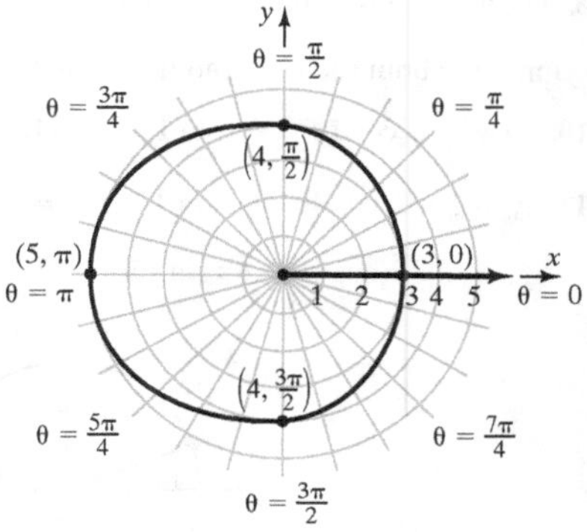

25. $\sqrt{2}(\cos 225° + i \sin 225°)$ **27.** $5(\cos 323.1° + i \sin 323.1°)$

29. $-\sqrt{3} + i$

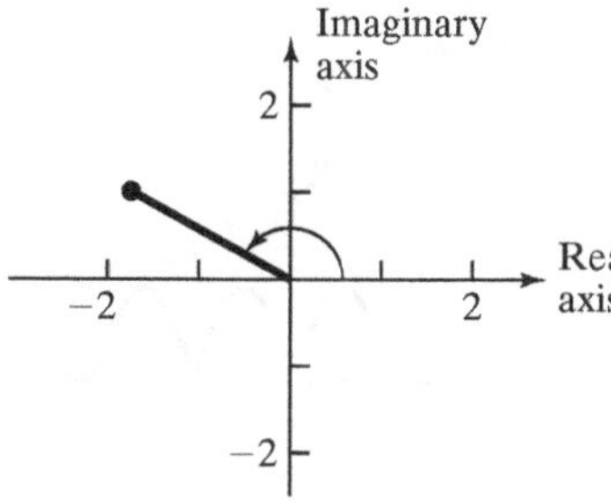

31. $-\dfrac{3}{2} + \dfrac{3\sqrt{3}}{2}i$

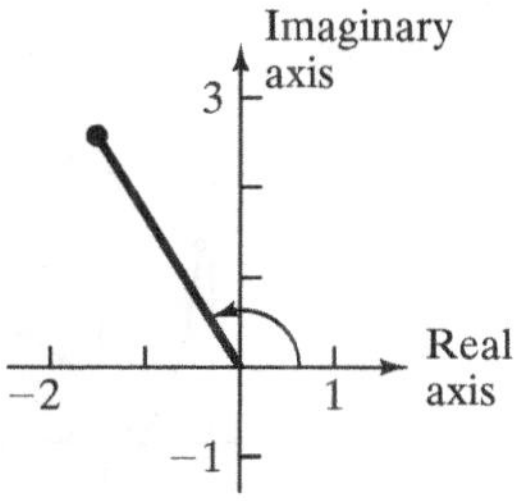

33. $0.10 - 0.02i$

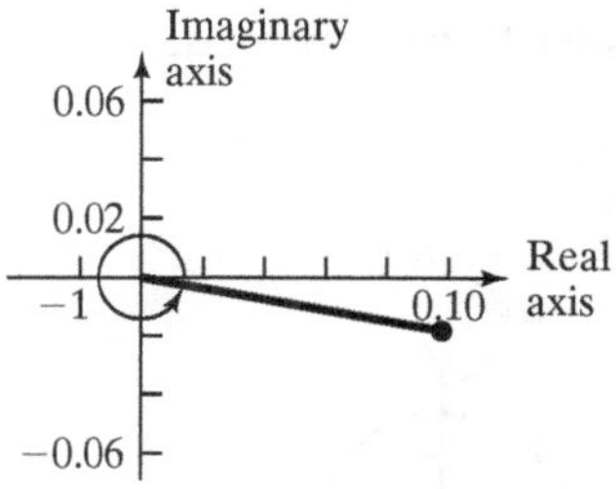

35. $zw = \cos 130° + i \sin 130°; \dfrac{z}{w} = \cos 30° + i \sin 30°$ **37.** $zw = 6(\cos 0 + i \sin 0) = 6; \dfrac{z}{w} = \dfrac{3}{2}\left(\cos\dfrac{8\pi}{5} + i \sin\dfrac{8\pi}{5}\right)$

39. $zw = 5(\cos 5° + i \sin 5°); \dfrac{z}{w} = 5(\cos 15° + i \sin 15°)$ **41.** $\dfrac{27}{2} + \dfrac{27\sqrt{3}}{2}i$ **43.** $4i$ **45.** 64 **47.** $-527 - 336i$

49. $3, 3(\cos 120° + i \sin 120°), \quad 3(\cos 240° + i \sin 240°)$ or $3, -\dfrac{3}{2} + \dfrac{3\sqrt{3}}{2}i, -\dfrac{3}{2} - \dfrac{3\sqrt{3}}{2}i$

51.

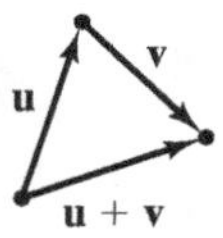

53.

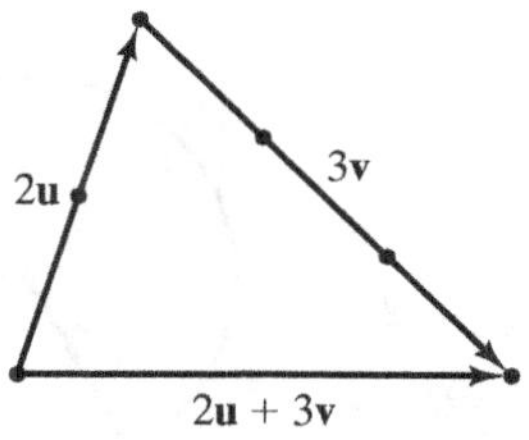

55. $\mathbf{v} = 2\mathbf{i} - 4\mathbf{j}; \|\mathbf{v}\| = 2\sqrt{5}$ **57.** $\mathbf{v} = -\mathbf{i} + 3\mathbf{j}; \|\mathbf{v}\| = \sqrt{10}$ **59.** $2\mathbf{i} - 2\mathbf{j}$ **61.** $-20\mathbf{i} + 13\mathbf{j}$ **63.** $\sqrt{5}$ **65.** $\sqrt{5} + 5 \approx 7.24$ **67.** $-\dfrac{2\sqrt{5}}{5}\mathbf{i} + \dfrac{\sqrt{5}}{5}\mathbf{j}$ **69.** $\mathbf{v} = \dfrac{3}{2}\mathbf{i} + \dfrac{3\sqrt{3}}{2}\mathbf{j}$ **71.** $\sqrt{43} \approx 6.56$ **73.** $\mathbf{v} = 3\mathbf{i} - 5\mathbf{j} + 3\mathbf{k}$ **75.** $21\mathbf{i} - 2\mathbf{j} - 5\mathbf{k}$ **77.** $\sqrt{38}$ **79.** 0 **81.** $3\mathbf{i} + 9\mathbf{j} + 9\mathbf{k}$ **83.** $\dfrac{3\sqrt{14}}{14}\mathbf{i} + \dfrac{\sqrt{14}}{14}\mathbf{j} - \dfrac{\sqrt{14}}{7}\mathbf{k}; -\dfrac{3\sqrt{14}}{14}\mathbf{i} - \dfrac{\sqrt{14}}{14}\mathbf{j} + \dfrac{\sqrt{14}}{7}\mathbf{k}$ **85.** $\mathbf{v} \cdot \mathbf{w} = -11; \theta \approx 169.7°$ **87.** $\mathbf{v} \cdot \mathbf{w} = -4; \theta \approx 153.4°$ **89.** $\mathbf{v} \cdot \mathbf{w} = 1; \theta \approx 70.5°$ **91.** $\mathbf{v} \cdot \mathbf{w} = 0; \theta = 90°$ **93.** Parallel **95.** Parallel **97.** Orthogonal

99. $\mathbf{v}_1 = \frac{4}{5}\mathbf{i} - \frac{3}{5}\mathbf{j}$; $\mathbf{v}_2 = \frac{6}{5}\mathbf{i} + \frac{8}{5}\mathbf{j}$ **101.** $\mathbf{v}_1 = \frac{9}{10}(3\mathbf{i} + \mathbf{j})$; $\mathbf{v}_2 = \frac{-7}{10}\mathbf{i} + \frac{21}{10}\mathbf{j}$ **103.** $\alpha \approx 56.1°$; $\beta \approx 138°$; $\gamma \approx 68.2°$ **105.** $2\sqrt{83}$ **107.** $-2\mathbf{i} + 3\mathbf{j} - \mathbf{k}$ **109.** $\sqrt{29} \approx 5.39$ mi/hr; 0.4 mi **111.** Left cable: 1843.21 lb; right cable: 1630.41 lb **113.** 50 foot-pounds

Chapter Test *(page 635)*

1–3.

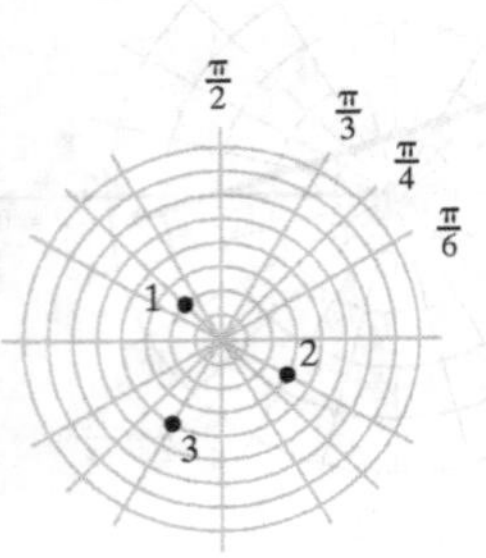

4. $\left(4, \frac{\pi}{3}\right)$

5. $x^2 + y^2 = 49$

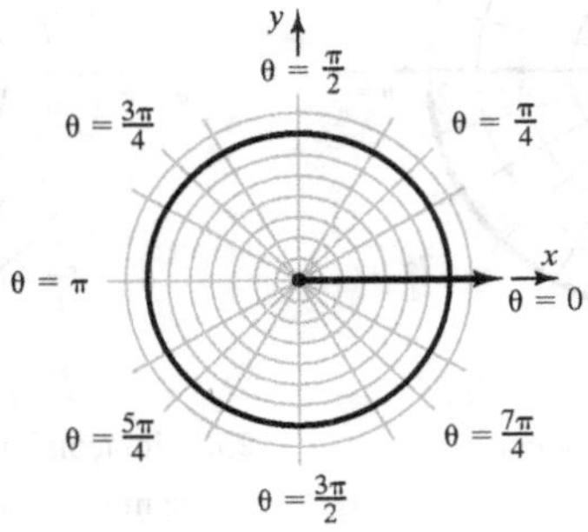

6. $\frac{y}{x} = 3$ or $y = 3x$

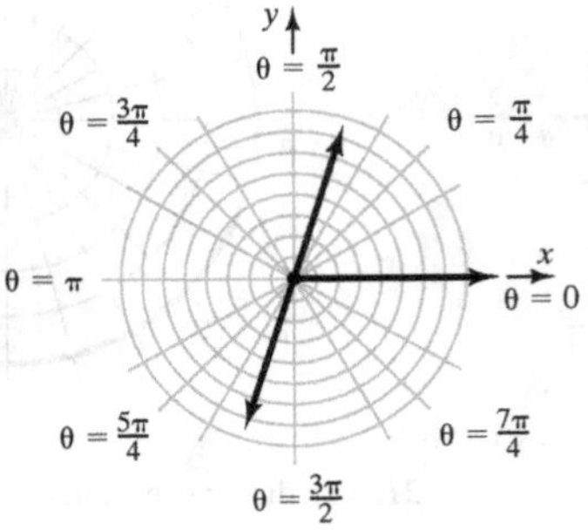

7. $8y = x^2$ or $4(2)y = x^2$
The graph is a parabola with vertex $(0, 0)$ and focus $(0, 2)$.

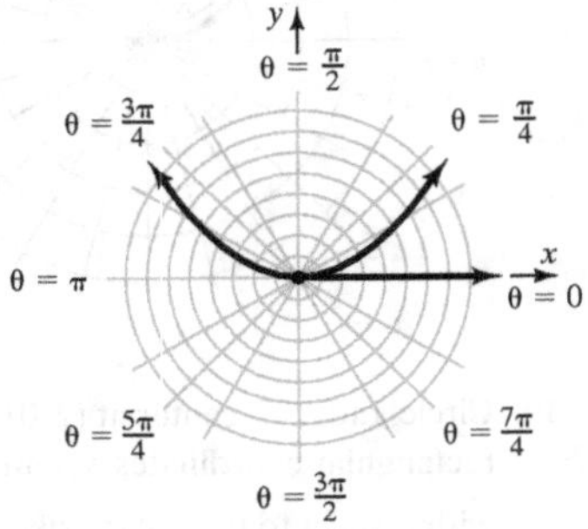

8. $r^2 \cos\theta = 5$ is symmetric about the pole, the polar axis, and the line $\theta = \frac{\pi}{2}$. **9.** $r = 5\sin\theta\cos^2\theta$ is symmetric about the line $\theta = \frac{\pi}{2}$. The tests for symmetry about the pole and the polar axis fail, so the graph of $r = 5\sin\theta\cos^2\theta$ may or may not be symmetric about the pole or polar axis.

10. $z \cdot w = 6(\cos 107° + i\sin 107°)$ **11.** $\frac{w}{z} = \frac{3}{2}(\cos 297° + i\sin 297°)$ **12.** $w^5 = 243(\cos 110° + i\sin 110°)$

13. $z_0 = 2\sqrt[3]{2}(\cos 40° + i\sin 40°)$, $z_1 = 2\sqrt[3]{2}(\cos 160° + i\sin 160°)$, $z_2 = 2\sqrt[3]{2}(\cos 280° + i\sin 280°)$

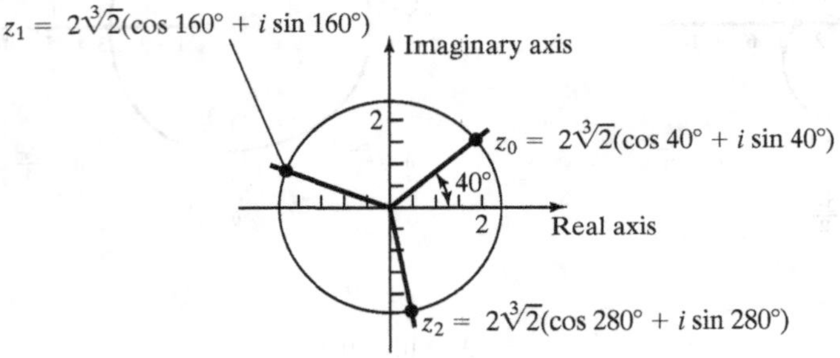

14. $\mathbf{v} = \langle 5\sqrt{2}, -5\sqrt{2}\rangle$ **15.** $\|\mathbf{v}\| = 10$

16. $\mathbf{u} = \frac{\mathbf{v}}{\|\mathbf{v}\|} = \left\langle \frac{\sqrt{2}}{2}, -\frac{\sqrt{2}}{2}\right\rangle$ **17.** 315° off the positive x-axis

18. $\mathbf{v} = 5\sqrt{2}\mathbf{i} - 5\sqrt{2}\mathbf{j}$ **19.** $\mathbf{v}_1 + 2\mathbf{v}_2 - \mathbf{v}_3 = \langle 6, -10\rangle$

20. Vectors $\mathbf{v}_1$ and $\mathbf{v}_4$ are parallel.

21. Vectors $\mathbf{v}_2$ and $\mathbf{v}_3$ are orthogonal.

22. 172.87° **23.** $-9\mathbf{i} - 5\mathbf{j} + 3\mathbf{k}$

24. $\alpha \approx 57.7°$, $\beta \approx 143.3°$, $\gamma \approx 74.5°$ **25.** $\sqrt{115}$

26. The cable must be able to endure a tension of approximately 670.82 lb.

Cumulative Review *(page 635)*

1. $\{-3, 3\}$

3. $x^2 + (y - 1)^2 = 9$

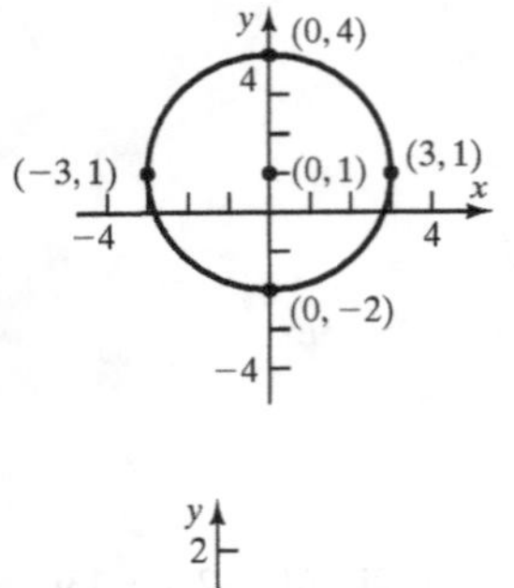

2. $y = \frac{\sqrt{3}}{3}x$

4. $\left\{x \,\middle|\, x < \frac{1}{2}\right\}$ or $\left(-\infty, \frac{1}{2}\right)$

5. Symmetry with respect to the y-axis

6.

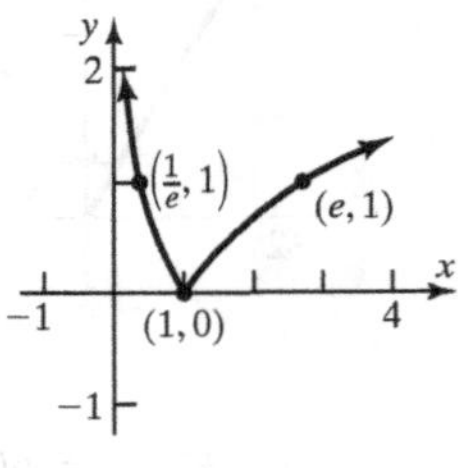

7.

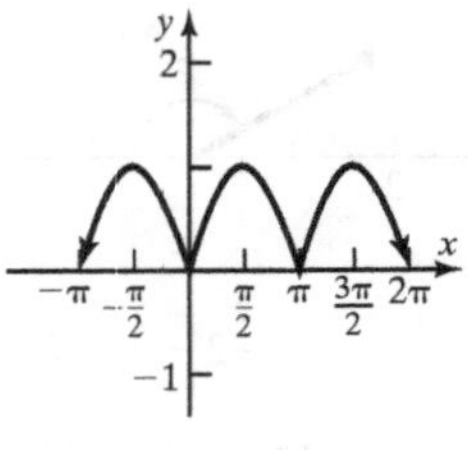

8.

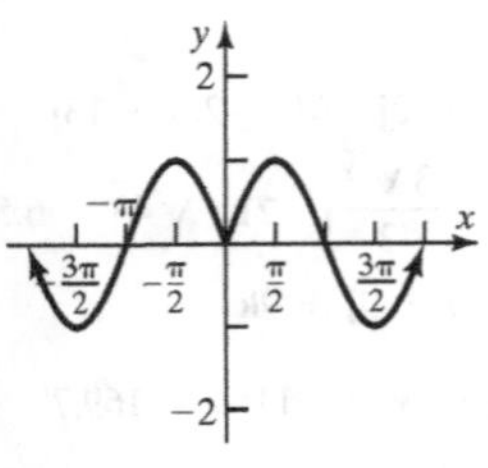

9. $-\frac{\pi}{6}$

10.

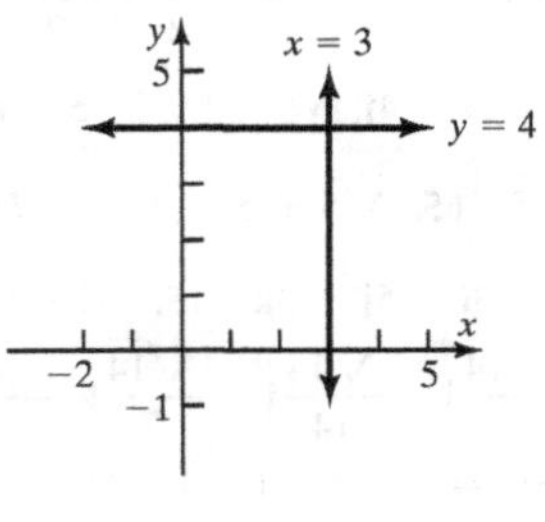

11.

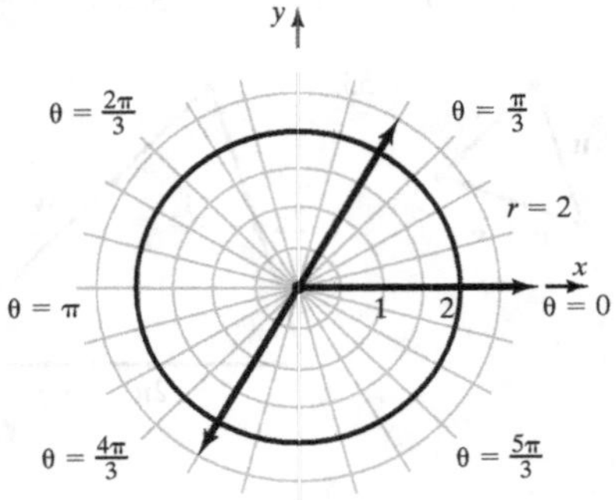

12. Amplitude: 4; period: 2

CHAPTER 10 Analytic Geometry

10.2 Assess Your Understanding *(page 646)*

6. parabola **7.** paraboloid of revolution **8.** T **9.** T **10.** T **11.** *B* **13.** *E* **15.** *H* **17.** *C*

19. $y^2 = 16x$

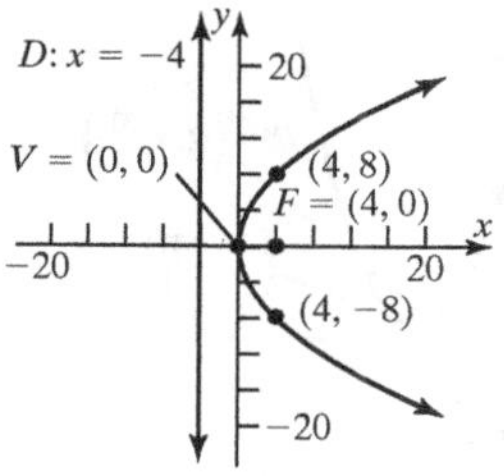

21. $x^2 = -12y$

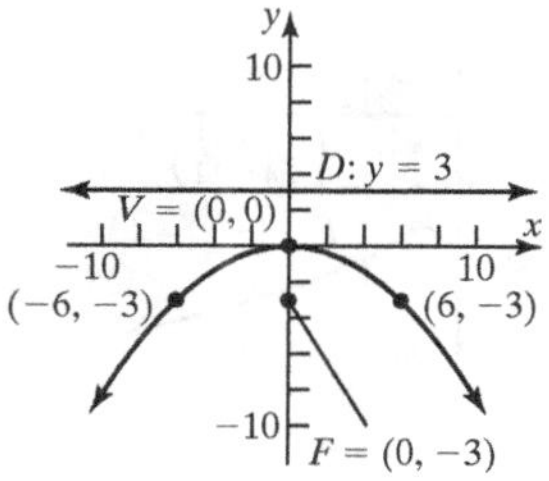

23. $y^2 = -8x$

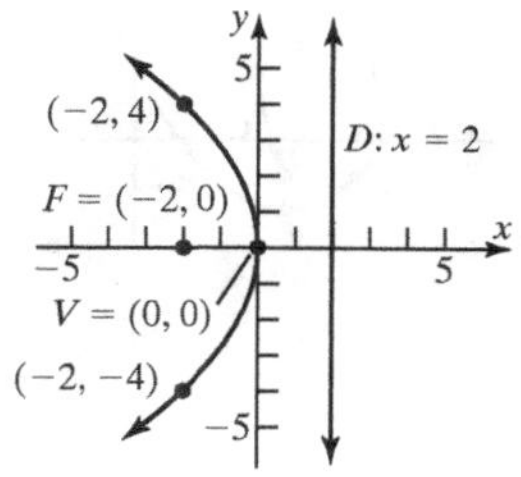

25. $x^2 = 2y$

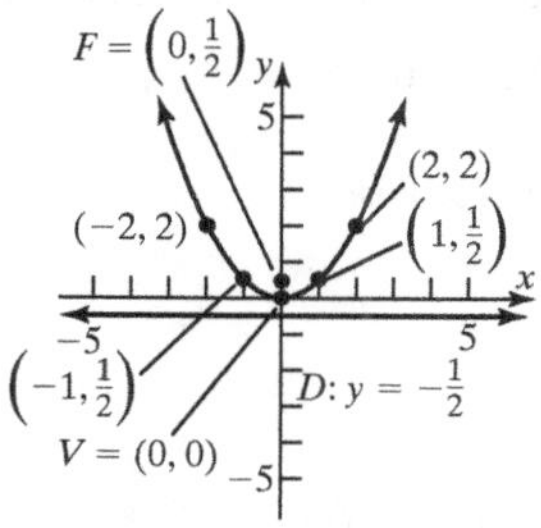

27. $x^2 = \frac{4}{3}y$

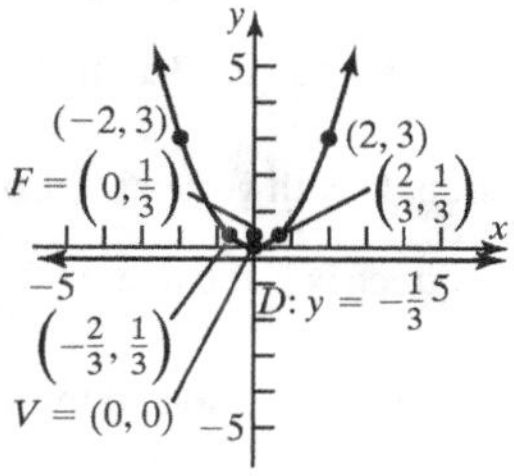

29. $(x - 2)^2 = -8(y + 3)$

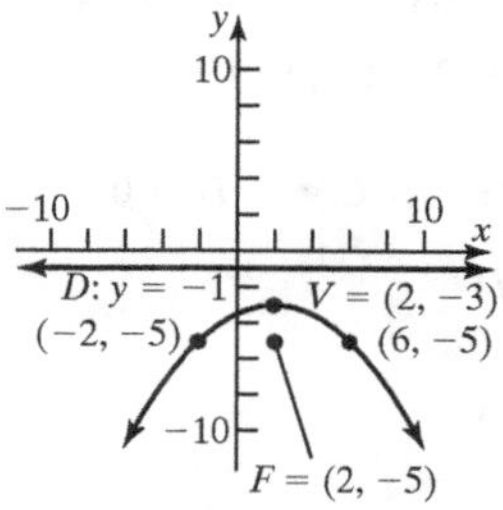

31. $(y + 2)^2 = 4(x + 1)$

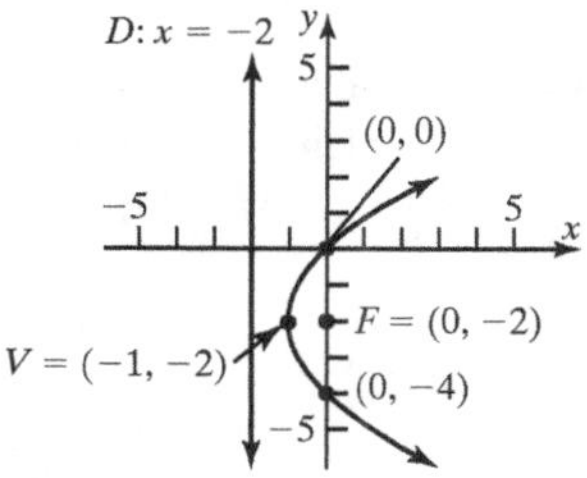

33. $(x + 3)^2 = 4(y - 3)$

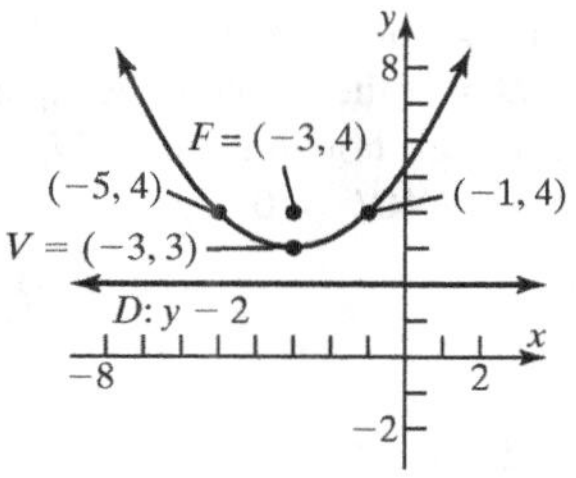

35. $(y + 2)^2 = -8(x + 1)$

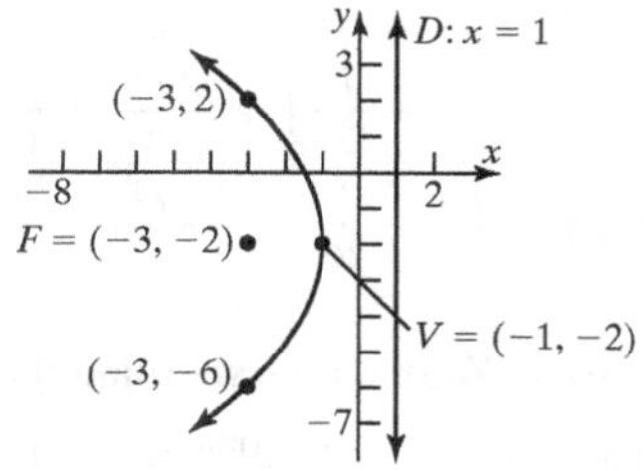

37. Vertex: (0, 0); focus: (0, 1); directrix: $y = -1$

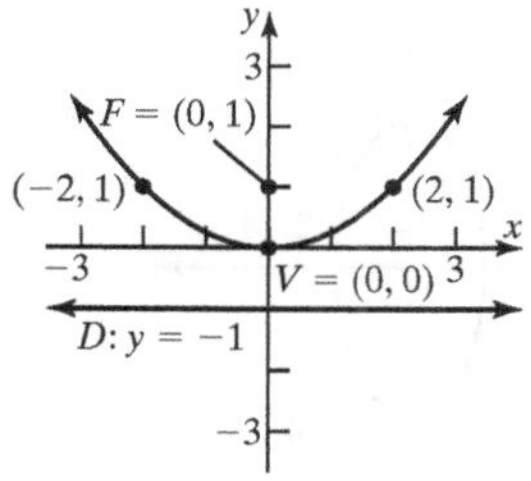

39. Vertex: (0, 0); focus: (−4, 0); directrix: $x = 4$

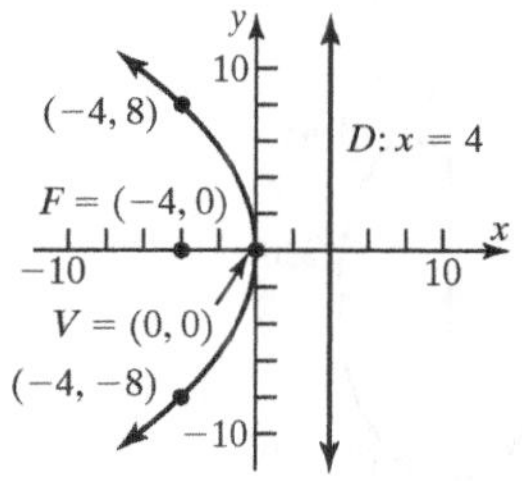

41. Vertex: (−1, 2); focus: (1, 2); directrix: $x = -3$

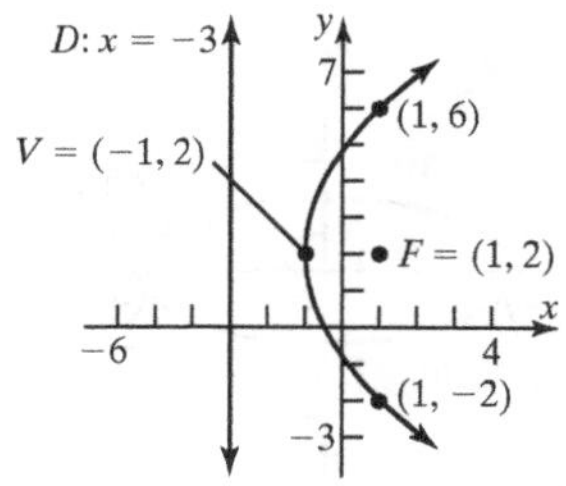

43. Vertex: (3, −1); focus: $\left(3, -\frac{5}{4}\right)$; directrix: $y = -\frac{3}{4}$

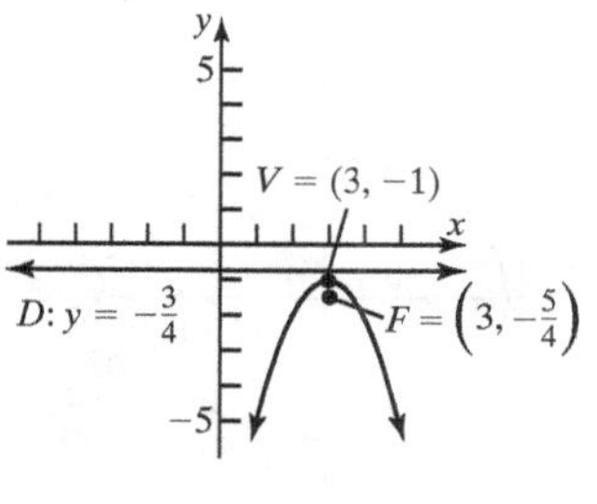

45. Vertex: (2, −3); focus: (4, −3); directrix: $x = 0$

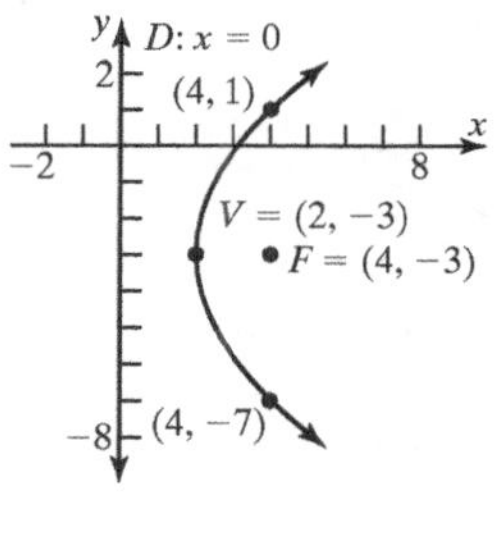

47. Vertex: (0, 2); focus: (−1, 2); directrix: $x = 1$

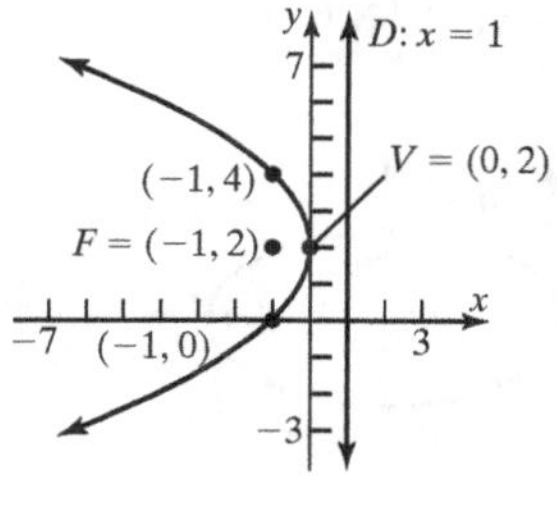

49. Vertex: $(-4, -2)$; focus: $(-4, -1)$; directrix: $y = -3$

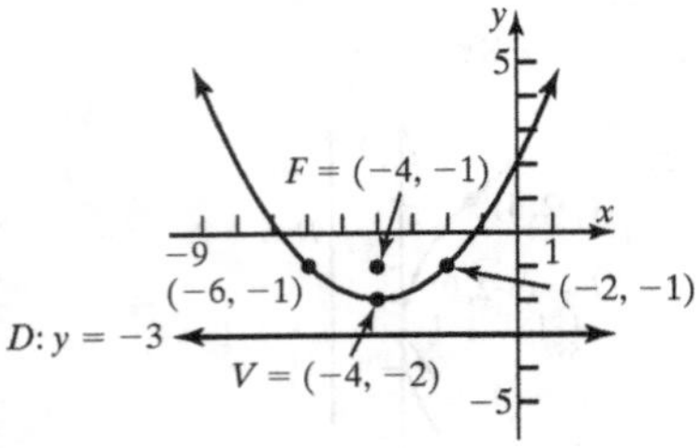

51. Vertex: $(-1, -1)$; focus: $\left(-\frac{3}{4}, -1\right)$; directrix: $x = -\frac{5}{4}$

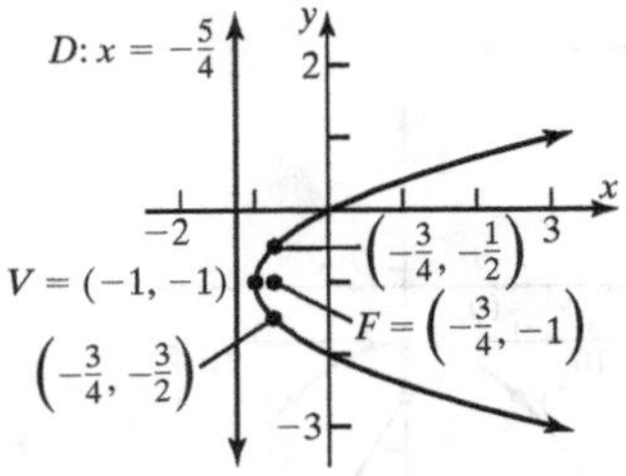

53. Vertex: $(2, -8)$; focus: $\left(2, -\frac{31}{4}\right)$; directrix: $y = -\frac{33}{4}$

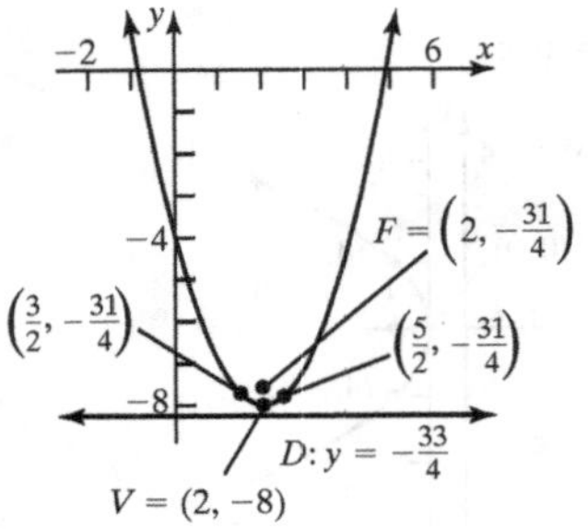

55. $(y - 1)^2 = x$ **57.** $(y - 1)^2 = -(x - 2)$ **59.** $x^2 = 4(y - 1)$ **61.** $y^2 = \frac{1}{2}(x + 2)$ **63.** 1.5625 ft from the base of the dish, along the axis of symmetry **65.** 1 in. from the vertex, along the axis of symmetry **67.** 20 ft **69.** 0.78125 ft **71.** 4.17 ft from the base, along the axis of symmetry **73.** 24.31 ft, 18.75 ft, 7.64 ft **75.** **(a)** $y = -\frac{625}{(299)^2}x^2 + 625$ **(b)** 567 ft: 63.12 ft; 478 ft: 225.67 ft; 308 ft: 459.2 ft **(c)** No

77. $Cy^2 + Dx = 0, C \neq 0, D \neq 0$

$Cy^2 = -Dx$

$y^2 = -\frac{D}{C}x$

This is the equation of a parabola with vertex at $(0, 0)$ and axis of symmetry the x-axis. The focus is $\left(-\frac{D}{4C}, 0\right)$; the directrix is the line $x = \frac{D}{4C}$. The parabola opens to the right if $-\frac{D}{C} > 0$ and to the left if $-\frac{D}{C} < 0$.

79. $Cy^2 + Dx + Ey + F = 0, C \neq 0$

$$Cy^2 + Ey = -Dx - F$$
$$y^2 + \frac{E}{C}y = -\frac{D}{C}x - \frac{F}{C}$$
$$\left(y + \frac{E}{2C}\right)^2 = -\frac{D}{C}x - \frac{F}{C} + \frac{E^2}{4C^2}$$
$$\left(y + \frac{E}{2C}\right)^2 = -\frac{D}{C}x + \frac{E^2 - 4CF}{4C^2}$$

(a) If $D \neq 0$, then the equation may be written as $\left(y + \frac{E}{2C}\right)^2 = -\frac{D}{C}\left(x - \frac{E^2 - 4CF}{4CD}\right)$.
This is the equation of a parabola with vertex at $\left(\frac{E^2 - 4CF}{4CD}, -\frac{E}{2C}\right)$ and axis of symmetry parallel to the x-axis.

(b)–(d) If $D = 0$, the graph of the equation contains no points if $E^2 - 4CF < 0$, is a single horizontal line if $E^2 - 4CF = 0$, and is two horizontal lines if $E^2 - 4CF > 0$.

10.3 Assess Your Understanding *(page 657)*

7. ellipse **8.** major **9.** $(0, -5)$; $(0, 5)$ **10.** F **11.** T **12.** T **13.** C **15.** B

17. Vertices: $(-5, 0)$, $(5, 0)$
Foci: $(-\sqrt{21}, 0)$, $(\sqrt{21}, 0)$

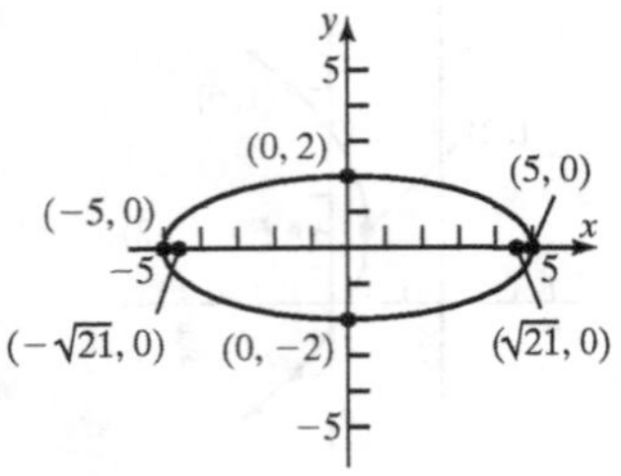

19. Vertices: $(0, -5)$, $(0, 5)$
Foci: $(0, -4)$, $(0, 4)$

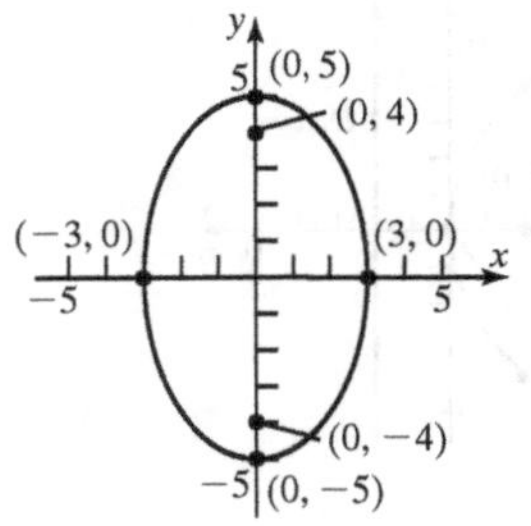

21. $\frac{x^2}{4} + \frac{y^2}{16} = 1$
Vertices: $(0, -4)$, $(0, 4)$
Foci: $(0, -2\sqrt{3})$, $(0, 2\sqrt{3})$

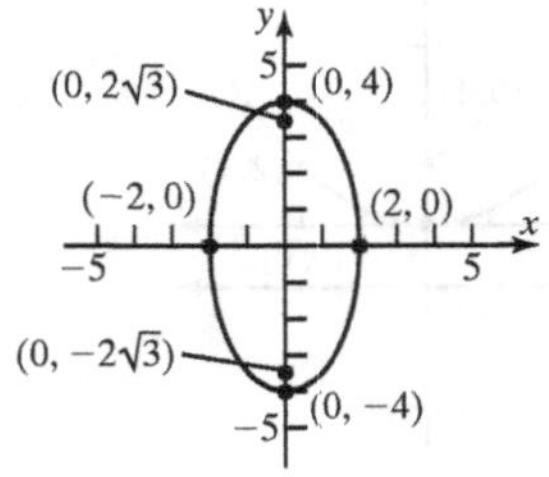

23. $\frac{x^2}{8} + \frac{y^2}{2} = 1$
Vertices: $(-2\sqrt{2}, 0)$, $(2\sqrt{2}, 0)$
Foci: $(-\sqrt{6}, 0)$, $(\sqrt{6}, 0)$

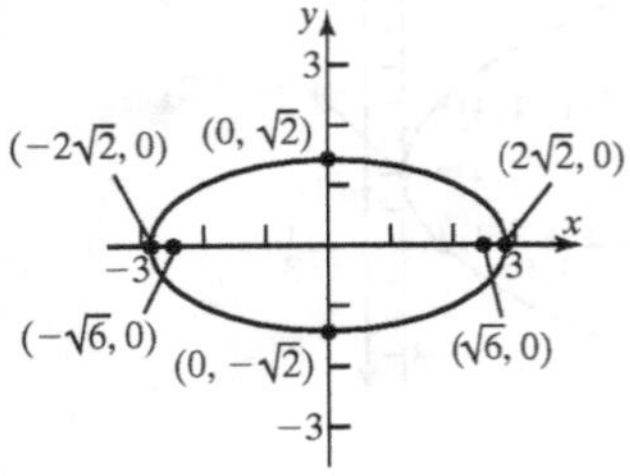

25. $\frac{x^2}{16} + \frac{y^2}{16} = 1$
Vertices: $(-4, 0)$, $(4, 0)$, $(0, -4)$, $(0, 4)$
Focus: $(0, 0)$

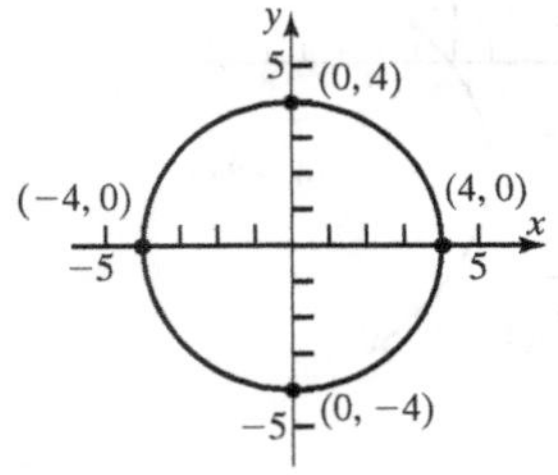

27. $\frac{x^2}{25} + \frac{y^2}{16} = 1$

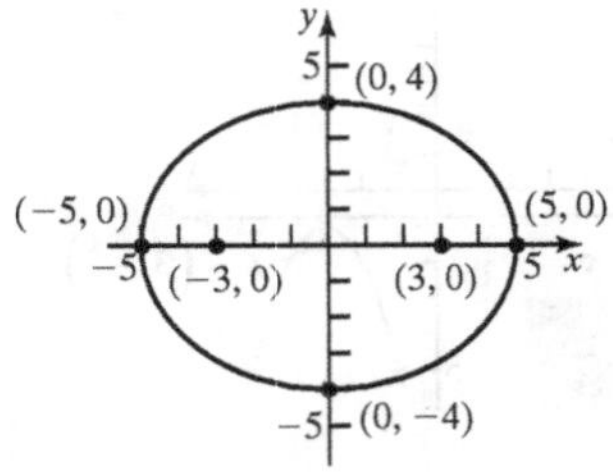

29. $\dfrac{x^2}{9} + \dfrac{y^2}{25} = 1$

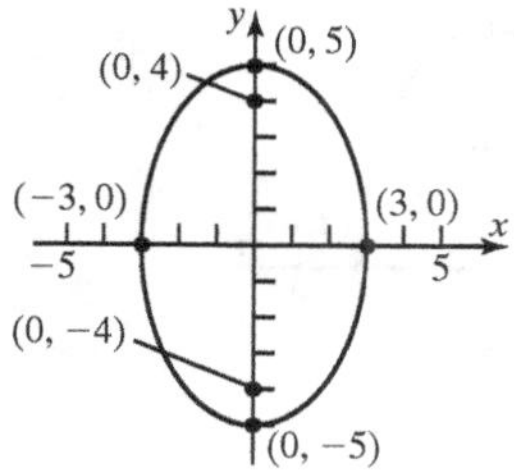

31. $\dfrac{x^2}{9} + \dfrac{y^2}{5} = 1$

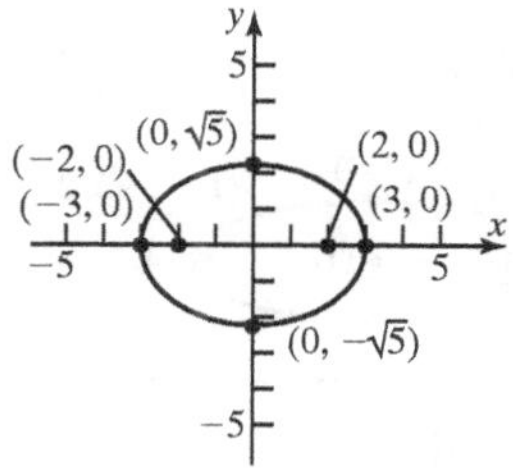

33. $\dfrac{x^2}{25} + \dfrac{y^2}{9} = 1$

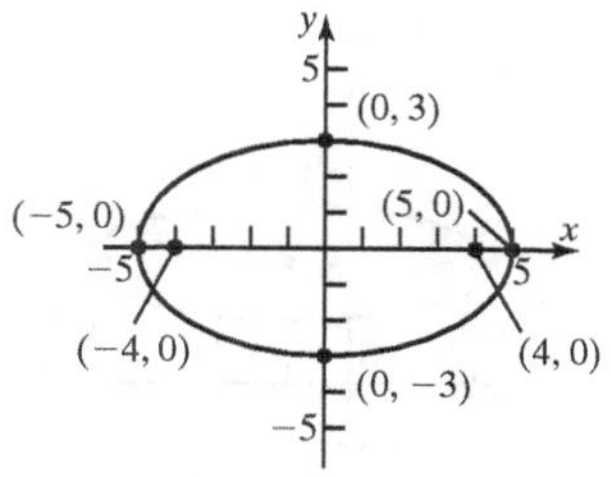

35. $\dfrac{x^2}{4} + \dfrac{y^2}{13} = 1$

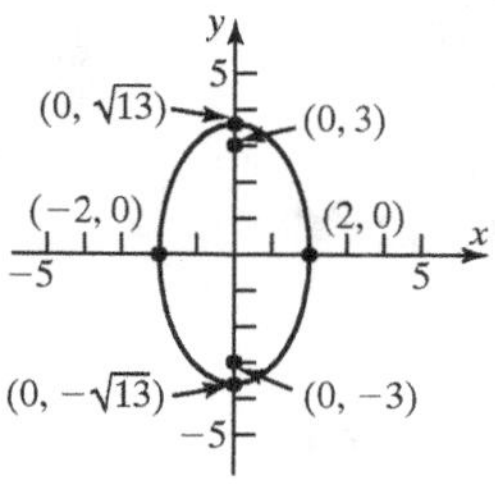

37. $x^2 + \dfrac{y^2}{16} = 1$

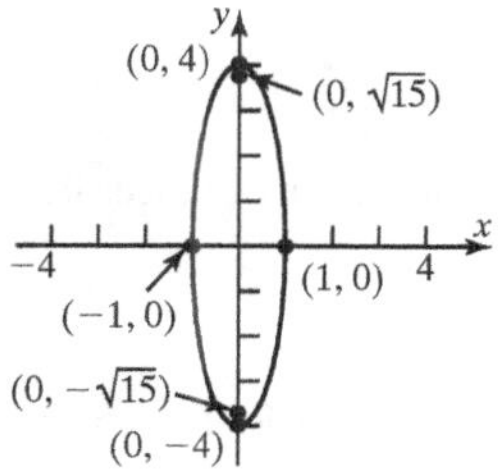

39. $\dfrac{(x + 1)^2}{4} + (y - 1)^2 = 1$

41. $(x - 1)^2 + \dfrac{y^2}{4} = 1$

43. Center: $(3, -1)$; vertices: $(3, -4)$, $(3, 2)$; foci: $\left(3, -1 - \sqrt{5}\right)$, $\left(3, -1 + \sqrt{5}\right)$

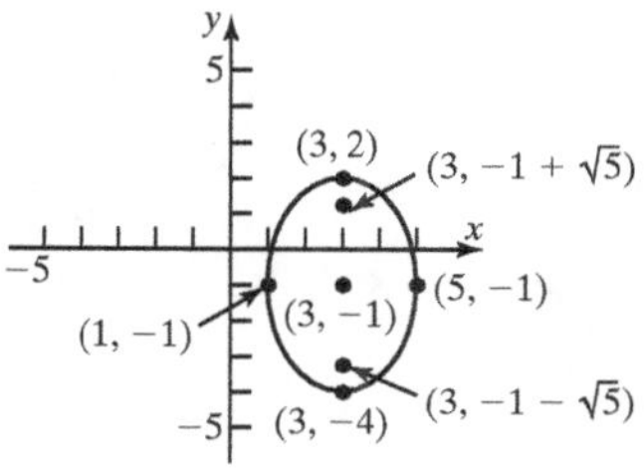

45. $\dfrac{(x + 5)^2}{16} + \dfrac{(y - 4)^2}{4} = 1$
Center: $(-5, 4)$; vertices: $(-9, 4)$, $(-1, 4)$; foci: $\left(-5 - 2\sqrt{3}, 4\right)$, $\left(-5 + 2\sqrt{3}, 4\right)$

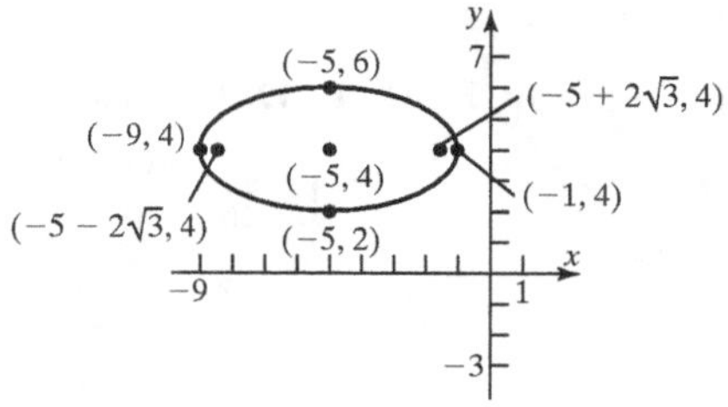

47. $\dfrac{(x + 2)^2}{4} + (y - 1)^2 = 1$
Center: $(-2, 1)$; vertices: $(-4, 1)$, $(0, 1)$; foci: $\left(-2 - \sqrt{3}, 1\right)$, $\left(-2 + \sqrt{3}, 1\right)$

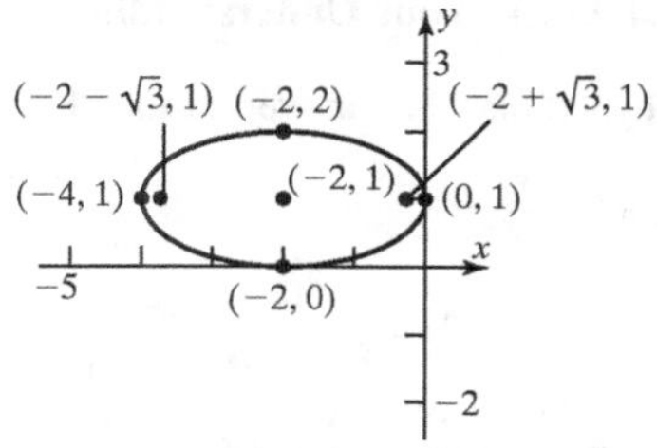

49. $\dfrac{(x - 2)^2}{3} + \dfrac{(y + 1)^2}{2} = 1$
Center: $(2, -1)$; vertices: $\left(2 - \sqrt{3}, -1\right)$; $\left(2 + \sqrt{3}, -1\right)$; foci: $(1, -1)$, $(3, -1)$

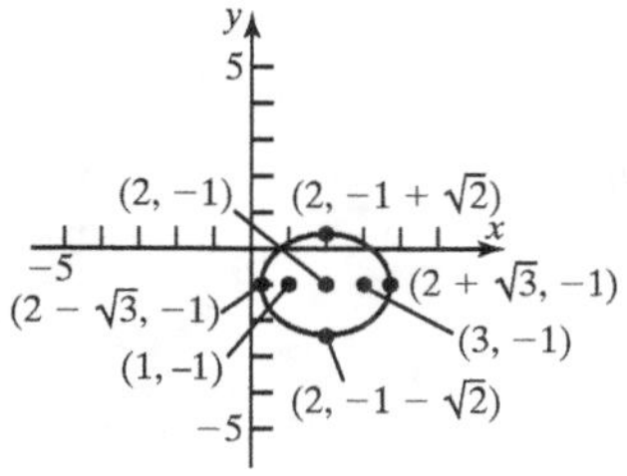

51. $\dfrac{(x - 1)^2}{4} + \dfrac{(y + 2)^2}{9} = 1$
Center: $(1, -2)$; vertices: $(1, -5)$, $(1, 1)$; foci: $\left(1, -2 - \sqrt{5}\right)$, $\left(1, -2 + \sqrt{5}\right)$

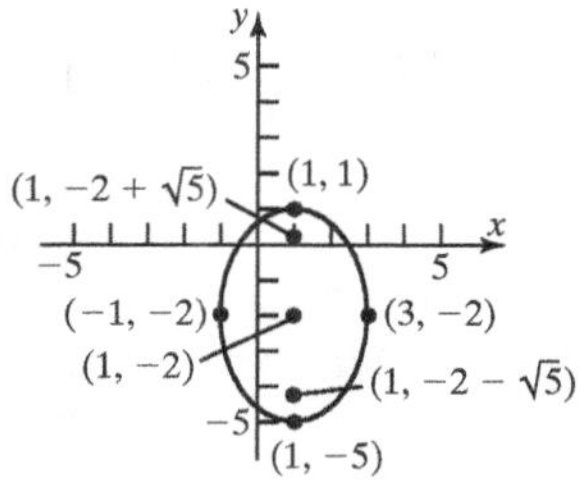

53. $x^2 + \dfrac{(y + 2)^2}{4} = 1$
Center: $(0, -2)$; vertices: $(0, -4)$, $(0, 0)$; foci: $\left(0, -2 - \sqrt{3}\right)$, $\left(0, -2 + \sqrt{3}\right)$

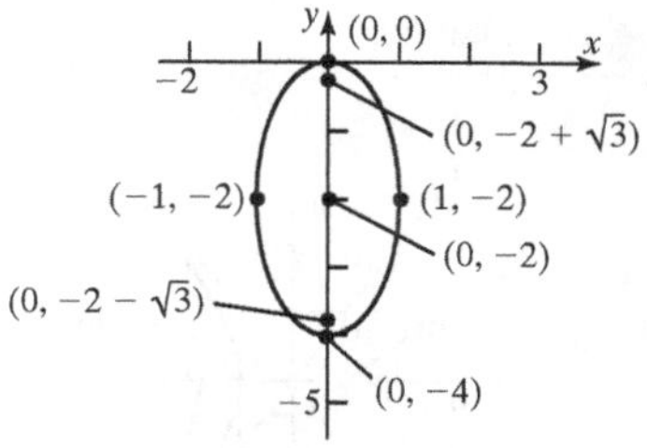

55. $\dfrac{(x - 2)^2}{25} + \dfrac{(y + 2)^2}{21} = 1$

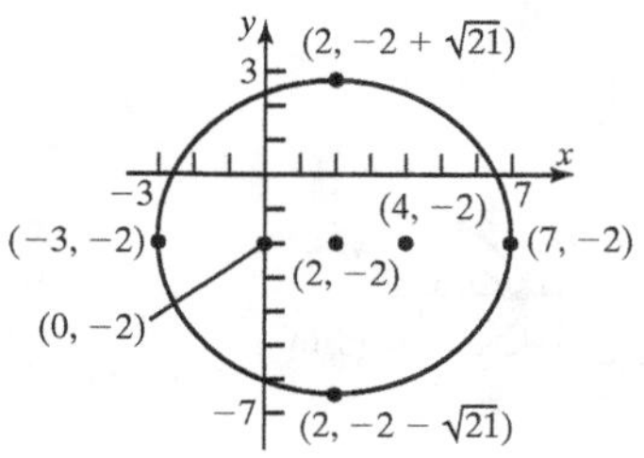

57. $\dfrac{(x - 4)^2}{5} + \dfrac{(y - 6)^2}{9} = 1$

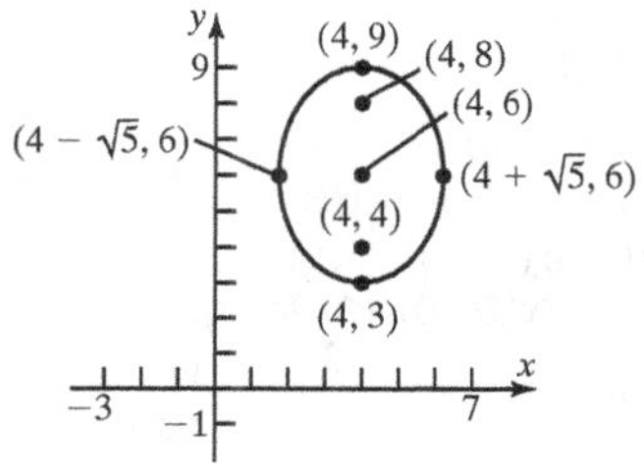

59. $\dfrac{(x - 2)^2}{16} + \dfrac{(y - 1)^2}{7} = 1$

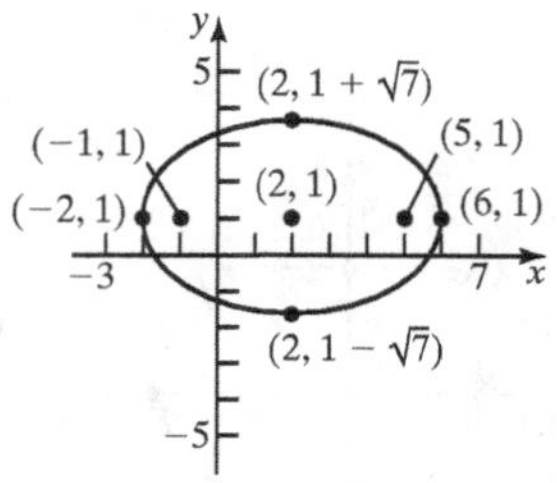

61. $\dfrac{(x-1)^2}{10} + (y-2)^2 = 1$

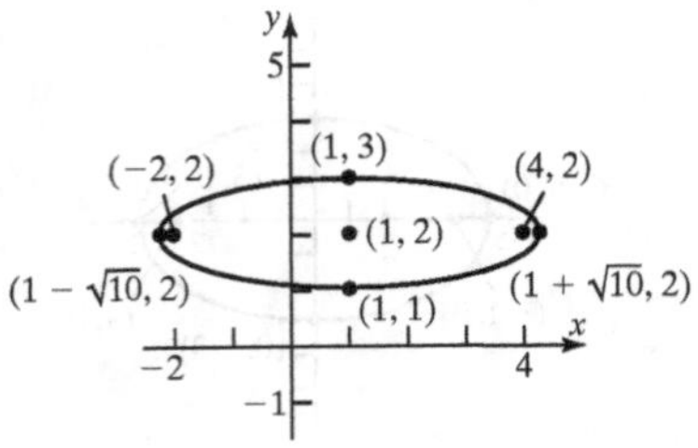

63. $\dfrac{(x-1)^2}{9} + (y-2)^2 = 1$

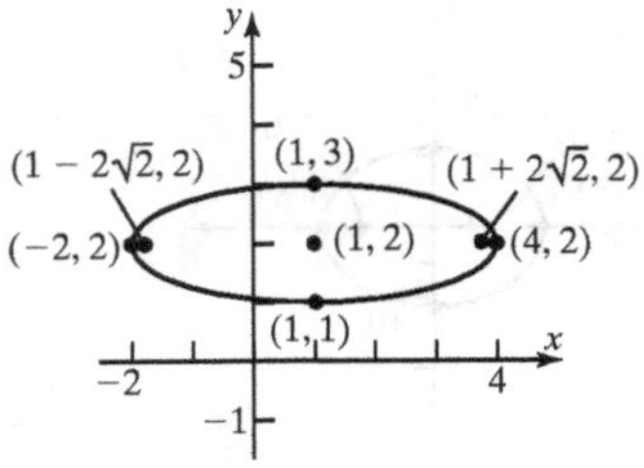

65.

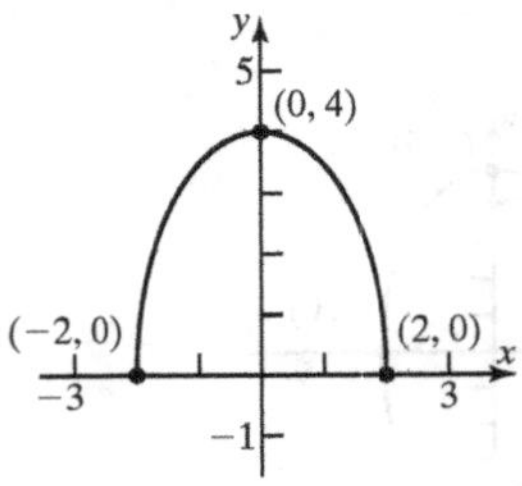

67.

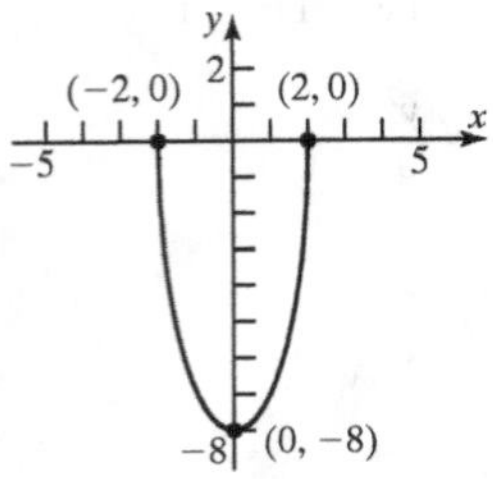

69. $\dfrac{x^2}{100} + \dfrac{y^2}{36} = 1$ **71.** 43.3 ft **73.** 24.65 ft, 21.65 ft, 13.82 ft **75.** 30 ft

77. The elliptical hole will have a major axis of length $2\sqrt{41}$ in. and a minor axis of length 8 in.

79. 91.5 million mi; $\dfrac{x^2}{8649} + \dfrac{y^2}{8646.75} = 1$

81. Perihelion: 460.6 million mi; mean distance: 483.8 million mi; $\dfrac{x^2}{233{,}482} + \dfrac{y^2}{233{,}524.2} = 1$

83. (a) $Ax^2 + Cy^2 + F = 0$

$Ax^2 + Cy^2 = -F$

If A and C are of the same sign and F is of opposite sign, then the equation takes the form

$\dfrac{x^2}{\left(-\dfrac{F}{A}\right)} + \dfrac{y^2}{\left(-\dfrac{F}{C}\right)} = 1$, where $-\dfrac{F}{A}$ and $-\dfrac{F}{C}$ are positive. This is the equation of an ellipse with center at $(0, 0)$.

(b) If $A = C$, the equation may be written as $x^2 + y^2 = \dfrac{-F}{A}$. This is the equation of a circle with center at $(0, 0)$ and radius equal to $\sqrt{-\dfrac{F}{A}}$.

10.4 Assess Your Understanding *(page 670)*

7. hyperbola **8.** transverse axis **9.** $y = \frac{3}{2}x$; $y = -\frac{3}{2}x$ **10.** F **11.** T **12.** F **13.** *B* **15.** *A*

17. $x^2 - \dfrac{y^2}{8} = 1$

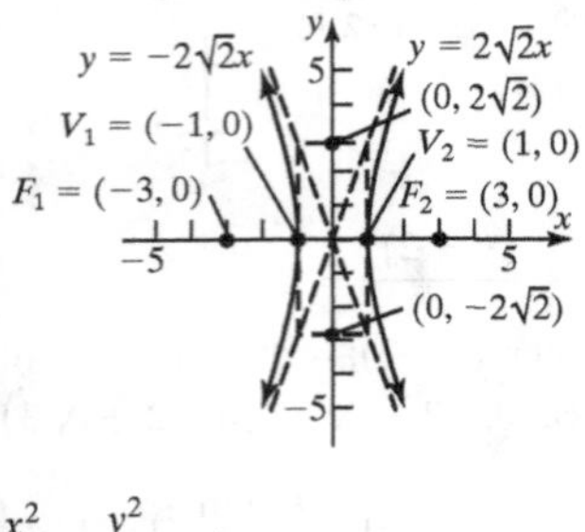

19. $\dfrac{y^2}{16} - \dfrac{x^2}{20} = 1$

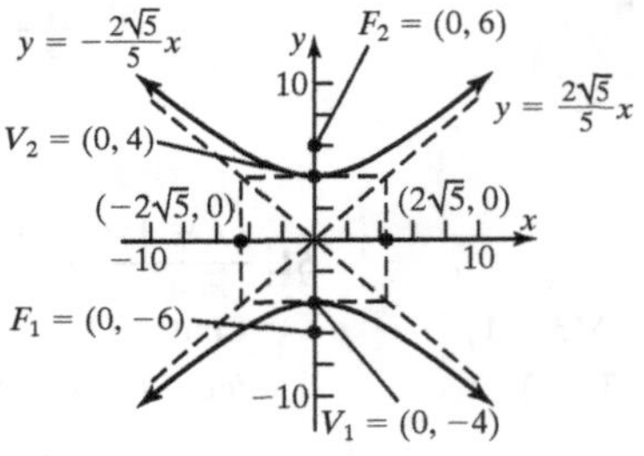

21. $\dfrac{x^2}{9} - \dfrac{y^2}{16} = 1$

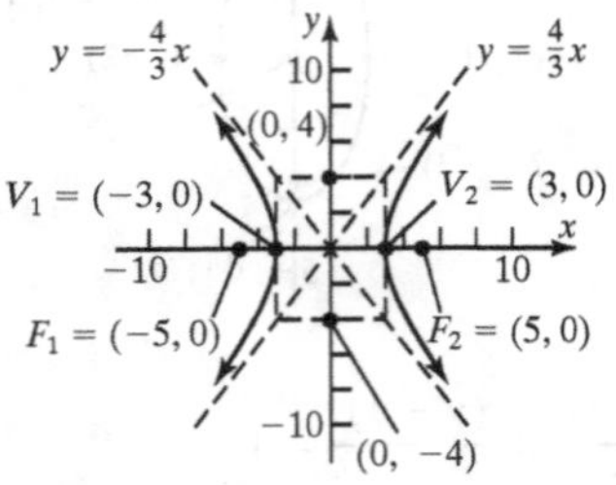

23. $\dfrac{y^2}{36} - \dfrac{x^2}{9} = 1$

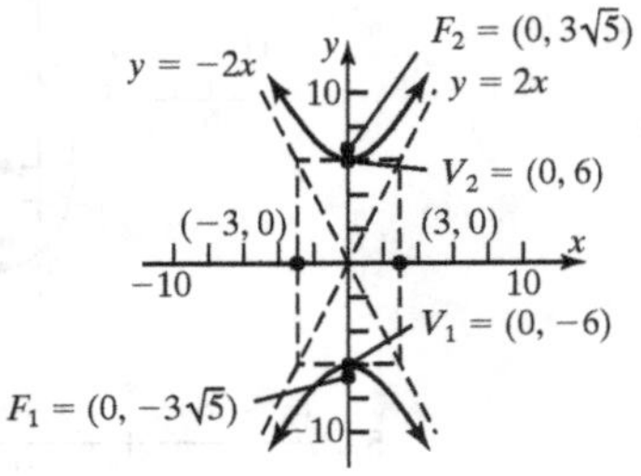

25. $\dfrac{x^2}{8} - \dfrac{y^2}{8} = 1$

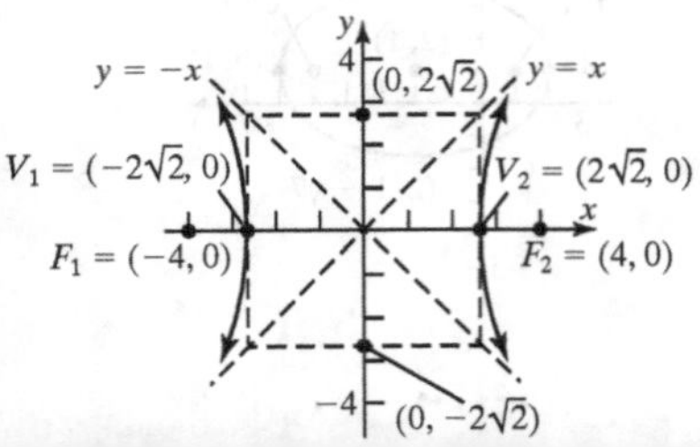

27. $\dfrac{x^2}{25} - \dfrac{y^2}{9} = 1$

Center: $(0, 0)$

Transverse axis: x-axis

Vertices: $(-5, 0)$, $(5, 0)$

Foci: $(-\sqrt{34}, 0)$, $(\sqrt{34}, 0)$

Asymptotes: $y = \pm\dfrac{3}{5}x$

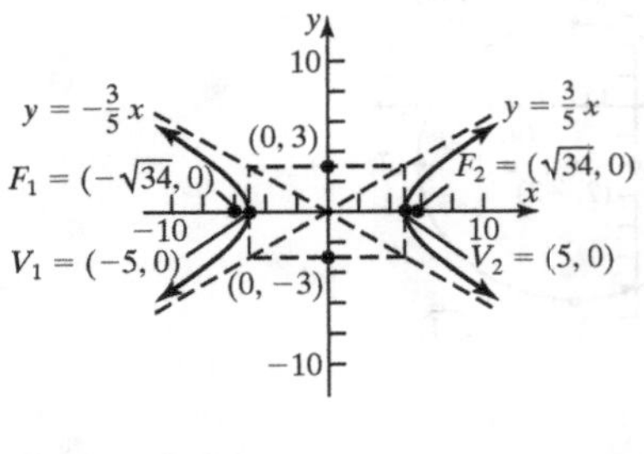

29. $\frac{x^2}{4} - \frac{y^2}{16} = 1$
Center: $(0, 0)$
Transverse axis: x-axis
Vertices: $(-2, 0)$, $(2, 0)$
Foci: $(-2\sqrt{5}, 0)$, $(2\sqrt{5}, 0)$
Asymptotes: $y = \pm 2x$

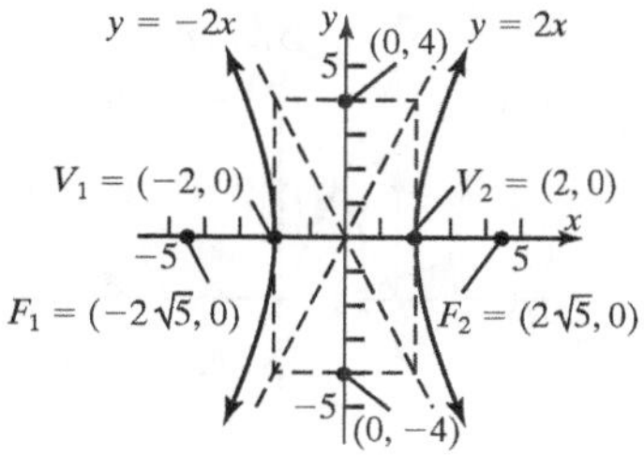

31. $\frac{y^2}{9} - x^2 = 1$
Center: $(0, 0)$
Transverse axis: y-axis
Vertices: $(0, -3)$, $(0, 3)$
Foci: $(0, -\sqrt{10})$, $(0, \sqrt{10})$
Asymptotes: $y = \pm 3x$

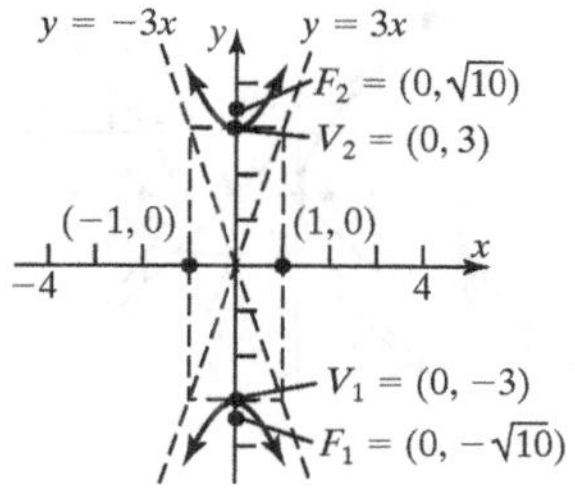

33. $\frac{y^2}{25} - \frac{x^2}{25} = 1$
Center: $(0, 0)$
Transverse axis: y-axis
Vertices: $(0, -5)$, $(0, 5)$
Foci: $(0, -5\sqrt{2})$, $(0, 5\sqrt{2})$
Asymptotes: $y = \pm x$

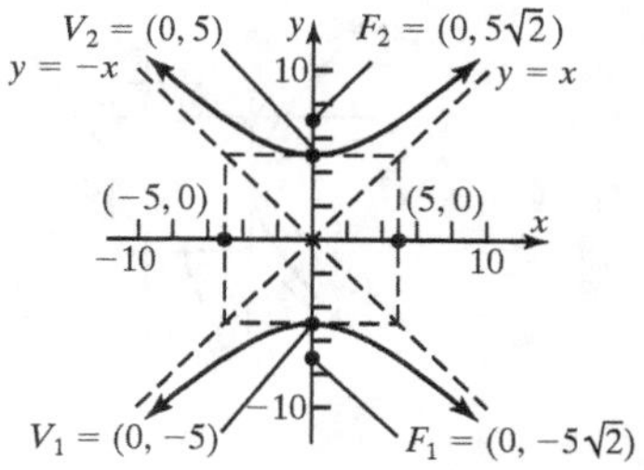

35. $x^2 - y^2 = 1$

37. $\frac{y^2}{36} - \frac{x^2}{9} = 1$

39. $\frac{(x-4)^2}{4} - \frac{(y+1)^2}{5} = 1$

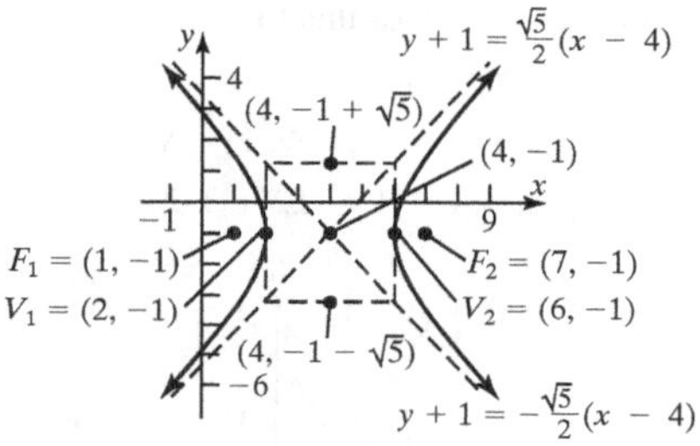

41. $\frac{(y+4)^2}{4} - \frac{(x+3)^2}{12} = 1$

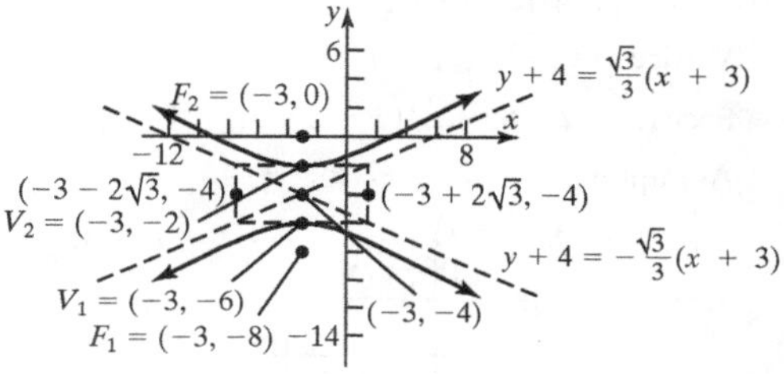

43. $(x-5)^2 - \frac{(y-7)^2}{3} = 1$

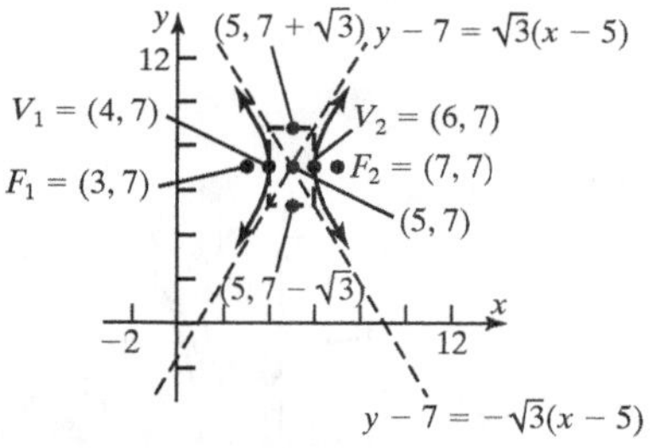

45. $\frac{(x-1)^2}{4} - \frac{(y+1)^2}{9} = 1$

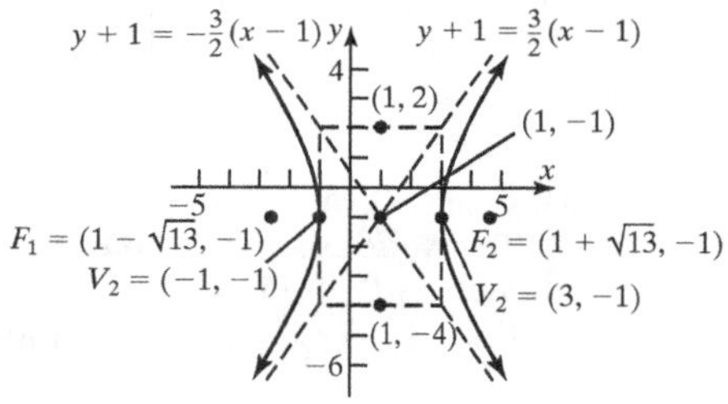

47. $\frac{(x-2)^2}{4} - \frac{(y+3)^2}{9} = 1$
Center: $(2, -3)$
Transverse axis: parallel to x-axis
Vertices: $(0, -3)$, $(4, -3)$
Foci: $(2 - \sqrt{13}, -3)$, $(2 + \sqrt{13}, -3)$
Asymptotes: $y + 3 = \pm\frac{3}{2}(x - 2)$

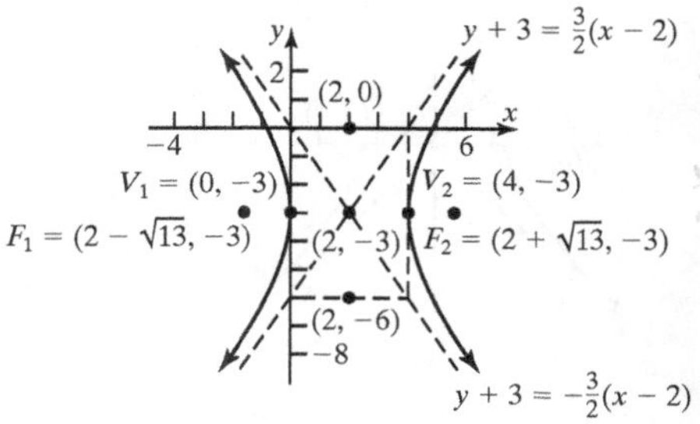

49. $\frac{(y-2)^2}{4} - (x+2)^2 = 1$
Center: $(-2, 2)$
Transverse axis: parallel to y-axis
Vertices: $(-2, 0)$, $(-2, 4)$
Foci: $(-2, 2 - \sqrt{5})$, $(-2, 2 + \sqrt{5})$
Asymptotes: $y - 2 = \pm 2(x + 2)$

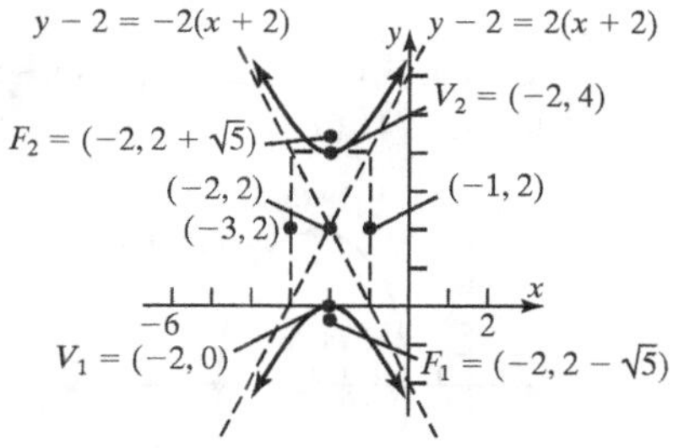

51. $\dfrac{(x+1)^2}{4} - \dfrac{(y+2)^2}{4} = 1$
Center: $(-1, -2)$
Transverse axis: parallel to x-axis
Vertices: $(-3, -2)$, $(1, -2)$
Foci: $\left(-1 - 2\sqrt{2}, -2\right)$, $\left(-1 + 2\sqrt{2}, -2\right)$
Asymptotes: $y + 2 = \pm(x + 1)$

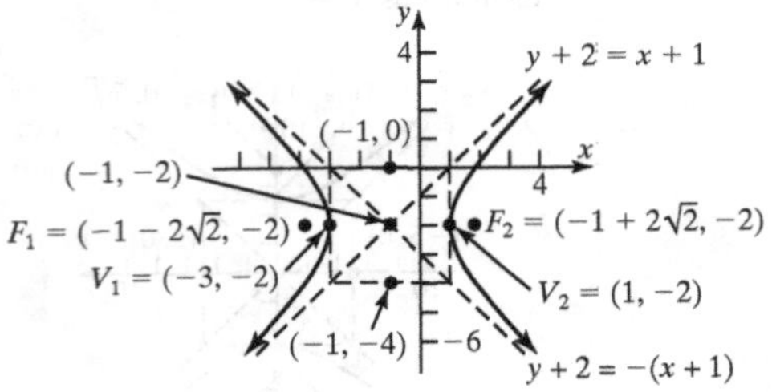

53. $(x-1)^2 - (y+1)^2 = 1$
Center: $(1, -1)$
Transverse axis: parallel to x-axis
Vertices: $(0, -1)$, $(2, -1)$
Foci: $\left(1 - \sqrt{2}, -1\right)$, $\left(1 + \sqrt{2}, -1\right)$
Asymptotes: $y + 1 = \pm(x - 1)$

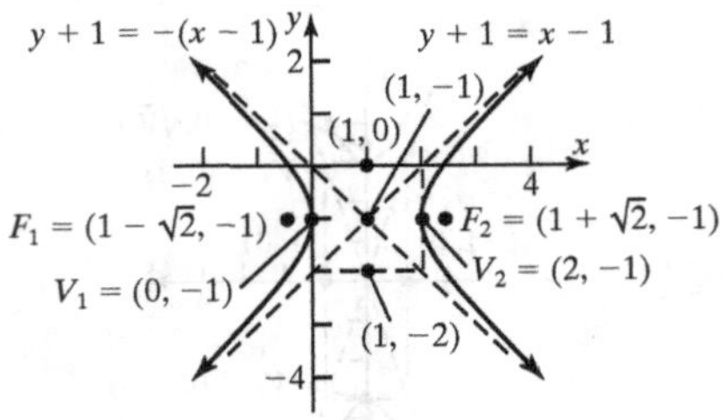

55. $\dfrac{(y-2)^2}{4} - (x+1)^2 = 1$
Center: $(-1, 2)$
Transverse axis: parallel to y-axis
Vertices: $(-1, 0)$, $(-1, 4)$
Foci: $\left(-1, 2 - \sqrt{5}\right)$, $\left(-1, 2 + \sqrt{5}\right)$
Asymptotes: $y - 2 = \pm 2(x + 1)$

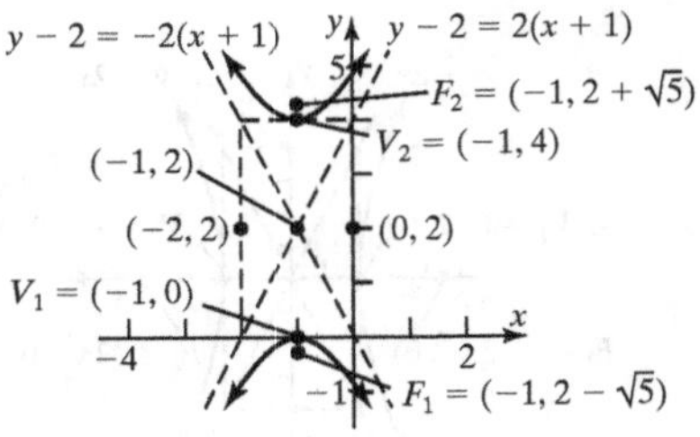

57. $\dfrac{(x-3)^2}{4} - \dfrac{(y+2)^2}{16} = 1$
Center: $(3, -2)$
Transverse axis: parallel to x-axis
Vertices: $(1, -2)$, $(5, -2)$
Foci: $\left(3 - 2\sqrt{5}, -2\right)$, $\left(3 + 2\sqrt{5}, -2\right)$
Asymptotes: $y + 2 = \pm 2(x - 3)$

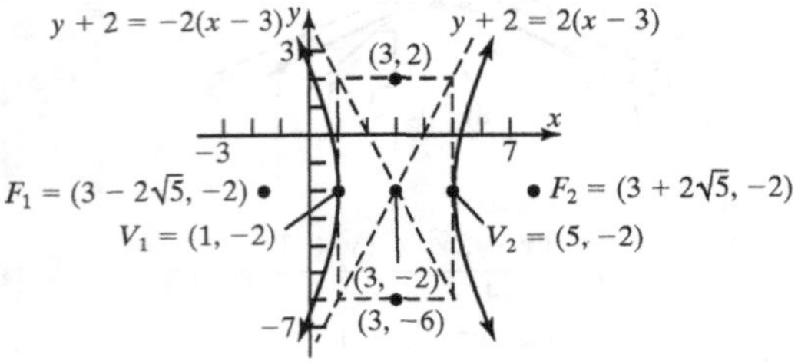

59. $\dfrac{(y-1)^2}{4} - (x+2)^2 = 1$
Center: $(-2, 1)$
Transverse axis: parallel to y-axis
Vertices: $(-2, -1)$, $(-2, 3)$
Foci: $\left(-2, 1 - \sqrt{5}\right)$, $\left(-2, 1 + \sqrt{5}\right)$
Asymptotes: $y - 1 = \pm 2(x + 2)$

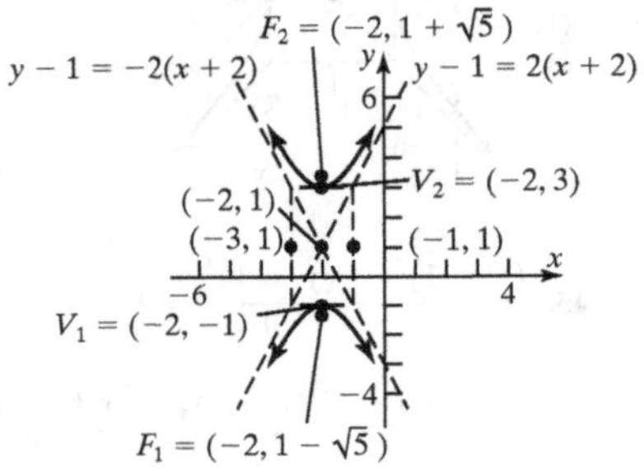

61.

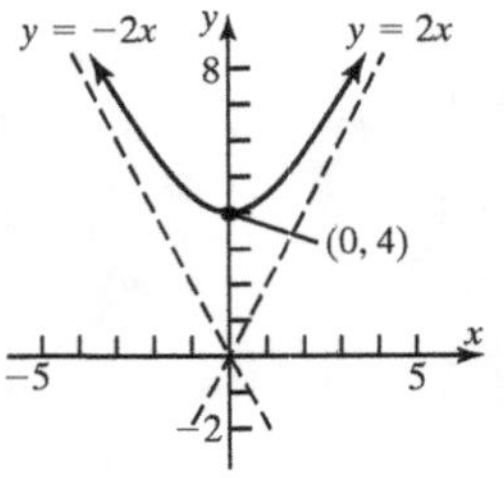

63.

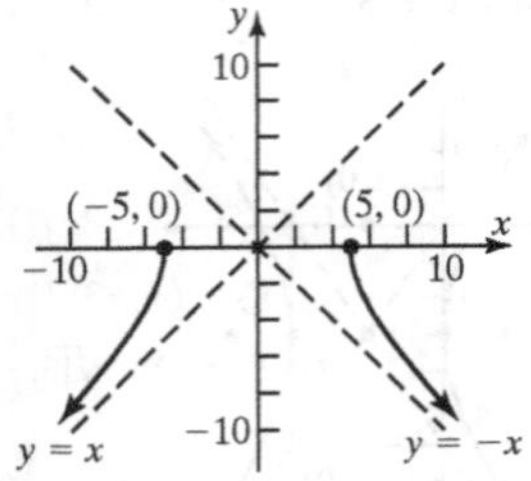

65. Center: $(3, 0)$
Transverse axis: parallel to x-axis
Vertices: $(1, 0)$, $(5, 0)$
Foci: $\left(3 - \sqrt{29}, 0\right)$, $\left(3 + \sqrt{29}, 0\right)$
Asymptotes: $y = \pm\dfrac{5}{2}(x - 3)$

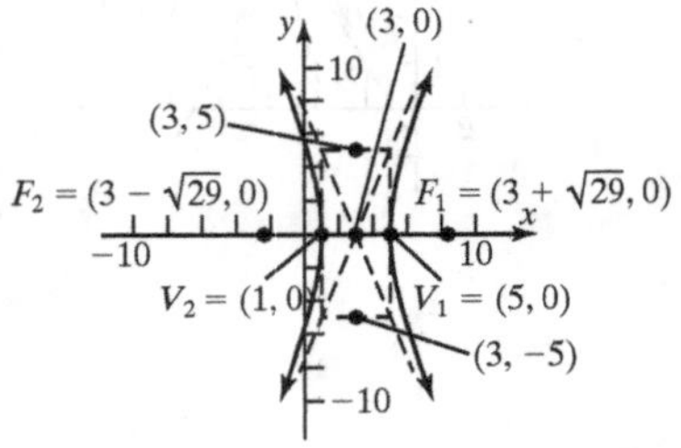

67. Vertex: $(0, 3)$; focus: $(0, 7)$; directrix: $y = -1$

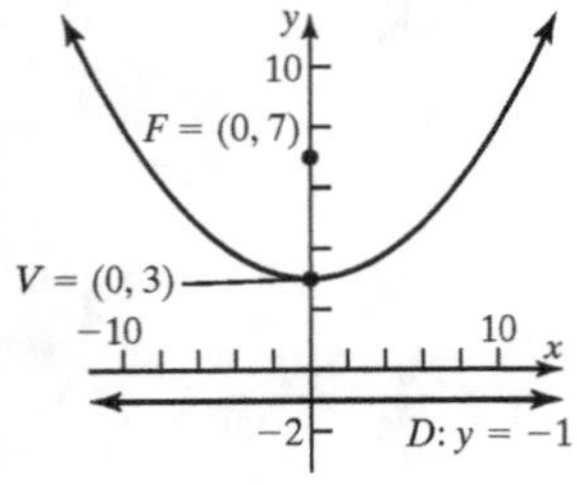

69. $\dfrac{(x-5)^2}{9} + \dfrac{y^2}{25} = 1$
Center: $(5, 0)$; vertices: $(5, 5)$, $(5, -5)$;
foci: $(5, -4)$, $(5, 4)$

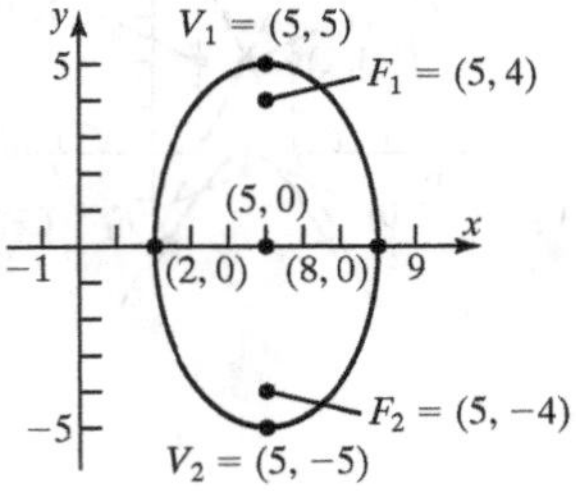

71. $(x - 3)^2 = 8(y + 5)$

Vertex: $(3, -5)$; foci: $(3, -3)$;

directrix: $y = -7$

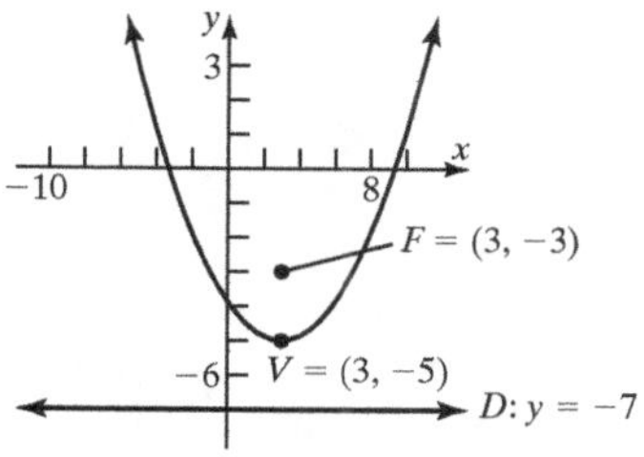

73. The fireworks display is 50,138 ft north of the person at point A. **75.** The tower is 592.4 ft tall.

77. **(a)** $y = \pm x$

(b) $\dfrac{x^2}{100} - \dfrac{y^2}{100} = 1, x \geq 0$

81. $\dfrac{x^2}{4} - y^2 = 1$: asymptotes $y = \pm\dfrac{1}{2}x$

$y^2 - \dfrac{x^2}{4} = 1$: asymptotes $y = \pm\dfrac{1}{2}x$

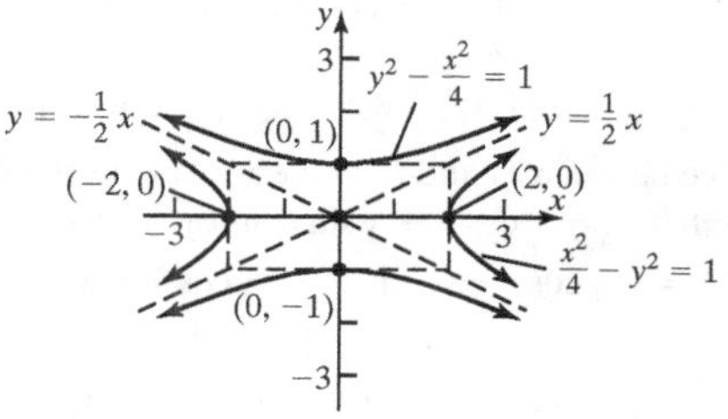

83. $Ax^2 + Cy^2 + F = 0$

$Ax^2 + Cy^2 = -F$

If A and C are of opposite sign and $F \neq 0$, this equation may be written as $\dfrac{x^2}{\left(-\dfrac{F}{A}\right)} + \dfrac{y^2}{\left(-\dfrac{F}{C}\right)} = 1$, where $-\dfrac{F}{A}$ and $-\dfrac{F}{C}$ are opposite in sign. This is the equation of a hyperbola with center $(0, 0)$. The transverse axis is the x-axis if $-\dfrac{F}{A} > 0$; the transverse axis is the y-axis if $-\dfrac{F}{A} < 0$.

10.5 Assess Your Understanding *(page 679)*

5. $\cot(2\theta) = \dfrac{A - C}{B}$ **6.** Hyperbola **7.** Ellipse **8.** T **9.** T **10.** F **11.** Parabola **13.** Ellipse **15.** Hyperbola **17.** Hyperbola **19.** Circle **21.** $x = \dfrac{\sqrt{2}}{2}(x' - y'), y = \dfrac{\sqrt{2}}{2}(x' + y')$ **23.** $x = \dfrac{\sqrt{2}}{2}(x' - y'), y = \dfrac{\sqrt{2}}{2}(x' + y')$ **25.** $x = \dfrac{1}{2}(x' - \sqrt{3}y'), y = \dfrac{1}{2}(\sqrt{3}x' + y')$ **27.** $x = \dfrac{\sqrt{5}}{5}(x' - 2y'), y = \dfrac{\sqrt{5}}{5}(2x' + y')$ **29.** $x = \dfrac{\sqrt{13}}{13}(3x' - 2y'), y = \dfrac{\sqrt{13}}{13}(2x' + 3y')$

31. $\theta = 45°$ (see Problem 21)

$x'^2 - \dfrac{y'^2}{3} = 1$

Hyperbola

Center at origin

Transverse axis is the x'-axis.

Vertices at $(\pm 1, 0)$

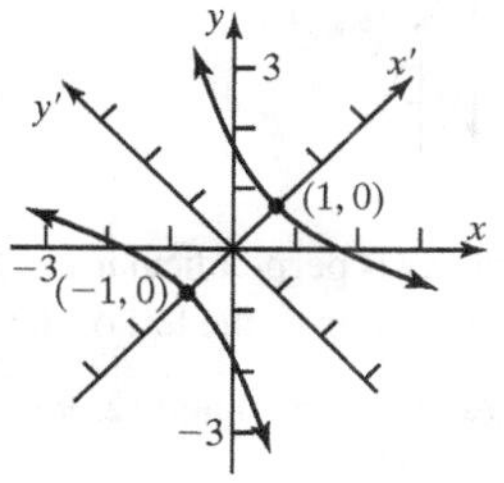

33. $\theta = 45°$ (see Problem 23)

$x'^2 + \dfrac{y'^2}{4} = 1$

Ellipse

Center at $(0, 0)$

Major axis is the y'-axis.

Vertices at $(0, \pm 2)$

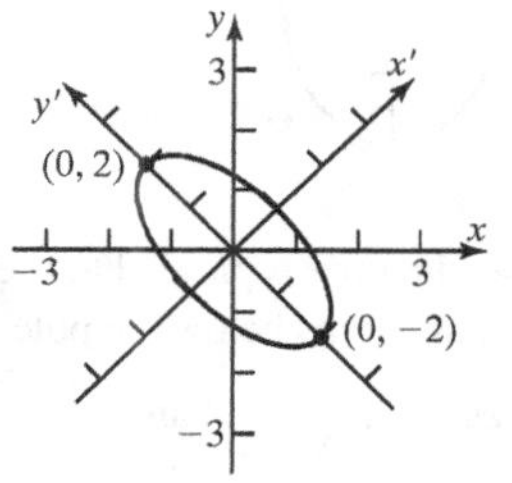

35. $\theta = 60°$ (see Problem 25)

$\dfrac{x'^2}{4} + y'^2 = 1$

Ellipse

Center at $(0, 0)$

Major axis is the x'-axis.

Vertices at $(\pm 2, 0)$

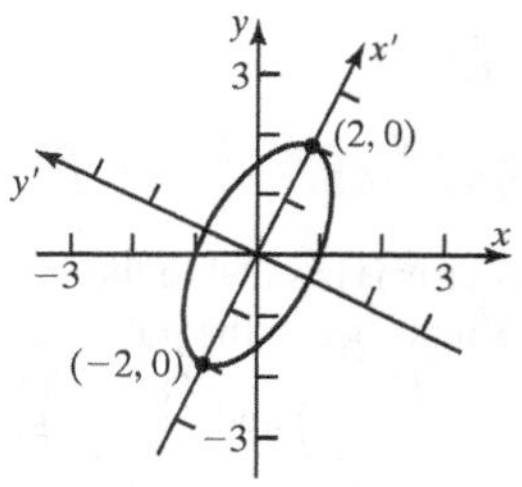

37. $\theta \approx 63°$ (see Problem 27)

$y'^2 = 8x'$

Parabola

Vertex at $(0, 0)$

Focus at $(2, 0)$

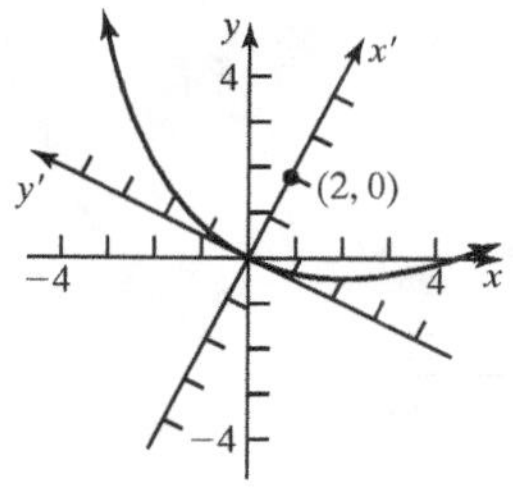

39. $\theta \approx 34°$ (see Problem 29)

$\dfrac{(x' - 2)^2}{4} + y'^2 = 1$

Ellipse

Center at $(2, 0)$

Major axis is the x'-axis.

Vertices at $(4, 0)$ and $(0, 0)$

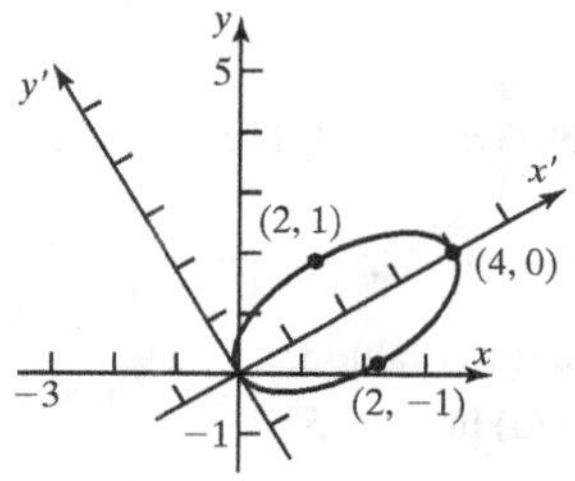

41. $\cot(2\theta) = \dfrac{7}{24}$;

$\theta = \sin^{-1}\left(\dfrac{3}{5}\right) \approx 37°$

$(x' - 1)^2 = -6\left(y' - \dfrac{1}{6}\right)$

Parabola

Vertex at $\left(1, \dfrac{1}{6}\right)$

Focus at $\left(1, -\dfrac{4}{3}\right)$

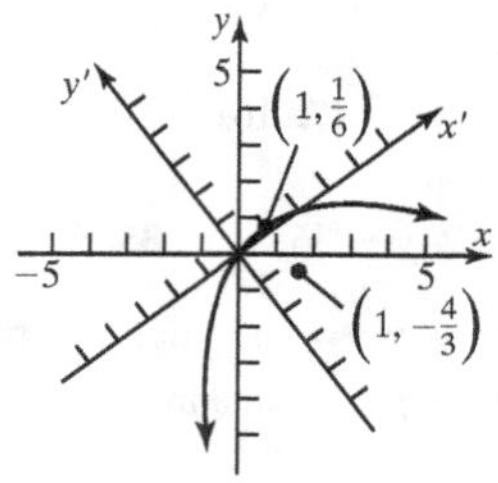

43. Hyperbola **45.** Hyperbola **47.** Parabola **49.** Ellipse **51.** Ellipse

53. Refer to equation (6):
$$\begin{aligned} A' &= A\cos^2\theta + B\sin\theta\cos\theta + C\sin^2\theta \\ B' &= B(\cos^2\theta - \sin^2\theta) + 2(C - A)(\sin\theta\cos\theta) \\ C' &= A\sin^2\theta - B\sin\theta\cos\theta + C\cos^2\theta \\ D' &= D\cos\theta + E\sin\theta \\ E' &= -D\sin\theta + E\cos\theta \\ F' &= F \end{aligned}$$

55. Use Problem 53 to find $B'^2 - 4A'C'$. After much cancellation, $B'^2 - 4A'C' = B^2 - 4AC$.

57. The distance between P_1 and P_2 in the $x'y'$-plane equals $\sqrt{(x_2' - x_1')^2 + (y_2' - y_1')^2}$.
Assuming that $x' = x\cos\theta - y\sin\theta$ and $y' = x\sin\theta + y\cos\theta$, then
$$\begin{aligned}(x_2' - x_1')^2 &= (x_2\cos\theta - y_2\sin\theta - x_1\cos\theta + y_1\sin\theta)^2 \\ &= \cos^2\theta(x_2 - x_1)^2 - 2\sin\theta\cos\theta(x_2 - x_1)(y_2 - y_1) + \sin^2\theta(y_2 - y_1)^2, \text{ and}\end{aligned}$$
$$(y_2' - y_1')^2 = (x_2\sin\theta + y_2\cos\theta - x_1\sin\theta - y_1\cos\theta)^2 = \sin^2\theta(x_2 - x_1)^2 + 2\sin\theta\cos\theta(x_2 - x_1)(y_2 - y_1) + \cos^2\theta(y_2 - y_1)^2.$$
Therefore, $(x_2' - x_1')^2 + (y_2' - y_1')^2 = \cos^2\theta(x_2 - x_1)^2 + \sin^2\theta(x_2 - x_1)^2 + \sin^2\theta(y_2 - y_1)^2 + \cos^2\theta(y_2 - y_1)^2$
$= (x_2 - x_1)^2(\cos^2\theta + \sin^2\theta) + (y_2 - y_1)^2(\sin^2\theta + \cos^2\theta) = (x_2 - x_1)^2 + (y_2 - y_1)^2.$

10.6 Assess Your Understanding *(page 685)*

3. $\frac{1}{2}$; ellipse; parallel; 4; below **4.** 1; <1; >1 **5.** T **6.** T **7.** Parabola; directrix is perpendicular to the polar axis 1 unit to the right of the pole.

9. Hyperbola; directrix is parallel to the polar axis $\frac{4}{3}$ units below the pole.

11. Ellipse; directrix is perpendicular to the polar axis $\frac{3}{2}$ units to the left of the pole.

13. Parabola; directrix is perpendicular to the polar axis 1 unit to the right of the pole; vertex is at $\left(\frac{1}{2}, 0\right)$.

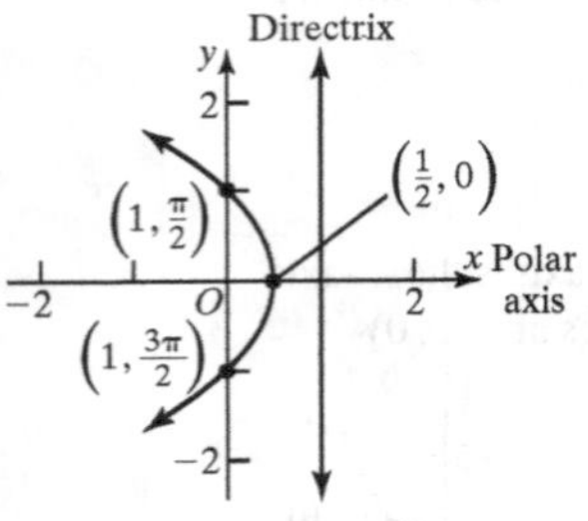

15. Ellipse; directrix is parallel to the polar axis $\frac{8}{3}$ units above the pole; vertices are at $\left(\frac{8}{7}, \frac{\pi}{2}\right)$ and $\left(8, \frac{3\pi}{2}\right)$.

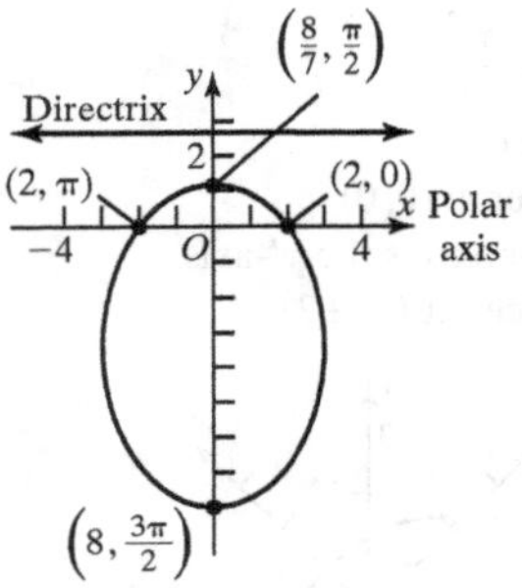

17. Hyperbola; directrix is perpendicular to the polar axis $\frac{3}{2}$ units to the left of the pole; vertices are at $(-3, 0)$ and $(1, \pi)$.

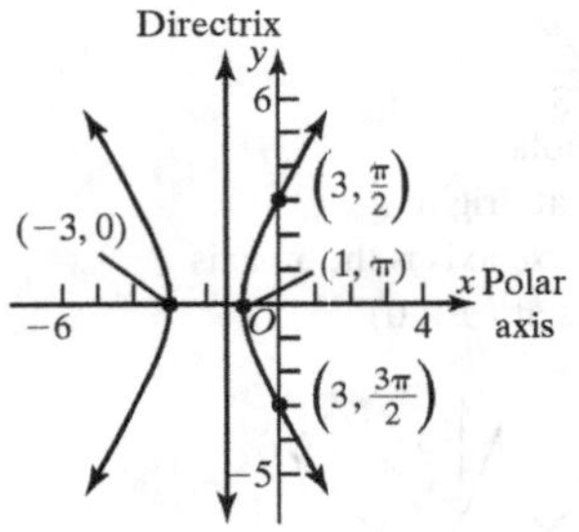

19. Ellipse; directrix is parallel to the polar axis 8 units below the pole; vertices are at $\left(8, \frac{\pi}{2}\right)$ and $\left(\frac{8}{3}, \frac{3\pi}{2}\right)$.

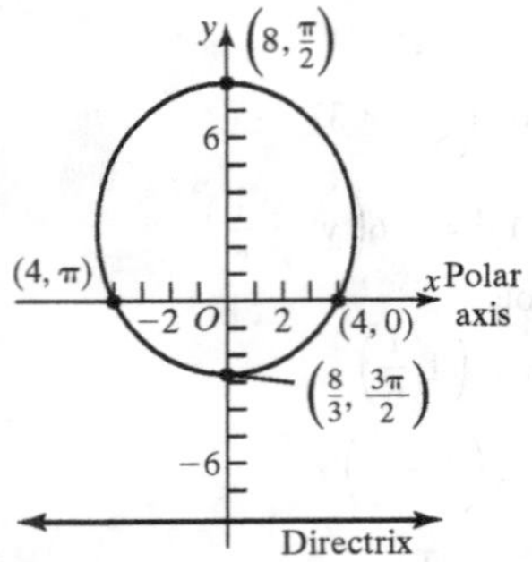

21. Ellipse; directrix is parallel to the polar axis 3 units below the pole; vertices are at $\left(6, \frac{\pi}{2}\right)$ and $\left(\frac{6}{5}, \frac{3\pi}{2}\right)$.

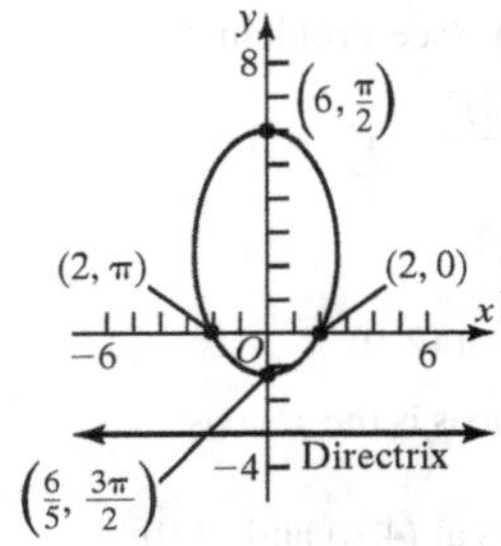

23. Ellipse; directrix is perpendicular to the polar axis 6 units to the left of the pole; vertices are at $(6, 0)$ and $(2, \pi)$.

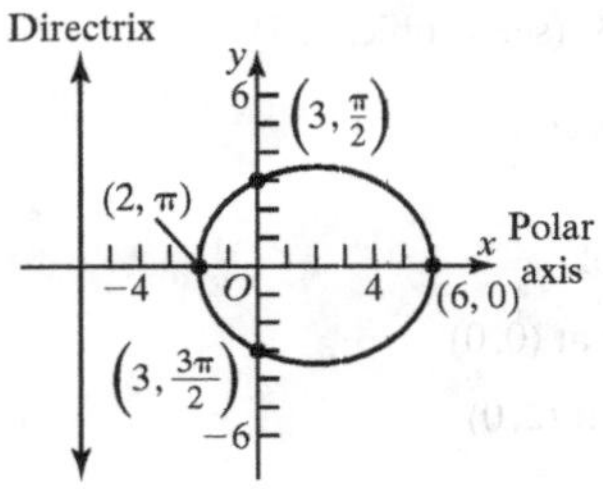

25. $y^2 + 2x - 1 = 0$ **27.** $16x^2 + 7y^2 + 48y - 64 = 0$ **29.** $3x^2 - y^2 + 12x + 9 = 0$ **31.** $4x^2 + 3y^2 - 16y - 64 = 0$

33. $9x^2 + 5y^2 - 24y - 36 = 0$ **35.** $3x^2 + 4y^2 - 12x - 36 = 0$ **37.** $r = \frac{1}{1 + \sin\theta}$ **39.** $r = \frac{12}{5 - 4\cos\theta}$ **41.** $r = \frac{12}{1 - 6\sin\theta}$

43. Use $d(D, P) = p - r\cos\theta$ in the derivation of equation (a) in Table 5.

45. Use $d(D, P) = p + r\sin\theta$ in the derivation of equation (a) in Table 5.

10.7 Assess Your Understanding *(page 697)*

2. plane curve; parameter **3.** ellipse **4.** cycloid **5.** F **6.** T

7.

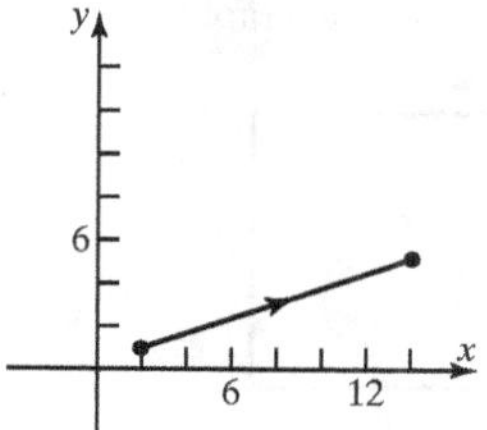

$x - 3y + 1 = 0$

9.

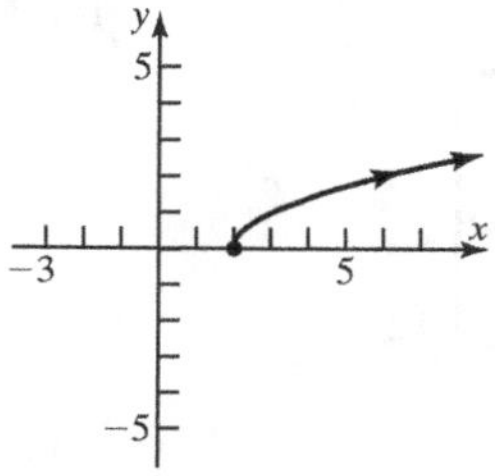

$y = \sqrt{x - 2}$

11.

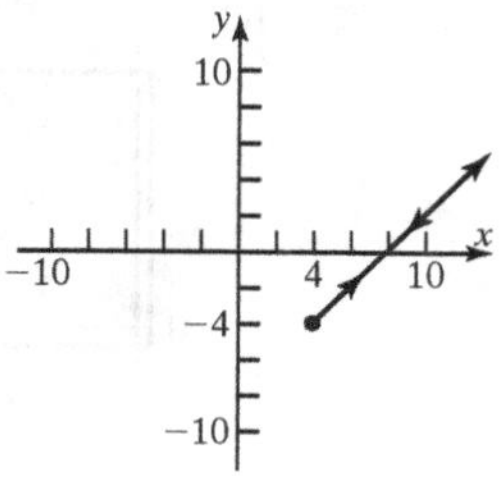

$y = x - 8$

13.

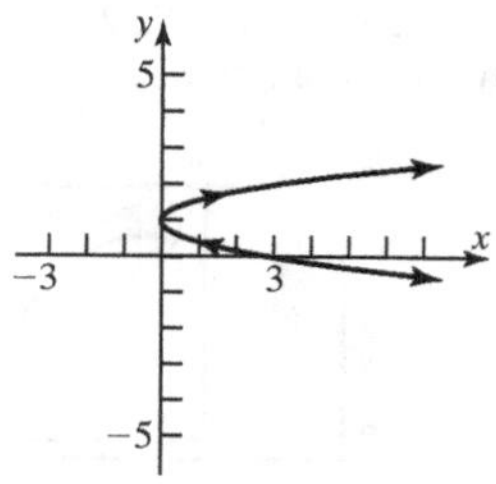

$x = 3(y - 1)^2$

15.

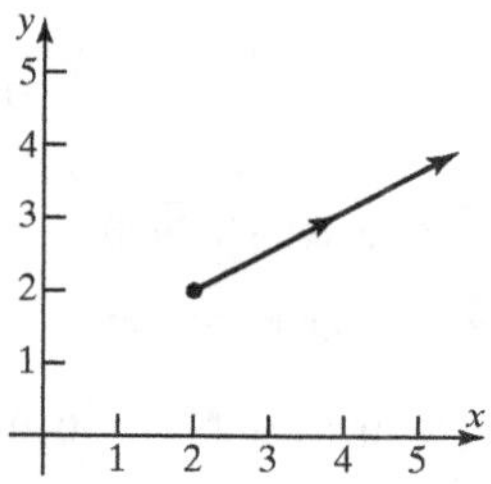

$2y = 2 + x$

17.

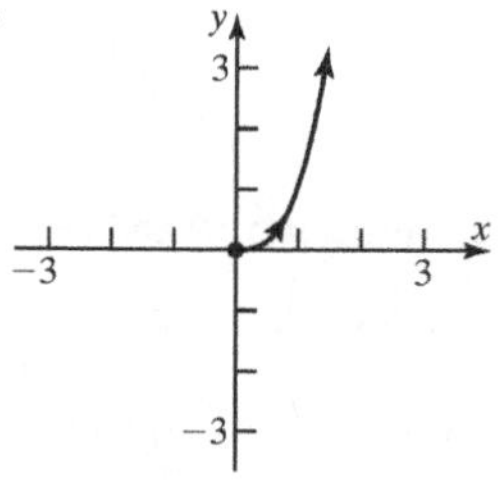

$y = x^3$

19.

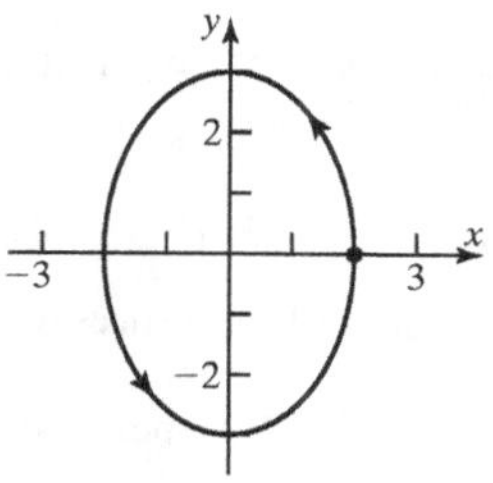

$\frac{x^2}{4} + \frac{y^2}{9} = 1$

21.

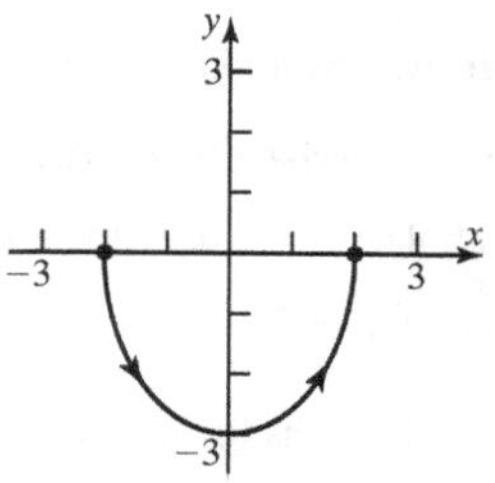

$\frac{x^2}{4} + \frac{y^2}{9} = 1$

23.

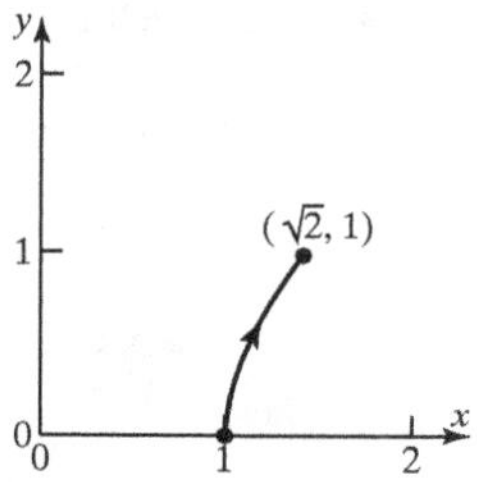

$x^2 - y^2 = 1$

25.

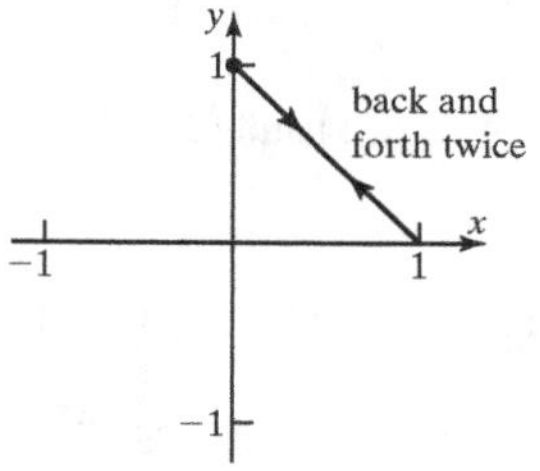

$x + y = 1$

27. $x = t$, $y = 4t - 1$ or $x = \frac{t+1}{4}$, $y = t$

29. $x = t$, $y = t^2 + 1$ or $x = t^3$, $y = t^6 + 1$

31. $x = t$, $y = t^3$ or $x = \sqrt[3]{t}$, $y = t$

33. $x = t$, $y = t^{2/3}$ or $x = t^3$, $y = t^2, t \geq 0$

35. $x = t + 2, y = t, 0 \leq t \leq 5$ **37.** $x = 3\cos t, y = 2\sin t, 0 \leq t \leq 2\pi$

39. $x = 2\cos(\pi t), y = -3\sin(\pi t), 0 \leq t \leq 2$

41. $x = 2\sin(2\pi t), y = 3\cos(2\pi t), 0 \leq t \leq 1$

43.

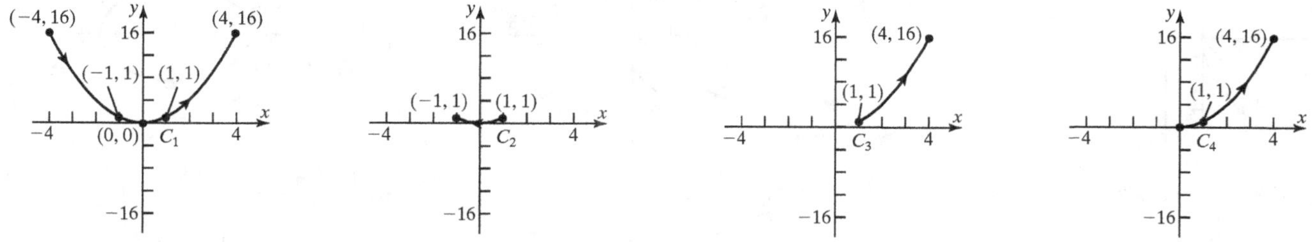

45.

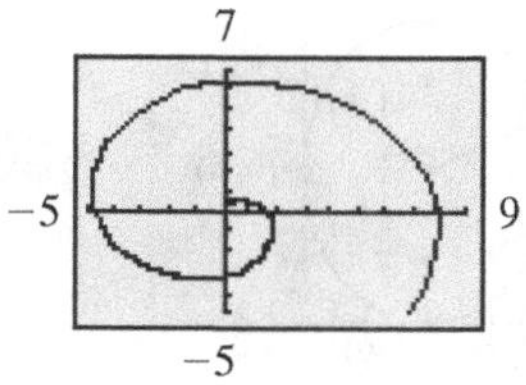

47.

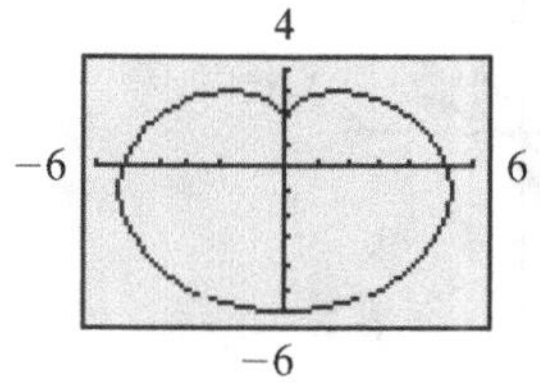

49. **(a)** $x = 3$
$y = -16t^2 + 50t + 6$
(b) 3.24 s
(c) 1.56 s; 45.06 ft
(d)

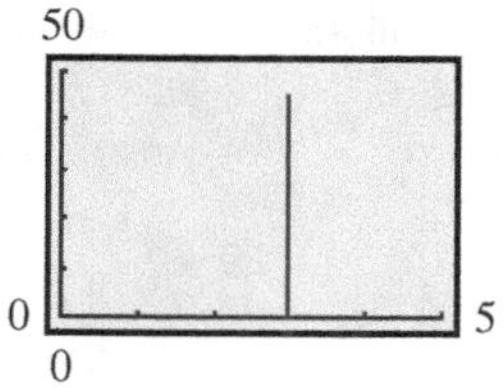

51. **(a)** Train: $x_1 = t^2, y_1 = 1$;
Bill: $x_2 = 5(t - 5), y_2 = 3$
(b) Bill won't catch the train.
(c)

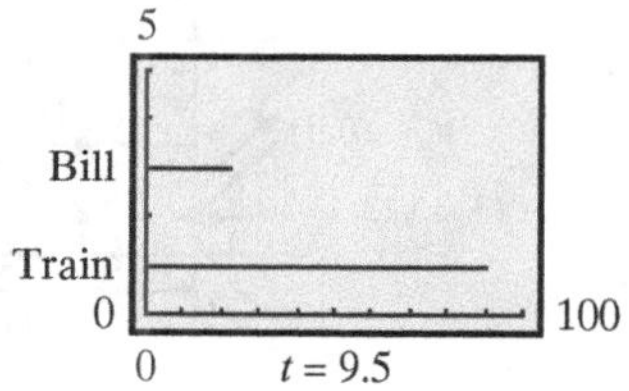

53. **(a)** $x = (145\cos 20°)t$
$y = -16t^2 + (145\sin 20°)t + 5$
(b) 3.20 s **(c)** 435.61 ft
(d) 1.55 s; 43.43 ft
(e)

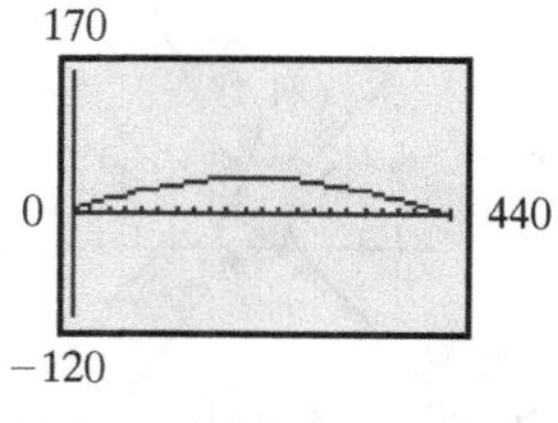

55. (a) $x = (40 \cos 45°)t$
$y = -4.9t^2 + (40 \sin 45°)t + 300$
(b) 11.23 s **(c)** 317.52 m
(d) 2.89 s; 340.82 m
(e)

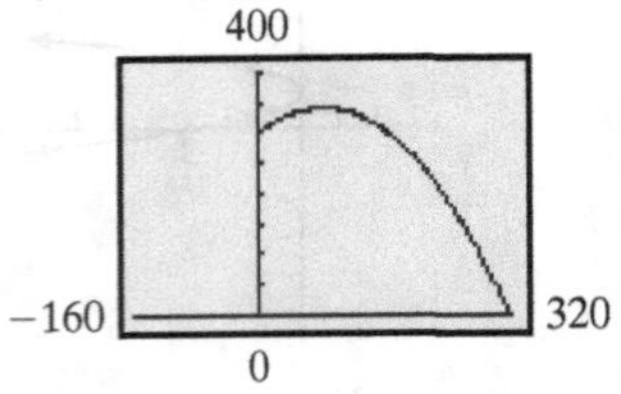

57. (a) Camry: $x = 40t - 5$, $y = 0$; Chevy Impala: $x = 0$, $y = 30t - 4$
(b) $d = \sqrt{(40t - 5)^2 + (30t - 4)^2}$
(c)

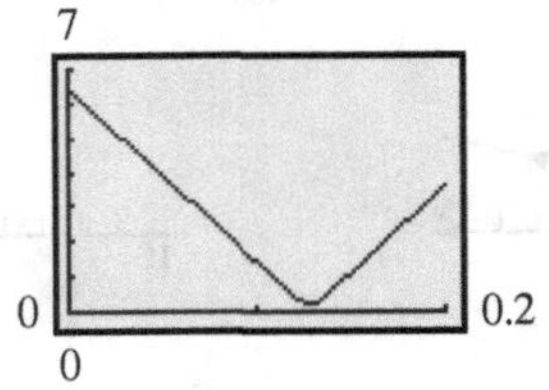

(d) 0.2 mi; 7.68 min
(e) Turn axes off to see the graph:

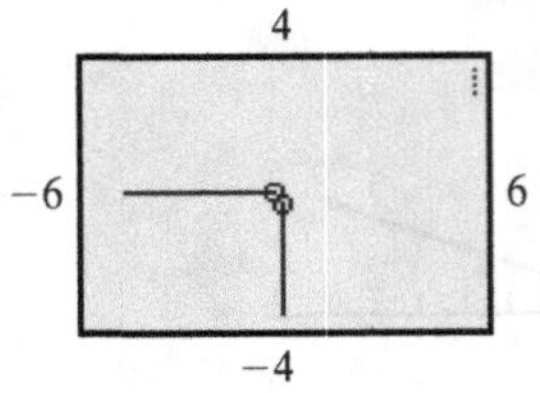

59. (a) $x = \dfrac{\sqrt{2}}{2} v_0 t$, $y = -16t^2 + \dfrac{\sqrt{2}}{2} v_0 t + 3$ **(b)** Maximum height is 139.1 ft. **(c)** The ball is 272.25 ft from home plate. **(d)** Yes, the ball will clear the wall by about 99.5 ft. **61.** The orientation is from (x_1, y_1) to (x_2, y_2).

Review Exercises *(page 701)*

1. Parabola; vertex $(0, 0)$, focus $(-4, 0)$, directrix $x = 4$ **3.** Hyperbola; center $(0, 0)$, vertices $(5, 0)$ and $(-5, 0)$, foci $(\sqrt{26}, 0)$ and $(-\sqrt{26}, 0)$, asymptotes $y = \frac{1}{5}x$ and $y = -\frac{1}{5}x$ **5.** Ellipse; center $(0, 0)$, vertices $(0, 5)$ and $(0, -5)$, foci $(0, 3)$ and $(0, -3)$ **7.** $x^2 = -4(y - 1)$: Parabola; vertex $(0, 1)$, focus $(0, 0)$, directrix $y = 2$ **9.** $\frac{x^2}{2} - \frac{y^2}{8} = 1$: Hyperbola; center $(0, 0)$, vertices $(\sqrt{2}, 0)$ and $(-\sqrt{2}, 0)$, foci $(\sqrt{10}, 0)$ and $(-\sqrt{10}, 0)$, asymptotes $y = 2x$ and $y = -2x$ **11.** $(x - 2)^2 = 2(y + 2)$: Parabola; vertex $(2, -2)$, focus $\left(2, -\frac{3}{2}\right)$, directrix $y = -\frac{5}{2}$

13. $\frac{(y - 2)^2}{4} - (x - 1)^2 = 1$: Hyperbola; center $(1, 2)$, vertices $(1, 4)$ and $(1, 0)$, foci $(1, 2 + \sqrt{5})$ and $(1, 2 - \sqrt{5})$, asymptotes $y - 2 = \pm 2(x - 1)$

15. $\frac{(x - 2)^2}{9} + \frac{(y - 1)^2}{4} = 1$: Ellipse; center $(2, 1)$, vertices $(5, 1)$ and $(-1, 1)$, foci $(2 + \sqrt{5}, 1)$ and $(2 - \sqrt{5}, 1)$

17. $(x - 2)^2 = -4(y + 1)$: Parabola; vertex $(2, -1)$, focus $(2, -2)$, directrix $y = 0$

19. $\frac{(x - 1)^2}{4} + \frac{(y + 1)^2}{9} = 1$: Ellipse; center $(1, -1)$, vertices $(1, 2)$ and $(1, -4)$, foci $(1, -1 + \sqrt{5})$ and $(1, -1 - \sqrt{5})$

21. $y^2 = -8x$

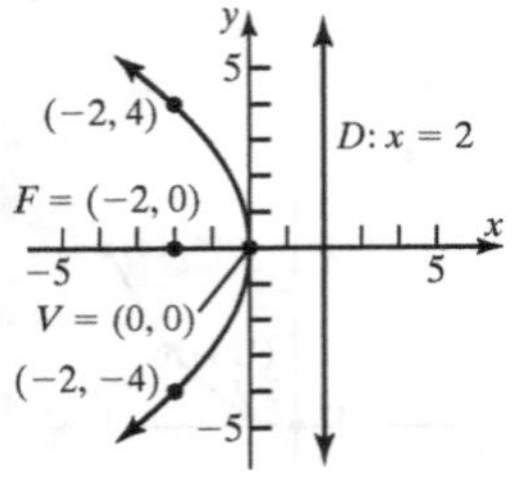

23. $\frac{y^2}{4} - \frac{x^2}{12} = 1$

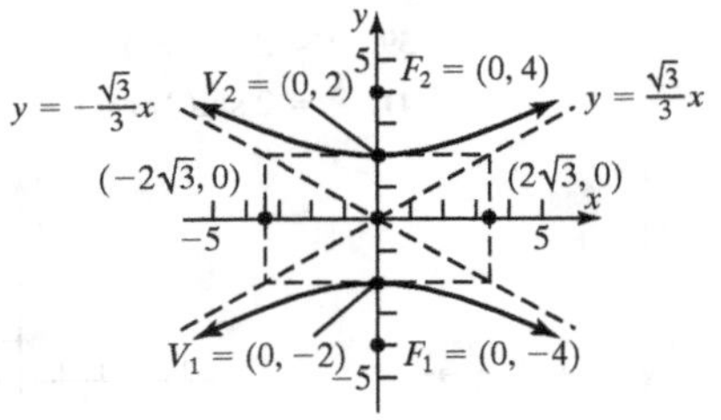

25. $\frac{x^2}{16} + \frac{y^2}{7} = 1$

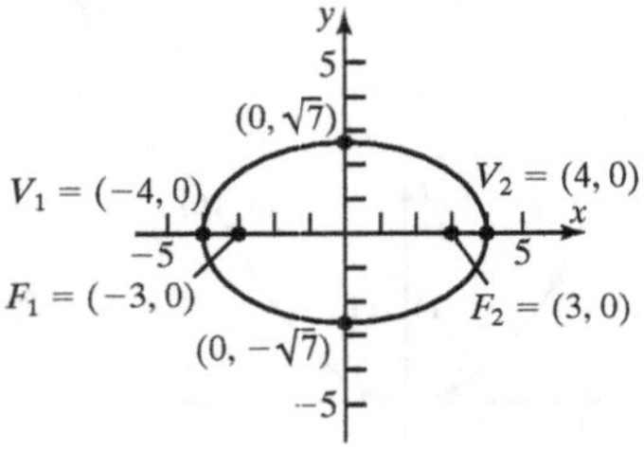

27. $(x - 2)^2 = -4(y + 3)$

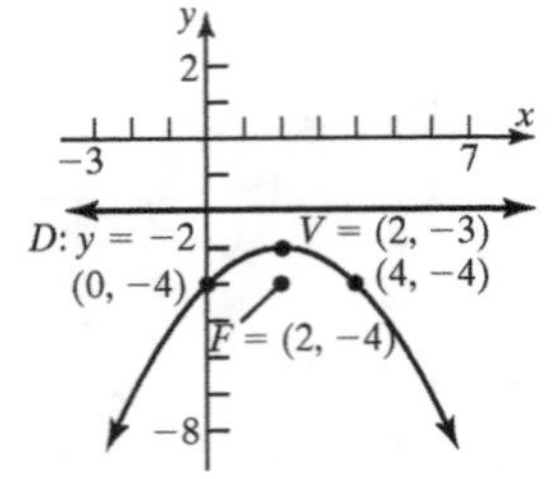

29. $(x + 2)^2 - \frac{(y + 3)^2}{3} = 1$

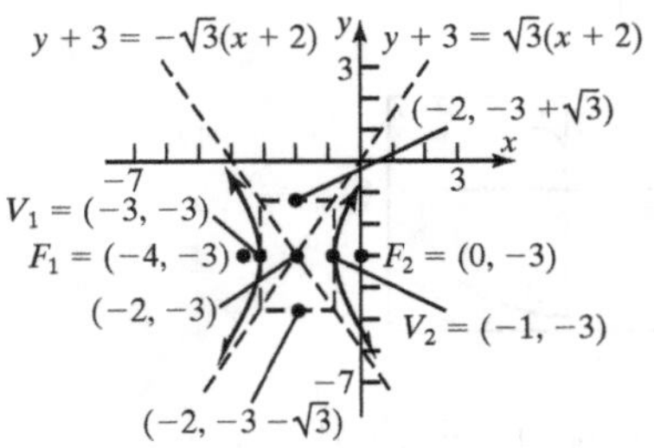

31. $\frac{(x + 4)^2}{16} + \frac{(y - 5)^2}{25} = 1$

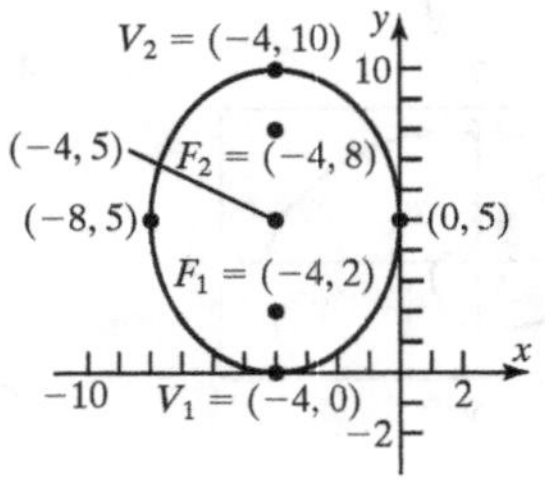

33. $\frac{(x + 1)^2}{9} - \frac{(y - 2)^2}{7} = 1$

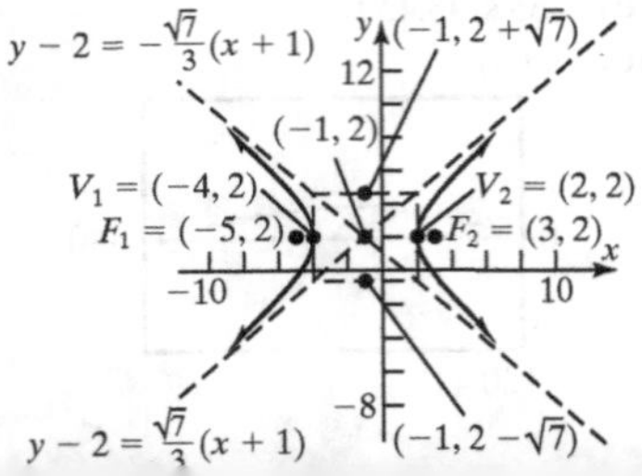

35. $\frac{(x - 3)^2}{9} - \frac{(y - 1)^2}{4} = 1$

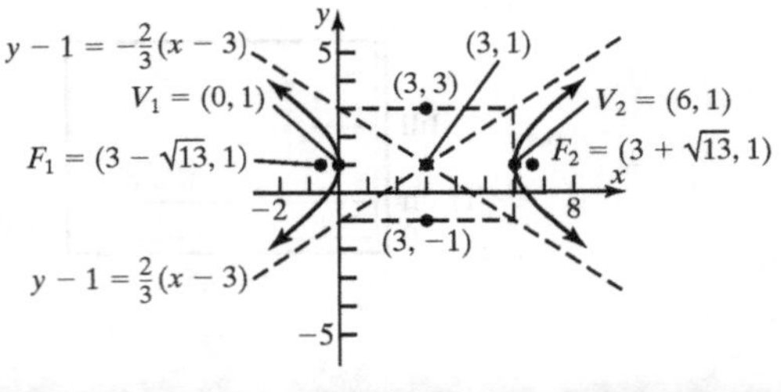

37. Parabola **39.** Ellipse
41. Parabola **43.** Hyperbola
45. Ellipse

47. $x'^2 - \dfrac{y'^2}{9} = 1$
Hyperbola
Center at the origin
Transverse axis the x'-axis
Vertices at $(\pm 1, 0)$

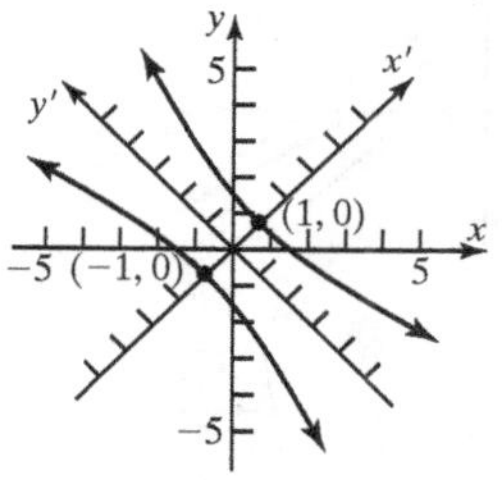

49. $\dfrac{x'^2}{2} + \dfrac{y'^2}{4} = 1$
Ellipse
Center at origin
Major axis the y'-axis
Vertices at $(0, \pm 2)$

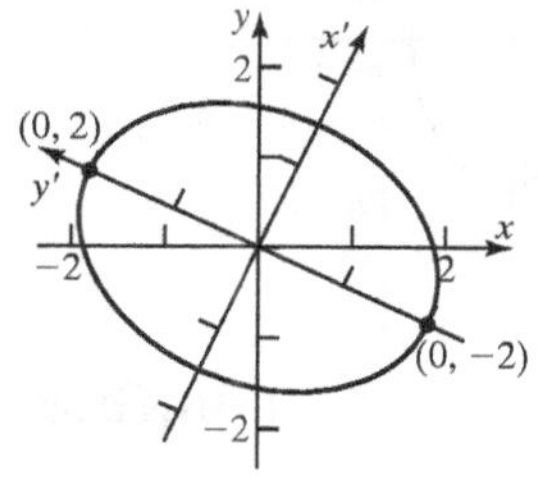

51. $y'^2 = -\dfrac{4\sqrt{13}}{13}x'$
Parabola
Vertex at the origin
Focus on the x'-axis at $\left(-\dfrac{\sqrt{13}}{13}, 0\right)$

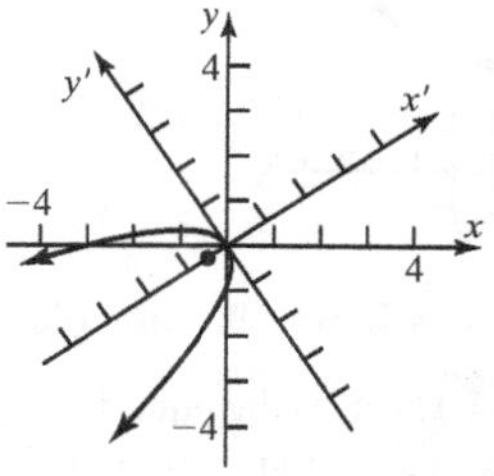

53. Parabola; directrix is perpendicular to the polar axis 4 units to the left of the pole; vertex is $(2, \pi)$.

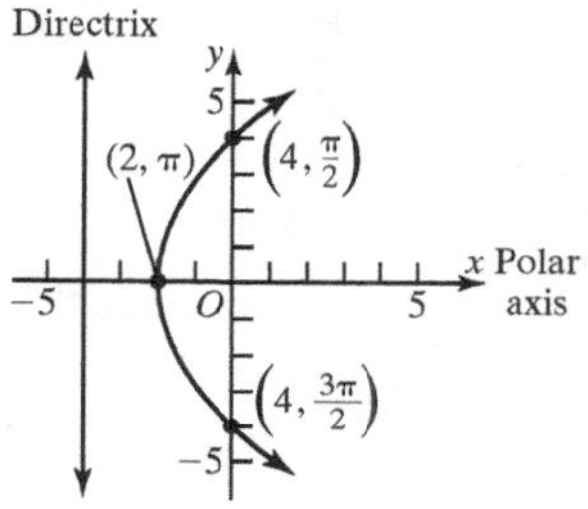

55. Ellipse; directrix is parallel to the polar axis 6 units below the pole; vertices are $\left(6, \dfrac{\pi}{2}\right)$ and $\left(2, \dfrac{3\pi}{2}\right)$.

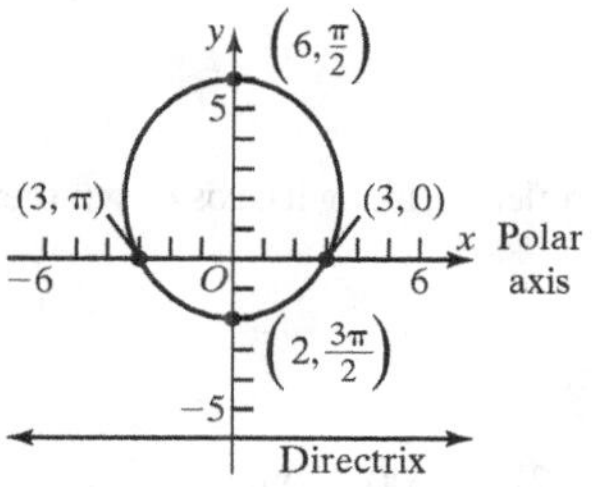

57. Hyperbola; directrix is perpendicular to the polar axis 1 unit to the right of the pole; vertices are $\left(\dfrac{2}{3}, 0\right)$ and $(-2, \pi)$.

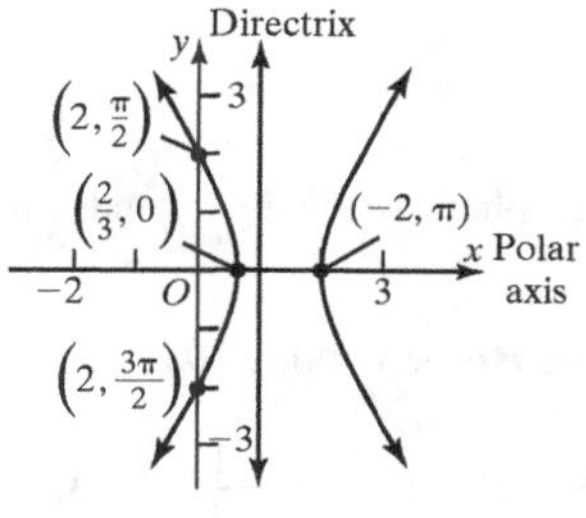

59. $y^2 - 8x - 16 = 0$ **61.** $3x^2 - y^2 - 8x + 4 = 0$

63.

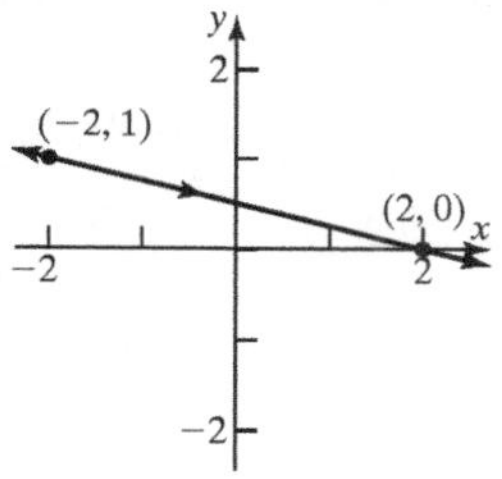

$x + 4y = 2$

65.

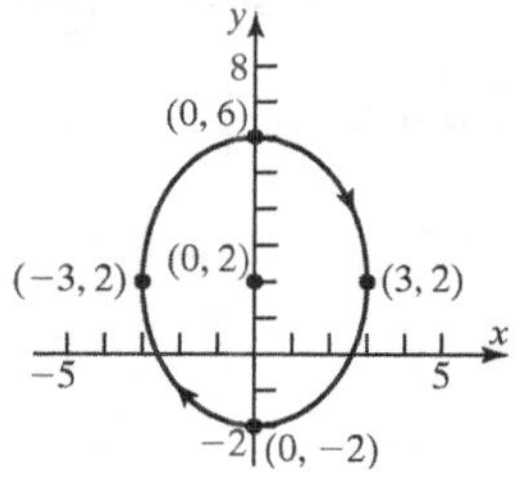

$\dfrac{x^2}{9} + \dfrac{(y-2)^2}{16} = 1$

67.

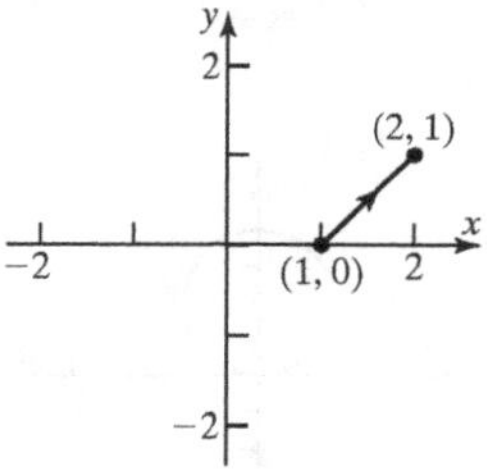

$1 + y = x$

69. $x = t, y = -2t + 4, -\infty < t < \infty$; $x = \dfrac{t-4}{-2}, y = t, -\infty < t < \infty$ **71.** $x = 4\cos\left(\dfrac{\pi}{2}t\right), y = 3\sin\left(\dfrac{\pi}{2}t\right), 0 \le t \le 4$

73. $\dfrac{x^2}{5} - \dfrac{y^2}{4} = 1$ **75.** The ellipse $\dfrac{x^2}{16} + \dfrac{y^2}{7} = 1$ **77.** $\dfrac{1}{4}$ ft or 3 in. **79.** 19.72 ft, 18.86 ft, 14.91 ft **81.** 450 ft

83. **(a)** $x = (80\cos 35°)t$

$y = -16t^2 + (80\sin 35°)t + 6$

(b) 2.9932 s
(c) 1.4339 s; 38.9 ft
(d) 196.15 ft

(e)

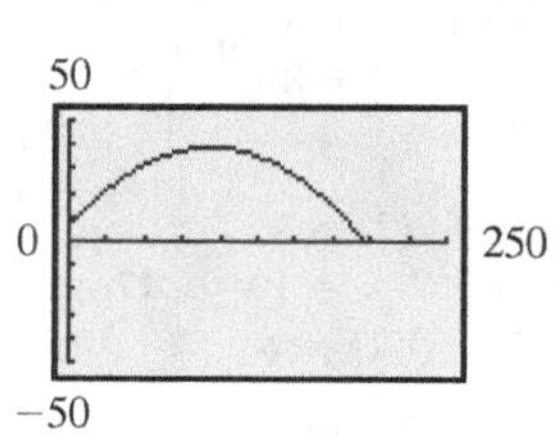

Chapter Test *(page 703)*

1. Hyperbola; center: $(-1, 0)$; vertices: $(-3, 0)$ and $(1, 0)$; foci: $(-1-\sqrt{13}, 0)$ and $(-1+\sqrt{13}, 0)$; asymptotes: $y = -\dfrac{3}{2}(x+1)$ and $y = \dfrac{3}{2}(x+1)$

2. Parabola; vertex: $\left(1, -\dfrac{1}{2}\right)$; focus: $\left(1, \dfrac{3}{2}\right)$; directrix: $y = -\dfrac{5}{2}$

3. Ellipse; center: $(-1, 1)$; foci: $(-1-\sqrt{3}, 1)$ and $(-1+\sqrt{3}, 1)$; vertices: $(-4, 1)$ and $(2, 1)$

4. $(x + 1)^2 = 6(y - 3)$

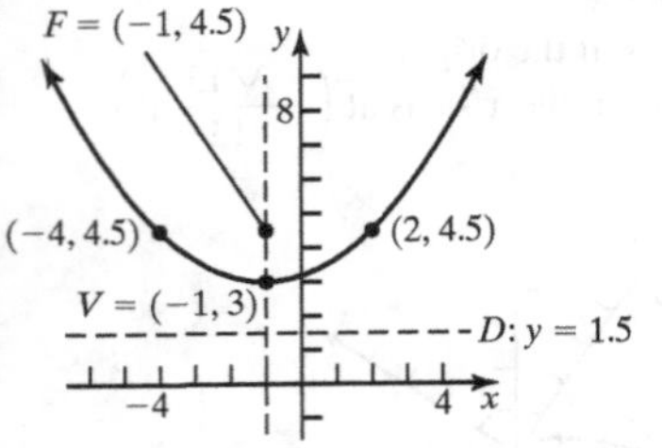

5. $\dfrac{x^2}{7} + \dfrac{y^2}{16} = 1$

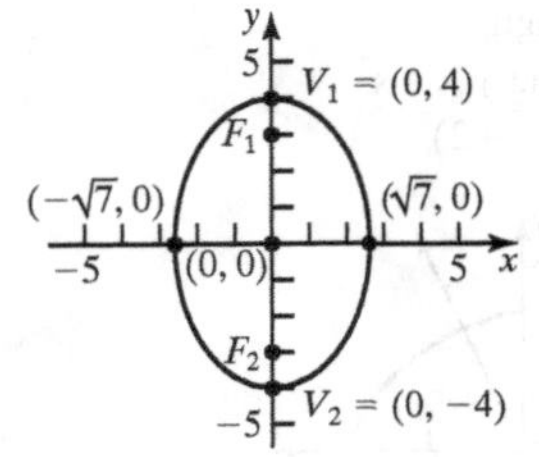

6. $\dfrac{(y - 2)^2}{4} - \dfrac{(x - 2)^2}{8} = 1$

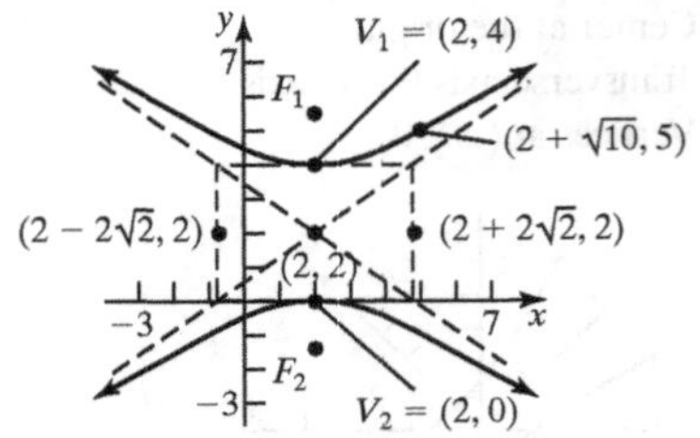

7. Hyperbola **8.** Ellipse **9.** Parabola

10. $x'^2 + 2y'^2 = 1$. This is the equation of an ellipse with center at $(0, 0)$ in the $x'y'$-plane. The vertices are at $(-1, 0)$ and $(1, 0)$ in the $x'y'$-plane.

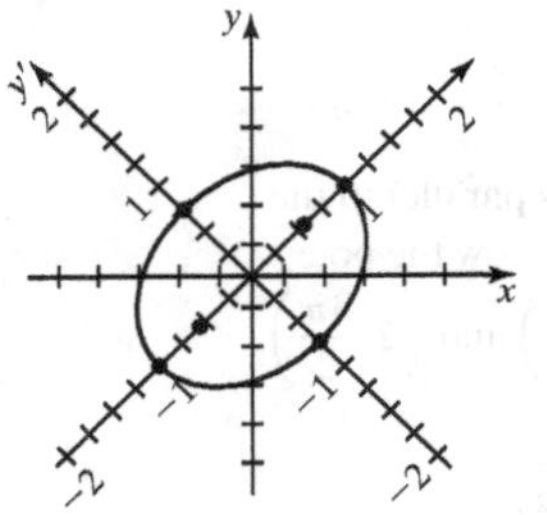

11. Hyperbola; $(x + 2)^2 - \dfrac{y^2}{3} = 1$ **12.** $y = 1 - \sqrt{\dfrac{x + 2}{3}}$

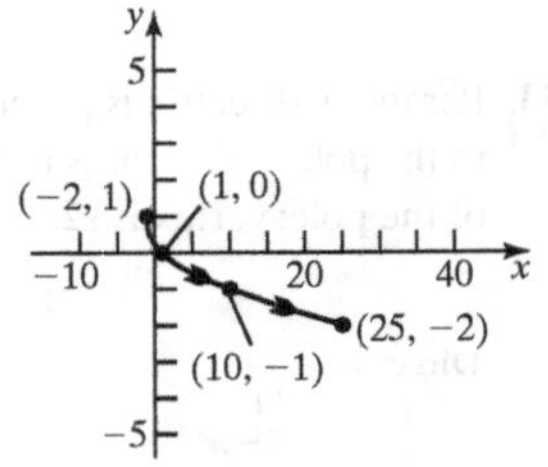

13. The microphone should be located $\dfrac{2}{3}$ ft from the base of the reflector, along its axis of symmetry.

Cumulative Review *(page 703)*

1. $-6x + 5 - 3h$ **2.** $\left\{-5, -\dfrac{1}{3}, 2\right\}$ **3.** $\{x \mid -3 \le x \le 2\}$ or $[-3, 2]$ **4. (a)** Domain: $(-\infty, \infty)$; range: $(2, \infty)$ **(b)** $y = \log_3(x - 2)$; domain: $(2, \infty)$; range: $(-\infty, \infty)$ **5. (a)** $\{18\}$ **(b)** $(2, 18]$ **6. (a)** $y = 2x - 2$ **(b)** $(x - 2)^2 + y^2 = 4$ **(c)** $\dfrac{x^2}{9} + \dfrac{y^2}{4} = 1$ **(d)** $y = 2(x - 1)^2$ **(e)** $y^2 - \dfrac{x^2}{3} = 1$ **(f)** $y = 4^x$ **7.** $\theta = \dfrac{\pi}{12} \pm \pi k$, k is any integer; $\theta = \dfrac{5\pi}{12} \pm \pi k$, k is any integer **8.** $\theta = \dfrac{\pi}{6}$

9. $r = 8 \sin\theta$

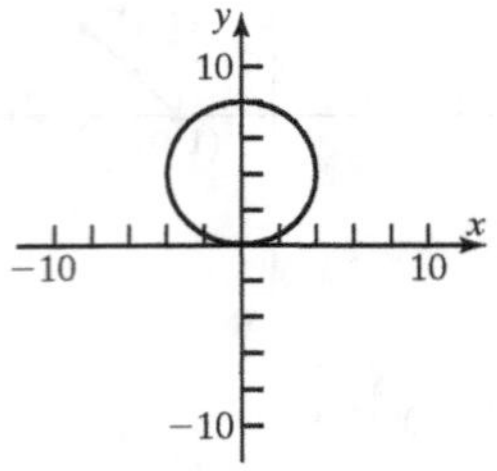

10. $\left\{x \,\middle|\, x \ne \dfrac{3\pi}{4} \pm \pi k, k \text{ is an integer}\right\}$ **11.** $\{22.5°\}$ **12.** $y = \dfrac{x^2}{5} + 5$

CHAPTER 11 Systems of Equations and Inequalities

11.1 Assess Your Understanding *(page 716)*

3. inconsistent **4.** consistent **5.** F **6.** T **7.** $\begin{cases} 2(2) - (-1) = 5 \\ 5(2) + 2(-1) = 8 \end{cases}$ **9.** $\begin{cases} 3(2) - 4\left(\dfrac{1}{2}\right) = 4 \\ \dfrac{1}{2}(2) - 3\left(\dfrac{1}{2}\right) = -\dfrac{1}{2} \end{cases}$ **11.** $\begin{cases} 4 - 1 = 3 \\ \dfrac{1}{2}(4) + 1 = 3 \end{cases}$

13. $\begin{cases} 3(1) + 3(-1) + 2(2) = 4 \\ 1 - (-1) - 2 = 0 \\ 2(-1) - 3(2) = -8 \end{cases}$ **15.** $\begin{cases} 3(2) + 3(-2) + 2(2) = 4 \\ 2 - 3(-2) + 2 = 10 \\ 5(2) - 2(-2) - 3(2) = 8 \end{cases}$ **17.** $x = 6, y = 2$; $(6, 2)$ **19.** $x = 3, y = -6$; $(3, -6)$

21. $x = 8, y = -4$; $(8, -4)$ **23.** $x = \dfrac{1}{3}, y = -\dfrac{1}{6}$; $\left(\dfrac{1}{3}, -\dfrac{1}{6}\right)$ **25.** Inconsistent **27.** $x = \dfrac{3}{2}, y = 3$; $\left(\dfrac{3}{2}, 3\right)$

29. $\{(x, y) \mid x = 4 - 2y, y \text{ is any real number}\}$ or $\left\{(x, y) \,\middle|\, y = \dfrac{4 - x}{2}, x \text{ is any real number}\right\}$ **31.** $x = 1, y = 1$; $(1, 1)$ **33.** $x = \dfrac{3}{2}, y = 1$; $\left(\dfrac{3}{2}, 1\right)$

35. $x = 4, y = 3$; $(4, 3)$ **37.** $x = \dfrac{4}{3}, y = \dfrac{1}{5}$; $\left(\dfrac{4}{3}, \dfrac{1}{5}\right)$ **39.** $x = \dfrac{1}{5}, y = \dfrac{1}{3}$; $\left(\dfrac{1}{5}, \dfrac{1}{3}\right)$ **41.** $x = 8, y = 2, z = 0$; $(8, 2, 0)$

43. $x = 2, y = -1, z = 1$; $(2, -1, 1)$ **45.** Inconsistent **47.** $\{(x, y, z) \mid x = 5z - 2, y = 4z - 3; z \text{ is any real number}\}$

49. Inconsistent **51.** $x = 1, y = 3, z = -2; (1, 3, -2)$ **53.** $x = -3, y = \frac{1}{2}, z = 1; \left(-3, \frac{1}{2}, 1\right)$ **55.** Length 30 ft; width 15 ft

57. There were 18 commercial launches and 37 noncommercial launches in 2005. **59.** 22.5 lb

61. Average wind speed 25 mph; average airspeed 175 mph **63.** 80 \$25 sets and 120 \$45 sets **65.** \$9.96

67. Mix 50 mg of first compound with 75 mg of second. **69.** $a = \frac{4}{3}, b = -\frac{5}{3}, c = 1$ **71.** $Y = 9000, r = 0.06$ **73.** $I_1 = \frac{10}{71}, I_2 = \frac{65}{71}, I_3 = \frac{55}{71}$

75. 100 orchestra, 210 main, and 190 balcony seats **77.** 1.5 chicken, 1 corn, 2 milk

79. If x = price of hamburgers, y = price of fries, and z = price of colas, then $x = 2.75 - z, y = \frac{41}{60} + \frac{1}{3}z, \$0.60 \le z \le \$0.90.$ There is not sufficient information:

x	\$2.13	\$2.01	\$1.86
y	\$0.89	\$0.93	\$0.98
z	\$0.62	\$0.74	\$0.89

81. It will take Beth 30 hr, Bill 24 hr, and Edie 40 hr.

11.2 Assess Your Understanding *(page 732)*

1. matrix **2.** augmented **3.** T **4.** T

5. $\left[\begin{array}{cc|c} 1 & -5 & 5 \\ 4 & 3 & 6 \end{array}\right]$ **7.** $\left[\begin{array}{cc|c} 2 & 3 & 6 \\ 4 & -6 & -2 \end{array}\right]$ **9.** $\left[\begin{array}{cc|c} 0.01 & -0.03 & 0.06 \\ 0.13 & 0.10 & 0.20 \end{array}\right]$ **11.** $\left[\begin{array}{ccc|c} 1 & -1 & 1 & 10 \\ 3 & 3 & 0 & 5 \\ 1 & 1 & 2 & 2 \end{array}\right]$ **13.** $\left[\begin{array}{ccc|c} 1 & 1 & -1 & 2 \\ 3 & -2 & 0 & 2 \\ 5 & 3 & -1 & 1 \end{array}\right]$ **15.** $\left[\begin{array}{ccc|c} 1 & -1 & -1 & 10 \\ 2 & 1 & 2 & -1 \\ -3 & 4 & 0 & 5 \\ 4 & -5 & 1 & 0 \end{array}\right]$

17. $\begin{cases} x - 3y = -2 & (1) \\ 2x - 5y = 5 & (2) \end{cases}$ $\left[\begin{array}{cc|c} 1 & -3 & -2 \\ 0 & 1 & 9 \end{array}\right]$ **19.** $\begin{cases} x - 3y + 4z = 3 & (1) \\ 3x - 5y + 6z = 6 & (2) \\ -5x + 3y + 4z = 6 & (3) \end{cases}$ **(a)** $\left[\begin{array}{ccc|c} 1 & -3 & 4 & 3 \\ 0 & 4 & -6 & -3 \\ -5 & 3 & 4 & 6 \end{array}\right]$ **(b)** $\left[\begin{array}{ccc|c} 1 & -3 & 4 & 3 \\ 3 & -5 & 6 & 6 \\ 0 & -12 & 24 & 21 \end{array}\right]$

21. $\begin{cases} x - 3y + 2z = -6 & (1) \\ 2x - 5y + 3z = -4 & (2) \\ -3x - 6y + 4z = 6 & (3) \end{cases}$ **(a)** $\left[\begin{array}{ccc|c} 1 & -3 & 2 & -6 \\ 0 & 1 & -1 & 8 \\ -3 & -6 & 4 & 6 \end{array}\right]$ **(b)** $\left[\begin{array}{ccc|c} 1 & -3 & 2 & -6 \\ 2 & -5 & 3 & -4 \\ 0 & -15 & 10 & -12 \end{array}\right]$

23. $\begin{cases} 5x - 3y + z = -2 & (1) \\ 2x - 5y + 6z = -2 & (2) \\ -4x + y + 4z = 6 & (3) \end{cases}$ **(a)** $\left[\begin{array}{ccc|c} 1 & 7 & -11 & 2 \\ 2 & -5 & 6 & -2 \\ -4 & 1 & 4 & 6 \end{array}\right]$ **(b)** $\left[\begin{array}{ccc|c} 1 & -2 & 5 & 4 \\ 2 & -5 & 6 & -2 \\ -4 & 1 & 4 & 6 \end{array}\right]$

25. $\begin{cases} x = 5 \\ y = -1 \end{cases}$ Consistent; $x = 5, y = -1$ or $(5, -1)$

27. $\begin{cases} x = 1 \\ y = 2 \\ 0 = 3 \end{cases}$ Inconsistent

29. $\begin{cases} x + 2z = -1 \\ y - 4z = -2 \\ 0 = 0 \end{cases}$ Consistent: $\begin{cases} x = -1 - 2z \\ y = -2 + 4z \\ z \text{ is any real number or} \end{cases}$ $\{(x, y, z) \mid x = -1 - 2z, y = -2 + 4z, z \text{ is any real number}\}$

31. $\begin{cases} x_1 = 1 \\ x_2 + x_4 = 2 \\ x_3 + 2x_4 = 3 \end{cases}$ Consistent: $\begin{cases} x_1 = 1, x_2 = 2 - x_4 \\ x_3 = 3 - 2x_4 \\ x_4 \text{ is any real number or} \end{cases}$ $\{(x_1, x_2, x_3, x_4) \mid x_1 = 1, x_2 = 2 - x_4, x_3 = 3 - 2x_4, x_4 \text{ is any real number}\}$

33. $\begin{cases} x_1 + 4x_4 = 2 \\ x_2 + x_3 + 3x_4 = 3 \\ 0 = 0 \end{cases}$ Consistent: $\begin{cases} x_1 = 2 - 4x_4 \\ x_2 = 3 - x_3 - 3x_4 \\ x_3, x_4 \text{ are any real numbers or} \end{cases}$ $\{(x_1, x_2, x_3, x_4) \mid x_1 = 2 - 4x_4, x_2 = 3 - x_3 - 3x_4, x_3, x_4 \text{ are any real numbers}\}$

35. $\begin{cases} x_1 + x_4 = -2 \\ x_2 + 2x_4 = 2 \\ x_3 - x_4 = 0 \\ 0 = 0 \end{cases}$ Consistent: $\begin{cases} x_1 = -2 - x_4 \\ x_2 = 2 - 2x_4 \\ x_3 = x_4 \\ x_4 \text{ is any real number or} \end{cases}$ $\{(x_1, x_2, x_3, x_4) \mid x_1 = -2 - x_4, x_2 = 2 - 2x_4, x_3 = x_4, x_4 \text{ is any real number}\}$

37. $x = 6, y = 2; (6, 2)$ **39.** $x = \frac{1}{2}, y = \frac{3}{4}; \left(\frac{1}{2}, \frac{3}{4}\right)$ **41.** $x = 4 - 2y$, y is any real number; $\{(x, y) \mid x = 4 - 2y, y \text{ is any real number}\}$

43. $x = \frac{3}{2}, y = 1; \left(\frac{3}{2}, 1\right)$ **45.** $x = \frac{4}{3}, y = \frac{1}{5}; \left(\frac{4}{3}, \frac{1}{5}\right)$ **47.** $x = 8, y = 2, z = 0; (8, 2, 0)$ **49.** $x = 2, y = -1, z = 1; (2, -1, 1)$ **51.** Inconsistent

53. $x = 5z - 2, y = 4z - 3$, where z is any real number; $\{(x, y, z) \mid x = 5z - 2, y = 4x - 3, z \text{ is any real number}\}$

55. Inconsistent **57.** $x = 1, y = 3, z = -2; (1, 3, -2)$ **59.** $x = -3, y = \frac{1}{2}, z = 1; \left(-3, \frac{1}{2}, 1\right)$ **61.** $x = \frac{1}{3}, y = \frac{2}{3}, z = 1; \left(\frac{1}{3}, \frac{2}{3}, 1\right)$

63. $x = 1, y = 2, z = 0, w = 1; (1, 2, 0, 1)$ **65.** $y = 0, z = 1 - x$, x is any real number; $\{(x, y, z) \mid y = 0, z = 1 - x, x \text{ is any real number}\}$

67. $x = 2, y = z - 3$, z is any real number; $\{(x, y, z) \mid x = 2, y = z - 3, z \text{ is any real number}\}$ **69.** $x = \frac{13}{9}, y = \frac{7}{18}, z = \frac{19}{18}; \left(\frac{13}{9}, \frac{7}{18}, \frac{19}{18}\right)$

71. $x = \frac{7}{5} - \frac{3}{5}z - \frac{2}{5}w, y = -\frac{8}{5} + \frac{7}{5}z + \frac{13}{5}w$, where z and w are any real numbers; $\left\{(x, y, z, w) \mid x = \frac{7}{5} - \frac{3}{5}z - \frac{2}{5}w, y = -\frac{8}{5} + \frac{7}{5}z + \frac{13}{5}w, z \text{ and } w \text{ are any real numbers}\right\}$ **73.** $y = -2x^2 + x + 3$ **75.** $f(x) = 3x^3 - 4x^2 + 5$ **77.** 1.5 salmon steak, 2 baked eggs, 1 acorn squash

79. \$4000 in Treasury bills, \$4000 in Treasury bonds, \$2000 in corporate bonds **81.** 8 Deltas, 5 Betas, 10 Sigmas **83.** $I_1 = \frac{44}{23}, I_2 = 2, I_3 = \frac{16}{23}, I_4 = \frac{28}{23}$

85. (a)

Amount Invested At		
7%	**9%**	**11%**
0	10,000	10,000
1000	8000	11,000
2000	6000	12,000
3000	4000	13,000
4000	2000	14,000
5000	0	15,000

(b)

Amount Invested At		
7%	**9%**	**11%**
12,500	12,500	0
14,500	8500	2000
16,500	4500	4000
18,750	0	6250

(c) All the money invested at 7% provides \$2100, more than what is required.

87.

First Supplement	Second Supplement	Third Supplement
50 mg	75 mg	0 mg
36 mg	76 mg	8 mg
22 mg	77 mg	16 mg
8 mg	78 mg	24 mg

11.3 Assess Your Understanding *(page 743)*

1. determinants **2.** $ad - bc$ **3.** F **4.** F **5.** 2 **7.** 22 **9.** -2 **11.** 10 **13.** -26 **15.** $x = 6, y = 2; (6, 2)$ **17.** $x = 3, y = 2; (3, 2)$ **19.** $x = 8, y = -4; (8, -4)$ **21.** $x = 4, y = -2; (4, -2)$ **23.** Not applicable **25.** $x = \frac{1}{2}, y = \frac{3}{4}; \left(\frac{1}{2}, \frac{3}{4}\right)$ **27.** $x = \frac{1}{10}, y = \frac{2}{5}; \left(\frac{1}{10}, \frac{2}{5}\right)$ **29.** $x = \frac{3}{2}, y = 1; \left(\frac{3}{2}, 1\right)$ **31.** $x = \frac{4}{3}, y = \frac{1}{5}; \left(\frac{4}{3}, \frac{1}{5}\right)$ **33.** $x = 1, y = 3, z = -2; (1, 3, -2)$ **35.** $x = -3, y = \frac{1}{2}, z = 1; \left(-3, \frac{1}{2}, 1\right)$ **37.** Not applicable **39.** $x = 0, y = 0, z = 0; (0,0,0)$ **41.** Not applicable **43.** -4 **45.** 12 **47.** 8 **49.** 8 **51.** -5 **53.** $\frac{13}{11}$ **55.** 0 or -9

57.
$$\begin{aligned}
(y_1 - y_2)x - (x_1 - x_2)y + (x_1y_2 - x_2y_1) &= 0\\
(y_1 - y_2)x + (x_2 - x_1)y &= x_2y_1 - x_1y_2\\
(x_2 - x_1)y - (x_2 - x_1)y_1 &= (y_2 - y_1)x + x_2y_1 - x_1y_2 - (x_2 - x_1)y_1\\
(x_2 - x_1)(y - y_1) &= (y_2 - y_1)x - (y_2 - y_1)x_1\\
y - y_1 &= \frac{y_2 - y_1}{x_2 - x_1}(x - x_1)
\end{aligned}$$

59. The triangle has an area of 5 square units.

61. If $a = 0$, we have
$$by = s$$
$$cx + dy = t$$
Thus, $y = \frac{s}{b}$ and
$$x = \frac{t - dy}{c} = \frac{tb - ds}{bc}$$
Using Cramer's Rule, we get
$$x = \frac{sd - tb}{-bc} = \frac{tb - sd}{bc}$$
$$y = \frac{-sc}{-bc} = \frac{s}{b}$$

If $b = 0$, we have
$$ax = s$$
$$cx + dy = t$$
Since $D = ad \neq 0$, then $a \neq 0$ and $d \neq 0$.
Thus, $x = \frac{s}{a}$ and
$$y = \frac{t - cx}{d} = \frac{ta - cs}{ad}$$
Using Cramer's Rule, we get
$$x = \frac{sd}{ad} = \frac{s}{a}$$
$$y = \frac{ta - cs}{ad}$$

If $c = 0$, we have
$$ax + by = s$$
$$dy = t$$
Since $D = ad \neq 0$, then $a \neq 0$ and $d \neq 0$.
Thus, $y = \frac{t}{d}$ and
$$x = \frac{s - by}{a} = \frac{sd - bt}{ad}$$
Using Cramer's Rule, we get
$$x = \frac{sd - bt}{ad}$$
$$y = \frac{at}{ad} = \frac{t}{d}$$

If $d = 0$, we have
$$ax + by = s$$
$$cx = t$$
Since $D = -bc \neq 0$, then $b \neq 0$ and $c \neq 0$.
Thus, $x = \frac{t}{c}$ and
$$y = \frac{s - ax}{b} = \frac{sc - at}{bc}$$
Using Cramer's Rule, we get
$$x = \frac{-tb}{-bc} = \frac{t}{c}$$
$$y = \frac{at - sc}{-bc} = \frac{sc - at}{bc}$$

63.
$$\begin{aligned}
\begin{vmatrix} a_{11} & a_{12} & a_{13} \\ ka_{21} & ka_{22} & ka_{23} \\ a_{31} & a_{32} & a_{33} \end{vmatrix} &= -ka_{21}(a_{12}a_{33} - a_{32}a_{13}) + ka_{22}(a_{11}a_{33} - a_{31}a_{13}) - ka_{23}(a_{11}a_{32} - a_{31}a_{12})\\
&= k[-a_{21}(a_{12}a_{33} - a_{32}a_{13}) + a_{22}(a_{11}a_{33} - a_{31}a_{13}) - a_{23}(a_{11}a_{32} - a_{31}a_{12})] = k\begin{vmatrix} a_{11} & a_{12} & a_{13} \\ a_{21} & a_{22} & a_{23} \\ a_{31} & a_{32} & a_{33} \end{vmatrix}
\end{aligned}$$

65.
$$\begin{aligned}
\begin{vmatrix} a_{11} + ka_{21} & a_{12} + ka_{22} & a_{13} + ka_{23} \\ a_{21} & a_{22} & a_{23} \\ a_{31} & a_{32} & a_{33} \end{vmatrix} &= (a_{11} + ka_{21})(a_{22}a_{33} - a_{32}a_{23}) - (a_{12} + ka_{22})(a_{21}a_{33} - a_{31}a_{23}) + (a_{13} + ka_{23})(a_{21}a_{32} - a_{31}a_{22})\\
&= a_{11}a_{22}a_{33} - a_{11}a_{32}a_{23} + \cancel{ka_{21}a_{22}a_{33}} - \cancel{ka_{21}a_{32}a_{23}} - a_{12}a_{21}a_{33} + a_{12}a_{31}a_{23}\\
&\quad - \cancel{ka_{22}a_{21}a_{33}} + \cancel{ka_{22}a_{31}a_{23}} + a_{13}a_{21}a_{32} - a_{13}a_{31}a_{22} + \cancel{ka_{23}a_{21}a_{32}} - \cancel{ka_{23}a_{31}a_{22}}\\
&= a_{11}a_{22}a_{33} - a_{11}a_{32}a_{23} - a_{12}a_{21}a_{33} + a_{12}a_{31}a_{23} + a_{13}a_{21}a_{32} - a_{13}a_{31}a_{22}\\
&= a_{11}(a_{22}a_{33} - a_{32}a_{23}) - a_{12}(a_{21}a_{33} - a_{31}a_{23}) + a_{13}(a_{21}a_{32} - a_{31}a_{22})\\
&= \begin{vmatrix} a_{11} & a_{12} & a_{13} \\ a_{21} & a_{22} & a_{23} \\ a_{31} & a_{32} & a_{33} \end{vmatrix}
\end{aligned}$$

Historical Problems *(page 759)*

1. (a) $2 - 5i \longleftrightarrow \begin{bmatrix} 2 & -5 \\ 5 & 2 \end{bmatrix}, 1 + 3i \longleftrightarrow \begin{bmatrix} 1 & 3 \\ -3 & 1 \end{bmatrix}$ **(b)** $\begin{bmatrix} 2 & -5 \\ 5 & 2 \end{bmatrix}\begin{bmatrix} 1 & 3 \\ -3 & 1 \end{bmatrix} = \begin{bmatrix} 17 & 1 \\ -1 & 17 \end{bmatrix}$ **(c)** $17 + i$ **(d)** $17 + i$

2. $\begin{bmatrix} a & b \\ -b & a \end{bmatrix}\begin{bmatrix} a & -b \\ b & a \end{bmatrix} = \begin{bmatrix} a^2+b^2 & 0 \\ 0 & b^2+a^2 \end{bmatrix}$; the product is a real number.

3. (a) $x = k(ar + bs) + l(cr + ds) = r(ka + lc) + s(kb + ld)$
$y = m(ar + bs) + n(cr + ds) = r(ma + nc) + s(mb + nd)$ **(b)** $A = \begin{bmatrix} ka + lc & kb + ld \\ ma + nc & mb + nd \end{bmatrix}$

11.4 Assess Your Understanding *(page 759)*

1. inverse **2.** square **3.** identity **4.** F **5.** F **6.** F

7. $\begin{bmatrix} 4 & 4 & -5 \\ -1 & 5 & 4 \end{bmatrix}$ **9.** $\begin{bmatrix} 0 & 12 & -20 \\ 4 & 8 & 24 \end{bmatrix}$ **11.** $\begin{bmatrix} -8 & 7 & -15 \\ 7 & 0 & 22 \end{bmatrix}$ **13.** $\begin{bmatrix} 28 & -9 \\ 4 & 23 \end{bmatrix}$ **15.** $\begin{bmatrix} 1 & 14 & -14 \\ 2 & 22 & -18 \\ 3 & 0 & 28 \end{bmatrix}$ **17.** $\begin{bmatrix} 15 & 21 & -16 \\ 22 & 34 & -22 \\ -11 & 7 & 22 \end{bmatrix}$ **19.** $\begin{bmatrix} 25 & -9 \\ 4 & 20 \end{bmatrix}$

21. $\begin{bmatrix} -13 & 7 & -12 \\ -18 & 10 & -14 \\ 17 & -7 & 34 \end{bmatrix}$ **23.** $\begin{bmatrix} -2 & 4 & 2 & 8 \\ 2 & 1 & 4 & 6 \end{bmatrix}$ **25.** $\begin{bmatrix} 5 & 14 \\ 9 & 16 \end{bmatrix}$ **27.** $\begin{bmatrix} 9 & 2 \\ 34 & 13 \\ 47 & 20 \end{bmatrix}$ **29.** $\begin{bmatrix} 1 & -1 \\ -1 & 2 \end{bmatrix}$ **31.** $\begin{bmatrix} 1 & -\frac{5}{2} \\ -1 & 3 \end{bmatrix}$ **33.** $\begin{bmatrix} 1 & -\frac{1}{a} \\ -1 & \frac{2}{a} \end{bmatrix}$

35. $\begin{bmatrix} 3 & -3 & 1 \\ -2 & 2 & -1 \\ -4 & 5 & -2 \end{bmatrix}$ **37.** $\begin{bmatrix} -\frac{5}{7} & \frac{1}{7} & \frac{3}{7} \\ \frac{9}{7} & \frac{1}{7} & -\frac{4}{7} \\ \frac{3}{7} & -\frac{2}{7} & \frac{1}{7} \end{bmatrix}$ **39.** $x = 3, y = 2; (3, 2)$ **41.** $x = -5, y = 10; (-5, 10)$ **43.** $x = 2, y = -1; (2, -1)$

45. $x = \frac{1}{2}, y = 2; \left(\frac{1}{2}, 2\right)$ **47.** $x = -2, y = 1; (-2, 1)$ **49.** $x = \frac{2}{a}, y = \frac{3}{a}; \left(\frac{2}{a}, \frac{3}{a}\right)$ **51.** $x = -2, y = 3, z = 5; (-2, 3, 5)$

53. $x = \frac{1}{2}, y = -\frac{1}{2}, z = 1; \left(\frac{1}{2}, -\frac{1}{2}, 1\right)$ **55.** $x = -\frac{34}{7}, y = \frac{85}{7}, z = \frac{12}{7}; \left(-\frac{34}{7}, \frac{85}{7}, \frac{12}{7}\right)$ **57.** $x = \frac{1}{3}, y = 1, z = \frac{2}{3}; \left(\frac{1}{3}, 1, \frac{2}{3}\right)$

59. $\left[\begin{array}{cc|cc} 4 & 2 & 1 & 0 \\ 2 & 1 & 0 & 1 \end{array}\right] \rightarrow \left[\begin{array}{cc|cc} 1 & \frac{1}{2} & \frac{1}{4} & 0 \\ 2 & 1 & 0 & 1 \end{array}\right] \rightarrow \left[\begin{array}{cc|cc} 1 & \frac{1}{2} & \frac{1}{4} & 0 \\ 0 & 0 & -\frac{1}{2} & 1 \end{array}\right]$ **61.** $\left[\begin{array}{cc|cc} 15 & 3 & 1 & 0 \\ 10 & 2 & 0 & 1 \end{array}\right] \rightarrow \left[\begin{array}{cc|cc} 1 & \frac{1}{5} & \frac{1}{15} & 0 \\ 10 & 2 & 0 & 1 \end{array}\right] \rightarrow \left[\begin{array}{cc|cc} 1 & \frac{1}{5} & \frac{1}{15} & 0 \\ 0 & 0 & -\frac{2}{3} & 1 \end{array}\right]$

63. $\left[\begin{array}{ccc|ccc} -3 & 1 & -1 & 1 & 0 & 0 \\ 1 & -4 & -7 & 0 & 1 & 0 \\ 1 & 2 & 5 & 0 & 0 & 1 \end{array}\right] \rightarrow \left[\begin{array}{ccc|ccc} 1 & 2 & 5 & 0 & 0 & 1 \\ 1 & -4 & -7 & 0 & 1 & 0 \\ -3 & 1 & -1 & 1 & 0 & 0 \end{array}\right] \rightarrow \left[\begin{array}{ccc|ccc} 1 & 2 & 5 & 0 & 0 & 1 \\ 0 & -6 & -12 & 0 & 1 & -1 \\ 0 & 7 & 14 & 1 & 0 & 3 \end{array}\right]$

$\rightarrow \left[\begin{array}{ccc|ccc} 1 & 2 & 5 & 0 & 0 & 1 \\ 0 & 1 & 2 & 0 & -\frac{1}{6} & \frac{1}{6} \\ 0 & 1 & 2 & \frac{1}{7} & 0 & \frac{3}{7} \end{array}\right] \rightarrow \left[\begin{array}{ccc|ccc} 1 & 2 & 5 & 0 & 0 & 1 \\ 0 & 1 & 2 & 0 & -\frac{1}{6} & \frac{1}{6} \\ 0 & 0 & 0 & \frac{1}{7} & \frac{1}{6} & \frac{11}{42} \end{array}\right]$

65. $\begin{bmatrix} 0.01 & 0.05 & -0.01 \\ 0.01 & -0.02 & 0.01 \\ -0.02 & 0.01 & 0.03 \end{bmatrix}$ **67.** $\begin{bmatrix} 0.02 & -0.04 & -0.01 & 0.01 \\ -0.02 & 0.05 & 0.03 & -0.03 \\ 0.02 & 0.01 & -0.04 & 0.00 \\ -0.02 & 0.06 & 0.07 & 0.06 \end{bmatrix}$ **69.** $x = 4.57, y = -6.44, z = -24.07$ or $(4.57, -6.44, -24.07)$

71. $x = -1.19, y = 2.46, z = 8.27$ or $(-1.19, 2.46, 8.27)$ **73.** $x = -5, y = 7; (-5, 7)$ **75.** $x = -4, y = 2, z = \frac{5}{2}; \left(-4, 2, \frac{5}{2}\right)$

77. Inconsistent; $\varnothing$ **79.** $x = -\frac{1}{5}z + \frac{1}{5}, y = \frac{1}{5}z - \frac{6}{5}$, where z is any real number; $\left\{(x, y, z) \middle| x = -\frac{1}{5}z + \frac{1}{5}, y = \frac{1}{5}z - \frac{6}{5}, z \text{ is any real number}\right\}$

81. (a) $A = \begin{bmatrix} 6 & 9 \\ 3 & 12 \end{bmatrix}; B = \begin{bmatrix} 71.00 \\ 158.60 \end{bmatrix}$ **(b)** $AB = \begin{bmatrix} 1853.40 \\ 2116.20 \end{bmatrix}$; Nikki's total tuition is \$1853.40, and Joe's total tuition is \$2116.20.

83. (a) $\begin{bmatrix} 500 & 350 & 400 \\ 700 & 500 & 850 \end{bmatrix}; \begin{bmatrix} 500 & 700 \\ 350 & 500 \\ 400 & 850 \end{bmatrix}$ **(b)** $\begin{bmatrix} 15 \\ 8 \\ 3 \end{bmatrix}$ **(c)** $\begin{bmatrix} 11{,}500 \\ 17{,}050 \end{bmatrix}$ **(d)** $[0.10 \quad 0.05]$ **(e)** \$2002.50

85. (a) $K^{-1} = \begin{bmatrix} 1 & 0 & -1 \\ -1 & 1 & 1 \\ 0 & -1 & 1 \end{bmatrix}$ **(b)** $M = \begin{bmatrix} 13 & 1 & 20 \\ 8 & 9 & 19 \\ 6 & 21 & 14 \end{bmatrix}$ **(c)** Math is fun.

87. If $D = ad - bc \neq 0$, then $a \neq 0$ and $d \neq 0$, or $b \neq 0$ and $c \neq 0$. Assuming the former,

$$\left[\begin{array}{cc|cc} a & b & 1 & 0 \\ c & d & 0 & 1 \end{array}\right] \rightarrow \left[\begin{array}{cc|cc} 1 & \frac{b}{a} & \frac{1}{a} & 0 \\ c & d & 0 & 1 \end{array}\right] \rightarrow \left[\begin{array}{cc|cc} 1 & \frac{b}{a} & \frac{1}{a} & 0 \\ 0 & \frac{D}{a} & -\frac{c}{a} & 1 \end{array}\right] \rightarrow \left[\begin{array}{cc|cc} 1 & \frac{b}{a} & \frac{1}{a} & 0 \\ 0 & 1 & -\frac{c}{D} & \frac{a}{D} \end{array}\right] \rightarrow \left[\begin{array}{cc|cc} 1 & 0 & \frac{d}{D} & -\frac{b}{D} \\ 0 & 1 & -\frac{c}{D} & \frac{a}{D} \end{array}\right]$$

$$R_1 = \frac{1}{a}r_1 \qquad R_2 = -cr_1 + r_2 \qquad R_2 = \frac{a}{D}r_2 \qquad R_1 = -\frac{b}{a}r_2 + r_1$$

11.5 Assess Your Understanding *(page 769)*

5. Proper **7.** Improper; $1 + \frac{9}{x^2 - 4}$ **9.** Improper; $5x + \frac{22x - 1}{x^2 - 4}$ **11.** Improper; $1 + \frac{-2(x - 6)}{(x + 4)(x - 3)}$ **13.** $\frac{-4}{x} + \frac{4}{x - 1}$ **15.** $\frac{1}{x} + \frac{-x}{x^2 + 1}$ **17.** $\frac{-1}{x - 1} + \frac{2}{x - 2}$ **19.** $\frac{\frac{1}{4}}{x + 1} + \frac{\frac{3}{4}}{x - 1} + \frac{\frac{1}{2}}{(x - 1)^2}$ **21.** $\frac{\frac{1}{12}}{x - 2} + \frac{-\frac{1}{12}(x + 4)}{x^2 + 2x + 4}$ **23.** $\frac{\frac{1}{4}}{x - 1} + \frac{\frac{1}{4}}{(x - 1)^2} + \frac{-\frac{1}{4}}{x + 1} + \frac{\frac{1}{4}}{(x + 1)^2}$ **25.** $\frac{-5}{x + 2} + \frac{5}{x + 1} + \frac{-4}{(x + 1)^2}$ **27.** $\frac{\frac{1}{4}}{x} + \frac{1}{x^2} + \frac{-\frac{1}{4}(x + 4)}{x^2 + 4}$ **29.** $\frac{\frac{2}{3}}{x + 1} + \frac{\frac{1}{3}(x + 1)}{x^2 + 2x + 4}$ **31.** $\frac{\frac{2}{7}}{3x - 2} + \frac{\frac{1}{7}}{2x + 1}$ **33.** $\frac{\frac{3}{4}}{x + 3} + \frac{\frac{1}{4}}{x - 1}$ **35.** $\frac{1}{x^2 + 4} + \frac{2x - 1}{(x^2 + 4)^2}$ **37.** $\frac{-1}{x} + \frac{2}{x - 3} + \frac{-1}{x + 1}$ **39.** $\frac{4}{x - 2} + \frac{-3}{x - 1} + \frac{-1}{(x - 1)^2}$ **41.** $\frac{x}{(x^2 + 16)^2} + \frac{-16x}{(x^2 + 16)^3}$ **43.** $\frac{-\frac{8}{7}}{2x + 1} + \frac{\frac{4}{7}}{x - 3}$ **45.** $\frac{-\frac{2}{9}}{x} + \frac{-\frac{1}{3}}{x^2} + \frac{\frac{1}{6}}{x - 3} + \frac{\frac{1}{18}}{x + 3}$

Historical Problem *(page 776)*

$x = 6$ units, $y = 8$ units

11.6 Assess Your Understanding *(page 776)*

5.

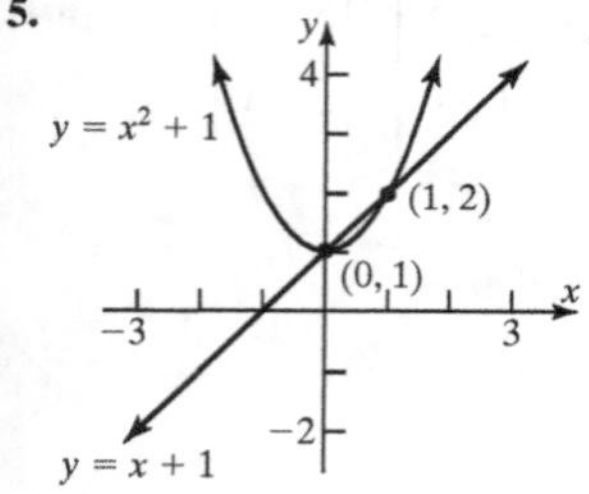

7.

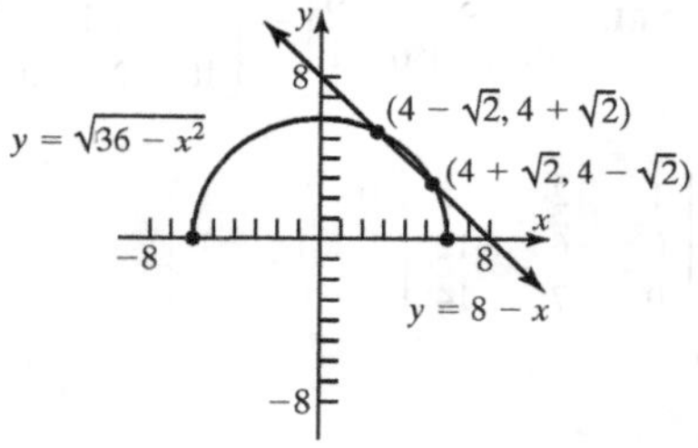

9.

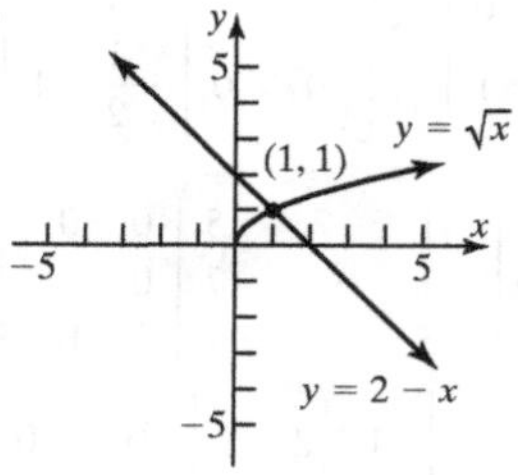

11.

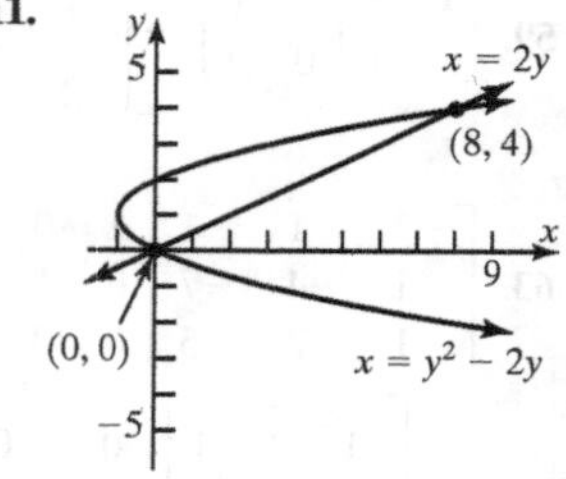

13.

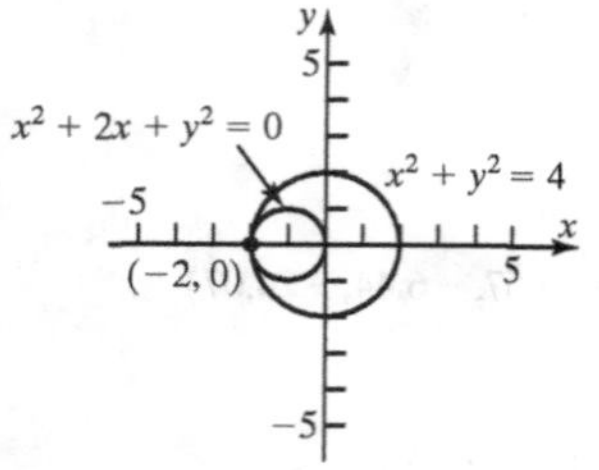

15.

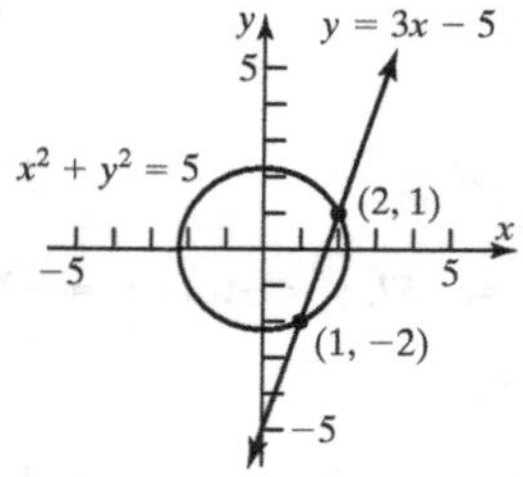

17.

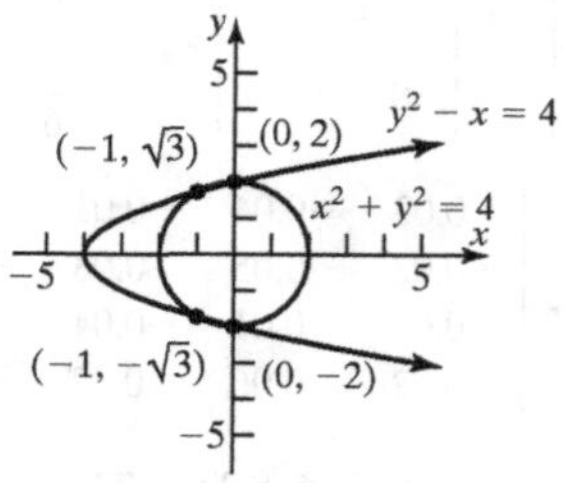

19.

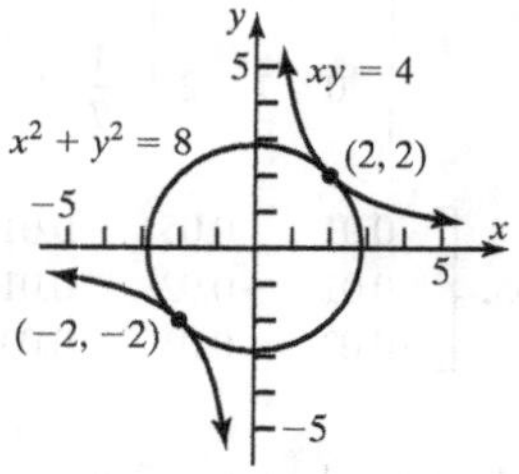

21. No points of intersection

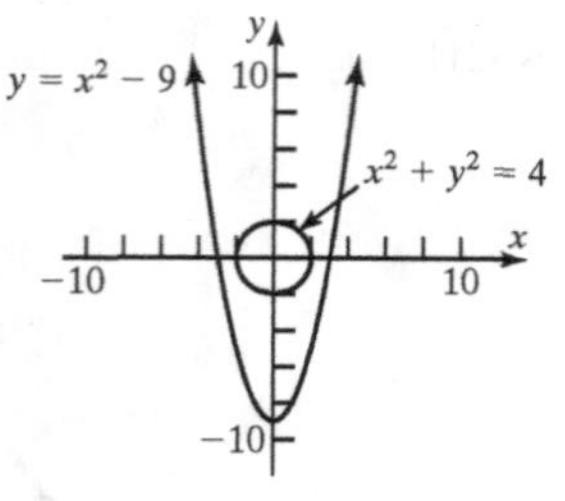

23.

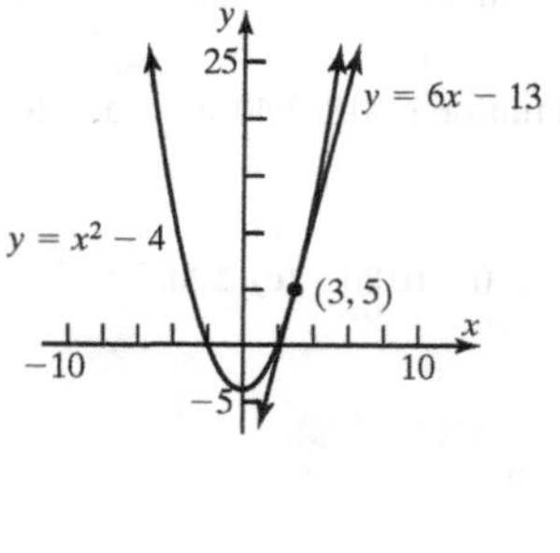

25. $x = 1, y = 4; x = -1, y = -4; x = 2\sqrt{2}, y = \sqrt{2}; x = -2\sqrt{2}, y = -\sqrt{2}$ or $(1, 4), (-1, -4), \left(2\sqrt{2}, \sqrt{2}\right), \left(-2\sqrt{2}, -\sqrt{2}\right)$

27. $x = 0, y = 1; x = -\frac{2}{3}, y = -\frac{1}{3}$ or $(0, 1), \left(-\frac{2}{3}, -\frac{1}{3}\right)$ **29.** $x = 0, y = -1; x = \frac{5}{2}, y = -\frac{7}{2}$ or $(0, -1), \left(\frac{5}{2}, -\frac{7}{2}\right)$

31. $x = 2, y = \frac{1}{3}; x = \frac{1}{2}, y = \frac{4}{3}$ or $\left(2, \frac{1}{3}\right), \left(\frac{1}{2}, \frac{4}{3}\right)$ **33.** $x = 3, y = 2; x = 3, y = -2; x = -3, y = 2; x = -3, y = -2$ or $(3, 2), (3, -2), (-3, 2), (-3, -2)$ **35.** $x = \frac{1}{2}, y = \frac{3}{2}; x = \frac{1}{2}, y = -\frac{3}{2}; x = -\frac{1}{2}, y = \frac{3}{2}; x = -\frac{1}{2}, y = -\frac{3}{2}$ or $\left(\frac{1}{2}, \frac{3}{2}\right), \left(\frac{1}{2}, -\frac{3}{2}\right), \left(-\frac{1}{2}, \frac{3}{2}\right), \left(-\frac{1}{2}, -\frac{3}{2}\right)$

37. $x = \sqrt{2}, y = 2\sqrt{2}; x = -\sqrt{2}, y = -2\sqrt{2}$ or $\left(\sqrt{2}, 2\sqrt{2}\right), \left(-\sqrt{2}, -2\sqrt{2}\right)$ **39.** No real solution exists.

41. $x = \frac{8}{3}, y = \frac{2\sqrt{10}}{3}; x = -\frac{8}{3}, y = \frac{2\sqrt{10}}{3}; x = \frac{8}{3}, y = -\frac{2\sqrt{10}}{3}; x = -\frac{8}{3}, y = -\frac{2\sqrt{10}}{3}$ or $\left(\frac{8}{3}, \frac{2\sqrt{10}}{3}\right), \left(-\frac{8}{3}, \frac{2\sqrt{10}}{3}\right), \left(\frac{8}{3}, -\frac{2\sqrt{10}}{3}\right), \left(-\frac{8}{3}, -\frac{2\sqrt{10}}{3}\right)$

43. $x = 1, y = \frac{1}{2}; x = -1, y = \frac{1}{2}; x = 1, y = -\frac{1}{2}; x = -1, y = -\frac{1}{2}$ or $\left(1, \frac{1}{2}\right), \left(-1, \frac{1}{2}\right), \left(1, -\frac{1}{2}\right), \left(-1, -\frac{1}{2}\right)$ **45.** No real solution exists.

47. $x = \sqrt{3}, y = \sqrt{3}; x = -\sqrt{3}, y = -\sqrt{3}; x = 2, y = 1; x = -2, y = -1$ or $\left(\sqrt{3}, \sqrt{3}\right), \left(-\sqrt{3}, -\sqrt{3}\right), (2, 1), (-2, -1)$

49. $x = 0, y = -2; x = 0, y = 1; x = 2, y = -1$ or $(0, -2), (0, 1), (2, -1)$ **51.** $x = 2, y = 8$ or $(2, 8)$ **53.** $x = 81, y = 3$ or $(81, 3)$

55.

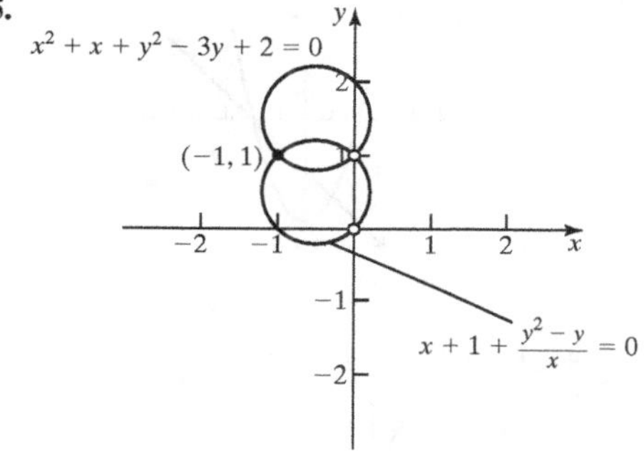

57. $x = 0.48, y = 0.62$ **59.** $x = -1.65, y = -0.89$

61. $x = 0.58, y = 1.86; x = 1.81, y = 1.05; x = 0.58, y = -1.86; x = 1.81, y = -1.05$

63. $x = 2.35, y = 0.85$

65.

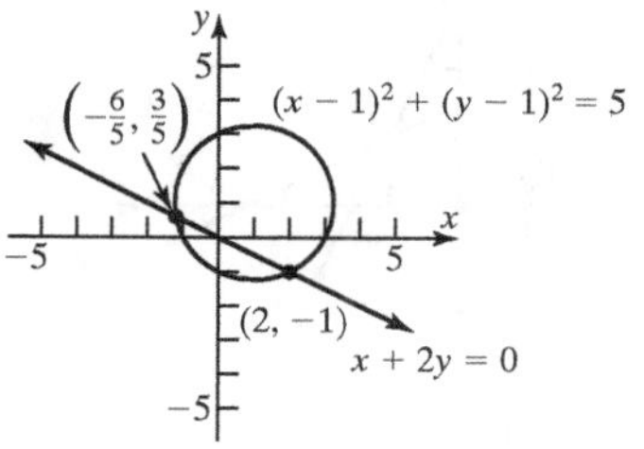

67.

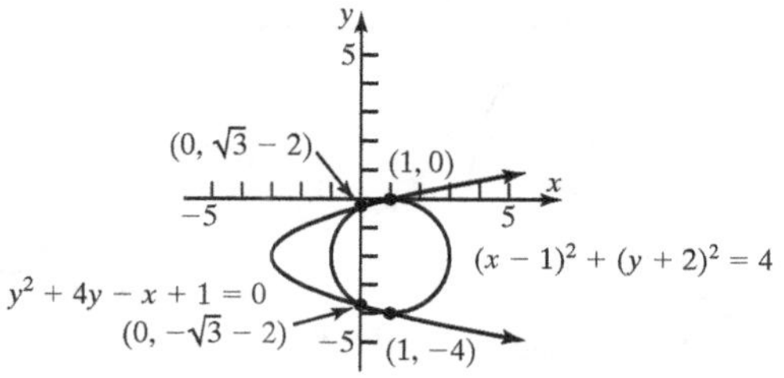

69.

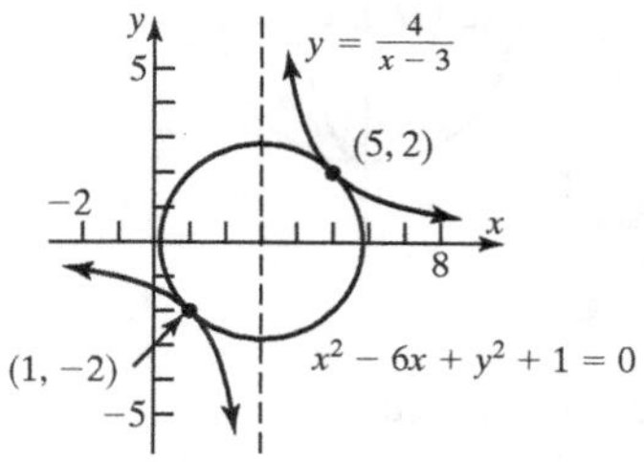

71. 3 and 1; −1 and −3 **73.** 2 and 2; −2 and −2 **75.** $\frac{1}{2}$ and $\frac{1}{3}$ **77.** 5 **79.** 5 in. by 3 in. **81.** 2 cm and 4 cm **83.** tortoise: 7 m/hr, hare: $7\frac{1}{2}$ m/hr

85. 12 cm by 18 cm **87.** $x = 60$ ft; $y = 30$ ft **89.** $l = \frac{P + \sqrt{P^2 - 16A}}{4}; w = \frac{P - \sqrt{P^2 - 16A}}{4}$ **91.** $y = 4x - 4$ **93.** $y = 2x + 1$

95. $y = -\frac{1}{3}x + \frac{7}{3}$ **97.** $y = 2x - 3$ **99.** $r_1 = \frac{-b + \sqrt{b^2 - 4ac}}{2a}; r_2 = \frac{-b - \sqrt{b^2 - 4ac}}{2a}$ **101.** **(a)** 4.274 ft by 4.274 ft or 0.093 ft by 0.093 ft

11.7 Assess Your Understanding *(page 786)*

7. satisfied **8.** half-plane **9.** F **10.** T

11.

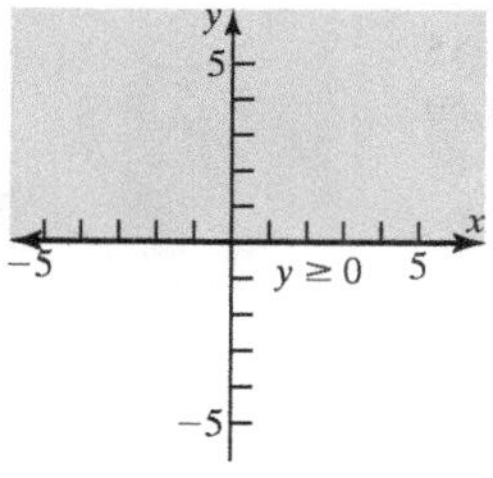

13.

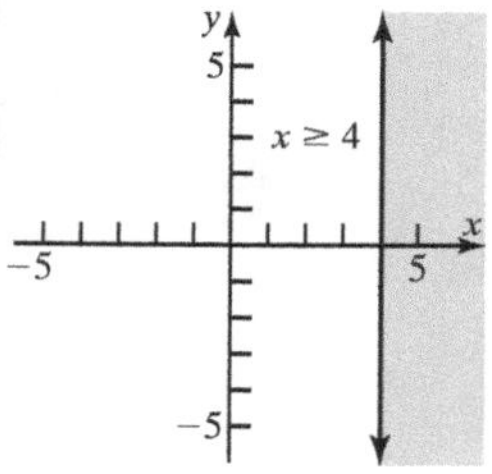

15.

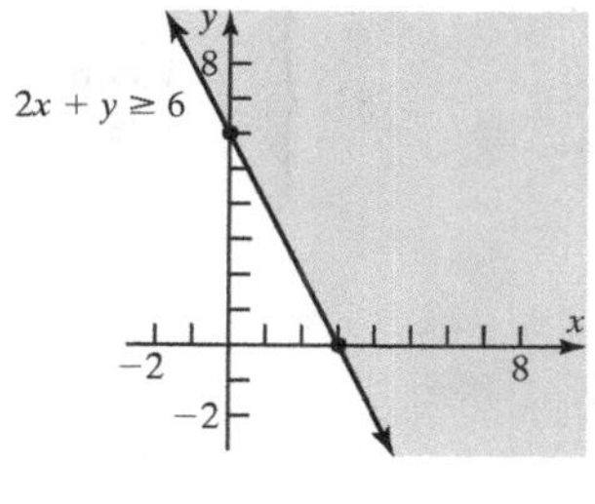

17.

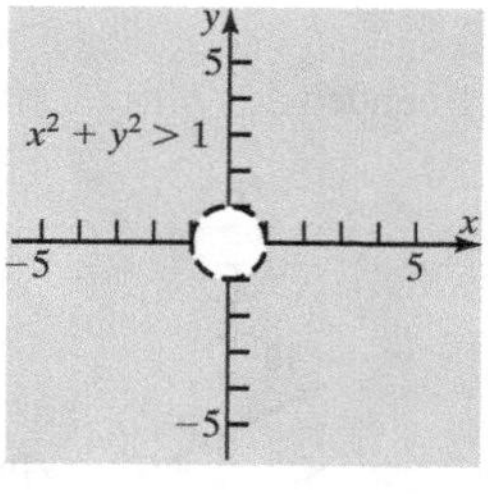

19.

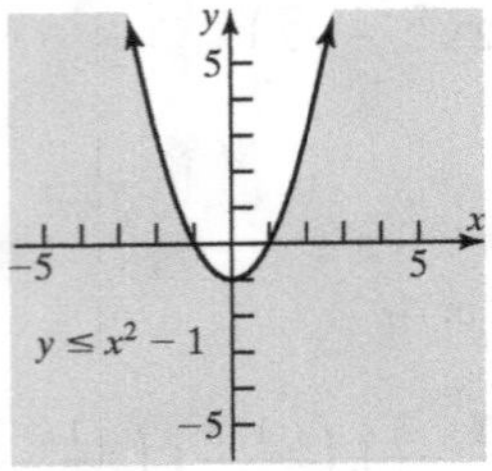

21.

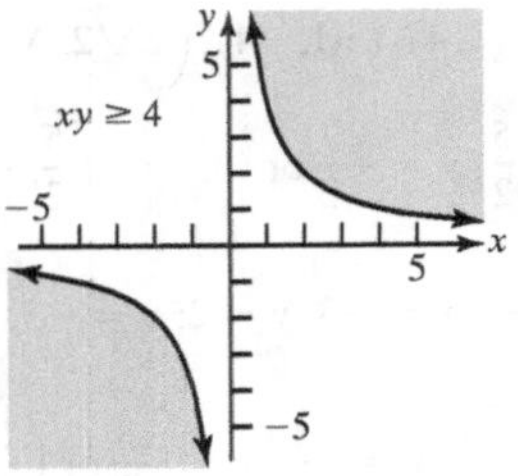

23.

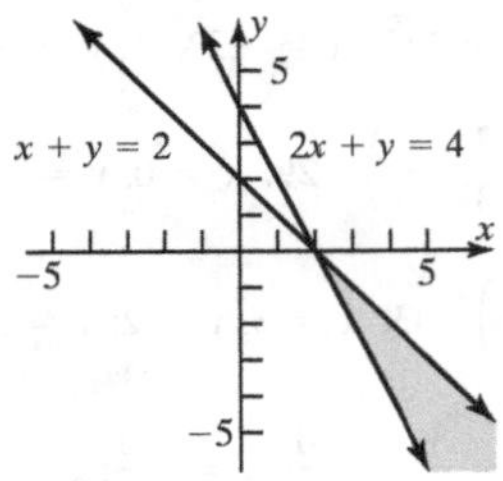

25.

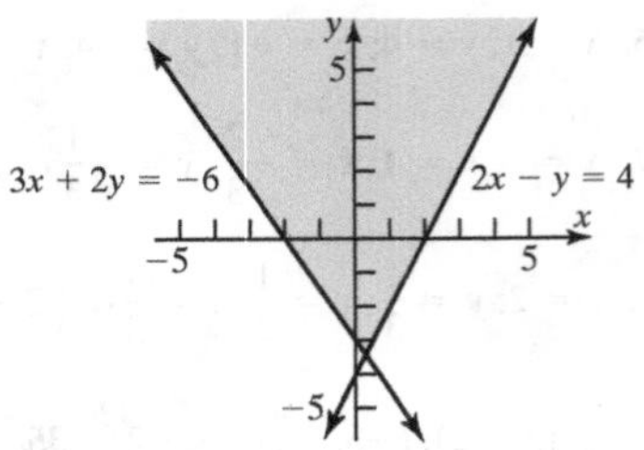

27.

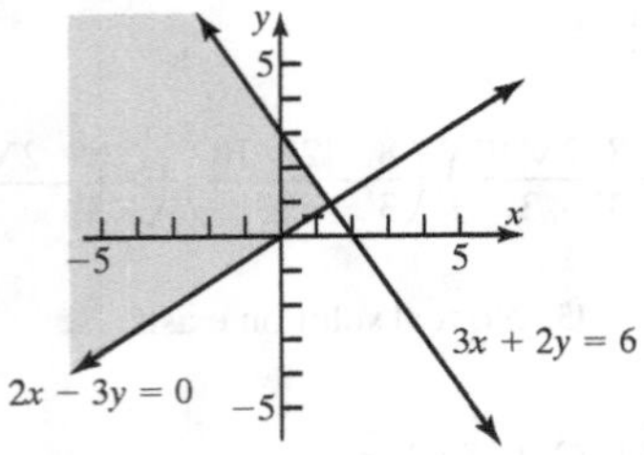

29.

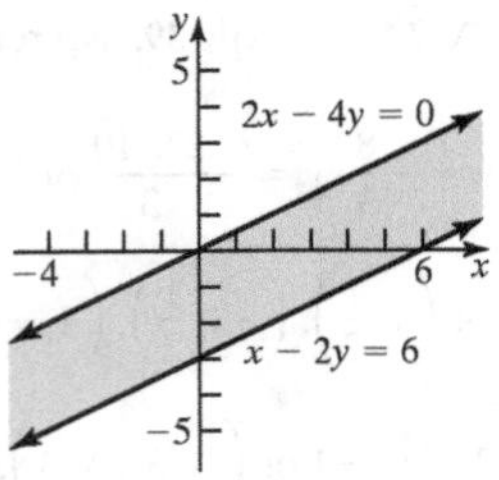

31.

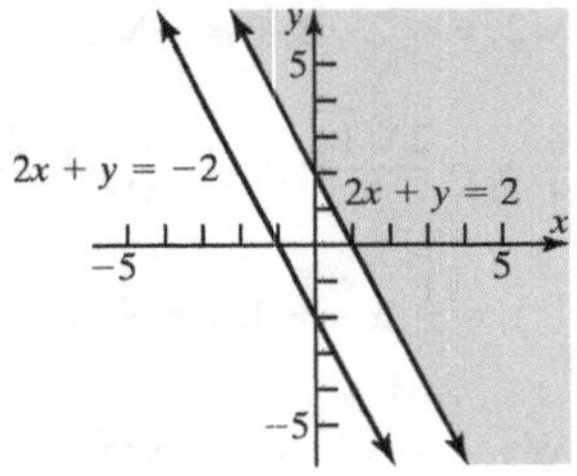

33. No solution

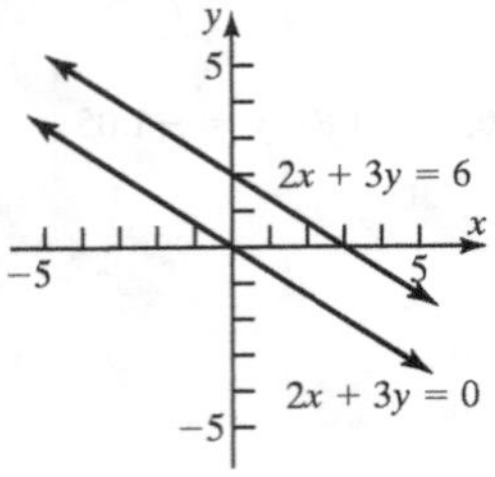

35.

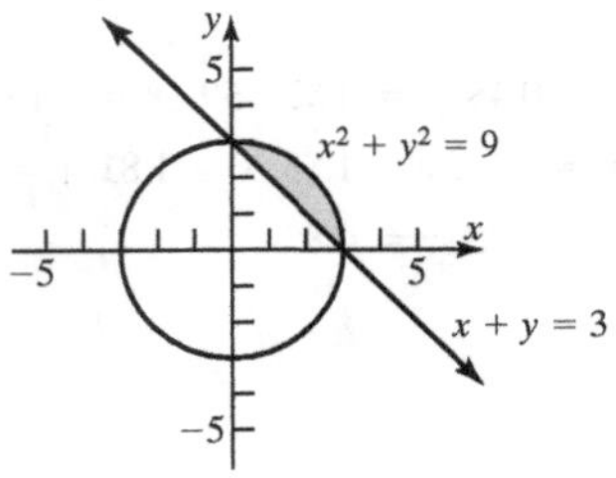

37.

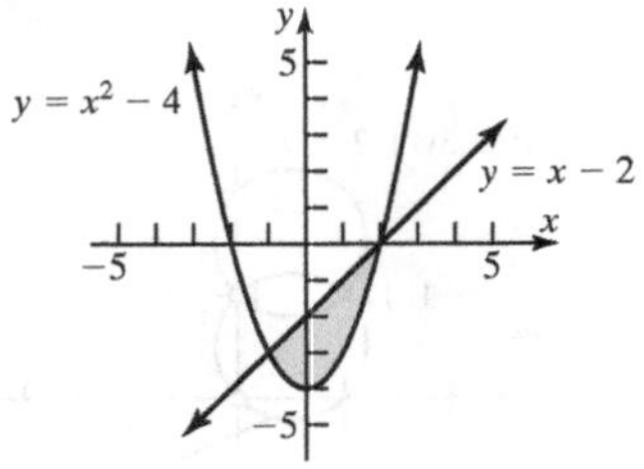

39.

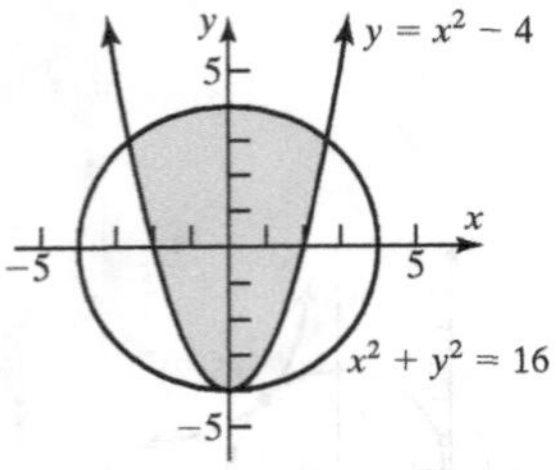

41.

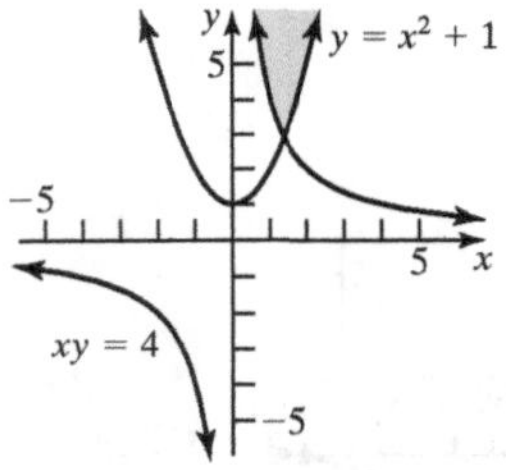

43. Bounded

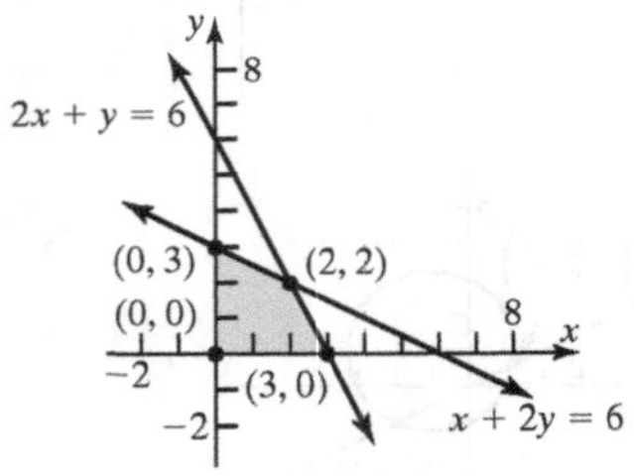

45. Unbounded

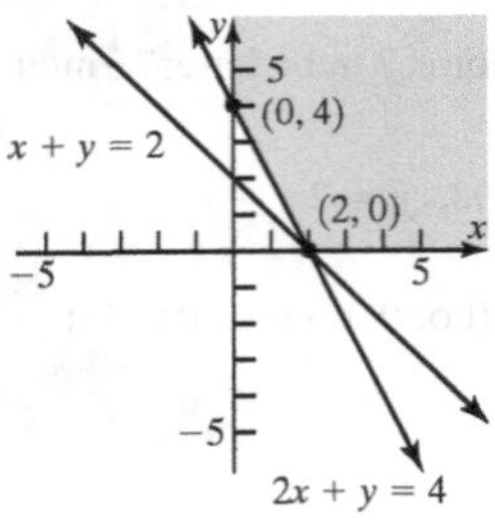

47. Bounded

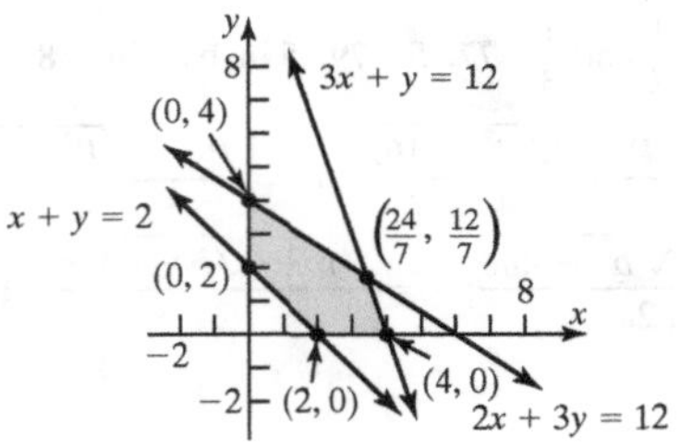

49. Bounded

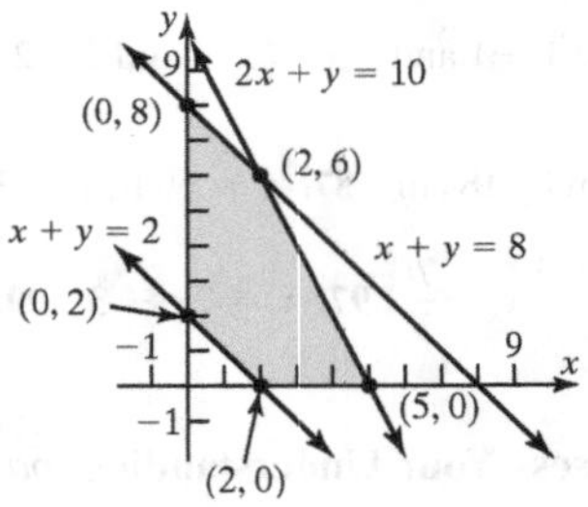

51. Bounded

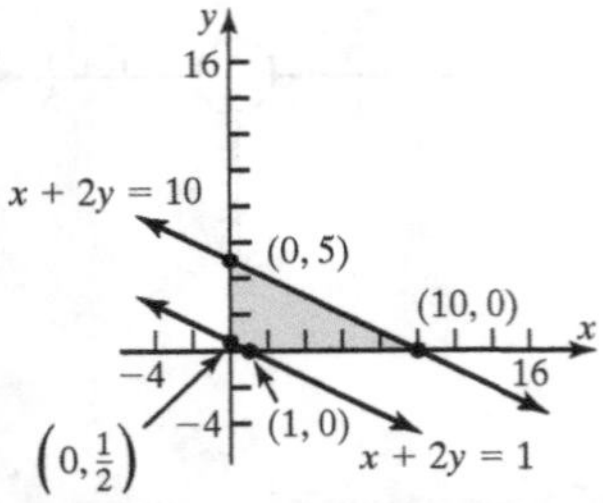

53. $\begin{cases} x \le 4 \\ x + y \le 6 \\ x \ge 0 \\ y \ge 0 \end{cases}$

55. $\begin{cases} x \le 20 \\ y \ge 15 \\ x + y \le 50 \\ x - y \le 0 \\ x \ge 0 \end{cases}$

57. **(a)** $\begin{cases} x + y \le 50{,}000 \\ x \ge 35{,}000 \\ y \le 10{,}000 \\ y \ge 0 \end{cases}$

(b)

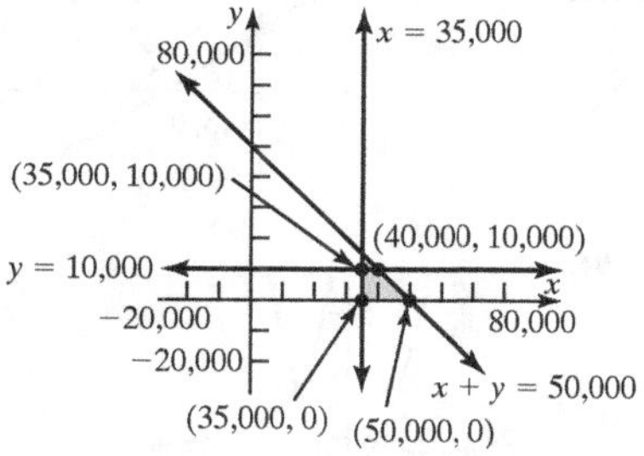

59. **(a)** $\begin{cases} x \ge 0 \\ y \ge 0 \\ x + 2y \le 300 \\ 3x + 2y \le 480 \end{cases}$

(b)

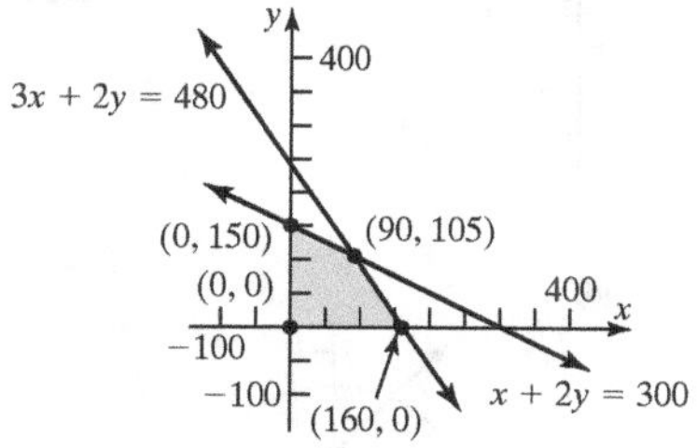

61. **(a)** $\begin{cases} 3x + 2y \le 160 \\ 2x + 3y \le 150 \\ x \ge 0 \\ y \ge 0 \end{cases}$

(b)

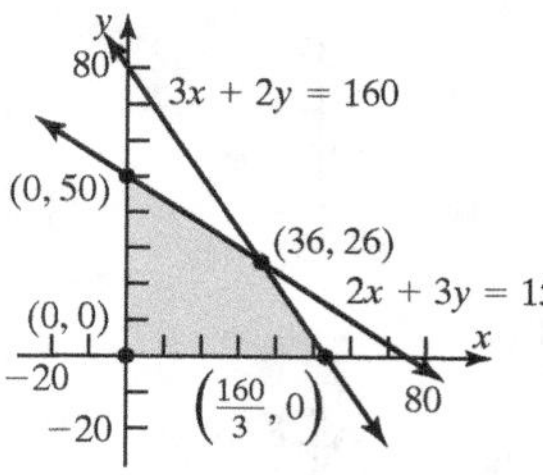

11.8 Assess Your Understanding *(page 793)*

1. objective function **2.** T **3.** Maximum value is 11; minimum value is 3. **5.** Maximum value is 65; minimum value is 4. **7.** Maximum value is 67; minimum value is 20. **9.** The maximum value of z is 12, and it occurs at the point (6, 0). **11.** The minimum value of z is 4, and it occurs at the point (2, 0). **13.** The maximum value of z is 20, and it occurs at the point (0, 4). **15.** The minimum value of z is 8, and it occurs at the point (0, 2). **17.** The maximum value of z is 50, and it occurs at the point (10, 0). **19.** Produce 8 downhill and 24 cross-country; \$1760; \$1920 which is the profit when producing 16 downhill and 16 cross-country. **21.** Rent 15 rectangular tables and 16 round tables for a minimum cost of \$1252. **23.** **(a)** \$10,000 in a junk bond and \$10,000 in Treasury bills **(b)** \$12,000 in a junk bond and \$8000 in Treasury bills **25.** 100 lb of ground beef should be mixed with 50 lb of pork. **27.** Manufacture 10 racing skates and 15 figure skates. **29.** Order 2 metal samples and 4 plastic samples; \$34 **31.** **(a)** Configure with 10 first class seats and 120 coach seats. **(b)** Configure with 15 first class seats and 120 coach seats.

Review Exercises *(page 796)*

1. $x = 2, y = -1$ or $(2, -1)$ **3.** $x = 2, y = \frac{1}{2}$ or $\left(2, \frac{1}{2}\right)$ **5.** $x = 2, y = -1$ or $(2, -1)$ **7.** $x = \frac{11}{5}, y = -\frac{3}{5}$ or $\left(\frac{11}{5}, -\frac{3}{5}\right)$ **9.** Inconsistent

11. $x = 2, y = 3$ or $(2, 3)$ **13.** Inconsistent **15.** $x = -1, y = 2, z = -3$ or $(-1, 2, -3)$ **17.** $x = \frac{7}{4}z + \frac{39}{4}, y = \frac{9}{8}z + \frac{69}{8}$, where z is any real number or $\left\{(x, y, z,) \mid x = \frac{7}{4}z + \frac{39}{4}, y = \frac{9}{8}z + \frac{69}{8}, z \text{ is any real number}\right\}$ **19.** $\begin{cases} 3x + 2y = 8 \\ x + 4y = -1 \end{cases}$ **21.** $\begin{bmatrix} 4 & -4 \\ 3 & 9 \\ 4 & 4 \end{bmatrix}$ **23.** $\begin{bmatrix} 6 & 0 \\ 12 & 24 \\ -6 & 12 \end{bmatrix}$ **25.** $\begin{bmatrix} 4 & -3 & 0 \\ 12 & -2 & -8 \\ -2 & 5 & -4 \end{bmatrix}$

27. $\begin{bmatrix} 8 & -13 & 8 \\ 9 & 2 & -10 \\ 22 & -13 & -4 \end{bmatrix}$ **29.** $\begin{bmatrix} \frac{1}{2} & -1 \\ -\frac{1}{6} & \frac{2}{3} \end{bmatrix}$ **31.** $\begin{bmatrix} -\frac{5}{7} & \frac{9}{7} & \frac{3}{7} \\ \frac{1}{7} & \frac{1}{7} & -\frac{2}{7} \\ \frac{3}{7} & -\frac{4}{7} & \frac{1}{7} \end{bmatrix}$ **33.** Singular **35.** $x = \frac{2}{5}, y = \frac{1}{10}$ or $\left(\frac{2}{5}, \frac{1}{10}\right)$

37. $x = 9, y = \frac{13}{3}, z = \frac{13}{3}$ or $\left(9, \frac{13}{3}, \frac{13}{3}\right)$ **39.** $x = -\frac{1}{2}, y = -\frac{2}{3}, z = -\frac{3}{4}$ or $\left(-\frac{1}{2}, -\frac{2}{3}, -\frac{3}{4}\right)$ **41.** $z = -1, x = y + 1$, where y is any real number or $\{(x, y, z) \mid x = y + 1, z = -1, y \text{ is any real number}\}$ **43.** $x = 4, y = 2, z = 3, t = -2$ or $(4, 2, 3, -2)$ **45.** 5 **47.** 108 **49.** -100

51. $x = 2, y = -1$ or $(2, -1)$ **53.** $x = 2, y = 3$ or $(2, 3)$ **55.** $x = -1, y = 2, z = -3$ or $(-1, 2, -3)$ **57.** 16 **59.** $\dfrac{-\frac{3}{2}}{x} + \dfrac{\frac{3}{2}}{x - 4}$

61. $\dfrac{-3}{x - 1} + \dfrac{3}{x} + \dfrac{4}{x^2}$ **63.** $\dfrac{-\frac{1}{10}}{x + 1} + \dfrac{\frac{1}{10}x + \frac{9}{10}}{x^2 + 9}$ **65.** $\dfrac{x}{x^2 + 4} + \dfrac{-4x}{(x^2 + 4)^2}$ **67.** $\dfrac{\frac{1}{2}}{x^2 + 1} + \dfrac{\frac{1}{4}}{x - 1} + \dfrac{-\frac{1}{4}}{x + 1}$

69. $x = -\frac{2}{5}, y = -\frac{11}{5}; x = -2, y = 1$ or $\left(-\frac{2}{5}, -\frac{11}{5}\right), (-2, 1)$ **71.** $x = 2\sqrt{2}, y = \sqrt{2}; x = -2\sqrt{2}, y = -\sqrt{2}$ or $\left(2\sqrt{2}, \sqrt{2}\right), \left(-2\sqrt{2}, -\sqrt{2}\right)$

73. $x = 0, y = 0; x = -3, y = 3; x = 3, y = 3$ or $(0, 0), (-3, 3), (3, 3)$ **75.** $x = \sqrt{2}, y = -\sqrt{2}; x = -\sqrt{2}, y = \sqrt{2};$ $x = \frac{4}{3}\sqrt{2}, y = -\frac{2}{3}\sqrt{2}; x = -\frac{4}{3}\sqrt{2}, y = \frac{2}{3}\sqrt{2}$ or $\left(\sqrt{2}, -\sqrt{2}\right), \left(-\sqrt{2}, \sqrt{2}\right), \left(\frac{4}{3}\sqrt{2}, -\frac{2}{3}\sqrt{2}\right), \left(-\frac{4}{3}\sqrt{2}, \frac{2}{3}\sqrt{2}\right)$ **77.** $x = 1, y = -1$ or $(1, -1)$

79.

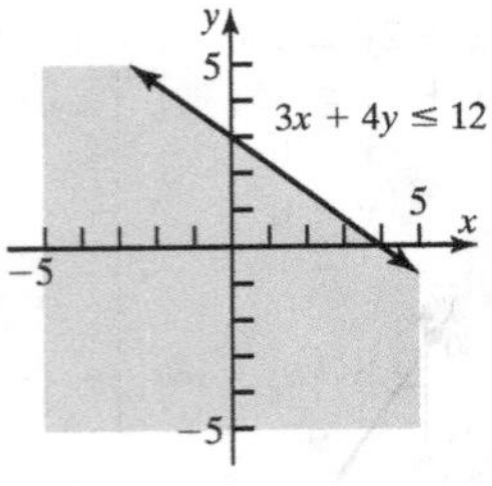

81.

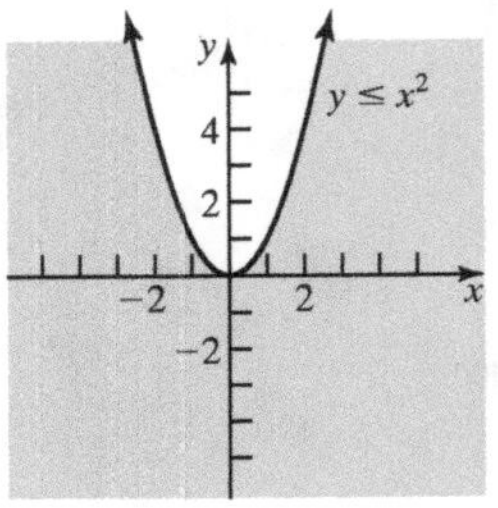

83. Unbounded

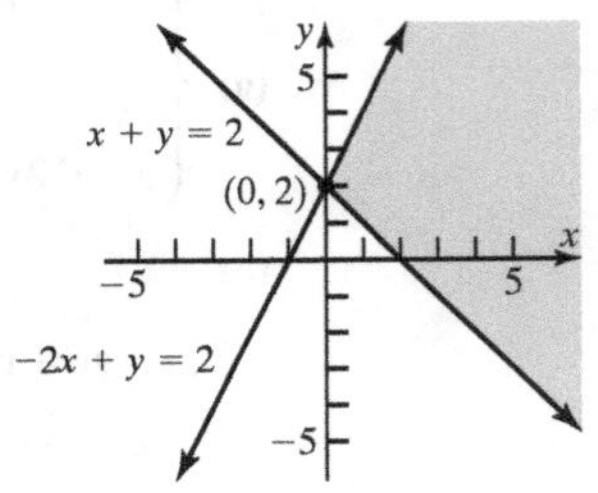

85. Bounded

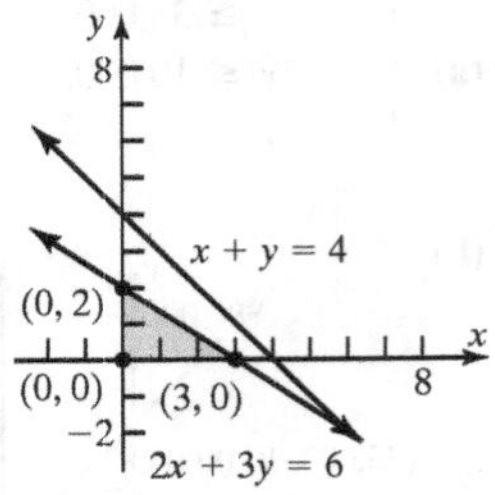

87. Bounded

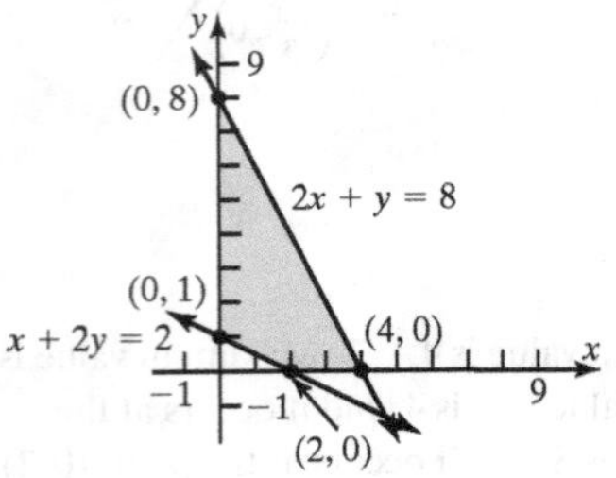

89.

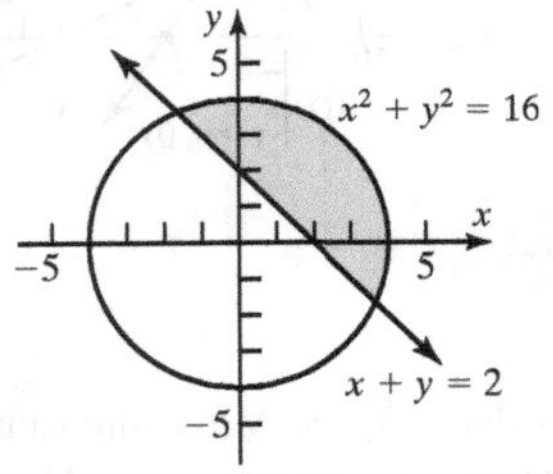

91.

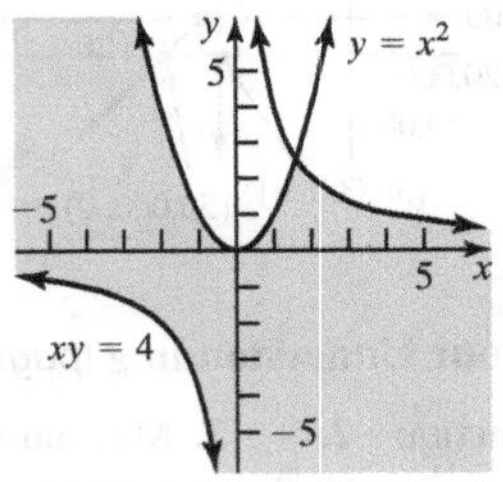

93. The maximum value is 32 when $x = 0$ and $y = 8$. **95.** The minimum value is 3 when $x = 1$ and $y = 0$. **97.** 10 **99.** $y = -\frac{1}{3}x^2 - \frac{2}{3}x + 1$
101. Mix 70 lb of \$6.00 coffee and 30 lb of \$9.00 coffee. **103.** Buy 1 small, 5 medium, and 2 large.
105. Speedboat: 36.67 km/hr; Aguarico River: 3.33 km/hr **107.** Bruce: 4hr; Bryce: 2hr; Marty: 8hr
109. Produce 35 gasoline engines and 15 diesel engines; the factory is producing an excess of 15 gasoline engines and 0 diesel engines.

Chapter Test *(page 799)*

1. $x = 3, y = -1$ or $(3, -1)$ **2.** Inconsistent. **3.** $x = -z + \frac{18}{7}, y = z - \frac{17}{7}$, where z is any real number or $\left\{(x, y, z) \mid x = -z + \frac{18}{7}, y = z - \frac{17}{7}, z \text{ is any real number}\right\}$ **4.** $x = \frac{1}{3}, y = -2, z = 0$ or $\left(\frac{1}{3}, -2, 0\right)$ **5.** $\left[\begin{array}{ccc|c} 4 & -5 & 1 & 0 \\ -2 & -1 & 0 & -25 \\ 1 & 5 & -5 & 10 \end{array}\right]$

6. $\begin{cases} 3x + 2y + 4z = -6 \\ 1x + 0y + 8z = 2 \\ -2x + 1y + 3z = -11 \end{cases}$ or $\begin{cases} 3x + 2y + 4z = -6 \\ x + 8z = 2 \\ -2x + y + 3z = -11 \end{cases}$ **7.** $\begin{bmatrix} 6 & 4 \\ 1 & -11 \\ 5 & 12 \end{bmatrix}$ **8.** $\begin{bmatrix} -11 & -19 \\ -3 & 5 \\ 6 & -22 \end{bmatrix}$ **9.** The operation cannot be performed. **10.** $\begin{bmatrix} 16 & 17 \\ 3 & -10 \end{bmatrix}$

11. $\begin{bmatrix} 2 & -1 \\ -\frac{5}{2} & \frac{3}{2} \end{bmatrix}$ **12.** $\begin{bmatrix} 3 & 3 & -4 \\ -2 & -2 & 3 \\ -4 & -5 & 7 \end{bmatrix}$ **13.** $x = \frac{1}{2}, y = 3$ or $\left(\frac{1}{2}, 3\right)$ **14.** $x = -\frac{1}{4}y + 7$, where y is any real number or $\left\{(x, y) \mid x = -\frac{1}{4}y + 7, y \text{ is any real number}\right\}$ **15.** $x = 1, y = -2, z = 0$ or $(1, -2, 0)$ **16.** Inconsistent

17. -29 **18.** -12 **19.** $x = -2, y = -5$ or $(-2, -5)$ **20.** $x = 1, y = -1, z = 4$ or $(1, -1, 4)$ **21.** $(1, -3)$ and $(1, 3)$ **22.** $(3, 4)$ and $(1, 2)$

23.

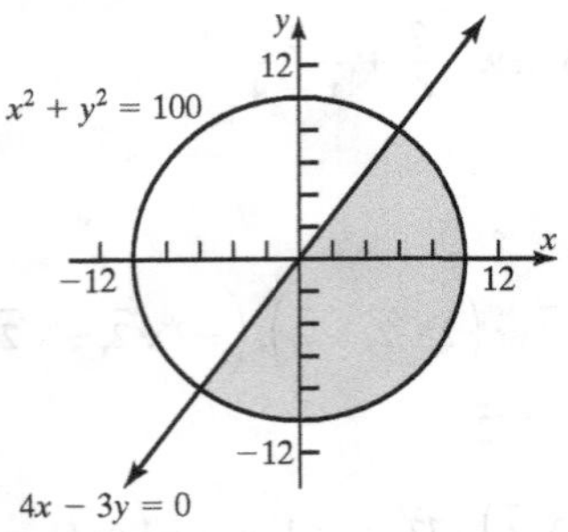

24. $\frac{3}{x + 3} + \frac{-2}{(x + 3)^2}$

25. $\frac{-\frac{1}{3}}{x} + \frac{\frac{1}{3}x}{(x^2 + 3)} + \frac{5x}{(x^2 + 3)^2}$

26. Unbounded

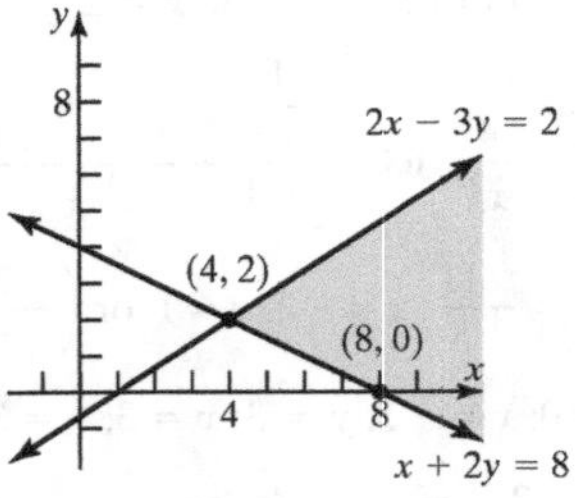

27. The maximum value of z is 64, and it occurs at the point $(0, 8)$. **28.** Flare jeans cost \$24.50, camisoles cost \$8.50, and T-shirts cost \$6.00.

Cumulative Review *(page 800)*

1. $\left\{0, \frac{1}{2}\right\}$ **2.** $\{5\}$ **3.** $\left\{-1, -\frac{1}{2}, 3\right\}$ **4.** $\{-2\}$ **5.** $\left\{\frac{5}{2}\right\}$ **6.** $\left\{\frac{1}{\ln 3}\right\}$ **7.** Odd; symmetric with respect to the origin

8. Center: $(1, -2)$; radius $= 4$

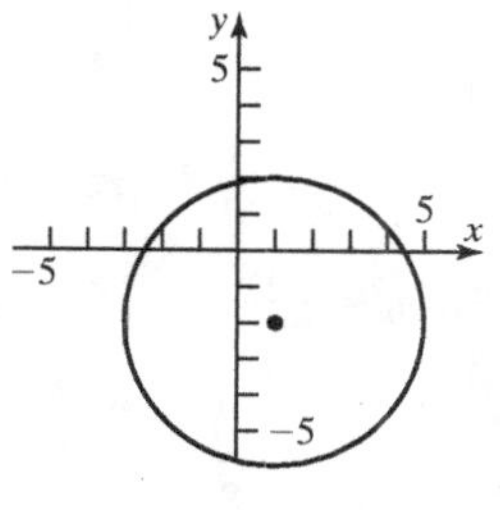

9. Domain: all real numbers
Range: $\{y \mid y > 1\}$
Horizontal asymptote: $y = 1$

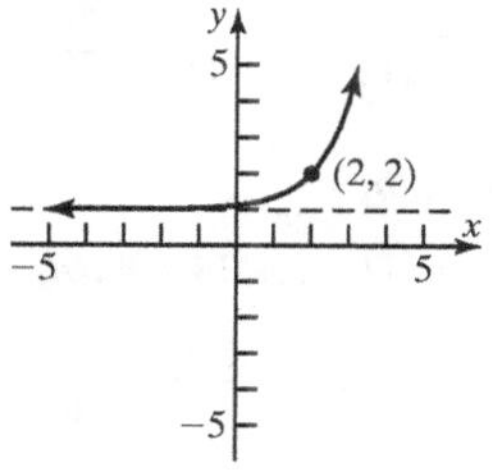

10. $f^{-1}(x) = \dfrac{5}{x} - 2$
Domain of f: $\{x \mid x \neq -2\}$
Range of f: $\{y \mid y \neq 0\}$
Domain of f^{-1}: $\{x \mid x \neq 0\}$
Range of f^{-1}: $\{y \mid y \neq -2\}$

11. (a)

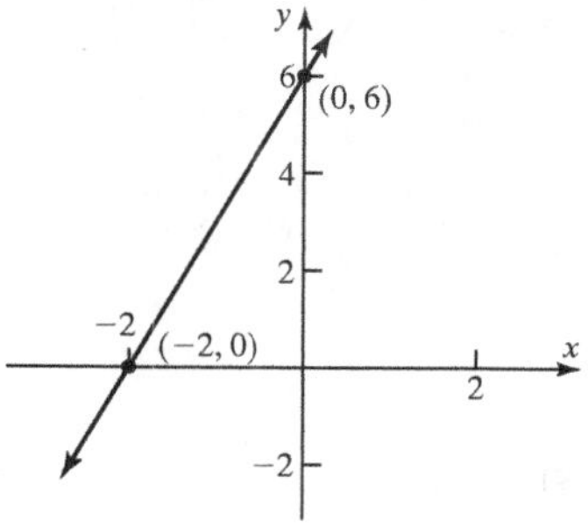

(b)

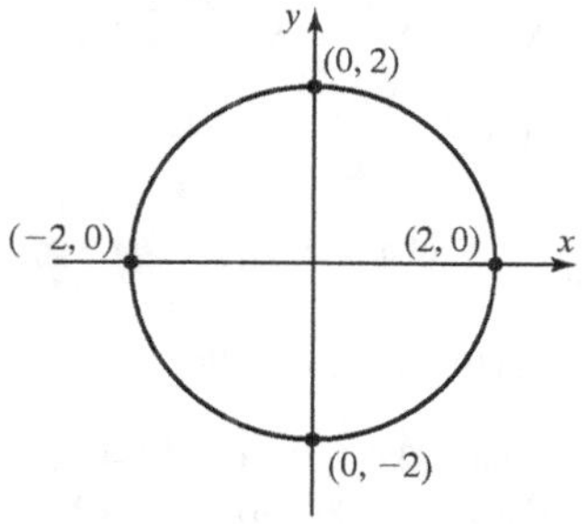

(c)

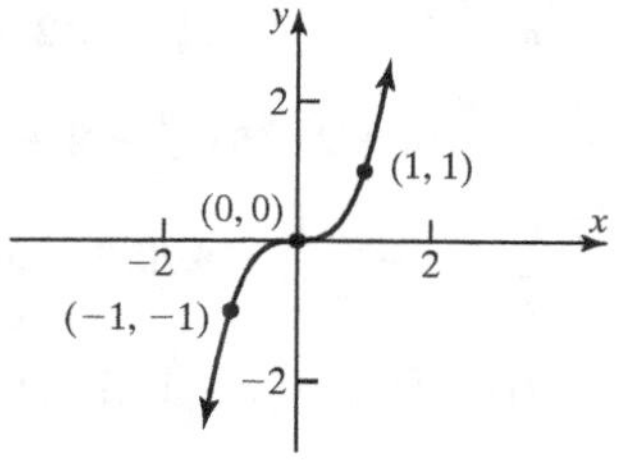

(d)

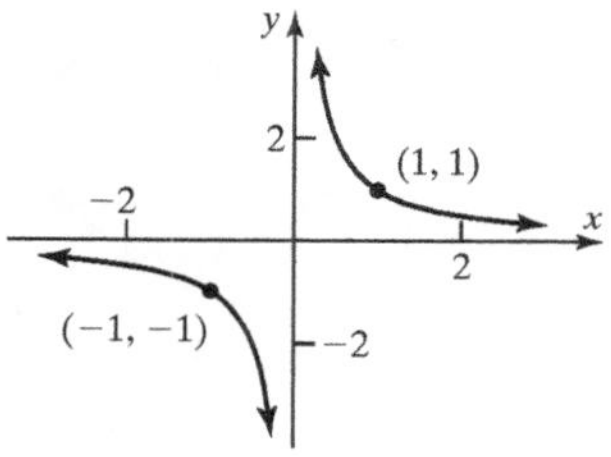

(e)

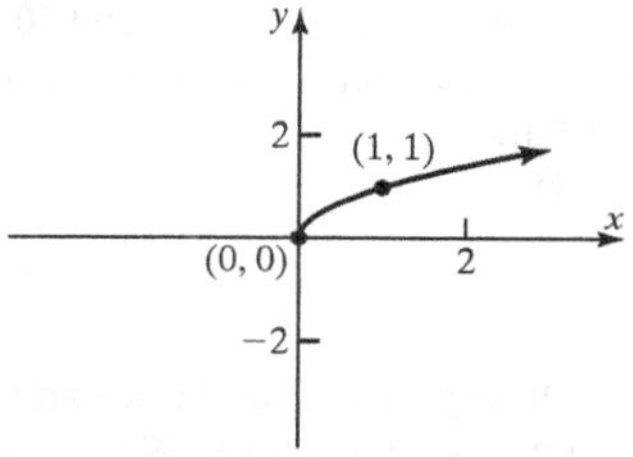

(f)

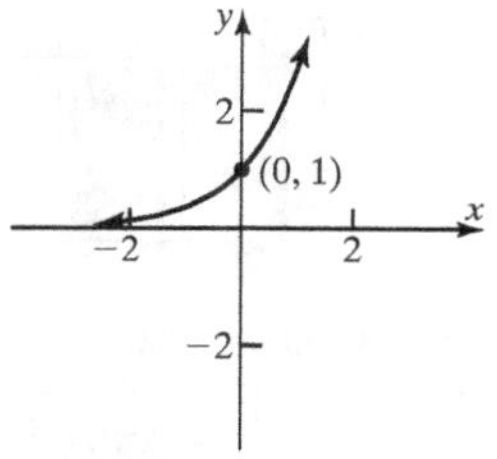

(g)

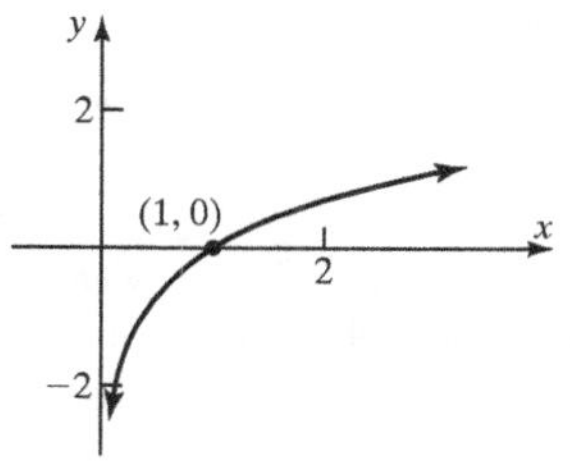

(h)

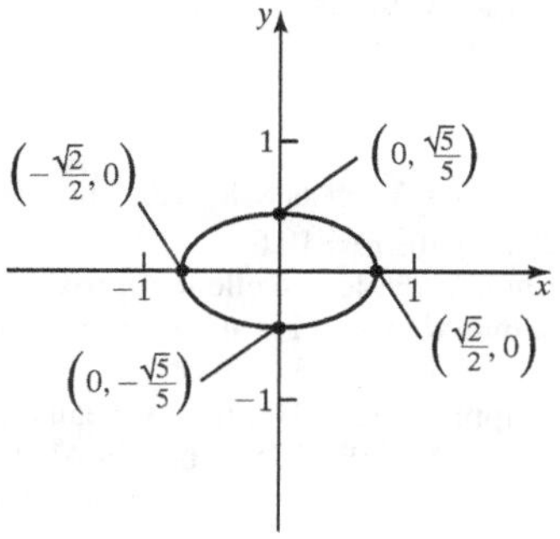

(i)

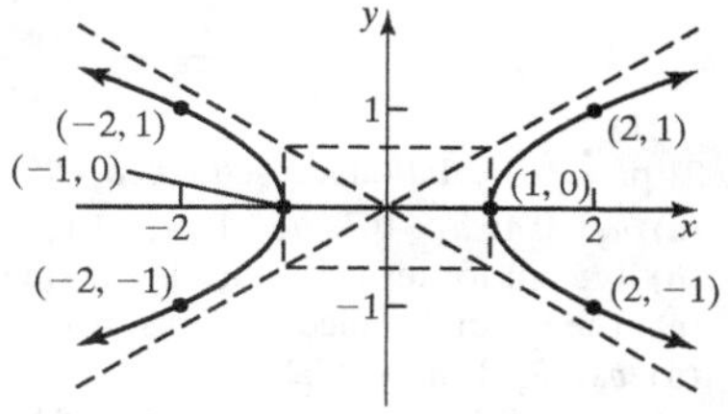

(j)

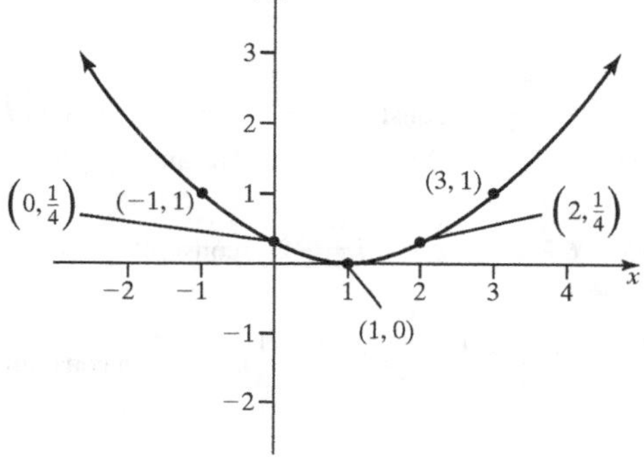

(k)

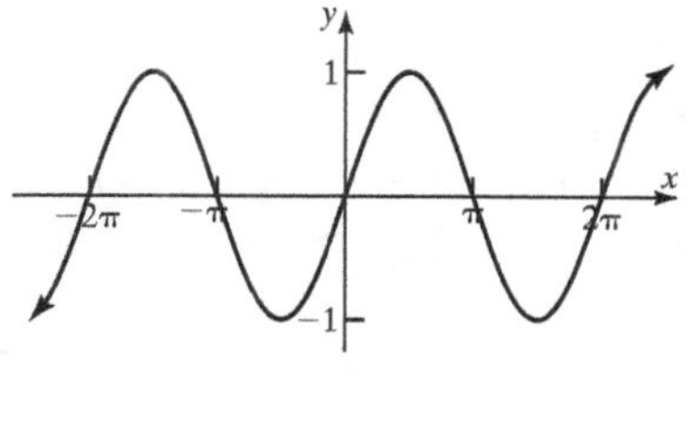

(l)

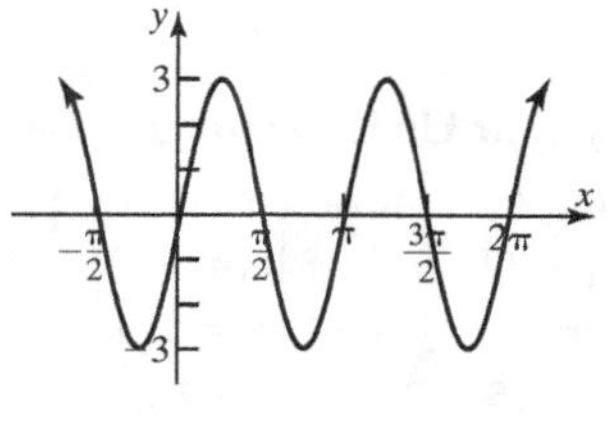

12. (a)

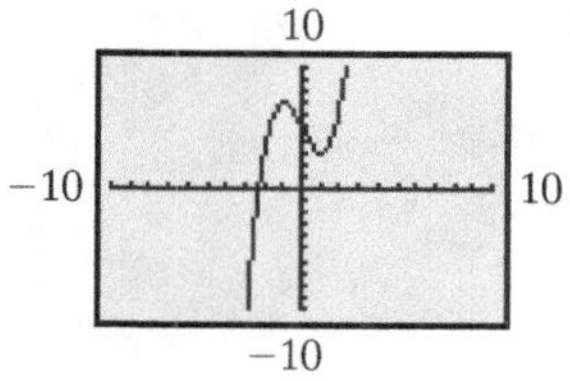

; −2.28

(b) Local maximum of 7 at $x = -1$; local minimum of 3 at $x = 1$

(c) $(-\infty, -1), (1, \infty)$

13. $\left\{x \mid x = \pm \dfrac{\pi}{3} + 2\pi k, k \text{ any integer}\right\}$

CHAPTER 12 Sequences; Induction; the Binomial Theorem

12.1 Assess Your Understanding *(page 813)*

5. sequence **6.** 3; 15 **7.** 20 **8.** T **9.** T **10.** T **11.** 3,628,800 **13.** 504 **15.** 1260 **17.** $s_1 = 1, s_2 = 2, s_3 = 3, s_4 = 4, s_5 = 5$

19. $a_1 = \frac{1}{3}, a_2 = \frac{1}{2}, a_3 = \frac{3}{5}, a_4 = \frac{2}{3}, a_5 = \frac{5}{7}$ **21.** $c_1 = 1, c_2 = -4, c_3 = 9, c_4 = -16, c_5 = 25$ **23.** $s_1 = \frac{1}{2}, s_2 = \frac{2}{5}, s_3 = \frac{2}{7}, s_4 = \frac{8}{41}, s_5 = \frac{8}{61}$

25. $t_1 = -\frac{1}{6}, t_2 = \frac{1}{12}, t_3 = -\frac{1}{20}, t_4 = \frac{1}{30}, t_5 = -\frac{1}{42}$ **27.** $b_1 = \frac{1}{e}, b_2 = \frac{2}{e^2}, b_3 = \frac{3}{e^3}, b_4 = \frac{4}{e^4}, b_5 = \frac{5}{e^5}$ **29.** $a_n = \frac{n}{n+1}$ **31.** $a_n = \frac{1}{2^{n-1}}$

33. $a_n = (-1)^{n+1}$ **35.** $a_n = (-1)^{n+1}n$ **37.** $a_1 = 2, a_2 = 5, a_3 = 8, a_4 = 11, a_5 = 14$ **39.** $a_1 = -2, a_2 = 0, a_3 = 3, a_4 = 7, a_5 = 12$

41. $a_1 = 5, a_2 = 10, a_3 = 20, a_4 = 40, a_5 = 80$ **43.** $a_1 = 3, a_2 = \frac{3}{2}, a_3 = \frac{1}{2}, a_4 = \frac{1}{8}, a_5 = \frac{1}{40}$ **45.** $a_1 = 1, a_2 = 2, a_3 = 2, a_4 = 4, a_5 = 8$

47. $a_1 = A, a_2 = A + d, a_3 = A + 2d, a_4 = A + 3d, a_5 = A + 4d$

49. $a_1 = \sqrt{2}, a_2 = \sqrt{2 + \sqrt{2}}, a_3 = \sqrt{2 + \sqrt{2 + \sqrt{2}}}, a_4 = \sqrt{2 + \sqrt{2 + \sqrt{2 + \sqrt{2}}}}, a_5 = \sqrt{2 + \sqrt{2 + \sqrt{2 + \sqrt{2 + \sqrt{2}}}}}$

51. $3 + 4 + \cdots + (n + 2)$ **53.** $\frac{1}{2} + 2 + \frac{9}{2} + \cdots + \frac{n^2}{2}$ **55.** $1 + \frac{1}{3} + \frac{1}{9} + \cdots + \frac{1}{3^n}$

57. $\frac{1}{3} + \frac{1}{9} + \frac{1}{27} + \cdots + \frac{1}{3^n}$ **59.** $\ln 2 - \ln 3 + \ln 4 - \cdots + (-1)^n \ln n$ **61.** $\sum_{k=1}^{20} k$ **63.** $\sum_{k=1}^{13} \frac{k}{k+1}$ **65.** $\sum_{k=0}^{6} (-1)^k\left(\frac{1}{3^k}\right)$ **67.** $\sum_{k=1}^{n} \frac{3^k}{k}$

69. $\sum_{k=0}^{n} (a + kd)$ or $\sum_{k=1}^{n+1} [a + (k-1)d]$ **71.** 200 **73.** 820 **75.** 1110 **77.** 1560 **79.** 3570 **81.** 44,000

83. **(a)** \$2930 **(b)** 14 payments have been made. **(c)** 36 payments; \$3584.62 **(d)** \$584.62

85. **(a)** 2162 **(b)** After 26 months **87.** **(a)** $a_0 = 0, a_n = (1.02)a_{n-1} + 500$ **(b)** After 82 quarters **(c)** \$156,116.15

89. **(a)** $a_0 = 150{,}000, a_n = (1.005)a_{n-1} - 899.33$

(b) \$149,850.67 **(c)**

n	u(n)
0	150000
1	149851
2	149701
3	149550
4	149398
5	149246
6	149093

n=0

(d) After 58 payments or 4 years and 10 months later
(e) After 359 payments of \$899.33, plus last payment of \$895.10
(f) \$173,754.57

(g) (a) $a_0 = 150{,}000, a_n = (1.005)a_{n-1} - 999.33$

(b) \$149,750.67 (c)

n	u(n)
0	150000
1	149751
2	149500
3	149248
4	148995
5	148741
6	148485

n=0

(d) After 37 payments or 3 years and 1 month later
(e) After 278 payments of \$999.33, plus last payment of \$353.69(1.005) = \$355.46
(f) \$128,169.20

91. 21 pairs **93.** Fibonacci sequence **95.** **(a)** 3.630170833 **(b)** 3.669060828 **(c)** 3.669296668 **(d)** 12

97. **(a)** $a_1 = 0.4$; $a_2 = 0.7$; $a_3 = 1$; $a_4 = 1.6$; $a_5 = 2.8$; $a_6 = 5.2$; $a_7 = 10$; $a_8 = 19.6$
(b) Except for term 5, which has no match, Bode's formula provides excellent approximations for the mean distances of the planets from the sun.
(c) The mean distance of Ceres from the sun is approximated by $a_5 = 2.8$ and that of Uranus is $a_8 = 19.6$.
(d) $a_9 = 38.8$; $a_{10} = 77.2$
(e) Pluto's distance is approximated by a_9, but no term approximates Neptune's mean distance from the sun.
(f) According to Bode's Law, the mean orbital distance of 2003 UB 313 will be 154 AU from the sun.

99. $a_0 = 3$; $a_5 = 2.828427125$; 2.828427125

101. $a_0 = 9$; $a_5 = 9.433981132$; 9.433981132

12.2 Assess Your Understanding *(page 821)*

1. arithmetic **2.** F **3.** $s_n - s_{n-1} = (n + 4) - [(n - 1) + 4] = n + 4 - (n + 3) = n + 4 - n - 3 = 1$, a constant; $d = 1$; $s_1 = 5, s_2 = 6, s_3 = 7, s_4 = 8$

5. $a_n - a_{n-1} = (2n - 5) - [2(n - 1) - 5] = 2n - 5 - (2n - 2 - 5) = 2n - 5 - (2n - 7) = 2n - 5 - 2n + 7 = 2$, a constant; $d = 2$; $a_1 = -3, a_2 = -1, a_3 = 1, a_4 = 3$

7. $c_n - c_{n-1} = (6 - 2n) - [6 - 2(n - 1)] = 6 - 2n - (6 - 2n + 2) = 6 - 2n - (8 - 2n) = 6 - 2n - 8 + 2n = -2$, a constant; $d = -2$; $c_1 = 4, c_2 = 2, c_3 = 0, c_4 = -2$

9. $t_n - t_{n-1} = \left(\frac{1}{2} - \frac{1}{3}n\right) - \left[\frac{1}{2} - \frac{1}{3}(n - 1)\right] = \frac{1}{2} - \frac{1}{3}n - \left(\frac{1}{2} - \frac{1}{3}n + \frac{1}{3}\right) = \frac{1}{2} - \frac{1}{3}n - \left(\frac{5}{6} - \frac{1}{3}n\right) = \frac{1}{2} - \frac{1}{3}n - \frac{5}{6} + \frac{1}{3}n = -\frac{1}{3}$, a constant; $d = -\frac{1}{3}$; $t_1 = \frac{1}{6}, t_2 = -\frac{1}{6}, t_3 = -\frac{1}{2}, t_4 = -\frac{5}{6}$

11. $s_n - s_{n-1} = \ln 3^n - \ln 3^{n-1} = n \ln 3 - (n-1)\ln 3 = n \ln 3 - (n \ln 3 - \ln 3) = n \ln 3 - n \ln 3 + \ln 3 = \ln 3$, a constant; $d = \ln 3; s_1 = \ln 3, s_2 = 2 \ln 3, s_3 = 3 \ln 3, s_4 = 4 \ln 3$

13. $a_n = 3n - 1; a_{51} = 152$ **15.** $a_n = 8 - 3n; a_{51} = -145$ **17.** $a_n = \frac{1}{2}(n-1); a_{51} = 25$ **19.** $a_n = \sqrt{2}n; a_{51} = 51\sqrt{2}$ **21.** 200 **23.** –266

25. $\frac{83}{2}$ **27.** $a_1 = -13; d = 3; a_n = a_{n-1} + 3; a_n = -16 + 3n$ **29.** $a_1 = -53; d = 6; a_n = a_{n-1} + 6; a_n = -59 + 6n$

31. $a_1 = 28; d = -2; a_n = a_{n-1} - 2; a_n = 30 - 2n$ **33.** $a_1 = 25; d = -2; a_n = a_{n-1} - 2; a_n = 27 - 2n$ **35.** n^2 **37.** $\frac{n}{2}(9 + 5n)$

39. 1260 **41.** 324 **43.** 30,919 **45.** 10,036 **47.** 6080 **49.** –1925 **51.** 15,960 **53.** $-\frac{3}{2}$ **55.** 24 terms **57.** 1185 seats
59. 210 of beige and 190 blue **61.** $\{T_n\} = \{-5.5n + 67\}$; $T_5 = 39.5$°F **63.** The amphitheater has 1647 seats. **65.** 8 yr

Historical Problems *(page 830)*

1. $1\frac{2}{3}$ loaves, $10\frac{5}{6}$ loaves, 20 loaves, $29\frac{1}{6}$ loaves, $38\frac{1}{3}$ loaves **2. (a)** 1 person **(b)** 2401 kittens **(c)** 2800

12.3 Assess Your Understanding *(page 830)*

1. geometric **2.** $\frac{a}{1-r}$ **3.** annuity **4.** T **5.** F **6.** T

7. $\frac{s_n}{s_{n-1}} = \frac{3^n}{3^{n-1}} = 3^{n-(n-1)} = 3$, a constant; $r = 3; s_1 = 3, s_2 = 9, s_3 = 27, s_4 = 81$

9. $\frac{a_n}{a_{n-1}} = \frac{-3\left(\frac{1}{2}\right)^n}{-3\left(\frac{1}{2}\right)^{n-1}} = \left(\frac{1}{2}\right)^{n-(n-1)} = \frac{1}{2}$, a constant; $r = \frac{1}{2}; a_1 = -\frac{3}{2}, a_2 = -\frac{3}{4}, a_3 = -\frac{3}{8}, a_4 = -\frac{3}{16}$

11. $\frac{c_n}{c_{n-1}} = \frac{\frac{2^{n-1}}{4}}{\frac{2^{(n-1)-1}}{4}} = 2^{n-1-[(n-1)-1]} = 2$, a constant; $r = 2; c_1 = \frac{1}{4}, c_2 = \frac{1}{2}, c_3 = 1, c_4 = 2$

13. $\frac{e_n}{e_{n-1}} = \frac{2^{n/3}}{2^{(n-1)/3}} = 2^{n/3-(n-1)/3} = 2^{1/3}$, a constant; $r = 2^{1/3}; e_1 = 2^{1/3}, e_2 = 2^{2/3}, e_3 = 2, e_4 = 2^{4/3}$

15. $\frac{t_n}{t_{n-1}} = \frac{\frac{3^{n-1}}{2^n}}{\frac{3^{(n-1)-1}}{2^{n-1}}} = \frac{3^{n-1}}{2^n} \cdot \frac{2^{n-1}}{3^{(n-1)-1}} = 3^{n-1-[(n-1)-1]} \cdot 2^{n-1-n} = 3 \cdot 2^{-1} = \frac{3}{2}$, a constant; $r = \frac{3}{2}; t_1 = \frac{1}{2}, t_2 = \frac{3}{4}, t_3 = \frac{9}{8}, t_4 = \frac{27}{16}$

17. $a_5 = 162; a_n = 2 \cdot 3^{n-1}$ **19.** $a_5 = 5; a_n = 5 \cdot (-1)^{n-1}$ **21.** $a_5 = 0; a_n = 0$ **23.** $a_5 = 4\sqrt{2}; a_n = (\sqrt{2})^n$ **25.** $a_7 = \frac{1}{64}$ **27.** $a_9 = 1$

29. $a_8 = 0.00000004$ **31.** $a_n = 7 \cdot 2^{n-1}$ **33.** $a_n = -3 \cdot \left(-\frac{1}{3}\right)^{n-1} = \left(-\frac{1}{3}\right)^{n-2}$ **35.** $a_n = -(-3)^{n-1}$ **37.** $a_n = \frac{7}{15}(15)^{n-1} = 7 \cdot 15^{n-2}$

39. $-\frac{1}{4}(1 - 2^n)$ **41.** $2\left[1 - \left(\frac{2}{3}\right)^n\right]$ **43.** $1 - 2^n$

45.

47.

49.

51. Converges; $\frac{3}{2}$ **53.** Converges; 16 **55.** Converges; $\frac{8}{5}$ **57.** Diverges **59.** Converges; $\frac{20}{3}$ **61.** Diverges **63.** Converges; $\frac{18}{5}$

65. Converges; 6 **67.** Arithmetic; $d = 1$; 1375 **69.** Neither **71.** Arithmetic; $d = -\frac{2}{3}$; –700 **73.** Neither **75.** Geometric; $r = \frac{2}{3}$; 1.999999997

77. Geometric; $r = -2$; $3.752999689 \times 10^{14}$ **79.** Geometric; $r = 3^{1/2}$; $2.004706374 \times 10^{12}$ **81.** –4 **83.** \$21,879.11

85. (a) 0.775 ft **(b)** 8th swing **(c)** 15.88 ft **(d)** 20 ft **87.** 1.845×10^{19} grains **89.** 10 **91.** \$72.67 per share **93.** December 20, 2007; \$9999.92
95. Option *B* results in more money (\$524,287 versus \$500,500). **97.** Total pay: \$41,943.03; pay on day 22: \$20,971.52

12.4 Assess Your Understanding *(page 836)*

1. (I) $n = 1: 2(1) = 2$ and $1(1 + 1) = 2$

(II) If $2 + 4 + 6 + \cdots + 2k = k(k + 1)$, then $2 + 4 + 6 + \cdots + 2k + 2(k + 1) = (2 + 4 + 6 + \cdots + 2k) + 2(k + 1)$ $= k(k + 1) + 2(k + 1) = k^2 + 3k + 2 = (k + 1)(k + 2) = (k + 1)[(k + 1) + 1]$.

3. (I) $n = 1: 1 + 2 = 3$ and $\frac{1}{2}(1)(1 + 5) = \frac{1}{2}(6) = 3$

(II) If $3 + 4 + 5 + \cdots + (k + 2) = \frac{1}{2}k(k + 5)$, then $3 + 4 + 5 + \cdots + (k + 2) + [(k + 1) + 2]$

$= [3 + 4 + 5 + \cdots + (k + 2)] + (k + 3) = \frac{1}{2}k(k + 5) + k + 3 = \frac{1}{2}(k^2 + 7k + 6) = \frac{1}{2}(k + 1)(k + 6) = \frac{1}{2}(k + 1)[(k + 1) + 5]$.

5. (I) $n = 1: 3(1) - 1 = 2$ and $\frac{1}{2}(1)[3(1) + 1] = \frac{1}{2}(4) = 2$

(II) If $2 + 5 + 8 + \cdots + (3k - 1) = \frac{1}{2}k(3k + 1)$, then $2 + 5 + 8 + \cdots + (3k - 1) + [3(k + 1) - 1]$

$= [2 + 5 + 8 + \cdots + (3k - 1)] + (3k + 2) = \frac{1}{2}k(3k + 1) + (3k + 2) = \frac{1}{2}(3k^2 + 7k + 4) = \frac{1}{2}(k + 1)(3k + 4)$

$= \frac{1}{2}(k + 1)[3(k + 1) + 1]$.

7. (I) $n = 1: 2^{1-1} = 1$ and $2^1 - 1 = 1$

(II) If $1 + 2 + 2^2 + \cdots + 2^{k-1} = 2^k - 1$, then $1 + 2 + 2^2 + \cdots + 2^{k-1} + 2^{(k+1)-1} = (1 + 2 + 2^2 + \cdots + 2^{k-1}) + 2^k$ $= 2^k - 1 + 2^k = 2(2^k) - 1 = 2^{k+1} - 1$.

9. (I) $n = 1: 4^{1-1} = 1$ and $\frac{1}{3}(4^1 - 1) = \frac{1}{3}(3) = 1$

(II) If $1 + 4 + 4^2 + \cdots + 4^{k-1} = \frac{1}{3}(4^k - 1)$, then $1 + 4 + 4^2 + \cdots + 4^{k-1} + 4^{(k+1)-1} = (1 + 4 + 4^2 + \cdots + 4^{k-1}) + 4^k$

$= \frac{1}{3}(4^k - 1) + 4^k = \frac{1}{3}[4^k - 1 + 3(4^k)] = \frac{1}{3}[4(4^k) - 1] = \frac{1}{3}(4^{k+1} - 1)$.

11. (I) $n = 1: \frac{1}{1\cdot 2} = \frac{1}{2}$ and $\frac{1}{1 + 1} = \frac{1}{2}$

(II) If $\frac{1}{1\cdot 2} + \frac{1}{2\cdot 3} + \frac{1}{3\cdot 4} + \cdots + \frac{1}{k(k + 1)} = \frac{k}{k + 1}$, then $\frac{1}{1\cdot 2} + \frac{1}{2\cdot 3} + \frac{1}{3\cdot 4} + \cdots + \frac{1}{k(k + 1)} + \frac{1}{(k + 1)[(k + 1) + 1]}$

$= \left[\frac{1}{1\cdot 2} + \frac{1}{2\cdot 3} + \frac{1}{3\cdot 4} + \cdots + \frac{1}{k(k + 1)}\right] + \frac{1}{(k + 1)(k + 2)} = \frac{k}{k + 1} + \frac{1}{(k + 1)(k + 2)} = \frac{k(k + 2) + 1}{(k + 1)(k + 2)}$

$= \frac{k^2 + 2k + 1}{(k + 1)(k + 2)} = \frac{(k + 1)^2}{(k + 1)(k + 2)} = \frac{k + 1}{k + 2} = \frac{k + 1}{(k + 1) + 1}$.

13. (I) $n = 1: 1^2 = 1$ and $\frac{1}{6}\cdot 1\cdot 2\cdot 3 = 1$

(II) If $1^2 + 2^2 + 3^2 + \cdots + k^2 = \frac{1}{6}k(k + 1)(2k + 1)$, then $1^2 + 2^2 + 3^2 + \cdots + k^2 + (k + 1)^2$

$= (1^2 + 2^2 + 3^2 + \cdots + k^2) + (k + 1)^2 = \frac{1}{6}k(k + 1)(2k + 1) + (k + 1)^2 = \frac{1}{6}(k + 1)[k(2k + 1) + 6(k + 1)]$

$= \frac{1}{6}(k + 1)(2k^2 + 7k + 6) = \frac{1}{6}(k + 1)(k + 2)(2k + 3) = \frac{1}{6}(k + 1)[(k + 1) + 1][2(k + 1) + 1]$.

15. (I) $n = 1: 5 - 1 = 4$ and $\frac{1}{2}(1)(9 - 1) = \frac{1}{2}\cdot 8 = 4$

(II) If $4 + 3 + 2 + \cdots + (5 - k) = \frac{1}{2}k(9 - k)$, then $4 + 3 + 2 + \cdots + (5 - k) + [5 - (k + 1)]$

$= [4 + 3 + 2 + \cdots + (5 - k)] + 4 - k = \frac{1}{2}k(9 - k) + 4 - k = \frac{1}{2}(9k - k^2 + 8 - 2k) = \frac{1}{2}(-k^2 + 7k + 8)$

$= \frac{1}{2}(k + 1)(8 - k) = \frac{1}{2}(k + 1)[9 - (k + 1)]$.

17. (I) $n = 1: 1\cdot(1 + 1) = 2$ and $\frac{1}{3}\cdot 1\cdot 2\cdot 3 = 2$

(II) If $1\cdot 2 + 2\cdot 3 + 3\cdot 4 + \cdots + k(k + 1) = \frac{1}{3}k(k + 1)(k + 2)$, then

$1\cdot 2 + 2\cdot 3 + 3\cdot 4 + \cdots + k(k + 1) + (k + 1)[(k + 1) + 1] = [1\cdot 2 + 2\cdot 3 + 3\cdot 4 + \cdots + k(k + 1)] + (k + 1)(k + 2)$

$= \frac{1}{3}k(k + 1)(k + 2) + \frac{1}{3}\cdot 3(k + 1)(k + 2) = \frac{1}{3}(k + 1)(k + 2)(k + 3) = \frac{1}{3}(k + 1)[(k + 1) + 1][(k + 1) + 2]$.

19. (I) $n = 1$: $1^2 + 1 = 2$, which is divisible by 2.
(II) If $k^2 + k$ is divisible by 2, then $(k + 1)^2 + (k + 1) = k^2 + 2k + 1 + k + 1 = (k^2 + k) + 2k + 2$. Since $k^2 + k$ is divisible by 2 and $2k + 2$ is divisible by 2, $(k + 1)^2 + (k + 1)$ is divisible by 2.

21. (I) $n = 1$: $1^2 - 1 + 2 = 2$, which is divisible by 2.
(II) If $k^2 - k + 2$ is divisible by 2, then $(k + 1)^2 - (k + 1) + 2 = k^2 + 2k + 1 - k - 1 + 2 = (k^2 - k + 2) + 2k$. Since $k^2 - k + 2$ is divisible by 2 and $2k$ is divisible by 2, $(k + 1)^2 - (k + 1) + 2$ is divisible by 2.

23. (I) $n = 1$: If $x > 1$, then $x^1 = x > 1$.
(II) Assume, for an arbitrary natural number k, that if $x > 1$ then $x^k > 1$. Multiply both sides of the inequality $x^k > 1$ by x. If $x > 1$, then $x^{k+1} > x > 1$.

25. (I) $n = 1$: $a - b$ is a factor of $a^1 - b^1 = a - b$.
(II) If $a - b$ is a factor of $a^k - b^k$, then $a^{k+1} - b^{k+1} = a(a^k - b^k) + b^k(a - b)$.
Since $a - b$ is a factor of $a^k - b^k$ and $a - b$ is a factor of $a - b$, then $a - b$ is a factor of $a^{k+1} - b^{k+1}$.

27. (I) $n = 1$: $(1 + a)^1 = 1 + a \geq 1 + 1 \cdot a$
(II) Assume that there is an integer k for which the inequality holds. So $(1+a)^k \geq 1+ka$. We need to show that $(1+a)^{k+1} \geq 1+(k+1)a$.
$(1+a)^{k+1} = (1+a)^k(1+a) \geq (1+ka)(1+a) = 1+ka^2+a+ka = 1+(k+1)a+ka^2 \geq 1+(k+1)a$.

29. If $2 + 4 + 6 + \cdots + 2k = k^2 + k + 2$, then $2 + 4 + 6 + \cdots + 2k + 2(k + 1)$
$= (2 + 4 + 6 + \cdots + 2k) + 2k + 2 = k^2 + k + 2 + 2k + 2 = k^2 + 3k + 4 = (k^2 + 2k + 1) + (k + 1) + 2$
$= (k + 1)^2 + (k + 1) + 2$.
But $2 \cdot 1 = 2$ and $1^2 + 1 + 2 = 4$. The fact is that $2 + 4 + 6 + \cdots + 2n = n^2 + n$, not $n^2 + n + 2$ (Problem 1).

31. (I) $n = 1$: $[a + (1 - 1)d] = a$ and $1 \cdot a + d\dfrac{1 \cdot (1 - 1)}{2} = a$.
(II) If $a + (a + d) + (a + 2d) + \cdots + [a + (k - 1)d] = ka + d\dfrac{k(k - 1)}{2}$, then

$$a + (a + d) + (a + 2d) + \cdots + [a + (k - 1)d] + [a + ((k + 1) - 1)d] = ka + d\frac{k(k - 1)}{2} + a + kd$$
$$= (k + 1)a + d\frac{k(k - 1) + 2k}{2} = (k + 1)a + d\frac{(k + 1)(k)}{2} = (k + 1)a + d\frac{(k + 1)[(k + 1) - 1]}{2}.$$

33. (I) $n = 3$: The sum of the angles of a triangle is $(3 - 2) \cdot 180° = 180°$.
(II) Assume for some $k \geq 3$ that the sum of the angles of a convex polygon of k sides is $(k - 2) \cdot 180°$. A convex polygon of $k + 1$ sides consists of a convex polygon of k sides plus a triangle (see the illustration). The sum of the angles is
$(k - 2) \cdot 180° + 180° = (k - 1) \cdot 180° = [(k + 1) - 2] \cdot 180°$.

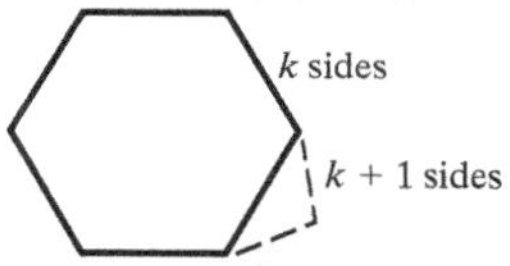

12.5 Assess Your Understanding *(page 842)*

1. Pascal triangle **2.** 15 **3.** F **4.** Binomial Theorem **5.** 10 **7.** 21 **9.** 50 **11.** 1 **13.** $\approx 1.8664 \times 10^{15}$ **15.** $\approx 1.4834 \times 10^{13}$
17. $x^5 + 5x^4 + 10x^3 + 10x^2 + 5x + 1$ **19.** $x^6 - 12x^5 + 60x^4 - 160x^3 + 240x^2 - 192x + 64$ **21.** $81x^4 + 108x^3 + 54x^2 + 12x + 1$
23. $x^{10} + 5x^8y^2 + 10x^6y^4 + 10x^4y^6 + 5x^2y^8 + y^{10}$ **25.** $x^3 + 6\sqrt{2}x^{5/2} + 30x^2 + 40\sqrt{2}x^{3/2} + 60x + 24\sqrt{2}x^{1/2} + 8$
27. $a^5x^5 + 5a^4bx^4y + 10a^3b^2x^3y^2 + 10a^2b^3x^2y^3 + 5ab^4xy^4 + b^5y^5$ **29.** 17,010 **31.** $-101{,}376$ **33.** 41,472 **35.** $2835x^3$
37. $314{,}928x^7$ **39.** 495 **41.** 3360 **43.** 1.00501
45. $\dbinom{n}{n-1} = \dfrac{n!}{(n-1)!\,[n-(n-1)]!} = \dfrac{n!}{(n-1)!\,1!} = \dfrac{n \cdot (n-1)!}{(n-1)!} = n$; $\dbinom{n}{n} = \dfrac{n!}{n!\,(n-n)!} = \dfrac{n!}{n!0!} = \dfrac{n!}{n!} = 1$
47. $2^n = (1 + 1)^n = \dbinom{n}{0}1^n + \dbinom{n}{1}(1)^{n-1}(1) + \cdots + \dbinom{n}{n}1^n = \dbinom{n}{0} + \dbinom{n}{1} + \cdots + \dbinom{n}{n}$

49. 1

Review Exercises *(page 844)*

1. $a_1 = -\frac{4}{3}, a_2 = \frac{5}{4}, a_3 = -\frac{6}{5}, a_4 = \frac{7}{6}, a_5 = -\frac{8}{7}$ **3.** $c_1 = 2, c_2 = 1, c_3 = \frac{8}{9}, c_4 = 1, c_5 = \frac{32}{25}$ **5.** $a_1 = 3, a_2 = 2, a_3 = \frac{4}{3}, a_4 = \frac{8}{9}, a_5 = \frac{16}{27}$

7. $a_1 = 2, a_2 = 0, a_3 = 2, a_4 = 0, a_5 = 2$ **9.** $6 + 10 + 14 + 18 = 48$ **11.** $\sum_{k=1}^{13} (-1)^{k+1}\frac{1}{k}$ **13.** Arithmetic; $d = 1$; $S_n = \frac{n}{2}(n + 11)$ **15.** Neither

17. Geometric; $r = 8$; $S_n = \frac{8}{7}(8^n - 1)$ **19.** Arithmetic; $d = 4$; $S_n = 2n(n - 1)$ **21.** Geometric; $r = \frac{1}{2}$; $S_n = 6\left[1 - \left(\frac{1}{2}\right)^n\right]$

23. Neither **25.** 3825 **27.** 1125 **29.** $\frac{1093}{2187} \approx 0.49977$ **31.** 35 **33.** $\frac{1}{10^{10}}$ **35.** $9\sqrt{2}$ **37.** $\{a_n\} = \{5n - 4\}$ **39.** $\{a_n\} = \{n - 10\}$

41. Converges; $\frac{9}{2}$ **43.** Converges; $\frac{4}{3}$ **45.** Diverges **47.** Converges; 8

49. (I) $n = 1: 3 \cdot 1 = 3$ and $\frac{3 \cdot 1}{2}(1 + 1) = 3$

(II) If $3 + 6 + 9 + \cdots + 3k = \frac{3k}{2}(k + 1)$, then $3 + 6 + 9 + \cdots + 3k + 3(k + 1) = (3 + 6 + 9 + \cdots + 3k) + (3k + 3)$
$= \frac{3k}{2}(k + 1) + (3k + 3) = \frac{3k}{2}(k + 1) + 3(k + 1) = 3(k + 1)\left(\frac{k}{2} + 1\right) = \frac{3}{2}(k + 1)(k + 2) = \frac{3(k + 1)}{2}[(k + 1) + 1]$.

51. (I) $n = 1: 2 \cdot 3^{1-1} = 2$ and $3^1 - 1 = 2$

(II) If $2 + 6 + 18 + \cdots + 2 \cdot 3^{k-1} = 3^k - 1$, then $2 + 6 + 18 + \cdots + 2 \cdot 3^{k-1} + 2 \cdot 3^{(k+1)-1} = (2 + 6 + 18 + \cdots + 2 \cdot 3^{k-1}) + 2 \cdot 3^k$
$= 3^k - 1 + 2 \cdot 3^k = 3 \cdot 3^k - 1 = 3^{k+1} - 1$.

53. (I) $n = 1: (3 \cdot 1 - 2)^2 = 1$ and $\frac{1}{2} \cdot 1 \cdot [6(1)^2 - 3(1) - 1] = 1$

(II) If $1^2 + 4^2 + 7^2 + \cdots + (3k - 2)^2 = \frac{1}{2}k(6k^2 - 3k - 1)$, then $1^2 + 4^2 + 7^2 + \cdots + (3k - 2)^2 + [3(k + 1) - 2]^2$

$= [1^2 + 4^2 + 7^2 + \cdots + (3k - 2)^2] + (3k + 1)^2 = \frac{1}{2}k(6k^2 - 3k - 1) + (3k + 1)^2 = \frac{1}{2}(6k^3 - 3k^2 - k) + (9k^2 + 6k + 1)$

$= \frac{1}{2}(6k^3 + 15k^2 + 11k + 2) = \frac{1}{2}(k + 1)(6k^2 + 9k + 2) = \frac{1}{2}(k + 1)[6(k + 1)^2 - 3(k + 1) - 1]$.

55. 10 **57.** $x^5 + 10x^4 + 40x^3 + 80x^2 + 80x + 32$ **59.** $32x^5 + 240x^4 + 720x^3 + 1080x^2 + 810x + 243$

61. 144 **63.** 84 **65. (a)** 8 bricks **(b)** 1100 bricks

67. (a) $20\left(\frac{3}{4}\right)^3 = \frac{135}{16}$ ft
(b) $20\left(\frac{3}{4}\right)^n$ ft
(c) 13 times
(d) 140 ft

69. (a) \$4975
(b)

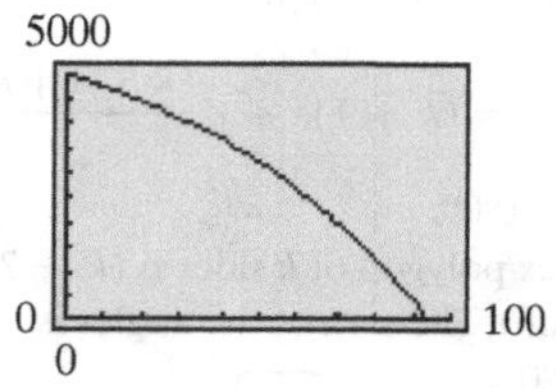

(c) At the beginning of the thirty-third month the balance is less than \$4000. At this time, 32 payments of \$100 each have been made.
(d) 93 payments of \$100 plus 1 payment of \$11.18; \$9311.18
(e) \$4311.18

Chapter Test *(page 846)*

1. $0, \frac{3}{10}, \frac{8}{11}, \frac{5}{4}, \frac{24}{13}$ **2.** 4, 14, 44, 134, 404 **3.** $2 - \frac{3}{4} + \frac{4}{9} = \frac{61}{36}$ **4.** $-\frac{1}{3} - \frac{14}{9} - \frac{73}{27} - \frac{308}{81} = -\frac{680}{81}$ **5.** $\sum_{k=1}^{10}(-1)^k\left(\frac{k + 1}{k + 4}\right)$ **6.** Neither

7. Geometric; $r = 4$; $S_n = \frac{2}{3}(1 - 4^n)$ **8.** Arithmetic: $d = -8$; $S_n = n(2 - 4n)$ **9.** Arithmetic; $d = -\frac{1}{2}$; $S_n = \frac{n}{4}(27 - n)$

10. Geometric; $r = \frac{2}{5}$ $S_n = \frac{125}{3}\left[1 - \left(\frac{2}{5}\right)^n\right]$ **11.** Neither **12.** Converges; $\frac{1024}{5}$ **13.** $243m^5 + 810m^4 + 1080m^3 + 720m^2 + 240m + 32$

14. First we show that the statement holds for $n = 1$. $\left(1 + \frac{1}{1}\right) = 1 + 1 = 2$. The equality is true for $n = 1$, so Condition I holds. Next we assume that $\left(1 + \frac{1}{1}\right)\left(1 + \frac{1}{2}\right)\left(1 + \frac{1}{3}\right)\cdots\left(1 + \frac{1}{n}\right) = n + 1$ is true for some k, and we show the formula then holds for $k + 1$. We assume that $\left(1 + \frac{1}{1}\right)\left(1 + \frac{1}{2}\right)\left(1 + \frac{1}{3}\right)\cdots\left(1 + \frac{1}{k}\right) = k + 1$. Now we need to show that $\left(1 + \frac{1}{1}\right)\left(1 + \frac{1}{2}\right)\left(1 + \frac{1}{3}\right)\cdots\left(1 + \frac{1}{k}\right)\left(1 + \frac{1}{k + 1}\right)$ $= (k + 1) + 1 = k + 2$. We do this as follows:

$\left(1 + \frac{1}{1}\right)\left(1 + \frac{1}{2}\right)\left(1 + \frac{1}{3}\right)\cdots\left(1 + \frac{1}{k}\right)\left(1 + \frac{1}{k + 1}\right) = \left[\left(1 + \frac{1}{1}\right)\left(1 + \frac{1}{2}\right)\left(1 + \frac{1}{3}\right)\cdots\left(1 + \frac{1}{k}\right)\right]\left(1 + \frac{1}{k + 1}\right) = (k + 1)\left(1 + \frac{1}{k + 1}\right)$

(induction assumption) $= (k + 1) \cdot 1 + (k + 1) \cdot \frac{1}{k + 1} = k + 1 + 1 = k + 2$

Condition II also holds. Thus, the formula holds true for all natural numbers.

15. After 10 years, the Durango will be worth \$6103.11. **16.** The weight lifter will have lifted a total of 8000 pounds after 5 sets.

Cumulative Review *(page 847)*

1. $\{-3, 3, -3i, 3i\}$ **2. (a)**

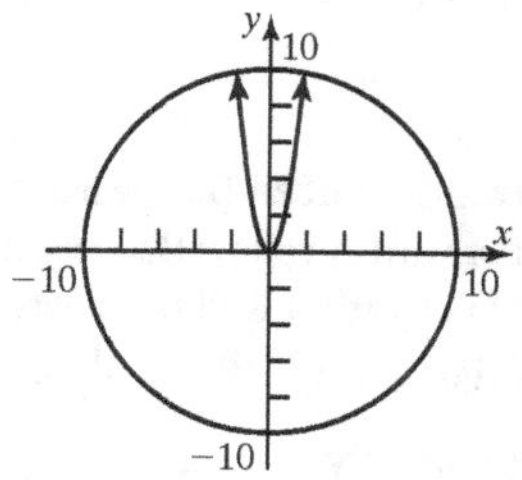

(b) $\left\{\left(\sqrt{\frac{-1+\sqrt{3601}}{18}}, \frac{-1+\sqrt{3601}}{6}\right), \left(-\sqrt{\frac{-1+\sqrt{3601}}{18}}, \frac{-1+\sqrt{3601}}{6}\right)\right\}$

(c) The circle and the parabola intersect at

$\left(\sqrt{\frac{-1+\sqrt{3601}}{18}}, \frac{-1+\sqrt{3601}}{6}\right), \left(-\sqrt{\frac{-1+\sqrt{3601}}{18}}, \frac{-1+\sqrt{3601}}{6}\right).$

3. $\left\{\ln\left(\frac{5}{2}\right)\right\}$ **4.** $y = 5x - 10$ **5.** $x^2 + y^2 + 2x - 4y - 20 = 0$

6. (a) 5 **(b)** 13 **(c)** $\frac{6x+3}{2x-1}$ **(d)** $\left\{x \middle| x \neq \frac{1}{2}\right\}$ **(e)** $\frac{7x-2}{x-2}$ **(f)** $\{x|x \neq 2\}$ **(g)** $g^{-1}(x) = \frac{1}{2}(x-1)$; all reals **(h)** $f^{-1}(x) = \frac{2x}{x-3}$; $\{x|x \neq 3\}$

7. $\frac{x^2}{7} + \frac{y^2}{16} = 1$ **8.** $(x+1)^2 = 4(y-2)$ **9.** $r = 8\sin\theta$; $x^2 + (y-4)^2 = 16$ **10.** $\left\{\frac{3\pi}{2}\right\}$ **11.** $\frac{2\pi}{3}$

12. (a) $-\frac{\sqrt{15}}{4}$ **(b)** $-\frac{\sqrt{15}}{15}$ **(c)** $-\frac{\sqrt{15}}{8}$ **(d)** $\frac{7}{8}$ **(e)** $\sqrt{\frac{1+\frac{\sqrt{15}}{4}}{2}} = \frac{\sqrt{4+\sqrt{15}}}{2\sqrt{2}}$

CHAPTER 13 Counting and Probability

13.1 Assess Your Understanding *(page 854)*

5. $n(A) + n(B) - n(A \cap B)$ **6.** F **7.** $\emptyset$, $\{a\}$, $\{b\}$, $\{c\}$, $\{d\}$, $\{a, b\}$, $\{a, c\}$, $\{a, d\}$, $\{b, c\}$, $\{b, d\}$, $\{c, d\}$, $\{a, b, c\}$, $\{a, b, d\}$, $\{a, c, d\}$, $\{b, c, d\}$, $\{a, b, c, d\}$ **9.** 25 **11.** 40 **13.** 25 **15.** 37 **17.** 18 **19.** 5 **21.** 15 different arrangements **23.** 9000 numbers **25.** 175; 125

27. (a) 15 **(b)** 15 **(c)** 15 **(d)** 25 **(e)** 40 **29. (a)** 11,923 thousand **(b)** 75,241 thousand **31.** 480 portfolios.

13.2 Assess Your Understanding *(page 861)*

3. permutation **4.** combination **5.** T **6.** T **7.** 30 **9.** 24 **11.** 1 **13.** 1680 **15.** 28 **17.** 35 **19.** 1 **21.** 10,400,600 **23.** {*abc, abd, abe, acb, acd, ace, adb, adc, ade, aeb, aec, aed, bac, bad, bae, bca, bcd, bce, bda, bdc, bde, bea, bec, bed, cab, cad, cae, cba, cbd, cbe, cda, cdb, cde, cea, ceb, ced, dab, dac, dae, dba, dbc, dbe, dca, dcb, dce, dea, deb, dec, eab, eac, ead, eba, ebc, ebd, eca, ecb, ecd, eda, edb, edc*}; 60
25. {123, 124, 132, 134, 142, 143, 213, 214, 231, 234, 241, 243, 312, 314, 321, 324, 341, 342, 412, 413, 421, 423, 431, 432}; 24
27. {*abc, abd, abe, acd, ace, ade, bcd, bce, bde, cde*}; 10 **29.** {123, 124, 134, 234}; 4 **31.** 16 **33.** 8 **35.** 24 **37.** 60 **39.** 18,278 **41.** 35
43. 1024 **45.** 120 **47.** 132,860 **49.** 336 **51.** 90,720 **53. (a)** 63 **(b)** 35 **(c)** 1 **55.** 1.157×10^{76} **57.** 362,880 **59.** 660 **61.** 15
63. (a) 125,000 **(b)** A better name for a *combination* lock would be a *permutation* lock because the order of the numbers matters.

Historical Problems *(page 871)*

1. (a) {*AAAA, AAAB, AABA, AABB, ABAA, ABAB, ABBA, ABBB, BAAA, BAAB, BABA, BABB, BBAA, BBAB, BBBA, BBBB*};
$P(A \text{ wins}) = \frac{11}{16}$; $P(B \text{ wins}) = \frac{5}{16}$; *A* should get $\frac{11}{16}$ of the stakes and *B* should set $\frac{5}{16}$ of the stakes.

(b) $P(A \text{ wins}) = \frac{C(4,2) + C(4,3) + C(4,4)}{2^4} = \frac{6+4+1}{16} = \frac{11}{16}$; $P(B \text{ wins}) = \frac{C(4,3) + C(4,4)}{2^4} = \frac{4+1}{16} = \frac{5}{16}$

2. (a) $\$\frac{3}{2} = \$1.50$ **(b)** $\$\frac{1}{2} = \$0.50$

13.3 Assess Your Understanding *(page 871)*

1. equally likely **2.** complement **3.** F **4.** T **5.** 0, 0.01, 0.35, 1 **7.** Probability model

9. Not a probability model **11.** $S = \{\text{HH, HT, TH, TT}\}$; $P(\text{HH}) = \frac{1}{4}$, $P(\text{HT}) = \frac{1}{4}$, $P(\text{TH}) = \frac{1}{4}$, $P(\text{TT}) = \frac{1}{4}$

13. S = {HH1, HH2, HH3, HH4, HH5, HH6, HT1, HT2, HT3, HT4, HT5, HT6, TH1, TH2, TH3, TH4, TH5, TH6, TT1, TT2, TT3, TT4, TT5, TT6}; each outcome has a probability of $\frac{1}{24}$.

15. $S = \{HHH, HHT, HTH, HTT, THH, THT, TTH, TTT\}$; each outcome has a probability of $\frac{1}{8}$.
17. $S = \{$1 Yellow, 1 Red, 1 Green, 2 Yellow, 2 Red, 2 Green, 3 Yellow, 3 Red, 3 Green, 4 Yellow, 4 Red, 4 Green$\}$; each outcome has a probability of $\frac{1}{12}$; thus, $P(2\text{ Red}) + P(4\text{ Red}) = \frac{1}{12} + \frac{1}{12} = \frac{1}{6}$.
19. $S = \{$1 Yellow Forward, 1 Yellow Backward, 1 Red Forward, 1 Red Backward, 1 Green Forward, 1 Green Backward, 2 Yellow Forward, 2 Yellow Backward, 2 Red Forward, 2 Red Backward, 2 Green Forward, 2 Green Backward, 3 Yellow Forward, 3 Yellow Backward, 3 Red Forward, 3 Red Backward, 3 Green Forward, 3 Green Backward, 4 Yellow Forward, 4 Yellow Backward, 4 Red Forward, 4 Red Backward, 4 Green Forward, 4 Green Backward$\}$; each outcome has a probability of $\frac{1}{24}$; thus, $P(1\text{ Red Backward}) + P(1\text{ Green Backward}) = \frac{1}{24} + \frac{1}{24} = \frac{1}{12}$.
21. $S = \{$11 Red, 11 Yellow, 11 Green, 12 Red, 12 Yellow, 12 Green, 13 Red, 13 Yellow, 13 Green, 14 Red, 14 Yellow, 14 Green, 21 Red, 21 Yellow, 21 Green, 22 Red, 22 Yellow, 22 Green, 23 Red, 23 Yellow, 23 Green, 24 Red, 24 Yellow, 24 Green, 31 Red, 31 Yellow, 31 Green, 32 Red, 32 Yellow, 32 Green, 33 Red, 33 Yellow, 33 Green, 34 Red, 34 Yellow, 34 Green, 41 Red, 41 Yellow, 41 Green, 42 Red, 42 Yellow, 42 Green, 43 Red, 43 Yellow, 43 Green, 44 Red, 44 Yellow, 44 Green$\}$; each outcome has a probability of $\frac{1}{48}$; thus, $P(22\text{ Red}) + P(22\text{ Green}) + P(24\text{ Red}) + P(24\text{ Green})$
$= \frac{1}{48} + \frac{1}{48} + \frac{1}{48} + \frac{1}{48} = \frac{1}{12}$.
23. A, B, C, F **25.** B **27.** $P(H) = \frac{4}{5}$; $P(T) = \frac{1}{5}$ **29.** $P(1) = P(3) = P(5) = \frac{2}{9}$; $P(2) = P(4) = P(6) = \frac{1}{9}$
31. $\frac{3}{10}$ **33.** $\frac{1}{2}$ **35.** $\frac{1}{6}$ **37.** $\frac{1}{8}$ **39.** $\frac{1}{4}$ **41.** $\frac{1}{6}$ **43.** $\frac{1}{18}$ **45.** 0.55 **47.** 0.70 **49.** 0.30 **51.** 0.87 **53.** 0.66 **55.** 0.95 **57.** $\frac{17}{20}$ **59.** $\frac{11}{20}$ **61.** $\frac{1}{2}$
63. $\frac{3}{10}$ **65.** $\frac{2}{5}$ **67.** **(a)** 0.57 **(b)** 0.95 **(c)** 0.83 **(d)** 0.38 **(e)** 0.29 **(f)** 0.05 **(g)** 0.78 **(h)** 0.71 **69.** **(a)** $\frac{25}{33}$ **(b)** $\frac{25}{33}$
71. 0.167 **73.** 0.000033069

Review Exercises *(page 875)*

1. $\varnothing$, {Dave}, {Joanne}, {Erica}, {Dave, Joanne}, {Dave, Erica}, {Joanne, Erica}, {Dave, Joanne, Erica} **3.** 17 **5.** 29 **7.** 7 **9.** 25 **11.** 336 **13.** 56 **15.** 60 **17.** 128 **19.** 3024 **21.** 1680 **23.** 91 **25.** 1,600,000 **27.** 216,000 **29.** 1260 **31.** **(a)** 381,024 **(b)** 1260
33. **(a)** $8.634628387 \times 10^{45}$ **(b)** 0.6531 **(c)** 0.3469 **35.** **(a)** 0.045 **(b)** 0.955 **37.** $\frac{4}{9}$ **39.** 0.2; 0.26

Chapter Test *(page 876)*

1. 22 **2.** 3 **3.** 8 **4.** 45 **5.** 5040 **6.** 151,200 **7.** 462 **8.** There are 54,264 ways to choose 6 colors from the 21 available colors. **9.** There are 840 distinct arrangements of the letters in the word REDEEMED. **10.** There are 56 different exacta bets for an 8-horse race. **11.** There are 155,480,000 possible license plates using the new format. **12.** **(a)** 0.95 **(b)** 0.30 **13.** **(a)** 0.25 **(b)** 0.55 **14.** 0.19
15. $P(\text{win on \$1 play}) = \frac{1}{120{,}526{,}770} \approx 0.0000000083$ **16.** $P(\text{exactly 2 fours}) = \frac{1250}{7776} \approx 0.1608$

Cumulative Review *(page 877)*

1. $\left\{\frac{1}{3} - \frac{\sqrt{2}}{3}i, \frac{1}{3} + \frac{\sqrt{2}}{3}i\right\}$

2.
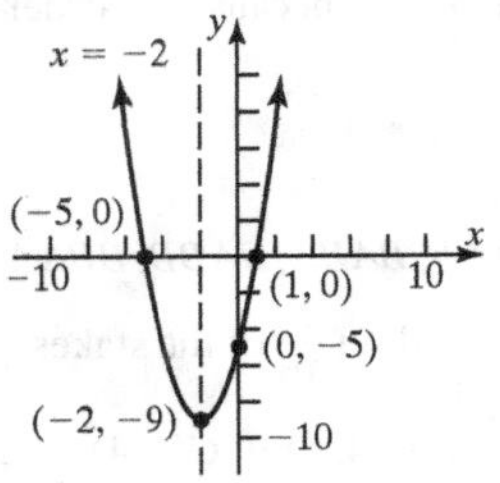

3.
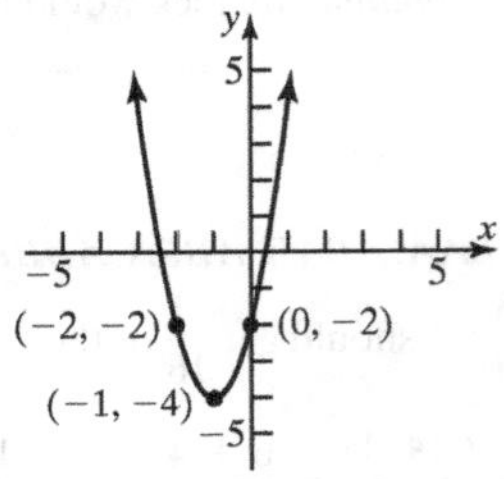

4. $\{x \mid 3.99 \le x \le 4.01\}$ or $[3.99, 4.01]$

5. $\left\{-\frac{1}{2} + \frac{\sqrt{7}}{2}i, -\frac{1}{2} - \frac{\sqrt{7}}{2}i, -\frac{1}{5}, 3\right\}$

6.
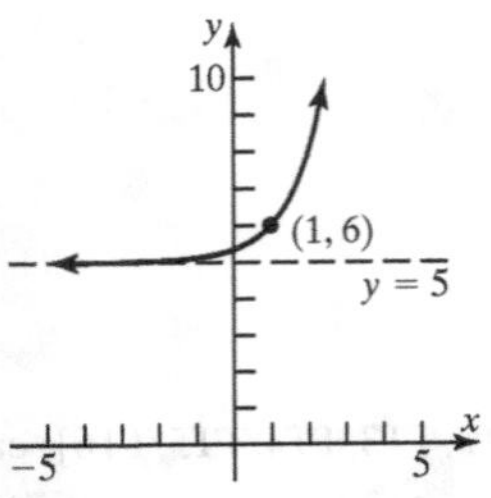

Domain: all real numbers or $(-\infty, \infty)$
Range: $\{y \mid y > 5\}$ or $(5, \infty)$
Horizontal asymptote: $y = 5$

7. 2

8. $\left\{\frac{8}{3}\right\}$

9. $x = 2, y = -5, z = 3$

10. 125; 700

11.
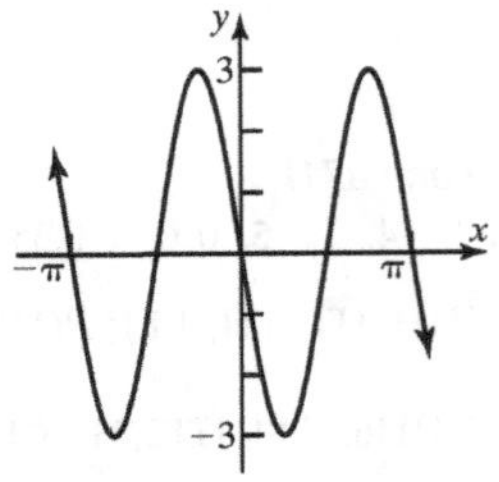

12.
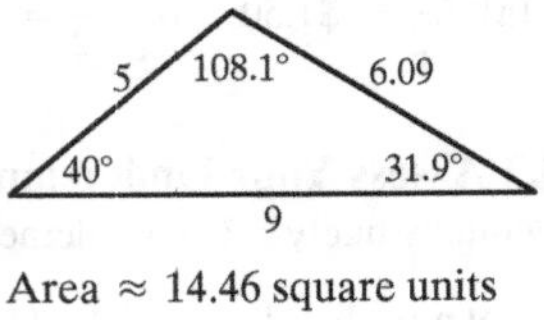

Area ≈ 14.46 square units

CHAPTER 14 A Preview of Calculus: The Limit, Derivative, and Integral of a Function

14.1 Assess Your Understanding *(page 883)*

3. $\lim_{x \to c} f(x)$ **4.** does not exist **5.** T **6.** F **7.** 32 **9.** 1 **11.** 4 **13.** 2 **15.** 0 **17.** 3 **19.** 4 **21.** Does not exist

23.
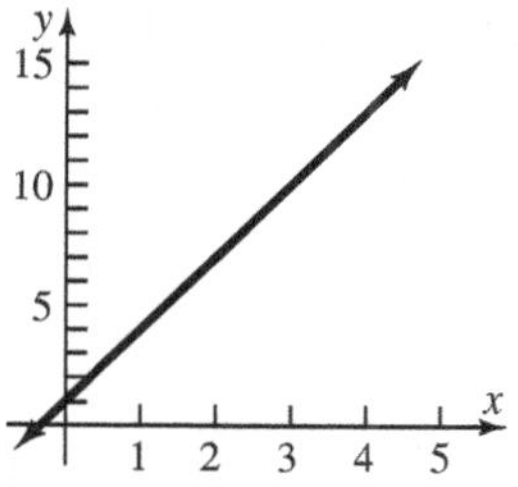

$\lim_{x \to 4} f(x) = 13$

25.
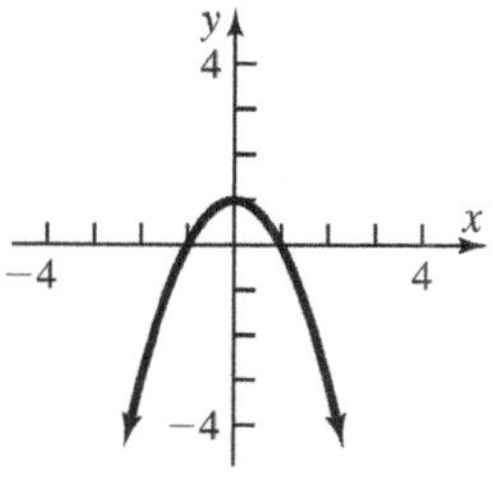

$\lim_{x \to 2} f(x) = -3$

27.
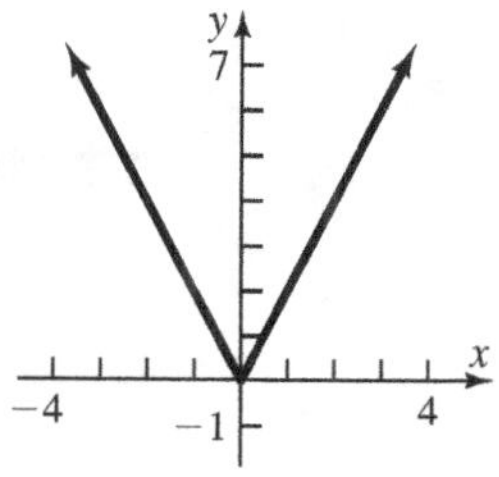

$\lim_{x \to -3} f(x) = 6$

29.
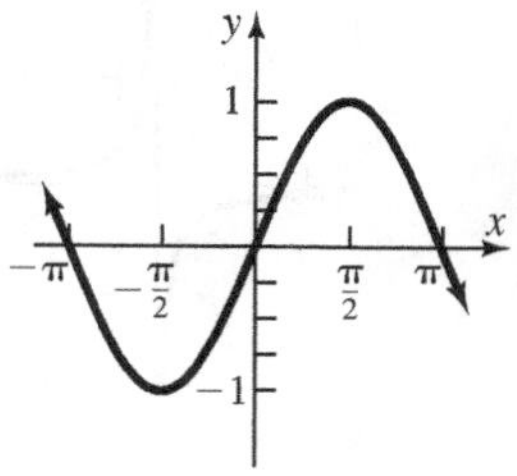

$\lim_{x \to \pi/2} f(x) = 1$

31.
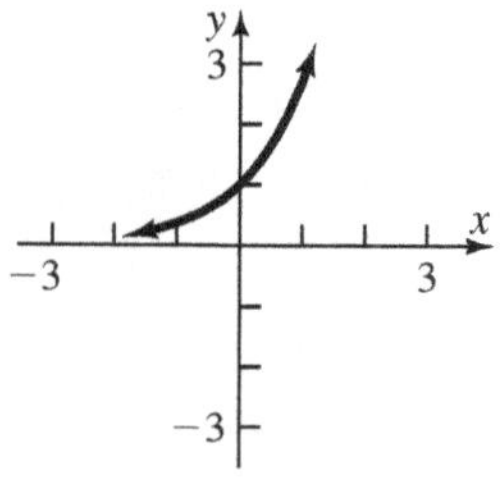

$\lim_{x \to 0} f(x) = 1$

33.
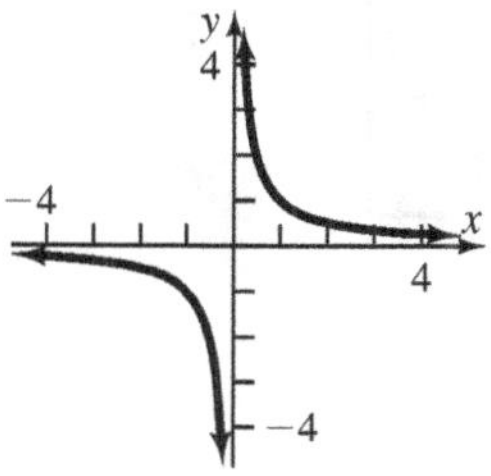

$\lim_{x \to -1} f(x) = -1$

35.
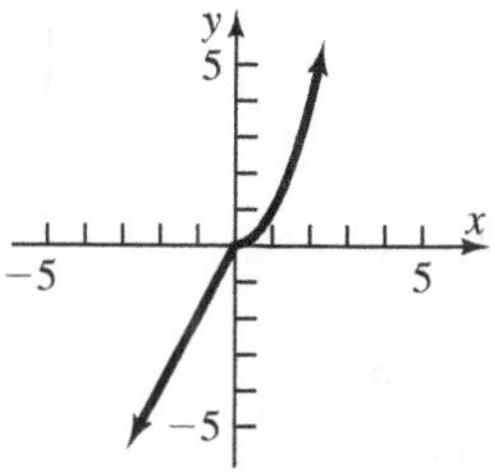

$\lim_{x \to 0} f(x) = 0$

37.
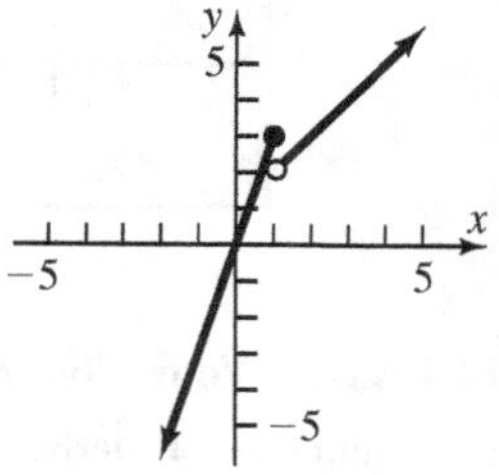

$\lim_{x \to 1} f(x)$ does not exist.

39.
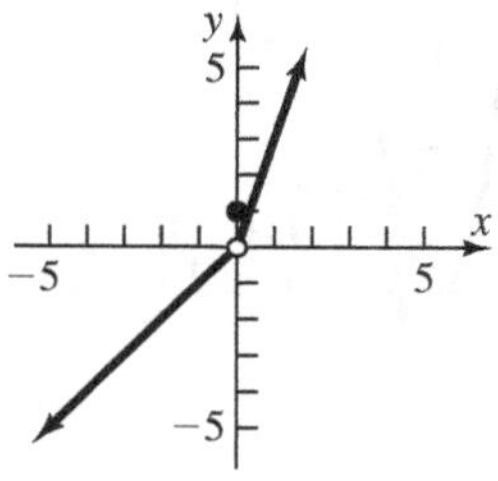

$\lim_{x \to 0} f(x) = 0$

41.
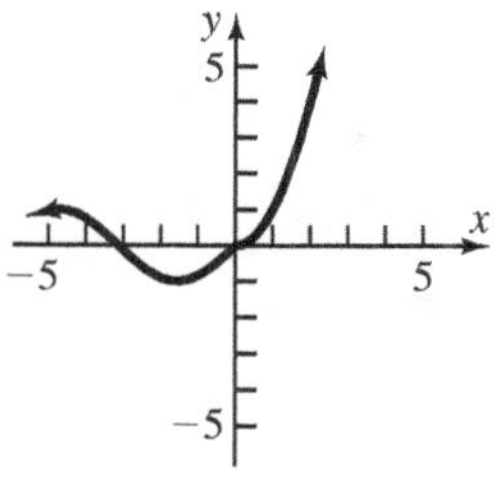

$\lim_{x \to 0} f(x) = 0$

43. 0.67 **45.** 1.6 **47.** 0

14.2 Assess Your Understanding *(page 891)*

1. product **3.** 1 **5.** F **7.** 5 **9.** 4 **11.** −10 **13.** 80 **15.** 8 **17.** 8 **19.** −1 **21.** 8 **23.** 3 **25.** −1 **27.** 32 **29.** 2 **31.** $\frac{7}{6}$ **33.** 3 **35.** 0 **37.** $\frac{2}{3}$ **39.** $\frac{8}{5}$ **41.** 0 **43.** 5 **45.** 6 **47.** 0 **49.** 0 **51.** −1 **53.** 1 **55.** $\frac{3}{4}$

14.3 Assess Your Understanding *(page 897)*

7. one-sided **8.** $\lim_{x \to c^+} f(x) = R$ **9.** continuous; c **10.** F **11.** T **12.** T **13.** $\{x \mid -8 \le x < -6 \text{ or } -6 < x < 4 \text{ or } 4 < x \le 6\}$ **15.** −8, −5, −3 **17.** $f(-8) = 0$; $f(-4) = 2$ **19.** ∞ **21.** 2 **23.** 1 **25.** Limit exists; 0 **27.** No **29.** Yes **31.** No **33.** 5 **35.** 7 **37.** 1 **39.** 4 **41.** $-\frac{2}{3}$ **43.** $\frac{3}{2}$ **45.** Continuous **47.** Continuous **49.** Not continuous **51.** Not continuous **53.** Not continuous **55.** Continuous **57.** Not continuous **59.** Continuous **61.** Continuous for all real numbers **63.** Continuous for all real numbers **65.** Continuous for all real numbers **67.** Continuous for all real numbers except $x = \frac{k\pi}{2}$, where k is an odd integer **69.** Continuous for all real numbers except $x = -2$ and $x = 2$ **71.** Continuous for all positive real numbers except $x = 1$

73. Discontinuous at $x = -1$ and $x = 1$; $\lim_{x\to 1} R(x) = \frac{1}{2}$: Hole at $\left(1, \frac{1}{2}\right)$ $\lim_{x\to -1^-} R(x) = -\infty$; $\lim_{x\to -1^+} R(x) = \infty$; vertical asymptote at $x = -1$

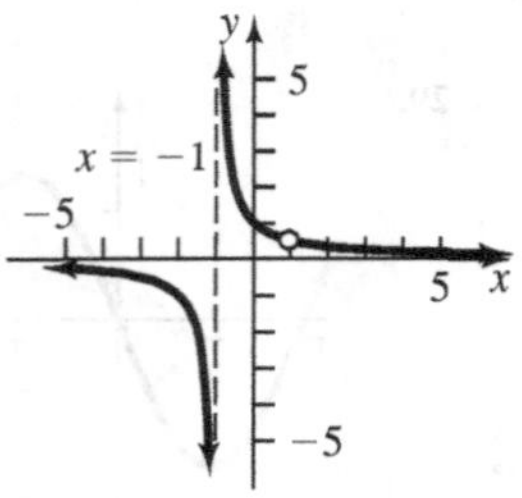

75. Discontinuous at $x = -1$ and $x = 1$; $\lim_{x\to -1} R(x) = \frac{1}{2}$: Hole at $\left(-1, \frac{1}{2}\right)$ $\lim_{x\to 1^-} R(x) = -\infty$; $\lim_{x\to 1^+} R(x) = \infty$; vertical asymptote at $x = 1$

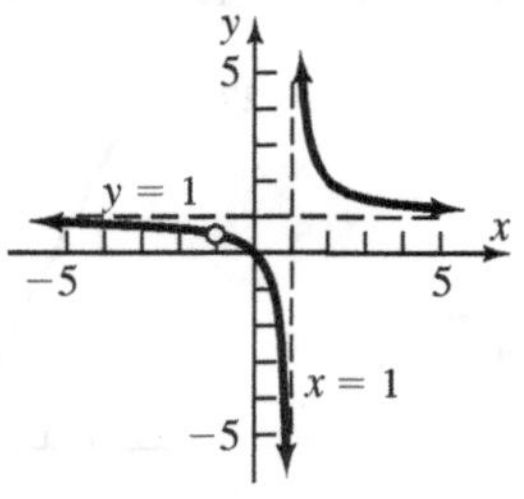

77. (a) $x = -\sqrt[3]{2}$: Asymptote; $x = 1$: Hole

(b)

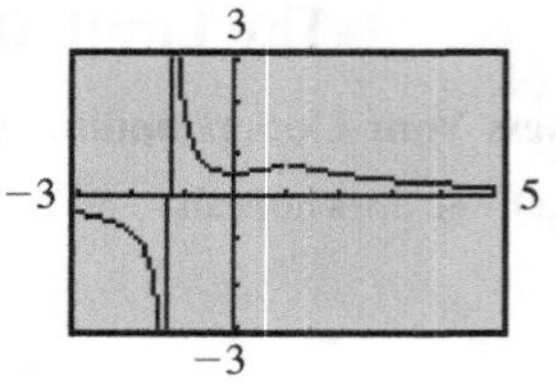

79. (a) $x = -3$: Asymptote; $x = 2$: Hole

(b)

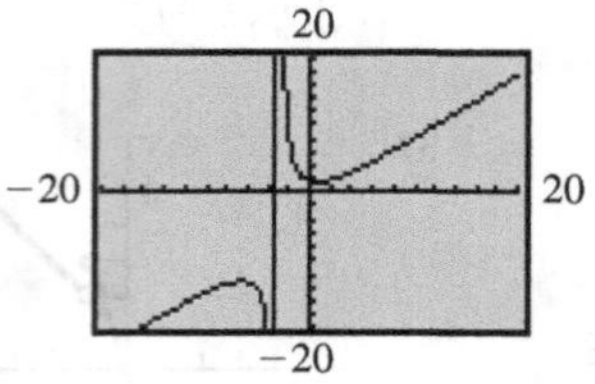

81. (a) $x = -\sqrt[3]{2}$: Asymptote; $x = -1$: Hole

(b)

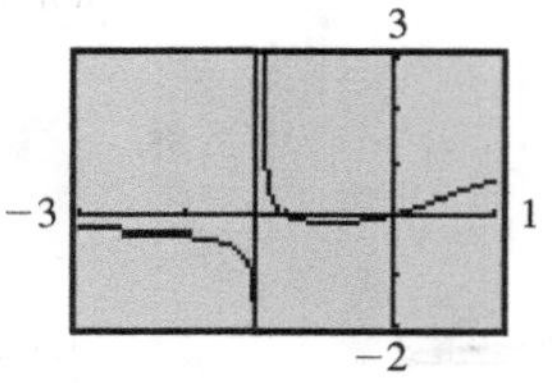

14.4 Assess Your Understanding *(page 905)*

3. tangent line **4.** derivative **5.** velocity **6.** T **7.** T **8.** T

9. $m_{tan} = 3$

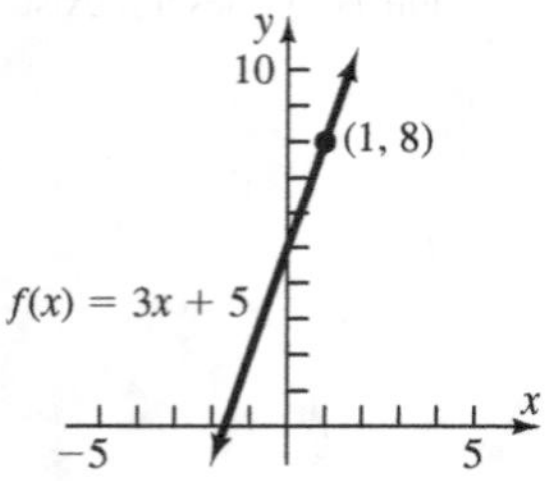

11. $m_{tan} = -2$

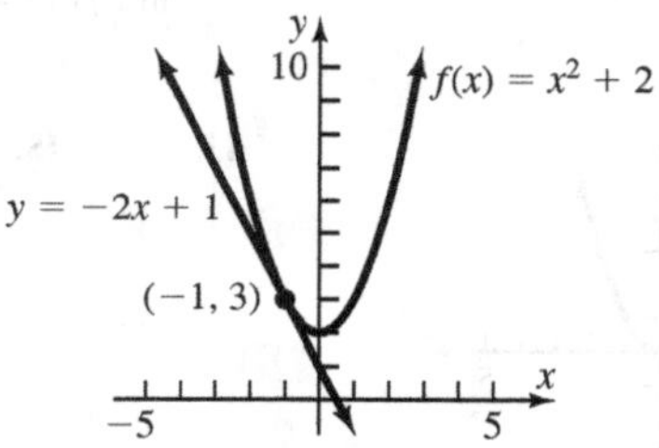

13. $m_{tan} = 12$

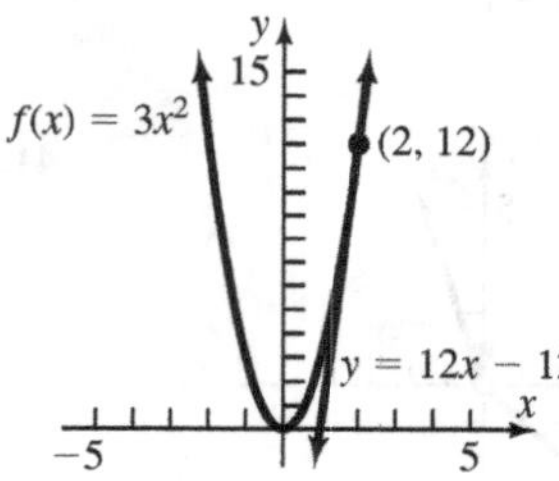

15. $m_{tan} = 5$

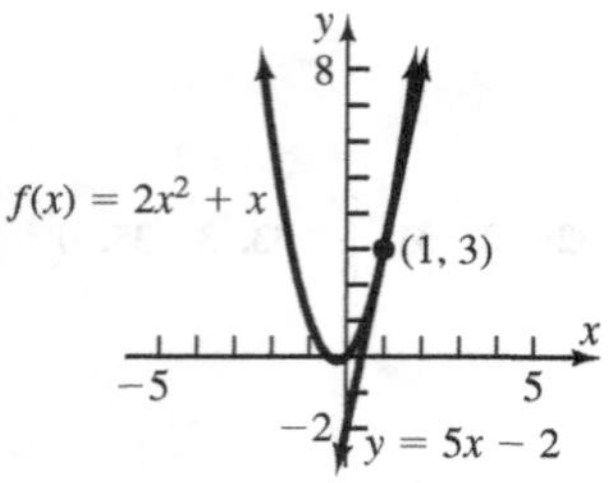

17. $m_{tan} = -4$

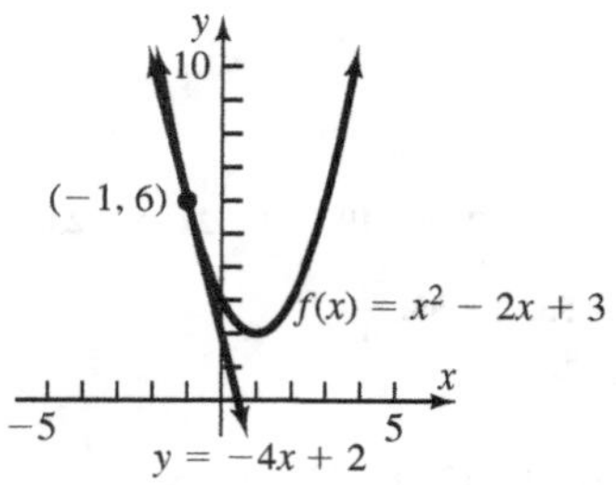

19. $m_{tan} = 13$

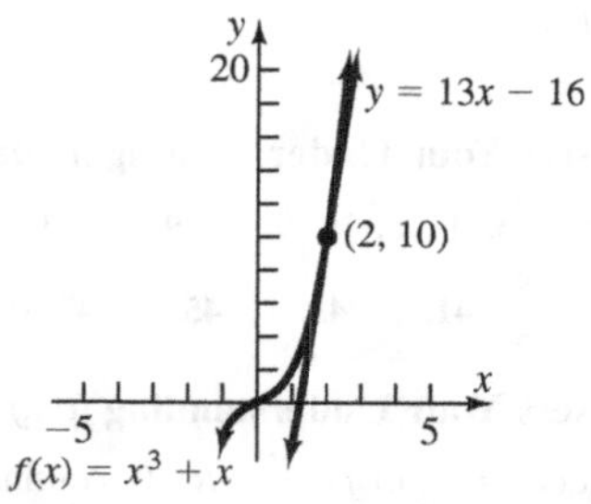

21. -4 **23.** 0 **25.** 7 **27.** 7 **29.** 3 **31.** 1 **33.** 60 **35.** -0.8587776956 **37.** 1.389623659 **39.** 2.362110222 **41.** 3.643914112 **43.** 18π ft³/ft **45.** 16π ft³/ft **47. (a)** 6 sec **(b)** 64 ft/sec **(c)** $(-32t + 96)$ ft/sec **(d)** 32 ft/sec **(e)** 3 sec **(f)** 144 ft **(g)** -96 ft/sec **49. (a)** $-23\frac{1}{3}$ ft/sec **(b)** -21 ft/sec **(c)** -18 ft/sec **(d)** $s(t) = -2.631t^2 - 10.269t + 999.933$ **(e)** Approximately -15.531 ft/sec

14.5 Assess Your Understanding *(page 912)*

3. $\int_a^b f(x)\,dx$ **4.** $\int_a^b f(x)\,dx$ **5.** 3 **7.** 56

9. (a)

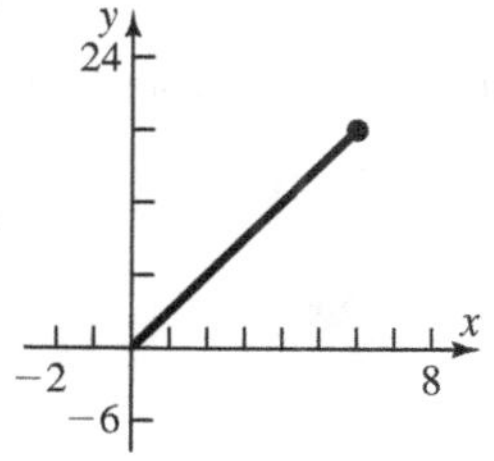

(b) 36 **(c)** 72

(d) 45 **(e)** 63 **(f)** 54

11. (a)

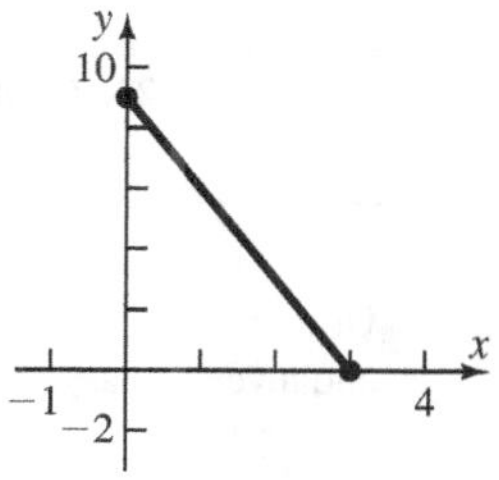

(b) 18 **(c)** 9

(d) $\frac{63}{4}$ **(e)** $\frac{45}{4}$ **(f)** $\frac{27}{2}$

13. (a)

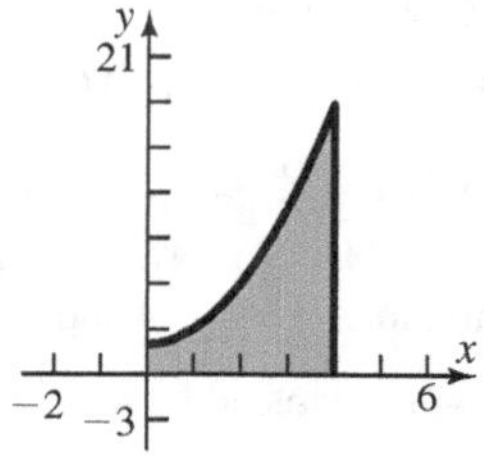

(b) 22 **(c)** $\frac{51}{2}$

(d) $\int_0^4 (x^2 + 2)\,dx$ **(e)** $\frac{88}{3}$

15. (a)

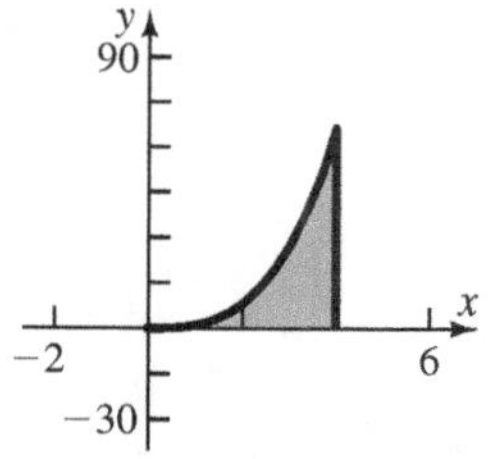

(b) 36 **(c)** 49

(d) $\int_0^4 x^3\,dx$ **(e)** 64

17. (a)

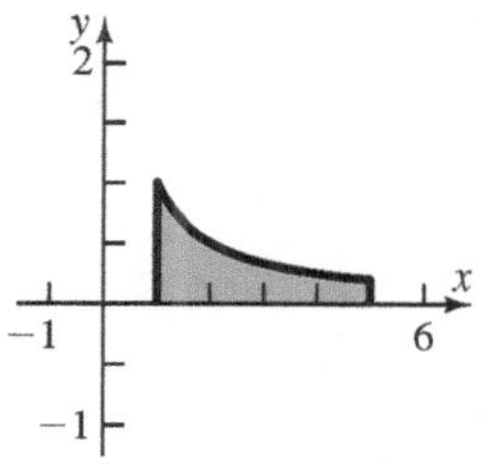

(b) $\frac{25}{12}$ **(c)** $\frac{4609}{2520}$

(d) $\int_1^5 \frac{1}{x}\,dx$ **(e)** 1.609

19. (a)

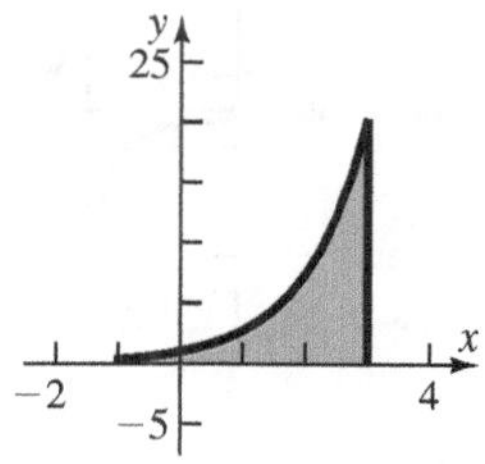

(b) 11.475 **(c)** 15.197

(d) $\int_{-1}^3 e^x\,dx$ **(e)** 19.718

21. (a)

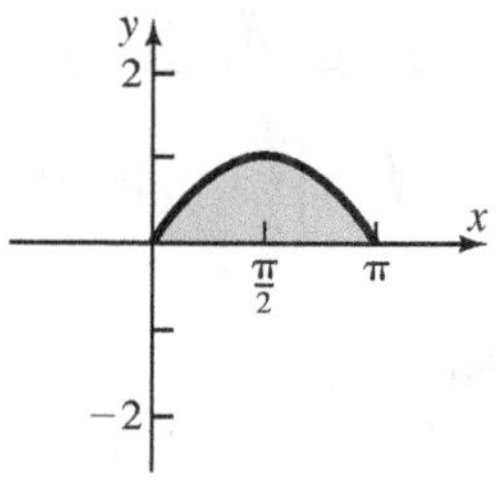

(b) 1.896 **(c)** 1.974

(d) $\int_0^{\pi} \sin x\,dx$ **(e)** 2

23. (a) Area under the graph of $f(x) = 3x + 1$ from 0 to 4

(b)

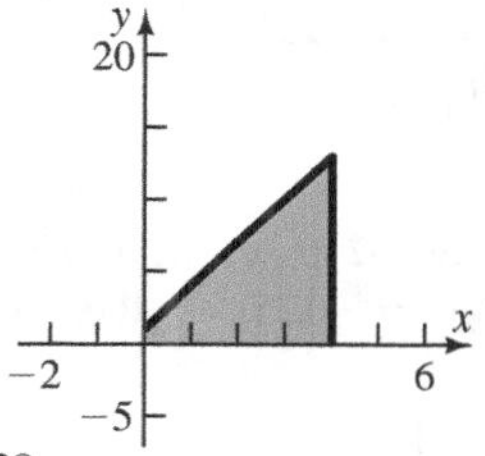

(c) 28

25. (a) Area under the graph of $f(x) = x^2 - 1$ from 2 to 5

(b)

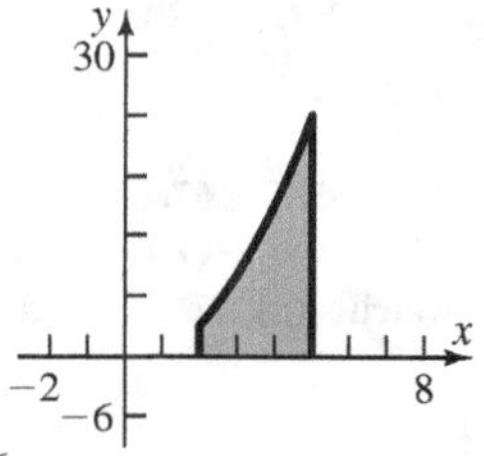

(c) 36

27. (a) Area under the graph of $f(x) = \sin x$ from 0 to $\frac{\pi}{2}$

(b)

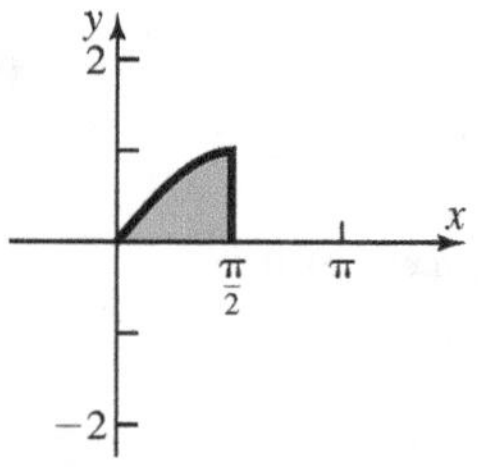

(c) 1

29. (a) Area under the graph of $f(x) = e^x$ from 0 to 2

(b)

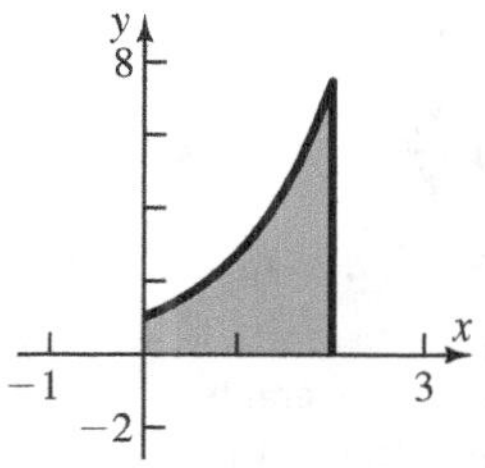

(c) 6.389

31. Using left endpoints: $n = 2$: $0 + 0.5 = 0.5$; $n = 4$: $0 + 0.125 + 0.25 + 0.375 = 0.75$;

$n = 10$: $0 + 0.02 + 0.04 + 0.06 + \cdots + 0.18 = \frac{10}{2}(0 + 0.18) = 0.9$;

$n = 100$: $0 + 0.0002 + 0.0004 + 0.0006 + \cdots + 0.0198 = \frac{100}{2}(0 + 0.0198) = 0.99$;

Using right endpoints: $n = 2$: $0.5 + 1 = 1.5$; $n = 4$: $0.125 + 0.25 + 0.375 + 0.5 = 1.25$;

$n = 10$: $0.02 + 0.04 + 0.06 + \cdots + 0.20 = \frac{10}{2}(0.02 + 0.20) = 1.1$;

$n = 100$: $0.0002 + 0.0004 + 0.0006 + \cdots + 0.02 = \frac{100}{2}(0.0002 + 0.02) = 1.01$

Review Exercises *(page 914)*

1. 9 **3.** 25 **5.** 4 **7.** 0 **9.** 64 **11.** $-\frac{1}{4}$ **13.** $\frac{1}{3}$ **15.** $\frac{6}{7}$ **17.** 0 **19.** $\frac{3}{2}$ **21.** $\frac{28}{11}$ **23.** Continuous **25.** Not continuous **27.** Not continuous **29.** Continuous **31.** $\{x \mid -6 \le x < 2 \text{ or } 2 < x < 5 \text{ or } 5 < x \le 6\}$ **33.** 1, 6 **35.** $f(-6) = 2$; $f(-4) = 1$ **37.** 4 **39.** -2 **41.** $-\infty$
43. Does not exist **45.** No **47.** No **49.** Yes

51. R is discontinuous at $x = -4$ and $x = 4$.
$\lim_{x \to -4} R(x) = -\frac{1}{8}$: Hole at $\left(-4, -\frac{1}{8}\right)$
$\lim_{x \to 4^-} R(x) = -\infty$; $\lim_{x \to 4^+} R(x) = \infty$:
The graph of R has a vertical asymptote at $x = 4$.

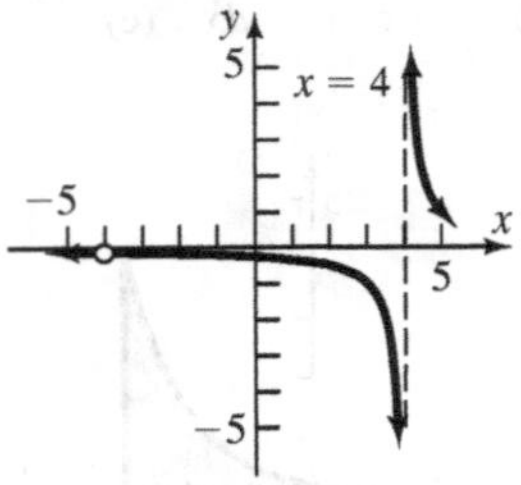

53. Undefined at $x = 2$ and $x = 9$; R has a hole at $x = 2$ and a vertical asymptote at $x = 9$.

55. $m_{\tan} = 12$

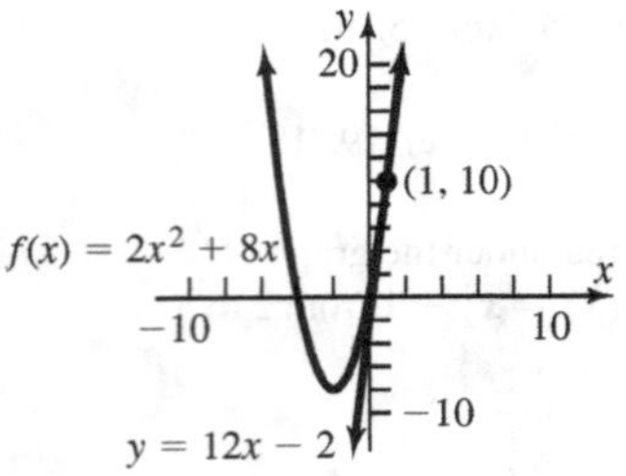

57. $m_{\tan} = 0$

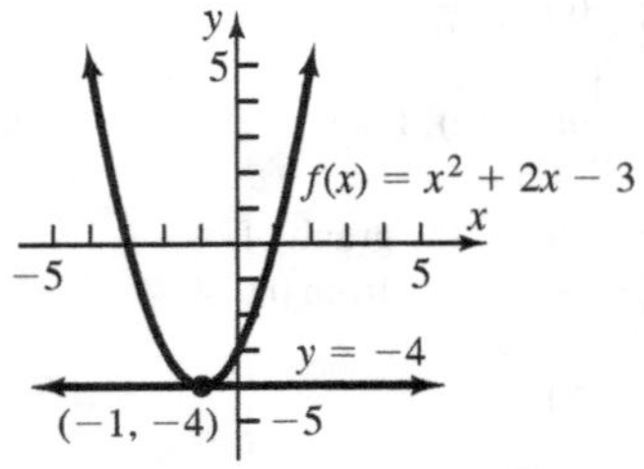

59. $m_{\tan} = 16$

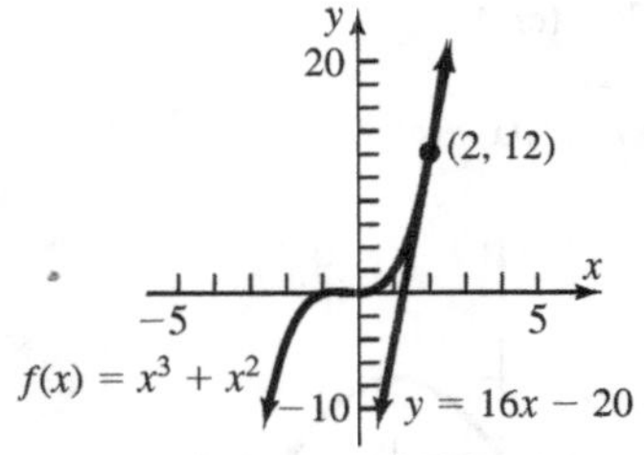

61. -24 **63.** -3 **65.** 7 **67.** -158 **69.** 0.6662517653
71. **(a)** 7 sec **(b)** 6 sec **(c)** 64 ft/sec **(d)** $(-32t + 96)$ ft/sec **(e)** 32 ft/sec **(f)** At $t = 3$ sec **(g)** -96 ft/sec **(h)** -128 ft/sec
73. **(a)** \$61.29/watch **(b)** \$71.31/watch **(c)** \$81.40/watch **(d)** $R(x) = -0.25x^2 + 100.01x - 1.24$ **(e)** Approximately \$87.51/watch

75. **(a)**

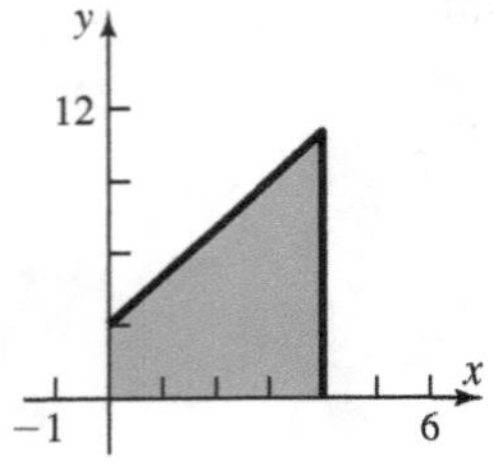

(b) 24 **(c)** 32
(d) 26 **(e)** 30 **(f)** 28

77. **(a)**

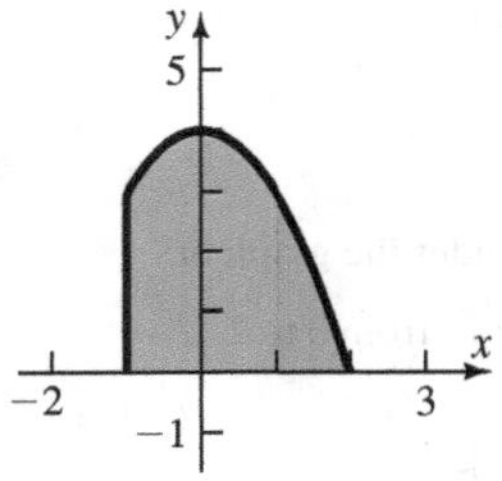

(b) 10 **(c)** $\frac{77}{8}$
(d) $\int_{-1}^{2} (4 - x^2)\, dx$ **(e)** 9

79. **(a)**

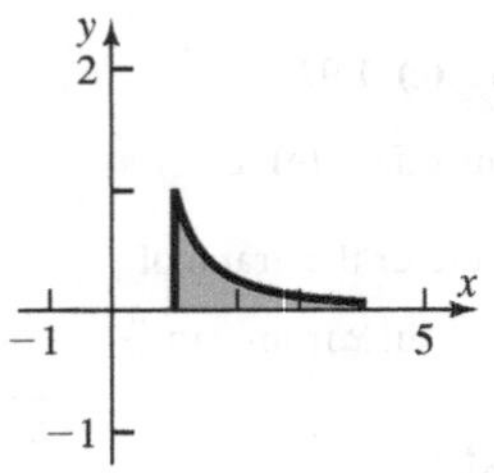

(b) $\frac{49}{36} \approx 1.36$ **(c)** 1.02
(d) $\int_{1}^{4} \frac{1}{x^2}\, dx$ **(e)** 0.75

81. **(a)** Area under the graph of $f(x) = 9 - x^2$ from -1 to 3
(b)

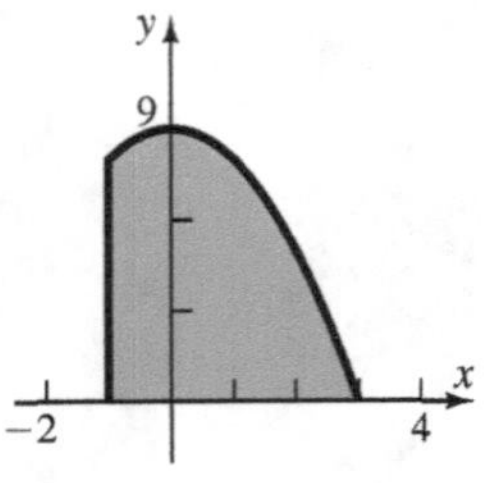

(c) $\frac{80}{3}$

83. **(a)** Area under the graph of $f(x) = e^x$ from -1 to 1
(b)

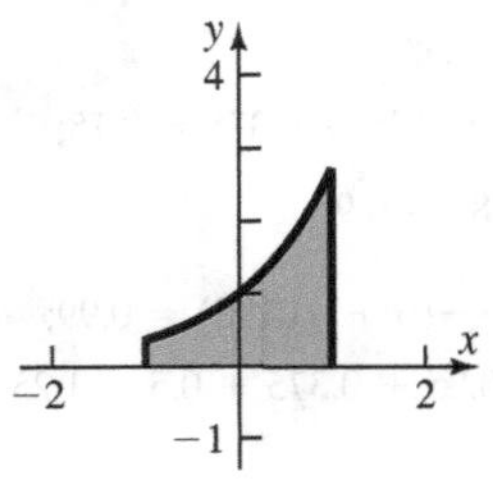

(c) 2.35

Chapter Test *(page 917)*

1. -5 **2.** $\frac{1}{3}$ **3.** 5 **4.** -2 **5.** 135 **6.** $\frac{2}{3}$ **7.** -1 **8.** -3 **9.** 5 **10.** 2 **11.** Limit exists; 2 **12. (a)** No; $f(-2)$ is not defined **(b)** No; $\lim_{x\to 1} f(x) \neq f(1)$ **(c)** No; $\lim_{x\to 3^+} f(x) \neq f(3)$ **(d)** Yes **13.** $x = -7$: asymptote; $x = 2$: hole

14. (a) 5
(b) $y = 5x - 19$
(c)

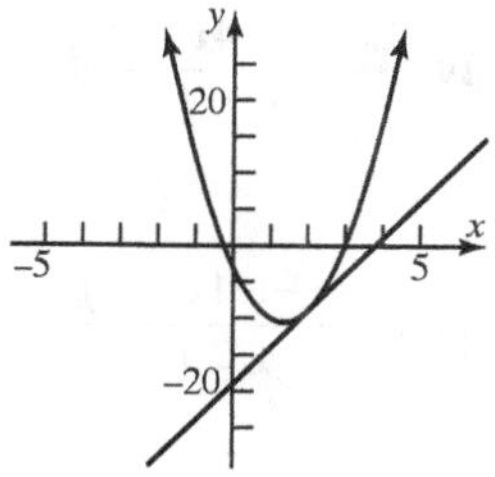

15. (a)

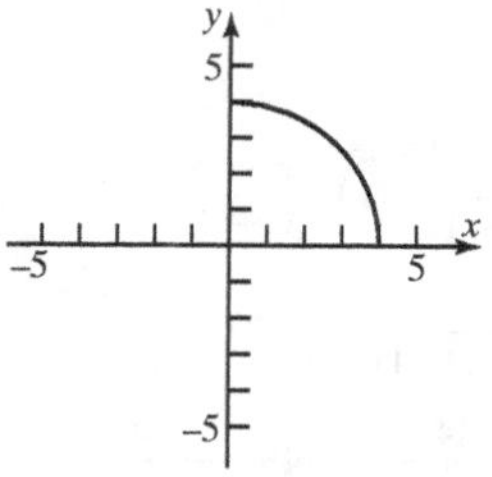

(b) 13.359 **(c)** $4\pi \approx 12.566$

16. $\int_1^4 (-x^2 + 5x + 3)\,dx$ **17.** $35\frac{1}{3}$ ft/sec

APPENDIX A

A.1 Assess Your Understanding *(page A10)*

1. variable **3.** strict **5.** T **7.** F **9.** $\{1, 2, 3, 4, 5, 6, 7, 8, 9\}$ **11.** $\{4\}$ **13.** $\{1, 3, 4, 6\}$ **15.** $\{0, 2, 6, 7, 8\}$ **17.** $\{0, 1, 2, 3, 5, 6, 7, 8, 9\}$ **19.** $\{0, 1, 2, 3, 5, 6, 7, 8, 9\}$ **21.**

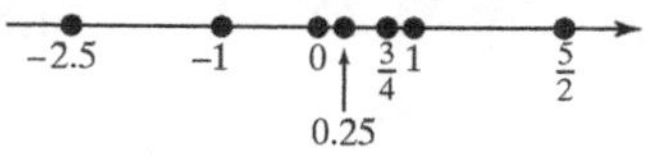

23. $>$ **25.** $>$ **27.** $>$ **29.** $=$ **31.** $<$ **33.** $x > 0$ **35.** $x < 2$

37. $x \le 1$ **39.**

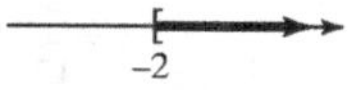

41.

43. 1 **45.** 2 **47.** 6 **49.** 4 **51.** -28 **53.** $\frac{4}{5}$ **55.** 0 **57.** 1 **59.** 5 **61.** 1 **63.** 22 **65.** 2 **67.** $x = 0$ **69.** $x = 3$ **71.** None **73.** $x = 0, x = 1, x = -1$ **75.** $\{x \mid x \neq 5\}$ **77.** $\{x \mid x \neq -4\}$ **79.** 0°C **81.** 25°C **83.** 16 **85.** $\frac{1}{16}$ **87.** $\frac{1}{9}$ **89.** 9 **91.** 5 **93.** 4 **95.** $64x^6$ **97.** $\frac{x^4}{y^2}$ **99.** $\frac{x}{y}$ **101.** $-\frac{8x^3z}{9y}$ **103.** $\frac{16x^2}{9y^2}$ **105.** -4 **107.** 5 **109.** 4 **111.** 2 **113.** $\sqrt{5}$ **115.** $\frac{1}{2}$ **117.** 10; 0 **119.** 81 **121.** 304,006.671 **123.** 0.004 **125.** 481.890 **127.** 0.000 **129.** $A = lw$ **131.** $C = \pi d$ **133.** $A = \frac{\sqrt{3}}{4}x^2$ **135.** $V = \frac{4}{3}\pi r^3$ **137.** $V = x^3$ **139. (a)** \$6000 **(b)** \$8000 **141.** $|x - 4| \ge 6$ **143. (a)** $2 \le 5$ **(b)** $6 > 5$ **145. (a)** Yes **(b)** No **147.** No; $\frac{1}{3}$ is larger; 0.000333... **149.** No

A.2 Assess Your Understanding *(page A20)*

1. right; hypotenuse **3.** $C = 2\pi r$ **5.** T **7.** F **9.** T **11.** 13 **13.** 26 **15.** 25 **17.** Right triangle; 5 **19.** Not a right triangle **21.** Right triangle; 25 **23.** Not a right triangle **25.** 8 in.^{2} **27.** 4 in.^{2} **29.** $A = 25\pi$ m^2; $C = 10\pi$ m **31.** $V = 224$ ft^3; $S = 232$ ft^2 **33.** $V = \frac{256}{3}\pi$ cm^3; $S = 64\pi$ cm^2 **35.** $V = 648\pi$ in.^{3}; $S = 306\pi$ in.^{2} **37.** π square units **39.** 2π square units **41.** $x = 4$ units; $A = 90°$; $B = 60°$; $C = 30°$ **43.** $x = 67.5$ units; $A = 60°$; $B = 95°$; $C = 25°$ **45.** About 16.8 ft **47.** 64 ft^2 **49.** $24 + 2\pi \approx 30.28$ ft^2; $16 + 2\pi \approx 22.28$ ft **51.** 160 paces **53.** About 5.477 mi **55.** From 100 ft: 12.2 mi; From 150 ft: 15.0 mi

A.3 Assess Your Understanding *(page A29)*

1. 4; 3 **3.** $x^3 - 8$ **5.** F **7.** $3x(x - 2)(x + 2)$ **9.** T **11.** Monomial; variable: x; coefficient: 2; degree: 3 **13.** Not a monomial; the exponent of the variable is not a nonnegative integer **15.** Not a monomial; it has more than one term **17.** Not a monomial; the exponent of one of the variables is not a nonnegative integer **19.** Not a monomial; it has more than one term **21.** Yes; 2 **23.** Yes; 0 **25.** No; the variable of one of the terms is not a nonnegative integer **27.** Yes; 3 **29.** No; the polynomial of the denominator has a degree greater than 0 **31.** $x^2 + 7x + 2$ **33.** $x^3 - 4x^2 + 9x + 7$ **35.** $-2x^3 + 18x^2 - 18$ **37.** $15y^2 - 27y + 30$ **39.** $x^3 + x^2 - 4x$ **41.** $x^2 + 6x + 8$ **43.** $2x^2 + 9x + 10$ **45.** $x^2 - 49$ **47.** $4x^2 - 9$ **49.** $x^2 + 8x + 16$ **51.** $4x^2 - 12x + 9$ **53.** $x^3 - 6x^2 + 12x - 8$ **55.** $8x^3 + 12x^2 + 6x + 1$ **57.** $4x^2 - 11x + 23$; remainder -45 **59.** $4x - 3$; remainder $x + 1$ **61.** $5x^2 - 13$; remainder $x + 27$ **63.** $2x^2$; remainder $-x^2 + x + 1$ **65.** $x^2 - 2x + \frac{1}{2}$; remainder $\frac{5}{2}x + \frac{1}{2}$ **67.** $-4x^2 - 3x - 3$; remainder -7 **69.** $x^2 - x - 1$; remainder $2x + 2$ **71.** $x^2 + ax + a^2$; remainder 0 **73.** $(x + 6)(x - 6)$ **75.** $2(1 + 2x)(1 - 2x)$ **77.** $(x + 1)(x + 10)$ **79.** $(x - 7)(x - 3)$ **81.** $4(x^2 - 2x + 8)$ **83.** Prime **85.** $-(x - 5)(x + 3)$ **87.** $3(x + 2)(x - 6)$ **89.** $y^2(y + 5)(y + 6)$ **91.** $(2x + 3)^2$ **93.** $2(3x + 1)(x + 1)$ **95.** $(x - 3)(x + 3)(x^2 + 9)$ **97.** $(x - 1)^2(x^2 + x + 1)^2$ **99.** $x^5(x - 1)(x + 1)$ **101.** $(4x + 3)^2$ **103.** $-(4x - 5)(4x + 1)$ **105.** $(2y - 5)(2y - 3)$ **107.** $-(3x - 1)(3x + 1)(x^2 + 1)$ **109.** $(x + 3)(x - 6)$ **111.** $(x + 2)(x - 3)$ **113.** $(3x - 5)(9x^2 - 3x + 7)$ **115.** $(x + 5)(3x + 11)$ **117.** $(x - 1)(x + 1)(x + 2)$ **119.** $(x - 1)(x + 1)(x^2 - x + 1)$ **121.** $2(3x + 4)(9x + 13)$ **123.** $2x(3x + 5)$ **125.** $5(x + 3)(x - 2)^2(x + 1)$ **127.** $3(4x - 3)(4x - 1)$ **129.** $6(3x - 5)(2x + 1)^2(5x - 4)$ **131.** The possibilities are $(x \pm 1)(x \pm 4) = x^2 \pm 5x + 4$ or $(x \pm 2)(x \pm 2) = x^2 \pm 4x + 4$, none of which equals $x^2 + 4$.

A.4 Assess Your Understanding *(page A34)*

1. quotient; divisor; remainder **3.** T **5.** $x^2 + x + 4$; remainder 12 **7.** $3x^2 + 11x + 32$; remainder 99 **9.** $x^4 - 3x^3 + 5x^2 - 15x + 46$; remainder -138 **11.** $4x^5 + 4x^4 + x^3 + x^2 + 2x + 2$; remainder 7 **13.** $0.1x^2 - 0.11x + 0.321$; remainder -0.3531 **15.** $x^4 + x^3 + x^2 + x + 1$; remainder 0 **17.** No **19.** Yes **21.** Yes **23.** No **25.** Yes **27.** -9

A.5 Assess Your Understanding *(page A43)*

1. lowest terms **3.** T **5.** $\frac{3}{x-3}$ **7.** $\frac{x}{3}$ **9.** $\frac{4x}{2x-1}$ **11.** $\frac{y+5}{2(y+1)}$ **13.** $\frac{x+5}{x-1}$ **15.** $-(x+7)$ **17.** $\frac{3}{5x(x-2)}$ **19.** $\frac{2x(x^2+4x+16)}{x+4}$ **21.** $\frac{8}{3x}$ **23.** $\frac{x-3}{x+7}$ **25.** $\frac{4x}{(x-2)(x-3)}$ **27.** $\frac{4}{5(x-1)}$ **29.** $-\frac{(x-4)^2}{4x}$ **31.** $\frac{(x+3)^2}{(x-3)^2}$ **33.** $\frac{(x-4)(x+3)}{(x-1)(2x+1)}$ **35.** $\frac{x+5}{2}$ **37.** $\frac{(x-2)(x+2)}{2x-3}$ **39.** $\frac{3x-2}{x-3}$ **41.** $\frac{x+9}{2x-1}$ **43.** $\frac{4-x}{x-2}$ **45.** $\frac{2(x+5)}{(x-1)(x+2)}$ **47.** $\frac{3x^2-2x-3}{(x+1)(x-1)}$ **49.** $\frac{-(11x+2)}{(x+2)(x-2)}$ **51.** $\frac{2(x^2-2)}{x(x-2)(x+2)}$ **53.** $(x-2)(x+2)(x+1)$ **55.** $x(x-1)(x+1)$ **57.** $x^3(2x-1)^2$ **59.** $x(x-1)^2(x+1)(x^2+x+1)$ **61.** $\frac{5x}{(x-6)(x-1)(x+4)}$ **63.** $\frac{2(2x^2+5x-2)}{(x-2)(x+2)(x+3)}$ **65.** $\frac{5x+1}{(x-1)^2(x+1)^2}$ **67.** $\frac{-x^2+3x+13}{(x-2)(x+1)(x+4)}$ **69.** $\frac{x^3-2x^2+4x+3}{x^2(x+1)(x-1)}$ **71.** $\frac{-1}{x(x+h)}$ **73.** $\frac{x+1}{x-1}$ **75.** $\frac{(x-1)(x+1)}{2x(2x+1)}$ **77.** $\frac{2(5x-1)}{(x-2)(x+1)^2}$ **79.** $\frac{-2x(x^2-2)}{(x+2)(x^2-x-3)}$ **81.** $\frac{-1}{x-1}$ **83.** $\frac{3x-1}{2x+1}$ **85.** $\frac{19}{(3x-5)^2}$ **87.** $\frac{(x+1)(x-1)}{(x^2+1)^2}$ **89.** $\frac{x(3x+2)}{(3x+1)^2}$ **91.** $-\frac{(x+3)(3x-1)}{(x^2+1)^2}$ **93.** $f = \frac{R_1 \cdot R_2}{(n-1)(R_1+R_2)}; \frac{2}{15}$ m

A.6 Assess Your Understanding *(page A57)*

5. equivalent equations **6.** identity **7.** F **8.** T **9.** add; $\frac{25}{4}$ **10.** discriminant; negative **11.** F **12.** F **13.** $\{7\}$ **15.** $\{-3\}$ **17.** $\{4\}$ **19.** $\left\{\frac{5}{4}\right\}$ **21.** $\{-1\}$ **23.** $\{-18\}$ **25.** $\{-3\}$ **27.** $\{-16\}$ **29.** $\{0.5\}$ **31.** $\{2\}$ **33.** $\{2\}$ **35.** $\{3\}$ **37.** $\{0, 9\}$ **39.** $\{0, 9\}$ **41.** $\{21\}$ **43.** $\{-2, 2\}$ **45.** $\{6\}$ **47.** $\{-3, 3\}$ **49.** $\{-4, 1\}$ **51.** $\left\{-1, \frac{3}{2}\right\}$ **53.** $\{-4, 4\}$ **55.** $\{2\}$ **57.** No real solution **59.** $\{-2, 2\}$ **61.** $\{-1, 3\}$ **63.** $\{-2, -1, 0, 1\}$ **65.** $\{0, 4\}$ **67.** $\{-6, 2\}$ **69.** $\left\{-\frac{1}{2}, 3\right\}$ **71.** $\{3, 4\}$ **73.** $\left\{\frac{3}{2}\right\}$ **75.** $\left\{-\frac{2}{3}, \frac{3}{2}\right\}$ **77.** $\left\{-\frac{3}{4}, 2\right\}$ **79.** $\{-6\}$ **81.** $\{-2, -1, 1, 2\}$ **83.** $\{-6, -5\}$ **85.** $\left\{-\frac{3}{2}, 2\right\}$ **87.** $\{-1, 0, 4\}$ **89.** $\{-1, 1\}$ **91.** $\left\{-2, \frac{1}{2}, 2\right\}$ **93.** $\{-5, 5\}$ **95.** $\{-1, 3\}$ **97.** $\{-3, 0\}$ **99.** 16 **101.** $\frac{1}{16}$ **103.** $\frac{1}{9}$ **105.** $\{-7, 3\}$ **107.** $\left\{-\frac{1}{4}, \frac{3}{4}\right\}$ **109.** $\left\{\frac{-1-\sqrt{7}}{6}, \frac{-1+\sqrt{7}}{6}\right\}$ **111.** $\{2-\sqrt{2}, 2+\sqrt{2}\}$ **113.** $\left\{\frac{5-\sqrt{29}}{2}, \frac{5+\sqrt{29}}{2}\right\}$ **115.** $\left\{1, \frac{3}{2}\right\}$ **117.** No real solution **119.** $\left\{\frac{-1-\sqrt{5}}{4}, \frac{-1+\sqrt{5}}{4}\right\}$ **121.** $\left\{\frac{-\sqrt{3}-\sqrt{15}}{2}, \frac{-\sqrt{3}+\sqrt{15}}{2}\right\}$ **123.** No real solution **125.** Repeated real solution **127.** Two unequal real solutions **129.** $R = \frac{R_1R_2}{R_1+R_2}$ **131.** $R = \frac{mv^2}{F}$ **133.** $r = \frac{S-a}{S}$ **135.** $\frac{-b+\sqrt{b^2-4ac}}{2a} + \frac{-b-\sqrt{b^2-4ac}}{2a} = \frac{-2b}{2a} = \frac{-b}{a}$ **137.** $k = -\frac{1}{2}$ or $\frac{1}{2}$ **139.** The solutions of $ax^2 - bx + c = 0$ are $\frac{b+\sqrt{b^2-4ac}}{2a}$ and $\frac{b-\sqrt{b^2-4ac}}{2a}$. **141.** (b)

A.7 Assess Your Understanding *(page A67)*

4. real; imaginary; imaginary unit **5.** $-2i, 2i$ **6.** F **7.** T **8.** F **9.** $8 + 5i$ **11.** $-7 + 6i$ **13.** $-6 - 11i$ **15.** $6 - 18i$ **17.** $6 + 4i$ **19.** $10 - 5i$ **21.** 37 **23.** $\frac{6}{5} + \frac{8}{5}i$ **25.** $1 - 2i$ **27.** $\frac{5}{2} - \frac{7}{2}i$ **29.** $-\frac{1}{2} + \frac{\sqrt{3}}{2}i$ **31.** $2i$ **33.** $-i$ **35.** i **37.** -6 **39.** $-10i$ **41.** $-2 + 2i$ **43.** 0 **45.** 0 **47.** $2i$ **49.** $5i$ **51.** $5i$ **53.** $\{-2i, 2i\}$ **55.** $\{-4, 4\}$ **57.** $\{3 - 2i, 3 + 2i\}$ **59.** $\{3 - i, 3 + i\}$ **61.** $\left\{\frac{1}{4} - \frac{1}{4}i, \frac{1}{4} + \frac{1}{4}i\right\}$ **63.** $\left\{-\frac{1}{5} - \frac{2}{5}i, -\frac{1}{5} + \frac{2}{5}i\right\}$ **65.** $\left\{-\frac{1}{2} - \frac{\sqrt{3}}{2}i, -\frac{1}{2} + \frac{\sqrt{3}}{2}i\right\}$ **67.** $\{2, -1 - \sqrt{3}i, -1 + \sqrt{3}i\}$ **69.** $\{-2, 2, -2i, 2i\}$ **71.** $\{-3i, -2i, 2i, 3i\}$ **73.** Two complex solutions **75.** Two unequal real solutions **77.** A repeated real solution **79.** $2 - 3i$ **81.** 6 **83.** 25 **85.** $2 + 3i$

87. $z + \bar{z} = (a + bi) + (a - bi) = 2a$; $z - \bar{z} = (a + bi) - (a - bi) = 2bi$

89. $\overline{z + w} = \overline{(a + bi) + (c + di)} = \overline{(a + c) + (b + d)i} = (a + c) - (b + d)i = (a - bi) + (c - di) = \bar{z} + \bar{w}$

95. $\sqrt{a} \cdot \sqrt{b} = \sqrt{ab}$ only when $\sqrt{a}, \sqrt{b}$ are real numbers.

A.8 Assess Your Understanding *(page A74)*

1. mathematical modeling **3.** uniform motion **5.** T **7.** $A = \pi r^2$; r = radius, A = area **9.** $A = s^2$; A = area, s = length of a side **11.** $F = ma$; F = force, m = mass, a = acceleration **13.** $W = Fd$; W = work, F = force, d = distance

15. $C = 150x; C =$ total variable cost, $x =$ number of dishwashers **17.** Invest \$48,000 in bonds and \$36,000 in CDs. **19.** \$85,000 was loaned out at 8%. **21.** Mix 75 lb of Earl Grey tea with 25 lb of Orange Pekoe tea. **23.** Mix 160 lb of cashews with the almonds. **25.** The speed of the current is 2.286 mi/hr. **27.** The speed of the current is 5 mi/hr. **29.** Working together, it takes 12 min. **31. (a)** The dimensions are 10 ft by 5 ft. **(b)** The area is 50 sq ft. **(c)** The dimensions would be 7.5 ft by 7.5 ft. **(d)** The area would be 56.25 sq ft. **33.** The defensive back catches up to the tight end at the tight end's 45-yd line. **35.** Add $\frac{2}{3}$ gal of water. **37.** Approximately 4.05 ft/s. **39.** hp 1300; 30 min; 20 pages/min; hp 2420; 20 min; 30 pages/min **41.** Evaporate 10.67 oz of water. **43.** 40 g of 12-karat gold should be mixed with 20 g of pure gold. **45.** Mike passes Dan $\frac{1}{3}$ mi from the start, 2 min from the time Mike started to race. **47.** Start the auxiliary pump at 9:45 A.M. **49.** The tub will fill in 1 hr. **51.** The distance of the run is 12 mi. The distance of the bicycle race is 75 mi. **53.** Lewis would beat Burke by 16.75 m. **57.** The average speed is 49.5 mi/hr.

A.9 Assess Your Understanding *(page A85)*

5. negative **6.** closed interval **7.** $-5, 5$ **8.** $-5 < x < 5$ **9.** T **10.** T **11.** $[0, 2]; 0 \le x \le 2$ **13.** $[2, \infty); x \ge 2$ **15.** $[0, 3); 0 \le x < 3$
17. (a) $6 < 8$ **(b)** $-2 < 0$ **(c)** $9 < 15$ **(d)** $-6 > -10$ **19. (a)** $7 > 0$ **(b)** $-1 > -8$ **(c)** $12 > -9$ **(d)** $-8 < 6$
21. (a) $2x + 4 < 5$ **(b)** $2x - 4 < -3$ **(c)** $6x + 3 < 6$ **(d)** $-4x - 2 > -4$

23. $[0, 4]$

25. $[4, 6)$

27. $[4, \infty)$
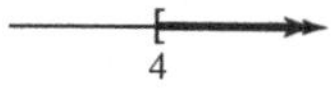

29. $(-\infty, -4)$
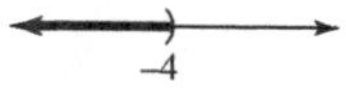

31. $2 \le x \le 5$

33. $-3 < x < -2$

35. $x \ge 4$
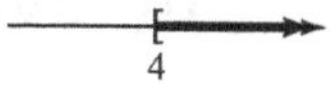

37. $x < -3$
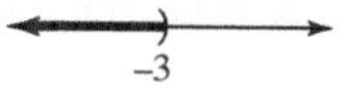

39. $<$ **41.** $>$ **43.** $\ge$ **45.** $<$ **47.** $\le$ **49.** $>$ **51.** $\ge$

53. $\{x \mid x < 4\}$ or $(-\infty, 4)$

55. $\{x \mid x \ge -1\}$ or $[-1, \infty)$
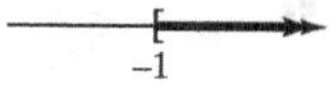

57. $\{x \mid x > 3\}$ or $(3, \infty)$

59. $\{x \mid x \ge 2\}$ or $[2, \infty)$
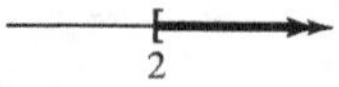

61. $\{x \mid x > -7\}$ or $(-7, \infty)$
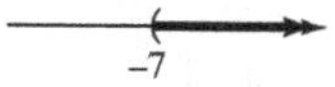

63. $\left\{x \middle| x \le \frac{2}{3}\right\}$ or $\left(-\infty, \frac{2}{3}\right]$
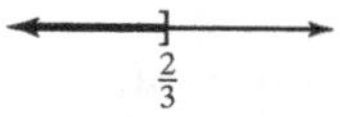

65. $\{x \mid x < -20\}$ or $(-\infty, -20)$
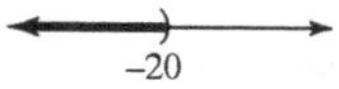

67. $\left\{x \middle| x \ge \frac{4}{3}\right\}$ or $\left[\frac{4}{3}, \infty\right)$
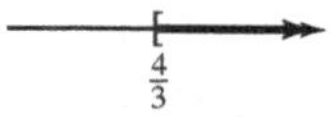

69. $\{x \mid 3 \le x \le 5\}$ or $[3, 5]$

71. $\left\{x \middle| \frac{2}{3} \le x \le 3\right\}$ or $\left[\frac{2}{3}, 3\right]$

73. $\left\{x \middle| -\frac{11}{2} < x < \frac{1}{2}\right\}$ or $\left(-\frac{11}{2}, \frac{1}{2}\right)$
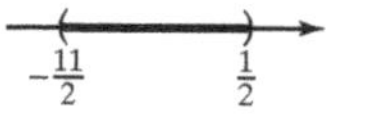

75. $\{x \mid -6 < x < 0\}$ or $(-6, 0)$

77. $\{x \mid x < -5\}$ or $(-\infty, -5)$
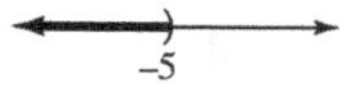

79. $\{x \mid x \ge -1\}$ or $[-1, \infty)$
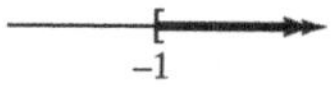

81. $\left\{x \middle| \frac{1}{2} \le x < \frac{5}{4}\right\}$ or $\left[\frac{1}{2}, \frac{5}{4}\right)$

83. $\left\{x \middle| x < -\frac{1}{2}\right\}$ or $\left(-\infty, -\frac{1}{2}\right)$
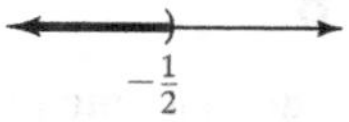

85. $\left\{x \middle| x > \frac{10}{3}\right\}$ or $\left(\frac{10}{3}, \infty\right)$
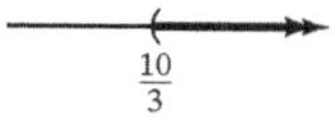

87. $\{x \mid x > 3\}$ or $(3, \infty)$
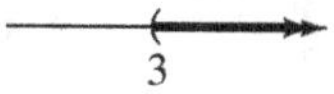

89. $\{x \mid -4 < x < 4\}; (-4, 4)$

91. $\{x \mid x < -4 \text{ or } x > 4\}; (-\infty, -4) \cup (4, \infty)$

93. $\{x \mid 0 \le x \le 1\}; [0, 1]$

95. $\{x \mid x < -1 \text{ or } x > 2\}; (-\infty -1) \cup (2, \infty)$

97. $\{x \mid -1 \le x \le 1\}; [-1, 1]$

99. $\{x \mid x \le -2 \text{ or } x \ge 2\}; (-\infty, -2] \cup [2, \infty)$

101. $|x - 2| < \frac{1}{2}; \left\{x \middle| \frac{3}{2} < x < \frac{5}{2}\right\}$ **103.** $|x + 3| > 2; \{x \mid x < -5 \text{ or } x > -1\}$

105. $\{x \mid x \ge -2\}$ **107.** $21 < \text{Age} < 30$ **109. (a)** Male $\ge$ 79.66 years **(b)** Female $\ge$ 83.58 years **(c)** A female can expect to live 3.92 years longer. **111.** The agent's commission ranges from \$45,000 to \$95,000, inclusive. As a percent of selling price, the commission ranges from 5% to 8.6%, inclusive. **113.** The amount withheld varies from \$98.30 to \$148.30, inclusive. **115.** The usage varies from 675.41 kW · hr to 2500.91 kW · hr, inclusive.

117. The dealer's cost varies from \$15,254.24 to \$16,071.43, inclusive.

119. (a) You need at least a 74 on the fifth test. **(b)** You need at least a 77 on the fifth test.

121. $\frac{a+b}{2} - a = \frac{a+b-2a}{2} = \frac{b-a}{2} > 0$; therefore, $a < \frac{a+b}{2}$. $b - \frac{a+b}{2} = \frac{2b-a-b}{2} = \frac{b-a}{2} > 0$; therefore, $b > \frac{a+b}{2}$.

123. $(\sqrt{ab})^2 - a^2 = ab - a^2 = a(b-a) > 0$; thus $(\sqrt{ab})^2 > a^2$ and $\sqrt{ab} > a$.
$b^2 - (\sqrt{ab})^2 = b^2 - ab = b(b-a) > 0$; thus $b^2 > (\sqrt{ab})^2$ and $b > \sqrt{ab}$.

125. $h - a = \frac{2ab}{a+b} - a = \frac{ab-a^2}{a+b} = \frac{a(b-a)}{a+b} > 0$; thus $h > a$.

$b - h = b - \frac{2ab}{a+b} = \frac{b^2-ab}{a+b} = \frac{b(b-a)}{a+b} > 0$; thus $h < b$.

127. Since $0 < a < b$, then $a - b < 0$ and $\frac{a-b}{ab} < 0$.

So $\frac{a}{ab} - \frac{b}{ab} < 0$, or $\frac{1}{b} - \frac{1}{a} < 0$. Therefore, $\frac{1}{b} < \frac{1}{a}$. And $0 < \frac{1}{b}$ because $b > 0$.

A.10 Assess Your Understanding *(page A93)*

3. index **4.** T **5.** cube root **6.** F **7.** 3 **9.** -2 **11.** $2\sqrt{2}$ **13.** $-2x\sqrt[3]{x}$ **15.** x^3y^2 **17.** x^2y **19.** $6\sqrt{x}$ **21.** $6x\sqrt{x}$ **23.** $15\sqrt[3]{3}$ **25.** $12\sqrt{3}$ **27.** $7\sqrt{2}$ **29.** $\sqrt{2}$ **31.** $2\sqrt{3}$ **33.** $-\sqrt[3]{2}$ **35.** $x - 2\sqrt{x} + 1$ **37.** $(2x-1)\sqrt[3]{2x}$ **39.** $(2x-15)\sqrt{2x}$ **41.** $-(x+5y)\sqrt[3]{2xy}$ **43.** $\frac{\sqrt{2}}{2}$ **45.** $-\frac{\sqrt{15}}{5}$ **47.** $\frac{(5+\sqrt{2})\sqrt{3}}{23}$ **49.** $\frac{8\sqrt{5}-19}{41}$ **51.** $\frac{5\sqrt[3]{4}}{2}$ **53.** $\frac{2x+h-2\sqrt{x^2+xh}}{h}$ **55.** 4 **57.** -3 **59.** 64 **61.** $\frac{1}{27}$ **63.** $\frac{27\sqrt{2}}{32}$ **65.** $\frac{27\sqrt{2}}{32}$ **67.** $x^{7/12}$ **69.** xy^2 **71.** $x^{2/3}y$ **73.** $\frac{8x^{5/4}}{y^{3/4}}$ **75.** $\frac{3x+2}{(1+x)^{1/2}}$ **77.** $\frac{x(3x^2+2)}{(x^2+1)^{1/2}}$ **79.** $\frac{22x+5}{10\sqrt{(x-5)(4x+3)}}$ **81.** $\frac{2+x}{2(1+x)^{3/2}}$ **83.** $\frac{4-x}{(x+4)^{3/2}}$ **85.** $\frac{1}{x^2(x^2-1)^{1/2}}$ **87.** $\frac{1-3x^2}{2\sqrt{x}(1+x^2)^2}$ **89.** $\frac{1}{2}(5x+2)(x+1)^{1/2}$ **91.** $2x^{1/2}(3x-4)(x+1)$ **93.** $(x^2+4)^{1/3}(11x^2+12)$ **95.** $(3x+5)^{1/3}(2x+3)^{1/2}(17x+27)$ **97.** $\frac{3(x+2)}{2x^{1/2}}$ **99.** 1.41 **101.** 1.59 **103.** 4.89 **105.** 2.15 **107. (a)** 15,660.4 gal **(b)** 390.7 gal **109.** $2\pi\sqrt{2} \approx 8.89$ s **111.** $\frac{\pi\sqrt{3}}{6} \approx 0.91$ s

APPENDIX B

Assess Your Understanding *(page A103)*

1. limit **3.** converges **5.** converges; 2 **7.** diverges **9.** converges; $\frac{1}{2}$ **11.** converges; 0 **13.** diverges **15.** converges; 0 **17.** converges; 3 **19.** converges; 4 **21.** converges; 1 **23.** diverges **25.** diverges **27.** diverges **29.** $1, \frac{4}{3}, \frac{13}{9}, \frac{40}{27}, \frac{121}{81}$ **31.** 1, 3, 6, 10, 15

Index

LICENSING AGREEMENT
SULLIVAN / SULLIVAN, III
Chapter Test Prep Video CDs Precalculus: Enhanced with Graphing Utilities, 5e

ISBN: 0-13-235620-1/978-0-13-235620-6

Pearson Prentice Hall
Pearson Education, Inc.
Upper Saddle River, NJ 07458

YOU SHOULD CAREFULLY READ THE TERMS AND CONDITIONS BEFORE USING THE CD-ROM PACKAGE. USING THIS CD-ROM PACKAGE INDICATES YOUR ACCEPTANCE OF THESE TERMS AND CONDITIONS.

Pearson Education, Inc. provides this program and licenses its use. You assume responsibility for the selection of the program to achieve your intended results, and for the installation, use, and results obtained from the program. This license extends only to use of the program in the United States or countries in which the program is marketed by authorized distributors.

LICENSE GRANT: You hereby accept a nonexclusive, nontransferable, permanent license to install and use the program ON A SINGLE COMPUTER at any given time. You may copy the program solely for backup or archival purposes in support of your use of the program on the single computer. You may not modify, translate, disassemble, decompile, or reverse engineer the program, in whole or in part.

TERM: The License is effective until terminated. Pearson Education, Inc. reserves the right to terminate this License automatically if any provision of the License is violated. You may terminate the License at any time. To terminate this License, you must return the program, including documentation, along with a written warranty stating that all copies in your possession have been returned or destroyed.

LIMITED WARRANTY: THE PROGRAM IS PROVIDED "AS IS" WITHOUT WARRANTY OF ANY KIND, EITHER EXPRESSED OR IMPLIED, INCLUDING, BUT NOT LIMITED TO, THE IMPLIED WARRANTIES OF MERCHANTABILITY AND FITNESS FOR APARTICULAR PURPOSE. THE ENTIRE RISK AS TO THE QUALITY AND PERFORMANCE OF THE PROGRAM IS WITH YOU. SHOULD THE PROGRAM PROVE DEFECTIVE, YOU (AND NOT PEARSON EDUCATION, INC. OR ANY AUTHORIZED DEALER) ASSUME THE ENTIRE COST OF ALL NECESSARY SERVICING, REPAIR, OR CORRECTION. NO ORAL OR WRITTEN INFORMATION OR ADVICE GIVEN BY PEARSON EDUCATION, INC., ITS DEALERS, DISTRIBUTORS, OR AGENTS SHALL CREATE A WARRANTY OR INCREASE THE SCOPE OF THIS WARRANTY. SOME STATES DO NOT ALLOW THE EXCLUSION OF IMPLIED WARRANTIES, SO THE ABOVE EXCLUSION MAY NOT APPLY TO YOU. THIS WARRANTY GIVES YOU SPECIFIC LEGAL RIGHTS AND YOU MAY ALSO HAVE OTHER LEGAL RIGHTS THAT VARY FROM STATE TO STATE.

Pearson Education, Inc. does not warrant that the functions contained in the program will meet your requirements or that the operation of the program will be uninterrupted or error-free. However, Pearson Education, Inc. warrants the CD-ROM(s) on which the program is furnished to be free from defects in material and workmanship under normal use for a period of ninety (90) days from the date of delivery to you as evidenced by a copy of your receipt. The program should not be relied on as the sole basis to solve a problem whose incorrect solution could result in injury to person or property. If the program is employed in such a manner, it is at the user's own risk and Pearson Education, Inc. explicitly disclaims all liability for such misuse.

LIMITATION OF REMEDIES: Pearson Education, Inc.'s entire liability and your exclusive remedy shall be:

1. the replacement of any CD-ROM not meeting Pearson Education, Inc.'s "LIMITED WARRANTY" and that is returned to Pearson Education, or
2. if Pearson Education is unable to deliver a replacement CD-ROM that is free of defects in materials or workmanship, you may terminate this agreement by returning the program.

IN NO EVENT WILL PEARSON EDUCATION, INC. BE LIABLE TO YOU FOR ANY DAMAGES, INCLUDING ANY LOST PROFITS, LOST SAVINGS, OR OTHER INCIDENTAL OR CONSEQUENTIAL DAMAGES ARISING OUT OF THE USE OR INABILITY TO USE SUCH PROGRAM EVEN IF PEARSON EDUCATION, INC. OR AN AUTHORIZED DISTRIBUTOR HAS BEEN ADVISED OF THE POSSIBILITY OF SUCH DAMAGES, OR FOR ANY CLAIM BY ANY OTHER PARTY.

SOME STATES DO NOT ALLOW FOR THE LIMITATION OR EXCLUSION OF LIABILITY FOR INCIDENTAL OR CONSEQUENTIAL DAMAGES, SO THE ABOVE LIMITATION OR EXCLUSION MAY NOT APPLY TO YOU.

GENERAL: You may not sublicense, assign, or transfer the license of the program. Any attempt to sublicense, assign or transfer any of the rights, duties, or obligations hereunder is void.

This Agreement will be governed by the laws of the State of New York. Should you have any questions concerning this Agreement, you may contact Pearson Education, Inc. by writing to:

ESM Media Development
Higher Education Division
Pearson Education, Inc.
1 Lake Street
Upper Saddle River, NJ 07458

Should you have any questions concerning technical support, you may write to:

New Media Production
Higher Education Division
Pearson Education, Inc.
1 Lake Street
Upper Saddle River, NJ 07458

YOU ACKNOWLEDGE THAT YOU HAVE READ THIS AGREEMENT, UNDERSTAND IT, AND AGREE TO BE BOUND BY ITS TERMS AND CONDITIONS. YOU FURTHER AGREE THAT IT IS THE COMPLETE AND EXCLUSIVE STATEMENT OF THE AGREEMENT BETWEEN US THAT SUPERSEDES ANY PROPOSAL OR PRIOR AGREEMENT, ORAL OR WRITTEN, AND ANY OTHER COMMUNICATIONS BETWEEN US RELATING TO THE SUBJECT MATTER OF THIS AGREEMENT.

System Requirements

Macintosh:
Power PC G3 233 MHz or better
Mac OS 10.x
64 MB RAM
19 MB available hard drive space for Mac OS X (optional – if QuickTime installation is needed)
800 × 600 resolution
8x or faster CD-ROM drive
QuickTime 6.x

Windows:
Pentium II 300 MHz processor
Windows 2000, XP, Vista Ultimate
64 MB RAM (128 MB RAM required for Windows XP)
4.3 MB available hard drive space (optional-for minimum QuickTime installation)
800 × 600 resolution
8x or faster CD-ROM drive
QuickTime 6.x
Sound Card

Support Information

If you are having problems with this software, you can get support by filling out the web form located at: http://247pearsoned.custhelp.com/

Our technical staff will need to know certain things about your system in order to help us solve your problems more quickly and efficiently. If possible, please be at your computer when you call for support. You should have the following information ready:

- ISBN
- CD-ROM ISBN
- corresponding product and title
- computer make and model
- Operating System (Windows or Macintosh) and Version
- RAM available
- hard disk space available
- Sound card? Yes or No
- printer make and model
- network connection
- detailed description of the problem, including the exact wording of any error messages.

NOTE: Pearson does not support and/or assist with the following:

- third-party software (i.e. Microsoft including Microsoft Office suite, Apple, Borland, etc.)
- homework assistance
- Textbooks and CD-ROMs purchased used are not supported and are non-replaceable. To purchase a new CD-ROM, contact Pearson Individual Order Copies at 1-800-282-0693.

CONICS

Parabola

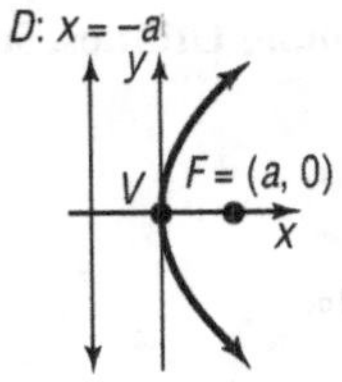

$y^2 = 4ax$

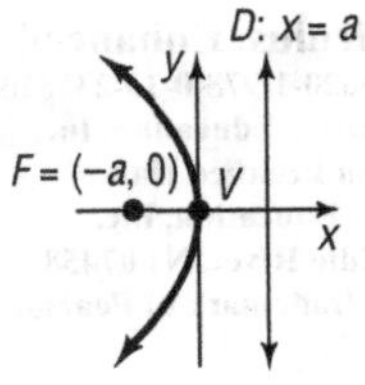

$y^2 = -4ax$

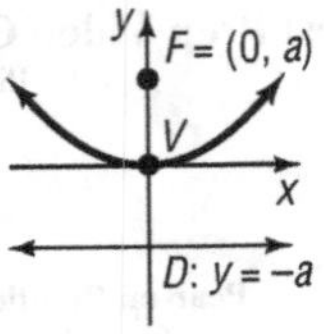

$x^2 = 4ay$

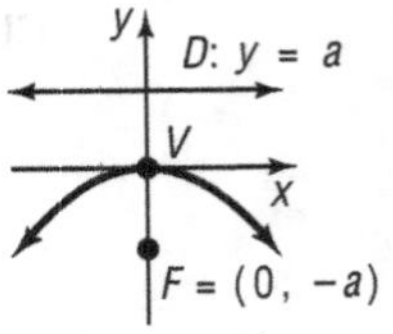

$x^2 = -4ay$

Ellipse

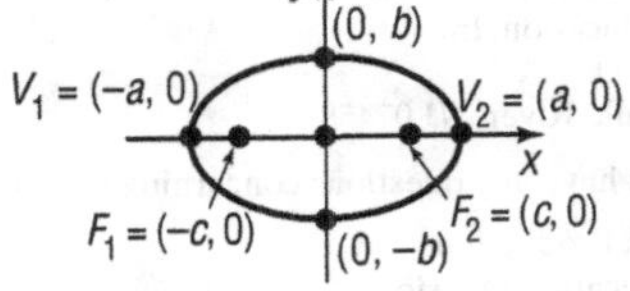

$$\frac{x^2}{a^2} + \frac{y^2}{b^2} = 1, \quad a > b, \quad c^2 = a^2 - b^2$$

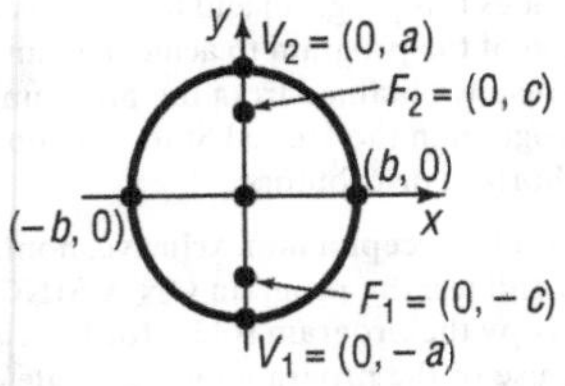

$$\frac{x^2}{b^2} + \frac{y^2}{a^2} = 1, \quad a > b, \quad c^2 = a^2 - b^2$$

Hyperbola

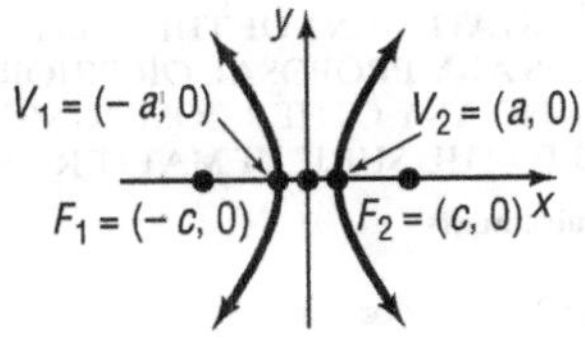

$$\frac{x^2}{a^2} - \frac{y^2}{b^2} = 1, \quad c^2 = a^2 + b^2$$

Asymptotes: $y = \frac{b}{a}x, \quad y = -\frac{b}{a}x$

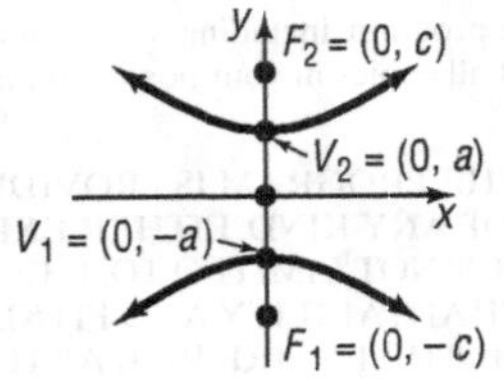

$$\frac{y^2}{a^2} - \frac{x^2}{b^2} = 1, \quad c^2 = a^2 + b^2$$

Asymptotes: $y = \frac{a}{b}x, \quad y = -\frac{a}{b}x$

PROPERTIES OF LOGARITHMS

$\log_a(MN) = \log_a M + \log_a N$

$\log_a\left(\frac{M}{N}\right) = \log_a M - \log_a N$

$\log_a M^r = r \log_a M$

$\log_a M = \frac{\log M}{\log a} = \frac{\ln M}{\ln a}$

PERMUTATIONS/COMBINATIONS

$0! = 1 \qquad 1! = 1$

$n! = n(n-1) \cdot \ldots \cdot (3)(2)(1)$

$P(n, r) = \frac{n!}{(n-r)!}$

$C(n, r) = \binom{n}{r} = \frac{n!}{(n-r)!\,r!}$

BINOMIAL THEOREM

$$(a+b)^n = a^n + \binom{n}{1}ba^{n-1} + \binom{n}{2}b^2a^{n-2} + \cdots + \binom{n}{n-1}b^{n-1}a + b^n$$

ARITHMETIC SEQUENCE

$$a_1 + (a_1 + d) + (a_1 + 2d) + \cdots + [a_1 + (n-1)d] = \frac{n}{2}[2a_1 + (n-1)d] = \frac{n}{2}[a_1 + a_n]$$

GEOMETRIC SEQUENCE

$$a_1 + a_1r + a_1r^2 + \cdots + a_1r^{n-1} = a_1 \cdot \frac{1 - r^n}{1 - r}$$

GEOMETRIC SERIES

If $|r| < 1$, $a_1 + a_1r + a_1r^2 + \cdots = \sum_{k=1}^{\infty} a_1r^{k-1} = \frac{a_1}{1-r}$

LIBRARY OF FUNCTIONS

Identity Function
$f(x) = x$

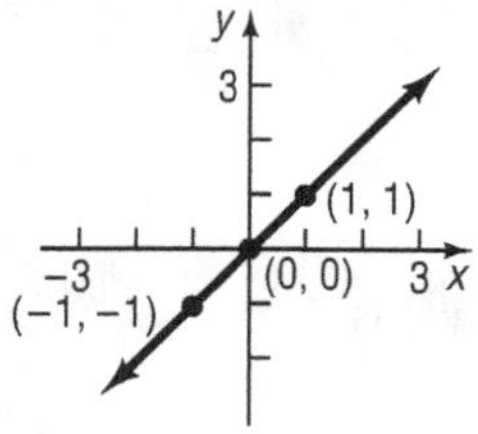

Square Function
$f(x) = x^2$

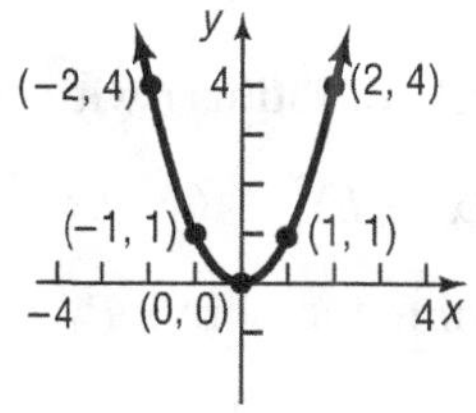

Cube Function
$f(x) = x^3$

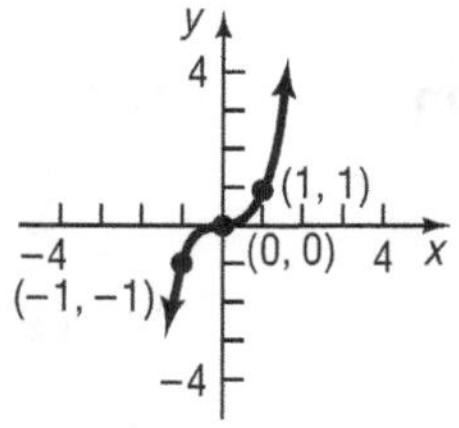

Square Root Function
$f(x) = \sqrt{x}$

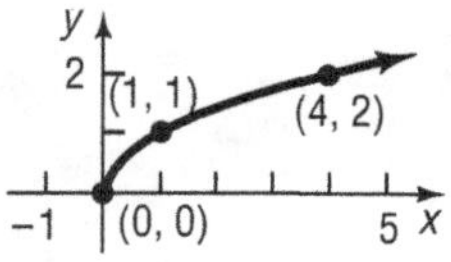

Reciprocal Function
$f(x) = \dfrac{1}{x}$

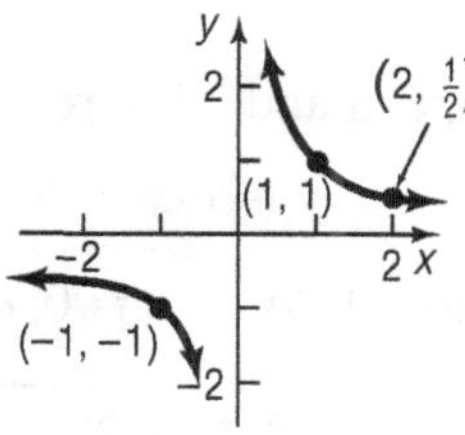

Cube Root Function
$f(x) = \sqrt[3]{x}$

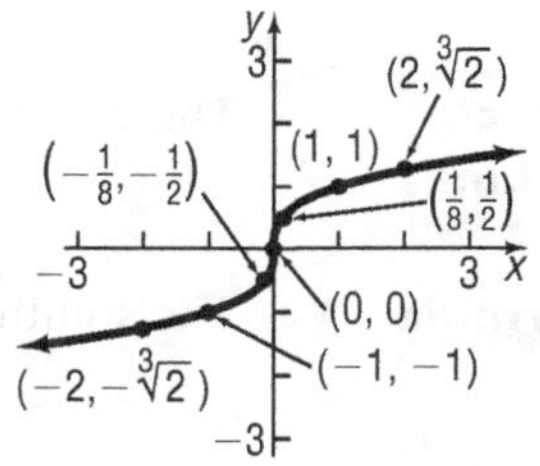

Absolute Value Function
$f(x) = |x|$

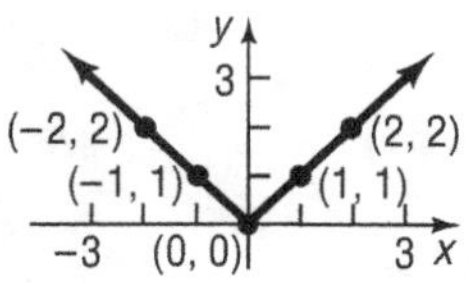

Exponential Function
$f(x) = e^x$

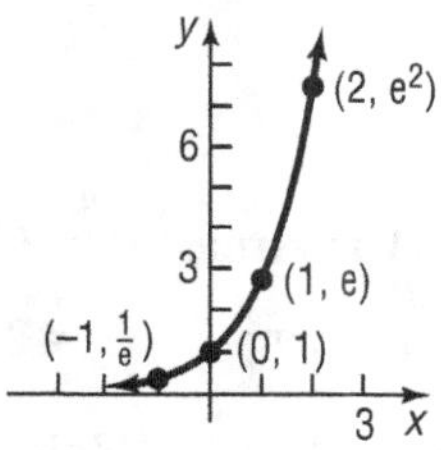

Natural Logarithm Function
$f(x) = \ln x$

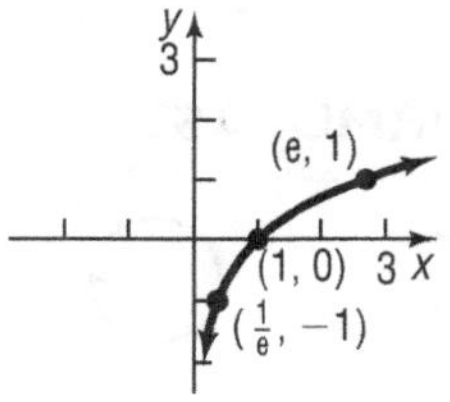

Sine Function
$f(x) = \sin x$

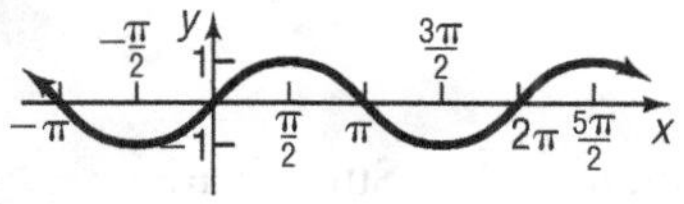

Cosine Function
$f(x) = \cos x$

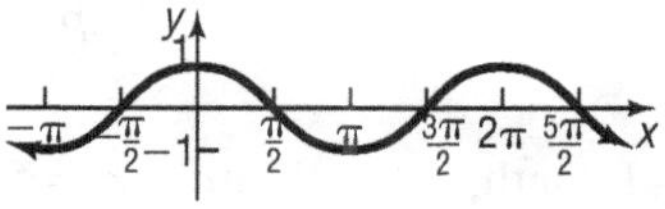

Tangent Function
$f(x) = \tan x$

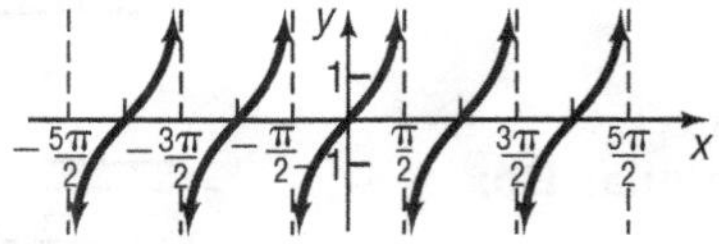

Cosecant Function
$f(x) = \csc x$

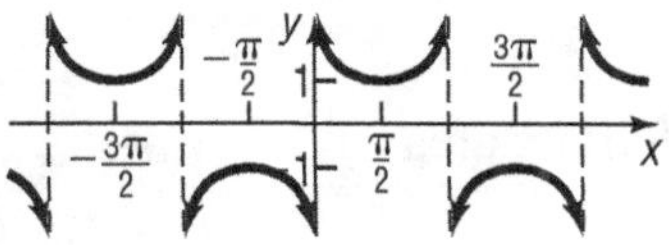

Secant Function
$f(x) = \sec x$

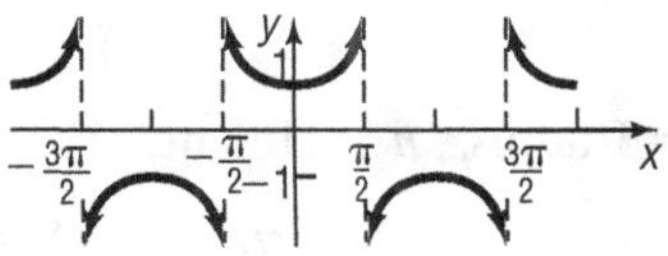

Cotangent Function
$f(x) = \cot x$

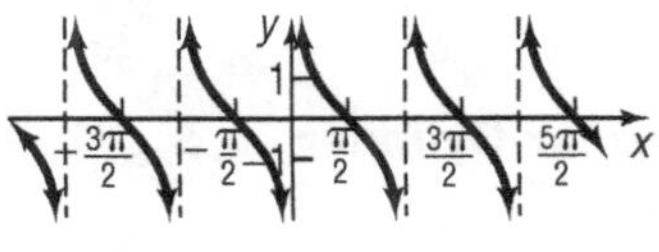

FORMULAS/EQUATIONS

Distance Formula

If $P_1 = (x_1, y_1)$ and $P_2 = (x_2, y_2)$, the distance from P_1 to P_2 is

$$d(P_1, P_2) = \sqrt{(x_2 - x_1)^2 + (y_2 - y_1)^2}$$

Standard Equation of a Circle

The standard equation of a circle of radius r with center at (h, k) is

$$(x - h)^2 + (y - k)^2 = r^2$$

Slope Formula

The slope m of the line containing the points $P_1 = (x_1, y_1)$ and $P_2 = (x_2, y_2)$ is

$$m = \frac{y_2 - y_1}{x_2 - x_1} \qquad \text{if } x_1 \neq x_2$$

$$m \text{ is undefined} \qquad \text{if } x_1 = x_2$$

Point–Slope Equation of a Line

The equation of a line with slope m containing the point (x_1, y_1) is

$$y - y_1 = m(x - x_1)$$

Slope–Intercept Equation of a Line

The equation of a line with slope m and y-intercept b is

$$y = mx + b$$

Quadratic Formula

The solutions of the equation $ax^2 + bx + c = 0$, $a \neq 0$, are

$$x = \frac{-b \pm \sqrt{b^2 - 4ac}}{2a}$$

If $b^2 - 4ac > 0$, there are two unequal real solutions.
If $b^2 - 4ac = 0$, there is a repeated real solution.
If $b^2 - 4ac < 0$, there are two complex solutions that are not real.

GEOMETRY FORMULAS

Circle

r = Radius, A = Area, C = Circumference

$$A = \pi r^2 \qquad C = 2\pi r$$

Triangle

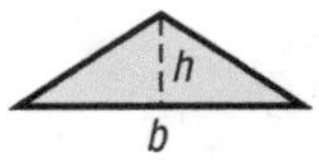

b = Base, h = Altitude (Height), A = area

$$A = \tfrac{1}{2}bh$$

Rectangle

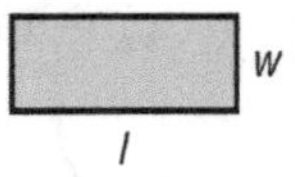

l = Length, w = Width, A = area, P = perimeter

$$A = lw \qquad P = 2l + 2w$$

Rectangular Box

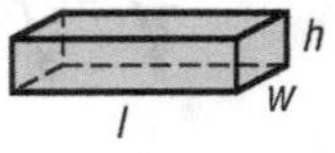

l = Length, w = Width, h = Height, V = Volume, S = Surface area

$$V = lwh \qquad S = 2lw + 2lh + 2wh$$

Sphere

r = Radius, V = Volume, S = Surface area

$$V = \tfrac{4}{3}\pi r^3 \qquad S = 4\pi r^2$$

Right Circular Cylinder

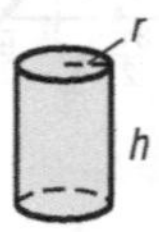

r = Radius, h = Height, V = Volume, S = Surface area

$$V = \pi r^2 h \qquad S = 2\pi r^2 + 2\pi rh$$